GEORGINA CAMPBELL'S

JAMESON
IRISH WHISKEY

GUIDE

The Best Places to Eat, Drink & Stay

IRELAND
2003

Georgina Campbell's Guides

Editor: Georgina Campbell

Georgina Campbell's Guides Ltd.,
PO Box 6173
Dublin 13
Ireland

website: www.ireland-guide.com
email: info@ireland-guide.com

Front Cover Photographs:	Ballymaloe House, Shanagarry, Co Cork
	Pub Scene courtesy of Old Jameson Distillery, Dublin
	Ivyleigh House, Portlaoise, Co Laois
Back Cover from top:	Doyle's, Dingle, Co Kerry
	Farran House, Farran, Co Cork
	Dromoland Castle, Newmarket-on-Fergus, Co Clare
	The Green Gate, Ardara, Co Donegal
	Brennans, Public House, Bundoran, Co Donegal
	Hunters Hotel, Rathnew, Co Wicklow

Design and Artwork by The Design Station, Dublin
Printed in Ireland by Beta Print Ltd.

First published 2002 by Georgina Campbell Guides Ltd.

ISBN: 1 903164-08-7

Georgina Campbell's Guides Awards

Cashel House Hotel
Hotel of the Year

Thornton's
Restaurant of the Year

Maura Foley
Chef of the Year

Café en Seine
Pub of the Year

Avoca Cafés
Féile Bia Awards

Ty Ar Mor
Seafood Restaurant of the Year

The full list of awards is on page 11

How to Use the Guide

Location/Establishment name
- Cities, towns and villages arranged in alphabetical order within counties, with the exception of Dublin, Cork, Belfast, Galway and Limerick which come first within their categories
- Establishments arranged alphabetically within location
- In Dublin city, postal codes are arranged in numerical order. Even numbers are south of the River Liffey and uneven numbers on the north, with the exception of Dublin 8 which straddles the river. Dublin 1 and 2 are most central; Dublin 1 is north of the Liffey, Dublin 2 is south of it (see map). Within each district establishments are listed in alphabetical order.

Category(ies) of Establishment

Address/contact details
(please phone/fax/email ahead for additional directions if required)
- includes an email address and website address if available

Rating - for outstanding cooking and accommodation

☆	- Demi-Star: restaurant approaching full star status
★	- For cooking and service well above average
★★	- Consistent excellence, one of the best restaurants in the land
★★★	- The highest restaurant grading achievable
⛪	- Outstanding Accommodation of its type
⛪⛪	- De Luxe Hotel
♙	- Outstanding Pub - good food and atmosphere
féile bia	- Denotes establishments committed to the Féile Bia Charter
◇	- Times/prices not confirmed at time of going to press
Ⓝ	- Establishments new to this edition of the Guide

Maps are intended for reference only; Ordnance Survey maps are recommended and available from Tourist Information Offices.

PRICES & OPENING HOURS
PLEASE NOTE THAT PRICES AND OPENING HOURS MAY HAVE CHANGED SINCE THE GUIDE WENT TO PRESS. TIMES & PRICES ARE GIVEN AS A GUIDELINE ONLY AND SHOULD BE CHECKED BEFORE TRAVELLING OR WHEN MAKING A RESERVATION.

Prices in the Republic of Ireland are given in Euros and those in Northern Ireland in pounds Sterling.

Thanks and Acknowledgements

The publication of this guide would not have been possible without the support and encouragement of a large number of organisations, companies and individuals. Particular thanks must go to all the sponsors, of course, for having faith in this fifth edition which is an all-Irish project. Those who have given invaluable assistance are too numerous to mention individually but, on behalf the Guide, I would like to thank you all.

Georgina Campbell,
Editor.

A Word from the Sponsor

by Kieran Tobin
Communications and Corporate Affairs Director
Irish Distillers Wines and Spirits

Jameson is once again delighted to be associated with a Guide which will help you to sample some of the best of Ireland's hospitality, food and drink.

Jameson, and indeed Irish Whiskey in general, is an intrinsic part of the renowned welcome and hospitality to be found in Ireland. Whiskey is woven into the fabric of Irish life, whether you are enjoying the warmth of an Irish pub, relaxing in a hotel or country house, enjoying an aperitif or relaxing after a memorable meal, there is always an appropriate occasion to savour a glass of Jameson.

As with many of the best things in Ireland, the traditions of the past are combined with the expertise of the present in the crafting of Jameson Irish Whiskey. The special qualities of Jameson are achieved through distilling the whiskey three times, ensuring a product that is particularly smooth and pure. During maturation in bourbon and sherry oak casks, which are stored for many years in dark, aromatic warehouses, Jameson mellows and takes on its rich golden colour. This combination of heritage, smoothness and expertise has helped to make Jameson the World's most popular Irish Whiskey.

A culinary revolution has taken place in Ireland over the past two decades and Irish cuisine is now taking its place among the best in the world. Good food, a personal welcome and friendly pubs are amongst the most frequently cited attractions for visitors to Ireland and these can be found in establishments, both large and small, throughout the country. Irish cuisine is widely acknowledged as using natural, pure and local ingredients combined with contemporary preparation and presentation, to achieve great things. Jameson has always set itself similar standards and uses only the finest malted and unmalted barley and pure Irish water as its principal ingredients.

I hope you will enjoy using this guide to find the best that Irish hospitality, food and – of course – Whiskey, has to offer.

Kieran Tobin

Kieran Tobin
Communications and Corporate Affairs Director

Introduction

by Georgina Campbell
Editorial Director

Hospitality has for centuries been the cornerstone of Irish life, and in uncertain times its value is brought ever more sharply into focus. World events may be the catalyst for reassessment in all areas of our lives, and a frequent comment now made is that people are determined to find more time for themselves - an admirable ambition, we think, and there are some very enjoyable ways to achieve it, right here in Ireland.

The great hosts and chefs selected for this year's guide have chosen to spend their lives making it possible for the rest of us to relax and discover, not just ourselves, but this wonderful country. So you have only to while away a little time browsing through our selection of memorable places to visit and some special corner of this extraordinarily diverse country will soon begin to exert its unique magnetism. This is a particularly good time to travel in Ireland, as extra efforts are being made everywhere to ensure that visitors enjoy their stay and pass on the good news to others.

You might begin your journey by looking through our list of award-winners, a breathtakingly accomplished group of dedicated people if ever there was one. All year, we seek out those very special places where professional pride is at its peak in order to reward perfectionism with public recognition of the very best that Ireland has to offer - and also to encourage those who aspire to similar standards.

This year, when searching for award winners, quality and value were the characteristics we sought and every individual and establishment in the awards pages contributes in some way to this theme. Close examination of the list will reveal great diversity (not least in price) but every one of these outstanding places has a unique contribution to make in terms of quality and service - and where prices are high, they are justified by exceptional standards. Each year only a tiny number of establishments receive awards, but many more of a similar standard are listed in our 'Best of the Best' selection, which should be the next point of reference for the discerning traveller.

An over-riding interest which is always our minds is the search for those with a sound philosophy of food, regardless of price. There is growing recognition of the need to demonstrate commitment to quality produce by, for example, giving the provenance of ingredients on menus. Similarly, we seek accomplished but simple cooking that relies on quality ingredients for its success - and many of these awards reflect that philosophy.

International groups like Euro-Toques and the Slow Food Movement, backed by the demands of increasingly well-informed consumers, support and encourage the artisan producers who ensure quality and diversity of ingredients. Bord Bia and other organisations are working to a similar end with Féile Bia, the national celebration of quality Irish produce and cooking, which is detailed in the guide.

Wherever your travels take you, on business or for pleasure, we hope that you will enjoy using this Guide - and that it will lead you on many a memorable outing.

Georgina Campbell.

The Best of the Best

★★ / ★ / ☆

REPUBLIC OF IRELAND

2 Star: ★★
Dublin, Restaurant Patrick Guilbaud
Dublin, Thornton's

1 Star: ★
Dublin, Chapter One
Dublin, L'Ecrivain
Co Clare, Dromoland Castle
Co Cork, Ballymaloe House, Shanagarry
Co Cork, Longueville House, Mallow
Co Kerry, Park Hotel, Kenmare
Co Kerry, Sheen Falls Lodge, Kenmare
Co Kildare, Kildare Hotel, Straffan
Co Sligo, Cromleach Lodge, Castlebaldwin

Demi-Star: ☆
Dublin, Clarence Hotel, Tea Room
Dublin, The Commons Restaurant
Dublin, Mermaid Café
Dublin, Morrison, Halo Restaurant
Dublin, O'Connell's in Ballsbridge
Dublin, One Pico Restaurant
Co Dublin, Portmarnock Hotel,
    Osborne Restaurant
Co Cavan, MacNean Bistro, Blacklion
Cork city, Café Paradiso
Cork city, Jacob's on the Mall

Demi-Star *(continued):* ☆
Cork city, Jacques
Co Cork, Blairs Cove House, Durrus
Co Cork, Casino House, Kilbrittain
Co Cork, Customs House, Baltimore
Co Kerry, Packie's, Kenmare
Co Kerry, Lime Tree, Kenmare
Co Kerry, Restaurant David Norris, Tralee
Co Limerick, Mustard Seed at Echo Lodge,
    Ballingarry
Co Mayo, Ashford Castle, Cong
Co Tipperary, Clifford's at The Bell, Cahir
Co Waterford, Tannery, Dungarvan
Co Wexford, Dunbrody House, Arthurstown
Co Wexford, La Marine at Kelly's Hotel,
    Rosslare

NORTHERN IRELAND

2 Star: ★★
Belfast, Restaurant Michael Deane

1 Star: ★
Belfast, Cayenne

Demi-Star: ☆
Belfast, Aldens
Belfast, Porcelain @TENsq
Co Down, Shanks, Bangor

REPUBLIC OF IRELAND

Dublin, Berkeley Court, Ballsbridge
Dublin, The Clarence, Temple Bar
Dublin, Four Seasons Hotel, Ballsbridge
Dublin, The Merrion, Merrion Street
Dublin, Morrison, Ormond Quay
Dublin, The Shelbourne, St Stephen's Green
Dublin, The Westbury, Grafton Street
Dublin, The Westin Hotel, College Green
Cork city, Hayfield Manor Hotel

Co Clare, Dromoland Castle,
    Newmarket-on Fergus
Co Kerry, Park Hotel, Kenmare
Co Kerry, Sheen Falls Lodge, Kenmare
Co Kildare, Kildare Hotel, Straffan,
Co Kilkenny, Mount Juliet, Thomastown
Co Limerick, Adare Manor, Adare
Co Mayo, Ashford Castle, Cong,
Co Wexford, Marlfield House, Gorey

NORTHERN IRELAND
Co Down, Culloden Hotel, Holywood

OUTSTANDING ACCOMMODATION

REPUBLIC OF IRELAND
Dublin, The Conrad, Earslfort Terrace
Dublin, The Towers, Lansdowne Road,
    Ballsbridge
Dublin, Clarion IFSC
Co Dublin, Portmarnock
    Hotel & Golf Links
Cork city, Maryborough Hotel
Co Cork, Aherne's, Youghal
Co Cork, Assolas House, Kanturk
Co Cork, Ballymaloe House, Shanagarry
Co Cork, Ballyvolane House, Castlelyons
Co Cork, Farran House, Farran
Co Cork, Longueville House, Mallow
Co Cork, Seaview House, Ballylickey
Co Clare, Carnelly House, Clarecastle,
Co Clare, Gregans Castle Hotel, Ballyvaughan
Co Clare, Moy House, Lahinch
Co Clare Sheedy's Hotel, Lisdoonvarna
Galway city, Killeen House, Bushypark
Galway city, SAS Radisson Hotel
Co Galway, Cashel House Hotel, Connemara
Co Galway, Dolphin Beach, Clifden
Co Galway, Fermoyle Lodge, Costello
Co Galway, The Quay House, Clifden
Co Kerry, Barrow House, Tralee
Co Kerry, Caragh Lodge, Caragh Lake
Co Kerry, Emlagh Lodge, Dingle
Co Kerry, Hotel Europe, Killarney

Co Kerry, Killarney Park Hotel, Killarney
Co Kerry, Shelburne Lodge, Kenmare
Co Kildare, Barberstown Castle, Straffan
Co Kildare, Kilkea Castle, Castledermot
Co Kildare, Moyglare Manor, Maynooth
Co Laois, Ivyleigh House, Portlaoise
Co Limerick, Clarion Hotel, Limerick
Co Limerick, Radisson SAS Hotel, Limerick
Co Limerick, Dunraven Arms Hotel, Adare
Co Limerick, Echo Lodge, Ballingarry
Co Limerick, Glin Castle, Glin
Co Mayo, Ardmore House, Westport
Co Mayo, Newport House, Newport
Co Monaghan, Hilton Park, Clones
Co Sligo, Coopershill House, Riverstown
Co Sligo, Cromleach Lodge, Castlebaldwin
Co Waterford, Hanora's Cottage, Nire Valley
Co Westmeath, Wineport Lodge, Glasson
Co Wexford, Dunbrody House, Arthurstown
Co Wicklow, Humewood Castle, Kiltegan
Co Wicklow, Rathsallagh House, Dunlavin
Co Wicklow, Tinakilly House, Rathnew

NORTHERN IRELAND
Belfast, TENsq Hotel
Co Antrim, Galgorm Manor, Ballymena
Co Londonderry, Ardtara House, Upperlands
Co Londonderry, Beech Hill House Hotel
Co Londonderry, Streeve Hill, Limavady
Co Tyrone, Grange Lodge, Dungannon

OUTSTANDING PUBS (for good food & atmosphere)

REPUBLIC OF IRELAND
Dublin, Café en Seine
Dublin, The Porterhouse
Co Cork, The Bosun, Monkstown
Co Cork, Bushe's, Baltimore
Co Cork, Mary Ann's, Castletownshend
Co Cork, Hayes Bar, Glandore
Co Galway, Moran's Oyster Cottage, Kilcolgan
Co Kerry, The Point Bar, Caherciveen
Co Kildare, The Ballymore Inn,
    Ballymore Eustace
Co Kilkenny, Marble City Bar

Co Leitrim, The Oarsman, Carrick-on-Shannon
Co Mayo, Gaughan's, Ballina
Co Offaly, The Thatch, Crinkle
Co Tipperary, The Derg Inn, Terryglass
Co Tipperary, Sean Tierney's, Clonmel
Co Waterford, Buggy's Glencairn Inn
Co Wexford, Kehoe's, Kilmore Quay
Co Wicklow, Roundwood Inn, Roundwood

NORTHERN IRELAND
Belfast, Crown Liquor Salon
Co Down, Grace Neill's, Donaghadee
Co Down, The Plough, Hillsborough

Georgina Campbell's Guides
gratefully acknowledges the support of the following sponsors:

Jameson Irish Whiskey
Sponsors of:
Hotel of the Year Award
Restaurant of the Year Award
Pub of the Year Award
International Hospitality Award

Bord Bia
Sponsors of:
Féile Bia Award

Martell
Sponsors of:
Host of the Year Award

Bord Iascaigh Mhara
Sponsors of:
Seafood Restaurant of the Year Award

Wyndham Estate
Sponsors of:
Wine Award of the Year

Bord Glas
Sponsors of:
Creative Use of Vegetables Award

Cork Dry Gin
Sponsors of:
Business Hotel of the Year Award

Rathborne Candles
Sponsors of:
Atmospheric Restaurant
of the Year Award

Wodka Wyborowa
Sponsors of:
Newcomer of the Year Award

Euro-Toques
Joint sponsors of:
Natural Food Award

Kerry Foods
Sponsors of:
Denny Irish Breakfast Awards

Irish Heart Foundation
Sponsors of:
Happy Heart Eat Out Award

Awards of Excellence

Annual awards for the best establishments and staff in a variety of categories, sponsored by leading Irish companies and organisations

Hotel of the Year

Dermot and Kay McEvilly were among the pioneers of the Irish country house hotel movement when they opened Cashel House as an hotel in 1968. The following year General and Madame de Gaulle chose to stay for two weeks, an historic visit of which the McEvilly's are justly proud. It brought immediate recognition for the hotel, but it did even more for Ireland by putting the Gallic seal of approval on Irish hospitality and food - and helping to raise standards by attracting discerning continental guests who were not afraid to complain when necessary. Comfort abounds here, even luxury, yet it's tempered by common sense, a love of gardening and the genuine sense of hospitality that ensures each guest will benefit as much as possible from their stay. The gardens, which run down to their own private beach, contribute greatly to the atmosphere, and accommodation includes especially comfortable ground floor garden suites. Relaxed hospitality combined with professionalism have earned an international reputation for this outstanding hotel and its qualities are perhaps best seen in details - log fires that burn throughout the year, day rooms furnished with antiques and filled with fresh flowers from the garden, rooms that are individually decorated with many thoughtful touches. Service is impeccable and superb breakfasts include a wonderful buffet display of home-made and local produce: this is Irish hospitality at its best.

2002 Winner:
Killarney Park Hotel, Kerry

Cashel House Hotel
Connemara, Co Galway

Jameson
congratulates

Cashel House Hotel

winner of
Hotel of the Year

Restaurant of the Year

When Kevin Thornton moved his team here from their famous little Portobello premises over the summer of 2002 and quietly opened at this lofty city-centre restaurant, early in September, without so much as a whisper of the PR hype that usually accompanies such occasions, it was the most significant opening Dublin has seen for some time. Seriously good cooking in a seriously good restaurant is to be found here and, under the supervision of the warmly professional maître d', Olivier Meisonnave, an excellent team of mostly French waiting staff set the tone from the outset, providing highly professional service to complement Kevin Thornton's superb cooking. As in the previous premises, the decor is stunningly simple and elegant, leaving you in no doubt that the food - offered in relatively short menus which, quite literally, bear the hand of the master on the cover in another stroke of understated originality - is to be the star. Kevin Thornton has a name for generosity with the finest ingredients, notably truffles, and he will not disappoint. Variations on a series of luxurious signature dishes appear throughout an 8-course Surprise Menu which is just that - there is nothing written and the menu created for each table is unique. This is creative cooking of the highest class, conceived with brilliance to utilise first-rate seasonal ingredients, and presented with a perfectionist's eye for detail and a palate to match: despite the occasional flash of gold leaf this is far from the show-off creations commonly associated with top chefs: Kevin Thornton's cooking has soul.

2002 Winner:
Cayenne, Belfast

Thornton's
St Stephen's Green, Dublin

Jameson
congratulates

Thornton's

winner of
Restaurant of the Year

Chef of the Year

Tom and Maura Foley's little Kenmare restaurant is stylish but unpretentious, with small tables and a big heart - and a devoted following of discerning diners from throughout Ireland (and beyond). Great local ingredients, especially organic produce and seafood, mingle with imports from sunnier climes and, in Maura's skilful hands, result in imaginative Ireland-meets-the-Med food that is memorable for its simplicity and intense flavouring. First impressions are of world cuisine and there's a clear awareness of international trends, but the cooking here is far above the influence of fashion. Maura modestly describes her food as "simple, with an emphasis on local ingredients" but what makes it special, apart from very accomplished cooking, is her sure judgement of complementary food combinations. Many of these are traditional and that is why they have lasted - rack of lamb with mint & redcurrant sauce for example - while others, like pan-fried fillet of plaice with coriander, lime & orange butter sound modern but are actually based on a time-honoured combination of flavours. Close examination of menus will probably reveal more dishes that have stood the test of time than new ones, but what is most impressive is the sheer quality of both food – especially local seafood – and cooking, also that new flavours will only be introduced when they make genuinely good partnerships. "Faites simple" was the famous (and, alas, largely ignored) dictum of the great Escoffier: Maura Foley is one of the few chefs with the confidence to do just that and the result is invariably memorable.

2002 Winner:
Rory O'Connell, Ballymaloe House, Co Cork

Maura Foley
Packie's, Kenmare

Georgina Campbell's Guides
congratulates

Maura Foley

winner of
Chef of the Year

Winner

Pub of the Year

The first of the continental style café-bars to open in Dublin, in 1993, Café en Seine is still ahead of the fashion a decade later - after closing for complete refurbishment, it re-opened in 2002 to reveal a stunning new interior in an opulent art deco style reminiscent of turn-of-the-century France. Not so much a bar as a series of bars (a mobile phone could be your most useful accessory if you arrange to meet somebody here), the soaring interior is truly awe-inspiring, with glass-panelled ceilings, forty foot trees, enormous glass lanterns and a 19th century French hotel lift among its many amazing features. No expense has been spared in ensuring the quality of design, materials and craftsmanship necessary to create this beautiful Aladdin's cave of a bar. It's the judicious mixture of old and new which make it a true orginal. Although the overall theme is based on tradition, it is far from pastiche and the final result is refreshingly different - and its many 'bars within bars' create intimate spaces that are a far cry from the impersonality of the superpub. Good food is a major part of its appeal too - notably a popular Jazz Brunch every Sunday - and it's little wonder that so many people of all ages see theis well-run bar as the coolest place in town.

2002 Winner:
The Bosun, Monkstown, Cork

Café en Seine
Dublin

Jameson
congratulates

Café en Seine

winner of
Pub of the Year

Irish Food Board

Féile Bia Award

Leylie Hayes has been supervising the production of the famously wholesome home-cooked food at Avoca Handweavers since 1990 and people home in to the cafés in county Wicklow and Dublin city, to tuck into fare which is as healthy as it is delicious. The importance of using only the very best ingredients has always been recognised at Avoca. Their food is based on the best available produce, as much of it as possible local and artisan and, when the Féile Bia programme was initiated, Leylie Hayes was one of the first to recognise its benefits and sign up to the Féile Bia Charter - which is a commitment to using products from recognised Quality Assurance Schemes, identifying the origin of these quality products on their menus and developing dishes and menus to profile local foods. "Quality in, quality out" is the motto at the heart of the Avoca philosophy: they have always strived to source the highest quality, least processed, best raw materials to make good, honest food which is produced with passion and attention to detail. More than ever, says Leylie Hayes, they have a sense of the critical importance of fresh, top quality seasonal ingredients: organic is great but if it has travelled half way around the world to reach us in a suspended state of refrigeration there is no point in that. So an emphasis on quality and sourcing the best ingredients locally has become a cornerstone of the Avoca ethic.

2002 Winner:
O'Connells, Ballsbridge, Dublin

Bord Bía
Irish Food Board

Avoca Cafés
Co Wicklow & Dublin

Bord Bia
congratulates

Avoca Cafés

winner of
Féile Bia Award

Seafood Restaurant of the Year

Michel Philippot and Rosaleen O'Shea's delightful little Breton restaurant in the centre of Skibbereen has a lively maritime theme and gives high quality at prices which are moderate for seafood. Michel takes pride in taking freshly-caught seafood from Irish waters, and enhancing it with real Breton cooking - just close your eyes and taste the sea! A Menu Gastronomique offers great value, (only lobster attracts a supplement) and, in true French style, there's also a modestly priced Menu Touristique with just two choices on each course. Traditional Breton fish soup with rouille and croûtons, Rossmore oysters with shallot sauce & lemon and cassolette of prawns & squid with lobster & Armagnac sauce all appear regularly along with classic main courses like black sole on the bone with garlic butter and grilled fillet of turbot beurre blanc (either of which would cost the price of this entire menu in many east coast restaurants). And desserts will not disappoint either: a rich gateau maison is made with chocolate and Grand Mariner, and there are other French classics such as île flottante or a wonderful caramelised tarte tatin - and, if you can find the appetite to appreciate them, local farmhouse cheeses are beautifully presented, French style, with a walnut salad. The value for money is exceptional and professional service under Rosaleen's supervision, from a mixture of local and French staff, matches the food: this place is a little gem.

2002 Winner:
Barrtra Seafood Restaurant, Co Clare

 **Ireland**

Ty Ar Mor
Skibbereen, Co Cork

BIM
congratulates

Ty Ar Mor

winner of
Seafood Restaurant of the Year

Cork Dry Gin

Business Hotel Award

Just 20 miles south of Dublin, adjacent to the famous Druids Glen Golf Club, this stunningly located new hotel is particularly attractive for the business guest, conferences and corporate events; Marriott Hotels have long experience in this field and the hotel is exceptionally well-equipped to meet demand. Convenient to the capital and easy to reach, there's a feeling of space throughout which is increasingly difficult to achieve in the city - and an away-from-it-all atmosphere conducive to productive meetings. Public areas are impressive - the tone is set in the large marbled foyer with its dramatic feature fireplace and seating areas, bars and dining areas lead off it in an open plan arrangement. There are eight conference rooms and seven meeting rooms (with natural light, overlooking the golf course and hotel grounds), with all the necessary back-up facilities and well-trained, helpful staff. Very spacious bedrooms have generous, well-organised desk space, phones with message light, data port, voice mail, in-room safe (big enough for a laptop) etc. In-room dining is also comfortably provided for - and all bathrooms have separate bath and walk-in shower. On-site recreational activities are equally impressive - as well as golf (preferential rates at Druids Glen), the hotel has an excellent spa and health club and other activities nearby include horse riding, archery, quad biking, orienteering and team building. A place to relax and unwind after doing business.

2002 Winner:
Clarion Hotel, IFSC, Dublin

Cork Dry Gin

Marriott Hotel
Druid's Glen, Co Wicklow

Cork Dry Gin
congratulates

Marriott Hotel

winner of
Business Hotel Award

International Hospitality Award

Often quoted as 'the luxury country house hotel par excellence', Marlfield House was once the residence of the Earls of Courtown and, thanks to the dedication and professionalism of Ray and Mary Bowe, has now been a leading light in the quest for excellence in Irish hospitality for 25 years. During that time they have lavished care and attention on this lovely house, creating an elegant oasis of unashamed luxury, where guests are cosseted and pampered in sumptuous surroundings - and matching these exceptional standards with a reputation for outstanding hospitality and service. Imposing gates, a wooded drive, a fine kitchen garden all set the scene - and the interior features marble fireplaces, antiques, notable paintings, glittering chandeliers and fine fabrics: all the creation of Mary Bowe, who has also ensured that housekeeping is immaculate throughout, service from committed staff thoughtful and unobtrusive. These are all qualities that have made Marlfield an important destination for the most discerning of international guests, people who value the exceptional level of comfort and care provided for them - and return home to pass on the good word about high standards and warm hospitality in Ireland. By aiming for the stars and having the determination and dedication to reach them, Mary and Ray Bowe - now joined by their daughter Margaret Bowe, who is continuing the family tradition as manager of Marlfield - are contributing a great service to Ireland's hospitality industry.

2002 Winner:
Pat McCann, Jurys Doyle Hotel Group

Mary Bowe
Marlfield House, Gorey, Co Wexford

Jameson
congratulates

Mary Bowe

winner of

International Hospitality Award

WÓDKA
WYBOROWA

Newcomer of the Year

This charming boutique hotel has been open little over a year, yet has already established a special niche for discerning visitors to Belfast. It is situated in a particularly attractive listed Victorian building and the location - just opposite the City Hall and within walking distance of the whole city centre area - is superb. Renovation throughout the building has been completed to an exceptionally high standard and, although the end result is refreshingly contemporary, it has been achieved with great sensitivity to the original building: a striking feature, for example, is the lovely old stained glass in many of the original windows, which is now subtly echoed in the interior design. Accommodation - in generous high-windowed rooms. theatrically decorated in an uncompromisingly modern style - is both simple and very luxurious; even the most dyed-in-the-wool traditionalist would be won over by the sheer style - and unexpected homeliness - of these rooms and, of course, they have wonderful bathrooms to match. The restaurant and bar attract discerning non-residents and it is a bonus for residential guests to have amenities of this standard on-site. Staff are warm, welcoming and generally efficient, with none of the stuffiness sometimes encountered in exclusive hotels. This stylish and increasingly accomplished hotel is a tremendous asset to Belfast - and a worthy winner of our Newcomer of the Year Award for 2003.

WÓDKA
WYBOROWA

TENsq Hotel
Belfast

Wodka Wyborowa
congratulates

TENsq Hotel

winner of
Newcomer of the Year

Wine Award of the Year

This 'Nissen hut' hidden away near Merrion Square is something of a Dublin institution, having been run since 1978 under the close supervision of owner John O'Byrne and manager Patrick Walsh. A visit to this unique oasis is always a treat and, along with great hospitality and delicious food, they're renowned for wine, which has always been at the centre of their philosophy: twenty five years ago people started recognising their food when coming to Dobbins for the best glass of good quality wines around at that time - and today it's not just 'the list' that is special, but a system John O'Byrne put in place some years ago, whereby the exclusive 'Front Page Wines' on the regular list are available for off-sales, by the bottle or case - which greatly pleases the many wine buffs who frequent the restaurant, as they are sold at half the list price. The wines selected change regularly and, as they're bought specially for Dobbins and their own internet company, offer exceptional quality and value to customers. They also hold a wine fair every December, buying bin ends and selling them a vineyard prices; needless to say it's very popular with customers and their friends - and sorts out the Christmas shopping very pleasantly too. Dobbins may well have the most extensive - and probably the most eclectic - wine list in Ireland and their customers certainly have fun trying them. Leisurely lunches have been known to run on a bit too long, hence the warning on the menu: "Bar closes at 5.30pm and re-opens at 7.30 for dinner service."

2002 Winner:
L'Ecrivain, Dublin

WYNDHAM ESTATE

ESTABLISHED 1828
HUNTER VALLEY

Dobbins
Dublin

Wyndham Estate
congratulates

Dobbins

winner of

Wine Award of the Year

Host of the Year

Jim McCarthy's informal restaurant brought a new element to Dingle's dining scene when it opened in 1997 and it quickly became established as one of the leading restaurants in an area exceptionally well-endowed with good eating places. Built in local stone to a low-key design that matches the proportions of the town well, it has a smart little bar just inside the door - and Jim McCarthy, the perfect host, always seems to be there meeting, seating and seamlessly ensuring that everyone is well looked after and generally having a good time. This warm professionalism is, to some extent, a gift - but one which was recognised and developed during his time at Francis Brennan's superb Park Hotel Kenmare (which is known in the industry as Ireland's unofficial hotel training school for top talents). Jim's special gifts and professionalism perfectly suited the philosophy of friendly perfection that prevails at The Park and, in due course, it helped him to channel his special skills into running his own restaurant here at The Chart House. And the rest, as they say, is history. He has great kitchen and front of house teams to match his own management and hospitality skills and the restaurant has become a destination address: great hospitality and accomplished cooking keep people coming back for more. And, never a man to miss a trick, Jim keeps a close eye on his wines - there's always a Chateau MacCarthy in stock!

2002 Winner:
Tom Reade-Duncan, The Motte, Co Kilkenny

Jim McCarthy
Chart House, Dingle, Co Kerry

Martell
congratulates

Jim McCarthy

winner of
Host of the Year

Hideaway of the Year

Since the opening of stunning new accommodation beside their famous restaurant, Ray Byrne and Jane English's lovely lakeside retreat, Wineport Lodge, now styles itself as Ireland's first wine hotel - and it has certainly brought something sensationally different to the Midlands. A covered boardwalk brings you to the front door: enter your guest key card and step into a different world. A lofty residents' lounge with a stove and its own bar simply oozes style and comfort, a hint of the high pamper quota waiting above in the ten spacious new bedrooms, all with private balconies overlooking the lake. Superbly comfortable beds face the view - a clear invitation to relax and take it all in; so why not have a little drink courtesy of your hosts - Ray and Jane decided to build on the history of the townland of Wineport by naming each room after a wine and including related artefacts in the decor - and a little taste of each wine to enjoy with their compliments! Seriously luxurious bathrooms have separate double-ended bath and walk-in shower, de-mist mirrors, underfloor heating and many little extras; complimentary drinks trays include individual cafetières - and fresh milk in the fridge. Nothing has been overlooked - even the decor, which is designed around a palette of warm neutrals and natural materials, complements the view rather than distracting from it and has universal appeal. Luxurious, romantic, beautiful, this boutique hotel is the perfect hideaway.

IRISH WHISKEY

Wineport Lodge
Glasson, Co Westmeath

Jameson
congratulates

Wineport Lodge

winner of

Hideaway of the Year

RATHBORNES
ESTABLISHED 1488

Atmospheric Restaurant of the Year

Blairs Cove enjoys a stunning waterside location in west Cork, at the head of Dunmanus Bay. While later additions include an elegant conservatory overlooking an intriguing courtyard garden (an attractive option on fine summer evenings), the original room at this remarkable restaurant is lofty, stone-walled and black-beamed: but, although characterful, any tendency to rusticity is immediately offset by the choice of a magnificent chandelier as the central feature, gilt-framed family portraits on the walls and the superb insouciance of using their famous grand piano to display an irresistible array of desserts. They have things down to a fine art at Blairs Cove - and what a formula: an enormous central buffet groans under the weight of the legendary hors d'oeuvre display, a speciality that is unrivalled in Ireland. Main course specialities of local seafood or the best of meat and poultry are char-grilled at a special wood-fired grill right in the restaurant and, in addition to those desserts, full justice is done to the ever-growing selection of local farmhouse cheese for which West Cork is rightly renowned. Theatrical it may be, but some of the best food in Ireland is served here. And, with its immense candelabras, wall sconces and candlesticks on every table - freshly lit each night and casting a magical glow on the entranced diners - it is undoubtedly one of our most atmospheric restaurants. This place is truly an original.

2002 Winner:
The Belfry, Mullingar, Co Westmeath

RATHBORNES
ESTABLISHED 1488

Blairs Cove House
Durrus, Co Cork

Rathborne Candles
congratulates

Blairs Cove House
winner of
Atmospheric Restaurant of the Year

IRISH
HEART
FOUNDATION

Happy Heart Eat Out Award

An attractive modern café-bar, Lennons is run by Sinéad and Liam Byrne - and their stylish contemporary design and deliciously healthy, reasonably priced food have clearly been a hit with both local business professionals and visitors to the town. Simple, uncluttered tables and speedy service of jugs of iced water bode well for menus that include a host of wholesome dishes: delicious home-made soups; open sandwiches (on freshly-baked home-made bread); ciabattas, wraps, some very tempting salads (with low fat options) and a range of hot specials. Lots of must-have mainstream dishes happen to be meatless and are highlighted as suitable for vegetarians, eg couscous with roasted Mediterranean vegetables served with homemade bread, or aubergine, courgette & tomato cheese bake with tossed salad - and the light lunch and healthy options are very popular too. Everything is freshly made to order from top quality ingredients (some local sources are named on the menu) and really wholesome - all at very accessible prices, so it's a winning formula. Leave room for delicious home-made desserts - hazelnut meringue roulade with raspberry sauce, perhaps, or hot apple crumble. This is well-balanced, good home cooking which is as healthy as it is delicious, meeting the Irish Heart Foundation's definition of a Healthy Choice - i.e. dishes with lots of fruit and vegetables that are high in fibre and low in fat, especially saturated fat - and a worthy winner of the Happy Heart Eat Out Award for 2003.

2002 Winner:
Preston House, Abbyleix, Co Laois

IRISH
HEART
FOUNDATION

Lennon's Café Bar
Carlow

Irish Heart Foundation
congratulates

Lennon's Café Bar

winner of
Happy Heart Eat Out Award

Bord Glas

Developing Horticulture

Creative Use of
Vegetables Award

Interesting decor and imaginative French and American-inspired cooking are the hallmarks at Ben Gorman and Mark Harrell's unusual restaurant on the edge of Temple Bar. Cooking at The Mermaid is innovative, seasonal and often memorable for inspired combinations of flavour, texture and colour - terrific vegetarian main courses such as steamed globe artichoke stuffed with basil pesto & niçoise salad rub shoulders with hearty meat dishes which vary with the seasons but are invariably full of interest. Vegetables, always used imaginatively, are beautifully integrated into main courses - loin of lamb with beetroot and couscous is a good, colourful example, and there are many more like it on each day's menus. Autumn is a particularly satisfying season to visit the Mermaid, as they revel in the rich harvest of good local produce there is to choose from, notably root vegetables; there is an earthy tone to cooking at The Mermaid that responds well to hearty late season produce - although, in summer, when desserts like gooseberry & elderflower fool with pistachio biscotti are well worth leaving room for, it is a different story. And, of course, there are Irish cheeses like the wonderful, deeply flavoured Gabriel and Desmond from west Cork, served with celery biscuits... Magic.

2002 Winner:
Avoca Café, Co. Wicklow

Bord Glas
Developing Horticulture

Mermaid Café
Dublin

Bord Glas
congratulates

Mermaid Café
winner of
Creative Use of Vegetables Award

Natural Food Award

Built on the site of a deserted village in a Wicklow valley, this extraordinary food, drink and leisure complex exists thanks to the vision of three brothers, Evan, Eoin and Bernard Doyle. The driving force is Evan, a pioneer of the new organic movement when he ran The Strawberry Tree in Killarney, a fine restaurant which was outstanding for its commitment to using wild, free-range and organic produce long before these became buzz words among a wider public. Now their new "village" has taken root and is thriving, with an hotel and restaurant already receiving national recognition for their strong position on organic food, and a little "street" with an olde-worlde pub (Actons), a micro-brewery and gift shops selling home-made produce and related quality products. Organic food markets, held on the first Sunday of the month (first and third in summer) have proved a great success and attracta lot of regulars (both stall-holders and customers). After filling their shopping bags with organic goodies, many visitors drop into the hotel - which is spacious and welcoming, with elegant country house furnishings, open fires and plenty of places to sit quietly or meet for a sociable drink - and stay on to enjoy an organic lunch. It makes a terrific day out and it's a great credit to Evan and his team that such an unusual enterprise, built where there was nothing, should have become a favourite destination for real food enthusiasts from far and wide.

2002 Winner:
Otto's Creative Catering, Co Cork

BrookLodge Hotel
Macreddin, Co Wicklow

Euro-Toques
congratulates

BrookLodge Hotel

winner of
Natural Food Award

Georgina Campbell congratulates

Moy House
Lahinch, Co Clare
Country House of the Year

Killeen House
Galway City
Guesthouse of the Year

Greenhill House
Aghadowey, Co Londonderry
Farmhouse of the Year

2002 Winners:
St. Clerans, Co Galway,
Gorman's Clifftop House, Co Kerry,
Boltown House, Co Meath

Winners 2003

Moy House

Killeen House

Greenhill House

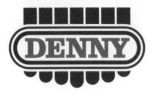

Irish Breakfast Awards

Kilkenny Café
Dublin
Dublin Winner

Old Workhouse
Dunshaughlin, Co Meath
Leinster Winner

Dolphin Beach
Clifden, Co Galway
Connaught Winner

St John's Country House
Fahan, Co Donegal
Ulster Winner

Winners 2003

Kilkenny Café

Old Workhouse

Dolphin Beach

St John's Country House

Munster & National Winner
Irish Breakfast Awards

Longueville House is a lovely Georgian mansion, beautifully located overlooking the famous River Blackwater - and the ruins of the O'Callaghan family's original home, Dromineen Castle. The house is elegantly furnished, and the river, farm and garden supply William O'Callaghan's kitchen with fresh salmon in season, the famous Longueville lamb and all the fruit and vegetables. Accommodation is sumptuous and, after a good night's sleep, a Longueville breakfast is a treat to be cherished: in addition to a wide range of more usual choices, you can have delicious pressed apple juice and seasonal compôtes from the walled garden, and there's home-mixed muesli, natural yogurt, farmhouse cheeses and slices off a mustard glazed baked ham. Then there are all the home-bakes - soda breads, scones, pain au chocolat and croissants - and house preserves, marmalade and Longueville honey. And that's just from the buffet - there's still a cooked breakfast menu to follow, including porridge and fish of the day as well as a superb rendition of the traditional cooked breakfast. Of all the wonderful breakfasts sampled during the Guide's travels throughout the length and breadth of Ireland during the past year, this was the best. Worth dropping in for even if you can't stay overnight - what a way to break a journey!

2002 Winner:
Hanora's Cottage, Co Waterford

Longueville House
Mallow, Co Cork

Denny
congratulates

Longueville House
National Winner of the
Irish Breakfast Awards

GETTING THE FLAVOUR
OF IRISH WHISKEY

Enjoyed by connoisseurs worldwide, Jameson enjoys universal brand awareness in Ireland. And it is a matter of national pride that this superb beverage, so much a part of Irish life, now has genuine international status.

Portrait of John Jameson by Raeburn

Unlike most other whiskeys, Jameson is distilled three times, ensuring a final product that is particularly smooth and pure. During maturation in sherry and bourbon oak casks, stored in dark aromatic warehouses, the whiskey mellows over the years, and takes on its rich golden colour.

The expertise required has a long history. Irish whiskey was invented as far back as the 6th Century, when monks discovered that an apparatus called the "alembic" - originally used to distill perfume in the Middle East - could be more usefully employed to produce "Uisce Beatha", the "Water of Life". Pronounced "ishka baahaa", it was later anglicised as "whiskey".

In time, the alembic, as used for whiskey distilling, became known as the "pot still". Ireland was already rich in whiskey's essential ingredients of pure water and golden barley. But it took the particular genius of the early distillers to discover that the barley used for the malt must first be dried in closed kilns to ensure that its honeyed taste shines through in the final product, giving Irish whiskey its distinctive mellow flavour.

John Jameson founded his distillery in Dublin in 1780, at a time when quality control in the industry was often perfunctory. Jameson set out with the clearcut ambition of creating the best whiskey in the world, distilled in the finest premises under the watchful supervision of highly motivated and experienced staff.

By 1996, Jameson had become the world's fastest growing spirit brand, retaining the loyalty of traditional drinkers while reaching new consumers through its versatility with mixers. Today, the Old Jameson Distillery in Dublin, together with the Jameson Heritage Centre in Midleton, Co Cork, are ranked among the most popular visitor attractions in the country.

Jameson whiskeys - for the brand has some very special even more mature variants - can be everything from an aperitif to a digestif, and a simple celebratory drink at all appropriate times. Richly imbued with history, it lends itself well to the most famous of Irish toasts and blessings:

Health and long life to you
Land without rent to you
The woman (or man) of your choice to you
A child every year to you
and may you be in heaven before
the Devil knows you're dead!

"Blas agus sasamh go bhfaighe tu air"

Feile Bia – a celebration of quality food – is now in its third year and continues to emphasise the importance of food sourcing and provenance in hotels, restaurants and pubs throughout the country. The programme is organised by Bord Bia (Irish Food Board) in conjunction with the Restaurants Association of Ireland and the Irish Hotels Federation and is supported by the farming community and Euro-Toques – the European community of chefs.

Participating members commit to sourcing beef, pigmeat, lamb, chicken and eggs from recognised Quality Assurance schemes and identify the country of origin of these quality products on their menus.

By signing the Charter, caterers are assuring consumers that they are committed to:

- Looking for assurances, as appropriate, that the listed products are produced under Bord Bia or other recognised Quality Assurance Schemes.

- Identifying the origin of these quality products on their menus.

- Developing dishes and menus to profile local food products.

Consumers can identify establishments with a commitment to Quality Assured food through the display of the blue framed Feile Bia certificate. It's well worth looking out for, as a reassurance that the establishment you have selected demonstrates a commitment to sourcing their ingredients through traceable systems and providing information to the consumer.

Those establishments recommended by the Guide which have signed up to the Charter are listed below and are identified within the body of the Guide by the use of the Feile Bia logo.

Féile Bia Members

CARLOW

Ballon, Sherwood Park House
Carlow Town, Lennons Café Bar
Carlow Town, The Beams Restaurant

CAVAN

Ballyconnell, The Anglers Rest
Blacklion, Mac Nean House & Bistro
Cavan Town, The Oak Room

CLARE

Bunratty, Fitzpatricks Hotel
Ennis, Hal Pino's Restaurant
Ennis, Temple Gate Hotel
Ennis, Woodstock Hotel
Lahinch, The Conch Shell Restaurant
Mountshannon, An Cupan Caife
Shannon, Great Southern Hotel

CORK

Baltimore, The Baltimore Harbour Hotel
Bantry, O'Connor's Seafood Restaurant
Ballylickey, Sea View House Hotel
Bantry, The Snug Bar
Blarney, Blairs Inn
Carrigaline, Gregorys Restaurant
Clonakilty, Dunmore House Hotel
Clonakilty, O'Keeffes & The Emmet Hotel
Cobh, Robin Hill House
Cork City, Farmgate Café
Cork City, Fenns Quay Restaurant
Cork City, Hayfield Manor Hotel
Cork City, Gresham Metropole
Cork City, Idaho.Café
Cork City, Isaac's Restaurant
Cork City, Jacobs On The Mall
Cork City, Jurys Inn Cork
Cork City, Maryborough Hotel
Cork City, Rochestown Park Hotel
Cork City, Silver Springs Hotel
Glengarriff, Glengarriff Eccles Hotel
Innishannon, Innishannon House Hotel
Kilbrittain, Casino House
Killeagh, Brownes Restaurant
Kinsale, Actons Hotel
Kinsale, Blue Haven
Kinsale, Crackpots Restaurant
Kinsale, Man Friday
Kinsale, Trident Hotel
Kinsale, The Old Bank House

Kinsale, The Vintage Restaurant
Macroom, The Castle Hotel
Midleton, Barnabrow Country House
Midleton, Farmgate Restaurant
Midleton, Midleton Park Hotel
Mitchelstown, O'Callaghans Delicatessen & Café
Roscarbery, Celtic Ross Hotel
Shanagarry, Ballymaloe House Hotel
Skibbereen, Ty Ar Mor Seafood Restaurant

DONEGAL

Fahan, St Johns Countryhouse & Restaurant

DUBLIN

Dublin 1, Chapter One Restaurant
Dublin 1, Gresham Hotel
Dublin 1, Jurys Inn Custom House
Dublin 2, Alexander Hotel
Dublin 2, Avoca Café, Suffolk Street
Dublin 2, Bewley's Grafton St
Dublin 2, Brooks Hotel
Dublin 2, Brownes Brasserie & Townhouse
Dublin 2, Bruno's Restaurant
Dublin 2, Buswells Hotel
Dublin 2, Davenport Hotel
Dublin 2, Fitzers
Dublin 2, Jacobs Ladder
Dublin 2, Kilkenny Restaurant & Café
Dublin 2, L'Ecrivain Restaurant
Dublin 2, Mont Clare Hotel
Dublin 2, Montys Of Katmandhu
Dublin 2, One Pico Restaurant
Dublin 2, Shalimar Indian Restaurant
Dublin 2, Shanahan's On The Green
Dublin 2, St Stephen's Green Hotel

Féile Bia Members

Dublin 2, Westbury Hotel
Dublin 4, Anglesea Town House
Dublin 4, Bella Cuba
Dublin 4, Berkeley Court Hotel
Dublin 4, Burlington Hotel
Dublin 4, Ernie's Restaurant
Dublin 4, Four Seasons Hotel
Dublin 4, Jurys Ballsbridge Hotel
Dublin 4, Jurys Montrose Hotel
Dublin 4, Mespil Hotel
Dublin 4, O'Connells In Ballsbridge
Dublin 4, Pembroke Townhouse
Dublin 4, Rolys Bistro
Dublin 4, The Towers
Dublin, 8 Jurys InnChristchurch
Dublin 18, Bistro One
Dublin 22, Jurys Green Isle Hotel
Dublin 22, Red Cow Moran Hotel
Dublin Airport, Great Southern Hotel
Dublin Airport, Holiday Inn
Dun Laoghaire, Brasserie Na Mara
Dun Laoghaire, Gresham Royal Marine Hotel
Glencullen, Johnnie Fox's Pub
Howth, King Sitric
Malahide, Bon Appetit Restaurant
Malahide, Cruzzo Restaurant
Saggart, Citywest Hotel
Skerries, Redbank House & Restaurant
Stillorgan, Stillorgan Park Hotel

GALWAY

Galway City, Ardilaun House Hotel
Galway City, Corrib Great Southern Hotel
Galway City, Great Southern Hotel
Galway City, Jurys Inn Galway
Galway City, Park House Hotel
Galway City, Radisson SAS Hote
Ballinasloe, Tohers Restaurant & Bar
Clarenbridge, The Old School House Restaurant
Clifden, Ardagh Hotel
Clifden, Mitchell's Restaurant
Furbo, Connemara Coast Hotel
Moycullen, Moycullen House Restaurant
Moycullen, White Gables Restaurant
Portmuna, Shannon Oaks Hotel & Country Club
Renvyle, Renvyle House Hotel
Salthill, Galway Bay Hotel
Tuam, Cre-Na-Cille Restaurant
Tuam, Finn's Restaurant

KERRY

Caherdaniel, Derrynane Hotel

Dingle, Chart House Restaurant
Dingle, Cleevaun Country House
Dingle, Dingle Skellig Hotel
Dingle, Doyles Seafood Restaurant
Dingle, Lord Bakers Restaurant
Listowel, Listowel Arms Hotel
Killarney, The Beaufort Bar & Restaurant
Killarney, The Great Southern Hotel
Parknasilla, Great Southern Hotel
Tralee, Ballygarry House Hotel
Tralee, Meadowlands Hotel
Tralee, The Abbey Gate Hotel
Tralee, Val's Bar & Bistro

KILDARE

Ballymore Eustace, Ballymore Inn
Straffan, The K-Club

KILKENNY

Kilkenny City, Hotel Kilkenny
Kilkenny City, Kilkenny Design Centre Restaurant
Kilkenny City, Lacken House
Kilkenny City, Newpark Hotel
Kilkenny City, The Kilkenny Rivercourt Hotel
Bennettsbridge, Calabash Bistro

LAOIS

Abbeyleix, Preston House
Portlaoise, Kingfisher Restaurant
Portlaoise, The Kitchen & Food Hall

LEITRIM

Carrick-on-Shannon, Bush Hotel

LIMERICK

Limerick City, Brulées Restaurant
Limerick City, Castletroy Park Hotel
Limerick City, Jurys Inn Limerick
Limerick City, The Locke Bar & Restaurant
Abbeyfeale, Whytes Restaurant
Adare, Adare Manor Hotel & Golf Resort
Adare, Dunraven Arms Hotel
Adare, The Wild Geese Restaurant
Adare, Woodlands House Hotel
Croom, The Mill-Race Restaurant

LOUTH

Carlingford, The Oystercatcher Bistro
Dundalk, Quaglino's Restaurant

Féile Bia Members

MAYO

Castlebar, Breaffy House Hotel

Foxford, Healys Hotel

Westport, Hotel Westport

Westport, Knockranny House Hotel

Westport, The Atlantic Coast Hotel

MEATH

Bettystown, Bacchus At The Coastguard

Dunboyne, Caldwells Restaurant

Kells, Headford Arms Hotel (Vanilla Pod)

Kells, The Ground Floor Restaurant

Navan, The Loft Restaurant

Slane, Conyngham Arms Hotel

Trim, Franzini O'Briens

MONAGHAN

Carrickmacross, Nuremore Hotel

Glaslough, Castle Leslie

Monaghan Town, Andy's Bar & Restaurant

OFFALY

Edenderry, Tyrrells Restaurant

Tullamore, Tullamore Court Hotel

ROSCOMMON

Roscommon Town, Abbey Hotel

Tarmonbarry, Keenan's

SLIGO

Rosses Point, Austies

Sligo town, Coach Lane Restaurant

Sligo town, Montmartre Restaurant

TIPPERARY

Cahir, Clifford's At The Bell

Cashel, Legends Townhouse & Restaurant

Clonmel, Angela's Restaurant

Clonmel, Hotel Minella

Roscrea, Fiacri Country House Restaurant

Terryglass, The Derg Inn

Thurles, Inch House

WATERFORD

Waterford City, Gatchells Restaurant

Waterford City, The Gingerman Bar

Waterford City, Granville Hotel

Waterford City, The Wine Vault

Ardmore, Whitehorses Restaurant

Cappoquin, Richmond House

Cheekpoint, McAlpin's Suir Inn

Dungarvan, Powersfield House

Tallow, Buggy's Glencairn Inn

WESTMEATH

Athlone, Hodson Bay Hotel

Athlone, Manifesto Restaurant

Athlone, Restaurant Le Chateau

Athlone, Wineport Lodge

Mullingar, Woodville House Restaurant

WEXFORD

Arthurstown, Dunbrody House

Duncannon, Sqigl Restaurant & Roche's Bar

Enniscorthy, Riverside Park Hotel

Kilmore Quay, Kehoe's Pub

Rosslare, Kelly's Resort Hotel

Rosslare Harbour, Great Southern Hotel

Wexford town, Ferrycarrig Hotel

Wexford town, Forde's Restaurant

Wexford town, Heavens Above The Sky & Ground

Wexford town, La Riva Restaurant

Wexford town, Talbot Hotel

WICKLOW

Arklow, Kitty's of Arklow

Arklow, Woodenbridge Hotel

Avoca Village, Avoca Café

Blessington, Downshire House Hotel

Dunlavin, Rathsallagh House

Greystones, The Hungry Monk

Kilmacanogue, Avoca Café

Powerscourt, Avoca Café

Roundwood, The Roundwood Inn

IRELAND

where the living is special...

Ireland today is a place of energising contrasts. The buzz of the towns and cities - particularly Dublin - is world class. Yet still there are large areas of breathtakingly beautiful scenery where life is lived at a much more gentle pace. And in town and country alike, there is enjoyment and appreciation of the good things in life, reflecting Ireland's long experience in warm hospitality, and our zest in contemporary prosperity. From the discerning traveller's point of view, the most striking recent change for the better has been the emergence of a new food culture that now makes Ireland a gourmet destination of the highest order - and with the high quality accommodation to match it.

Chic contemporary hotels are taking their place beside much-loved traditional establishments and the recent arrival of top international chains has put the leading Irish hotels on their mettle. But the newcomers, however prestigious their reputations may be, recognise that they have a challenge on their hands and there is fierce competition from Irish-owned hotel groups who are masters of hospitality.

Many Irish hotels now successfully operate both fine-dining and informal brasserie-style restaurants - and there's a bevy of talented and determined owner-chefs out there too, so it's definitely not a walk-over for the big names, who have to find a balance between providing the services demanded by an international clientèle and the need to give visitors a meaningful flavour of Ireland.

For generations, Irish chefs, trained in the classical tradition, have gone abroad to complete their training and on their return, as surely as the invaders of earlier centuries, brought back foreign culinary influences. The process continues to this day - as a glance at any popular menu shows - but, fortunately, the demands of discerning visitors are helping to re-awaken interest in Irish food culture.

THE 'FOOD ISLAND'

Ireland is a food exporting country and Bord Bia, the Irish Food Board, is responsible for promoting Irish food at home and abroad: their slogan "Ireland the Food Island" highlights this neatly. Although they have 700 food and drink companies to support, they are committed to the development of speciality foods, a sector that has grown in strength and variety, in particular those producers who take charge of every step in the process from

farm to consumer: craft sausage-makers, organic meat and poultry farmers, specialists in wild game and rare breeds, producers who work with fruits, herbs, and vegetables, and the farm cheesemakers who have gained wide respect in the international food community.

The success of niche-market foods, notably Irish farm cheeses, in recent decades has come to symbolise the hopes of food-lovers for the future of mainstream produce. It is a source of wonderment to Europeans that today's Irish farm cheeses are produced on just one farm, usually by one dedicated family. The variety and high quality is astonishing. One reason for this is the Irish climate. Our green grasslands in favoured areas are rich in wild, natural herbage and sheep, goats and cows are largely grass fed to produce flavoursome and distinctive milk. You can experience local farmhouse cheeses in restaurants, or visit local food markets in Dublin, Belfast, Cork, and many other small country markets. Food markets are a fun day out and feature innovative and traditional products from small food producers.

In the current cosmopolitan atmosphere - where global cuisine is the norm, even in many rural restaurants - the best Irish chefs are increasingly aware of the need to give the Irish table "a sense of place". The Féile Bia programme encourages chefs everywhere to think less about contemporary cooking fashions and look to their roots. Féile Bia, which began as a week-long festival celebrating Irish food and traditional Irish cooking, has been developed as a year-round programme. Working together, Bord Bia, the Restaurants Association of Ireland and the Irish Hotels Federation set up this scheme, with the support of the farming community. Establishments that undertake to source and use local/quality-assured products from named suppliers, and be subject to an annual audit, may display the blue-framed Féile Bia certificate. Consumer research shows that we place a high value on quality Irish food and assume when eating out that is what we are getting. At the top end of the market, especially where the chef is a member of Euro-Toques, this is generally the case; but it is not universally true.

Féile Bia aims to provide assurance for consumers that the food they eat is quality sourced. Beef, pork, bacon, lamb, chicken and eggs are included in the scheme, which is under continuous development. Concerned consumers should look out for the certificate and talk to owners or managers about their policy on sourcing other foods - showing this interest will help the Féile Bia scheme to grow and prosper.

EURO-TOQUES

Thanks to the dedication of many talented Irish chefs and small producers, progress on strengthening the regional quality of Irish food is promising. Dubbed variously "the new Irish cuisine" or "contemporary Irish cooking", a recognisably Irish cooking style is gradually emerging, producing lighter, modern food that is still based on traditional foodstuffs and themes. Through Féile Bia, and other programmes and organisations which recognise the value of quality Irish produce and traditions, chefs are encouraged to avoid the dangers of fashionable but bland

Ross Lewis, Ireland's Euro-Toques Commissioner General

internationalism and to bring a real Irish flavour back into their restaurants. Euro-Toques, the European Community of Chefs, is an organisation with just these issues at heart - and over 200 Irish chefs are enthusiastic members. Their charter commits them to supporting the quality of natural and traditional foods, to maintaining traditional dishes and traditional ways of preparing them in order to keep regional differences alive.

Ross Lewis, chef-proprietor of Dublin's Chapter One Restaurant, is Ireland's Commissioner General, leading a strong Irish 'chapter' which steals time to support social activities like mushroom hunts and visits to members' restaurants and to craft food producers. Euro-Toques nurtures young talent through the annual Baileys/Euro-Toques Young Chef of the Year Competition, and by selecting and coaching Ireland's representative for the world's most prestigious cooking competition, the Bocuse d'Or. But in no way is this an elitist group. All chefs are encouraged to join, providing they are prepared to follow the code of honour and use fine, non-genetically engineered, quality foods, and support local craft food producers.

SLOW FOOD

The Slow Food Movement is a focal point for small craft food producers in much the same way as Euro-Toques is for chefs. This international movement is dedicated to ensuring the future of small-scale, quality, farm-food production. Groups of small producers have formed convivia (local chapters) and hold open days throughout the country. Their goal is to spread and stimulate awareness of food culture (flavours and ancient production techniques), to safeguard the food and agricultural heritage (biodiversity, artisanal techniques and traditions), to protect the heritage of traditional eating places, and oppose the worldwide standardisation of tastes. Although only recently activated in Ireland, it has touched a chord of resonance and is, despite the name, a fast-growing movement that promises to become highly influential.

FOOD FOR VITALITY

A youthful, health-conscious population has taken to the fashion for juices and smoothies with enthusiasm and, judging by the great variety of vegetables and side salads on restaurant tables, the Bord Glas (horticultural development board) "Four or More" slogan, urging Irish people to eat more fruit and vegetables, is proving remarkably popular. Welcome trends include the growing availability of an ever-growing range of creative vegetarian dishes - often placed top of the menu; an increased use of seasonal and named foods from local growers and producers; and the increasing availability of Irish-grown organic foods. Most exciting of all, perhaps, is that the best vegetarian cooking is now very definitely mainstream and much of the most innovative cooking in Ireland at the moment focuses on the creative use of Irish fruit and vegetables in season.

HAPPY HEART EAT OUT

Most visitors lose a little bit of their heart to Ireland - and it's the Irish Heart Foundation's task to keep the hearts of natives and visitors alike physically healthy. The Irish Heart Foundation's aims coincide with those of Bord Glas and other food agencies, in that they want healthy eating to be a normal, enjoyable part of life. The Happy Heart Eat Out initiative is an imaginative (and very Irish way) of doing just that and has been a welcome annual feature of the dining scene for some years now. Restaurants, hotels, pubs and other eating establishments that join the programme offer

healthy eating options - look out for the smiling heart-shaped face on the menu. In a country with an abundance of home-grown vegetables, fruits, herbs, seafoods, and meat, it's not difficulty to offer "healthy" menu options. Increasingly, Irish restaurants recognise the need to care for their customers' health, with dishes low in fat and sodium highlighted on the menu, and a willingness to meet special dietary requirements: if you don't see what you need on the menu, "Just Ask".

Knowing that making "healthy" activities enjoyable is the secret of success, The Irish Heart Foundation invented Slí na Sláinte (the Path to Health) - a simple and successful concept that has since been adopted by 12 other countries. The signed (with a blue-pole) 1 kilometre routes allow walkers or runners to keep track of time and distance. Some run along the coast, or along lake and river banks, others go through parks and city centres. New routes are opened all the time and you'll rarely be far from one.

RICHES FROM LAND & SEA

If you wanted to create the perfect place to catch seafood—clean Atlantic waters warmed along much of the coast by the Gulf Stream—you'd probably invent Ireland: Bord Iascaigh Mhara, the Irish Sea Fisheries Board (BIM), is dedicated to developing the seafood industry and encouraging everyone to cook and enjoy seafood.

A number of current developments are of special interest: in one innovative scheme, BIM and Bord Glas work together to encourage combining of fruit and vegetables with fish—a healthy idea that also makes the most of expensive seafood. Deep-water species are appearing on menus (spurred on by EU fish quotas). The development of aquaculture and the trend towards organic fish farming is growing: organic mussels, trout and salmon are already available and, at Clare Island Sea Farm, the demand for organic salmon outstrips supply. Shellfish grown commercially include oysters, mussels, clams, and scallops - and prime fish such as turbot and halibut are being successfully farmed, even in unexpected locations, such as Turbord Iarthar Chonemara Teo, in Connemara.

BIM's successful pub-lunch programme, The Seafood Circle, is encouraging more pubs to serve seafood dishes for lunch, a meal for which more and more customers prefer lighter, healthier dishes. It's a practical programme and involves workshops and on-going guidance on every aspect of buying, storing, and cooking seafood. Only pubs that meet the criteria are allowed to join the circle following annual audits by Excellence Ireland, and a striking plaque makes them easy to identify.

COSMOPOLITAN TASTES
The current fashion for global cuisine has quickened pace recently; having a large cosmopolitan population with differing tastes and traditions is changing the way Irish people look at ethnic food and there is growing interest in authenticity, both in restaurants and ethnic cooking at home.

Shops, supermarkets and street markets specialising in ethnic cuisines are springing up all over - an example is the African market in the Parnell Street area of Dublin - and mainstream supermarkets are laden down with ethnic ingredients all all kinds. It's an exciting phase and highlights the value of restaurants that are true to a particular style or cuisine, many of which are included in the Guide - all the main cultures are well-represented with Thai and, most recently, Japanese restaurants making particular impact at the moment.

IRISH LOVE OF ATMOSPHERE

Assuming good food, atmosphere in restaurants is probably more important to the Irish dining public than anything else - and, while there's no sure recipe for making a restaurant somewhere people just love to be, genuine hospitality is the main ingredient for success. Relaxing decor and sympathetic lighting are the other magic ingredients and the Guide is privileged to have Rathborne Candles as a sponsor - Ireland's oldest established (AD 1488) surviving company, they have been lighting churches and dining rooms in the country for almost 600 years and are increasingly doing it again today as candles have become an essential "softening" feature in contemporary decor. So the next time you sit in a great candlelit dining-room overlooking a lake or a sunset-lit mountain, just think that for six centuries people have been doing something remarkably similar! Candles are also closely interwoven with traditional customs in Ireland - putting a lighted candle in the window on Christmas Eve, for example, goes back countless generations and there was also a tradition of shopkeepers and publicans giving a candle to customers at Christmas. A recent example was P.J. McCaffrey's, The Hole in the Wall pub in Dublin which is near the old candle factory at Dunsinea and continued the practice of giving out a red Rathbornes to every customer until a few years ago.

DRINKING A TOAST

Drink is an essential element of Irish hospitality, that some prize above food as a way of showing our pleasure in company, our delight in entertainment, and as nourishment for mind and body. The Irish have been brewing since earliest times and without a doubt, had the climate been favourable, there would have been a thriving wine industry, too. Not that the Irish did without wine. Records show that two thousand years ago French wine was being dispatched to Ireland for "feasts in the courts of the kings". Later, early Christian monks sailed to the mouth of the Loire to fetch wine for Irish monasteries and the Vikings paid tribute to Irish kings in vats of wine. The ordinary people were content with cider, ale, and later, with porter and stout.

It is generally accepted that the craft of distillation was brought to Ireland from the Mediterranean, possibly by missionary monks around fifteen hundred years ago. It was used originally to make perfumes and medicines; and later whiskey. Much as we'd like to, no one really knows the origins of whiskey. The Celtic culture was an oral one, particularly when it came to important secrets which were never written down. Historians search ancient texts for written evidence with good reason—our reputation for having invented whiskey is at stake.

We had aqua vitae of course, distilled from wine. We do know, from a wealth of written sources, that by the mid-16th Century the making of grain aqua vitae (known to the Irish as ische beatha and to English-speakers as whiskey) was widespread. Then, on Christmas Day 1661, a tax of 4p was imposed on every gallon distilled. Folklore has it that the making of the illicit spirit poitin began on Boxing Day!

The difference between legal and illicit whiskey was small. By the 18th Century there were 2,000 stills in operation and whiskey had become the spirit of the nation, inspiring poets and musicians and promoting friendship (and frequent disputes) between native and stranger. Irish whiskey is both spelled and made differently from other whiskeys. It is made only from kiln-dried barley (both malted and unmalted), yeast and pure Irish water. It is distilled three times in a pot still, then matured in oak barrels until judged ready for drinking. Visitors can relive this history by visiting three historic distilleries: The Old Jameson Distillery in Dublin, The Bushmills Distillery in Antrim, and the Midleton Distillery in County Cork. The tours are fascinating, covering all aspects of whiskey making - and end with a whiskey tasting.

Although whiskey is better known internationally, gin also has a long and honourable history in Ireland, and is an excellent product. It may hurt a Dubliner to admit it, but Ireland's best known gin is made, and always has been made, in Cork. Cork Dry Gin dates back to 1793 when the first stone of Cork's old Watercourse Distillery was laid. A 1798 recipe book details both the process and the recipe—grain from the rich lands of East Cork, flavoured with juniper berries (a native plant), angelica root, and citrus fruits (then a recent arrival in the port of Cork). Blending these exotic ingredients was the task of William Coldwell and his secret recipe migrated to Cork Distillers Company in 1876 inspiring the uniquely balanced taste of Cork Dry Gin.

THE PERFECT WAY TO START THE DAY

If enjoyment in restaurants and pubs around the country provides memorable evening entertainment, the next morning's breakfast is no small matter for visitors to Ireland - or, indeed, for the Irish on holiday, as having the leisure to indulge in a proper breakfast seems to symbolises escape from the workaday routine. The best hosts take great pride in offering guests a breakfast to remember, whether it be a meal with little choice that is cooked to perfection or a wide range of breakfast menus - in some areas the competition between neighbouring establishments is fierce and menus can run to several pages. They offer traditional country house breakfast dishes that have fallen from favour, fresh and cured fish, European-style salami and hams, wonderful and varied breads, Irish farm cheeses, and vegetarian options. Not that the traditional Irish breakfast is neglected; how could it be when it remains (particularly with visitors) the most popular way to start to the day?

"The full Irish" as it is affectionately known, is not for the faint-hearted—bacon rashers, eggs, sausages, black and white puddings, tomatoes, and fried bread. Once cooked on a great black cast-iron frying pan over a turf fire, it is more usually grilled nowadays (or oven-baked) except for the fried egg. The truly health-conscious will be glad to know you'll be offered a choice of poached, scrambled, or baked eggs (which, just to confuse, are often cooked in thick Irish cream). The Ulster Fry, on the other hand, remains defiantly unreconstructed—at least in name! Its additional ingredients include fried potato cakes, boxty, farls of soda (griddle) bread, mushrooms, and on occasion baked beans! Small wonder that the "all-day breakfast" is widely on offer!

You can forgive visitors for being confused sometimes; not only can they eat breakfast all day but there is a growing trend of serving Sunday lunch all day, too! You've heard of seamless hospitality? It's right here in Ireland.

IRELAND

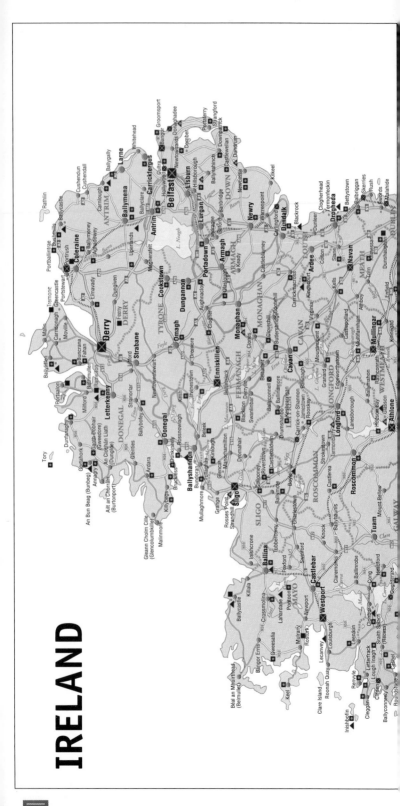

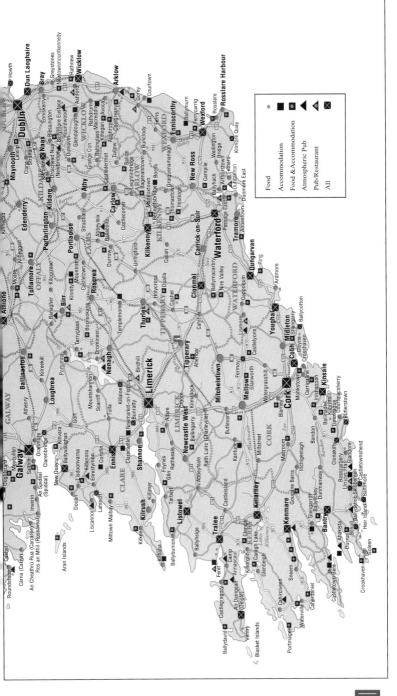

Food •

Accommodation ■

Food & Accommodation ◀

Atmospheric Pub ◁

Pub/Restaurant ⊠

All

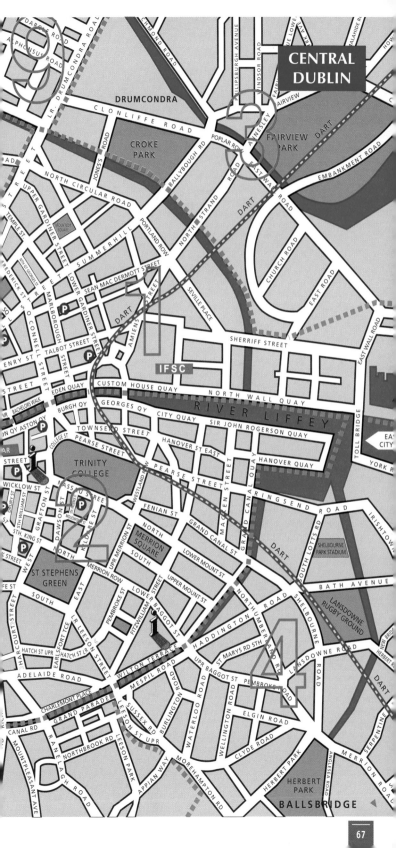

CENTRAL DUBLIN

DRUMCONDRA

CROKE PARK

FAIRVIEW PARK

IFSC

RIVER LIFFEY

TRINITY COLLEGE

MERRION SQUARE

ST STEPHENS GREEN

SHELBOURNE PARK STADIUM

LANSDOWNE RUGBY GROUND

HERBERT PARK

BALLSBRIDGE

DUBLIN
A Town for our Times

Dublin continues to be Western Europe's fastest expanding economic centre even in the uncertainties of 2003, its creative business and commercial energy matched by the vibrancy of its everyday life and hospitality. For Dublin is a city whose time has come. It's an old town whose many meandering stories have interacted and combined to create today's busy riverside and coastal metropolis. Through a wide variety of circumstances, it has become an entertaining place ideally suited for the civilised enjoyment of life in the 21st Century.

Dubliners tend to wear their city's history lightly, despite having in their environment so much of the past in the way of ancient monuments, historic buildings, gracious squares and fine old urban architecture that still manages to be gloriously alive. This if anything is emphasised by the city's impressive modern architecture, seen particularly in the area around the International Financial Services, and most spectacularly in the Gaelic Athletic Association's completely revamped headquarters at Croke Park, now the third largest stadium in Europe, and a masterpiece of contemporary design which provides a spectacular setting for epic matches of hurling and Gaelic football.

Dubliners may not quite take their city's dynamic interaction of classic and modern for granted, but nevertheless they have to get on with life. Indeed, these days they've a vigorous appetite for it. So they'll quickly deflate any visitor's excessive enthusiasm about their city's significance with some throwaway line of Dublin wit, or sweep aside highfalutin notions of some figure of established cultural importance by recalling how their grandfathers had the measure of that same character when he was still no more than a pup making a nuisance of himself in the neighbourhood pub.

The origins of the city's name are in keeping with this downbeat approach. From the ancient Irish there came something which derived from a makeshift solution to local inconvenience. Baile Atha Cliath - the official name today - means nothing more exciting than "the townland of the hurdle ford". Ancient Ireland being an open plan sort of place without towns, the future city was no more than a river crossing.

But where the Irish saw inconvenience, the Vikings saw an opportunity. When they brought their longships up the River Liffey, they found a sheltered berth in a place which the locals of the hurdle ford called Dubh Linn - "the black pool". Although the name was to go through many mutations as the Vikings were succeeded by the Normans who in turn were in the business of becoming English, today's name of Dublin is remarkably similar to the one which the Vikings came upon, although the old Irish would have pronounced it as something more like "doo-lin".

The name makes sense, for it was thanks to the existence of the black pool that Dublin became the port and trading base which evolved as the country's natural administrative centre. Thus your Dubliner may well think that the persistent official use of Baile Atha Cliath is an absurdity. But it most empatically isn't the business of any visitor to say so, for although Dublin came into existence almost by accident, it has now been around for a long time, and Dubliners have developed their own attitudes and their own way of doing things, while their seaport - still very much part of the city - has never been busier.

Located by a wide bay with some extraordinarily handsome hills and mountains near at hand, the city has long had as an important part of its makeup the dictates of stylish living, and the need to cater efficiently for individual tastes and requirements. From time to time the facade has been maintained through periods of impoverishment, but even in the earliest mediaeval period this was already a major centre of craftmanship and innovative shop-keeping. Today, the Dublin craftsmen and shop-keepers and their assistants are characterful subjects worthy of respectful academic study. And in an age when "going shopping" has become the world's favourite leisure activity, this old city has reinvented herself in the forefront of international trends.

For Dublin virtually shunned the Industrial Revolution, or at least took some care to ensure that it happened elsewhere. The city's few large enterprises tended to be aimed at personal needs and the consumer market, rather than some aspiration towards heavy industry. Typical of them was Guinness's Brewery, founded in 1759. Today, its work-force may be much slimmed in every sense, but it still creates the black nectar, and if a new mash is under way up at the brewery and the wind is coming damply across Ireland from the west, the aroma of Guinness in the making will be wafted right into the city centre, the moist evocative essence of Anna Livia herself, while the imaginatively renovated Guinness Storehouse - with its interactive museums, restaurants and bars - provides a visitor centre of international quality.

Although some of the vitality of the city faded in the periods when the focus of power had been moved elsewhere, today Dublin thrives as one of Europe's more entertaining capitals, and as a global centre of the computer, communications and financial services industries. While it may be trite to suggest that her history has been a fortuitous preparation for the needs of modern urban life in all its variety of work and relaxation, there is no denying Dublin's remarkable capacity to provide the ideal circumstances for fast-moving people-orientated modern industries, even if those same people find at times that their movement within the city is hampered by weight of traffic. Nevertheless it's a civilised city where the importance of education is a central theme of the strong family ethos, this high level of education making it a place of potent attraction in the age of information technology.

Such a city naturally has much of interest for historians of all kinds, and a vibrant cultural life is available for visitors and Dubliners alike. You can immerse yourself in it all as much or as little as you prefer, for today's Dublin is a city for all times and all tastes, and if you're someone who hopes to enjoy Dublin as we know Dubliners enjoy it, we know you'll find much of value here. And don't forget that there's enjoyment in Dublin well hidden from the familiar tourist trails.

History is well-matched by modernity, or a mixture of both. The glass palaces of the International Financial Services Centre point the way to a maturing new business district which is a pleasure to savour. To the westward, the award-winning transformation of the Smithfield area beside the popular Old Jameson Distillery Visitor centre is another magnet for the discerning visitor who enjoys a sense of the past interacting with the present.

When Dublin was starting to expand to its present size during the mid-20th Century, with people flocking in from all over Ireland to work in the city, it was said that the only "real Dub" was someone who didn't go home to the country for the weekend. Today, with Dublin so popular with visitors, the more cynical citizens might well comment that the surest test of a real Dub is someone who avoids Temple Bar...

But it is rather unfair of any Dubliner to dismiss that bustling riverside hotbed of musical pubs, ethnic restaurants, cultural events and nightclubs as being no more than a tourist ghetto. After all, in addition to its many places of entertainment and hospitality, Temple Bar is also home to at least 1,300 people, their needs being served locally by useful happenings such as the Natural Food Fair, held every Saturday (10am to 6pm) in Cow's Lane, with organic foods and the freshest of produce from land and sea matching the gourmet quality of the exotic products sold through the Specialist Market in Meeting House Square.

So there's real life here too. And at the very least, it is Temple Bar which maintains the Dubliner's international reputation as a round-the-clock party animal. So now that the area has settled down and achieved a certain mellowness in its new role, you will definitely meet "real Dubs" here, though in today's very cosmopolitan city, just how we'd define a "real Dub" is a moot point.

Nevertheless, come nightfall and your discerning Dubliner is more likely to be found in a pleasant pub or restaurant in one of the city's many urban villages, delightfully named places such as Ranelagh or Rathmines or Templeogue or Stoneybatter or Phibsborough or Donnybrook or Glasnevin or Ringsend or Dundrum or Clontarf or Drumcondra or Chapelizod, to name only a few. And then there are places like Stepaside or Howth or Glasthule or Foxrock or Dalkey which are at sufficient distance as scarcely to think of themselves as being part of Dublin at all. Yet that's where you'll find today's real Dubs enjoying their fair city every bit as much as city centre folk. Happy is the visitor who is able to savour it all, in and around this town for our times.

Local Attractions & Information

Abbey & Peacock Theatres Lower Abbey Street	01 8787222
Andrew's Lane Theatre off Exchequer Street	01 6795720
The Ark Arts Centre Eustace St., Temple Bar D2	01 6707788
Bank of Ireland (historic) College Green	01 6615933
Botanic Gardens Glasnevin, D9	01 8374388
Ceol - Irish Traditional Music Centre Smithfield	01 8173820
Christchurch Cathedral Christchurch Place, D8	01 6778099
City Arts Centre 23-25 Moss St., D2	01 6770643
Croke Park GAA Stadium and Museum D3	01 8558176
Drimnagh Castle (moat, formal 17c gardens) Longmile Rd	01 4502530
Dublin Airport	01 8144222
Dublin Castle Dame Street	01 6777129
Dublin Film Festival (April)	01 6792937

Dublin Garden Festival, RDS (June)	01 4900600
Dublin International Horse Show, RDS, (August)	01 6680866
Dublin International Organ & Choral Fest. (June)	01 6773066
Dublin Theatre Festival (October)	01 6778439
Dublin Tourism Centre (restored church) Suffolk St.	1850 230330
Dublin Writer's Museum Parnell Square	01 8722077
Dublinia (living history) Christchurch	01 4758137
Gaiety Theatre South King Street	01 6771717
Gate Theatre Cavendish Row	01 8744045
Guinness Brewery St Jame's Gate	01 4536700 ext 5155
Guinness Storehouse	01 4084800
Helix DCU Performing Arts Centre, Collins Avenue, D9	01 7007000
Hugh Lane Municipal Gallery Parnell Square	01 8741903
Irish Antique Dealers Fair, RDS (October)	01 2859294
Irish Film Centre Eustace Street	01 6793477
Irish Museum of Modern Art/Royal Hospital Kilmainham	01 6718666
Irish Music Hall of Fame Middle Abbey Street	01 8783345
Irish Tourist Board/Bord Failte Baggot St Bridge	01 6024000
Iveagh Gardens Earlsfort Terrace	01 4757816
Jameson Distillery Smithfield, Dublin 7	01 8072355
Kilmainham Gaol Kilmainham	01 4535984
Lansdowne Road Rugby Ground Ballsbridge	01 6684601
Mother Redcaps Market nr St Patricks/Christchurch Fri-Sun 10am-5.30pm	
National Botanic Gardens Glasnevin	01 8377596
National Concert Hall Earlsfort Terrace	01 6711888
National Gallery of Ireland Merrion Square West	01 6615133
National Museum of Ireland Kildare Street	01 6777444
National Museum of Ireland Collins Barracks	01 6777444
Natural History Museum Merrion Street	01 6777444
Newman House St Stephen's Green	01 4757255
Northern Ireland Tourist Board Nassau Street	01 6791977
Number 29 (18c House) Lower Fitzwilliam Street	01 7026155
Old Jameson Distillery Smithfield, Dublin 7	01 8072355
Olympia Theatre Dame Street	01 6777744
Point Depot (Concerts & Exhibitions) North Wall Quay	01 8366000
Powerscourt Townhouse South William Street	01 6794144
Pro Cathedral Marlborough Street	01 2874292
Project Arts Centre 39 East Sussex St, D2	01 6796622
RDS (Royal Dublin Society) Ballsbridge	01 6680866
Royal Hospital Kilmainham	01 6798666
St Michans Church (mummified remains) D7	01 8724154
St Patrick's Cathedral Patrick's Close	01 4539472
Shaw birthplace 33 Synge St., D8	01 4750854
Temple Bar Foodmarket Saturdays 11am - 4 pm (all year)	
The Dillon Garden 45 Sandford Rd, Ranelagh, D6	01 4971308
The Old Jameson Distillery Smithfield, D7	01 8072355
Tivoli Theatre Francis Street	01 4544472
Trinity College (Book of Kells & Dublin Experience)	01 6082308
Viking Adventure Essex St W, Temple Bar,	01 6796040
War Memorial Gardens (Sir Edwin Lutyens) Islandbridge	01 6770236
Zoological Gardens Phoenix Park	01 6771425

DUBLIN 1

Aya Deli @ IFSC

🅝 Restaurant   Mayor Street/Custom House Square IFSC Dublin 1 Tel: 01 672 1852

This younger sister of the highly successful Aya@ Brown Thomas (see entry) is run on similar lines, although with less seating and greater emphasis on food to go. Amex, MasterCard, Visa, Laser.

101 Talbot Restaurant

Restaurant   100-102 Talbot Street Dublin 1 **Tel: 01 874 5011** Fax: 01 874 5011

Margaret Duffy and Pascal Bradley's ground breaking northside restaurant was here a decade ahead of the current gold rush to service the growing needs of the new "city" area in and around the maturing International Financial Services Centre. Its potential may be more obvious today but it is they who created the buzz here and, while the nearby Abbey and Gate theatres and the constantly changing art exhibitions in the restaurant are partly responsible for drawing an interesting artistic/theatrical crowd, it is essentially their joyfully creative and healthy food that has earned the 101 such a fine reputation and that remains the case. Mediterranean and Middle Eastern influences explain the uniquely enjoyable wholesomeness across the complete range of dishes, always including strong vegetarian options - in signature dishes like spanakopita (spinach, flat mushrooms & feta cheese in filo, with creamy celeriac sauce) or a herby variation on traditional boxty cake, topped with spinach, roast peppers & Cashel blue cheese and served with a smoked garlic sauce - and dietary requirements are always willingly met. Children welcome. **Seats 80.** Open Tue-Sat, 5-11. A la carte. No-smoking area. Closed Sun & Mon, Christmas, New Year, bank hols. Amex, Diners, MasterCard, Visa, Laser. **Directions:** 5 minutes walk between Connolly Station and O'Connell Street.

Bangkok Café

Restaurant   106 Parnell Street Dublin 1 **Tel: 01 878 6618**

This cheap'n'cheerful café offers authentic Thai cooking with a minimum of frills in a part of town where good restaurants are, so far, thin on the ground. The helpfully-described menu offers degrees of spiciness to please every palate, and there's beer available as well as a short wine list. Good simple cooking, speedy service and great value - the Bangkok Cafe is hard to beat. Dinner only, 5.30-10.30 daily. **No credit cards**.

Bond

Restaurant/Café   5 Beresford Place Dublin 1
Tel: 01 8559244 Fax: 01 8881612 Email: info@bond.ie Web: www.bond.ie

Not exactly a restaurant, a bar or even a wine bar, this is really a wine cellar that also offers food. On arrival, restaurant guests place their order and are then brought downstairs to the seriously impressive cellar to select from over 300 wines sourced by proprietor Karl Purdy. A reasonable flat-rate corkage charge (€6.35) added to all cellar wine consumed on the premises instead of the usual restaurant percentage system encourages diners to choose better wines - the more expensive the wine, the greater the value. At the time of going to press exciting new menus are about to be introduced. Service is well informed, friendly and accommodating. A wine shop (with separate entrance) is run by sommelier Julien David le Gentil, who also hosts private tastings and dinners. **Seats 50.** L Mon-Fri 12-3, D Thu-Sat 6-9/10 A la carte. No smoking area. Service discretionary (except 12.5% on parties of 6+). Closed Christmas week, Mon of bank hol weekends. Amex, MasterCard, Visa, Laser. **Directions:** Bottom of Gardiner Street facing Dublin's Customs House.

Chapter One Restaurant

féile bia ★ Restaurant   18/19 Parnell Square Dublin 1 **Tel: 01 873 2266** Fax: 01 873 2330
Email: info@chapter.onerestaurant.com Web: www.chapteronerestaurant.com

Chef-proprietor Ross Lewis and his partner, restaurant manager Martin Corbett, operate this excellent restaurant in the basement beneath the Dublin Writers' Museum and near The Gate Theatre - which you can visit after your main course and return later for dessert and coffee. Ross has built up a well-deserved following for confident, creative cooking which is classic French with leanings towards modern Irish themes: dishes like white onion soup with Montgomery cheese & chive beignet and John Dory with basil crushed tomato, tomato essence, broad beans & gingered carrots illustrate the style. Menus are always based on first class seasonal ingredients and finish with lovely desserts - rhubarb crème brulée with a pistachio tuile, perhaps - or an unusual, informative Irish and French cheese menu to finish. Chapter One was our Restaurant of the Year in 2001, reflecting the consistently memorable dining experience created by great hospitality and service, excellent cooking, an interesting, informative wine list and the characterful atmosphere of this cellar restaurant. Recent changes have seen the introduction of an oyster counter in a spacious new reception area and a fine wine cellar. They also run the coffee shop in the Writers Museum, (10-5 pm Mon-Sat). Small conferences. Air conditioning. Parking by arrangement with nearby carpark. Children welcome. Seats 90 (private rooms,14 & 20). L 12.30-2.30 Fri, D 6-10.45 Tue-Sat. Set L E27.50. Pre-theatre menu E27.50, 6-7; D à la carte (except group dinner menu, E46.50). House wine E18.50. s.c.10%. Closed Sun, Mon, 2 wks Christmas, bank hols. Amex, Diners, MasterCard, Visa, Laser. Directions: Bottom of O'Connell Street, north side of Parnell Square, opp Garden of Remembrance.

Clarion Hotel Dublin IFSC

🏨 Hotel

Excise Walk IFSC Dublin 1 **Tel: 01 433 8822** Fax: 01 433 8811
Email: sales@clarionhotelifsc.com Web: www.info@clarionhotelifsc.com

This dashing contemporary hotel opened on the river side of the Financial Services Centre in March 2001. It is the first in the area to be built specifically for the mature 'city' district and is not only meeting the needs of business guests and the financial community admirably, but its high standards and central location have proved very popular with leisure guests as well, especially at weekends. Bright, airy and spacious, the style is refreshingly clean-lined yet comfortable, with lots of gentle neutrals and a somewhat eastern feel that is emphasised by the food philosophy of the hotel - a waft of lemongrass and ginger entices guests through to the Kudos Bar, where Asian wok cooking is served; the more formal restaurant, Sinergie, also features world cuisine, but with more European influences. Staff show a real desire to please,the standard of cooking and service are both consistently high and the house wine selection includes 'wine geese' bottles, named after suites and bottles specially for the Clarion. Uncluttered bedrooms have many facilities to appeal to the modern traveller, especially when on business: keycard, security eye and security chain are reassuring features and there are many other conveniences, including air conditioning, 2 phone lines (with voice mail and ISDN) also a pleasing element of self-containment, with tea/coffee-making, multi-channel TV, ironing facilities, power hairdryer mini-bar and safe. Generous semi-orthopaedic beds, good linen and bright bathrooms with power showers and bath, heated mirror, luxurious towels and top quality toiletries all add to the sense of thoughtful planning that attaches to every aspect of the hotel. There's even a 'Sleep Programme' to help you relax before bed! Leisure facilities, in the basement, are excellent and include an 18m pool and large, well-equipped gym. (Open to membership as well as residents' use). While this is not a place for huge conferences, there is a wide range of rooms for meetings of anything between 8 and 120 people, theatre style, with state-of-the art facilities. 24 hour room service. Leisure centre (indoor swimming pool, gym). Lift. Children welcome (under 12s free in parents' room, cot available free of charge). No pets. **Rooms 160** (17 suites, 68 executive, 80 no smoking). B&B €115pps; room rate €230. Kudos Bar & Restaurant: Mon-Fri,12-8.30; Sinergie Restaurant: L Mon-Fri 12.15-2.30, D daily, 6-9.30. Set L €25; Early D €24 (6-7); D €17.50-€40, also à la carte. House wines, from €16. Closed 24-26 Dec. [*Comfort Inn, Talbot Street (Tel: 01-874 9202) is in the same group and offers budget accommodation near the IFSC.] Amex, Diners, MasterCard, Visa. **Directions:** Heading east, take the left lane on Custom House Quay. Hotel is in the 3rd block, after 2 sets of traffic lights.

D.One Restaurant

Ⓝ Restaurant

North Wall Quay IFSC Dublin 1
Tel: 01 856 1622 Fax: 01 856 1622

Proudly laying claim to be only restaurant in Dublin built right on the walls of the River Liffey, this contemporary glass cube takes full advantage of its location on the river side of the road. Although not large and often very busy (especially at lunchtime when hordes of hungry workers pour out of the nearby offices), it succeeds surprisingly well in achieving a sense of spaciousness through simple, minimalist furnishing which combines comfort with eye appeal. Clean-lined surroundings seem to underline the stated aim "to offer first class food with great service and, above all, to offer outstanding value for money" which is very welcome in a part of the city where good value is not often the first concept to come to mind - starters begin at €5, main courses range from around €12.50 (pasta) to about €20 (fillet of beef with roast shallots & green peppercorn sauce) and the 3-course pre-theatre menu is a snip. The cooking style is contemporary, (which can be taken to mean a mixture of many styles and influences, some more successful than others) and specialities include D.One fish & chips and their variation on a modern Irish classic of roast breast of chicken stuffed with tomato & creamed cheese, wrapped in bacon, served with champ mash & wholegrain mustard cream. In the Guide's experience, starters tend to be a strong point and desserts a weak one, and the most successful main courses are the ones that don't attempt to marry too many flavours, so simplest choices are often the wisest. Perhaps reflecting demand from heady world of high finance across the road, a brief wine list rather surprisingly includes four champagnes, with a top price of €196.80. Not suitable for children. **Seats 80**. No smoking area. Air conditioning. Wheelchair accessible. Street parking available 7pm-7am and weekends. L Mon-Sat, 12-3; D Tue-Sat, 5-9 (Fri & Sat to 10). A la carte. House wine €14.60. Closed all Sun, D Mon, 23-31 Dec. MasterCard, Visa, Laser. **Directions:** Customs House Quay, opposite Clarion Hotel.

Epicurean Food Hall

Restaurants   Lr Liffey Street Dublin 1

The Epicurean Food Hall brings together a wide range of gourmet foods, cooked and uncooked - amd the wines to go with them. The hall is open during the day every (opens later on Sunday, stays open later for late shoppers on Thursday); there are lots of lovely little shops and cafes in the hall, these few are just a taster:

C-Bar (Tel 01 8656663) Little sister to Dublin's most popular restaurant, L'Ecrivain, C-Bar is a tiny fish restaurant where customers perching on high stools at an aluminium counter are treated to superb restaurant-quality seafood cooking, served in classy white porcelain dishes. Try the ultra-fresh seafood platter (with modish sauces alike salsa verde or aioli and a few baby potatoes). Open afternoons/early evening (later on Thu, to 9pm).

La Corte (Tel 01 873 4200) One of two north river outposts of Stefano Crescenzi and David Izzo's smart Bar Italia (see entry). Also at IFSC (Tel: 01 672 1929).

Miss Sushi (Tel 01 617 4820) Japanese food has taken great strides in Dublin over the last few years and Miss Sushi, which was opened here in 2000 by a well-travelled Laois lady, Margaret Scully, features food (mostly free range and organic) prepared by a team of professional sushi chefs at The Japanese Food Company and delivered twice daily. There's much more to sushi than raw fish, as Dublin diners are beginning to discover: sushi may have originated as a way to preserve fish in vinegared rice but it has long since taken on a wider meaning - the marriage of vinegared rice with other ingredients. There's a lunch special, changed daily, individual pieces can be selected to taste, or there are Bento(lunch) Boxes which are a good start. Soy sauce, wasabi (Japanese mustard), pickled ginger and rolling mats comes with all sushi. Part platters are available (24 hours notice) and, although Miss Sushi is mainly a gourmet take-away, plated sushi can be eaten on the premises.

Itsabagel (Tel 01 874 0486) Domini and Peaches Kemps' classy bagel bar is very popular with discerning lunchers: choose from bagels, savoury breads with fillngs, juices, muffins and cookies. Just delicious.

Expresso Bar Café I.F.S.C.

Café   6 Custom House Square I.F.S.C. Dublin 1
                    Tel: 01 6721812 Fax: 01 6721813 Email: expressobar@ireland.com

Following on the great success of the Expresso Bar Café in Ballsbridge - winner of our Bord Bia Bacon Award in 2001 - Ann Marie Nohl and Jane Cathcart applied the same winning formula to this stylish little contemporary restaurant in Dublin's financial heartland. Breakfasts worth getting in early for kick off with freshly squeezed orange juice and lead on to a wonderful menu of temptations, from the best of traditional fries through the likes of pancakes with crispy bacon and syrup or pain au choc. Lunches are in a class of their own too, offering lots of lovely, colourful dishes - baked cod with a parmesan & basil crust, potato cake & garden pea purée is typical - all based on the best ingredients, impeccably sourced. Desserts are given daily on a board and there's a wide choice of coffees, minerals and a compact, well-selected wine list. Outside seating is planned for 2003. **Seats 62** . Open 7-5 Mon-Fri, 10-5 Sat & Sun; L11.30-5. No-smoking area; air-conditioning. Closed 25 Dec, bank hols. Amex, MasterCard, Visa. **Directions:** New development behind The Clarion Hotel.

The Gresham

 Hotel   23 Upper O'Connell Street Dublin 1 **Tel: 01 874 6881** Fax: 01 878 7175
                    Email: info@thegresham.com Web: www.greshamhotels.com

This famous hotel has been at the centre of Dublin society since the early nineteenth century and is one of the city's best business hotels. It has recently undergone a major makeover throughout the ground floor, including the lobby lounge, which is a favourite meeting place and renowned for its

traditional afternoon tea, and also the Gresham and Toddy's Bars, both popular rendezvous for a pint. Business guests appreciate the newer air-conditioned bedrooms in the Lavery Wing, especially spacious and have ISDN lines and mini-bars, extra large beds and smart bathrooms with separate bath and shower, but others, including six penthouse suites, (one occupied for several months by Elizabeth Taylor and Richard Burton many years ago), offer similar facilities including voicemail and fax/modem points. The hotel prides itself on the quality of its staff.
Restaurant: An impressive new contemporary restaurant, No.23 opened shortly before the guide went to press and got off to a promising start. Conference/banqueting (350/270). Business centre; secretarial services; video conferencing. Fitness suite. Wheelchair access. Own secure multi-storey parking. No pets. **Rooms 288** (4 suites, 2 junior suites, 100 executive rooms, 60 no-smoking, 3 for disabled). Lifts. B&B €160pps, ss up to €140 (Room only rate €255, max 3 guests). Open all year. Amex, Diners, MasterCard, Visa, Laser. **Directions:** City centre, on north side of the River Liffey.

The Harbourmaster Bar and Restaurant

Restaurant/Pub   IFSC Dublin 1 **Tel: 01 670 1688** Fax: 01 670 1690

In a waterside setting at Dublin's thriving financial services centre this old Dock Offices building has genuine character and makes a fine restaurant and bar. The bar is very busy at times, but the development has been more towards the restaurant end of the business, now including an impressive contemporary upstairs restaurant, The Greenhouse, in a modern extension which has been designed in sympathy with the original building. Most tables have an interesting (and increasingly attractive) view of the development outside but, as there are now several dining areas, it is wise to ensure you get to the right one on arrival. For fine weather there's also a decked outdoor area overlooking the inner harbour and fountain, with extra seating. The Harbourmaster has that indefinable buzz that comes from being in the financial centre of a capital city and the food is appropriately international and contemporary in style.
The Greenhouse Restaurant: Mon-Fri L, 12-3. Restaurant closed evenings and weekends (except for functions). Bar open Mon-Wed, 12 noon-11.30; Thu-Sat 12 noon-12.30am, Sun 12.30-11. Brasserie food: Mon-Fri, 12-9; Sat 12-10; Sun, 12-7. Closed 25 Dec & Good Fri. Amex, Diners, MasterCard, Visa.
Directions: In IFSC, near Connolly train station. ◇

Insomnia

Café   Unit 2 Lower Mayor Street Custom House Quay IFSC Dublin 1 **Tel: 01 671 8651**

This speciality coffee company has a small chain of outlets around Dublin (some under the brand Bendini & Shaw, whose complementary speciality is in sandwiches). All coffees made on the premises are based on top quality beans (Kenya, Java, Colombia and House Blend) and the range is wide: you name it, if it's quality coffee connected you can get it here: espresso-based drinks like cappuccino, caffe latte, caffe mocha and caffe americano and their cousins ('essence of coffee'), espresso, espresso con panna (with whipped cream), espresso macchiato (with foamed milk), espresso ristretto (extra strong) and extras (espresso shot, flavoured syrup, whipped cream). Speciality teas, hot chocolates and chilled drinks like iced coffee are available too, and a selection of pastries (croissants, muffins, biscotti for dunking); Bendini & Shaw sandwiches also available. *Also at Charlotte Way, Dublin 1; Ballsbridge, Dublin 4; Main Street, Blackrock; Pavilion Shopping Centre, Swords. Seats 45 Open 7.30am-4pm daily. Closed 25-26 Dec. **Directions:** In IFSC.

Jurys Custom House Inn

 Hotel   Custom House Quay Dublin 1
                                          Tel: 01 607 5000 Fax: 01 829 0400

Right beside the Financial Services Centre, overlooking the Liffey and close to train and bus stations, this hotel meets the requirements of business guests with better facilities than is usual in budget hotels. Large bedrooms have all the usual facilities, but also fax/modem lines and a higher standard of finish than earlier sister hotels; fabrics and fittings are better quality with neat bathrooms, although bath tubs are still tiny. As well as a large bar, there is a full restaurant on site, plus conference facilities for up to 100 and a staffed business centre. No room service. Adjacent multi-storey car park has direct access to the hotel. **Rooms 239.** Room Rate from €75 (max 3 guests); breakfast from €6. Closed 24-26 Dec. Amex, Diners, MasterCard, Visa. **Directions:** IFSC.

Morrison Hotel

Hotel/Restaurant   Ormond Quay Dublin 1 **Tel: 01 887 2400** Fax: 01 874 4039
                          Email: info@morrisonhotel.ie Web: www.morrisonhotel.ie

Located in the heart of the city close to the new Millennium Bridge over the River Liffey, this stunning contemporary hotel is within walking distance of theatres, the main shopping areas and the financial district. It was a first for Dublin, with dazzling 'east meets west' interiors created by the internationally renowned designer, John Rocha. His simple, cool bedroom design - the essence of orderly thinking - contrasts pleasingly with the dramatic, even flamboyant, style of public areas. In addition to the more usual facilities, bedrooms have CD players (CD library available), individually controlled air conditioning, safe, modem and mini-bar. Public areas include a range of stylish bars and restaurants catering to the needs of different times - the Café Bar, for example, is ideal for morning coffee or light pre-post-theatre meals, while The Morrison Bar has become the place for cocktails and Lobo is a late night bar (open to 3 am on Friday and Saturday nights). Siting this highly original hotel on the north quays underlines the recent shift of emphasis across the river - to the area which is currently seeing Dublin's most exciting developments. No pets. **Rooms 94** (3 suites, 3 junior suites, 5 for disabled). Lift. B&B €153 pps (Room rate: €318) Closed Dec 25 & 26.

☆ **Halo:** High drama comes into its own in the restaurant, which is on two levels, with angled mirrors giving a sense of unity and acres of curtains - notably a rich purple velvet - falling the full height. Having taken some time to settle in the early days, Jean-Michel Poulot's stylish French and fusion cooking at this fashionable restaurant is reliably excellent and seafood dishes are a particular strength - a starter of baked oysters with smoked bacon, green cabbage, lemon & chive sabayon and main course aiguillette of John Dory with baby vegetables casserole, thyme flower, black olives and olive oil emulsion are typical - and imaginative vegetarian choices are highlighted on the main menu. Be sure to leave room for original desserts, spectacularly presented. Lunch offers especially good value. **Seats 95.** No-smoking area. Air conditioning. L& D daily,12.30-2.30 & 7-10.30; Set L €25, D à la carte; house wine € 22; sc 12.5%. Amex, Diners, MasterCard, Visa, Laser, Switch. **Directions:** North Quays between Capel Bridge and Millennium Bridge.

The Muse Café

🅝 Restaurant   Easons Bookshop O'Connell Street Dublin 1 **Tel: 01 858 3850**

Providing refreshments for the many people who spend hours browsing in bookshops is a good idea, and it is beginning to take off in Ireland. The aptly named Muse Café makes a good place to pop into for lunch whether you are shopping or not, as they specialise in simple, moderately priced food with a welcome emphasis on wholesomeness. Menus change through the day, starting off with a traditional bacon & egg breakfast and progressing to healthy hot lunches like lasagne, quiches, nut loaf and other vegetarian dishes. Open 8.30-6.30 (Thu to 7.30), Sun 1.30-5.30. Amex, Diners, MasterCard, Visa. **Directions:** In Easons bookshop, on O'Connell Street.

Panem

Café   Ha'penny Bridge House 21 Lower Ormond Quay Dublin 1
Tel: 01 872 8510 Fax: 01 872 8510

Ann Murphy's little bakery and café has been delighting discerning Dubliners - and providing a refuge from the thundering traffic along the quays outside - since 1996. Although tiny, it just oozes Italian chic - not surprisingly, perhaps, as Ann's Italian architect husband designed the interior - and was way ahead of its time in seeing potential north of the Liffey. Italian and French food is prepared on the premises from 3 am each day: melt-in-the-mouth croissants with savoury and sweet fillings, chocolate-filled brioches, traditional and fruit breads, filled foccacia breads are just a few of the temptations on offer. No cost is spared in sourcing the finest ingredients (Panem bread is baked freshly each day using organic flour) and special dietary needs are considered too: soups, for example, are usually suitable for vegans and handmade biscuits - almond & hazelnut perhaps - for coeliacs. They import their own 100% arabica coffee from Sicily and hot chocolate is a speciality, made with the best Belgian dark chocolate. Simply superb. Open Mon-St 9-5.30. Closed Sun & 24 Dec-8 Jan. No Credit Cards. **Directions:** North quays, opposite Millennium Bridge.

Pasta di Milano

🅝 Restaurant   38 Lower Ormond Quay Dublin 1 **Tel: 01 872 0003** Fax: 01 872 0004

Pasta, grills and salads are the mainstay of this informal contemporary restaurant which, like others in the group owned by the UK Pizza Express chain, is known for consistently high standards at moderate prices. Expect specialities like polpetta di Milano (Italian style char-grilled burgers) and a wide range of popular dishes that are modern Italian in style but based on well-sourced local ingredients, including at least two Irish cheeses. Other features that please a loyal young clientele include live jazz on Fridays and a play area on Saturdays (12 noon-5pm). There's also a room available for private dining, drinks receptions and meetings (up to 24 guests). Open all day, noon-midnight (Sun 11pm). Set L €17.65; Set D from €17.65. House wine €16.85. Closed 25/26 Dec. Amex, Diners, MasterCard, Visa, Laser. **Directions:** On the northern side of the Ha'penny Bridge.

Soup Dragon

Café   168 Capel Street Dublin 1 **Tel: 01 8723277** Fax: 01 8723277

A compact, smart little place with space for just ten bar stools, Soup Dragon offers a stylish way to have a hot meal on a budget. There's no need to book and, surprisingly, there's even a smoking section. A daily choice of soups and stews is available in three different sizes, with a medium portion and a selection of delicious home-made breads and a piece of fruit starting at about €5. Some change daily, while others stay on the menu for a week or a season. Choose from dahl (Indian lentil), potato & leek or carrot & coriander soup; or opt for something more substantial like beef chilli or a very fine Thai chicken curry from the blackboard menu. In keeping with their healthy philosophy, a range of wholesome and innovative breakfasts is offered, and also a range of freshly squeezed drinks (Red Dragon: strawberry, raspberry and cranberry or home-made lemon & lime lemonade) and smoothies, all made to order so they taste fresh and vibrant. Desserts include old favourites like rice pudding (served with cream) and a range of unusual home-made ice creams. Food to go is also available. **Seats 10.** Open Mon-Fri 8-5.30 & Sat 11-5. Closed Sun, bank hols, Christmas. [Opening times not confirmed at time of going to press.] No Credit Cards. **Directions:** Bridge of Capel Street. ◊

The Vaults

Ⓝ Pub/Restaurant   Harbourmaster Place IFSC Dublin 1 **Tel: 01 605 4700** Fax: 01 605 4701
Email: info@the vaults.ie Web: www.thevaults.ie

These ten soaring vaulted chambers underneath Connolly Station were built in the mid 19th century to support the railway between Amiens Street and the Royal Canal and have since found many uses, including the storage of Jameson whiskey, which used to occupy a tunnel running from Connolly to Westland Row! In May 2002 this wonderful space entered a new and exciting era when Michael Martin - previously best known for his culinary expertise as head chef of the Clarence Hotel restaurant, The Tea Rooms - opened it as a multi-purpose venue. The idea was inspired and the execution a great credit to Neil Burke Kennedy of NBK Designs, who has succeeded in creating a cool series of spaces in the massive 14,500 sq ft area. Despite the size - and a ceiling height of four metres - the atmosphere is surprisingly intimate: the Portland Stone floor is warm and welcoming and the vaults, which have been treated individually in styles ranging from sleek contemporary (brown leather booth seating) to neo-classical (salvaged lamps, aged sculptures) add up to a stylish and highly versatile place. Each has its own entrance, allowing a number of events to take place simultaneously and, in addition to high-resolution digital projectors allowing cinema quality audio-visual effects, surround sound and drop-down screens in three of the vaults, others have plasma screens - ideal for sports events (seats bookable in advance). Given Michael Martin's background, culinary expectations are high at The Vaults and Sardinian head chef Max Usai ensures that everything is made from scratch, including pasta, ice cream and breads; menus are simple - mainly grills, pizzas and pastas - but brilliantly executed and beautifully presented on plain white modern crockery. This place encapsulates the dramatic changes taking place north of the Liffey: simply stunning. **Seats 210.** Private room 120. (All spaces available to hire, for business or pleasure). No smoking area. Food served 12-8 daily. Various menus - lunch, afternoon/evening, Saturday brunch and Sunday roast - à la carte. Vegetarian dishes on main menu. House wine EUR17.50. Late night bar. Closed 25-26 Dec, 1 Jan. Amex, Diners, MasterCard, Visa, Laser. **Directions:** Under Connolly station; accessible from station or IFSC.

The Winding Stair Bookshop & Café

Restaurant/Café   40 Lower Ormond Quay Dublin 1 **Tel: 01 873 3292**

Everybody's favourite place for a wholesome daytime bite and a good browse - window tables at this delightfully higgledy-piggledy cafe beside the Ha'penny Bridge have terrific views across the Liffey. Open 7 days, 10am-5pm (Sun from 1 pm). [Times not confirmed at time of going to press.] Amex, MasterCard, Visa. **Directions:** North quays, beside Ha'penny Bridge. ◊

DUBLIN 2

Acapulco Mexican Restaurant

Restaurant   7 South Great Georges St. Dublin 2
                                              Tel: 01 677 1085

Reliable Tex-Mex fare at this bright, cheap and notably cheerful place on the edge of Temple Bar. Authentic Mexican - nachos with salsa & guacamole, enchiladas, burrito, sizzling fajitas - and good coffee. No smoking area. **Seats 70**. Open 7 days: L 12-3pm, D 6-10.30pm (Fri & Sat 12-4pm & 6-11pm, Sun 12 -10.30pm). House wine €15.87. 10% SC on parties of 6+. Amex, Diners, MasterCard, Visa, Laser. **Directions:** Bottom of South Gt George's St. ◇

Alexander Hotel

féile bia Hotel   Merrion Square Dublin 2 **Tel: 01 607 3900** Fax: 01 661 8663
                  Email: alexanderres@ocallaghanhotels.ie Web: www.ocallaghanhotels.ie

Very well situated at the lower end of Merrion Square within a stone's throw of Dail Éireann (Government Buildings), the National Art Gallery and History Museum as well as the city's premier shopping area, this large new hotel is remarkable for classic design that blends into the surrounding Georgian area quite inconspicuously. In contrast to its subdued public face, the interior is strikingly modern and colourful, both in public areas and bedrooms, which are all to executive standard, spacious and unusual. Perhaps its most positive attribute, however, is the exceptionally friendly and helpful attitude of the hotel's staff, who immediately make guests feel at home and take a genuine interest in their comfort during their stay. Conference/banqueting (400/400). Business centre. Secretarial services. Video conferencing. Gym. Children welcome (Under 2s free in parents' room; cots available). No pets. **Rooms 102** (4 suites, 40 no-smoking, 2 for disabled). Lift. B&B €175, ss150. Room-only rate €299 (max 2 guests). 12.5% s.c. Open all year. Amex, Diners, MasterCard, Visa. **Directions:** off Merrion Square.

Ar Vicoletto Osteria Romana

Restaurant   5 Crow Street Temple Bar Dublin 2 **Tel: 01 670 8662**

Genuine little Italian restaurant, doing authentic, restorative food in a relaxing atmosphere and at very moderate prices - a set two-course lunch which includes a glass of wine and tea or coffee, is particularly good value. Very friendly helpful staff too - one of the pleasantest spots in Temple Bar. Children welcome. **Seats 35**. L 1.15-4 (Sun 2-4); D 6.30-11.30 (Sun 4-11). Children welcome. Set L €15 (also à la carte); D à la carte No smoking restaurant. Air conditioning. Closed 24-26 Dec. Amex, MasterCard, Visa.

Avoca Café

féile bia Café   11-13 Suffolk St. Dublin 2
        Tel: 01 672 6019 Fax: 01 672 6021 Email: info@avoca.ie Web: www.avoca.ie

FÉILE BIA AWARD *(see page 20)*
City sister to the famous craftshop and café who have their flagship store in Kilmacanogue, County Wicklow, this large centrally located shop opened very near the Dublin Tourism office in July 2000 and has become a favourite daytime dining venue for discerning Dubliners. The restaurant (which is up rather a lot of stairs, where queues of devotees wait patiently at lunchtime) has low-key style and an emphasis on creative, healthy cooking that is common to all the Avoca establishments recommended in the guide. (Avoca Cafés received the Happy Heart Eat Out Award in 2000). Chic little menus speak volumes - together with careful cooking, meticulously sourced ingredients like Woodstock tuna, Hederman mussels, Gubbeen bacon and Hicks sausages lift dishes such as smoked fish platter, organic bacon panini and bangers & mash out of the ordinary. All this sits happily alongside the home baking for which Avoca is famous - much of which (along with other specialist produce) can be bought downstairs. Meals daily 10-5, (Sunday 11-5); à la carte. bookings accepted but not required. Amex, Diners, MasterCard, Visa. **Directions:** Turn left into Suffolk St. from the bottom of Grafton St.

Aya @ Brown Thomas

Restaurant   49/52 Clarendon Street Dublin 2
        Tel: 01 677 1544 Fax: 01 677 1546 Email: mail@aya.ie Web: www.aya.ie

This dashing contemporary Japanese restaurant was Dublin's first conveyor sushi bar, restaurant and food hall - and was a runaway success from the day it opened, in 1999. Aya is owned by the Hoashi family, who established Dublin's first Japanese restaurant, Ayumi-Ya, where authentic traditional Japanese cuisine was offered from 1983 until it closed in 2001. In order to build on the success of Aya, an Aya Deli (with seated area) has opened in the IFSC, offering all that is currently available from the Aya Deli in Clarendon Street. Thus, with its deep-red velvet and beech laminated tables providing wall-to-wall style, the youthful Aya @ Brown Thomas now becomes the parent operation. The dining highlight is a full on-line menu offering a wide range of sushi, all authentically Japanese, and Aya also offers takeaway sushi, fresh and frozen meals and a small selection of Japanese ingredients. The main menu covers all the bases and is impressively wide-ranging, serving everything from well-priced bento boxes at lunchtime to more exotic fare in the evening. Always innovative, promotions like Aya's "sushi 55" (55 minutes unlimited sushi for €22) and "happy zone" (plates on the conveyor belt from €2 during certain hours) have earned them a loyal following. The service is excellent and, to add to the fun, the staff wear very distinctive grey and red uniforms inspired by "Dr. No", of James Bond fame. Children welcome before 8pm. **Seats 60**. No-smoking area. Air conditioning. Open daily. L 12-4. D 5.30-11 (Sun to 10). Set L €16.90; Set D €29.90. Also à la carte. House wine €21. 12.5% sc, evenings only. Closed 25-26 Dec. Amex, MasterCard, Visa, Laser. **Directions:** Directly behind Brown Thomas off Wicklow Street.

The Bad Ass Café

Café/Restaurant   9-11 Crown Alley Temple Bar Dublin 2 **Tel: 01 671 2596** Fax: 01 671 2596
Email: bad_ass_@hotmail .com Web: www.badasscafe.com

Original and still the best - the Bad Ass Café has been charming youngsters (and a good few oldsters) with its particular brand of wackiness and good, lively food since 1983, when most people running Temple Bar restaurants were still at school. Kids love the food (the Bad Ass burger is still one of the favourites, and very good too), the warehouse atmosphere, the loopy menu and the cash shuttles (from an old shop) that whizz around the ceiling. Fifteen years after opening, young people still find it cool. Children welcome. **Seats 92**. Open daily 11.30-11.30. Set menu €14.95, all day. A la carte also available. House wine €16.50. No-smoking area. Air conditioning. sc 10%. Closed 25-26 Dec, Good Fri. Amex, MasterCard, Visa, Laser. **Directions:** Behind the Central Bank on the way to the Ha'penny Bridge.

The Bailey

Pub   2-3 Duke Street Dublin 2

Although it's now more of a busy lunchtime spot and after-work watering hole for local business people and shoppers, this famous Victorian pub has a special place in the history of Dublin life - literary, social, political - and attracts many a pilgrim seeking the ghosts of great personalities who have frequented this spot down through the years. Closed 25 Dec & Good Friday. ◇

Bang Café

Ⓝ Restaurant   11 Merrion Row Dublin 2
Tel: 01 676 0898 Fax: 01 676 0899 Web: www.bangrestaurant.com

Stylishly minimalist in natural tones of dark wood and pale beige leather complement simple white linen and glassware, this smart restaurant is well-located just yards from the Shelbourne Hotel. It is on two levels with a bar in the basement; upstairs, unstressed chefs can be seen at work in one of the open kitchens: an air of calm, relaxed and friendly professionalism prevails. Predictably, perhaps, as head chef Lorcan Cribbin will be representing Ireland in the prestigious 2003 Bocuse d'Or, the menu offers innovative, modern food: a starter of perfectly cooked foie gras served atop a crisp onion bahji with Sauternes jus is typical and well-balanced main course options include tempting fish dishes such as turbot with baby broad bean and pea risotto with parsley oil. Tempting desserts include several fruity finales (Scandinavian iced berries with hot white chocolate sauce, perhaps) as well as the ever-popular dark chocolate treats, or there's an Irish farmhouse cheese selection. Attention to detail is the keynote throughout and this, seen in carefully sourced food and excellent cooking combined with generous servings and professional service under the management of Kelvin Rynhart, ensures a memorable dining experience and value for money. **Seats 90**. Private room, 30. Air conditioning. No smoking area. L & D Mon-Sat 12.30-3, 6-10.30 (Thu-Sat to 11). Set L €35, Set D €40. Also à la carte. House wine €18. 10% sc on on parties of 6+. Closed Sun, bank hols. Amex, MasterCard, Visa, Laser. **Directions:** Just past Shelbourne Hotel, off St Stephen's Green.

Bewley's Oriental Café

féile bia Café   78-79 Grafton Street Dublin 2 **Tel: 01 635 5470** Fax: 01 679 9237
Email: manager@graftonstbewleys.ie Web: www.bewleys.com

Established in 1840, Bewleys Cafés - and especially the Grafton Street café - have a special place in the affection of Irish people. Bewleys has always been a great meeting place for everyone, whether native Dubliners or visitors to the capital 'up from the country'. Although they have changed hands and undergone renovations in recent years, they have retained a unique atmosphere and it's this - together with some outstanding architectural features, notably the Harry Clarke stained glass windows in the Grafton Street premises - which makes them special, rather than the food. It seems highly appropriate that this great Dublin institution should venture into theatre - there's a lunchtime event daily, 12.50-2.20 and cabaret on Thursday, Friday and Saturday (Phone for details.) Full licence. Open daily, from 7.30 am 'until late' Branches at: Westmoreland Street (Mon-Sat 7.30 am-9 pm; Sun 10 am- 11 pm) Mary Street, Dublin 1 (Mon-Sat, 7.30 am- 6 pm; closed Sun.). Also at Waterstones Bookshop. MasterCard, Visa, Laser. **Directions:** Halfway up Dublin's premier shopping street. ◇

The Bistro

Restaurant   4/5 Castle Market Dublin 2 **Tel: 01 671 5430** Fax: 01 677 3379

Well located in the pedestrianised walkway between the Powerscourt Centre and George's Street Market, this relaxed, family-run restaurant has natural warm-toned decor with open brickwork and cheerful yellow walls and a friendly atmosphere. This, plus good food cooked by co-owner Maire Block and caring service under the management of Martin and Robert Block add up to a formula that brings people back. Menus lean towards seafood and sound cooking includes classics like poached wild Irish salmon with new potatoes and chive hollandaise alongside more contemporary dishes such as wok fried chicken with an oyster and kecap manis sauce, julienne vegetables & cashew nuts. Desserts range from old favourites like peach melba to an intriguing spaghetti ice cream with fresh strawberries, or you can finish with an Irish cheese plate. Daily specials offer especially good value. A la carte. Outside seating for fine weather. House wine from €16.50. No sc. Open daily 12-11.30 (Sun to 8.30). Closed 25-26 Dec, 1 Jan, Good Fri. Amex, MasterCard, Visa, Laser.

Brooks Hotel

féile bia Hotel   59-62 Drury Street Dublin 2 **Tel: 01 670 4000** Fax: 01 670 4455
Email: reservations@brookshotel.ie Web: www.sinnotthotels.com

A city sister for the Sinnott family's hotels in Galway - the Connemara Gateway and the Connemara Coast - Brooks is very well located, close to the Drury Street multi-storey car park and just a couple of minutes walk from Grafton Street. Described as a 'designer/boutique' hotel, it's high on style in a comfortable country house-cum-club fashion and has been furnished and decorated with great attention to detail. The whole of the first floor has been designated no-smoking and all rooms have exceptionally good amenities, including well-designed bathrooms with power showers as well as full baths, air conditioning, ISDN lines, teletext TV and many other features. Children welcome (under 3s free in parents' room; cots available). No pets. Lift. **Rooms 75** (3 suites, 30 executive, 62 no-smoking, 3 for disabled). B&B from about €108, ss about €57. Open all year. Amex, Diners, MasterCard, Visa, Laser. **Directions:** Between Grafton and Great St. Georges Streets, 2 mins. from St. Stephen's Green. **Francescas Restaraunt:** This lower ground floor restaurant has a welcoming ambience, with wooden floors, plaid-covered seating and beautiful book tapestries on the walls creating a pleasant setting for head chef Patrick McLarnon's seasonal menus. Carefully sourced ingredients (wild salmon, organic chicken, dry aged steak) are used in imaginative dishes, with a strong emphasis on fish - although dedicated carnivores should not be disappointed here either, with tempting choices including a signature dishe of peat smoked loin of lamb (with fondant potatoes, caramelised shallots, tomato fondue and a caper jus) to turn to. **Seats 70** (private room, 30) No-smoking area. Air conditioning. Early D, 5-7 daily, about €8-15. D 6.30-10 (Sun 7-9.30). Set D from €26.60. A la carte also available. SC discretionary. [*Bar food is served from noon-7pm daily in the Butter Lane Bar.] ◇

Brownes Brasserie & Townhouse

féile bia Restaurant/Guesthouse   22 St Stephen's Green Dublin 2
Tel: 01 638 3939 Fax: 01 638 3900
Email: info@brownesdublin.com Web: www.brownesdublin.com

Stylish conversion of this fine period house on the stretch of St Stephen's Green between Grafton Street and the Shelbourne Hotel makes an impressive and exceptionally well-located restaurant and guesthouse. The house has something of the atmosphere of a private home about it and includes a front first floor junior suite which can be converted for meetings and private parties, as the bed swings up into the wall. The spacious bedrooms have quality reproduction furniture and well-finished bathrooms, with quality toiletries and towelling robes. An ironing board is tucked neatly into the wardrobe and there's a CD player as well as TV. Browne's was the Dublin winner of the 2002 Denny Irish Breakfast Awards, in association with the Guide, and is truly a feast worth allowing plenty of time for. Small conference/banqueting (24). **Rooms 12** (1 suitable for disabled). Lift. Fax/ISDN lines. Air conditioning. Children welcome (Under 6 free in parents' room; cots available without charge). No pets. 1 suitable for disabled). B&B €111 pps, ss €47.74

Brownes Brasserie: Up a short flight of granite steps, you pass through a reception area and small drawing area furnished with antiques (where aperitifs and digestifs can be served) into the restaurant, which is a long well-appointed split-level room, with big mirrors and plenty of decorative interest to occupy guests between courses. Good-sized tables, comfortable chairs and fresh flowers all create a good impression and well-balanced international menus offer a wide choice - home-smoked salmon is a speciality in, for example, an unusual main course of roast fillet, served with a spring onion mash and a red wine & mustard seed sauce - also char-grilled meats. Imaginative vegetarian dishes also feature - typically a starter of deep-fried halloumi cheese, served wit tzatziki & aubergine tomato salad and main courses like sesame-infused crêpes filled with wild mushrooms, leeks & blue cheese, served with a green salad. Finish with rather luscious desserts (pavlova filled with a crunchy cream, topped with summer berries, perhaps), or a cheese plate with home-made chutney. Children welcome. **Seats 75** (private room, 30). No-smoking area. Air conditioning. L&D daily: 12.30 -2.45 (Sun to 2.30), D 6:30-10.30 (Sun to 10). Set L €35 (Sun €27.95), Set D €47.95. A la carte also available. House wine from €19. SC discretionary. Closed 24 Dec-4 Jan. Amex, MasterCard, Visa, Laser. **Directions:** Stephens Green North, between Kildare & Dawson Street.

Bruno's - Kildare Street

féile bia Restaurant

21 Kildare Street Dublin 2
Tel: 01 662 4724 / 6623856 Fax: 01 6623857 Web: www.brunos.ie

Bruno Berta's conversion of a characterful cellar under Mitchell's wine shop into a sleek contemporary restaurant in 2000 dismayed many devotees of the previous establishment which highlighted its old-world charm, but even the style critics admit that it is a great success. Head chef Garrett Byrne - whose previous experience includes Nico's in London and The Tea Room and Chapter One in Dublin - sources carefully and is doing a consistently excellent job in the French/modern Irish genre, typically in house specialities like blanquette de veau and sauté of foie gras with black pudding & fried egg. Intriguing desserts like cherry clafoutis with nutmeg ice cream are hard to pass over - but Irish cheeses supplied by Sheridans cheesemongers are also hard to resist. Not suitable for children under 12 after 7 pm. No-smoking area; air-conditioning. **Seats 100.** L 12.30-2.30 & D 6-10.30 Mon-Sat. Set L & early D €18.50; L&D à la carte available. House wine €19. SC discretionary (12.5% on tables of 6+). Closed Sun, bank hol Mons, 25 Dec-3 Jan & 2 wks in Aug. [Also at: East Essex Street, Temple Bar, Dublin 2. Tel: 01 670 6767] Amex, Diners, MasterCard, Visa, Laser. **Directions:** Across the road from side door of Shelbourne Hotel.

Buswells Hotel

féile bia Hotel/Restaurant

25 Molesworth Street Dublin 2
Tel: 01 614 6500 Fax: 01 676 2090
Email: buswells@quinn-hotels.com Web: quinnhotels.com

Home from home to Ireland's politicians, this 18th century townhouse close to the Dail (parliament) has been an hotel since 1921 and is held in great affection by Dubliners. Since major refurbishment several years ago, it now offers a fine range of services for conferences, meetings and private dining. Accommodation is comfortable in the traditional style with good amenities for business guests and it's just a few yards from the city's prime shopping and cultural area, making it an ideal base for private visits. The lobby and characterful bar are handy meeting places. Conference/banqueting (85/50). Secretarial services. Video conferencing. Children welcome (Under 3s free in parents' room; cots available). No pets. **Rooms 69** (2 suites, 17 no-smoking, 1 for disabled). Lift. B&B about €110pps, ss about €33. Closed 24-26 Dec. [Times/prices not confirmed at time of going to press.]

Trumans Restaurant: This elegant well-appointed restaurant has a separate entrance from Kildare Street or access through the hotel. Menus feature lively modern dishes and have the little touches that endear guests to an establishment, such as a tasty little amuse-bouche presented before the meal ìcompliments of the chefî. Wisely, given the likely clientèle, simpler dishes are always an option - notably roast beef or steaks presented various ways - and vegetarian dishes are creative. Desserts are also interesting (eg, date-stuffed pear in a phyllo crown) or you can finish with Irish cheeses, which attract a small supplement on set menus. No children under 12 after 9pm. **Seats 45** (private room, 12). L 12:30-2 Mon - Fri. D 6-10 Mon - Sat. Set L&D; also à la carte. House wine around €16. SC discretionary. Closed lunch Sat, all Sun, 24-26 Amex, Diners, MasterCard, Visa. **Directions:** Close to Dail Eireann, 5 minutes walk from Grafton Street. ◇

Butlers Chocolate Café

Café   77 Sir John Rogersons Quay Dublin 2 **Tel: 01 671 0599**
Fax: 01 671 0480 Email: michelle@butlers.ie Web: butlerschocolates.com

Butlers Irish Handmade Chocolates combine coffee-drinking with complimentary chocolates - an over-simplification, as the range of drinks at this stylish little cafe also includes hot chocolate as well as lattes, cappuccinos and mochas and chocolate cakes and croissants are also available. But all drinks do come with a complimentary handmade chocolate on the side - and boxed or personally selected loose chocolates, caramels, fudges and fondants are also available for sale. Branches at: 51 Grafton Street Tel: 01 671 0599); 9 Chatham Street (Tel: 01 672 6333); 18 Nassau Street (Tel: 01 671 0772). Amex, Diners, MasterCard, Visa. **Directions:** 4 city centre locations. ◇

Café Bar Deli

Ⓝ Restaurant   12-13 Sth Great George's Street Dublin 2 **Tel: 01 677 1646**
Fax: 01 677 6044 Email: dublin@cafébardeli.ie Web: www.dublin@cafébardeli.ie

Despite its obvious contemporary appeal - paper place mat menus set the tone by kicking off with Tasters, the first of which is home-made breads with three dips and marinated olives - the friendly ghosts of the old Bewleys Café are still alive and well in Jay Bourke and Eoin Foyle's inspired reincarnation of one of Dublin's favourite comfort zones. Even the name is a play on what was the essence of a café in the old-fashioned sense - steaming pots of tea and milky coffee, with scones or a traditional fry; today it suggests a very different character. Tables may be old café style, with simple bentwood chairs, the original fireplace and a traditional brass railing remain but a smartly striped awning over the the large street window signals the real nature of the place from the outset. Imaginative salads are packed with colourful, flavoursome treats in the modern idiom - rocket, parmesan, anchovies, baby spinach, goat's cheese, hazelnuts, chickpeas, couscous, tapenade are the vocabulary of this menu - with pizza and pasta menus continuing in the same tone. The ten or so pizzas offered include a Café Bar Deli special, changed daily, as do the pastas - and there are also family sized bowls available. Vegetarian options are particularly appealing, the wine list is sensibly limited but well chosen to combine quality and style (sparkling and dessert wines included) with value, service is friendly and efficient and prices remarkably moderate - a winning formula. Two more outlets in existing sister establishments in Cork (Bodega) and Sligo (Garavogue). Children welcome. **Seats 150.** Open 12.30-11 daily. No smoking area; air conditioning. A la carte. House wine €15 & €18 (litre). No booking. Closed 25-26 Dec, 1 Jan, Good Fri. Amex, MasterCard, Visa, Laser.

Café en Seine

♟ Café/Pub   40 Dawson Street Dublin 2 **Tel: 01 677 4369** Fax: 01 671 7938

PUB OF THE YEAR

The first of the continental style café-bars to open in Dublin, in 1993, Café en Seine is still ahead of the fashion a decade later - after closing for complete refurbishment, it re-opened in December 2001 to reveal a stunning new interior in an opulent art deco style reminiscent of turn-of-the-century Paris. Not so much a bar as a series of bars (your mobile phone could be your most useful accessory if you arrange to meet somebody here), the soaring interior is truly awe-inspiring with a 3-storey atrium culminating in beautiful glass-panelled ceilings, forty foot trees, enormous art nouveau glass lanterns, and statues and a 19th century French hotel lift among its many amazing features. No expense has been spared in ensuring the quality of design, materials and craftsmanship necessary to create this beautiful Aladdin's cave of a bar. Among the many attractive features of this spectacular bar are the lush ferns, which create a deliciously decadent atmosphere; the judicious mixture of old and new which make it a true original - although theme is based on tradition, it is far from pastiche and the final result is refreshingly original - and the fact that its many 'bars within bars' create intimate spaces that are a far cry from the impersonality of the superpub. Good food is a major part of its appeal too - there's an informal range of contemporary dishes available over lunchtime every day (in the self-service food hall beyond the main bar on the left-hand side), light bites all day (baguettes, pastries, paninis etc, from the coffee dock near the front door) and a popular Jazz Brunch every Sunday. Little wonder that so many people of all ages see it as the coolest place in town. Lunch daily 12-3. Sunday brunch, 1-4 pm. Wheelchair access. Bar open 10.30am-2.30am daily. Carvery lunch 12-3. Snack menu 4-10. Closed 25-26 Dec & Good Fri.

Camden Court Hotel

Hotel
Camden Street Dublin 2 **Tel: 01 475 9666** Fax: 01 475 9677
Email: sales@camdencourthotel.com Web: www.camdencourthotel.com

This stylish modern hotel, in a thriving area convenient to St Stephen's Green, has two entrances - one next to the Bleeding Horse pub, the other via an arched passageway through a courtyard. The spacious reception area leads to a smart restaurant, where an enticing breakfast buffet is laid out each morning. Some bedrooms have their own fax machines; all have neat bathrooms, practical fitted furniture and the usual facilities (plus satellite TV which can show your room bill, speeding checkout). Friendly staff, business and leisure facilities facilities and reasonable rates for the location make this a good city centre base. Conferences (115). Leisure centre (swimming pool, gym, sauna, steam). Children (Under 2s free in parents' room; cots available). No pets. **Rooms 246** (1 suite, 13 no-smoking, 13 for disabled). Lift. B&B from about €86pps, ss about €60; no sc. Closed 24 Dec-2 Jan. Amex, Diners, MasterCard, Visa, Laser. **Directions:** City centre, near St Stephen's Green. ◇

Central Hotel

Hotel
1-5 Exchequer Street Dublin 2
Tel: 01 679 7302 Fax: 01 679 7303
Email: reservations@centralhotel.ie Web: www.centralhotel.ie

Very conveniently located on the corner of South Great George's Street, this hotel is over a hundred years old and is a handy place to stay on business or for short breaks. Extensive renovations have recently been completed, it's not unreasonably priced for the city centre and special offers are often available, including weekends. Conference/banqueting (120/100). Children welcome (Under 5s free in parents' room; cots available without charge). Lift. No pets. **Rooms 70** (3 suites, 1 junior suite, 1 executive, 16 shower only, 14 no smoking). B&B €105, ss €25. Closed 23-28 Dec. Amex, Diners, MasterCard, Visa, Laser. **Directions:** City centre, between Trinity College & Dublin Castle.

Chili Club

Restaurant
1 Anne's Lane South Annes Street Dublin 2
Tel: 01 677 3721 Fax: 01 635 1928 Web: www.adlib.ie

This cosy restaurant, in a laneway just off Grafton Street, was Dublin's first authentic Thai restaurant and is still as popular as ever a decade later. Owned and managed by Patricia Kenna, who personally supervises a friendly and efficient staff, it is small and intimate, with beautiful crockery and genuine Thai art and furniture. Supot Boonchouy, who has been head chef since 1996, prepares a fine range of genuine Thai dishes which are not 'tamed' too much to suit Irish tastes. Not suitable for children. **Seats 42** (private room, 16) L Mon-Sat 12.30-2.30, D daily 6-11; (early menu 6-7). Set L €15.50. Set D from €25. A la carte L&D also available. SC discretionary. No smoking area. Closed L Sun, 25-27 Dec,1 Jan. Amex, Diners, MasterCard, Visa, Laser. **Directions:** off Grafton Street.

The Clarence Hotel

 Hotel/Restaurant
6-8 Wellington Quay Dublin 2
Tel: 01 407 0800 Fax: 01 407 0820
Email: reservations@theclarence.ie Web: www.theclarence.ie

Dating back to 1852 this hotel has long had a special place in the hearts of Irish people - especially the clergy and the many who regarded it as a home from home when 'up from the country' for business or shopping in Dublin - largely because of its convenience to Heuston Station. Since the early '90s, however, it has achieved cult status through its owners - Bono and The Edge of U2 - who have completely refurbished the hotel, creating the coolest of jewels in the crown of Temple Bar. No expense was spared to get the details right, reflecting the hotel's original arts and crafts style whenever possible. Accommodation offers a luxurious combination of contemporary comfort and period style, with excellent amenities including mini-bar, private safe, PC/fax connections (fax available on request), remote control satellite television and video and temperature control panels. Public areas include the clublike, oak-panelled Octagon Bar, which is a popular Temple Bar meeting place, and The Study, a quieter room with an open fire. Parking in the area is difficult but, in addition to the hotel's own parking, there are several multi-storey carparks within walking distance. Conference/banqueting (50/60); secretarial services. Beauty salon. Children welcome (Under 12s free in parents' room, cots available without charge). No pets. **Rooms 49** (5 suites, 45 executive, 3 for disabled). Lift. Room rate from €300; no SC.

☆ **The Tea Room:** The restaurant, which has its own entrance on Essex Street, is a high-ceilinged room furnished in the light oak which is a feature throughout the hotel. Pristine white linen, designer cutlery and glasses, high windows softened by the filtered damson tones of pavement awnings, all combine to create an impressive dining room. Solicitous staff move quietly, quickly offering aperitifs and menus. Head chef Antony Ely presents fashionably international seasonal menus that offer plenty of choice, including vegetarian options, but are not overlong or overpriced. Lunch menus offer especially good value and an imaginative approach to the varying requirements of clientèle": in addition to The Tea Room menu, working lunch menus for meetings provide several no-choice options from €14 per person and there's an "all-day" lunch in The Octagon bar offering a light à la carte and a different main course dish every day of the week (all €10). Seasonal à la carte dinner menus offer around nine or ten starters and main courses in a modern European/Irish style that is bright and sassy, with strong but not overworked presentation - signature dishes include a modern Irish starter of deep-fried potato & bacon cakes with buttered curly kale & caper sauce and there are delicious contemporary main courses with traditional roots like Dale Orr's organic chicken with salardaise potatoes, spinach and Clonakilty jus. A wonderful 8-course Tasting Menu is also offered, at €70 per person (€124 with wine specially selected for each course). **Seats 80.** Toilets wheelchair accessible. No-smoking area. L 12:30-2.30 (Sun 12-3.30), D 6:30-10.30 daily. Set L from €17.25; Set D from €39.50 A la carte L available. House wine from €25. No SC. Octagon Bar Menu,11-5 daily. Closed 23-27 Dec. Amex, Diners, MasterCard, Visa, Laser. **Directions:** Overlooking the River Liffey at Wellington Quay, southside.

Clarion Stephen's Hall Hotel & Suites

Hotel   14-17 Lower Leeson Street Dublin 2 **Tel: 01 638 1111** Fax: 01 638 1122
Email: stephens@premgroup.com Web: www.premgroup.ie

Conveniently located just off St Stephen's Green, this 'all-suite' hotel consists of units (bedroom, bathroom, living room, kitchenette) each with modem point, fax machines and CD players. **Rooms 33** (all suites, 9 no-smoking). Wheelchair access. Lift. B&B from about €85 pps, ss about €70. Free underground parking. Open all year.
Romanza: George Sabongi took over this attractive semi-basement adjacent to the hotel in 2001 and with him came the piano bar concept for which he is well-known in Dublin. An enclosed coffee terrace at the back creates a pleasantly summery 'outdoor' atmosphere and, as the restaurant is accessible directly from the hotel and nearby offices, it's a popular lunchtime venue - and very convenient to the National Concert Hall in the evening too. Moderately priced menus include informal Italian fare like quality pizzas and pastas, but there's also a range of antipasti and substantial main courses like charcoal grilled rib eye of beef and barbecue leg of lamb, and Egyptian influence showing in a vegetarian dish such as koushery, which is based on black lentils. You can also just have a drink at the bar (10am-midnight); there's quite an extensive cocktail list and a short bar food menu,10.30-5.30. Live music at weekends. L Mon-Fri, 12.30-3; D Mon-Sat 5-12. A la carte. House wine €16. 10% s.c. on parties of 6+. Closed L Sat, all Sun. Amex, Diners, MasterCard, Visa, Laser. **Directions:** Just off St. Stephen's Green on Lower Leeson Street. ◇

The Commons Café

Café   The National Concert Hall Earlsfort Terrace Dublin 2 **Tel: 01 475 0060**
Fax: 01 478 5037 Email: info@thecommonscafe.ie Web: www.thecommonscafe.ie

An off-shoot of The Commons Restaurant at Newman House on St Stephen's Green, this spacious restaurant is in the main Concert Hall building and makes a good place to drop into before a concert, or just for a meal. The room is lovely - high-ceilinged, bright and airy room with a large mirrored bar area, blue banquettes and white walls setting off impressive paintings - and friendly staff under the skilful direction of restaurant manager Michael Andrews are anxious to please. Menus are quite short and flexible, with no distinction between starters and main courses, but proceed in a fairly logical way from soup and lighter dishes like focaccia and pasta through to more substantial fare. The Commons Café club sandwich has become a signature dish or, for those with a hankering for comfort food, haddock deep-fried in beer batter and served with potato wedges and pea purée is the business. The cooking is good, the quality of carefully sourced ingredients shines through and it's also good value for money: a winning formula. Children welcome. **Seats 60.** No smoking area. Toilets wheelchair accessible. Open Mon-Sat, 9.30am-11pm (but closes at 6pm on non-concert evenings), Sun D 6 - "late" on concert evenings. A la carte. House wine from €19. No SC except 10% on groups of 6+. Amex, Diners, MasterCard, Visa, Laser. **Directions:** St Stephen's Green South, oposite Conrad Hotel.

The Commons Restaurant

☆ Restaurant   Newman House 85-86 St Stephen's Green Dublin 2 **Tel: 01 478 0530**
Fax: 01 478 0551 Email: siobhandooley@thecommons Web: www.thecommons.ie

Sited on the South of the Green, in the basement of Newman House - considered one of Dublin's finest examples of Georgian splendour - this restaurant was formerly the college dining room of University College Dublin and still evokes literary memories, with specially commissioned works by eleven of Ireland's top artists, including Louis Le Broquy, Brian King and Brian Bourke, dedicated to James Joyce, a scholar at the turn of the last century. Other luminaries associated with the Palladian building are Cardinal John Henry Newman, former rector, and Gerald Manley Hopkins, professor. Newman House has always been notable for its elegance and recent changes have restored it to its original Palladian style splendour, introducing richer, warmer colours in lavish redecoration of the rooms - including the Newman Room, used for private dining and suitable for corporate and social events, including weddings. French doors open from the restaurant onto a secluded south-facing terrace which is perfect for aperitifs on a warm summer's day and can be used for dining when the weather is kind enough to allow al fresco meals. Head chef Aiden Byrne's commitment to using only the highest quality ingredients is seen in some fine modern dishes and he is not afraid to try out new ideas. His menus are extensive, but a starter example of pan-roasted foie gras with spiced pineapple and pineapple sorbet and main course of roast lobster with pressed Serrano ham, tomato confit and leeks convey the luxurious style of dishes on evening menus. Wide-ranging à la carte menus do not come cheap, with starters from €19 (soup of sweet garlic and new season almond) and main courses in the €33-58 range (making the 10-course Menu Gourmand seem a snip at €85) but, on the whole, the cost is justified by the quality of food, cooking, service and details (little canapés on arrival, amuse-bouches, excellent breads) and, of course, the surroundings. Lunch offers very good value: both classic and innovative, it offers simpler but very accomplished dishes- typically a beautifully arranged mille feuille of duck confit with girolles and an inspired main course of pan-fried black sole with vichyssoise sauce and crisp baby squid. An imaginative dessert menu may include a themed "Plate", perhaps of lemon: iced lemon & thyme parfait, lemon ice cream and lemon curd tartlet. Teamwork is admirable and, although not always perfect, service under the supervision of restaurant manager David Devereaux is good and the contribution of sommelière Natalie Greve adds an extra dimension to the enjoyment of a meal at The Commons. Entrance to the Iveagh Gardens, behind the restaurant, is via Clonmel Street (Admission Free). **Seats 75** (private room 220). No-smoking area; air conditioning. L Mon-Sat 12.30-2, D Mon-Sat, D 7-10.15. Set L €32; early D €40 (7pm); Set D €55; Gourmet menu €85. A la carte also available, L&D. Wines from €22. No SC. Closed Sun, Christmas-New Year, first 2 wks Aug. Amex, Diners, MasterCard, Visa, Laser. **Directions:** Next door to University Church, south side of Stephens Green.

Conrad Dublin

🏨 Hotel   Earlsfort Terrace Dublin 2 **Tel: 01 602 8900** Fax: 01 676 5424
Email: dublininfo@conradhotels.com Web: www.conradhotels.com

Just a stroll away from the beautiful St Stephen's Green and right in the heart of the city centre, this fine hotel celebrated its tenth anniversary in 1999 - and was our Business Hotel of the Year in 2001. Service by committed staff is excellent and facilities are constantly upgraded. Many of the bedrooms enjoy views of the piazza below and across the city, and all have recently been refurbished in a contemporary style, offering luxuriously comfortable accommodation with individual temperature control, internet access, mini bar, trouser press, executive writing desk, safe and CD player. Conference space is flexible, with a variety of syndicate meeting rooms, all with ISDN lines and individually temperature and light controlled. A state of the art fitness centre is reserved exclusively for the use of hotel guests. Public areas include a raised lounge, two restaurants, the Alexandra and Plurabelle Brasserie (breakfast, lunch and dinner served here), and Alfie Byrne's Pub, which is home to locals and visitors alike and opens on to a sheltered terrace. Conference/banqueting(250/250). Executive boardroom (12). Business centre; secretarial services. Hairdresser. Underground carpark. Children welcome (cots available without charge). **Rooms 191** (9 suites, 1 for disabled). Lift. B&B €120 pps, ss €120; room-only rate €210, SC incl. Open all year. Amex, MasterCard, Visa. **Directions:** On the south-eastern corner of St Stehen's Green, opposite the National Concert Hall.

Cornucopia

Restaurant   Wicklow Street Dublin 2 **Tel: 01 677 7583**

You don't have to be vegetarian to enjoy this long-established wholefood restaurant and it's very well located for a wholesome re-charge if you're shopping around the Grafton Street area. It was originally a wholefood store with a few tables at the back and, although it has now been a dedicated restaurant for some time, a welcoming waft of that unmistakable aroma remains. The atmosphere is informal, especially during the day (when window seats are well placed for people watching) and people like it for its simple wholesomeness, redolent of good home cooking. Vegetarian breakfasts are a speciality (lots of freshly squeezed juices to choose from) and all ingredients are organic, as far as possible. In the evening, menus are more ambitious and the cooking moves up a notch or two - with organic wines to accompany. **Seats 40.** Mon-Sat 8.30am-8pm (Thurs to 9pm), Sun 12-6. All à la carte (menus change daily); organic house wine from €16 (large glass €3.95). Closed 25-27 Dec & 1 Jan. MasterCard, Visa, Laser.

Da Pino

Restaurant   38-40 Parliament Street Dublin 2
Tel: 01 671 9308 Fax: 01 677 3409 Email: m.jimenez@tinet.ie

Just across the road from Dublin Castle, this busy youthful Italian/Spanish restaurant is always full - and no wonder, as they serve cheerful, informal, well cooked food that does not make too many concessions to trendiness and is sold at very reasonable prices. Paella is a speciality and the pizzas, which are especially good, are prepared in full view of customers. Children welcome. No-smoking area. **Seats 80.** Open 12-11.30 daily. 2-course L (Mon-Fri), € 6.25; also à la carte. Wine from €14.50. Closed 25-26 Dec & Good Fri. Amex, Diners, MasterCard, Visa, Laser. **Directions:** Opposite Dublin Castle. ◇

The Davenport Hotel

féile bia Hotel   Merrion Square Dublin 2 **Tel: 01 607 3900** Fax: 01 661 5663
Email: davenportres@ocallaghenhotels.ie Web: www.ocallaghenhotels.ie

On Merrion Square, close to the National Gallery, the Dail (Parliament Buildings) and Trinity College, this striking hotel is fronted by the impressive 1863 facade of the Alfred Jones designed Merrion Hall, which was restored as part of the hotel building project in the early '90s. Inside, the architectural theme is continued in the naming of rooms - Lanyon's Restaurant, for example honours the designer of Queen's University Belfast and Gandon Suite is named after the designer of some of Dublin's finest buildings, including the Custom House. The hotel, which is equally suited to leisure and business guests, has been imaginatively designed to combine interest and comfort, with warm, vibrant colour schemes and a pleasing mixture of old and new in both public areas and accommodation. Bedrooms are furnished to a high standard with orthopaedic beds, air conditioning, voicemail, modem lines, personal safes and turndown service in addition to the more usual amenities - all also have ample desk space, while the suites also have fax and laser printer. Conference/banqueting (390/400). Business centre. Gym. Children welcome (Under 2s free in parents' room; cots available). No pets. **Rooms 120** (2 suites, 10 junior suites, 60 no-smoking, 2 for disabled). Lift. B&B €175 pps, ss €150. Room-only rate €299 (max 3 guests). Open all year.
Lanyon's Restaurant: James Whelan, previously head chef at Conrad Gallagher's controversial restaurant Peacock Alley, joined The Davenport shortly before the Guide went to press. Early menus for the hotel's elegant Dining room, Lanyon's Restaurant, are promising - and favourably priced for the quality of food and service to be expected. Set lunch and evening menus are especially reasonable. **Seats 90.** No smoking area; air conditioning. L Mon-Fri, D Daily. Set L €25, Set D €35, House wine €20. SC discretionary. Closed L Sat, L Sun. Amex, Diners, MasterCard, Visa. **Directions:** Lower Merrion Street off Merrion Square.

Davy Byrnes

Pub   21 Duke Street Dublin 2
Tel: 01 677 5217 Fax: 01 671 7619 Web: www.davybyrnes.com

Just off Grafton Street, Davy Byrnes is one of Dublin's most famous pubs - references in Joyce's Ulysses mean it is very much on the tourist circuit. Despite all this fame it remains a genuine, well-run place and equally popular with Dubliners, who find it a handy meeting place and also enjoy the bar food. The style is quite traditional, providing 'a good feed' at reasonable prices (most meals, with hearty vegetables, are under €15). Oysters with brown bread & butter, Irish stew, beef & Guinness pie and deep-fried plaice with tartare sauce are typical and there's always a list of daily specials like sautéed lambs liver with bacon & mushroom sauce, pheasant in season - and, in deference to the Joycean connections, there's also a Bloomsday Special (gorgonzola and burgundy). Not suitable for children under 7. Outside eating area. Bar food served daily, 12-9. Closed 25-26 Dec & Good Fri. MasterCard, Visa, Laser. **Directions:** Off Grafton Street, opposite side entrance to Marks & Spencer.

Diep Le Shaker

Restaurant   55 Pembroke Lane Dublin 2
Tel: 01 661 1829 Fax: 01 661 5905 Web: www.diep.net

This fashionable two-storey restaurant is elegantly appointed with comfortable high-back chairs, good linen and fine glasses, while sunny yellow walls and a long skylight along one side of the upper floor create a bright, summery atmosphere. The cuisine is mainly Thai, offering a wide range from the famed Tom Yum hot & sour soup with lemon grass and kaffir lime leaves to a selection of the equally typical green and red curries - and, in between, a wide choice including many based on luxurious ingredients like fresh lobster, seabass and black sole. Also a few Chinese favourites like sizzling dishes, crispy fried pork and sweet & sour king prawns. No children after 8 pm. No smoking area, air conditioning. Jazz Mon & Tue night. **Seats 120.** L Mon-Fri 12.30-2.15, D Mon-Wed 6.30-10.30, Thu-Sat 6.30-11.15). Set D from €36.25; also à la carte. Wines from €18.90. SC 10%. Closed L Sat, all Sun. Amex, Diners, MasterCard, Visa, Laser. **Directions:** First Lane on Left Off Pembroke Street. ◇

Dobbins Wine Bistro

Restaurant   15 Stephens Lane Dublin 2
Tel: 01 661 3321 / 676 4679 Fax: 01 661 3331
Email: dobbinswinebistro@eircom.net

WINE AWARD OF THE YEAR - *(see page 30)*

This 'Nissen hut' hidden away near Merrion Square is something of an institution, and has operated since 1978 under the close supervision of owner John O'Byrne and manager Patrick Walsh. A unique oasis in the centre of the city, it has a conservatory area with a sliding roof and a patio at the far end which is very popular in summer, and a dark intimate atmosphere in the main restaurant, where the booths for four lining the long walls are always in great demand. Pleasing details which hint at the good things to come include include generous, plain wine glasses and lovely home-baked brown bread. Gary Flynn, head chef since 1979, has attracted a loyal following for consistently good cooking in a style which has not abandoned tradition but incorporates new ideas too: thus a starter of pork terrine studded with prune and served with apple chutney appears alongside marinated Asian chicken with French beans, rocket & Caesar style dressing and a main course escalope of veal holstein precedes tomato risotto with basil & Mediterranean roasted vegetables; either way, Dobbins sticky toffee pudding is a likely choice from the gloriously old-fashioned dessert list. A visit to Dobbins is a treat and, along with great hospitality and delicious food, they're renowned for their wines: weekend wine sales are sometimes held at the restaurant and the exclusive 'Front Page Wines' on the regular list are available for off-sales, by the bottle or case. Leisurely lunches have been known to run on a bit too long, hence the warning on the lunch menu: "Bar closes at 5.30pm and re-opens at 7.30 for dinner service." The only down side to this conviviality is that tables for two can seem a little forlorn, so it's best to make up a party. Children welcome. No-smoking area; air conditioning. **Seats 120** (private room, 40). L Mon-Fri12.30-2.30, D Tue-Sat 7.30-10. Set L €23, D à la carte. House wine from €19.50. SC discretionary. Closed L Sat, all Sun, D Mon, bank hols, Christmas week. Amex, Diners, MasterCard, Visa, Laser. **Directions:** Between Lower & Upper Mount Street.

Doheny & Nesbitt

Pub   5 Lower Baggot Street Dublin 2
Tel: 01 676 2945 Fax: 01 676 0655

Only a stone's throw from Toner's (see entry), Doheny & Nesbitt is another great Dublin institution, but there the similarity ends. Just around the corner from the Dail (Irish Parliament), this solid Victorian pub has traditionally attracted a wide spectrum of Dublin society - politicians, economists, lawyers, business names, political and financial journalists - all with a view to get across or some new scandal to divulge, so a visit here can often be unexpectedly rewarding. Like the Horseshoe Bar at the nearby Shelbourne Hotel which has a similar reputation and shares the clientèle, half the fun of drinking at Nesbitt's is anticipation of 'someone' arriving or 'something' happening, both more likely than not. Aside from that it's an unspoilt, very professionally run bar with an attractive Victorian ambience and a traditional emphasis on drinking. Traditional music on Sunday nights. Closed 25 Dec & Good Fri. ◇

The Dome Restaurant

Restaurant/Café   St Stephens Green Shopping Centre St Stephens Green Dublin 2
Tel: 01 478 1287

At the top of the shopping centre is this bright and airy daytime restaurant has a lot going for it before you take a bite: beautiful views over St Stephen's Green, a friendly atmosphere, fresh flowers - and even live background music. In the guide's experience hot meals may be hit and miss, but the large salad bar offers a wide-ranging and colourful selection. But the real strength here is the baking - all cakes are home-made, there's a wide choice of desserts and confectionery which would be very hard to beat - and an off sales cake shop too. Service is polite and prompt, with table service for teas and coffees. Children welcome. **Seats 200** No-smoking area. Air conditioning. Open Mon-Sat, 9-5.30. Set L around €10, otherwise à la carte. Wines (1/4 bottles) from about €4.50. SC discretionary. Closed Sun, bank hols, Christmas. **No Credit Cards. Directions:** Very top floor of St Stephens Green Shopping Centre. ◇

Dunne & Crescenzi

Restaurant   14 South Frederick Street Dublin 2 **Tel: 01 677 3815** Fax: 01 677 3815

This tiny Italian restaurant and deli very near the Nassau Street entrance to Trinity College delights Dubliners with its unpretentiousness and the simple good food it offers at reasonable prices. It's the perfect place to shop for genuine Italian ingredients - risotto rice, pasta, oils, vinegars, olives, cooked meats, cheeses, wines and much more - and a great example of how less can be more. Menus offer sandwiches or panini, antipasti and desserts: How good to sit down with a glass of wine (bottles on sale can be opened for a small corkage charge) and, perhaps, a plate of antipasti - with wafer-thin Parma ham, perhaps, several salamis, peppers preserved in olive oil, olives and a slice of toasted ciabatta drizzled with extra virgin olive oil... There are even a couple of little tables on the pavement, if you're lucky enough to get them on a sunny day. Indoors or out, expect to queue: this place has a loyal following. An extension into 16 Nassau Street is planned for next year and will specialise in primi piatti (gnocchi, ravioli etc). **Seats 30.** No smoking area; air conditioning. Open 9-7 Mon & Tue, to 10 pm Wed-Sat. Closed Sun. A la carte; wine from €10.16 (€3 by the glass). Amex, MasterCard, Visa, Laser. **Directions:** Off Nassau Street, between Kilkenny and Blarney stores.

Eden

Restaurant   Meeting House Square Temple Bar Dublin 2
Tel: 01 670 5373 / 2 Fax: 01 670 3330

On Sycamore Street, next to the Irish Film Theatre and opposite Diceman's Corner (The Diceman, Thom McGinty, was a popular Dublin street performer, famous for his costumes), this spacious two-storey restaurant has its own outdoor terrace on the square. Modern, with lots of greenery and hanging baskets, there's an open kitchen which adds to the buzz and provides entertainment if service is slow. Executive chef Eleanor Walshe has established a house style which suits the restaurant and has become very popular. Seasonal menus make use of organic produce where possible and lunch menus change weekly. Salmon tartare with crème fraîche and paprika, spicy lamb meat balls with lemon rice and tomato sauce, sticky toffee pudding with caramel sauce are all typical of the style. Classic desserts could include a caramelised lemon tart served with a scoop of blackcurrant sorbet. A well-balanced and not-too-expensive wine list offers several wines by the glass. Children welcome. **Seats 110** (private room, 12). No-smoking area. Air conditioning. L 12.30-3 daily (Sat & Sun from 12). D 6-10:30 daily. Set L from €18; also à la carte. SC discretionary. Closed bank hols, 3 days Christmas/New Year. Amex, Diners, MasterCard, Visa. ◇

Elephant & Castle

Restaurant   18 Temple Bar Dublin 2 **Tel: 01 679 3121** Fax: 01 679 1399

This buzzy Temple Bar restaurant was one of the first new-wave places in the area and is still doing a consistently good job. Ingredients are carefully sourced and served in a range of big, generous and wholesome salads (their special Caesar salad is renowned), pasta dishes, home made burgers and great big baskets of chicken wings. Service can sometimes be a problem - waiting staff are usually foreign students and, although willing and friendly, it can take longer than anticipated to finish a meal here. Children welcome. No-smoking area. Air conditioning. **Seats 85**. Open Mon-Fri, 8am-11.30pm; Sat, 10.30am-11.30pm, Sun from 12. Toilets wheelchair accessible. Closed 24-26 Dec & Good Fri. Amex, Diners, MasterCard, Visa. **Directions:** Behind Central Bank, Dame Street. ◇

Ely Winebar & Café

Restaurant/Café   22 Ely Place Dublin 2 **Tel: 01 676 8986** Fax: 01 661 7288

Just around the corner from The Shelbourne and a stone's throw from the Merrion Hotel, Erik Robson's recently opened wine bar and café occupies the ground floor and basement of an imaginatively renovated Georgian townhouse - polished wooden floors, brick arches and contemporary furnishings are completely at home here, a successful and refreshing blend of old and new. Ely's unusual wine list is the main attraction, offering a huge number of carefully selected wines, with over seventy available by the glass thus providing the opportunity to taste wines which would otherwise be completely unaffordable to most people. Although not the first restaurant to try this, it is done with great dedication and style at Ely - and the exceptional wine list is backed up by other specialities including a list of premium beers and cigars. On the food side, organic produce, notably meats from the family farm in Co Clare, are a special feature - and not just premium cuts, but also products like black pudding and home-made sausages which make all the difference to simple dishes like sausages and mash. Although food was originally presented more or less as an accompaniment to the exceptional wines, quite extensive lunch and evening menus are now offered - including, many visitors will be glad to hear, Kilkee oysters with brown bread and traditional Irish stew made with Burren lamb as well as many contemporary dishes - and wine suggestions are given too. Mature Irish and continental cheeses make the ideal accompaniment to a glass of wine and there's a bar menu of small dishes like mini chicken kebabs with satay sauce, organic beef or lamb meatballs and organic black or white pudding crostini, which you can get in selections of two to four. They also serve great coffee, a perfect accompaniment for their fine selection of handmade Irish chocolates. Open Mon-Sat L 12-3, D 6-10 (Bar open to midnight). Closed Sun, Christmas week. Amex, Diners, MasterCard, Visa, Laser. **Directions:** Junction of Baggot Street/Merrion Street off St Stephens Green. ◇

Fado Restaurant

Restaurant   Mansion House Dawson Street Dublin 2
Tel: 01 676 7200 Fax: 01 676 7530 Email: info@fado.ie Web: www.fado.ie

The Mansion House has been the official residence of the Lord Mayor of Dublin since 1715 - the only mayoral residence in Ireland, it is older than any mayoral residence in Britain. The room previously known as The Supper Room has been imaginatively renovated as a restaurant - the room itself is of sufficient interest to be worth a look even if you haven't time to eat - and the contemporary food served somehow seems very appropriate to this sparkling restoration. Since opening in 2000, Myles Tuthill's team have worked hard to achieve a well-earned reputation for hospitality and attention to detail, in both food and service. Well-balanced menus, which include a quick set lunch, an early dinner and a nice little children's menu as well as quite extensive à la carte menus, perhaps lean a little towards seafood - specialities include salmon & herb fish cakes with creamed rocket & cucumber salad - but meat and poultry are well-represented and vegetarian options are imaginative: a main course of goat's cheese & tomato tortellini with a herb broth and green vegetables is a typical example from a lunch menu. Desserts tend to be classic, sometimes with a twist (Bordeaux chocolate tart with Jaffa cake ice cream) and there's always a cheese plate (supplied by Sheridans cheesemongers). The wine list includes some serious bottles, including plenty of bubbles, a fair choice of half bottles and wines by the glass. Open Mon-Sat, 12-10. Set L €18, early D (5-7pm) €14; also à la carte. House wines from €15. Closed Sun, 25 Dec, Good Fri & bank hols. Amex, Diners, MasterCard, Visa, Laser. **Directions:** City centre, beside the Mansion House.

Fitzers Restaurant

féile bia Restaurant   51 Dawson Street Dublin 2
Tel: 01 677 1155 Fax: 01 670 6575 Email: fitzcat@indigo.ie

Reliable Cal-Ital influenced cooking in a dashing contemporary setting with a heated al fresco dining area on the pavement. Open daily 11.30am-11pm. Closed Dec 25/26, Jan 1, Good Friday. Amex, Diners, MasterCard, Visa. Also at: *Temple Bar Square, Tel: 01-679 0440(12-11 daily, cl 25 Dec & Good Fri) *National Gallery, Merrion Square Tel: 01-663 3500 Mon-Sat 9.30-5, Sun 12-4.30, closed Gallery Opening days). ◇

The Fitzwilliam Hotel

Hotel/Restaurant St Stephens Green Dublin 2 **Tel: 01 478 7000** Fax: 01 478 7878
Email: enq@fitzwilliamhotel.com Web: www.fitzwilliamhotel.com

This stylish contemporary hotel enjoys a superb location on the north-western corner of St Stephen's Green. Behind its deceptively low-key frontage lies an impressively sleek interior created by Sir Terence Conran's design group CD Partnership. Public areas combine elegant minimalism with luxury fabrics and finishes, notably leather upholstery and a fine pewter counter in the bar, which is a chic place to meet in the Grafton Street area. In addition to the hotels' premier restaurant, Thornton's (see separate entry), breakfast, lunch and diner are served daily in Citron, on the mezzanine level. Bedrooms, while quite compact for a luxury hotel, are finished to a high standard with air-conditioning, safe, fax/modem point, stereo CD player and minibar, and care has been lavished on the bathrooms too, down to details such as high quality toiletries. Conference/banqueting (80/60). Secretarial services. Children welcome; (under12s free in parents' room; cots available free of charge). 24 hour room service. **Rooms 128** (2 suites, 128 executive, 90 no-smoking, 4 for disabled). Lift. Room rate about €305 (max 2 guests). No service charge. Open all year.
Citron: On a mezzanine with a balcony overlooking a floating indoor bridge connecting two sides of the hotel, this city-centre restaurant is modern and vibrant with citrus recessed neon lighting, soft greys, mirrors, and dark woods. Ideal for Grafton Street shoppers, it offers high quality food ranging from superior snack food - perfect for a quick lunch - to more elaborate dishes that befit a lingering meal. Typically, a refreshing Gazpacho comes with cucumber spaghetti and a selection of delicious warm breads, a main course of chargrilled chicken is served atop a perfectly mixed Caesar dressing and roast cod and clams accompany well-dressed papardella pasta. There is also a choice of sushi – from Ebi or Californian Maki to a fish-based Mariawase selection of prawn, mackerel, salmon, tuna and squid. Service is professional and friendly - and there's a great wine list too. Open all day. Informal meals also served at fashionable 'The Inn on the Green' bar. Amex, Diners, MasterCard, Visa, Laser.

Good World Chinese Restaurant

Restaurant 18 South Great Georges Street Dublin 2
Tel: 01 677 5373 Fax: 01 677 5373

One of a cluster of interesting ethnic restaurants around Wicklow Street and South Great George's Street, the Good World has been owner-managed by Thomas Choi since opening a decade ago. Its large selection of Dim Sum, served daily, has made it a favourite of the local Chinese community. The restaurant also prides itself on an especially full range of other Chinese dishes, suitable for both Chinese and European customers and Thomas Choi makes a welcoming and helpful host. **Seats 95.** Open 12.30pm-midnight daily; L Mon-Fri 12.30-2.15; Set D €22-28. Closed 25-26 Dec. Amex, Diners, MasterCard, Visa. **Directions:** Corner of Sth Gt George's St & Wicklow Street.

Gotham Café

Restaurant 8 South Anne Street Dublin 2 **Tel: 01 679 5266** Fax: 01 679 5280

A lively, youthful café-restaurant just off Grafton Street, the Gotham does good informal food and is specially noted for its gourmet pizzas - try the Central Park, for example, a Greek style vegetarian pizza with black olives, red onion & fresh tomato on a bed of spinach with feta & mozzarella cheeses and fresh hummus, which is just one of a choice of sixteen tempting toppings. Other specialities include Caesar salad, baby calzoni (two miniatures - one with with chèvre, prosciutto, basil & garlic; the other with baby potato, spinach, caramelised red onion, mozzarella & fresh pesto) and Asian chicken noodle salad (satay chicken fillets on a salad of egg noodles tossed in a light basil & crème fraîche dressing). There's a good choice of pastas too - and it's a great place for brunch on Sundays and bank holidays. [*A sister outlet, The Independent Pizza Company, is moving to new premises in Drumcondra at the time of going to press; previously mainly a pizza restaurant, the new menu will include Gotham favourites: 28 Lr Drumcondra Road, Dublin 9. Tel: 01 830 2044). Children welcome. No-smoking area. Air conditioning. **Seats 65.** Open daily: Mon-Sat 12 -12 (L 12-5, D 5-12); Sun brunch 111.30-4:30 & D 5-10:30. A la carte. House wine €14.60. SC discretionary (10% on parties of 6+). Closed 2 days Christmas & Good Fri. Amex, MasterCard, Visa, Laser. **Directions:** Just Off Grafton Street.

The Grafton Capital

Hotel Lower Stephens Street Dublin 2 **Tel: 01 475 0888** Fax: 01 475 0908
Email: info@graftoncapital-hotel.com Web: www.capital-hotels.com

In a prime city centre location just a couple of minutes walk from Grafton Street, this attractive hotel offers particularly well furnished rooms and good amenities (including fax/modem) at prices which are not unreasonable for the area. Rooms are also available for small conferences, meetings and interviews. The popular 'Break for the Border' nightclub next door is in common ownership with the hotel, offering guests live entertainment on Wednesday-Saturday nights. Small conference (25). Secretarial services. Wheelchair access. Parking by arrangement with nearby carpark. Children welcome (Under 12s free in parents' room; cots available). No Pets. **Rooms 75** (4 mini-suites, 30 executive rooms, 5 no-smoking, 4 for disabled). B&B about €100. Lift. Closed 24-26 Dec. Amex, Diners, MasterCard, Visa, Laser. **Directions:** From Stephen's Green (North), turn left into South King street, take a right and the hotel is on your left.

Harrington Hall

Accommodation   69/70 Harcourt Street Dublin 2 **Tel: 01 475 3497** Fax: 01 475 4544
Email: harringtonhall@eircom.net Web: www.harringtonhall.com

Conveniently located close to St Stephen's Green and within comfortable walking distance of the city's premier shopping areas, Trinity College and the National Concert Hall, this fine family-run guesthouse was once the home of a former Lord Mayor of Dublin and has been sympathetically and elegantly refurbished, retaining many original features. Echoes of Georgian splendour remain in the ornamental ceilings and fireplaces of the well-proportioned ground and first floor rooms, which include a peaceful drawing room. Bedrooms, which are both comfortable and practical, have neat en-suite bathrooms and have recently had all the windows sound-proofed and ceiling fans installed. All round this is a welcoming alternative to a city-centre hotel, offering good value and with the huge advantage of free parking behind the building. Secretarial services; fax; internet access. Small conferences (24). Children welcome (under 2s free in parents' room, cot available without charge). Lift. 24 hour room service. **Rooms 28** (3 junior suites, 2 shower only, 6 executive, 2 for disabled). B&B €82.50, ss €45. Open all year. Amex, MasterCard, Visa, Diners, Laser. **Directions:** Off southwest corner of St Stephens Green (one-way system approaches from Adelaide Road).

Hilton Dublin

Hotel   Charlemont Place Dublin 2 **Tel: 01 402 9988** Fax: 01 402 9966
Email: reservations_dublin@hilton.com Web: www.dublin.hilton.com

Overlooking the Grand Canal, this fairly new hotel, is just a few minutes walk from the city centre and caters well for the business guest. Each double-glazed bedroom provides a worktop with modem point, swivel satellite TV, individual heater, tea/coffee-making facilities, trouser press, hairdryer and compact bathroom (club rooms - which include a new floor of 39 rooms recently upgraded - also offer a bathrobe, additional toiletries and chocolates). A buffet-style breakfast is served in the well-appointed Conference/banqueting (350/270). Underground carpark. Children welcome (Under 12s free in parents' room; cots available). No pets. Lift. **Rooms 189** (78 no-smoking, 8 for disabled). Room rate from about €184 (max 2 guests). Open all year. Amex, MasterCard, Visa. **Directions:** Off Fitzwilliam Square. ◇

Hodges Figgis

Café   56-58 Dawson Street Dublin 2
Tel: 01 677 4754 Email: books@hodgesfiggis.ie

One of Europe's largest bookshops is also one of the oldest - they've been selling books here since 1768. Always innovative, they were also one of the first to hit on the idea of nourishing the book-hunter's body as well as the mind - their in-store café opened in 1995. As this is the kind of shop where you could easily lose a day, this was one of their best ideas. Café open 9.30-5.30, (Thursday to 7pm). **No Credit Cards. Directions:** At lower end of Dawson Street. ◇

Il Primo

Restaurant   16 Montague Street Dublin 2 **Tel: 01 478 3373** Fax: 01 478 3373
Email: alto.primo@iolfree.ie Web: www.ilprimoireland.com

Dieter Bergman's cheery little two storey restaurant and wine bar between Harcourt Street and Camden Street was way ahead of current fashions when it opened in 1991. Two separate dining rooms (both seating 30 and air-conditioned) are simply furnished (some would say spartan) but the essentials are right: warm hospitality and excellent, imaginative, freshly cooked modern Italian food that includes gourmet pizzas (with smoked salmon & spinach, for example), excellent pastas and lovely salads (try the insalata misto, with mixed leaves, cheese, olives & French beans). Unusual speciality dishes include Ravioli Il Primo - open ravioli filled with chicken breast, parma ham and wild mushrooms, in a cream sauce - and lasagne with crabmeat. The wines are Dieter's special passion: the list is impressive and 40 are available by the millilitre - you drink as much or as little as you want and that's the amount you pay for, which is a brilliant idea. Dieter also organises regular wine tastings and dinners. Food prices are quite moderate - most main courses are under €18 - but the bill can mount alarmingly if you don't watch the wine orders closely. Children welcome. **Seats 60.** No-smoking area. Air conditioning. L Mon-Sat, 12.30-3, D daily 6-11; à la carte. House wines €26-65. SC10%. Closed L Sun, bank hols. Amex, MasterCard, Visa, Laser. **Directions:** 5 mins from Stephens Green between Harcourt Street & Wexford Street.

Imperial Chinese Restaurant

Restaurant   12A Wicklow Street Dublin 2
Tel: 01 677 2580 Fax: 01 677 9851 Email: imperial@hotmail.com

Mrs Cheung's long-established city centre restaurant has enjoyed enduring popularity with Dubliners and has also a clear vote of confidence from the local Chinese community, who appreciate the authenticity of cooking by Chi Hung Lee and Ip Kay Yim. Crispy aromatic duck is a speciality and they are renowned for their Dim Sum on Sundays, when a wide selection of small, typically Chinese dishes is offered. Children welcome. **Seats 180.** Private room available. Open daily 12.30-11.30 (L12.30-2.10 Mon-Sat). Set L about €11, Set D about €28. Also à la carte. House wine about €16. SC 10%. Closed 25-26 Dec. Amex, MasterCard, Visa, Laser. **Directions:** On Wicklow Street near Brown Thomas.

The International Bar

Pub   23 Wicklow Street Dublin 2

Just a minute's walk from Grafton Street, this unspoilt Victorian bar makes a great meeting place - not a food spot, but good for chat and music. Closed 25 Dec. & Good Friday. **Directions:** Corner of Wicklow Street & St Andrew Street.

John Mulligan

Pub   8 Poolbeg Street Dublin 2 **Tel: 01 677 5582**

One of Dublin's oldest and best-loved pubs, Mulligan's 'wine & spirit merchant' is mercifully un-renovated and likely to stay that way - dark, with no decor (as such) and no music, it's just the way so many pubs used to be. However it's now so fashionable that it gets very crowded (and noisy) after 6pm - better to drop in during the day and see what it's really like. Closed 25 Dec & Good Fri.

Jacobs Ladder

féile bia Restaurant   4 Nassau Street Dublin 2
Tel: 01 670 3865 Fax: 01 670 3868 Web: www.jacobsladder.ie

Adrian and Bernie Roche's smart restaurant overlooks the playing fields of Trinity College and the contemporary decor provides an appropriate backdrop for Adrian's cooking, which is modern Irish with international influences and with a welcome heartiness to the style. Recent redecoration has seen the introduction of larger tables with classic white cloths and paintings for sale by new Irish artists. Wide ranging and well-balanced seasonal menus always include some vegetarian dishes - vegetarian and 'healthy eating' dishes are considerably highlighted - and seafood features strongly, typically in a speciality Dublin seafood coddle or seabass with orange & vanilla. Menus offered include a compact à la carte selection at lunch, and early 2/3 course set dinner which is very good value, as is the main dinner menu which offers a similarly restricted course but with more luxurious dishes including, perhaps, a speciality dish of roast wood pigeon with braised leg, paté, herb mash & port sauce. An 8-course tasting menu, for complete parties, is also offered. Service can sometimes be a little slow but food is cooked to order and, on the lunch menu, there's a warning to allow 25 minutes cooking time for the main course; it's worth allowing time to finish off with a classic dessert (raspberry mousse with almond sauce and tuiles, perhaps) or Irish farmhouse cheeses, which are served with tomato chutney & oat biscuits. The wine selection has recently been extended to include a fine wine list. Children welcome. **Seats 80** (private room, 50) No smoking area L Tue-Sat 12.30-2.30 (Sat to 2) D 6-10 (Sat from 7) Early D (6-7pm), from €19; Set D €31.74; Menu Surprise €70, L à la carte. House wine €19.50. No SC. Closed Sun & Mon,1 week Aug, 2 weeks from 24 Dec. Amex, Diners, MasterCard, Visa, Laser. **Directions:** City centre overlooking Trinity College.

Jaipur

Restaurant   41-46 South Great Georges Street Dublin 2 **Tel: 01 677 0999**
Fax: 01 677 0979 Email: dublin@jaipur.ie Web: www.jaipur.ie

This custom-built restaurant is named after the "Jewel of Rajasthan" and offers a different, more contemporary image of ethnic dining. It's a cool and spacious place, with a large modern spiral staircase leading up to an area that can be used for private parties and the main restaurant below it. Although the modern decor may seem strange in comparison with traditional Indian restaurants, warm colours send the right messages and it is a pleasing space. Kaushik Roy, who has been head chef since the restaurant opened and is very highly regarded in India, is keen to make the most of Irish ingredients, notably organic lamb (Khato Ghosth - Wicklow lamb braised in yoghurt with carrom seeds & mustard oil, finished with asafoetida and dried mango powder - is a signature dish), while importing fresh and dried spices directly. Menus offer an attractive combination of traditional and more creative dishes - try Jaipur Jugalbandi, an assortment of five appetisers, to set the tone. Jaipur was the first ethnic restaurant in Ireland to devise a wine list especially suited to spicy foods. Service is attentive and discreet. **Seats 105** (private room 22). D daily, 5-11.30, L Sun only (1-11.30). Early D €20; Set D from €22 A la carte. House wine from €16. * Also at: 21 Castle Street Dalkey, Co Dublin (same opening hours). Tel: 01 285 0552. A new sister restaurant, Mantra, is due to open in Malahide, Co Dublin, as we go to press. Amex, MasterCard, Visa, Laser, Switch. **Directions:** At the corner of Sth Great Georges St. and Lower Stephens St.

The Joose Bar

Café   7a, Poolbeg Street Dublin 2
Tel: 01 679 9611 Fax: 01 679 9642 Web: joosebar.com

Tucked away behind office blocks near Tara Street station, this cheerful café offers a wide variety of excellent drinks, all made to order, in regular and large sizes: Smoothies, made with low fat frozen yoghurt, include The Grind (blueberry, raspberry, banana & apple) and The Squash (blueberry, strawberry and OJ & banana) for example, while Joose Juices include a Stressbuster (orange, lemon, apple & lettuce) and the aptly named The Hair of the Dog (pink grapefruit, lemon, lime and orange) while City Squeezes are combinations of just one or two types of fruit and/or vegetable juice. They also have a soup of the day and a chill cabinet to the side, offering a selection of basic sandwiches, wraps and salads, along with tubs of muesli for the breakfast brigade. Open Mon to Fri. 7.30am-3pm. Closed Sat. Sun & Bank Hols. **No credit cards. Directions:** Beside Mulligans Pub. ◇

Kehoe's

Pub   9 South Anne Street Dublin 2 **Tel: 01 677 8312**

One of Dublin's best, unspoilt traditional pubs, Kehoe's is also one of the busiest in the evening - try it for a quieter daytime pint instead. Closes 25 Dec and Good Friday.

Khyber Tandoori

Restaurant   45 Sth William Street Dublin 2 **Tel: 01 670 4855** Fax: 01 670 4865

Easily recognised by the doorman, who is colourfully attired in full traditional costume, this large, well-appointed Pakistani restaurant is handy to Grafton Street. Cooking is sound and the menu wide-ranging - the selection offered goes beyond Pakistani specialities, offering a cross-section of popular eastern dishes like tandoori and balti. There's plenty of choice for vegetarians and a nice touch comes as you leave the restaurant and each departing guest is presented with a rose. Wheelchair accessible. **Seats 100.** (Private room 30) L Mon-Sat, 12-2.30, D daily 6-12 (Sun from 5). Closed L Sun. Amex, Diners, MasterCard, Visa, Laser. **Directions:** City centre, near Grafton Street.

Kilkenny Restaurant & Café

féile bia Restaurant/Café   5-6 Nassau Street Dublin 2 **Tel: 01 677 7066** Fax: 01 670 7735
Email: info@kilkennyshop.com Web: kilkennygroup.com

IRISH BREAKFAST AWARD - DUBLIN

Situated on the first floor of the shop now known simply as Kilkenny, with a clear view into the grounds of Trinity College, the refurbished Kilkenny Restaurant is one of the most pleasant places in Dublin to have a bite to eat - and the food matches the view. It looks good and the experience generally matches the anticipation. Ingredients are fresh and additive-free (as are all the products on sale in the shop's Food Hall) and food has a home-cooked flavour. Salads, quiches, casseroles, home-baked breads and cakes are the specialities of the Kilkenny Restaurant and they are very good. For quicker bites the shop has a second eating place, Kilkenny Café, where Italian panini and cappuccino are served and the same principles apply. They also do an excellent breakfast and its worth considering an early visit into town to have a good breakfast before getting into the business of the day: Fresh orange juice to start, various combinations of the traditional fare and lots of lighter options to choose from. Children welcome. **Seats 190.** Open Mon-Fri 8.30-5 (Thu to 7), Sat 9-5, Sun 11-5. L 12-3. A la carte. Licensed. No-smoking area. Air conditioning. Closed 25-26 Dec, 1 Jan. Easter Sun. Amex, Diners, MasterCard, Visa. **Directions:** Opposite TCD playing fields.

La Maison des Gourmets

Restaurant   15 Castle Market Dublin 2 **Tel: 01 672 7258** Fax: 01 855 5332

In a pedestrian area near Grafton Street, this French boulangerie has a smart little café on the first floor and also a couple of outdoor tables on the pavement for fine weather. Home-baked bread is the speciality, made by French bakers who work in front of customers throughout the day, creating a wonderful aroma that wafts through the entire premises. Their speciality is sourdough bread, which is used as the base for a selection of tartines - French open-style sandwiches served warm - on the lunch menu (€9.75-10.75): baked ham with thyme jus and smoked bacon cream; smoked salmon with crème fraîche, lemon confit & fresh dill and vegetarian ones like roast aubergine with plum tomato, fresh parmesan & basil pesto are all typical. Add to this a couple of delicious soups (French onion with Emmental croûtons, perhaps, €5), one or two salads (€9.25) and a charcuterie selection (€14.50) - and a simple dessert like strawberries with balsamic reduction and fresh cream - and the result is as tempting a little menu as any discerning luncher could wish for. On the down side, portions are on the small side and service can be haphazard, a combination which can make it seem pricey. But everything is very appetising, the atmosphere is chic and you can stock up on bread and croissants from the shop as you leave - just don't think in terms of a quick bite. **Seats 25.** Open Mon-Sat, 8-6 (L12-4). A la carte. SC discretionary. House wine €13. Closed Sun, Bank hols. MasterCard, Visa, Laser. **Directions:** Pedestrianised area between South William Street and Drury Street.

L'Ecrivain

féile bia ★ Restaurant   109a Lower Baggot Street Dublin 2 **Tel: 01 661 1919** Fax: 01 661 0617
Email: enquiries@lecrivain.com Web: www.lecrivain.com

Derry and Sallyanne Clarke's acclaimed city centre restaurant is light and airy with lots of pale wood and smoky mirrors - it's on two levels, spacious and very dashing with lovely formal table settings which promise seriously good food. Derry's cooking style - classic French with contemporary flair and a strong leaning towards modern Irish cooking - remains consistent although new ideas are constantly incorporated and the list of specialities keeps growing. Special treats to try include a wonderful starter of baked rock oysters with York cabbage & crispy cured bacon, with a Guinness sabayon - perhaps followed by a main course speciality of rack of baby Irish lamb (mountain lamb may be used in season), with tomato & mint chutney, fondant potato and rosemary & garlic jus. Thoughtful little touches abound - an exceptionally fine complimentary amuse-bouche before your first course, for example - and there are some major ones too, like the policy to add the price of your wine after the 10% service charge has been added to your bill, instead of

charging on the total as other restaurants do. While seafood, lamb, beef and game in season are all well-represented, menus may also include neglected ingredients like rabbit, which is always appealingly served. Wonderful puddings are presented with panache and might include a hot soufflé or a super crème brulée with armagnac. Presentation is impressive but not ostentatious and attention to detail - garnishes designed individually to enhance each dish, careful selection of plates, delicious home-made breads and splendid farmhouse cheeses - is excellent. A fine wine list is augmented by a tempting selection of coffees and digestifs - all this, plus excellent service, adds up to a very caring approach and an exceptional restaurant. **Seats 101.** L Mon-Fri 12.30-2, D Mon-Sat 7-11, Set L €27/€35. Set D €50. House wine €25. 10% SC (on food only). Closed L Sat, all Sun, Christmas week, bank hols. Amex, MasterCard, Visa, Laser. **Directions:** 10 minutes walk east of St Stephen's Green, opposite Bank of Ireland HQ.

La Cave Wine Bar & Restaurant

Restaurant   28 South Anne Street Dublin 2 **Tel: 01 679 4409** Fax: 01 670 5255
Email: lacave@iol.ie Web: lacavewinebar.com

Wine bars were not a noticeable feature of Dublin's hospitality scene until recently, but Margaret and Akim Beskri have run this characterful place just off Grafton Street since 1989 and it's well-known for its cosmopolitan atmosphere, late night opening and lots of chat. An excellent wine list of over 350 bins includes 15 bubblies, an exceptional choice of half bottles and 30 by the glass. With its traditional bistro atmosphere, classic French cooking ("food for the gourmet at reasonable prices"), it makes a handy place to take a break from shopping, for an evening out or for party. Classic menus with the occasional contemporary twist make a refreshing change from the ubiquitous eclectic fare that has taken over the restaurant scene in recent years: duck liver paté, crab & gruyère cheese tartlet, brochette of Wicklow lamb with a thyme jus, vegetable couscous with coriander & chickpeas and chocolate mousse with Grand Marnier all indicate the style. A private room upstairs (with bar) is ideal for parties and small functions - Christmas parties are a speciality, but it's ideal for any kind of party, family reunions or even small weddings. No children after 6pm. **Seats 20** (private room, 30). No smoking area; air conditioning. Open Mon-Sat 12.30-11, Sun 6-11. Set D €28.50; also à la carte. SC discretionary. Closed L Sun, 25-26 Dec, Good Fri. Amex, Diners, MasterCard, Visa, Laser. **Directions:** Just off Grafton Street.

La Mère Zou

Restaurant   22 St Stephen's Green Dublin 2
Tel: 01 661 6669 Fax: 01 661 6669 Email: merzou@indigo.ie

Eric Tydgadt's French/Belgian restaurant is situated in a Georgian basement on the north side of the Green. Although there are some concessions to current cuisine (especially on the lunch menu), this establishment's reputation is based on French country cooking, as in rillette of pork with toasted baguette or confit duck leg with braised lentils, mashed potato & red wine jus; specialities include steamed mussels (various ways) with French fries and prices are reasonable - a policy carried through to the wine list too. The lunch menu - which offers a choice of three dishes on each course - also suggests six or seven more luxurious seafood dishes from the à la carte, so you can make a feast of it if time allows or, at the other extreme, they offer a range of Big Plates, with a salad starter and a main course served together on a king size plate (all €13) which is great value and ideal if you're in a hurry. A recent visit confirmed that this remains one of Dublin's pleasantest and most reliable restaurants. [* The associated business, Supper's Ready - an enlightened takeaway doing real food like navarin of lamb and potée paysanne - now has three outlets: 51, Pleasant Street, Dublin, 8. (Tel: 01-475 4556); 58 Clontarf Road, Dublin 3 (Tel: 01 853 3555) and Monread Avenue, Naas, Co Kildare (Tel: 045 889554). Check the website for further details: www.suppersready.ie] **Seats 55** (private room, 8) No-smoking area. L Mon-Fri, 12.30-2.30. D6-11 (Sun to 9). Early D €20 (6-7.30), Set L €17.15; also à la carte. House wine €15.50. SC discretionary. Closed L Sat, L Sun, 24 Dec-6 Jan. Amex, Diners, MasterCard, Visa, Laser. **Directions:** Beside Shelbourne Hotel.

La Stampa Hotel & Restaurant

Restaurant/Hotel   35 Dawson Street Dublin 2 **Tel: 01 285 4851** Fax: 01 235 2240

Already well-established as a restaurant, La Stampa is now a hotel. There's an exotic lounge bar on the ground floor - to the right of the restaurant entrance - and the reception desk is upstairs, on the first floor. Rooms are very attractive, with sumptuous fabrics, and neat en-suite bathrooms. No pets. **Rooms 36** (6 suites, 6 junior suites). Room rate about €165.

La Stampa: Reminiscent of a grand French belle époque brasserie, this is one of Ireland's finest dining rooms - high-ceiling, large mirrors, wooden floor, Roman urns, statues, busts, candelabra, Victorian lamps, plants, flowers and various bits of bric-a-brac, all the noisily complemented by a constant bustle. There's a small bar with a few comfortable seats where you can sip a drink while studying menus that encompass dishes from around the world. Menus are changed fairly often and, although prices can mount rather quickly for the style and quality of food and service, this is a fun and lively place, offering international brasserie-style food in delightful surroundings. No children after 9pm. Smoking unrestricted; air conditioning. **Seats 150** (private room, 60). L 12.30-2.30 Mon-Fri. D 5.30-12am Mon-Fri, 6-12.30am Sat, 6:30-11.30 Sun. Early D 5.30-7, Mon-Fri. L&D à la carte. SC discretionary (10% on parties of 6+). Closed L Sat & L Sun.

Tiger Becs: Like its big sister upstairs, the interior of this trendy and busy basement restaurant is unusual and beautiful – Moroccan in flavour with wrought iron gates, small wall niches which hold either pottery or flickering candles, wooden latticed ceilings, brass lights and illuminated glass mosaic panels. Fresh flowers are everywhere and there's a great buzz. Staff are cheerful, efficient and knowledgeable, and food is primarily Thai with preambles into Chinese and Malay cuisines. It's quite pricey but an interesting and entertaining. Many of the wines on offer are unsuitable for spicy oriental food and there are no house wines (prices start at about €31, however, improvements in this area should be in place before the 2003 season. Open through the day (breakfast 8-12, L 12-3. Last orders are generously put at midnight. [Sam Sara Bar and Café is also part of the La Stampa complex.] Amex, Diners, MasterCard, Visa. ◊

Le Meridien Shelbourne

Hotel
Restaurant

27 St Stephen's Green Dublin 2 **Tel: 01 663 4500** Fax: 01 661 6006
Email: shelbourneinfo@lemeridian-hotels.com Web: www.shelbourne.ie

The Irish Constitution was drafted here and this opulent 18th-century hotel overlooking St Stephen's Green (Europe's largest garden square) is still central to Dublin life today - officially it may now be called Le Meridien Shelbourne, but to Dubliners it will always remain the dear old 'Shelbourne'. Under the direction of General Manager Jean Ricoux, who joined the hotel in 1997, major renovation has taken place, confirming its ranking among the world's great hotels: it has retained all its grandeur, and the entrance creates a strong impression with

its magnificent faux-marble entrance hall and Lord Mayor's Lounge, a popular meeting place for afternoon tea. The Shelbourne Bar on Kildare Street is relatively new (food served 12-8 daily - may vary on Sun - includes 'traditional daily specials', some more traditional than others) but the Horseshoe Bar, renowned as a meeting place for local politicians and theatrical society, is nothing short of a Dublin institution. The best rooms and suites are very luxurious but accommodation varies somewhat due to the age of the building; however all rooms are well-appointed, with good bathrooms, bathrobes, mini-bars and three telephones as standard. The hotel has two restaurants, No 27 The Green (see below) and The Side Door At The Shelbourne (12-11 daily) which has a separate entrance from Kildare Street and, with its striking minimalist decor and Cal-Ital menus, provides a complete contrast to the ultra-traditional atmosphere of the hotel. The Shelbourne Club, a fine leisure cpmplex with 18m swimming pool, sauna, jacuzzi, steam room and much else besides is situated within the hotel complex. Conference/banqueting (400/320). Business centre. 24 hour room service. Fitness centre (indoor swimming pool); hairdressing/beauty salon. Valet Parking. 24 hour room service. Children welcome. Lift. **Rooms 190** (22 suites, 101 no smoking) B&B from €137.50pps, ss€107.50, SC 15%. Open all year.

No. 27 The Green: This elegant and lofty dining-room offers some very good cooking, combining the best of Irish produce with some traditional/continental flair and expertise. Alongside the daily-changing table d'hôte menus (five choices of starter and main course), there's an à la carte offered at lunch and dinner. Specialities, which are strongly seasonal, typically include the best Irish beef in The Shelbourne Roast (sirloin on the trolley, with traditional garnish) and several other specialities on the evening menu, prime seafood such as No 27 Howth seafood Caesar salad and The Shelbourne Special (fricassée of lobster in its shell with tarragon keaves & bisque emulsion). The restaurant is a credit to the hotel, with excellent food and service to match. **Seats 60**. No-smoking area (no air conditioning).L Sun-Fri,12.30-230; D 6.30-10.30 Mon-Sat, Sun 6-10. Set menus from €31.L A la carte. House wine from about €15. SC15%. Closed L Sat. Amex, Diners, MasterCard, Visa.
Directions: From Trinity College take 3rd right, turn up Kildare Street, Shelbourne on left hand side.

Les Frères Jacques

Restaurant

74 Dame Street Dublin 2 **Tel: 01 679 4555** Fax: 01 679 4725
Email: info@lesfreresjacques.com Web: www.lesfreresjacques.com

One of the few genuinely French restaurants in Dublin, Les Frères Jacques opened beside the Olympia Theatre in 1986, well before the development of Temple Bar made the area fashionable. Most of the staff are French, the atmosphere is French - and the cooking is classic French. Seasonal menus are wide-ranging and well-balanced but - as expected when you notice the lobster tank just beside the door on entering - there is a strong emphasis fish and seafood, all of it from Irish waters; game also features in season. Lunch at Les Frères Jacques is a treat (and good value) but dinner is a feast. Lunch offers at least three choices on each course, plus a few luxurious options from the carte listed as extras; west coast mussel risotto with a saffron cream, roast lamb tian with aubergine, courgette & thyme juices and strawberry tiramisu with a red fruit coulis are all typical. The à la carte offers classics such as west coast oysters (native or rock) and grilled lobster, individually priced, and there may be game in season. Finish with cheeses (including some Irish ones) or a classic dessert like warm thin apple tart (baked to order), with a rum & raisin ice cream. The wine list naturally favours France and makes interesting reading, notably the two pages of "recommandations du patron" (en rouge et blanc). Children welcome. No-smoking area. Air conditioning. **Seats 60** (private room, 40). L Mon-Fri,12-2.30; D Mon-Sat 7.15-10.30 (Sat to 11). Set L€20; Set D €34; D also à la carte. House wine €17.15. SC 12.5%. Closed L Sat, all Sun, Christmas. Amex, MasterCard, Visa, Laser. **Directions:** Next to Olympia Theatre.

Little Caesar's Palace

Restaurant   Balfe Street Dublin 2 **Tel: 01 671 8714**

This genuine little pizza place is just a stone's throw from the door of the Westbury Hotel - fresh, tasty and inexpensive pizzas (with good crisp bases) cooked before your very eyes could be the perfect antidote to too much luxury, or too much shopping. Open 12noon-midnight. Closed 25 Dec & Good Fri. *There's also a Mediterranean food shop & café nearby on Chatham Street and Little Caesar branches at: Rathfarnham (Unit 2, Butterfield, The Orchard Inn. Tel: 01-493 4060); Blackrock, Co Dublin (Main Street. Tel: 01 278 1533). ◇

The Long Hall Bar

Pub   51 South Great George's Dublin 2 **Tel: 01 475 1590**

A wonderful old pub with magnificent plasterwork ceilings, traditional mahogany bar and Victorian lighting. One of Dublin's finest bars and well worth a visit. Closed 25 Dec & Good Fri.

Longfields Hotel

Hotel/Restaurant   10 Lower Fitzwilliam Street Dublin 2 **Tel: 01 676 1367**
Fax: 01 676 1542 Email: info@longfields.ie Web: www.longfields.ie

Located in a Georgian terrace between Fitzwilliam and Merrion Squares, this reasonably priced hotel is more like a well proportioned private house, furnished with antiques in period style - notably in elegant public areas. Comfortable bedrooms are individually furnished, some with four-posters or half-tester beds, although they vary considerably in size as rooms are smaller on the upper floors. Staff are friendly and there is morning coffee and afternoon tea available in The Drawing Room, which can also be used for private dining or small conferences (20). 24 hour room service. Children welcome (cots available). No pets. Lift. **Rooms 26** (2 executive, 16 shower only, 4 no smoking). B&B €107.50pps, ss €37.50 Open all year.
Kevin Arundel @ Number 10: In the basement, with direct access from Longfields Hotel or the street, this excellent restaurant is currently one of Dublin's best-kept secrets. In 2001 Kevin Arundel, previously second chef at L'Ecrivain, took over as chef-patron, and moved the kitchen up into a higher gear. Modern French is the style, seen in starters like a rich ballottine of foie gras with pickled cherries and toasted brioche and a speciality main course such as seared fillet of brill with new potatoes and fennel a la grèque with roast fish sauce. Careful sourcing and excellent cooking at fair prices add up to great value - it is impressive, for example, to find wild salmon on a set lunch menu. But be sure to leave room for a grand finale of wonderful desserts, such as an exemplary caramelised crème brulée wit vanilla ice cream, beautifully presented. Kevin also presents an 8-course Tasting Menu which features many of his specialities, with an option of specially selected wines with each course. Impeccable service complements the fine food, making this an equally good venue for lunch or dinner. Interesting wine list. Children welcome; wheelchair accessible. **Seats 35** (private room, 20). L Mon-Fri 12.30-2.30, D daily 6.30-10.30 (Sun 7-9). Set L €26, Set D €46; Tasting Menu €65 (with wines +€40); house wine €22. SC 12.5%. Closed L Sat, L Sun & Christmas. Amex, Diners, MasterCard, Visa, Laser. **Directions:** On corner of Fitzwilliam Street & Baggot Street.

Mao Café Bar

Restaurant   2-3 Chatham Row Dublin 2 **Tel: 01 670 4899** Fax: 01 670 4993
Email: info@cafemao.com Web: www.cafemao.com

In simple but stylish surroundings, Café Mao brings to the Grafton Street area the cuisines of Thailand, Malaysia, Indonesia, Japan and China - about as 'Asian Fusion' as it gets. The atmosphere is bright and very buzzy and interesting food is based on seasonal ingredients; the standard of cooking is consistently good and so is value for money, although the bill can mount up quickly if you don't watch the number of Asian beers ordered. Chilli squid, Nasi Goreng and Malaysian chicken are established favourites, also tempura sole with stir-fried vegetables in a citrus sauce; vegetarians might try a starter of Jakarta salad (crisp vegetables and fruits in a piquant chilli dressing) followed by Thai green vegetable curry, with Jasmine rice. Chilli strength is considerately indicated on the menu, also vegetarian and low fat dishes, dishes containing nuts. A compact but wide-ranging drinks menu includes cocktails, fresh juices and smoothies, a range of coffees and teas and speciality beers as well as wines. No reservations. Wheelchair access. Children welcome. **Seats 120**. No smoking area; air conditioning. Open daily, 12-11. Menu à la carte. House wine from €16.95; Asian beers from €4.50. SC discretionary. Closed 25-26 Dec, Good Fri. MasterCard, Visa, Laser. **Directions:** City centre - just off Grafton Street.

McDaids

Pub   3 Harry Street Dublin 2 **Tel: 01 679 4395**

Established in 1779, McDaids more recently achieved fame as one of the great literary pubs - and its association with Brendan Behan, especially, brings a steady trail of pilgrims from all over the world to this traditional premises just beside the Westbury Hotel. Dubliners, however, tend to be immune to this kind of thing and drink there because it's a good pub - and, although its character is safe, it's not a place set in aspic either, as a younger crowd has been attracted by recent changes. History and character are generally of more interest than food here, but sandwiches are available. Open Mon-Wed,10.30am-11.30pm; Thu-Sat, 10.30am-12.30am; Sun 12.30-11. Closed 25 Dec & Good Fri.

The Mermaid Café

☆ Restaurant   69-70 Dame Street Dublin 2 **Tel: 01 670 8205** Fax: 01 670 8205
Email: info.@mermaid.ie Web: www.mermaid.ie

CREATIVE USE OF VEGETABLES AWARD - (see page 40)

Interesting decor and imaginative French and American-inspired cooking are to be found at Ben Gorman and Mark Harrell's unusual restaurant on the edge of Temple Bar. The two dining areas have recently been supplemented by a new wine lounge, which still hasn't transformed it into a big restaurant - but every inch of space has always been used with style here. Cooking at The Mermaid is among the best in the area - innovative, mid-Atlantic, seasonal and often memorable for inspired combinations of flavour, texture and colour - and service, although not always notable for swiftness, is invariably courteous and helpful. Menus change frequently but there would be public outcry if specialities like New England crab cakes with piquant mayonnaise, the Giant Seafood Casserole (which changes daily depending on availability) or pecan pie were taken off. Terrific vegetarian main courses such as steamed globe artichoke stuffed with basil pesto & niçoise salad rub shoulders with and hearty meat dishes which vary with the seasons but are invariably full of interest

- slow cooked osso bucco, perhaps, with tarragon & white wine, cannellini beans & crispy pancetta. Deserts like gooseberry & elderflower fool with pistachio biscotti are well worth leaving room for - unless you can't resist Irish cheeses like the wonderful, deeply flavoured Gabriel and Desmond from west Cork, served with celery biscuits. Then teas and coffees arrive with crystallised pecan nuts: attention to detail right to the finish. Sunday brunch is not to be missed if you are in the area - kick off with restorative drinks ranging from freshly squeezed juice or home-made lemonade to champagne, then launch into splendid fare like home-made sourdough pancakes and a variety of good things, olive oil bread bruschetta with roast ham, mustard & gratinated Gabriel cheese sauce, West Cork hand smoked haddock & horseradhish with mash - and much else besides. Wines are imported privately and are exclusive to the restaurant. Children welcome. **Seats 55** (private room, 28) No-smoking area; air conditioning. L 12.30-3 (Sun to 3.30), D 6.30-11 (Sun to 9). Set L €21.95; Set D from €30; also à la carte. House wine from about €18. SC discretionary. Closed 24-26 Dec,31 Dec, 1 Jan, Good Fri. New Year, Good Fri. [*Next door, Gruel (Tel 01 670 7119), is a quality fast-food outlet under the same management; open Mon-Fri 7.30-9.30; Sat & Sun 10.30-4.30.] MasterCard, Visa, Laser. **Directions:** Next door to Olympia Theatre.

The Merrion Hotel

Hotel   Upper Merrion Street Dublin 2 **Tel: 01 603 0600** Fax: 01 603 0700
Email: info@merrionhotel.com Web: www.merrionhotel.com

Right in the heart of Georgian Dublin opposite the Government Buildings, the main house of this luxurious hotel comprises four meticulously restored Grade 1 listed townhouses built in the 1760s and now restored to their former glory; behind them, a contemporary garden wing overlooks two private period and formal landscaped gardens. Inside, Irish fabrics and antiques reflect the architecture and original interiors with rococo plasterwork ceilings and classically proportioned windows - and the hotel has one of the most important private collections of 20th-century art. Public areas include three interconnecting drawing rooms (one is the cocktail bar with a log fire), with French windows giving access to the gardens. Elegant and gracious bedrooms have individually controlled air-conditioning, three telephones, personalised voice-mail with remote access, fax/modem and ISDN lines and video conference facilities, also a mini-bar and safe (VCRs, CD players and tea/coffee making facilities are available on request). Sumptuous Italian marble bathrooms, with a separate walk-in shower, pampe guests to the extreme. The six meeting/private dining rooms combine state-of-the-art technology and Georgian splendour, while the splendid leisure complex, The Tethra Spa, with classical mosaics, i almost Romanesque. Staff, under the excellent direction of General Manager Peter MacCann, are quite exemplary and courteous, suggesting standards of hospitality from a bygone era. Complimentary underground valet parking. Restaurant Patrick Guilbaud (see separate entry) is also on site. Conference/banqueting (50). Secretarial services. Leisure centre; swimming pool. Garden. Children welcome (under 4s free in parents' room, cots available free of charge). No pets. Lift. Valet parking. **Rooms 145** (20 suites, 10 junior suites, 1 shower only, 80 no-smoking, 5 for disabled). Room rate from €300. Open all year.

Morningtons Brasserie: The contemporary style of this elegant dining-room is reflected on the plate where fine Irish ingredients combine with Mediterranean cooking influences - although tradition also comes into play here, as The Merrion fish & chips with mushy peas and tartars sauce is a house speciality. An inexpensive table d'hôte lunch menu contrasts with more choices in the evening, bu nonetheless shows off head chef Edward Cooney's competent and precise cooking, backed up by excellent service - and some dishes are usefully highlighted to make an Express Menu, which allow two courses with coffee within 45 minutes. The wine list is grand, but prices are not over the top fo such an illustrious establishment. Al fresco dining on the terrace in summer, weather permitting. No smoking area. Air conditioning. **Seats 66.** L 12:30-2 Mon-Fri, D 6-10 daily. Set L from €23. Pre theatre menu from €23, 6-7pm. D also à la carte. House wine from €23. Closed L Sat, L Sun. Amex, Diners, MasterCard, Visa. **Directions:** City centre, opposite Government Buildings.

Milano

Restaurant   38 Dawson Street Dublin 2   **Tel: 01 670 7744**   Fax: 01 679 271

This stylish contemporary restaurant at the top of Dawson Street is best known for its wide range o excellent pizzas (it's owned by the UK company Pizza Express), but it's more of a restaurant than the description implies. Children are welcome and they run a very popular crèche facility on Sunday afternoons (12-5). Branches also in Temple Bar and also Ormond Quay and IFSC. **Seats 140** (private room 80). No-smoking area; air conditioning. Open daily,12 noon-12 midnight (Sun to 11.30). Menu à la carte. House wine €16.85. SC discretionary (10% on parties of 7+). Closed Dec 25 & 26. Amex, MasterCard, Visa, Diners, Laser. **Directions:** Opposite Mansion House, off Stephens Green.

Moe's Restaurant

Restaurant   112 Lower Baggot Street Dublin 2   **Tel: 01 676 7610**   Fax: 01 676 761
              Email: moesrestaurant@hotmail.com   Web: www.moesdublin.com

Small though the reception area may be - not, perhaps, the most relaxing place to wait for your table in the busy restaurant - do not allow this to spoil your anticipation of the meal to come. The dining-room is in the crisp modern style, with light-wood floors, white walls, interesting prints and excellent lighting; good napery, sparkling crystal glasses and attractive modern cutlery say this as a place to reckon with, yet the pricing is very competitive. Serious reputations have been built in these premises - Derry Clarke, of the highly-acclaimed L'Ecrivain just a few doors away started here to name but one - and chef/proprietor Ian Connolly is in the same mould, if his current renditions of modern and classical international cooking are anything to go by. Menus are not over-long bu well-considered, offering a choice of about eight tempting starters and main courses at dinner rather less for lunch. A signature dish to look out for is a starter iof seared beef salad, brioche croûtons with parmesan, rocket and truffle oil - unusual and delicious. Updated versions o traditional Irish themes are to be found in dishes like confit pork belly with champ and Apricot jus and vegetarian dishes like parmesan potato cake with oyster mushrooms, sautéed spinach, truffle oi and chive crème fraîche are also tempting enough to lure the most ardent carnivore. And the cheeseboard features the best mature Irish farmhouse cheeses from Sheridans cheesemongers, served with organic leaves and apple chutney. **Seats 40.** L Mon-Sat, 12.30-3; D Mon-Sat, 6-11. Set L €22, D from €15 (before 7pm), Set D €41; also à la carte. House wine €17.75. SC discretionary. Closed Sun, Dec 24-26, Dec 31-Jan 1, bank hols. Amex, MasterCard, Visa, Laser, Switch. **Directions:** Corner Fitzwilliam/Baggot, opposite Larry Murphys.

Mont Clare Hotel

 Hotel

Merrion Square Dublin 2 **Tel: 01 607 3800** Fax: 01 661 5663
Email: montclareres@ocallaghanhotels.ie Web: www.ocallaghanhotels.ie

A few doors away from the National Gallery, this well-located and reasonably priced hotel is in common ownership with the nearby Davenport and Alexander Hotels. The hotel is imaginatively decorated in contemporary style - except the old stained glass and mahogany Gallery Bar, which retains its original pubby atmosphere. Compact bedrooms are well furnished and comfortable; executive rooms have full marbled bathrooms and good amenities, including air conditioning, three direct line phones, a personal safe, ISDN lines and fax - and multi-channel TV with video channel. Business centre, secretarial services; gym. Conference/banqueting. (150). Children welcome (Under 2s free in parents' room; cots available free of charge). No pets. **Rooms 80** (2 junior suites, 40 no-smoking). Lift. Room rate from about €150; SC 12.5%. Open all year. Amex, Diners, MasterCard, Visa, Laser. **Directions:** Corner of Clare Street. and Lower Merrion St.

Montys of Kathmandu

 Restaurant

28 Eustace Street Temple Bar Dublin 2 **Tel: 01 670 4911**
Fax: 01 494 4359 Email: montys@tinet.ie Web: www.montys.ie

At first glance this restaurant deep in the heart of Temple Bar seems ordinary enough, but the food here has real character - and at agreeably low prices. The chefs are all from Nepal and although all the familiar dishes are represented there are definite undertones of Nepalese cooking throughout the menu. Friendly staff are more than happy to offer suggestions or choose a well balanced meal for you. Sheesh kebabs are really good and other specialities include kachela (raw mincedlamb), Momo (Nepalese dumplings) and Tandoori butter chicken: deliciously moist pieces of tender, tandoori chicken off the bone, cooked in a well balanced creamy masala sauce. Attentive staff foresee problems almost before they arise and sort things out in flash - and they even have their own beer, 'Shiva', brewed exclusively for the restaurant. Children welcome. **Seats 60** (private room, 30) L Mon-Sat, 12-2.15; Set L €13, Early D €17 (6-7pm), D daily 6-11.30, (Sun to11), tasting Menu €27-40. L&D à la carte available. SC discretionary except on parties of 6+ (12.5%). House wine from €17. Closed L Sun, 25-26 Dec & Good Fri. Amex, MasterCard, Visa, Laser. **Directions:** Opposite the Irish Film Centre (IFC).

Morgan Hotel

Hotel

10 Fleet Street Temple Bar Dublin 2 **Tel: 01 679 3939** Fax: 01 679 3946
Email: sales@themorgan.com Web: www.themorgan.com

In deepest Temple Bar, this unusual boutique hotel is characterised by clean simple lines and uncluttered elegance. Bedrooms have 6' beds in light beech, with classic white cotton bedlinen and natural throws, while standard bedroom facilities include satellite TV and video, CD/hi-fi system, mini-bar, safe, voicemail and internet access. The stylish Morgan Bar is open all day and offers an oasis of comfort and relaxation amongst the hustle and bustle of Temple Bar - try an exotic Morgain Mai Tai, perhaps? Strangely, as it seems so much at odds with the cool, reserved style of the rest of the hotel, the brash All Sports Café next door is part of it. Wheelchair access. Children welcome (Under 12s free in parents' room; cots available). **Rooms 64** (1 suite, 1 junior suite, 13 executive, 29 shower only, 20 no-smoking). Lift. Room rate €229. Closed 23-28 Dec. Amex, Diners, MasterCard, Visa, Laser. **Directions:** off Wesrmoreland Street.

Neary's

Pub

1 Chatham Street Dublin 2 **Tel: 01 677 7371**

This unspoilt Edwardian pub off Grafton Street is popular at all times of day - handy for lunch or as a meeting place in the early evening and full of buzz later when a post-theatre crowd, including actors from the nearby Gaiety theatre, will probably be amongst the late night throng in the downstairs bar. Traditional values assert themslves through gleaming brass, well-polished mahogany and classic like oysters and smoked salmon amongst the bar fare. Closed 25 Dec & Good Fri.

Nude Restaurant

Café

21 Suffolk Street Dublin 2
Tel: 01 672 5577 Fax: 01 672 5773 Email: niamh@nude.ie

Nude brought a new concept in fast food to Dublin when it opened in 1999, providing fantastic very fresh food - organic whenever possible - in an ultra-cool, youthful environment. Just off Grafton Street it's a great place for a quick snack, with plenty of room to sit down at long canteen-style tables. Queue up, order and pay at the till, then collect your food if it's ready or it will be delivered to your table. Working on the theory that you eat with your eyes, just looking at the fresh fruit and vegetables hanging or racked up in the open kitchen should revive you while you wait! A choice of soups includes seafood chowder, chunky vegetable and Thai chicken broth, all served with freshly baked breads; there are hot wraps - chicken satay or vegetarian Jumpin Bean, for example - and paninis, including one with Gubeen cheese, or try the chill cabinet for salads like Caesar or tomato & mozzarella, and cold wraps such as hummus or spinach & peppers, or soft bread rolls (eg smoked salmon & cream cheese). Freshly squeezed juices, smoothies and organic Fair Trade coffees, teas and herbal teas are all very popular (drinks can be made up to order) and the menu caters for vegetarians, people with nut allergies and other dietary requirements. Nude won the Guide's Creative Use of Irish Vegetables Award 2001. **Seats 40**. Open Mon-Sat, 8am-9.30pm, Sun 11-7. MasterCard, Visa, Laser. **Directions:** Near Dublin Tourism office. ◇

Number 31

Guesthouse   31 Leeson Close Lower Leeson St. Dublin 2 **Tel: 01 676 5011**
Fax: 01 676 2929 Email: number31@iol.ie Web: www.number31.ie

Formerly the home of leading architect Sam Stephenson, Noel and Deirdre Comer's 'oasis of tranquillity and greenery' just off St Stephen's Green makes an excellent city centre base, with virtually everything within walking distance in fine weather. Warm hospitality, huge breakfasts and secure parking add greatly to the attraction and rooms have everything you could wish for, including phones, TVs and tea/coffee trays. Not suitable for children under 10. No pets. **Rooms 20** (all en-suite & no smoking). B&B about €85, ss €19.95. Open all year. Amex, MasterCard, Visa. **Directions:** From St. Stephens Green onto Baggot St., turn right on to Pembroke St. and left on to Leeson St.

O'Donoghue's

Pub   15 Merrion Row Dublin 2 **Tel: 01 676 2807**

O'Donoghues has long been the Dublin mecca for visitors in search of a lively evening with traditional music - live music every night is a major claim to fame - but a visit to this famous pub near the Shelbourne Hotel at quieter times can be rewarding too. Closed 25 Dec & Good Fri.

O'Neill's Pub & Guesthouse

Pub/Guesthouse   37 Pearse Street Dublin 2 **Tel: 01 671 4074** Fax: 01 8325218
Email: oneilpub@iol.ie Web: www.oneillsdublin.com

Established in 1885, this centrally located pub on the corner of Pearse Street and Shaw Street is easily recognised by the well-maintained floral baskets that brighten up the street outside. Inside, this cosy bar has kept its Victorian character and charm and serves a good range of reasonably priced home-cooked food - typically soft cheese & garlic stuffed mushrooms, traditional pies and Dublin Coddle, served with french fries and an attractive salad. (Accommodation is available in recently renovated rooms, with breakfast served in a pleasant room above the pub.) Bar food, Mon-Fri: L 12.30-2, D 5.30-9. Closed Christmas & Good Fri. Amex, MasterCard, Visa, Laser. **Directions:** Opposite Pearse Street side of Trinity College.

O'Neill's Public House

Pub   2 Suffolk Street Dublin 2
Tel: 01 679 3656 Fax: 01 679 0689 Email: mikeon@indigo.ie

A striking pub with its own fine clock over the door and an excellent corner location, it has been in the O'Neill family since 1920 and is popular with Dubliners and visitors alike. Students from Trinity and several other colleges nearby home into O'Neill's for its wide range of reasonably priced bar food, which includes a carvery with a choice of five or six roasts and an equal number of other dishes (perhaps including traditional favourites such as Irish Stew) each day; finish off with some home-made rhubarb pie, perhaps.. Wheelchair access. No children after 6pm. Bar food served daily: Mon-Thu,12-8; Fri 12-4.30; Sat 12-8; Sun 12.30-10. Closed 25 & 26 Dec, Good Fri. Amex, MasterCard, Visa, Laser. **Directions:** On the corner of Suffolk St and Church Lane, opposite the DublinTourist Centre.

Odessa Lounge & Grill

Restaurant/Pub   13/14 Dame Lane Dublin 2 **Tel: 01 670 7634**

Tucked away about 5 minutes from Grafton Street this is a favourite haunt for Dublin's bright young things and this lively place to eat and was one of the first places in Dublin to do brunch. The room downstairs is the perfect place to nurse a hangover with no natural light, subdued lighting, comfy chairs with plenty of room to spread out and read the papers in peace. The food is basic brunch fare but the atmosphere is a major attraction. Eggs Benedict or Florentine, huevos rancheros or a char-grilled steak sandwich (all around €8). The service is relaxed and friendly even when they are very busy there's never a feeling of being rushed. At night is just right for those who want more than a fast-food burger, but who do not want to dress for dinner - and it's also perfect for large groups with something to celebrate. **Seats 100.** No smoking area. Air conditioning. Sat & Sun open noon-midnight, brunch 12-4. D Mon-Wed 6-11, Thu & Fri 5-12. SC discretionary (10% on parties of 6+). Amex, MasterCard, Visa. **Directions:** Left off Dame Street onto George's Street, left onto Exchequer Street, then left again.

The Old Mill

Restaurant   14 Temple Bar Dublin 2 **Tel: 01 671 9262**

Long before this area became trendy Temple Bar, Moroccan chef-patron Lahcen Iouani had a loyal following in the area - since the mid 80s, in fact, when this restaurant delighted discerning Dubliners in an earlier guise as 'Pigalle'. The name change has relevance to local history (you can read all about it on the back of the menu) but other things have thankfully remained the same and Lahcen continues to offer admirably traditional French cooking at refreshingly modest prices. Giving good value to the customer is something he feels strongly about, so you will find most starters like traditional fish soup, salade niçoise and calmar frit in the €5.50 range, with main courses from around €9.50 for vegetarian dishes like lentil & leek gratin, rising to €22 for expensive fish like sole and seabass; in between there's a range of other fish and meats at €21 or less. An informative wine list follows the same admirable philosophy and all desserts (tarte tatin, fresh fruit sabayon) are home-made. **Seats 60.** Air conditioning. Open 5-11.30 daily. A la carte. House wine from €15.50. SC discretionary except on parties of 8+ (10%). MasterCard, Visa, Laser, Switch. **Directions:** Above Merchants Arch on Temple Bar Square (behind Central Bank).

The Old Stand

Pub   37 Exchequer Street Dublin 2 **Tel: 01 677 7220** Fax: 01 677 5849

This fine traditional pub, which is a sister establishment to Davy Byrnes, off Grafton Street, occupies a prominent position on the corner of Exchequer Street and St Andrew Street and lays claim to being "possibly the oldest public house in Ireland"!. Named after the Old Stand at the Lansdowne Road rugby grounds, it has a loyal following amongst the local business community, notably from the 'rag trade' area around South William Street, and also attracts a good mixture of sporting people and visitors, who enjoy the atmosphere. They offer no-nonsense traditional bar food at reasonable prices and a blackboard at the door proclaims daily specials as well as a selection of regulars from the menu - steaks (with or without sauce), grilled salmon with dill & white wine sauce, omelettes and chips, Irish stew and a vegetarian pasta dish of the day are all typical. Not suitable for children under 7. Bar food served daily 12.15-9. Closed 25-26 Dec & Good Fri. MasterCard, Visa, Laser. **Directions:** Grafton Street area.

One Pico Restaurant

féile bia ☆ Restaurant   5-6 Molesworth Place Schoolhouse Lane Dublin 2 **Tel: 01 676 0300**
            Fax: 01 676 0411 Email: eamonoreilly@ireland.com Web: www.onepico.com

In a magical location near St Stephen's Green, nicely tucked in a laneway just a couple of minutes walk from the Dail and Grafton Street, Eamonn O'Reilly's One Pico has become one of Dublin's most popular restaurants since moving here a year ago. The surroundings are elegant and cooking good - the style distinctly contemporary, with worldwide influences; sophisticated, technically demanding dishes are executed with confidence and flair. Eamonn has always based his menus on first class ingredients and it is their flavours that stand out, together with the precision of the cooking. Menus offered include a 2- and 3-course lunch which, as usual in restaurants of this calibre represents great value. Dinner is à la carte, with about ten quite luxurious dishes offered on each course, plus optional side dishes which may not be necessary as each main course is individually garnished. Dishes from the international side of the menu enjoyed on the Guide's most recent visit include a deliciously under-stated parsley & wild garlic soup with poached

Eamonn O'Reilly
Proprietor/Chef

101

quail egg (although this was less well received at a neighbouring table) and a main course of roast salted cod with vine ripened tomatoes, warm potato & spinach salad. Dishes with Irish influences are not much in evidence, alas - just a small nod to our own traditions in speciality starters of black pudding with scallion mash & apple confit and bacon & cabbage terrine with sauce grebiche & crackling - but be sure to sample an innovative and delicious cheese menu and/or beautifully presented desserts that taste as good as they look. An 8-course tasting menu is also offered, for whole tables up to a maximum of six. Service, under the direction of restaurant manager Pascal Michel, is professional. *A sister restaurant, Pacific, opened in Temple Bar in summer 2002 - see separate entry. **Seats 80** (private room, 20-50) No-smoking area; air conditioning. L& D Mon-Sat: L12-3, D 6-11. Set L from €22.50, Tasting Menu €70,also à la carte. House wine €20. SC 10%. Closed Sun, 1st 2 wks in Aug. Amex, Diners, MasterCard, Visa, Laser. **Directions:** 2 mins walk off St Stephens Green/Grafton Street.

Pacific Restaurant

Ⓝ Restaurant   17/19 Sycamore Street Dublin 2 **Tel: 01 677 4199** Fax: 01 677 4714
Email: eamonnoreilly@ireland.com Web: www.onepico/pacific.com

In the same ownership as Eamonn O'Reilly's One Pico, Pacific opened to some acclaim in July 2002. It's a very cool space with streamlined decor, lots of glass, cream leather - and beautiful people. There's a little bar where cocktails and aperitifs can be ordered from a compact drinks menu or you may be shown straight to your table. Tables are quite close together but fine glasses, lovely flowers and fine white china make a classy setting for head chef Nick Woollard's "new world cuisine". Patrons of the parent restaurant will recognise some of their specialities - a modern Irish bacon & cabbage terrine with sauce gribiche & crackling, for example - and devotees of contemporary cooking may find choices from lively and wide-ranging menus difficult, with a selection of 8-10 starters and a similar number of main courses at both lunch and dinner. With starters on the lunch menu ranging from €5.80 - €12.70 and main courses between €10.80 - €18.50, this is a pricey placeand will have to deliver consistently high standards all round to give good value. In the Guide's experience both cooking and service are a little mixed, but a serious new restaurant is very welcome in this area - it has great potential and should be a great success when it is fully "run in". Sky Bar (piano bar, jazz, cocktails) open Thu-Sat, from 8pm. **Seats 130** (private rooms 10/90). No smoking area; air conditioning. L& D daily: 12.30-3 , 5.30-11 (Sun to 9.30). A la carte. SC 10%. Closed bank hols. Amex, Diners, MasterCard, Visa, Laser. **Directions:** Off Dame Street, next to Olympia Theatre stage door.

The Palace Bar

Pub   21 Fleet Street Dublin 2 **Tel: 01 677 9290**

Just around the corner from the Irish Times offices, The Palace has had strong connections with writers and journalists for many a decade. Its unspoilt frosted glass and mahogany are impressive enough but the special feature is the famous sky-lighted snug, which is really more of a back room. Many would cite The Palace as their favourite Dublin pub. Closed 25 Dec & Good Fri.

Pasta Fresca

Restaurant   2-4 Chatham Street Dublin 2 **Tel: 01 679 2402** Fax: 01 668 4563

This long-established Italian restaurant in the Grafton Street shopping area specialises in fresh pasta. The popular all-day menu is based on good home-made pastas, thin-based crispy Neapolitan pizzas, a wide range of interesting salads with well-made dressings. There are plenty of vegetarian on offer as well as Tuscan favourites like pollo all Toscana (chargrilled marinated chicken served with Tuscan white beans and salad) and a speciality pasta salad (with Tuscan beans, sweetcorn, fresh vegetables, shaved Parmesan & house dressing). Evening menus offer a wider choice and shoppers and diners alike can buy Italian groceries, fresh pasta and sauces made on the premises from their deli counter. Children welcome. **Seats 90** (private rooms, 20/40). No-smoking area; air conditioning. Open all day Mon-Sat, 11.30-midnight, Sun 12 -10. L 11-5, D 5.30-12 (Sun to10); à la carte. House wine from €17.75. SC discretionary (12.5% on tables of 4+). Closed 25-26 Dec. Amex, Diners, MasterCard, Visa, Laser. **Directions:** Off top of Grafton Street.

Pearl Brasserie

Restaurant   20 Merrion Street Upper Dublin 2 **Tel: 01 661 3572** Fax: 01 661 3629
Email: info@pearl-brasserie.com Web: www.pearl-brasserie.com

Just a few doors away from The Merrion Hotel, this stylish basement restaurant with colourful blue banquettes and marble-topped tables is run by Sebastien Masi, previously head chef at The Commons on St Stephen's Green, and his partner Kirsten Batt, who is the restaurant manager. The style is contemporary international, with a classic French base and a pleasing emphasis on clean flavours, highlighting the quality of ingredients. Menus lean towards towards fish, which Sebastien cooks with accuracy and flair - nearly half of the starters and main courses on the à la carte menu are seafood of some sort and very attractive they are too - who could resist squid tempura with a mild chilli dressing and carrot salad, or a main course of seared king scallops served with a citrus salad? But there's plenty from the land too, with specialities including luscious pan-fried foie gras with toasted brioche with rhubarb and strawberry compôte and a modern Irish dish of pan-fried fillet of beef with colcannon, cèpe sauce & black pudding parcels. A place mat à la carte lunch menu offering a wide range of styles (so you can make it as informal as you like or go for a regular 3-course meal) includes salads and hot snacks (chicory & blue cheese salad with walnut & mustard dressing, perhaps, croque madame or creamy duck liver paté with toasted brioche & onion marmalade, pastas and main courses ranging from bangers & mash with red wine jus to sirloin steak shallot sauce & fries. Service is charming and well informed and the wine list is a good match for the food, balancing French and New World wines and offering a fair choice of half bottles and wines by the glass. **Seats 80** (private areas 12 & 6); no-smoking area; air-conditioning. L Tue-Fri 12-2.30, D daily 6-10.30; L à la carte; Early D €19 (6-7.30, Mon-Fri), Set D from €28; Gourmet menu €60. House wine €19. SC discretionary. Closed bank hols, 1st 2 wks Jan. Amex, MasterCard, Visa, Laser. **Directions:** Opposite Government Building, near Merrion Hotel.

The Pembroke

Pub/Restaurant   31/32 Lower Pembroke Street Dublin 2 **Tel: 01 676 2980**
Fax: 01 676 6579 Email: briancrowley@hotmail.com Web: www.pembroke.ie

There was consternation amongst traditionalists when this fine old pub was given a complete makeover several years ago, creating the bright and trendy bar that it is now - it even has a cyber café in the basement. But, even if the cosiness of old has now gone for ever, the spacious new bar that has been created has character of its own and, along with some striking design features (notably lighting), the atrium/ conservatory area at the back brings the whole place to life. Meeting the needs of those who get in to work before the traffic builds up, bar food begins with breakfast. **Seats 300.** Food served Mon-Sat, 7.30am-10pm; carvery lunch, 12-2:30. Closed Sun, 25-26 Dec & Good Fri. Amex, MasterCard, Visa, Laser. **Directions:** Near St Stephen's Green - off Lr Baggot Street.

Pizza Stop

Restaurant   6-10 Chatham House Chatam Lane Dublin 2
Tel: 01 679 6712 Fax: 01 679 6712

This cheap and cheerful little restaurant has been doing good pizzas and pastas in style since the late '80s. If you're not in the mood for pizza or pasta try one of their other Italian specialities - diced leg of Wicklow lamb with Medterranean sauce, perhaps. Just the place to meet up with the family for a tasty meal that won't break the bank. **Seats 70.** No-smoking area; air conditioning. Open Mon-Sat 12-12, Su 3-11. A la carte. Hpuse wine €15. SC5%. MasterCard, Visa, Laser. **Directions:** Beside Westbury Hotel ,Grafton Street.

The Porterhouse

🚩 Pub   16-18 Parliament Street Temple Bar Dublin 2
Tel: 01 679 8847 Fax: 01 670 9605 Email: porterh@indigo.ie

Dublin's first micro-brewery pub opened in 1996 and, although several others have since set up and are doing an excellent job, The Porterhouse was at the cutting edge. Ten different beers are brewed on the premises and beer connoisseurs can sample a special 'tasting tray' selection of plain porter (a classic light stout), oyster stout (brewed with fresh oysters, the logical development of a perfect partnership), Wrasslers 4X (based on a west Cork recipe from the early 1900s, and said to be Michael Collins' favourite tipple), Porter House Red (an Irish Red Ale with traditional flavour), An Brain Blasta (dangerous to know) and the wittily named Temple Brau. But you don't even have to like beer to love The Porterhouse. The whole concept is an innovative move away from the constraints of the traditional Irish pub and yet it stays in tune with its origins - it is emphatically not just another theme pub. The attention to detail which has gone into the decor and design is a constant source of pleasure to visitors and the food, while definitely not gourmet, is a cut above the usual bar food and, like the pub itself, combines elements of tradition with innovation. This is a real Irish pub in the modern idiom and was a respected winner of our Jameson Pub of the Year award in 1999. No children after 7pm. Bar food served 12:30-9:30 daily. Closed 25 Dec & Good Fri. MasterCard, Visa. [*The original Porterhouse is located on Strand Road on the seafront in Bray, Co Wicklow and, like its sister pub in Temple Bar, it offers bar food daily from 12:30-9:30. No children after 7pm. Closed 25 Dec & Good Fri. MasterCard, Visa. Tel/Fax: 01 286 1839. There is also a newer Porterhouse in London, located at Covent Garden, and one due to open in Phibsborough during 2003.

Principal Hotel

Hotel   19/20 Fleet Street Temple Bar Dublin 2
          Tel: 01 670 8122 Fax: 01 6708103 Email: bewleyshotel@eircom.net

Conveniently situated in the heart of Temple Bar, within easy walking distance of all the city's main attractions, this reasonably priced hotel is fairly small, allowing an intimate atmosphere and a welcome emphasis on service. Major renovations are planned at the time of going to press. Children welcome (under 12s free in parents' room; cots available without charge). No pets. **Rooms 70** (40 shower only, 35 no-smoking). Room rate €149). Lift. Closed 24-26 Dec. Amex, Diners, MasterCard, Visa. **Directions:** Heart of Temple Bar, near Fleet Street.

Queen of Tarts

🄽 Café   4 Cork Hill Dame Street Dublin 2 **Tel: 01 670 7499**

Behind this quaint traditional shopfront near Dublin Castle lies an equally quaint traditional tea room, with warmly welcoming friendly and efficient staff and wonderful smells wafting across the room as they struggle to make space for new arrivals to the comfortable, lived-in little room. Breakfast (including a vegetarian cooked breakfast) is served from 7.30 and the lunch/afternoon menu takes over at noon. Baking is a speciality, with home-made scones, buttermilk brown bread, hot savoury tarts, roast chicken & coriander tartlets, strawberry & rhubarb crumble and much else besides taking their place on a suprisingly extensive menu, which includes some seriously good sandwiches and salads - most people pop in for a snack, but you could just as easily have a 3-course lunch. Inexpensive (there's not much over €7), consistently excellent food and great service - what more could anyone ask? Well, another branch perhaps - and another has opened in the newly renovated City Hall (Open museum hours, Sat 10-5, Sun 2-5). **Seats 20.** No smoking restaurant; air conditioning. Open daily: Mon-Fri 7.30-6; Sat 9-6; Sun 10-6. **No Credit Cards. Directions:** Opposite the gates of Dublin Castle.

QV2 Restaurant

Restaurant   14-15 St Andrew Street Dublin 2 **Tel: 01 677 3363** Fax: 01 677 3363
              Email: frontdesk@qv2restaurant.com Web: www.qv2restaurant.com

Handy to Grafton Street and all the city centre attractions, this popular restaurant accurately describes itself as offering 'International cuisine with an Irish twist'. Eoin McDonnell, head chef since 1991, builds his menus around fresh seasonal produce and hits just the right note on interesting menus that also give good value, especially for lunch and the early bird dinner. Among the international flavours you'll find comforting traditional Irish fare like corned beef with champ, buttered cabbage & parsley cream sauce and house specialities include Eoin's Fish Pie - lots of big chunks of fish in a white wine & parsley sauce, with a crispy filo crust - and rosettes of lamb with sautéed spinach, potatoes Anna & mint mayonnaise. The street level room has more atmosphere, but the basement improves as it fills up. Lunch and early bird menus are keenly priced. Nice, helpful staff; reasonably priced wine list. Children welcome. **Seats 140** (private room, 40) No-smoking area; air conditioning. L Mon-Sat 12-2.45, D Mon-Sat 6-10.45. A la carte. House wine €19. SC discretionary (10% on parties of 8+). Closed Sun, Bank Hols, Christmas wk & Good Fri. Amex, Diners, MasterCard, Visa, Laser. **Directions:** Near Dublin Tourism Centre.

Rajdoot Tandoori

Restaurant   26 -28 Clarendon Street Dublin 2 **Tel: 01 679 4274** / 80 Fax: 01 679 4274
              Email: info@rajdoottandoori.com Web: www.rajdoottandoori.com

A member of a small UK chain of restaurants specialising in subtle, aromatic North Indian cuisine, this restaurant has had a fine reputation for its food and service since it opened in 1984. Tandoori dishes are the main speciality, based on a wide range of ingredients authentically cooked - this is possibly the only restaurant in Ireland that still uses the traditional charcoal-fired clay ovens rather than gas. Speciality dishes include duck jaipur (with spring onions, green peppers, mushrooms, garlic

& red wine), chicken johl (a spicy Nepalese dish with ginger, garlic, fresh coriander & fenugreek) and lamb chili garlic. There is also plenty of choice for vegetarians. Set menus include a keenly priced 3-course lunch and pre-theatre dinner. Children over 6 welcome until 7pm. **Seats 120.** No smoking area; air conditioning. L Mon-Sat 12-2.30, Sun 1.30-5.30. D 6-11 daily. Set L €11.35 Set D from €21.59. Early D €20.32 (6-7pm). House wine €14.60. No-smoking area. Air conditioning. SC discretionary. Closed 25-26 Dec. Amex, Diners, MasterCard, Visa, Laser, Switch. **Directions:** Top of Grafton Street, behind Westbury Hotel.

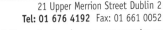
Restaurant Patrick Guilbaud

★★ Restaurant

21 Upper Merrion Street Dublin 2
Tel: 01 676 4192 Fax: 01 661 0052

The capital's premier French restaurant occupies an elegant ground-floor restaurant in the Main House of The Merrion Hotel, opening on to a terrace and landscaped garden (with al fresco eating in fine weather). Although access can also be gained via the hotel, the main entrance is through the original front door to the 1760s Georgian townhouse. Fine works by Irish artists (look out especially for Harry Kernoff's 'Jammet's Restaurant', probably Dublin's finest restaurant in the Sixties) are a major decorative feature, making a very fine setting for one of Ireland's most renowned restaurants. Head chef Guillaume Lebrun has presided over this fine kitchen since the restaurant opened in its original premises in 1982 and presents wide-ranging à la carte and set menus - the table d'hôte lunch (changed daily) is a snip at €28 and, at the other end of the spectrum there's a luxurious 7-course Menu Célébration, which was created to celebrate the 20th anniversary of the restaurant and is for complete parties only, as is the 10-course Menu Dégustation (both available until 9.30 pm). Contemporary French cooking at its best is what you get, albeit with a nod to traditional Irish influences, so the best of Irish ingredients, combined with the precision and talents of a team of gifted chefs, produces dishes of dexterity, appeal and flavour - a recent visit by the Guide confirmed that consistent excellence remains the order of the day at RPG and, given that the small portions are frequently the target of criticism, it was noted with approval that a bowl of extra potatoes was brought up from the kitchen for a hungry young diner without condescension. Desserts are particularly interesting, cheeses are supplied by Sheridans cheesemongers, breads are home-made, and the mostly French wine list includes some great classics, with some reasonably-priced offerings. Service, under the supervision of Stephane Robin, is immaculate and Patrick Guilbaud himself is almost invariably present to greet guests personally and, discreetly working the tables, he makes a point of having a chat with everyone - whether a resident at the Merrion Hotel, local business person or simply an individual bent on a gastronomic treat in Dublin's most famous restaurant - and making sure that all is well. Children welcome. **Seats 80** (private room, 25) No-smoking area; air conditioning. L Tue-Sat 12.30-2.15, D Tue-Sat 7.30-10.15. Set L €28. Menu Célébration €114, Menu Dégustation €125.. L&D à la carte available. House wine from €32. SC discretionary. Closed Sun & Mon, Christmas, 1st week Jan. Amex, Diners, MasterCard, Visa, Laser. **Directions:** Opposite Government Buildings.

Saagar Indian Restaurant

Restaurant

16 Harcourt Street Dublin 2 **Tel: 01 475 5060** / 5012 Fax: 01 475 5741
Email: info@saagarindianrest.com Web: www.saagarindianrest.com

Meera and Sunil Kumar's highly-respected basement restaurant just off St Stephen's Green offers a wide range of speciality dishes, all prepared from fresh ingredients and thoughtfully coded with a range of one to four stars to indicate the heat level. Thus Malai Kabab is a safe one-star dish, while traditional Lamb Balti and Lamb Aayish (marinated with exotic spices and cooked in a cognac-flavoured sauce) is a three-star and therefore pretty hot. Beef and pork are not served but this is balanced by a good vegetarian selection and the side dishes, such as Naan breads which are made to order in the tandoori oven, are excellent. The Kumars also have restaurants in Athlone and Mullingar. Children welcome but not very young babies (under 1), or after 10pm. **Seats 60.** Toilets wheelchair accesible. L Mon-Fri, 12.30-2.30; D 6-11 daily. L&D à la carte available. House wine €15. SC discretionary. Closed L Sat,L Sun & Christmas week. Amex, Diners, MasterCard, Visa, Laser, Switch. **Directions:** Opposite Children's Hospital on Harcourt Street (off Stephen's Green).

Salamanca

N Restaurant   1 St Andrew's Street Dublin 2 **Tel: 01 670 8628**

Hundred watt smiles are the norm at this atmospheric tapas bar and Spanish restaurant in the heart of Dublin. There's no waiting space for new arrivals, but the entrance is pleasant - past a bar with flowers on the counter - and you go straight to a simple marble-topped table. The menu - which is in Spanish with English explanations - is flexible enough to suit anything from a light lunch to a full dinner and offers an embarrassment of good choices: three tapas plates will make a generous lunch for two. Decor is warm and bright, with interesting Spanish details to enjoy in the unlikely event that service might be slow. Food is tasty and Spanish staples are well-handled - garlic roast chicken, langoustines with serrano ham, squid in chilli butter and patatas bravas are all delicious and there are no short cuts on ingredients, including the quality of olive oil used for frying; presentation is simple and traditional, oval plates and shallow casseroles are used, with nice little touches like fresh parsley and drizzles of sour cream set off the food and their lovely frothy-topped mocha served in a tall glass makes a great post-prandial reviver. Excellent food, delightful staff and very good value (individual tapas from €3.75) make this place a sure fire winner; food is served throughout the day and they don't take bookings - so be prepared to wait at peak times. Wine list includes a range of sherries by the glass - the traditional accompaniment for tapas. No smoking area. Meals: Mon-Thur, 12 noon-11 pm, Fri & Sat to midnight. Closed Sun. MasterCard, Visa. **Directions:** Near Dublin Tourism.

Shalimar Indian Restaurant

féile bia Restaurant   17 South Great Georges Street Dublin 2
Tel: 01 671 0738 Fax: 01 677 3478 Email: shalimar@iol.ie

Just across the road from the Central Hotel this welcoming, well-appointed basement restaurant serves generous portions of a wide-range of Indian dishes. Balti dishes are a speciality - diners are invited to mix and match items on the menu to suit individual tastes - and there's also a wide choice of Tandoori and Biryani basmati rice dishes. This is a friendly, relaxing restaurant and prices are reasonable. Wheelchair access. Parking by arrangement with nearby carpark. Children welcome. **Seats 100** (private room, 50) Set L&D & à la carte available. No-smoking area. Air conditioning. SC 10%. Closed Christmas & Good Fri. Amex, Diners, MasterCard, Visa, Laser. **Directions:** Opposite Central Hotel.

Shanahan's on the Green

féile bia Restaurant   119 St. Stephen's Green Dublin 2
Tel: 01 407 0939 Fax: 01 407 0940 Web: www.shanahans.ie

Located on the west side of the Green, this opulent restaurant is Dublin's first dedicated American style steakhouse - although the wide-ranging menu also offers plenty of other meats, poultry and seafood. However, the big attraction for many of the hungry diners who have headed for Shanahan's is their certified Irish Angus beef, which is seasoned and cooked in a special broiler, 1600-1800°F, to sear the outside and keep the inside tender and juicy. Their steaks range from a 'petit filet' at a mere 8 oz/225g right up to The Shanahan Steak (24 oz/700g), which is a sight to gladden the heart of many a traditionally-minded Irishman - and many of his trendier young friends too. Strange to think that steak was passé such a short time ago... Just bring a good appetite - and a fat wallet. (Portions tend to be very large, so regulars often order less courses than in other restaurants, which makes for better value.) The wide-ranging wine list includes many special bottles - with, naturally, a strong presence from Californian producers. No children. **Seats 120.** No smoking area; air conditioning. D daily, 6-10.30. A la carte. (SC discretionary, except 15% on parties of 6+). Closed Christmas week. Amex, Diners, MasterCard, Visa, Laser. **Directions:** On the west side of Stephen's Green.

Silk Road Café

N Café   Chester Beatty Library Dublin Castle Dublin 2
Tel: 01 407 0770 Fax: 01 407 0788 Email: aljamal@gofree.indigo.ie

In a fine location in the heart of the city centre, Dublin Castle provides wonderful gardens and historic architecture which greatly enhance the enjoyment of a visit to this unusual restaurant, which is situated in the clock tower beside the Chester Beatty Library (which was awarded the title of European Museum of the Year in 2002). Middle eastern, Mediterranean and vegetarian and organic are the themes brought together by a dedicated small team who create inspired versions of classics like Greek moussaka, Moroccan cous cous, falafel and spinach & feta pie to the delight of their many returning customers. Fresh organic herbs are used in all dishes and, in line with halal/kosher rules, all dishes are made without the use of pork or beef. Prices are very reasonable - an average main course served with rice or salad is around €10. Children welcome. **Seats 60** (private room 25). No smoking restaurant; air conditioning. Open daily, 12-4 (Sun 1-5); à la carte. No service charge. Closed Mon off-season (Oct-Apr). Visa, Laser. **Directions:** Beside Chester Beatty Library in Dublin Castle.

Sonar Gaon

Restaurant   6 Crow Street Dublin 2 **Tel: 01 672 8822** Fax: 01 672 8877
Email: sonargoan@eircom.net

Right in the heart of Temple Bar, this friendly Indian restaurant has brought something new to the ethnic dining scene in Ireland and is earning a reputation for authenticity. Decor in the light, airy room is not unusual, but the food is - notably a range of street foods not found before in Ireland. These 'Sonar Chaat Bazaar' are mostly served cold although several hot ones are offered (pastry dumplings, for example, served stuffed with potatoes, peas herbs & spices or with mung lentils and peas) and the range of dishes offered throughout the menu is wide and unusual. The well-known cooking styles are represented, including tandoori dishes, but also unfamiliar dishes such as Dosai - a thin, crispy crepe of rice and lentil from southern India with various stuffings - which have never been offered in Ireland before. Vegetarian dishes are particularly attractive and the choice extensive; they may sound expensive at first, but the standard of cooking and excellent flavour spells value for money. There are none of the familiar set menus for groups, so it may take some time to get to grips with the menu, but staff are knowledgeable and helpful. Accompaniments include a range of breads - chapatt, poori, paratha and various nan breads; limited wine list but Indian beer and beverages (lassi, tea) are available. An early dinner menu offers especially good value. MasterCard, Visa.

The Stag's Head

Pub   1 Dame Court Dublin 2 **Tel: 01 679 3701**

In Dame Court, just behind the Adams Trinity Hotel, this impressive establishment has retained its original late-Victorian decor and is one of the city's finest pubs. It can get very busy at times - sometimes dusty and sticky surfaces suggest that the volume of business makes it difficult to keep up with routine housekeeping, but this lovely pub is still worth a visit. Closed 25 Dec & Good Fri.

Stauntons on the Green

Guesthouse   83 St Stephen's Green Dublin 2
Tel: 01 478 2300 Fax: 01 487 2263 Email: hotels@indigo.ie

Well-located with views over St Stephen's Green at the front and its own private gardens at the back, this guesthouse - which is in an elegant Georgian terrace on the south of the Green and has fine period reception rooms - offers moderately priced accommodation of a good standard, with all the usual amenities. It's in the heart of the business and banking district and the Grafton Street shopping area is just a stroll across the Green. Meeting rooms are available, with secretarial facilities on request - and here's private parking. Children welcome. No pets. **Rooms 36** (all en-suite, 20 shower only). B&B about €75 pps, ss £15. Closed 24-27 Dec. Amex, Diners, MasterCard, Visa.

Stephen's Green Hotel

féile bia Hotel   St Stephen's Green Dublin 2 **Tel: 01 607 3600** Fax: 01 661 5663
Email: stephensgreenres@ocallaghanhotels.ie Web: www.ocallaghanhotels.ie

This striking landmark hotel on the south-western corner site overlooking St Stephen's Green is the newest of the O'Callaghan Hotels group (Alexander, Davenport, Mont Clare - see entries). Public areas include an impressive foyer and, in memory of the writer George Fitzmaurice who used to live here, 'Pie Dish' restaurant and 'Magic Glasses' bar - both named after titles from his work. It's a great location for business or leisure and bedrooms have exceptionally good facilities, particularly for business travellers, including air conditioning, 3 direct line telephones, voice mail and modem line, desk, mini-bar as standard. (Small conference 35). Business centre. ISDN lines. Gym. Children welcome (Under 2s free in parents' room; cots available). No pets. **Rooms 75** (9 suites, including 2 studio terrace suites, 3 penthouse suites, junior suites; 40 no-smoking rooms, 2 for disabled). Lift. B&B €150, ss €100 (Room-only rate €298, max 2 guests). SC 12.5%. Open all year. Amex, Diners, MasterCard, Visa, Switch. **Directions:** Corner of Harcourt St. and St. Stephen's Green.

Steps of Rome

Restaurant   1 Chatham Street Dublin 2 **Tel: 01 670 5630**

For some reason good, inexpensive little Italian places specialising in pizza have clustered around Balfe and Chatham Streets. Each has its following and this authentic one-room café just beside Neary's pub is a favourite lunch spot for discerning Dubliners. (Branch at Ciao Bella Roma, Parliament St.) **Seats 18.** Open 12 noon-11pm Mon-Sat, Sun 1-10pm. House wine €13.50. No service charge. **No Credit Cards.**

Tante Zoes

Restaurant   1 Crow Street Temple Bar Dublin 2 **Tel: 01 679 4407** Fax: 01 670 7559
Email: robbief@indigo.ie Web: indigo.ie/~ robbief/

Tante Zoe's is a dark, relaxing place - dark wood, bamboo and cloth covered tables, with old posters and signs from the deep south on the walls - great for a group of pals out for the night. Cajun popcorn - a huge mound of juicy baby shrimps coated in crispy spiced breadcrumbs and served with a Marie Rose-style sauce or crab cakes, Shrimp Creole (spicy tomato sauce with plump jumbo shrimps), blackened chicken with spiced cream sauce are all typical and side dishes include Maque choux (sweetcorn cooked with peppers, onion and tomato). Bread pudding with whiskey sauce could make a great finale on a chilly night. Attentive waiting staff contribute to the relaxed atmosphere - and make informed suggestions. Not suitable for children under 10. **Seats 150** (private room, 100) No-smoking area (no air conditioning). Open daily 12 noon-midnight, (Sun 12-4 & 6-12) Set L €11. Early D €15 (6-8pm). Also à la carte, L&D. SC discretionary (12.5% on parties of 6+). Closed 25 Dec & Good Fri. Amex, Diners, MasterCard, Visa, Laser. **Directions:** Temple Bar off Dame Street.

Temple Bar Hotel

Hotel   Fleet Street Temple Bar Dublin 2 **Tel: 01 677 3333** Fax: 01 677 3088
Email: reservations@tbh.ie Web: ww.templebarhotel.com

This pleasant hotel is handy for both sides of the river. Spacious reception and lounge areas create a good impression and bedrooms are generally larger than average, almost all with a double and single bed and good amenities. Neat, well-lit bathrooms have over-bath showers and marble wash basin units. Room service menu (6-10pm) No parking, but the hotel has an arrangement with a nearby car park. Conference/banqueting (8-/70). Wheelchair access. Children welcome (Under 3s free in parents' room, cots available without charge). No pets. **Rooms 129** (10 no-smoking, 2 for disabled). Lift. B&B €90pps, ss €55. Closed 23-27 Dec. Amex, Diners, MasterCard, Visa, Laser.

Thomas Read

Café/Pub   Parliament Street Dublin 2 **Tel: 01 677 1487**

This bustling café-bar was one of the first of its type and it is still one of the best. Attracting a wide variety of customers (including literary types from Trinity College and nearby newspapers) it serves a good cup of coffee, with (or without) light food. Its corner position and large windows looking down to Dame Street make this a fine place to sit and watch the world go by. Closed 25 Dec & Good Fri.

Thornton's Restaurant

★★ Restaurant   128 St Stephen's Green Dublin 2
Tel: 01 478 7008

RESTAURANT OF THE YEAR

Seriously good cooking in a seriously good restaurant is to be found at this lofty city-centre restaurant. Kevin Thornton moved his team here from their famous little Portobello premises over the summer of 2002 and quietly opened, without so much as a whisper of the PR hype that usually accompanies such occasions, early in September. The restaurant is on the top floor of the Fitzwilliam Hotel and can be reached by lift from the lobby, but is best approached from its own entrance on St Stephen's Green: mounting the wide staircase, deep-carpeted in dark blue, conveys a sense of occasion. Once inside - as in the previous premises -the decor is stunningly simple and elegant: a striking flower arrangement catches the eye on arrival; a deep wine carpet and comfortable high-back chairs in green velvet paint a strong background for pastels and neutrals that leave you in no doubt that the food is to be the star here: pale walls washed with reflected colour from heavy primrose silk curtains highlight a series of wonderfully subtle oil paintings (commissioned from the talented young Monaghan artist, Siobhán McDonald) while linen-clad tables each have a silver candlestick and a simple white candle, classical modern cutlery and glasses and restrained china with just a silver rim. A superb team of French waiting staff set the tone from the outset, providing highly professional service to complement Kevin Thornton's superb cooking; the neat reception area which divides the restaurant has room for only half a dozen or so guests to assemble, so the warmly professional maître d', Olivier Meisonnave may show you straight to your table to consider a menu which, literally, bears the hand of the master on the cover, in another stroke of understated originality. Relatively short à la carte dinner menus offer about eight luxurious choices on each course - Kevin Thornton has a name for generosity with truffles and he will not disappoint: a first course terrine of foie gras and rabbit is served with truffle and leek...a main course of black-legged chicken comes with truffle and foie gras, potato purée and truffle sauce...Seafood is well-represented, in a signature dish of sautéed foie gras with scallops and cep sauce, served with warm brioche, another starter of ravioli of lobster with quinoa (a Peruvian grain dating back to the Incas) with lobster consommé, and striking main courses include fillet of turbot served with little piles of lime and beetroot powder and a squid ink sauce. Other signature dishes include braised suckling pig, and trotter served with Maxim potato, glazed turnip and a light poitín - and variations on these creations appear throughout an 8-course Surprise Menu (€120) which is just that - there is nothing written and the menu created for each table is unique. This is creative cooking of the highest class, conceived with confidence to utilise first-rate seasonal ingredients, and beautifully (but not flamboyantly) presented with a perfectionist's eye for detail and a palate to match: this is extraordinarily intense, deeply flavoured food and - despite the occasional flash of gold leaf - it is far from the show-off creations commonly associated with top chefs: Kevin Thornton's cooking has soul. Service throughout is impeccable, from the moment a basket of breads arrive to the final presentation of assorted petits fours accompanying coffees and teas. An outstanding Irish and French cheese trolley deserves special mention (cheese supplied by Sheridans cheesemongers and dispensed with knowledge and infectious enthusiasm by Kevin's brother, Garrett Thornton); there's also excellent wine list - and a fine sommelier, Julien Herbert, to steer you through it, which is especially important for those who opt for the Surprise Menu. Children welcome. No-smoking area. Air conditioning. **Seats 70** (private room, 24). L Tue-Sat, 12.30-1.45; D Tue-Sat, 7.00-10.30. Set L €29. Set D €70. Tasting Menu €100, A la carte also available. House wine from €20. SC discretionary. Closed Sun & Mon, 2 wks Christmas & Aug. Amex, Diners, MasterCard, Visa, Laser. **Directions:** St Stephen's Green (corner at top of Grafton Street); entrance beside Fitzwilliam Hotel.

Toners

Pub   139 Lower Baggot Street Dublin 2 **Tel: 01 676 3090** Fax: 01 676 2617

One of the few authentic old pubs left in Dublin, Toners is definitely worth a visit (or two). Among many other claims to fame, it is said to be the only pub ever frequented by the poet W.B. Yeats. Closed 25 Dec & Good Fri.

Trinity Capital Hotel

Hotel   Pearse Street Dublin 2 **Tel: 01 648 1000** Fax: 01 648 1010
Email: info@trinitycapital-hotel.com Web: www.capital-hotels.com

A stylish new hotel right beside the headquarters of Dublin's city centre fire brigade (inspiring the name 'Fireworks' for its unusual club-style bar) and opposite Trinity college. Very centrally located for business and leisure, the hotel is within easy walking distance of all the main city centre attractions on both sides of the Liffey and the lobby wine and coffee bar make handy meeting places. Rooms have a safe, interactive TV, phone, data ports, hair dryer, trouser press, tea/coffee trays, comfortable beds and good bathrooms -junior suites suites have jacuzzi powered bath, hi-fi system and mini-bar. Guests have free admission all 13 bars and clubs in the city centre owned by Capital Bars, including the adjacent Fireworks night club. Conference/banqueting 45/80. Meeting rooms; business centre; secretarial services. Children welcome (under 12s free in parents' room; cots available without charge). **Rooms 82** (4 suites, 20 no-smoking, 2 shower only, 6 for disabled). B&B €89pps, s.c. included. Amex, Diners, MasterCard, Visa, Laser. **Directions:** City centre.

Trocadero Restaurant

Ⓝ Restaurant   3/4 St Andrew Street Dublin 2
Tel: 01 677 5545 Fax: 01 679 2385 Web: www.restaurantsindublin.ie

The Dublin theatrical restaurant par excellence with deep blood-red walls and gold-trimmed stage curtains, black and white pictures of the celebrities who've passed through the place – dimly lit, intimate tables with individual beaded lampshades and snug, cosy seating, the 'Troc' is one of Dublin's longest-established restaurants and has presided over St Andrew Street since 1956. It has atmosphere in spades, food and service to match. Comforting menus reminiscent of the seventies offer starters like French onion soup, deep-fried brie, chicken liver pâté and avocado prawn Marie Rose, followed by ever-popular grills - fillet steak (with Cashel Blue cheese perhaps), Wicklow rack of lamb and sole on the bone are the mainstays of the menu, also wild Irish salmon and Dublin Bay Prawns from Clogherhead, naturally all with a sprinkling of freshly chopped parsley. Desserts include apple and cinnamon strudel and wicked chocolate and Baileys slice and a better-value winelist will be hard to find. There's privacy too – sound-absorbing banquettes and curtains allow you to hear everything at your own table with just a pleasing murmur in the background. Lovely friendly service too: magic. **Seats 100.** No smoking area; air conditioning. Children welcome (up to 9pm). D Mon-Sat, 5-12. D à la carte (pre-theatreD 5-7.30m €17.70). House wine from €18.50. Closed Sun, 25-26 dec, 31 Dec, Good Fri. Amex, Diners, MasterCard, Visa, Laser. **Directions:** Beside Dublin Tourism Centre.

Trinity Lodge

Guesthouse   12 South Frederick Street Dublin 2 **Tel: 01 679 5044** Fax: 01 679 5223
Email: trinitylodge@eircom.net Web: www.trinitylodge.com

As centrally located as it is possible to get, this owner-run guesthouse offers a high standard of accommodation at a reasonable price just yards away from Trinity College. Air-conditioned rooms have a safe, direct-dial phone, tea/coffee making facilities, multi-channel TV and trouser press, Children welcome (Under 12s free in parents' room; cots available free of charge). No pets. **Rooms 13** (3 suites, 6 executive, 8 no-smoking). B&B €75pps, ss €25. Closed 22-29 Dec. Amex, Diners, MasterCard, Visa, Laser, Switch. **Directions:** Off Nassau Street, near Trinity College.

Tulsi

(N) Restaurant   17a Lr Baggot Street Dublin 2 **Tel: 01 676 4578**

One of a small chain of authentic Indian restaurants, this bustling place has a compact reception area leading into a pleasingly elegant restaurant with echoes of the Raj in the decor. Tables are set up with plate warmers, fresh flowers, sauces and pickles and service is brisk so you will quickly be presented with menus offering a broad range of Indian styles - there's a slight leaning towards Punjabi style cooking, with its use of nuts and fruit in sauces, but also tandoori, tikka, biryani, balti and an extensive vegetarian menu. A selection of nan breads is offered and the food quality overall is consistently high; this, together with good value, make booking at both lunch and dinner advisable. A range of special menus offers variety and value; Indian beer available. *Also at: Galway city & Castlebar, Co Mayo. Amex, Diners, MasterCard, Visa. **Directions:** 2 minutes walk from St Stephens Green (Shelbourne Hotel side).

Unicorn Restaurant

Restaurant   12B Merrion Court off Merrion Row Dublin 2
Tel: 01 676 2182 / 662 4752 Fax: 01 662 8584

In a lovely, secluded location just off a busy street near the Shelbourne Hotel, this informal and perennially fashionable restaurant is famous for its buffet hors d'oeuvres selection, piano bar and exceptionally friendly staff. It's particularly charming in summer, as the doors open out onto a terrace which is used for al fresco dining in fine weather - and the Number Five piano bar, which now extends to two floors, is also a great atttraction for after-dinner relaxation with live music (Wed-Sat 9pm-3 am). Good food (regional and modern Italian), efficient service and atmosphere all partially explain The Unicorn's enduring succcess - another element is the constant quest for further improvement. Many of the Italian wines listed are exclusive to The Unicorn: uniquely, in Ireland, they stock the full collection of Gava wines and the Pio Cesare range will also be exclusive in the near future. Not suitable for children after 9 pm. **Seats 85** (private room 14). No-smoking area; air conditioning. Open Mon-Sat, L12.30-4, D 6-11.15. A la carte. House wine €20. SC discretionary. Closed Sun, 10 days at Christmas Amex, Diners, MasterCard, Visa, Laser. **Directions:** Near Shelbourne Hotel.

Wagamama

Restaurant   Unit 4B South King Street Dublin 2 **Tel: 01 478 2152** Fax: 01 478 2154
Email: chris@wagamama-dublin.com Web: www.wagamama-dublin.com

The Dublin branch of this justly popular London-based noodle bar is full of groovy young things, who find it cool - both for the food and the interior, which is a huge basement canteen, simple and functional, but strikingly designed with high ceilings. The large portions of noodles consist of ramen (thread noodles), udon (fat noodles) or soba (a round buckwheat noodle) served in soups or pan-fried, well seasoned and colourfully decorated with South Asian ingredients. The large menu gives plenty of information about ingredients and dishes - and also explains how orders are taken (kids love the elctronic notepads used by servers); it includes a few Japanese dishes such as teriyaki (mouth-watering little kebabs) and edamame (freshly steamed geen soya beans, served sprinkled with salt), also an excellent selection of fruit and vegetable juices, some rice dishes and plenty of great vegetarian options. All food served wagamama nodle bars is GMO free. Sake and interesting soft drinks such as kombucha ('cleanses body & soul') take their place on the drinks menu alongside wines and coffees. Service is friendly and efficient but all those fashionable bare surfaces make it very noisy. Multi-storey carpark nearby. Children welome. **Seats 136**. No-smoking restaurant; air conditioning. Open daily, 12-11 (Sun to 10). A la carte. SC discretionary. Closed 25-26 Dec. Amex, Diners, MasterCard, Visa, Laser.

Westbury Hotel

  Hotel/Restaurant   Grafton Street Dublin 2 **Tel: 01 679 1122** Fax: 01 679 7078
Email: westbury@jurysdoyle.com Web: www.jurysdoyle.com

Possibly the most conveniently situated of all the central Dublin hotels, the Westbury is a very small stone's throw from the city's premier shopping street and has all the benefits of luxury hotels - notably free valet parking - to offset any practical disadvantages of the location. Unashamedly sumptuous, the hotel's public areas drip with chandeliers and have accessories to match - like the grand piano on The Terrace, a popular first floor meeting place for afternoon tea and frequently used for fashion shows. Accommodation is similarly luxurious, with bedrooms that include penthouse suites and a high proportion of suites, junior suites and executive rooms. With conference facilities to match its quality of accommodation and service, the hotel is understandably popular with business guests, but it also makes a luxurious base for a leisure break in the city. Laundry/dry cleaning. Mini-gym. Conference/banqueting (220/200). Business centre. Secretarial services. ISDN lines. Children welcome (Under 12s free in parents' room; cots available). No pets. **Rooms 204** (suites:1 presidential, 3 luxury, 14 junior; 24 executive rooms,130 no-smoking, 3 for disabled). Lifts. B&B €186, ss €141. SC15%. Open all year. Amex, Diners, MasterCard, Visa, Laser. **Directions:** The Westbury is approx 11km from the airport near Trinty College & Stephens Green.

Russell Room: After a drink in one of the hotel's two bars - the first floor Terrace bar and the Sandbank Bistro, an informal seafood restaurant and bar accessible from the back of the building - the Russell Room offers classic French dining, with some global cuisine and modern Irish influences. **Seats 100** (private room, 14) No-smoking area. Air conditioning. SC 15%. L daily,12 30-2.30; D daily 6.30-10.30 (Sun to 9). Set L from about €30, D à la carte. House wine about €20.

The Westin Dublin

 Hotel   College Green Dublin 2 **Tel: 01 645 1000** Fax: 01 645 1401
Email: sales.dublin@westin.com Web: www.westin.com

It would be hard to imagine a more central location for the impressive new hotel that emerged after massive reconstruction of the former mid-nineteenth century AIB and Pearl Buildings. Much of the original was gutted, although part of the former bank was glassed over to create a dramatic lounging area, The Atrium, which has a huge palm tree feature and bedroom windows giving onto it like a courtyard - very effective. The magnificent Banking Hall provides the main conference and banqueting room and the adjacent Teller Room now makes an unusual circular boardroom, while the vaults have found a new lease of life as The Mint, a bar with its own access from College Street. Other special features of the new hotel include a split-level suite, which has views over Trinity College and has a living room, board room and private exercise area; the business traveller's Westin Guest Office, designed to combine the efficiency and technology of a modern office with comfort of a luxurious bedroom; and the so-called 'Heavenly Bed' designed by Westin and 'worlds apart from any other bed'. The inner man will also be well looked after - in the hotel's elegant restaurant The Exchange. Very limited parking (some valet parking if it is arranged at the time of booking accommodation). Fitness room. **Rooms 163** (13 suites, 5 junior suites, 19 for disabled). Lift. B&B €167pps, ss €152; Room rate €319 (max 2 guests). Open all year. Amex, Diners, MasterCard, Visa, Laser. **Directions:** On Westmoreland Street, opposite Trinity College.

The Exchange: An elegant, spacious room in 1930s style, The Exchange has a welcome emphasis on comfort and simply oozes luxury. Everything about it, from the classily understated decor in tones of cream and brown to the generous-sized, well-spaced tables and large carver chairs says expensive but worth it. And, in the Guide's recent experience, that promise follows through onto the plate in head chef Darrin Parrish's well-executed menus - fairly contemporary but not overburdened with fusion overtones and distinguished by clear flavours and accurate cooking. From a 3-course lunch menu (excellent value at €25.50), for example, an excellent fillet of tuna fully three inches thick was perfectly cooked I and calves' liver was a joy: three thick slices browned on the outside and just pink within, accompanied by a mild mustard and cream sauce. Accompanying vegetables included asparagus and bok choi - a refreshing and well-judged choice. Desserts might include a tangy short pastry rhubarb tart and there's a generous cheese plate. Top quality fresh ingredients, generous portions and confident, unfussy cooking will all endear this restaurant to Dublin diners.Westin Smart Dining options (moderate in calories and fat) and vegetarian options are highlighted on menus. Friendly service from knowledgeable young waiting staff. More extensive, luxurious evening menus are à la carte, except for a 3-course pre-theatre menu which (like Chapter One - see entry) allows you to return to your table for dessert after the performance. **Seats 75.** Breakfast daily 6.30-10, L Sun-Fri 12-2.30, D daily 6.30-10 (Fri, Sat, Sun to 10.30). Restaurant closed L Sat.

The Winter Garden

Ⓝ Café   The National Gallery Merrion Square West Dublin 2 **Tel: 01 661 5133**

A soaring glass-ceilinged space in the stunning new Millennium Wing of the National Gallery, provides an appropriately dramatic (if rather noisy) space or a break before or after a visit to the exhibition. It's minimalist and self-service, there's no menu except a blackboard (which may not have everything listed and can be confusing) but staff are very pleasant and helpful. International food is the order of the day and most of it is microwaved, but (with the strange exception of the coffee, which is inexplicably unreliable) it still manages to be better than average gallery fare - just be careful to choose something robust which should stand reheating. Prices are reasonable. No smoking restaurant. Open 12-5 daily; annual closures as for the gallery. **Directions:** In the new Millennium Wing of the national Gallery.

Yamamori Noodles

Restaurant   71 South Great George's Street Dublin 2 **Tel: 01 475 5001** Fax: 01 475 5001

Good value speedy cooking with lots of flavour is the secret of Yamamori's success - and atmosphere too. It's just the kind of buzzy place that young people of all ages like to hang about in - a cool place for family outings. Specialities include Yamamori ramen, sushi and sashimi served in generous portions that give great value. Separate lunch and dinner menus are offered, with a more extensive choice in the evening. House wine (quarter bottles), from €4.75. **Seats 130.** Open daily, 12.30-11.30: L 12-5.30, D 5.30-11 (Sun-Wed 4-11). Closed 25-26 dec, 1 Jan, Good Fri. Amex, MasterCard, Visa, Laser. **Directions:** City centre - 5 mins walk from Grafton Street.

DUBLIN 3

Clontarf Castle Hotel

Hotel   Castle Avenue Clontarf Dublin 3 **Tel: 01 833 2321** Fax: 01 833 2279
                    Email: info@clontarfcastle.ie Web: www.clontarfcastle.ie

This historic 17th century castle is convenient to both the airport and city centre. A major refurbishment and extension programme recently added banqueting, conference and business facilities (business centre and secretarial services, same day laundry and dry cleaning and exercise room for guests) as well as major changes to public areas and the addition of 111 rooms. Bedrooms, are furnished to a high standard and well-equipped for business guests with ISDN lines, voicemail and US electrical sockets in addition to the usual amenities; all south-facing rooms have air conditioning and bathrooms are well-designed and finished. The new building has been imaginatively incorporated into the old castle structure, retaining the historic atmosphere - some rooms, such as the restaurant and the original bar, have been left untouched and bedrooms have old-world details to remind guests of their castle surroundings, although it is a pity that so little of the original grounds now remain. Conference/banqueting (550/450). Business centre. Secretarial services. Leisure centre. Children welcome (Under 12s free in parents' room; cots available). No pets.Lift. **Rooms 111** (3 suites, 2 junior suites, 4 executive rooms, 30 no-smoking, 6 for disabled). B&B €143pps, ss €80. Templars Bistro:D Mon-Sat, 6.30-10.30 (Sun 6-9); L 12.30 -3 (Sun to 2.30). Closed 25 Dec. Amex, Diners, MasterCard, Visa, Laser. **Directions:** Off coast road from Dublin- Howth, signed left 2 miles from city centre.

Kinara Restaurant

(N) Restaurant   318 Clontarf Road Dublin 3 **Tel: 01 833 6759** Fax: 01 833 6651
                                           Email: info@kinara.ie Web: www.kinara.ie

This smart two-storey restuarant specialising in authentic Pakistani and Northern Indian cuisine opened in the autumn of 2001 in a scenic location overlooking Bull Island. Fine views - especially from the first floor dining room - are a feature at lunch time or on summer evenings, and there's a cosy upstairs bar with Indian cookbooks to inspire guests waiting for a table or relaxing after dinner. A warm welcome from the Sudanese doorman Muhammad ensures a good start as, with a mighty grin and a swirl of the traditional costume that has become the restaurant's trademark, he sweeps arriving guests into the little foyer. The menu is unusual, beginning with a useful introduction to the cuisine that explains the four fundamental flavours - tomato, garlic, ginger and onions - and their uses, then offering a series of styles to choose from, opening with a range of traditional starters like kakeragh (local crab claws with garlic, yogurt, spices and a tandoori masala sauce) and main courses (like Shimla chicken, simmered with chopped onions & tomato, garnished with fresh coriander). There is a declared commitment to local produce - notably organic beef, lamb and chicken - and a section of the menu devoted to organic and 'lighter fare' main courses (typically Loki Mushroom, a vegetarian dish of courgettes and mushrooms in a light spicy yogurt sauce). Head chef Ashok Kumar and his team have over 80 years experience between them and Dublin has clearly taken them to her heart as there is already talk of expansion in 2003. **Seats 75** (private room 35). No smoking area; air conditioning. Children welcome. L Thu, Fri & Sun, 12.30-3; D daily, 6-11.30. Set L €14; D à la carte (also available at L). House wine €16. Closed 25-26 Dec, 1 Jan. Amex, MasterCard, Visa, Laser. **Directions:** 1.5 miles north of city centre on coast road to Howth (opposite wooden bridge).

DUBLIN 4

Aberdeen Lodge

Guesthouse   53 Park Avenue Ballsbridge Dublin 4 **Tel: 01 283 8155** Fax: 01 283 7877
                                       Email: aberdeen@iol.ie Web: www.halpinsprivatehotels.com

Centrally located (close to the Sydney Parade DART station) yet away from the heavy traffic of nearby Merrion Road, this handsome period house offers all the advantages of an hotel at guesthouse prices. Elegantly furnished executive bedrooms and four-poster suites offer air conditioning and all the little comforts expected by the discerning traveller, there's a drawing room and room service menu (with wine list). Boardroom, business and fitness facilities for business guests - and mature secluded gardens. Small conferences (50). Children welcome. No pets. **Rooms 17** (2 suites, 15 executive rooms, 5 no-smoking). B&B €60pps, ss €35 Residents' meals available: D €30 + all-day menu. House wines from €25. 24-hr room service. SC discretionary. Open all year. Amex, Diners, MasterCard, Visa, Laser. **Directions:** Minutes from the city centre by DART or by car, take the Merrion Road towards Sydney Parade DART station and then first left into Park Avenue.

Anglesea Townhouse

féile bia Guesthouse   63 Angelsea Road Ballsbridge Dublin 4
                                                  Tel: 01 668 3877 Fax: 01 668 3461

Helen Kirrane's guesthouse brings all the best 'country' house qualities to urban Dublin - a delightful building and pleasant location near Herbert Park, Ballsbridge; comfortable, attractive bedrooms; good housekeeping; a warm, welcoming drawing room with a real period flavour and wonderful breakfasts that prepare guests for the rigours of the most arduous of days. Thoroughly recommended for its creativity and perfectionism in re-defining what a guesthouse can be, Anglesea Townhouse was the winner of our 1999 Irish Breakfast Award. Garden. Children welcome (Under 3s free in parents' room; cots available without charge). No pets. **Rooms 7** (5 shower only, all no-smoking). B&B €65pps, no ss. Closed Christmas and New Year. Amex, MasterCard, Visa, Laser. **Directions:** South of city centre.

Baan Thai

Restaurant   16 Merrion Road Ballsbridge Dublin 4 **Tel: 01 660 8833**

Delicious aromas and oriental music greet you as you climb the stairs to Lek and Eamon Lancaster's well-appointed first floor restaurant opposite the RDS. Friendly staff, Thai furniture and woodcarvings create an authentic oriental feeling and intimate atmosphere - and, as many of the staff are Thai, it's almost like being in Thailand. A wide-ranging menu includes various set menus that provide a useful introduction to the cuisine (or speed up choices for groups) as well as an à la carte. The essential fragrance and spiciness of Thai cuisine is very much in evidence throughout and there's Thai beer as well as a fairly extensive wine list. D only, Sun-Thu 6-11, Fri & Sat to 11.30. Amex, Diners, MasterCard, Visa, Laser. ◇

Bahay Kubo

Ⓝ Restaurant

14 Bath Avenue Sandymount Dublin 4
Tel: 01 660 5572 Fax: 01 668 2006

Don't be put off by trains rumbling overhead as you approach this unusual Filipino restaurant - the smart carpeted entrance and stairway which quickly reassure the fainthearted. Upstairs, you will find yourself in a clean-lined modern room with pale beech flooring and matching panels on a vaulted roof space which, together with fresh flowers at the entrance (and on each table), uncluttered decor in warm colours and crisp white linen on the tables, creates a spacious, airy and welcoming atmosphere. Friendly staff seat new guests immediately and bring iced water with menus that are well organised with explanations about dishes - which are probably very necessary as most guests will not be familiar with the cuisine, which is related to Chinese food, with Malaysian, Indonesian and Thai influences. Several set menus are offered (a good choice on a first visit, perhaps), and an à la carte which is, by oriental standards, quite restrained; anyone who likes Chinese food should enjoy the Filipino versions, which are similar but with generally fresher flavours of lemongrass, ginger, chili and coconut; no MSG is used and soups are refreshingly free of cornstarch. As in some other oriental cuisines, the weakness is in the dessert menu, so make the most of the excellent savoury dishes and don't worry about saving space for the finale. Service is attentive, making up in willingness anything it may occasionally lack in training. No smoking area. Meals: D Tue-Sat, 6-11 (Sun 5-10), L Thu & Fri, 12-2.30. MasterCard, Visa, **Directions:** Above Lansdowne Bar, at railway bridge.

Bella Cuba Restaurant

féile bia Restaurant

11 Ballsbridge Terrace Dublin 4 **Tel: 01 6605539** Fax: 01 6605539
Email: info@bella-cuba.com Web: www.bella-cuba.com

Authentic Cuban cuisine is presented at its best in this small, intimate restaurant, which demonstrates the Spanish, Caribbean and South American influences on this unique country's cooking, with pork dishes prepared particularly well. Well worth a visit to experience something genuinely different. The wine list, which offers a choice fairly balanced between the old world and the new, includes a pair of Cuban bottles. Not suitable for children after 7pm. **Seats 26.** D only, 5.30-11 daily. A la carte. House wine about €18. SC discretionary. Closed 25-26 Dec. Amex, MasterCard, Visa, Laser. **Directions:** Near the RDS. ◇

Berkeley Court Hotel

féile bia 🏨 Hotel/Restaurant

Lansdowne Road Ballsbridge Dublin 4
Tel: 01 660 1711 Fax: 01 661 7238
Email: berkeley_court@jurysdoyle.com Web: www.jurysdoyle.com

Set in its own grounds yet convenient to the city centre, this luxurious hotel is well-known as a haunt of the rich and famous when in Dublin. The tone is set by an impressively spacious chandeliered foyer, with bars, restaurants and private conference rooms leading off it. The hotel is renowned for its high standards of service and accommodation - bedrooms have a safe, computer modem, mini-bars and extras such as robes and slippers as well as the more usual amenities, and refurbished rooms also have air conditioning. Health & beauty treatments; barber shop; gift shop/newsagent. Conference/banqueting (400/380), Video-conferencing, business centre, secretarial services, ISDN lines. **Rooms 188** (1 penthouse suite, 4 luxury suites, 24 executive rooms, 35 no-smoking, 4 for disabled). Lift. B&B €165pps, ss€145. SC15%. Open all year.
Berkeley Room: A fine restaurant with very professional staff and some reliable specialities - seafood dishes are especially good and they are renowned for their roast beef. **Seats 60.** No smoking area; air conditioning. L Sun-Fri,12.30-2.15; D Mon-Sat, 6.30-9.15. A la carte. SC 15%. Toilets wheelchair accessible. SC 15%. Restaurant closed L Sat, D Sun (L&D available daily in the Palm Court Café). Amex, Diners, MasterCard, Visa, Laser. **Directions:** The Berkley Court is near Lansdowne Road Rugby Stadium and approx. 13km from Airport.

Berman & Wallace

(N) Restaurant   Belfield Office Park Beaver Row Clonskeagh Dublin 4
Tel: 01 219 6252 Fax: 01 219 6219
Email: bermanandwallace@eircom.net Web: www.bermanandwallace.com

This pavilion-style restaurant, in a courtyard surrounded by office buildings, supplies the local business community with reliable and wide-ranging daytime food, revitalising drinks and there's a daily health lunch special. Wines by the glass or by bottle. Full breakfast; takeaway/corporate platters. Restaurant. available for evening functions **Seats 70**. Open Mon-Fri, 7.30-3.30; Sun 11.30-3. Closed Sun; Christmas, bank hols. **Directions:** Towards city, turn left at Donnybrook Bus Station; last turn on left.

Bewley's Hotel, Ballsbridge

Hotel/Restaurant   Merrion Road Ballsbridge Dublin 4 **Tel: 01 668 1111** Fax: 01 668 1999
Email: bb@bewleyshotels.com Web: www.bewleyshotels.com

This new hotel has been cleverly built to incorporate a landmark period building next to the RDS (entrance by car is on Simmonscourt Road, via Merrion Road or Anglesea Road; underground carpark). Like its sister hotel at Newlands Cross (see entry), you get a lot of comfort here at a very reasonable cost. *Restaurant: See O'Connells in Ballsbridge. Small conferences (30). ISDN lines. Garden. Parking. Children welcome. No pets. Lift. **Rooms 220** (80 suites, 100 no-smoking, 20 disabled). Room rate €99 (max 2 adult guests). Closed 6pm 24 Dec - 6pm 26 Dec. Amex, Diners, MasterCard, Visa, Laser. **Directions:** At Junction of Simmonscourt and Merrion Roads.

Blakes Townhouse

Guesthouse   50 Merrion Road Ballsbridge Dublin 4 **Tel: 01 668 8324** Fax: 01 668 4280
Email: blakestownhouse@iol.ie Web: www.halpinsprivatehotels.com

The latest addition to Pat Halpin's small chain of quality guesthouses, Blakes is very handily situated for anyone attending exhibitions in Dublin, as it's directly opposite the RDS, and offers an attractive alternative to hotel accommodation. Comfortable bedrooms are well-equipped for business and professional travellers and executive rooms and four-poster suites also have whirlpool spas. Drawing room menu available all day (selection of quality wines, from €25) and 24 hour room service. Children over 2 welcome. No pets. Complimentary use of nearby leisure centre. **Rooms 12** (2 suites,10 executive, 4 no smoking). B&B €60 pps, ss €35; SC 10%. Open all year. Amex, Diners, MasterCard, Visa, Laser. **Directions:** Opposite the RDS in Ballsbridge.

Burlington Hotel

féile bia Hotel   Upper Leeson Street Dublin 4 **Tel: 01 660 5222** Fax: 01 660 8496
Email: burlington@jurysdoyle.com Web: www.jurysdoyle.com

Ireland's largest hotel, the Burlington has more experience of dealing with very large numbers efficiently and enjoyably than any other in the country. All bedrooms have been recently refurbished and banquets for huge numbers are not only catered for but can have a minimum choice of three main courses on all menus. The Burlington also offers good facilities for business guests; a high proportion of bedrooms are designated executive, with ISDN lines, fax machines and air conditioning. On-site entertainment is provided at Anabels night club and their bar, Buck Mulligans, has won numerous awards. Conference/banqueting (1200/1000). Business centre. Secretarial services. Video conferencing. No pets. Special offers often available. **Rooms 506** (2 suites, 4 junior suites, 200 executive rooms, 76 no-smoking, 3 for disabled). Lift. B&B €124pps, ss €98. Open all year. Amex, Diners, MasterCard, Visa, Laser.

Butlers Town House

Guesthouse   44 Lansdowne Road Ballsbridge Dublin 4 **Tel: 01 667 4022** Fax: 01 667 3960
Email: info@butlers-hotel.com Web: butlers-hotel.com

On a corner site in Dublin's 'embassy belt' and close to the Lansdowne Road stadium, this large townhouse/guesthouse has been extensively refurbished and luxuriously decorated in a Victorian country house style and is a small hotel in all but name. Public rooms include a comfortable drawing room and an attractive conservatory-style dining room where breakfast is served; there's also an attractive all-day menu available, offering light and colourful Mediterranean/modern Irish fare ranging from grilled St Tola goats cheese with basil & tomato salad to lobster with garlic butter & sauté potatoes, or Butlers Famous Seafood Plate: smoked salmon, prawns, poached fish, crab claws & home-made cocktail sauce. Rooms are individually decorated and furnished to a high standard, some with four-poster beds. Small conferences (30), secretarial services. Wheelchair access. Parking. Children welcome (Under 4s free in parents' room; cots available without charge). No pets. **Rooms 19** (5 executive rooms, 4 no smoking, 1 for disabled). B&B €95, ss about €45. All day menu, 12-10; D 6-9, à la carte. House wine €20.95. Closed 23 Dec-3 Jan. Amex, Diners, MasterCard, Visa, Laser, Switch. **Directions:** Corner of Lansdowne Road and Shelbourne Road.

Cedar Lodge

Guesthouse   98 Merrion Road Ballsbridge Dublin 4 **Tel: 01 668 4410** Fax: 01 668 4533
Email: info@cedarlodge.ie Web: www.cedarlodge.ie

Conveniently located near the RDS show grounds and conference centre, this friendly owner-run guesthouse has been recently refurbished and is moderately priced. Spacious double-glazed rooms have a full range of amenities and some are on the ground floor. Public rooms are comfortably furnished and the emphasis is on relaxataion and creating a 'home from home'. Children over 3 welcome. No pets. **Rooms 15** (all no-smoking, 1 for disabled). B&B €70pps, ss €18. Closed Dec 23-29. Amex, MasterCard, Visa, Laser. **Directions:** Directly opposite British Embassy on Merrion Road.

Dish Restaurant

Restaurant   146 Upper Leeson Street Dublin 4 **Tel: 01664 2135** Fax: 01 664 2136
Email: dish@indigo.ie Web: www.dishrestaurant.net

Gerard Foote moved his well-known restaurant from Temple Bar to exciting new premises in 2002 with great success, but the same principles apply: he uses only the best ingredients - organic beef and lamb, free-range chicken and a wide variety of fresh fish daily - to provide the wholesome basis for menus that change regularly to make the most of seasonal produce. Roast fillet of monkfish with savoy cabbage, baby potatoes & cream and organic fillet steak are typical - and cheeses are supplied by Sheridans cheesemongers, of South Anne Street. Children welcome. **Seats 55**. No-smoking area, air conditioning. Open 12-4, 6-11 daily. L from about €20, D from €35. House wine from about €17.50. SC 10% on parties of 6+. Closed 24-28 Dec & Good Fri. Amex, Diners, MasterCard, Visa, Laser. **Directions:** Near Burlington Hotel. ◇

Ernie's Restaurant

féile bia Restaurant   Mulberry Gardens Donnybrook Dublin 4
Tel: 01 269 3300 Fax: 01 269 3260

Named after the late Ernie Evans and still owned by the family, the dining-room of this famous restaurant overlooks a pretty courtyard garden, floodlit at night, though its main feature is the fantastic art collection, mostly of Ernie's beloved Kerry, that cover the walls entirely. Both the cooking and service are straightforward and some dishes have real old-fashioned classic sauces - a welcome respite in this era of global cuisine and minimalist restaurants. However, although some old favourites are kept in demand by regular patrons, there is young blood in the kitchen so a hint of modernism and a nod to foreign influences is creeping into some dishes - starters like chorizo, artichoke & pinenut salad or tian of crab, apple & avocado with chilli & ginger dressing are typical. Modern Irish cooking is also a feature as, perhaps, in Valentia scallops with Clonakilty black pudding. Desserts are deliciously classic - chocolate tart fondant with Cointreau oranges, perhaps - and a selection of teas and coffees is served with petits fours. Good wine list, strong on clarets. Not suitable for children under 12. No-smoking area; air conditioning. **Seats 60**. Open Mon-Sat, L12.30-2, D 7.30-10. Set L from €15, Set D from €25 midweek (weekend €40). A la carte also available L&D. House wine from €19. SC discretionary. Closed Sun, Mon & 22 Dec-3 Jan. Amex, Diners, MasterCard, Visa. **Directions:** From city first left after Victoria Avenue; to city right turn opposite Ulster Bank Donnybrook.

Expresso Bar Café

Café   1 St Mary's Road Ballsbridge Dublin 4
Tel: 01 660 0685 Fax: 01 660 0585 Email: expressosbmenus@hotmail.com

Ann-Marie Nohl's cool, informal eating place is notable for clean-lined minimalism, and colourful Cal-Ital food and classic brunches: diligently sourced ingredients are well-prepared and carefully presented. The lively breakfasts for which they have become famous are served all morning and feature many of the best classic dishes, with a twist: thus a simple poached egg on toast comes with crispy bacon (from Dorans of Dalkey) and relish, or cooked-to-order pancakes are served with crispy bacon and maple syrup and french toast comes with bacon or winter berries and syrup. Lunch and dinner menus tend to favour an international style, but the same high standards apply: whether it's caesar salad with bacon lardons, Parmesan cheese and croûtons (with smoked chicken as an option), char-grilled fillet of beef with red onion marmalade or pan-seared scallops with chilli dressing, the concept is simple enough but it's the quality of the ingredients and cooking that make the difference. Weekend brunch is a must. Not suitable for children under 2 after 6pm. No-smoking area; air conditioning. *Also at IFSC (see entry). A new branch is due to open in The Gables, Foxrock Village at the time of going to press; in partnership with McCabe Wines it heralds an exciting new development, with seasonal foods from France as well as Irish produce, cooked in a rustic style, with a wide selection of wines by the glass and access to the 1,500 wines stocked next door. **Seats 50.** Open Mon-Fri, 7.30am-9.30pm (B'fst 7.30-11.30, L12-5, D 6-9.30), Sun brunch 10-5. Closed 25 Dec. Amex, MasterCard, Visa, Laser. **Directions:** Opposite Hibernan Hotel, off Baggot Street.

Four Seasons Hotel

 Hotel

Simmonscourt Road Ballsbridge Dublin 4
Tel: 01 665 4805 Fax: 01 665 4880
Email: ben.trodd@fourseasons.com Web: www.fourseasons.com

Set in its own gardens on a three and a half acre site of the Royal Dublin Society's 42-acre show grounds, this luxurious hotel opened in 2001. The location is magnificent, allowing a sense of spaciousness while also being convenient to the city centre - the scale is generous throughout and there are views of the Wicklow Mountains or Dublin Bay from many bedrooms. Public areas are designed to impress, although the cherrywood panelled Lobby Bar was too small from the outset and a second, larger, bar is due to open early in 2003. Accommodation is very luxurious and, with two-line speaker phones, data port, hi-speed internet access, satellite TV, CD players, bar and safe, the air-conditioned rooms are designed to appeal equally to leisure and business guests. A choice of pillows (down and non allergenic foam) is provided as standard, the large marble bathrooms have separate bath and shower, and robes among many desirable features - and there's twice daily housekeeping service, overnight laundry and dry cleaning, one hour pressing and complimentary overnight shoe shine. Meeting planners will appreciate the hotel's state of the art conference and meeting spaces, which can accommodate corporate events, business meetings and parties in groups from 5-500. But the Spa in the lower level of the hotel is perhaps its most outstanding feature, offering: separate men's and women's saunas and steamrooms, a wide range of body and facial treatments, aromatherapy and massage services, plus a gym (with intructors) - and a naturally lit 14m lap pool and adjacent jacuzzi pool, overlooking an outdoor sunken garden. **Rooms 259** (67 suites, 192 executive rooms, 4 floors no-smoking rooms, 12 rooms for disabled). Room rate from €395 (max 2 guests). SC included. Off-season special breaks available. Open all year.

Seasons Restaurant: Guests dining in Seasons Restaurant can have an aperitif in the (attractive) bar or, as there is no dedicated reception area/cocktail bar for the restaurant, you may go straight to your table - a procedure which can sometimes get a meal off to a shaky start. Also, although no expense has been spared on the decor, the dining ambience lacks atmosphere and the restaurant has yet to reach the consistently high standard of food and service expected in this price range: on the basis of a visit by the Guide shortly before going to press, Seasons has some way to go before it reaches its full potential. However, although this is not immediately obvious from descriptions of dishes on the menus, Executive Head Chef Terry White states a commendable commitment to sourcing the best Irish ingredients for his contemporary international menus - citing, for example, organic produce from a west Cork farm, as well as Irish farmhouse cheeses and other speciality foods. No-smoking area; air conditioning. **Seats 90** (private room, 12). Breakfast 7-11 daily, L 12-2.30 daily, D 6.30-10 daily. Set L from €31 (Set Sun L €24); Set D €45; à la carte also available L&D). House wine from €24. No SC.*Less formal dining, including a range of "Irish Home Style Dining" dishes, is available in The Café, open daily 11 am-midnight. Amex, Diners, MasterCard, Visa, Laser. **Directions:** Located on the RDS Grounds corner of Merrion and Simmonscourt Road.

The French Paradox

Ⓝ Restaurant

53 Shelbourne Road Ballsbridge Dublin 4
Tel: 01 660 4068 Fax: 01 663 1026
Email: tastingroom@thefrenchparadox.net Web: www.thefrenchparadox.com

On a busy road near the RDS, this inspired and stylish operation has brought a new dimension (and a whiff of the south of France) to the concept of wine and food in Dublin. Upstairs, over a continental style open fronted wine shop with a couple of pavement tables sectioned off with green canvas, there's a smart little bar - pale wood, glass, vases of lilies - with a display area for charcuterie and cheese and five tables set up with quality modern cutlery, a single flower and white linen napkins (even at lunch time). A warm welcome sets the tone for an experience characterised by caring service, knowledge of the (short) menu and - the big story here - the wide range of wines (25, mostly French) available by the glass (from €7). Food is simple - and superb: plates of charcuterie (cured meats from the Basque country and Spain); cured fish; pâtés (French style, with cornichons) and artisan cheeses, individual plates or shred ones for two, served with crusty bread baked twice daily on the premises and a green salad. If there is a signature dish it is probably the smoked duck breast salad, with qualis eggs, griottine and walnuts, with mixed leaves (€12.50) but salade Bill Hogan (Desmond and Gabriel cheese, mixed leaves & extra virgin oil dressing €7.90) is a worthy contender. Given the simplicity of the food, bills can mount alarmingly fast - probably because the seductive atmosphere of the place makes it too tempting to linger over another glass (or two) of wine - but this is quality and worth paying for. Open wine bottles are kept fresh by a method new to Ireland - the white spot nitrogen 'Wine Keeper' - which ensures that wine is kept in good condition down to the last glass. Wines offered change regularly, food can be purchased from the deli-counter to take home - and there's a more extensive menu in the evening, including tapas. Not very suitable for children. **Seats 23.** no smoking area; air conditioning. Toilets wheelchair accessible. L Mon-Sat, 12-3; D Mon-Say, 5-9.30. A la carte. House wine €15.95. Closed Sun, bank hols. Amex, Diners, MasterCard, Visa, Laser. **Directions:** Opposite Ballsbridge Post Office.

Furama Restaurant

Restaurant   G/F Eirpage House Donnybrook Dublin 4 **Tel: 01 283 0522** Fax: 01 668 7623
Email: info@furama.ie Web: www.furama.ie

In the sleek black interior of Rodney Mak's long-established restaurant Freddie Lee, who has been head chef since the restaurant opened in 1989, produces terrific food with an authenticity which is unusual in Ireland. Even the menu does not read like other Chinese restaurants - dishes aren't numbered, for a start, and they are also presented and described individually. They do offer Set Dinners, which are more predictable - and many traditional Chinese dishes on the à la carte menu - but the option is there to try something different. Specialities include steamed seafood, roasted duck and Chinese vegetables. Service, under the supervision of Rodney Mak and manager Stephen Lee, is friendly and efficient. A Special Chinese Menu can be arranged for banqueting with one week's notice (up to 30 people) and outside catering is also available. Parking. **Seats 100** L Mon-Fri 12.30-2, Sun 1.30-4; D daily: Mon-Fri 6-11, Sun. 30 4-11. Various set menus from €35 pp. A la carte available. House wine from €17. No-smoking area. Air conditioning. SC 10%. Closed 24-26 Dec & Good Fri. Amex, Diners, MasterCard, Visa, Laser. **Directions:** Opposite Bective Rugby Ground, Near RTE.

Glenogra House

Guesthouse   64 Merrion Road Ballsbride Dublin 4 **Tel: 01 668 3661** Fax: 01 668 3698
Email: glenogra@indigo.ie Web: www.glenogra.com

Seamus and Cherry McNamee make a point of providing personal service and good breakfasts at their comfortable Ballsbridge guesthouse. Old and new are carefully combined to create a homelike atmosphere and three new rooms were recently added. Conveniently located for the RDS and within 3 minutes walk of the Sandymount DART station. Children welcome (Under 12s free in parents' room; cots available free of charge). No pets. **Rooms 12** (2 shower only, all no-smoking). B&B €55pps, ss €25. Closed Christmas & New Year. Amex, MasterCard, Visa, Diners, Laser. **Directions:** Opposite 4 Seasons Hotel, RDS.

Herbert Park Hotel

Hotel   Ballsbridge Dublin 4 **Tel: 01 667 2200** Fax: 01 667 2595
Email: reservations@herbertparkhotel.ie Web: www.herbertparkhotel.ie

This large, Irish-owned contemporary hotel is set in an 'urban plaza' near the RDS and the public park after which it is named. It is approached over a little bridge, which leads to an underground carpark and, ultimately, to a chic lower ground foyer and the lift up to the main lobby. Public areas on the ground floor are impressively light and spacious, with excellent light meals and drinks provided by efficient waiting staff. The bright and modern style is also repeated in the bedrooms, which have views over Ballsbridge and Herbert Park and are stylishly designed and well-finished with a high standard of amenities, including air conditioning, individual temperature control, 2 line ISDN phones with voice mail, mini bar, safe, interactive TV with email, internet, PlayStation, in house movies and bill view facility. Suites also have extras like robes, CD player, jacuzzi bath,

complimentary mineral water, fruit and chocolates and a daily newspaper. Breakfast, lunch and dinner are all served in the hotel's attractive Pavilion restaurant; snacks and light lunches are available all day in The Terrace lounge (8am-10pm). Team building, jazz events, golf packages and special breaks are all offered. A good choice for the business guest or corporate events, the hotel has a range of meeting rooms and video-conferencing facilities. Conference/banqueting (120/150). Business centre. Secretarial services. Gym. Garden. Children welcome (under 12s free in parents' room, cots available free of charge, playground. Pets by arrangement. **Rooms 153** (3 suites, 27 executive rooms, 65 no-smoking, 7 disabled). Lift. Room rate from about €275. No SC. Open all year.
The Pavilion: This is a bright, elegant, contemporary room which is pleasingly devoid of hard-edged minimalism and overlooks a garden terrace (where tables can be set up in fine weather). Fashionable international menus, mainly based on well-sourced Irish ingredients and offer a choice of about four dishes on each course on set menus and seven or eight on the à la carte. Irish themes are sometimes introduced - as in stuffed chicken supreme, black pudding & bacon roulade and herb mash - and desserts often include refreshingly simple things like fresh fruit salad with crème fraîche or warm apple pie with vanilla ice cream as well as some more flamboyant dishes. Prices are reasonable, especially when seen in comparison with nearby competition, and the lunch menu offers particularly good value. **Seats 150.** No smoking area; air conditioning. L daily, 12.30-2.30 (to 3 on Sunday); D Mon-Sat, 5.30-9.30. Set L & early D (5.30-7.30) from €19.68; D à la carte. House wine €19. Closed D Sun & D bank hols. *Informal dining is offered at The Terrace, 8am-10pm daily. Amex, Diners, MasterCard, Visa, Laser.
Directions: In Ballsbridge, shortly before RDS heading out of city.

The Hibernian Hotel

Hotel/Restaurant

Eastmoreland Place Ballsbridge Dublin 4
Tel: 01 668 7666 Fax: 01 660 2655
Email: info@hibernianhotel.com Web: www.hibernianhotel.com

It feels as if it's in a peaceful backwater, yet this splendid Victorian building is only yards from one of Dublin's busiest city centre roads. It's very friendly, with a country house feeling in the size and proportions of its rooms and an elegant decorative style with warm country colours. The names of the rooms evoke a homely atmosphere too - the drawing room, the library and so on. Individually decorated bedrooms have excellent bathrooms featuring a wide range of amenities. Service is exemplary. Small conference/private parties (45/45). Board room (20). Business centre. Secretarial services. Small garden. Children under 2 free in parents' room; cots available free of charge. No pets. **Rooms 40** (3 shower only, 10 junior suites, 14 no-smoking, 2 disabled). Lift. B&B €110 pps Closed Dec 24-26.
The Patrick Kavanagh Room: In keeping with the rest of the hotel, the restaurant is well-appointed, with elegance and charm - and there's a nice little patio area where tables can be set up on fine summer days. lunch and dinner menus change weekly and include unusal vegetarian choice - typically a tian of aubergine with ratatouille, herb crust and cauliflower sauce. Global influences are certainly at work here, but you will also find more traditional dishes, such as grilled sirloin beef with confit shallots & black pudding mash. Desserts tend to be quite classic - bruléed lemon tart with citrus sorbet, pehaps - and Irish and European cheeses are an option. Service is friendly and efficient. **Seats 45** (private room 20). No-smoking area (no air conditioning). L Mon-Fri 12.30-2.30; D Mon-Sat 6.30-10, Sun 7-9. Set L €25, Set D €39; D also à la carte. House wine €21.95. SC 12.5%. Closed L Sat & Sun, 24-26 Dec, bank hol Mons. Amex, Diners, MasterCard, Visa, Laser, Switch.
Directions: Turn off Upper Baggot Street just below Searsons pub (right turn heading into town).

Jury's Ballsbridge The Towers

 Hotel

Lansdowne Road Dublin 4 **Tel: 01 667 0033** Fax: 01 660 5540
Email: towers@jurysdoyle.com Web: www.jurysdoyle.com

 The Towers is a quieter, more exclusive section of the main Jurys Hotel in Ballsbridge, a hotel within a hotel located to the rear of the main block with its own entrance on Lansdowne Road and a high level of security - entry to the inner foyer and thus to accommodation is by card key. Business and corporate guests are well looked after and constant maintenance and upgrading, plus a high level of service from a committed and well-trained staff, keep this hotel up with the leaders in an increasingly competitive market. The many little extras that make The Towers especially desirable for business guests include complimentary tea, coffee and biscuits, served all day in a seating area known as the hospitality lounge, where a light

breakfast (included in the room rate) is also served each morning and complimentary drinks are served, 6-7pm Monday-Thursday. Guests at The Towers also have the benefit of spacious rooms, queen/king size beds, dedicated work desk and lamp, luxurious bathrooms and towelling robes in addition to or of a higher grade than the usual 'executive' extras. There is direct access to the main hotel and all its amenities from The Towers. **Rooms 105** (4 suites, 101 executive, 50 no-smoking, 2 for disabled). Lift. B&B €160, ss130, SC12.5%. Open all year. Amex, Diners, MasterCard, Visa, Laser. **Directions:** Approx 11 km from the airport, 1 km from city centre.

Jurys Ballsbridge Hotel

féile bía Hotel　　Pembroke Road Ballsbridge Dublin 4 **Tel: 01 660 5000** Fax: 01 660 5540
Email: ballsbridge@jurysdoyle.com Web: wwwjurysdoyle.com

Centrally located in the Ballsbridge area, always busy, Jurys has the distinction of being both an international hotel providing high levels of service to business and leisure guests, while remaining a popular local hotel for Dubliners. Rooms and service are of a high standard (24 hour room service and laundry and dry cleaning services) and executive rooms also have a modem line, voice mail, mini-bar and 24 hour sports and news channels as well as multi-channel TV. The facilities offered by the hotel generally are excellent - Jurys was for a long time the only Dublin hotel with a swimming pool; the leisure centre currently also has a whirlpool, saunas and gym and there's a health & beauty salon, hairdresser and newsagent on site. There are two restaurants, Raglans and the informal Coffee Dock, and two bars - the larger Dubliner Bar is a great meeting places, especially when matches are played at the nearby Lansdowne Road rugby stadium. Conference/banqueting (850/600). Business centre, secretarial services. Cabaret (May-Oct). No pets. Special offers available. **Rooms 303** (3 suites, 500 executive rooms, 150 no-smoking, 2 for disabled). Lifts. B&B €140, ss €110. SC12.5%. Open all year. **Raglans Restaurant: Seats 120.** No-smoking area. Air conditioning. Open for L&D daily. Toilets wheelchair accessible. Open all year. Amex, Diners, MasterCard, Visa, Laser. **Directions:** About 11 km from the Airport & 1 km from city centre.

Jurys Montrose Hotel

féile bía Hotel　　Stillorgan Road Dublin 4 **Tel: 01 269 3311** Fax: 01 2691164
Email: montrose@jurysdoyle.com Web: www. jurysdoyle.com

This south-city hotel near the University College campus has undergone extensive refurbishment. Removing balconies and rebuilding the whole front has updated the exterior, while interior improvements include the addition of more rooms to executive standard and some wheelchair friendly accommodation. All rooms have quite good facilities (direct dial phone, multi-channel TV, tea/coffee-making facilities and trouser press/iron) and there's 12 hour room service and laundry/dry cleaning services. Executive rooms also have a modem line and complimentary newspaper and business magazines. Although conference facilities are not extensive (max 70 delegates), there's a business centre, seven meeting rooms and free parking, making this an attractive venue for small events. Children welcome (cots available) **Rooms 180** (35 executive). B&B €79.50pps, ss €79.50; weekend specials available. Open all year. Amex, Diners, MasterCard, Visa. **Directions:** On Stillorgan dual carriageway near RTE studios.

Kites Restaurant

Restaurant　　15-17 Ballsbridge Terrace Ballsbridge Dublin 4
Tel: 01 660 7415 Fax: 01 660 5978

Lots of natural light with white painted walls, dark wooden fittings and a rich, dark carpet create a good first impression at this split-level Ballsbridge restaurant, and a mix of diners (Chinese and non-Chinese, business and pleasure) tucking into tasty, well prepared food gives the place a nice buzz. The cuisine is combination of Cantonese, Szechuan, peking and Thai and menus range from the standard set meals to a decent list of specials. An excellent house platter of appetisers (€8.89 per person) make a good begining, offering a fine selection of spring rolls, wontons, sesame prawn toasts, spare ribs along with some more unusual additions. Duckling and seafood are sepcialities: half a crispy aromatic duck (€22.86) has well-textured meat and comes with fresh steaming pancakes, while a combination dish of salt & pepper jumbo king prawns and a stir-fry is really mouth-watering - or you could try chicken Szechuan, notable for its well judged spicing. Desserts are not a strong point, but courteous, good humoured and charming service adds considerably to the experience. No-smoking area. Air conditioning. **Seats 100.** L Mon-Sat 12.30-2, D daily 6.30-11.30 (Sun to 11). Set L €18.40, Set D €33. House wine €18.40. SC 10%. Closed 25-26 Dec, Good Fri. Amex, Diners, MasterCard, Visa, Laser. **Directions:** In the heart of Ballsbridge.

Kwai

Restaurant   41-43 Shelbourne Road Dublin 4 **Tel: 01 667 0959**

Friendly staff, a good buzz and an informal café-style atmosphere are some of the things that draw people to this contemporary Ballsbridge restaurant. It's a place where you could find yourself spending some time: chairs which have a hard-edged minimalist look turn out to be surprisingly comfortable and tables - which are simply but attractively laid, with fresh flowers - are well-spaced for privacy. Eclectic menus cover a wide range of south-east asian cuisines (notably Thai-style curries, noodles and satays, teriyaki steak) and a good deal of thought seems to go into them - somebody in the kitchen is certainly trying hard to please, with interesting food and flavour combinations presented attractively and generously in large bowls. Efficient and knowledgeable service by friendly staff adds greatly to the enjoyment of a meal here. A short lunch menu offers especially good value. There's a wide selection of fresh fruit juices and smoothies as well as beers and wine. L&D daily: L 12-4, D 5.30-10.30 (Thu-Sat to 11.30). Closed 25 Dec, 1 Jan, Good Fri.

Langkawi Malaysian Restaurant

Restaurant   46 Upper Baggot Street Dublin 4
Tel: 01 6682760 Fax: 01 6682760 Email: hosey@indigo.ie

The three main distinct national cuisines that influence Malaysian cuisine - Malay, Chinese and Indian - produce a distinctive culinary range, from hot, fiery dishes through to more subtle flavours. The now very popular Langkawi sets out to do all styles justice, but there is an understandable emphasis on Malay dishes since this is the rarer cuisine in Ireland. Satays make a good start for the cautious, while more adventurous diners have plenty to choose from (with clear menu guidance on heat levels). Chef Alex Hosey uses genuine imported ingredients to achieve an authentic Malaysian taste. Well worth visiting for a lunch or dinner that is out of the ordinary. Wheelchair access. Children welcome. No-smoking area. **Seats 50.** L Mon-Sat 12.30-2, D Mon-Sat 6-11. Set L €16.50, Set D from €25, also à la carte. House wine €15. SC 12.5%. Closed Sun. Amex, Diners, MasterCard, Visa, Laser. **Directions:** Beside Searsons Pub. ◇

Lansdowne Manor

Guesthouse   46-48 Lansdowne Road Ballsbridge Dublin 4 **Tel: 01 668 8848** Fax: 01 668 8873
Email: lansdownemanor@eircom.net Web: lansdownemanor.ie

Situated in the heart of 'embassyland', Lansdowne Manor comprises two early Victorian mansions which have been recently refurbished and decorated in period style. It now offers some of the most comfortable guesthouse accommodation in the city, with an elegant period drawing room for guests use and bedrooms - which have specially commissioned furniture reminiscent of 18th century France - with all the amenities usually expected of hotels, including multi-channel TV, trouser press, tea/coffee-making facility and hairdryer; a full laundry and dry cleaning service is also offered. There are facilities for small conference/private parties (16), with full secretarial services available. Children welcome (under 8s free in parents' room, cots available free of charge). No pets. **Rooms 22** (9 junior suites, 7 shower only). B&B about €70ps, ss about €20. Closed 23 Dec-2 Jan. Amex, Diners, MasterCard, Visa, Laser. **Directions:** At Corner of Lansdowne/Shelbourne Road. ◇

The Lobster Pot

Restaurant   9 Ballsbridge Terrace Ballsbridge Dublin 4 **Tel: 01 660 9170** Fax: 01 668 0025

On the first floor of a redbrick Ballsbridge terrace, conspicuously located near the Herbert Park Hotel - and just a few minutes walk from all the major Ballsbridge hotels - this long-established restaurant has lost none of its charm or quality over the years. The whole team - owner Tommy Crean, Restaurant manager (and sommelier) John Rigby and head chef Don McGuinness - have been working here together since 1980 and the system is running very sweetly. How good it is to see old favourites like dressed Kilmore crab, home-made chicken liver paté and fresh prawn bisque on the menu, along with fresh prawns Mornay and many other old friends, including kidneys turbigo and game in season. The menu is a treat to read but there's also a daily fish tray display for specials - dishes are explained and diners are encouraged to choose their own combinations. All this and wonderfully old-fashioned service too, including advice from John Rigby on the best wine to match your meal. If only there were more places like this - long may it last. L 12.30-2.30pm, D 6.45-9.45pm Mon-Sat. Closed Sun, 24 Dec-4 Jan & Good Fri. Amex, Diners, MasterCard, Visa, Laser.

Georgina Campbell's Jameson Guide to Ireland

Merrion Hall

Guesthouse   54 Merrion Road Ballsbridge Dublin 4 **Tel: 01 668 1426** Fax: 01 668 4280
Email: merrionhall@iol.ie Web: halpinsprivatehotels.com

This Edwardian style townhouse opposite the RDS is handy to the DART (suburban rail) and makes a good base for business or leisure, offering great value in comparison with hotels in the area. Major renovation has taken place over the last year and an additional 12 rooms were added; some rooms have four-posters and the suites have air conditioning and whirlpool spa baths. There's a well-stocked library and a comfortable big drawing room where an all day menu is available (also 24 hour room service), with a wine selection to complement it. Off-street parking at the back. Small conference/private parties (50/50). Garden. Children welcome (cots available free of charge). No pets. **Rooms 34** (6 suites, 2 junior suites, 14 executive, 20 no smoking, 2 for less able guests). Lift. B&B €60pps, ss €35. Food available 7am-9pm; house wine €25. 10% sc. Open all year. Amex, Diners, MasterCard, Visa, Laser. **Directions:** Merrion Hall is located opposite the RDS in the Ballsbridge area of Dublin.

Merrion Inn

Pub   188 Merrion Road Dublin 4 **Tel: 01 269 3816** Fax: 01 269 7669

The McCormacks are a great pub family (see separate entry for their Mounttown establishment) and this attractive contemporary pub on the main road between Dublin and Dun Laoghaire has always had a name for food. At lunchtime there's a good buffet, with a selection of hot main courses as well as a wide range of salads; it's a well-organised operation and details (such as having chilled drinks to hand) are well-planned. In the evening the style moves up a notch or two, with a menu including the likes of warm crispy bacon & croûton salad, pastas and serious main courses such as chargrilled sirloin steak (served with a choice of sauces and salads) as well as some good fish dishes, vegetarian options and the day's specials. Homely desserts always include homemade apple pie. Bar food served daily 12-10 (L12-3, D 3.30-10). Buffet/ à la carte. House wine from €15.95. Closed 25 Dec & Good Fri. Amex, Diners, MasterCard, Visa, Laser. **Directions:** Opposite St. Vincent's Hospital.

Mespil Hotel

 Hotel   Mespil Road Dublin 4 **Tel: 01 667 1222** Fax: 01 667 1244
Email: marketing@leehotels.ie Web: www.leehotels.ie

This fine modern hotel enjoys an excellent location in the Georgian district of the city, overlooking the Grand Canal and within easy walking distance of St Stephen's Green and all the city centre attractions. Public areas are spacious and elegant in an easy contemporary style and bright, generously-sized bedrooms are comfortably furnished with good amenities including fax/modem connection and voicemail. Dining options include the 180-seater restaurant 'Glaze Restaurant, which is open for lunch and dinner daily and offers a well-balanced choice of traditional and contemporary fare based on carefully sourced ingredients at fair prices (main courses from €11.95), and the Terrace Bar (due for renovation, completion due January 2003), where lunch and light snacks are served. The hotel takes pride in the friendliness and efficiency of the staff and special breaks offer good value. Small meeting and seminars (20). Children welcome (Under 12s free in parents' room; cots available free of charge). No pets. **Rooms 256** (3 shower only, 68 no-smoking, 12 for disabled). Lift. Room rate €135 (max 3 guests). Closed 23-27 Dec. Amex, Diners, MasterCard, Visa, Laser. **Directions:** On the Grand Canal at Baggot St. Bridge.

O'Connells Restaurant

 ☆ Restaurant   Bewleys Hotel Merrion Road Dublin 4 **Tel: 01 647 3304** Fax: 01 647 3398
Email: info@oconnellsballsbridge.com Web: www.oconnellsballsbridge.com

Located in a large semi-basement under Bewley's Hotel, this remarkable restaurant continues to strive for the highest standards. It's run by Tom O'Connell, previously the general manager of the Berkeley Court Hotel and a brother of Darina Allen (of Ballymaloe Cookery School in County Cork) and what you will get here is quality ingredient driven modern Irish cooking - simple food, with natural flavours, often emphasised by cooking in a special wood-fired oven. It has dark wood-panelled walls and floor to ceiling windows overlooking a courtyard used for al fresco dining in summer and the atmosphere (which was a little canteen-like) has been improved with the introduction of more divisions, allowing more privacy - and there's no doubt that arriving by the courtyard steps rather than through the hotel helps the ambience considerably. A Swiss-trained executive chef, Felix Zund, joined the team in July 2002 and, together with west Cork head chef Brian McCarthy, works closely with Rory O'Connell of Ballymaloe House, who visits regularly. Menus, which are arranged by course and price, are very reasonable for the quality, beginning with soups, paté and sorbet at only €4.95 to a main course maximum of €19.95 (including vegetables). Carefully sourced food is the star here and the menu not only states that pork, beef, eggs and catering supplies are sourced using Bord Bia's Quality Assurance Schemes, but also credits a number of individual producers and suppliers, often in dishes that have become house sepcialities - typically, a starter salad is made with Fingal Ferguson's Gubbeen smoked bacon, from Schull in Co Cork, an East Cork smoked fish plate comprises a selection from Frank Hederman's smokery in Cobh and smoked salmon from Bill Casey at Shanagarry (both Co Cork) and beef comes from the Irish Hereford Prime Beef Society, Co Offaly and Slaney Foods, Co Wexford. Irish farmhouse cheese, matured on the premises, is served with home-made biscuits and excellent classic desserts range from deliciously homely sugar crust apple tart served with lightly whipped cream to a light summery strawberry délice or (genuinely) home-made ice creams. A highly informative wine list, which includes an extensive selection of house wines, reflects the same philosophy and gives details of vintage, region, grape, grower/shipper, merchant, taster's notes, suggested food partnership, bottle size (including some magnums) and price - invariably moderate for the quality offered - for every wine on the list. Inconsistent service has been a weak point but, with the appointment of Andy Woodyatt as joint restaurant manager with Linda Dignam, this problem is clearly being addressed and major improvements are anticipated. For wonderful quality and sheer value for money this busy restaurant is a shining example of the direction Irish dining should be taking. In recognition of their commitment to quality ingredient driven cooking, O'Connell's was awarded the Guide's prestigious Feile Bia Award in 2002. **Seats 160** (+ summer courtyard 60). No smoking area; air conditioning. Buffet L daily 12.30-2.30 (Sun to 3). D daily 6-10.30 (Sun to 9.30). Buffet L €16, Set Sun L €16.30 Early D from €19 (6-7pm). Set D from €21 A la carte D available. SC discretionary (10% on parties of 6+). Closed 24 Dec (after lunch)-26 Dec. Amex, Diners, MasterCard, Visa, Laser. **Directions:** On the junction of Simmonscourt & Merrion Road, next to the RDS in Ballsbridge.

Ocean Bar

Pub   Charlotte Quay Ringsend Road Dublin 4 **Tel: 01 668 8862**

Dramatically situated on the water's edge with lots of glass and outdoor seating to take full advantage of views over the Grand Canal Basin, Ocean has great atmosphere and makes an excellent meeting place for people of all ages. The location, style and frindliness of the staff all make it a great place to relax - and a particularly good choice for visitors to the city. There are three bars and dining areas to choose from and, while menus offering a wide range of contemporary favourites may not contain any suprises (and can seem a little expensive for what you get), food is well sourced, freshly prepared and competently cooked - and the ambience is exceptional. Tables are laid as you order - simple cutlery, paper napkins - and food is served modern bistro style on big white plates. After a rocky start a couple of years ago, Ocean seems to have found its sea legs - and the Sunday jazz brunches are a particular success. Children welcome. **Seats 160** (private room, 80). No smoking area; air conditioning. Food served daily, 12.30-10. (L12.30-6, D6-10). Set L €15 (Sun €12), Set D from €12. House wine €19. Closed 15 Dec, Good Fri. Amex, MasterCard, Visa, Laser.

Pembroke Townhouse

féile bia Guesthouse   90 Pembroke Road Ballsbridge Dublin 4 **Tel: 01 660 0277** Fax: 01 660 0291
Email: info@pembroketownhouse.ie Web: www.pembroketownhouse.ie

Conveniently located close to the RDS and Lansdowne Road, this luxurious guesthouse has all the amenities usually expected of an hotel, including a lift. There's a drawing room and study for residents' use and individually designed rooms have a safe and fax facilities (on request) for business guests, as well as direct dial phone, cable television, tea/coffee facilities and trouser press. Breakfast is the only meal served but it is a point of pride (a Gourmet Menu offers dishes like sautéed lambs liver served on a bed of sautéed onions and topped with bacon as well as the traditional cooked breakfast). Small conference (12). Children welcome (cots available free of charge). No pets. Lift. **Rooms 48** (7 suites, 2 shower only, 20 no-smoking, 4 for disabled). B&B €98 pps, ss €15. Closed 22 Dec-4 Jan. Diners, MasterCard, Visa.

Radisson SAS St Helen's Hotel

Hotel/Restaurant   Stillorgan Road Dublin 4 **Tel: 01 218 6000** Fax: 01 218 6030
Email: info.dublin@radissonsas.com Web: www.radissonsas.com

Set in formal gardens just south of Dublin's city centre, with views across Dublin Bay to Howth Head, the fine 18th century house at the heart of this impressive new hotel was once a private residence. Careful restoration and imaginative modernisation have created interesting public areas, including the Orangerie bar and a pillared ballroom with minstrels' gallery and grand piano. Bedrooms, in a new four-storey block adjoining the main building, all have garden views (some of the best rooms also have balconies) and air conditioning and are well-equipped for business guests (with desks and fax machines). Rooms are comfortably furnished to a high standard in contemporary style, although less spacious than might be expected in a new development; small bathrooms, especially, fail to live up to the opulence that the old house promises The hotel has two restaurants (see below) and lighter menus are also offered all day in the Orangerie bar and Ballroom lounge. Conference/banqueting (350/220). Fitness centre; beauty salon. Garden; snooker. Ample parking. Children welcome (Under 17s free in parents' room; cots available). **Rooms 151** (25 suites, 70 no-smoking, 8 for disabled). Room rate about €205 (max 3 guests). Open all year.

Le Panto: The hotel's fine dining restaurant, offers international fine dining, including a 7-course "Chefs Surprise Menu". In common with other rooms at St Helen's, the name of the restaurant has military connections - a copper representation of the battle of Le Panto (as described in the G.K. Chesterton poem) hangs over the fire - but it's easy to forget all that when enjoying the view over the gardens. An à la carte menu tends towards the luxurious, with words like truffles and foie gras scattered across the page and pruces to match. Although mainly an evening restaurant, Le Panto is also open for lunch on Sundays and can be used for private lunch parties. **Seats 60.** No smoking area; air conditioning, toilets wheelchair accessible. D Tue-Sat, 7-10.30; L Sun only, 12.30-3. A la carte. Closed Mon, all Aug.

Talavera: In four interconnecting rooms in the lower ground floor, this informal Italian restaurant is decorated in warm Mediterranean colours and is atmospheric when candle-lit at night. It specialises in authentic dishes from Tuscany and Basilicata and features a fine antipasti buffet; high standards of both food and service were experienced on a recent visit by the Guide - a Tuscan main course of rabbit with rosemary was singled out for particular praise, also a delicious pannacotta with caramelised pears; the wine list offers a strong selection of regional Italian bottles to match the food. **Seats 110.** No smoking area; air conditioning. Toilets accessible by wheelchair. L Mon-Sat 12.30-2.30; D daily, 6.30-10.30. Set L €29, D à la carte. Closed L Sun. Amex, Diners, MasterCard, Visa, Laser. **Directions:** Just 3 miles from the City Centre, on N11.

Raglan Lodge

Guesthouse   10 Raglan Road Ballsbridge Dublin 4 **Tel: 01 660 6697** Fax: 01 660 6781

Helen Moran's elegant mid 19th-century residence is peacefully situated near the US embassy, yet convenient to the city centre - and reasonably priced too. Well-proportioned, high-ceilinged reception rooms are reminiscent of more leisurely times and the en-suite bedrooms are exceptionally comfortable. Raglan Lodge is renowned for the high level of comfort and service provided, and particularly for outstanding breakfasts: a white-clothed sideboard displays freshly squeezed orange juice, fresh fruits and compôtes, home-made muesli and cereals, creamy porridge, yogurt and cheeses, then you can have a choice of kippers, scrambled eggs with smoked salmon or a fine traditional breakfast of rashers, sausages, tomatoes and all the trimmings, delivered piping hot under silver domes covers - a great start to the day. (Raglan Lodge was the Dublin winner of our Denny Irish Breakfast awards in 2001). Theatre reservations can be arranged. Children welcome. **Rooms 7** (all en-suite, some shower only 2 no-smoking). B&B €63pps, ss €13. Closed 2 wks Christmas. Amex, Diners, MasterCard, Visa. **Directions:** Follow signs for South city to Baggot Street which becomes Pembroke Road, turn right onto Raglan Road, Raglan Lodge is on the left.

Roly's Bistro

féile bia Restaurant   7 Ballsbridge Terrace Ballsbridge Dublin 4 **Tel: 01 668 2611**
Fax: 01 660 8535 Email: ireland@rolysbistro.ie Web: www.rolysbistro.ie

This bustling Ballsbridge bistro has been a smash hit since the day it opened. Chef-patron Colin O'Daly (one of Ireland's most highly regarded chefs) and head chef Paul Cartright present imaginative, reasonably priced seasonal menus at lunch and an evening à la carte menu. A lively style is based on Colin's classical French training but it also gives more than a passing nod to Irish traditions, world cuisines and contemporary styles. Carefully sourced ingredients are the sound foundation for cooking that never disappoints - Dublin Bay Prawns are always in demand and may be served Newburg (this has become something of a speciality and comes with a tian of mixed long grain and wild rice), or in prawn cocktail, when using fresh Dublin Bay prawns moves that old favourite up into a different class. Chicken stuffed with Clonakilty black pudding - which uses one of Ireland's best-loved contemporary products, made by Edward Twomey in west Cork - is another favourite, but the cooking is always innovative, colourful and appealing. Wholesomely delicious puddings are worth saving a little space for: red apple tart tatin, perhaps, with chunky caramel ice cream and maple fudge sauce, or white chocolate and strawberry slice. Service is generally efficient but discreet. Offering quality with good value has been the philosophy of the restaurant from the outset and it continues to fulfil this promise well. **Seats 140.** No smoking area; air conditioning. L daily 12-3, D daily 6-10 Set L €17.75; carte. Early D menu (6-6.45); L&D also à la carte. SC10%. Amex, Diners, MasterCard, Visa.

Rumm's D 4

Pub   Shelbourne Road Ballsbridge Dublin 4 **Tel: 01 6676422** Fax: 01 6676423
Email: cj@rummsd4.com Web: www.rummsd4.com

Good bar food and comfortable surroundings are a combination that's suprisingly hard to find in Dublin, so this large, well-maintained pub (which is quite handy to the RDS), could be a useful spot to bear in mind. Varied menus and chef's specials lunch and dinner daily. Closed 25 Dec & Good Fri. Amex, MasterCard, Visa. **Directions:** Prominent corner position on Shelbourne Road. ◇

Schoolhouse Hotel

Hotel   2-8 Northumberland Road Ballsbridge Dublin 4 **Tel: 01 667 5014** Fax: 01 667 5015
Email: reservations@schoolhousehotel.com Web: www.schoolhousehotel.com

Dating back to its opening in 1896 as a school, this building beside Mount Street Bridge has seen many changes lately, culminating in its opening in 1998 as one of Dublin's trendiest small hotels. The Inkwell Bar is always a-buzz with young business people of the area. Rooms are finished to a high standard, with air conditioning, power showers and the usual amenities expected of a quality hotel. Small conference (20). Wheelchair access. Parking. Children welcome (Under 5s free in parents' room; cots available). No pets. Lift. **Rooms 31** (15 no-smoking, 2 for disabled). B&B €125pps, ss €55. SC discretionary. Closed 24-27 Dec. Amex, Diners, MasterCard, Visa. **Directions:** Southbound from Trinity College, at the end of Mount Street across the Grand Canal.

Waterloo House

Guesthouse   8-10 Waterloo Road Ballsbridge Dublin 4 **Tel: 01 660 1888** Fax: 01 667 1955
Email: waterloohouse@tinet.ie Web: waterloohouse.ie

Evelyn Corcoran has combined two Georgian townhouses to make a luxurious base in a quiet location very convenient to the city centre and also Lansdowne Road (rugby), RDS (equestrian & exhibitions) and several of the city's most famous restaurants. Equally attractive to the business or leisure traveller. ISDN lines. Conservatory & Garden. Wheelchair access. Own parking. Children welcome. No pets. Lift. **Rooms 19** (8 shower only, 1 disabled). B&B about €70pps. Closed Christmas week. MasterCard, Visa. **Directions:** South on Stephens Green on Merrion Row for 1 mile. First turn right after Baggot Street Bridge. ◇

DUBLIN 6

Antica Venezia

Ⓝ Restaurant   97 Ashfield Road Ranelagh Dublin 6 **Tel: 01 497 4112**

A real throw-back in time and refreshingly so: this entirely Italian-run restaurant has a classic Italian 70's interior with stained wooden floors and ceiling beams, Venetian trompe-l'oeil scenes on the walls and candlewax-dripped Chianti bottles on every table. The food is traditional Italian too, with a menu that could easily date back to the seventies: old-fashioned favourites like stuffed mushrooms and antipasto misto of Italian meats are followed by classics like chicken breast with mushroom and white wine sauce, salmon with lemon butter sauce, pork with marsala sauce and a choice of pasta dishes and pizzas, with predictable but good desserts such as banoffi, tiramisu and cassata as well as a selection of ice creams. Reliably consistent, with service that is laid back but attentive - a perfect recipe for a popular neighbourhood restaurant. **Seats 45.** Air conditioning. MasterCard, Visa, Laser.

Bijou Bistro

Ⓝ Restaurant   47 Highfiield Road Rathgar Dublin 6
Tel: 01 496 1518 Fax: 01 491 1410 Email: bijourestaurant@eircom.net

An intimate restaurant with four smallish rooms on two floors and a distinctly French atmosphere with curtained doorways, colourful turn-of-the-century style paintings, frilled lampshades and vases of lilies - and charming, efficient staff. A generous selection of well made breads (quickly replaced if necessary) accompanies an innovative menu with a dozen or so choices on each course and several fish specialities each evening (typically chargrilled loin of swordfish with chive mash and spiced chickpea salsa); other specialities include risotto of spiced cajun chicken with parmesan herb salad, while more traditional tastes will welcome dishes like pork fillet with sage & bacon potato cake, apple & raisin chutney and Vermouth cream, cooked with accuracy and style - and served on plates decorated with a colourful art deco flourish. Finish with classic desserts or an Irish cheese selection with muscat grapes. A good wine list is augmented by a couple of weekly specials. Booking at this popular neighbourhood restaurant is essential. Children welcome. **Seats 70** (private room, 14). No smoking area; air conditioning. D daily, 5-11, L Sun only 12-3. Set Sun L €19, early D €16 (Mon-Fri, 5-6.45); house wines from €16. SC discretionary. Closed 25-27 Dec, 31 Dec, 1 Jan. Amex, Diners, MasterCard, Visa, Laser. **Directions:** Rathgar cross roads.

Elysium

Ⓝ Restaurant   25 Dunville Avenue Ranelagh Dublin 6
Tel: 01 496 8181 Fax: 01 491 5483 Email: ledadeforge@hotmail.com

This popular neighbourhood restaurant is in premises previously occupied by Dunville Place - a long narrow room with a conservatory at the end, and new decor in fashionable browns and beiges, softened by scatter cushions. The welcome has been known to be a little cool and service off-hand, notably at opening time when they may not be quite ready for early arrivals - but any slight lapse in hospitality is quickly countered by an imaginative menu and sound, creative cooking: well-flavoured aubergine, feta and mint samosas, for example, come with a subtle cardamom yoghurt dip and an earthy oxtail & black pudding terrine is accompanied by a potato salad. Delicious Peking Duck is served with a scrumptious bok choy roll filled with all sorts of vegetarian goodies, while excellent scallops are served with raw, dressed baby spinach and an unusual accompaniment of crushed butternut squash. Desserts are classical and very good - mocha crème caramel with cinnamon espresso reduction, for example, or sticky toffee pudding with vanilla icecream. **Seats 45**. No smoking area; air conditioning. L Tue-Sun, 12-3; D Tue-sat, 6-11. A la carte; house wine from €18.Closed D Sun, all Mon. Amex, MasterCard, Visa, Laser, Switch.

Ivy Court Restaurant

Restaurant   88 Rathgar Road Dublin 6 **Tel: 01 492 0633**

Swiss chef Josef Frei has been doing a good job at this reliable neighbourhood restaurant for many a year now, and it's greatly to his credit that he has maintained the standard of food - and kept prices to a reasonable level - at a time when the reverse is true in many more fashionable establishments. **Seats 80**. D only, Mon-Sat. Closed Sun, Christmas week. MasterCard, Visa.

Poppadom Indian Restaurant

Restaurant   91a Rathgar Road Dublin 6 **Tel: 01 490 2383** Fax: 01 492 3900

Behind a neat but unremarkable frontage in a row of modern shops lies a treat: colourful and airy, with deep yellow walls, linen-clad tables and comfortable chairs (and a new bar recently added), this new wave Indian restaurant demonstrates the delicious diversity of Indian cooking and offers some appealingly unusual dishes. Complimentary poppadoms with fresh chutney dips are brought before menus which offer regional specialities including a starter of Karwari Prawns - deep-fried jumbo prawns marinated in ginger, garlic, yoghurt, garam masal and barbecued in the tandoor, then served with a fresh mint chutney - and main courses ranging in heat from Chicken Avadh, a mild and creamy dish with nuts that was a speciality of the erstwhile Avadh empire of central India, to Lamb Chettinad, a fiery festive dish of the Chettiyar clan in Tamil Nadu. Vegetarians are spoilt for choice, with plenty of dishes available as main courses or side orders. Variations like garlic, onion & coriander naan and lime rice offer a subtle change from the standard acompaniments, food presentation is contemporay and service solicitous. Make a point of trying the masala tea, made with leaf tea and cardamom pods. The wine list helpfully begins with some advice on the styles that partner spicy food well, wisely suggesting Alsace wines, notably Gewurztraminer as the best all-rounder. Children welcome. **Seats**

44. No-smoking area. Air conditioning. D only, 6-12 daily. A la carte. House wine €16. SC discretionary. Toilets wheelchair accessible. Closed 25-26 Dec. Amex, MasterCard, Visa, Laser, Switch. **Directions:** A minute away on the same side as Comans Pub, Rathgar.

Quality Charleville Hotel & Suites

Hotel/Restaurant   121 Lr Rathmines Road Dublin 6 **Tel: 01 4066100** Fax: 01 4066200
Email: charleville@charleville.pressgroup.ie Web: www.pressgroup.ie

Well-equipped new hotel, mostly with suites (including sitting room kitchenette). Good business choice: fax machines, CD players, ISDN lines, modem sockets, cable TV, hairdryer, trouser press with ironing board and tea/coffee-making facilities all included as standard. Own parking. Children welcome (under 4s free in parents' room; cots available). No pets. **Rooms 53** (43 suites, 4 shower only, 25 no-smoking rooms). Room rate from about €85.50. Lift. Amex, Diners, MasterCard, Visa. **Directions:** 15 minutes stroll from the city centre on the South Side.
Carmines Restaurant: Perhaps reflecting demands of the student population in the neighbourhood, pizzas and pastas are the backbone of menus which actually offer a wide choice. Closed 24-26 Dec.

Taipo Restaurant

🅝 Restaurant   2 Terenure Road East Rathgar Dublin 6
Tel: 01 490 0206 Fax: 01 490 0207

Situated above a well-known Rathgar pub, this new Chinese restaurant is on two levels and creates an excellent impression on arrival. It's an elegant and welcoming space, elegant, with well-spaced tables, comfortable seating and tables attractively laid with fresh flowers, crisp white linen tablecloths and napkins. The menu is shorter than most oriental restaurants, and all the better for that, offering Chinese cuisine with some diversions into neighbouring cultures with dishes such as Malaysian satay and some Thai dishes - and, while most of the dishes offered look quite familiar - dishes like sweet & sour king prawn and sizling dishes like fillet steak with peppers and blackbean sauce, but are there - there are also simpler dishes like steamed black sole with ginger & spring onion (predictably expensive at €27.30) and a number of duck specialities lincluding Cantonese roast duck (€16.51). Although still a newcomer to the area, Taipo has the potential to become a reliable neighbourhood restaurant - and it is greatly enhanced by charming Chinese staff, who are eager to please. **Seats 100** (private room 40). No smoking area. Children welcome. L Sun only, 1-3, D 6-11 daily. Set Sun L €19, D à la carte. Hpouse wine €17.15. Closed 25-26 Dec, Good Fri. Amex, Diners, MasterCard, Visa, Laser. **Directions:** Above Comans pub.

Tribeca

Restaurant   65 Ranelagh Village Dublin 6 **Tel: 01 497 4174** Fax: 01 491 1584

An outpost of the well-known Dublin restaurant Dish (previously Temple Bar, recently moved to Upper Leeson Street), Tribeca opened in Ranelagh in 2001 and this New York style restaurant was an immediate hit with its good fast food and relaxed, casual feel, with bright and airy decor and wooden floors and tables. It's just right for food like carefully sourced burgers (made from 100% organic beef), salads, omelettes and chicken wings, which take their place beside the fusion inspired dishes that keep the more adventurous diners happy. It's not cheap, but portions are generous so it works out as quite good value for money - although the level of service is not as good as it was at the outstet and there can be inexplicably long delays. However, a new computerised ordering system had just been started at the time of going to press to increase efficiency, so there should be an improvement in this area. No-smoking area. Air conditioning. **Seats 70** (outside seating 20). Open daily, 12-11. A la carte plus daily blackboard specials. Toilets wheelchair accessible. No reservations. Closed Dec 24-26, Good Fri. MasterCard, Visa, Laser. **Directions:** Heading southbound from city centre, halfway along Ranelagh main street, on right.

Vermilion

🅝 Restaurant   94-96 Terenure Road North Terenure Dublin 6W **Tel: 01 499 1400**
Fax: 01 499 1300 Email: mail@vermilion.ie Web: www.vermilion.ie

This purpose-built restaurant on the first floor above the Terenure Inn pub is another of the new-wave ethnic restaurants that are taking Dublin by storm, and opened to acclaim in December 2001. The decor - contemporary and smart interior in soft primary colours - is carried through into the food which offers colourful, beautifully presented and updated versions of many Indian favourites. Nibbles include little bowls of various condiments such as a rich tomato sauce, a vibrantly yellow, fragrant custard dip and grated carrots with ginger and black mustard seeds, whilst the menu includes specialities from Kerala, Tamil-Nadu and Goa. Pride is clearly taken in the quality of ingredients and cooking, reflecting attention to detail in every aspect of the operation including a good wine list (due for revision at the time of going to press) and friendly service. A small selection of desserts is much more tempting than is usual in oriental restaurants (although only the kulfi is an Indian speciality), an innovative children's menu (main course, dessert and soft drink €10) offers a very mild Chicken Tikka Masala, served with either rice or pasta, and Indian cheese and tomato-topped naan Pizza. The early bird dinner menu includes a good range of dishes and great value (tables to be vacated by 8pm) and the Sunday lunch menu is also well-constructed to give a real taste of the main menu. All round a very welcome addition to the city's ethnic dining scene. **Seats 85** (private area 35). No smoking area; air conditioning. L Sun only, 1.30-5.30, D daily 6-11.30. Set Sun L, €20; early D, 6-7, €20; D à la carte. House wine €18. Closed 25 Dec, Good Fri. Amex, Diners, MasterCard, Visa, Laser, Switch. **Directions:** 200 yards from Terenure crossroads.

Zen Restaurant

Restaurant   89 Upper Rathmines Road Dublin 6 **Tel: 01 497 9428** Fax: 01 497 9428

Denis O'Connor's unusual Chinese restaurant in a converted church (now with the added comfort of stained glass roof windows, opening by remote control) has a well-earned reputation for authenticity. Staff are sourced in Beijing and, although there are plenty of popular dishes on their menus, this is one of the relatively small number of oriental restaurants in Dublin where more adventurous diners are rewarded with food that is well spiced. Zhenquan Fang, who has been head chef since 1993, offers a range of menus including one "For A Sichuan Palate" (for a minimum table of four, about €35 per person) and a speciality "Sichuan Crispy Duck Dinner" for at least two people, which has to be ordered 24 hours in advance (about €70 for two). D daily, 6-11; L Thurs, Fri & Sun only, 12.30-2.30. Set D menus from €19, Set L from €15; also à la carte. Closed L Mon-Wed, L Sat, 25-27 Dec. Amex, Diners, MasterCard, Visa, Laser. **Directions:** Veer left for 750 yards at top of Rathmines Road.

DUBLIN 7

Chief O'Neill's Hotel

Hotel   Smithfield Village Dublin 7 **Tel: 01 817 3818** Fax: 01 817 3839
Email: reservations@chiefoneills.com Web: www.chiefoneills.com

This unusual hotel is central to the complex now known as Smithfield Village - and part of the ongoing upgrading of the areas along Dublin's north quays. Accommodation is in a strikingly modern style which guests will either love or loathe - the bathroom arrangements, for example, are more sculptural than practical - but bedrooms have good facilities, including CD hi-fi systems, ISDN lines, multi-channel TV, while penthouse suites have jacuzzis and rooftop balconies. Lines are simple, colours strong and there's a distinctly youthful air about the place. State of the art conference facilities and meeting rooms attract corporate guests and, for relaxation, Chief O'Neill's Café Bar features live traditional music at weekends and offers a combination of traditional and contemporary Irish food. Unusual attractions incorporated into the hotel complex include The Chimney viewing tower, which was once part of the distillery next door and now has two galleries reached by a glass-walled lift. It's open every day and panoramic views over the city can be spectacular on a good day (also available for private parties of up to 50 guests). Video-conferencing. Conference/banqueting (120/150). Children welcome (Under 12s free in parents' room; cots available free of charge). **Rooms 73** (3 suites, 70 executive rooms, 63 shower only,19 no-smoking, 4 for disabled). Lift. 24 hour room service. B&B €115pps. Amex, MasterCard, Visa, Laser.

The Halfway House

Pub   Navan Road Ashtown Dublin 7 **Tel: 01 838 3358** Fax: 01 868 3088

A well-supported local and handy meeting place just off the West-Link motorway, this well-known pub is very large, well-run and offers good quality popular bar food. Wheelchair access. Parking. No children after 7pm. Bar food every day 12-8. Closed 25 Dec & Good Fri. Amex, Diners, MasterCard, Visa.

The Hole in the Wall

Pub   Blackhorse Avenue Phoenix Park Dublin 7
Tel: 01 838 9491 Fax: 01 868 5160 Email: h/w@eircom.net

PJ McCaffrey's remarkable pub beside the Phoenix Park is named in honour of a tradition which existed here for around a hundred years -the practice of serving drinks through a hole in the wall of Phoenix Park to members of the army garrison stationed nearby. Today the Hole in the Wall also claims to be the longest pub in Ireland - and it is certainly one of the most interesting, best-run and most hospitable. They do good food too - there's a carvery lunch (12.30-3pm) and a bar menu available throughout the day offers a wide choice including traditional Irish dishes like Beef & Guinness Pie, Dublin Coddle and Irish Stew. Children welcome. Pets allowed in certain areas. Music nightly and all day Sun. Wheelchair access. Parking. Bar menu served daily (12-9). Closed 25 Dec & Good Fri. Amex, MasterCard, Visa, Laser. **Directions:** Beside Phoenix Park.

Kelly & Ping, Bar & Restaurant

Restaurant/Hotel   Smithfield Village Dublin 7 Tel: 01 817 3840 Fax: 01 817 3841
                              Email: info@kellyandping.com Web: www.kellyandping.com

In common ownership with Chief O'Neill's Hotel but with its own separate entrance from Duck Lane, this colourful, glass-fronted two-storey restaurant offers generous portions of keenly priced, mainly Asian, food including a range of Thai curries which can be ordered red (hot), green (medium) or yellow (mild). Other dishes can also be adjusted to taste on request and there's a useful glossary of ingredients and sauces. As well as an inexpensive wine list, there's a good choice of Asian beers. Open all day Mon-Fri, noon-11pm. Closed L Sat, all Sun, Dec 23-26. Amex, MasterCard, Visa, Laser. **Directions:** Behind the Four Courts, beside Old Jameson Distillery.

Mero Mero

Ⓝ Café   57a Manor Street Stoneybatter Dublin 7
                              Tel: 01 670 7799 Email: sabormex@indigo.ie

This tiny little place is packed around lunchtime for the very good value, truly Mexican dishes: quesadilla about €2.90, burrito, about €4.30, fajitas about €5.20 with a choice of authentic toppings such as guacamole, re-fried beans, salsa and sour cream. Cheerful staff, genuine and delicious food make this a great little neighbourhood café - be prepared to queue. L, daily. **No Credit Cards. Directions:** Near Phoenix Park (NCR entrance).

The Old Jameson Distillery

Pub/Café   Bow Street Smithfield Dublin 7 Tel: 01 807 2355 Fax: 01 807 2369
                              Email: raydempsey@idl.ie Web: www.whiskey-tours.com

While most visitors to Dublin will visit the recently restored Old Jameson Distillery to do the tour (which is fascinating), it's also a good spot for a bite to eat. There are special menus for groups (including evening functions, when the Distillery is not otherwise open) but The Still Room Restaurant is also open to individuals - light food served all day and lunch, featuring Irish specialities like bacon & cabbage soup, John Jameson beef casserole and Jameson farnhouse whiskey cake - and the standard of cooking is generally high. Downstairs, the 1780 Bar is open from 12 noon daily, with bar food available at lunchtime (12.30-3). Conference centre recently opened. Wheelchair access. Children welcome. **Seats 80** Food served daily, 9-5; L 12.30-2.30. A la carte: carvery main courses from €7. House wine about €16. No-smoking area; air conditioning. Closed 25 Dec & Good Fri. Amex, Diners, MasterCard, Visa, Laser, Switch.

Ta Se Mahogani Gaspipes

Restaurant   17 Manor Street Dublin 7
                    Tel: 01 679 8138 Fax: 01 670 5353 Email: mahoganigaspipes@indigo.ie

In Stoneybatter, a very pleasant neighbourhood of the city in the 'undiscovered' Dublin near Phoenix Park, Drina and Roy Kinsley's small American style restaurant was way ahead of its time when it opened in 1991. What was then eclectic food is now (usually less accurately) called fusion, they were way ahead of others with their spicy food, their 'waitpersons' - and, of course, the jazz (Friday and Saturday nights 9.30-11.30). Drina's menus are still hot on spices in dishes like mandarin scallop & prawn with mangetout, scallions, garlic & ginger in garlic blackbean sauce; vegetarian choices are there in force and highlighted throughout the menu, there are a couple of unusual pasta dishes and a range of main course salads for lunch and dinner - and a good sprinkling of classics like chicken cordon bleu and glazed pork Calvados. Sourcing has always been meticulous at this unusual restaurant - organic meats are supplied by Danny O'Toole, for example, herbs from Eden. Informative wine list, good selection of half bottles. Outdoor seating in mature garden, weather permitting. Not suitable for children after 8 pm. **Seats 50.** No-smoking area. L Tue-Fri,12-3; D Tue-Sat 6-10 (Fri & Sat to11.30). A la carte. Wines from about €14. Closed Sun, Mon, 25-26 Dec & 1 month Jul/Aug. Diners, MasterCard, Visa. **Directions:** North Quays towards O'Connell Street. Left turn on Blackhall Place which becomes Manor Street, half way at North Circular Road.

DUBLIN 8

Bar Italia

Ⓝ Café/Restaurant

Lr Exchange Street Essex Quay Dublin 8
Tel: 01 679 5128 Email: acrobat_ltd@yahoo.it

In a modern office block on the edge of Temple Bar and close to the Civic Offices known disparagingly to Dubliners as 'The Bunkers', this little Italian café has floor-to-ceiling glass to make the most of a splendid view across the Liffey to the magnificent Four Courts - and there's plenty of space outside to enjoy lunch 'al fresco' when the weather's right. Attentive Italian waiters quickly seat new arrivals, service throughout is quick and professional and the banter lends a relaxed atmosphere - matched by colourful, flavoursome food, simply presented. The minestrone soup alone can be memorable, paninis and pasta dishes are the business, and it's a place worth seeking out for their espressos alone. And it's great value too: magic. **Seats 25.** Open every day: Mon-Fri, 8-6, Sat 9-6, Sun 12-6. A la carte. Closed Christmas/New Year. MasterCard, Visa. **Directions:** South quays, west end of Temple Bar (near Dublin Corporation head office).

Brazen Head

Pub

20 Lower Bridge Street Dublin 8
Tel: 01 679 5186 Fax: 01 677 9549 Email: info@brazenhead.com

Dublin's (possibly Ireland's) oldest pub was built on the site of a tavern dating back to the 12th century - and it's still going strong. Full of genuine character, this friendly, well-run pub has lots of different levels and dark corners. Food is wholesome and middle-of-the-road at reasonable prices. Live music nightly in the Music Lounge. L & D daily. Closed 25 Dec & Good Fri.

Footplate Brasserie

Restaurant   Johns Road Heuston Station Dublin 8 **Tel: 01 7032 250** Fax: 01 6718 969

Conveniently located right beside the platform where the Cork train departs, this is a place to consider for a meeting (could save having to go into town at all), when collecting someone off a train or to ensure due care of the inner man before leaving on a train which may have questionable dining arrangements - it certainly takes the rush out of catching a train and, given the difficulties of estimating journey time in Dublin these day, that in itself is sufficient recommendation. However, although short on atmosphere, the food is far better than might be expected of a railway station and they make a real effort to meet special dietary requirements, with vegetarian, gluten-free dishes and any containing nuts highlighted on the menu and a note to coeliacs to ask about any dish that appeals in case it can be adapted. The style is fairly modern - grilled goats cheese with char-grilled vegetables & red onion marmalade, seared tuna steak with Mediterranean style vegetables - and there's a short sandwich menu if you're in a hurry. Open all day, 11-6.30. A la carte. House wine from €15.17. Closed Dec 25, Jan 1, Sun & bank hols. Visa, Laser. **Directions:** Heuston Station, Platform 2.

Gallic Kitchen

Restaurant   49 Francis Street Dublin 8 **Tel: 01 455 4912**

This little spot in Dublin's "antique" district has been delighting locals and visitors alike for the last five years. Patissière Sarah Webb - who also has a stall at the Saturday market in Temple Bar - is renowned for quality baking (quiches, roulades, wraps) and also salads and delicious little numbers to have with coffee. Sourcing is immaculate, cooking skilful and prices reasonable, so you may have to queue. Open Mon-Sat, 9-4.

The Grass Roots Café

Ⓝ Café

Irish Museum of Modern Art Royal Hospital Kilmainham Dublin 8
Tel: 01 612 9900

This self-service café is a pleasant place for an informal meal, whether or not you are visiting the museum - it has good parking facilities and the spacious room, which is attractively located overlooking a new garden area, has a pleasingly cool modern ambience. An appetising small menu offers home-made soup, salads and quiches, tarts and cakes plus several hot dishes - tortellini with pesto cream, perhaps, or tasty pork tacos, generously served - and about half the daily selection is vegetarian. Food quality and presentation is good (large white plates) and cafeteria style service is efficient - and it's a handier choice for a quick lunch than city centre venues, perhaps. Wine choices are restricted to a few quarter bottles. Open: Museum opening hours. MasterCard, Visa. **Directions:** At Royal Hospital Kilmainham museum. ◇

Guinness Storehouse

Visitor Centre/Pub

St James's Gate Dublin 8
Tel 01 408 4800 Web: www.guinness.com

The most spectacular pint of Guinness in Dublin - indeed, in all Ireland - awaits you in Gravity, the modern glass-walled bar providing panoramic views of the city from its unique position atop the impressive Guinness Storehouse, a handsome 1904 building. The Storehouse is commodious - with 170,000 square feet of floor space, it is one of the choicest pieces of real estate in Dublin. The space is imaginatively used to house the Guinness Museum, the story - told with fascinating high tech exhibits - of the famous company's 250-plus years in business. It also includes (on Level 5) the traditional Brewery Bar, serving nourishing Irish fare, and the contemporary-style Source Bar. Opened in the Autumn of 2000, the Guinness Storehouse welcomed its millionth visitor in September 2002. It has so much to offer that some folk spend an entire day there. The Storehouse is open daily 9.30-5. Entrance: Adult €12, Senior Citizen €5.30, Student €8, Family €26 (under 6s free). Bureau de Change. Free parking. Bureau Bar **Seats 150.** Food served 11-4 daily. Closed 25-26 Dec, 31 Dec, 1 Jan, Good Fri.

Havana Tapas Bar

Café

Grantham Street Dublin 8
Tel: 01 476 0046 Email: info@havana.ie Web: www.havana.ie

This smashing little tapas bar is tucked away on a little street off Camden Street and, although understandably extremely popular with locals and people working in the area, it's otherwise one of Dublin's best kept secrets. Prices are very reasonable and lunch is a real bargain. Home-cooked food freshly made on the premises is the philosophy: Spanish tortilla, paella, Serrano ham and delicious breads from the famous Bretzel Bakery is the kind of food you'll get, along with tapas like marinated jumbo prawns. For music, be there on Saturday nights at 10 o'clock (until "late") for live percussion and salsa music. **Seats 60** (private room 20). No smoking area. Live music. Open Mon-Sat 12-10.30 (later Thu-Sat). Tapas from €4.80-€7.30. Closed Sun. Amex, MasterCard, Visa, Laser.

Jurys Christchurch Inn

féile bia Hotel

Christchurch Place Dublin 8
Tel: 01 454 0000 Fax: 01 454 0012 Email: info@jurys.com

Jurys Christchurch Inn is well placed for both tourist and business travellers, within walking distance of the main city centre areas on both sides of the Liffey and close to attractions in Temple Bar, Dublin Castle and Dublinia (the museum of medieval Dublin). Rooms are comfortable and spacious (though occasionally in need of greater attention to upgrading and maintenance), with large, well positioned work desks and small but practical bathrooms with economy baths and overbath showers. A large multi-storey car park at the rear has convenient access to the hotel. **Rooms 182.** Room rate from €96 (up to 3 adults or 2 adults and 2 children); breakfast from €6. Closed 24-26 Dec. Amex, Diners, MasterCard, Visa. ◇

Locks Restaurant

Restaurant   1 Windsor Terrace Portobello Dublin 8 **Tel: 01 454 3391** Fax: 01 453 8352

In an old building with a lovely canalside setting, this long-established two-storey restaurant is furnished and decorated in a warm country house style with soft lighting, open fires and a soothing atmosphere. There's a timelessness about the place which is extremely refreshing in contrast to the overdose of chic minimalism and international menus that has hit Dublin: short set menus for lunch and dinner offer the kind of food that might be served in a good country house; the seasonal à la carte menu is more ambitious in scale, but offers a similar combination of classic and country French and modern Irish cooking, with just a nod towards world cuisine here and there. For example, an extremely luxurious starter - sauté of Dublin Bay prawns with seared duck foie gras, galette potatoes & a balsamic reduction - is a speciality and might be followed by roast rack of lamb with rataouille, mash potatoes with rosemary jus-lié or other classics like monkfish or lobster thermidor and sole meunière. Some dishes are more contemporary, but the classic base is sound - and service is gloriously old-fashioned professional. The wine list favours France, notably Bordeaux, and offers several house choices (all French) by the glass. A la carte prices are high, but the set lunch and dinner menus offer good value. Children welcome. **Seats 60** (private room, 30). No-smoking area. L Mon-Fri,12.15-2.15; D Mon-Sat, 7-11. Set L €26, Set D €46; L&D à la carte available. House wine €19.95. SC 12.5%. Closed Sat L, all Sun, Bank Hols, Dec 25-7 Jan. Amex, Diners, MasterCard, Visa, Laser. **Directions:** Half way between Portobello and Harolds Cross Bridges.

The Lord Edward

Restaurant/Pub   23 Christchurch Place Dublin 8
Tel: 01 4542 420 Fax: 01 4542 420 Email: ledward@indigo.ie

Dublin's oldest seafood restaurant bar span three floors of a tall, narrow building overlooking Christchurch cathedral. Traditional in a decidedly old-fashioned way, The Lord Edward provides a complete contrast to the current wave of trendy restaurants that has taken over Dublin recently, which is just the way a lot of people seem to like it. There are a few non-seafood options - traditional dishes like Irish stew, perhaps or corned beef and cabbage - and the seafood can be excellent: simplest choices are usually best. Bar food is also available Mon-Fri, 12-2.30. Children welcome. **Seats 40**. L Mon-Fri, 12-3. D 6-10.30 Mon-Sat. Set menu €33. Closed Sun, Dec 23 - 2 Jan, bank hols. Amex, Diners, MasterCard, Visa, Laser. **Directions:** Opposite Christchurch Cathedral.

Nancy Hands

Restaurant/Pub   30-32 Parkgate Street Dublin 8 **Tel: 01 677 0149** Fax: 01 677 0187
Email: nancyh@indigo.ie Web: www.nancyhands.com

A sister establishment to the Hole in the Wall (see entry), Nancy Hands is a newish pub, based on tradition but far from being a theme pub. It's a characterful place for a drink and the selection stocked is unusually extensive and includes a wide choice of wines on an unusually informative list (including about 10 by the glass and two wines of the week), also a range of vodkas, whiskeys and cocktails. Food was an important aspect of Nancy Hands from the outset and, on the whole, it is well done: Roland McLaughlin (who has been head chef since 2000) clearly takes it seriously. In both the bar and first floor restaurant his menus successfully straddle the divide between traditional bar food (seafood chowder, brie parcels, steaks) and the lighter international fare that is becoming increasingly popular in pubs: spicy lamb wrap, crispy Japanese chicken, even Tahitian tuna - examples are from the restaurant menu, but bar food shares the same philosophy. The 'Big Breakfast Menu' (10-12.30) is free of all outside influences, however, and remains faithful to tradition, down to the white bread. Children welcome (but not after 8pm). Live music 7 nights. No-smoking area. Air conditioning. Toilets wheelchair accessible. Restaurant: **Seats 120**, L 12-3 (Sun to 4.30), D 6-10; Set L €16, Set D €30; à la carte L&D available. Bar meals available Mon-Fri 3.30-7.30, Sat 10-6. Closed 25 Dec & Good Fri. Amex, Diners, MasterCard, Visa. **Directions:** North quays, opposite Heuston Station.

The Old Dublin Restaurant

Restaurant   90/91 Francis Street Dublin 8
Tel: 01 454 72028 Fax: 01 454 1406 Email: olddub@indigo.ie

Eamonn Walsh's oasis of civilised dining is one of Dublin's longest-established fine restaurants. The standard of cooking is high and the food is lively, with new dishes regularly taking their place alongside established favourites. The dining area is in several domestic-sized rooms with special features - a marble fireplace, some very good pictures - creating a cosy old-world atmosphere. While most famous for its Russian and Scandinavian specialities like blini (buckwheat pancake with cured salmon, prawns and herrings), and planked sirloin Hussar, which still feature on the à la carte, recent menus have been noticeably modern. Set lunch and early evening menus are very good value. Hospitable, thoughtful service. Children welcome. **Seats 65** (private room, 32) No-smoking area. L Mon-Fri,D Mon-Sat. Closed L Sat, all Sun, bank hols. Amex, Diners, MasterCard, Visa, Laser. ◇

Ryans of Parkgate Street

Pub   28 Parkgate Street Dublin 8 **Tel: 01 671 9352** Fax: 01 671 3590
Ryans is one of Ireland's finest and best-loved original Victorian pubs, with magnificent stained glass, original mahogany bar fixtures and an outstanding collection of antique mirrors all contributing to its unique atmosphere. Good bar food is available at lunch time and in the evening, and there's a separate restaurant upstairs. Closed 25 Dec, Good Fri, first 2 wks Jan & Bank Hols.

DUBLIN 9

Egans House

Guesthouse   7-9 Iona Park Glasnevin Dublin 9 **Tel: 01 830 3611** Fax: 01 830 3312
Email: info@eganshouse.com Web: www.eganshouse.com

Within walking distance of the Botanic Gardens and convenient to the airport, north Dublin golf clubs, Dublin port and the city centre, this family-run guesthouse offers comfortable, well-maintained accommodation at a reasonable price. All rooms have full bath, phone, tea/coffee trays. Wine licence. Wheelchair access. Parking. Children welcome (Under 2s free in parents' room; cots available). No pets. **Rooms 30** (2 suites, 5 superior, all no-smoking). B&B €59, ss€10. Closed 23-27 Dec. MasterCard, Visa, Laser. **Directions:** North of city centre - Dorset Street - St Alphonsus Road- Iona Park.

John Kavanagh (Grave Diggers)

Pub   1 Prospect Square Glasnevin Dublin 9
Tel: 01 8307 978 Email: antokav@gofree.indigo.ie

John Kavanagh's lays claim to being the oldest family pub in Dublin - it was established in 1833 and the current family are the 6th generation in the business. Also known as "The Gravediggers' because of its location next to the Glasnevin cemetery and its attached folk history, this is a genuine Victorian bar, totally unspoilt - and it has a reputation for serving one of the best pints in Dublin. No music, "piped or otherwise". Theme pub owners eat your hearts out. Parking. No children after 7pm. Bar food served weekdays 12-2. Closed Good Fri & Christmas. **No credit cards. Directions:** Old Glasnevin Cemetery Gate,off Botanic Road. ◇

DUBLIN 13

Marine Hotel

Hotel   Sutton Cross Dublin 13 **Tel: 01 839 0000** Fax: 01 839 0442
Email: info@marinehotel.ie Web: www.marinehotel.ie

Well-located on the sea side of a busy junction, this attractive hotel has ample car parking in front and a lawn reaching down to the foreshore at the rear. Recently renovated public areas give a good impression: a smart foyer and adjacent bar, an informal conservatory style seating area overlooking the garden and a well-appointed restaurant. Refurbishment of bedrooms, some of which have sea views, is continuing. A popular venue for conferences and social gatherings, especially weddings, the Marine is also the only hotel in this area, providing for the business guest. 24 hour room service. Conference/banqueting (100/180). Indoor swimming pool. Garden. Children welcome (Under 4s free in parents' room; cots available). No pets. **Rooms 48** (4 shower only, 31 executive rooms, 8 no-smoking, 2 for disabled). Lift. B&B about €100pps, ss about €24. Closed 25-27 Dec. Amex, Diners, MasterCard, Visa, Laser. **Directions:** Take coast road towards Howth from city centre, on right at Sutton Cross. ◇

DUBLIN 14

Indian Brasserie

Restaurant   Main Street Rathfarnham Dublin 14 **Tel: 01 492 0261**

Samir Sapru's Indian Brasserie is just a minute's walk from Rathfarnham Castle, at the Butterfield Avenue end of the village. The restaurant, which is run as a buffet, offers freshly prepared wholesome food, aiming to make it the nearest to home cooking that can be achieved in a restaurant. The selection usually includes around eight starters, five or six salads and seven or eight main courses, with each dish individually prepared from scratch and the selection worked out so that all the dishes complement each other. Breads - which are baked quickly at a very high temperature - are cooked to order. The hospitality is intended to make each guest feel as if they are visiting a private house - customers are encouraged to try a little of everything that has been prepared on the night. Own parking. No children after 7pm. **Seats 50.** No-smoking area. Air conditioning D 5:15-11:30 daily. L Sun only 12:30-3. Set D about €20; early D, 5.30-7.30pm. House wine about €14. SC discretionary. Toilets wheelchair accessible. Closed 25-26 Dec. Amex, Diners, MasterCard, Visa. **Directions:** At the Butterfield Avenue end of Rathfarnham village, under TSB Bank. ◇

The Yellow House

Pub   Willbrook Road Rathfarnham Dublin 14 **Tel: 01 493 2994** Fax: 01 494 2441

Named after the unusual shade of the bricks with which it is built, the landmark pub of Rathfarnham makes a perfect rendezvous, with no chance of confusion. The tall and rather forbidding exterior gives little hint of the warmth inside, where pictures and old decorative items relevant to local history repay closer examination. Traditional bar food is served in the lounge and there's a restaurant upstairs serving evening meals and Sunday lunch. Closed 25-6 Dec & Good Fri. Amex, Diners, MasterCard, Visa, Laser. ◇

DUBLIN 15

Ashbrook House

Country House

River Road Ashtown Castleknock Dublin 15
Tel: 01 838 5660 Fax: 01 838 5660

This beautiful Georgian country house is set in 10 acres of grounds and gardens beside the Phoenix park just 15 minutes from the city and the airport. Large beautifully furnished bedrooms have power showers and two family rooms have a single bed as well as doubles. There are two magnificent drawing rooms, tennis court and walled gardens. Direct dial phones in rooms. B&B from about €45 pps. Single supplement about €10. Closed 19 Dec-2 Jan. Amex, MasterCard, Visa, Laser. **Directions:** 15 minutes from airport, similar distance from city centre.

Wongs Chinese Restaurant

Restaurant

Ashley Centre, Main Street, Castleknock, Dublin 15. **Tel: 01 822 2330**

The darkly dramatic decor - ornate carved panelling, formal white-clothed tables - may come as a surprise to first-time visitors to this first-floor restaurant, but it will soon seem incidental in the whirl of entertainment provided by their teppanyaki chef, who skilfully flambés everything in front of you with style and panache. Forget about chafing dishes, this is light years away from any such sedate culinary practice and well worth the pretty high prices charged (set menus start at around €50). Meals, which consist of several small courses, are very different from the usual Chinese dining experience and outstanding for variety, quality of ingredients, accuracy of cooking and good saucing - and, in the case of teppanyaki (only quite recently introduced), entertainment is as important a part of the experience as the food: this, together with the high prices, mean it is very much a night out. The weak point, as usual in oriental restaurants, is dessert - better to settle for Chinese tea and be done with it. Pleasant staff, efficient service and consistently good food make this a place to remember when planning a big night out. Castleknock is generally recognised as the culinary flagship of the Wongs group but other restaurants are also at:

436 Clontarf Road Dublin 3. Tel: 01 833 4400

7 Sandford Road, Dublin 6. Tel: 01 496 7722

5a The Crescent, Monkstown. Tel: 01 230 1212

Directions: Straight through Phoenix Park to Castleknock Gate; into village - Ashley Centre carpark signposted on right. ◇

DUBLIN 16

Killakee House Restaurant

Restaurant

Killakee Road Rathfarnham Dublin 16 **Tel: 01 493 8849**

This famous old house - once the premises of the notorious Hellfire Club - was taken over in 2001 by George Smith, well known for his years as head chef at Kilkea Castle, Co Kildare. A great deal of renovation work was required and much has been done to improve the premises since the Guide's first visit. The restaurant operation has settled well too and a much more confident tone prevails: cheerful and willing staff provide a welcoming atmosphere, skilful cooking ensures that the promise of interesting menus (based on quality ingredients as ever) is carried through onto the plate - and lots of happy punters create a pleasing ambience. **Seats 75**. D Tue-Sat 7-10, L Sun 12.30-5. Closed 25 Dec. Amex, MasterCard, Visa, Laser. ◇

DUBLIN 18

Bistro One

féile bia Restaurant

3 Brighton Road Foxrock Village Dublin 18
Tel: 01 289 7711 Fax: 01 289 9858 Email: bistroone@eircom.ie

This popular first floor neighbourhood restaurant can get very busy but there is a little bar on the way in, where guests are greeted and set up in comfort, and the attitude throughout is laid back but not without care. Ingredients are carefully sourced - organic bacon and beef is from O'Tooles of Glasthule, cheeses from Sheridans cheesemongers, fish from Caviston's of Sandycove - and menus offer about 6 or 8 tempting choices per course. Starters might include seared parcels of crabmeat &

potato with stir-fried noodles, sweet chilli & honey or the ever-popular Bistro One's salad with pancetta, rocket & pine nuts, while the pasta and risotto selection can be starter or main course as preferred - typically, spaghetti with organic meatballs & fresh basil, perhaps, or risotto with fresh asparagus & a light lemon reduction. Main courses include classics - in seafood dishes, maybe, or roast duck - and updated club fare like lamb's liver with streaky bacon, scallion & horseradish mash. There are generous side vegetables and a choice of farmhouse cheese; home made ice creams or classic puddings to finish. Children welcome. **Seats 45** D Tue-Sat 6.45-10.30. A la carte. House wine €21.59. SC 10%. No-smoking area. Closed Sun, Mon & Dec 24-27. MasterCard, Visa, Laser. **Directions:** Southbound on N11, first right after Foxrock church.

Rodney's Bistro

Restaurant   Cabinteely Village Dublin 18 **Tel: 01 285 1664**

Busy, buzzy with closely packed tables, great atmosphere - this little restaurant could be described as the definitive bistro. Friendly service, good cooking and fairly reasonable prices explain its great popularity with the locals. The cooking style is updated classic, with moderate international influences: goujons of sole may come with caper aioli and salsa verde and spicy potato cake with chickpeas and coriander & tomato chilli jam, while main courses could include boned roast crispy duck with fresh herb stuffing, pear confit and port & orange jus - all combinations that work well. Fish is a particularly strong point - monkfish, plaice, cod and even lobster could be among the daily specials and game comes onto the menu in season. Informative wine list, with South African house wines and some half bottles. Not suitable for children. **Seats 38** D Tue-Sat, 7-10. Menu à la carte. House wine €18. No smoking area; air conditioning. SC10%. Closed Sun, Mon, 2 weeks Jan, 2 weeks Jul. Amex, MasterCard, Visa, Laser.

DUBLIN 22

Bewley's Hotel at Newlands Cross

Hotel   Newlands Cross Naas Road Dublin 22 **Tel: 01 464 0140** Fax: 01 464 0900
Email: res@bewleyshotels.com Web: www.bewleyshotels.com

The lobby gives a good first impression at this stylish budget hotel just off the N7. Bedrooms will confirm this feeling, especially at the price - a very reasonable room rate offers a large room with double, single and sofa-bed, a decent bathroom and excellent amenities including a trouser press, iron and ironing board and fax/modem lines. Many more expensive hotels might take note of these standards. Good business facilities too (boardrooms for meetings from only €63.49 per day). The adjacent Bewley's Restaurant provides very acceptable food and there is free parking for 200 cars. Small conference (20). Wheelchair access. Parking. Children welcome. (under 16s free in parents' room; cots available). No pets. Lift. **Rooms 260** (5 shower only, 160 no-smoking, 7 for disabled). Room rate about €70. (max 3 adults). Closed Dec 24-26. Amex, Diners, MasterCard, Visa. **Directions:** Off N7 - take junction 9 from M50.

Browns Barn

Restaurant/Pub   Citywest Bridge Naas Road Dublin 22 **Tel: 01 464 0903** Fax: 01 464 0929
Email: info@brownsbarn.ie Web: www.brownsbarn.ie

Prominently located opposite Citywest Business Park, this landmark listed building dates back to the late 17th century and once housed the Royal Garter Stables. It opened as a bar and restaurant early in 2001 and has proved an asset to the area. Imaginative restoration has created a contemporary interior while retaining many of the original features, including the original stone walls which makes such a welcome contrast to new industrial developments along this stretch of road. Especially attractive features include a courtyard that has been transformed into a light-filled bar - and a west-facing walled garden providing summer seating. Bar food is available all day (steak sandwiches, BLT etc) and the restaurant is open for "casual fine dining" at lunch and dinner every day. Menus are in the popular contemporary style - Caesar salad, goats cheese in filo and chargrilled steaks are typical, also more elaborate dishes such as seabass with braised fennel, black bean dressing & chilli hollandaise. Interesting vegetarian options are also given. Cooking, presentation and service are all generally good - and this, together with a friendly atmosphere, make it good value. Midweek visits might be more enjoyable as it gets very busy at weekends. No smoking area; air conditioning. **Seats 200** (private room, 10-100). Set L €24; D à la carte. House wine €18.98. SC discretionary, except 12.5% on parties of 6+. Amex, Diners, MasterCard, Visa, Laser. **Directions:** Opposite Citywest Business Park.

Jurys Green Isle Hotel

féile bia Hotel   Naas Road Dublin 22 **Tel: 01 459 3406** Fax: 01 459 2178
Email: greenisle@jurysdoyle.com Web: www.jurysdoyle.com

Situated on the Naas Road, close to the major industrial estates, this is a popular hotel for conferences and business. Over half of the bedrooms are executive rooms and there are conference facilities for up to 250 delegates, four meeting rooms for a maximum of 50 each and some business back-up service if required. Laundry/dry cleaning services available. **Rooms 90** (48 executive). B&B from €79pps, ss €79.50. Open all year. Amex, Diners, MasterCard, Visa. ◇

Kingswood Country House

Restaurant/Country House/Guesthouse   Naas Road Clondalkin Dublin 22
Tel: 01 459 2428 Fax: 01 459 2207
Email: kingswoodcountryhse@eircom.net

Just off the Naas Road and very close to the industrial estates around Newlands Cross, the country house atmosphere of this guesthouse and restaurant comes as a very pleasant surprise. The restaurant has a lovely cosy atmosphere and a loyal following, for service and friendliness as well as the food. This is an interesting combination of classic French and traditional and new Irish styles. Ingredients are top quality and the policy is to use as much local and free range produce as possible. Private rooms are available for groups and small business meetings. Small conference/private parties (16/30). Garden. Children welcome (under 2s freee in parents' room, cots available). **Seats 80** (private room, 30) No-smoking area. L 12:30-2:30 daily. D 6:30-10:30 Mon-Sat. SC 12.5%. Closed D Sun, 25-26 Dec & Good Fri. Open on Bank Hols. Accommodation: Guest rooms, like the rest of the house, have an old-fashioned charm. **Rooms 7** (all en-suite). Amex, Diners, MasterCard, Visa. **Directions:** 1.5 miles past Newlands Cross heading south on N7. ◇

Red Cow Moran's Hotel

féile bia Hotel   Red Cow Complex Naas Road Dublin 22
Tel: 01 459 3650 Fax: 01 459 1588
Email: info@morangroup.ie Web: www.morangroup.ie

Strategically located close to the motorway and known as a pub for many years, the Red Cow is now an impressive hotel. A grand staircase sweeping up from the marble lobby gives an indication of the style to follow and, although it will also be of interest to private guests, this is definitely a location to check out if you are considering visiting the area on business or wish to organise conferences or meetings. Bedrooms are all of executive standard, with excellent amenities for business guests including voice mail and fax/modem lines. The purpose-built conference centre offers a wide range of facilities and ample car parking. Conference/banqueting (720/550) Secretarial services. Video conferencing. Wheelchair access. Parking. Children welcome (Under 2s free in parents' room; cots available). No pets. **Rooms 123** (3 suites, 6 mini-suites, 44 no-smoking, 5 for disabled). Lift. B&B about €110pps, ss about €24. Closed 24-26 Dec. Amex, Diners, MasterCard, Visa. ◇

COUNTY DUBLIN

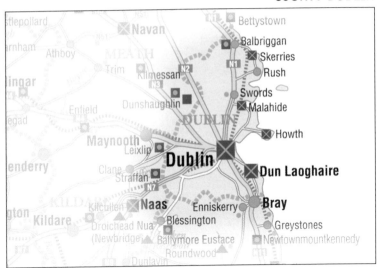

Dublin county is divided into three administrative counties - Dun Laoghaire-Rathdown to the southeast, South Dublin to the southwest, and the large territory of Fingal to the north. However, although these regions are among the most populous and economically active in all Ireland, the notion of Greater Dublin being in four parts is only slowly taking root - for instance, all postal addresses still either have a Dublin city code, or else they're simply "County Dublin".

Inevitably, it is in the counytryside and towns in the Greater Dublin Region that some of the pressures of the success of the Irish economy continue to be most evident. But although Dubliners of town and county alike will happily accept that they're part of a thrusting modern city, equally they'll cheerfully adhere to the old Irish saying that when God made time, He made a lot of it. So most folk are allowing themselves all the time in the world to get used to the fact that they are now either Fingallions, or South Dubliners, or - Heaven forbid - Hyphenators out in Dun Laoghaire-Rathdown.

It's good news for the visitor, for it means that if you feel that the frenetic pace of Dublin city is just a mite overpowering, you will very quickly find that nearby, in what used to be - and for many folk still is - County Dublin, there continue to be oases of a much more easy-going way of life waiting to be discovered.

Admittedly, the fact that the handsome Dublin Mountains overlook the city in spectacular style means that even up in the nearby hills, you can be well aware of the city's buzz. But if you want to find a vigorous contrast between modern style and classical elegance, you can find it in an unusual form at Dun Laoghaire's remarkable harbour, where one of the world's most modern ferryports is in interesting synergy with one of the world's largest Victorian artificial harbours. Now, a new element has been introduced with the opening of a showcase marina in the harbour, expensively built so that its style matches the harbour's classic elegance. In 2003, the facilities there will be in world focus, as Dun Laoghaire is to be the venue for the sailing events in the Special Olympics, and also the Admiral's Cup, the world championship of offshore racing.

Should you head northward into Fingal, you'll quickly discover an away-from-it-all sort of place of estuary towns, fishing ports, offshore islands alive with seabirds, and an environment of leisurely pace in which it's thought very bad form to hasten over meals in restaurants where portion control is either unknown, or merely in its infancy.

Civic pride is a growth industry in Fingal, the pace being set by the attractive modern County Hall in Swords. However, both Fingal and Dun Laoghaire-Rathdown, with their populations respectively at 196,000 and 191,000, are compact by comparison with South Dublin, which chimes in with an impressive 240,000 citizens in the survey of 2002. Yet here too, a new awareness of civic pride is leading to a significantly improved environment.

Local Attractions and Information

Balbriggan/Skerries Ardgillan Castle	01 8492212
Blackrock Deepwell House & Gardens	01 2887407
Donabate Newbridge House, Park & Traditional Farm	01 8436534
Dun Laoghaire National Maritime Museum, Haigh Terrace	01 2800969
Dun Laoghaire Tourist Information	01 2806984/5/6
Lucan Primrose Hill Garden (house attrib. James Gandon)	01 6280373
Malahide Malahide Castle & Demesne	01 8462184
Malahide Fry Model Railway (Malahide Castle)	01 8463779
Malahide Talbot Botanic Gardens (Malahide Castle)	01 8727530
Rathfarnham Marlay Demesne gardens	01 4937372
Sandycove James Joyce Museum (Martello Tower)	01 2809265
Sandyford Fernhill Gardens (Himalayan species)	01 2956000
Skerries Skerries Mills - Working Windmills, Craft and Visitor Centre	01 8495208
Tallaght Community Arts Centre, Old Blessington Rd	01 4621501

Blackrock   Blueberry's

Restaurant   15 Main Street Blackrock Co. Dublin
Tel: 01 2788900 Fax: 01 2788903 Email: blueberrys_dublin@hotmail.com

This fresh, bright first-floor restaurant has lots of polished wood and classy contemporary table settings - a fitting background for stylish food. The best fresh ingredients provide a sound foundation for confident, creative French-style cooking: well-balanced menus offer plenty of choice, with well-made soups, tempting starters and main courses that take vegetarian cooking seriously. Seafood is a strong option and there are modern dishes inspired by French and Irish traditions. Friendly, efficient service. **Seats 38**. No smoking area. Air conditioning. L 12-2 (Sun to 4); D 5.30-10 (Sun 6-9, bookings only). Amex, MasterCard, Visa. **Directions:** Above Jack O'Rourke's pub on the Main Street Blackrock. ◇

Blackrock   Dali's Restaurant

Restaurant   63-65 Main Street Blackrock Co. Dublin **Tel: 01 278 0660** Fax: 01 278 0661

Just across the road from the Library, these premises have been home to several of Dublin's most successful restaurateurs and the present establishment is no exception, having established a loyal local clientèle and a reputation beyond the immediate area. There's a chic little bar just inside the door and a dining area, at a slightly higher level,beyond - all very attractively set up in a style that is contemporary but without hard-edged minimalism. Menus are appealingly light and colourful, including zesty first courses like panfried prawns with a lime, ginger & coriander butter(available as a starter or main course) and salmon fishcakes with a chive beurre blanc, followed by main courses that include several slight variations on old favourites - rack of lamb might come with a salsa verde - and tempting vegetarian dishes such as chargrilled vegetable stack, layered with goats cheese & rocket pesto; prices are moderate, but side dishes are charged extra. Set lunch menus offer a choice of four or five dishes on each course and are very good value. Children welcome. No smoking area; air conditioning. **Seats 65**. L Tue-Sun, 12-3 D Tue-Sat 6-10.30. Set L €13.90, A la carte L&D available; house wine €17.14, sc discretionary except 10% on parties of 6+. Closed D Sun, all Mon, 25-27 Dec. Amex, Diners, MasterCard, Visa, Laser. **Directions:** Opposite Blackrock Library. ◇

Blackrock   Ristorante da Roberto

Restaurant   5 George's Avenue Blackrock Co. Dublin **Tel: 01 278 0759**

First impressions of this extremely popular Italian restaurant are a little confusing - stained glass windows and chandeliers seem at odds with a terracotta-style tiled floor and country kitchen chairs - but the regulars are unfazed. Proprietor-chef Roberto Morsiani offers quite a few house specialities featuring dshes like - Prawns Roberto's Way, Greedy Man's Ravioli, Chef's Rustic Veal - plus a wide choice of fish (mostly local), a page of pastas and a vegetarian section. People like the food, of course, but it's the atmosphere that really singles it out and the overall experience provides a down-to-earth contrast to the chic contemporary restaurants nearby. The best tables are in the front section; the back room (where non-smokers tend to end up) is very noisy. *Also at Roundwood Golf Club (Tel: 01 281 8488). **Seats 70**. Air conditioning D Sun-Sat. Closed Mon. Amex, MasterCard, Visa. **Directions:** Opposite the Post Office off the Main Street in Blackrock. ◇

Dalkey — Daniel Finnegan

Pub
2 Sorrento Road Dalkey Co. Dublin **Tel: 01 285 8505**

An immaculately maintained pub of great character, much-loved by locals and visitors alike, Finnegans, which is bright, comfortable and cosy, with wood panelling and traditional Irish seating in 'snugs', has now "blended in" the large extension opened in December 2001. Food is served at lunchtime only - a full hot bar lunch, including starters such as baked Dalkey crab, brie fritters with apple coulis and main courses like roast stuffed pork steak, honey roast half duck and grilled cod steak, followed by traditional desserts like applie pie and lemon cheesecake. The fresh fish (from the harbour nearby) is excellent, the vegetables predictable but tasty and value good. No reservations - get there early to avoid a long wait. Carpark nearby. Bar food 12.30-3pm Mon-Sat. Closed 25 Dec, Good Fri & & New Year. Amex, Diners, MasterCard, Visa, Laser. **Directions:** Near Dalkey DART station. ◇

Dalkey — Kish Restaurant

Restaurant
Coliemore Road Dalkey Co. Dublin **Tel: 01 285 0377** Fax: 01 285 0141
Email: book@kishrestaurant.ie Web: www.kishrestaurant.ie

The Delaney family, who previously owned the Dalkey Island Hotel, built their new restaurant in 2000 to take full advantage of views over Dublin Bay and Dalkey Island and it is now well-established as one of the area's leading restaurants. It's a great place for special treats like birthdays and anniversaries - the location is a real asset and, aside from the dining experience, there is always something to watch, whether it be wildlife or watersports. There have been several changes in the kitchen lately and the present head chef, Roisin Gavin, previously worked in Belfast with one of Ireland's finest chefs, Michael Deane. Her short seasonal à la carte menus offer about six choices on each course and favour seafood, notably local lobster - typically included in first course house specialities like lobster bisque with roasted langoustines & coconut (€12.50) and, perhaps, a ballotine of chicken served with a cold lobster salad (€14). Main courses which follow in a similar style also include rather more seafood than meat, with a speciality like seared scallops with Clonakilty black pudding and crispy bacon salad (€28) bridging the divide. Vegetarian dishes are available on request, so it would be wise to mention when booking if you would like a vegetarian choice. Charging €1.50 for a selection that would be complimentary in most restaurants is small meanness that will irritate guests out of all proportion to its importance. No smoking area; air conditioning. **Seats 55**. D Wed-Sun, 7-10.30, L Sun only 12.30-2.30. D à la carte; Set Sun L €38; house wine €21-23; SC 10%. Closed Mon,Tue, 7-14 Nov, 7-31 Jan, bank hols. Amex, Diners, MasterCard, Visa, Laser. **Directions:** 8 miles southh of Dublin City just outside Dalkey Village.

Dalkey — Munkberrys Restaurant

Restaurant
22 Castle Street Dalkey Co. Dublin
Tel: 01 284 7185 Email: info@munkberrys.com Web: www.munkberrys.com

This chic, minimalist restaurant in the heart of Dalkey village has earned the support of a local clientèle, who appreciate the stylish cooking and consistently high standard of cooking by head chef Stephen Doris, who has been with the restaurant since it opened in 1999. Several menus are offered- an early dinner menu with three choices on each course is excellent value and it is followed by a set dinner with more choice and quite an extensive à la carte; specialities such as cod fillet with zucchini, basil, pinenuts & currants and grilled beef fillet wrapped in bacon, with creamed spinach, pont neuf potatoes & wild mushroom butter enjoy enduring popularity. Dishes suitable for vegetarians and those containing nuts are thoughtfully highlighted on the menu. Sunday brunch is a speciality, bringing fans from far and wide for good food and live jazz. Interesting, informative wine list. **Seats 50**. D daily: Mon-Sat from 5.30 (early D 5.30-6.45), Sun 6-10; Sun brunch 12-6. Early D €21.75; Set D €32; also à la carte. House wine from €16.75. Closed 25 Dec, 1 Jan, Good Fri. Amex, Diners, MasterCard, Visa, Laser. **Directions:** Main Street Dalkey (5 miles south of Dublin on the Dart Rail Link).

Dalkey — Nosh

Restaurant
111 Coliemore Road Dalkey Co. Dublin **Tel: 01 2840666** Fax: 01 230 0383
Email: comments@nosh.ie Web: www.nosh.ie

Samantha and Sacha Farrell opened their bright, contemporary restaurant next to the famous Club Bar in December 2000 and, with its clean lines and lightwood furniture, no-nonsense menus, quality ingredients and fair prices, it immediately found a niche in the Dalkey dining scene. Paul Quinn (previously sous-chef at The Hungry Monk) has been head chef since they opened and presents seasonal menus that also change throughout the day. There's brunch (hot dishes, anything from French toast with maple syrup, bacon & banana to fish pie with Nosh mash and a wide range of coffees and other hot and cold drinks, including home-made lemonade) then lunch, where things ge a bit more serious, with some overlap from the Brunch menu and a dozen or so choices ranging u to the "Posh Nosh" special of the day. In the evening, you might begin with prawn pil-pils in sizzlin garlic & chilli oil (an enduring favourite) and proceed to fish & chips with home-made chips & tartare sauce (another speciality) or an unusual vegetarian dish such as rotolo (pasta stuffed wit spinach, shitake mushrooms & feta cheese with basil & cream sauce. Top prices range from aroun €15 for a vegetarian main course, to about €20.50 for fillet of lamb with honey-roasted vegetable with rocket mash and thyme jus. A selection of home-made desserts is always offered and there's limited but well-chosen wine list, with a few half bottles, offered throughout the day. Not suitabl for children after 8pm. Wheelchair accessible. No smoking area; air conditioning. **Seats 45.** L Tue Sun, 12-4; D Tue-Sun 6-10.30 (Sun to 10). A la carte. House wine €17.20. Closed Mon, all bank hols MasterCard, Visa, Laser. **Directions:** End of Dalkey Town take left.

Dalkey — The Queen's Bar & Restaurant

Pub/Restaurant
12 Castle Street Dalkey Co. Dubli
Tel: 01 285 4569 Fax: 01 285 8345 Email: queens@clubi.i

The oldest pub in Dalkey, and also one of the oldest in Ireland, The Queen's was originally license to 'dispense liquor' as far back as 1745. Recent renovations and improvements have been done with due respect for the age and character of the premises. There are two restaurants on the premises La Romana, which has offered good value Italian/Mediterranean food for some years and the firs floor restaurant and piano bar, The Vico, which offers contemporary international food in a mor formal atmosphere. Good bar food (member of BIM Seafood Circle)- chowders, salads, pies, stea sandwiches etc also available every afternoon and and evening, and can be served to patio areas a the back and front in fine weather. Wheelchair accessible; children welcome at La Romana, up t 7pm; The Vico is not suitable for children under 8. Restaurants both seat 70. Vico D only Tue-Sat 6-10.30 (Set D menu €28, also à la carte); Romana D daily 6-10.30m (à la carte). Bar menu daily,12 5, Bar Bites menu Mon-Fri, 5-8. Vico closed Mon, Tue; establishment closed 25 Dec & Good Fri. Amex Diners, MasterCard, Visa, Laser. **Directions:** Centre of town, beside Heritage centre.

Dalkey — Ragazzi

N Restaurant
109 Coliemore Road Dalkey Co Dublin **Tel 01 284 7280**

Possibly Dublin's buzziest little bistro, this is the pizza place where everyone goes to have thei spirits lifted by theatrical Italian waiters and great value. Lovely pastas, luscious bruschettas - bu best of all the pizzas, renowned for their thin, crisp bases and scrumptious toppings. But it's the atmosphere that counts - every town should have a place like this.

Dalkey — Thai House Restaurant

Restaurant
21 Railway Road Dalkey Co. Dublin **Tel: 01 284 7304** Fax: 01 284 7304
Email: info@thaihouseireland.com Web: www.thaihouseireland.com

Established in 1997, well before the current vogue for Thai food became established, Tony Ecock's restaurant has earned a loyal following and head chef Wilai Kruekcai has maintained a reputation for including dishes that do not pander too much to bland western tastes. In typical oriental style, a number of set menus are offered for groups of various sizes and there is also an extensive à la carte which offers a wider choice. Begin, perhaps, with the Thai House Special Starter Pack, a sampling plate of six starters, well-balanced in flavour and texture and including some vegetarian options: Thai prawn toast, chicken satay with peanut sauce, deep-fried corn cakes with herbs & curry paste, crispy vegetarian spring rolls, deep-fried prawn cakes with sweet chili sauce From a choice of soups that include the famous Tom Yam Gung (spicy prawn soup with lemon grass and chilli) Tom Yam Rumit - a spicy soup with prawns, squid, crab and mussels is perhaps the most interesting. Main courses include a range of curries - a speciality of is fresh monkfish dumplings in green curry sauce with wild ginger - and vegetarian dishes are listed separately. Groups of four can share a desser platter (mostly with coconut and/or banana). The wine list includes a page of house favourites (all under €25) and a Thai beer. Not suitable for children after 8pm. No smoking area. Air conditioning. **Seats 34.** D Tue-Sun, 6-11. Set D €32, house wine from €16; SC discretionary. Closed Mon, 3 wks late Sep/Oct. Amex, Diners, MasterCard, Visa, Laser. **Directions:** 100 metres from Dalkey Dart Station.

Dublin Airport — Great Southern Hotel

féile bia Hotel
Dublin Airport Co. Dublin **Tel: 01 844 6000** Fax: 01 844 6001
Email: res@dubairport-gsh.ie Web: www.gshotels.com

This large, spacious modern hotel opened in the airport complex in 1998 and has already been extended, with a new 82-bedroom wing added in 2002. It's just two minutes drive from the main terminal building (with a coach service available), rooms are all double-glazed and there's a high proportion of executive rooms (12 of which are designated lady executive). Its good choice for business guests and, should your flight be delayed, the large bar and Potters Bistro on the ground floor could be a welcome place to pass the time. Conference/banqueting (400/240); video conferencing; secretarial services; business centre. Children welcome (Under 2s free in parents' room; cots available free of charge). **Rooms 230** (2 suites, 4 junior suites, 82 executive rooms, 5 no-smoking floors, 4 rooms for disabled) Lifts. Room rate €250 (1 or 2 guests). Closed 24-26 Dec. Amex, Diners, MasterCard, Visa, Laser. **Directions:** Situated in airport complex.

Dun Airport — Holiday Inn Dublin Airport

féile bia Hotel — Dublin Airport Dublin Airport Co. Dublin **Tel: 01 808 0500** Fax: 01 844 6002
Email: reservations-dublinairport@6c.com Web: dublinairport.holiday-inn.com

Guests at this large, comfortable hotel may use the ALSAA Leisure Complex free of charge. Bedrooms all have TV and pay movies, mini-bar, trouser press and hair dryer; 24 hour room service. Two restaurants (Bistro and Sampan) offer contrasting styles of cuisine. Live music in the bar at weekends. The airport is an ideal place for business meetings and there are eight well-equipped meeting rooms/conference suites for groups of up to 130, with secretarial and business services support. Courtesy bus to and from the airport terminal (24 hr). Conference/banqueting (130/130). Parking. Children welcome (Under 12s free in parents' room; cots available without charge). Wheelchair accessible. **Rooms 249** (110 executive rooms, 102 no-smoking, 3 for disabled) B&B €78pps; Closed 24-25 Dec. Amex, Diners, MasterCard, Visa, Laser. **Directions:** In airport complex.

Dun Laoghaire — Bistro Vino

Restaurant — 56 Glasthule Road Dun Laoghaire Co. Dublin
Tel: 01 280 6097 Fax: 01 280 6097

Dermot Baker's small first floor evening restaurant (up steep stairs) is near the seafront at Sandycove. It pre-dates surrounding establishments in this now fashionable area by a long chalk. But it's still a hit with the locals, who appreciate the moderate prices, unpretentious, good food and informal atmosphere. A la carte except for an inexpensive early set menu. D daily, 5-"late". Amex, Diners, MasterCard, Visa. **Directions:** Opposite Eagle House pub. ◇

Dun Laoghaire — Brasserie Na Mara

féile bia Restaurant — 1 Harbour Road Dun Laoghaire Co. Dublin
Tel: 01 280 6767 Fax: 01 284 4649 Email: brasserienamara@irishrail.ie

The old Kingstown terminal building beside the Dun Laoghaire DART station makes a fine location for this harbourside restaurant. The current contemporary decor is stylish - and the bar faces in towards the reception area, so you look out over the harbour while enjoying your aperitif. Interesting menus are in a bright, modern style to suit the decor, include plenty of seafood as one would expect - and prices are not excessive. There's a fish special every night and non-fish eaters have sound choices too, such as rack of lamb with sautéed spinach, herb potatoes & garlic jus. No smoking area. **Seats 86.** L Mon-Fri 12.30-3, Long L Sun, from 12.30; D Mon-Sat, 6.30-10. Set early D (6.30-7.15); Set D about €30.15. A la carte available; house wine. SC discretionary except 10% on parties 8+. Closed L Sat, all Sun, 25-26 Dec & 1 Jan, Good Fri, bank hols. Amex, Diners, MasterCard, Visa, Laser, Switch. **Directions:** Coast road, beside Dart, opposite the Pavillion.

Dun Laoghaire — Caviston's Seafood Restaurant

Restaurant — 59 Glasthule Road Dun Laoghaire Co. Dublin **Tel: 01 280 9120**
Fax: 01 284 4054 Email: caviston@indigo.ie Web: cavistons.com

Caviston's of Sandycove has long been a mecca for lovers of good food and was the guide's Happy Heart Eat Out award-winner for 2001. Here you will find everything that is wonderful, from organic vegetables to farmhouse cheeses, cooked meats to specialist oils and other exotic items. But it was always for fish and shellfish that Caviston's were especially renowned - even providing a collection of well-thumbed recipe books for on-the-spot reference. At their little restaurant next door, they serve an imaginative range of healthy seafood dishes, washed down by a glass from a very tempting little wine list. Caviston's food is simple, colourful, perfectly cooked - it speaks volumes for how good seafood can be. Children welcome. **Seats 26.** No-smoking restaurant; air conditioning. L only Tues-Sat, 3 sittings: 12-1.30, 1.30-3, 3-5; all à la carte; sc discretionary. Toilets wheelchair accessible. Closed Sun, Mon & Christmas-New Year. Amex, Diners, MasterCard, Visa. **Directions:** Between Dun Laoghaire and Dalkey, 5 mins. walk from Glasthule DART station. ◇

Dun Laoghaire — Cumberland Lodge

Accommodation 54 York Road Dun Laoghaire Co. Dublin
Tel: 01 280 9665 Fax: 01 284 3227 Email: cumberlandlodge@eircom.net

Dating from about 1847, David and Mariea Jameson's handsome regency house convenient to the car ferry has retained its period features throughout. Well-proportioned rooms are furnished with antiques and all bedrooms have direct-dial phones, television and tea/coffee-making. Breakfast is a point of pride, with fresh juice, home-baked breads and hot food cooked to order. Garden. **Rooms 6** (5 en suite, 1 with private bathroom). B&B from €50, ss€10. Amex, MasterCard, Visa, Laser. **Directions:** Right at Cumberland Inn,approaching Dun Laoghaire from Monkstown.

Dun Laoghaire — Duzy's Café

Restaurant 18 Glasthule Road (over Eagle House Pub) Dun Laoghaire Co. Dublin
Tel: 01 230 0210 Fax: 01 230 0466 Email: duzyscafe@club.ie

On the first floor of the Eagle House pub (see entry) Duzy's is a more informal, youthful reinvention of one of Dublin's great success stories, Morels Bistro. It's decorated elegantly in deep reds and blues lightened by creams and plenty of mirrors, with comfortable furniture - and a fish tank clearly indicating what's likely to be on the menu. What you can expect is well-sourced seasonal food (some of it coming no further than from Caviston's across the road) and contemporary cooking with a classic base. Specialities include an unusual smoked cod and yellow pepper bisque with glazed goats cheese croûton and scallops with couscous and coriander & lime dressing. If you like jazz, go on a Friday or Saturday night. Coffees and light bites available outside meal times. No smoking area. Children welcome. **Seats 80** (private room 35). Open 12.30-10. Closed L Sat, 25-26 Dec, 1 Jan, Good Fri. Diners, Amex, MasterCard, Visa, Laser. **Directions:** In centre of village over Eagle House Pub. ◇

Dun Laoghaire — Eagle House

Pub 18 Glasthule Road Dun Laoghaire Co. Dublin **Tel: 01 280 4740**

This fine traditional establishment is full of interest and a great local. The interior is dark, but has a fascinating collection of model boats, ships and other nautical bric-à-brac and is arranged in comfortably sized alcoves and 'snugs' on different levels. Bar meals, available at lunchtime and in the evening, can be very good. Bar food daily, from 12.30. Closed 25 Dec & Good Fri. Amex, MasterCard, Visa, Laser. **Directions:** 5 mins walk from Glasthule DART station, opposite Caviston's. ◇

Dun Laoghaire — The Forty Foot

Ⓝ Pub/Café Pavilion Centre Dun Laoghaire Co. Dublin **Tel: 01 284 2982**

Named after a well-known local swimming place, this ultra-modern two-storey bar and restaurant in the redeveloped Pavilion Centre is designed to make the most of views over the harbour and Dublin Bay - particularly from the first floor restaurant - and to impress. Bright, spacious and airy, with acres of wood and huge windows the restaurant, especially, is a lovely space and, unless it is very busy and you have been directed down to the bar, you can settle into a comfortable sofa to read the menu before being shown to a table simply laid with good linen and cutlery and pleasingly plain glasses. The menu offers a wide choice and reads well: colourful, fresh-sounding starters are offered - typically mozzarella with roasted peppers, rocket salad with sundried tomatoes & pine nuts or tian of salmon & crab with crème fraîche and tomato & oil dressing and main courses in a similar vein: fillet of pork wrapped in pancetta, with a mushroom mash, perhaps, or chicken fillet with chorizo. Expect attractively presented food that pleasant rather than exciting and you will not be disappointed; caring service from well-informed and watchful staff who, together with the pleasing ambience, will ensure you wish to return. If you hit it on a sunny day the large terraces outside both the bar and restaurant might also be a draw. Closed 25 Dec, Good Fri. Visa, MasterCard. **Directions:** At Pavilion Centre. ◇

Dun Laoghaire — Gresham Royal Marine Hotel

féile bia Hotel Marine Road Dun Laoghaire Co. Dublin **Tel: 01 280 1911** Fax: 01 280 1089
Email: info@gresham-royalmarinehotel.com Web: www.gresham-hotels.com

Overlooking Dublin Bay and the ferry port, this grand old Victorian hotel has ample parking and extensive landscaped gardens, yet it's only a twenty minute DART ride to the centre of Dublin. On entering the marble floored foyer a few steps take you up and through arched columns into the Bay Lounge (popular for afternoon teas) and the Powerscourt Restaurant. Eight bay-windowed suites have four-poster beds and free-standing antique furniture - a reminder of the age and character of the original building - but most rooms have fitted furniture and standard facilities, including neat bathrooms. Reflecting its popularity as a venue for for functions, conferences and meetings, rooms on the executive floor provide extras for business travellers. Conference/banqueting (450/250). Garden. No pets. **Rooms 103** (8 junior suites, 55 executive, 24 no smoking, 2 for disabled). Lift. B&B about €85 pps, SC15%. Open all year. Amex, Diners, MasterCard, Visa, Laser. **Directions:** Town centre, 200 yards from ferry terminal.

Dun Laoghaire · Mao Café Bar

Café · The Pavilion Dun Laoghaire Co. Dublin **Tel: 01 214 8090** Fax: 01 214 7064

This large, informal contemporary café-restaurant near the harbour is a younger sister establishment to the popular Café Mao in the city centre, which was one Dublin's first fusion cafés. It is run on the same lines with the philosophy of providing simple, quick and healthy food with youthful appeal at a reasonable price. Dishes with nuts are highlighted on the menu, also chilli strength, low fat and vegetarian dishes. Daily specials are especially good value, and there's a daily cake selection - eg cappuccino with walnut gateau, toffee & apple gateau, pecan pie & mississippi mud pie (€4, or €4.50 with ice cream). It's a good place for brunch, with tables outside for fine weather. Open 7 days for coffee, lunch & dinner. Bookings accepted. Closed 25-26 Dec, Good Fri. MasterCard, Visa, Laser. **Directions:** Dun Laoghaire seafront, near station.

Dun Laoghaire · McCormack & Sons

Pub · 67 Lr Mounttown Dun Laoghaire Co. Dublin
Tel: 01 280 5519 Fax: 01 280 0145 Email: cormak@iol.ie

This fine pub (and 'emporium') has been run by the McCormack family since 1960. It's one of the neatest pubs around, with a landscaped carpark creating a pleasant outlook for an imaginative conservatory extension at the back of the pub. The main part of the pub is full of traditional character and the whole place has a well-run hum about it. Good bar food includes fresh fish available on the day as well as classics like home-made hamburger (with mixed leaf salad, fries & a choice of toppings), sandwiches and salds. Evening menus offer tasty light dishes: zucchini fritters, warm crispy bacon and croûton salad and steak sandwiches. Main dishes include a fish special, a 10 oz sirloin steak (with mushroom and Irish whiskey sauce perhaps) or pasta dishes with fresh parmesan. No children after 7pm. Wheelchair accessible. Bar food daily, 12-10 (Sun from 12.30). Closed 25 Dec, Good Fri. Amex, MasterCard, Visa, Diners, Laser. **Directions:** near Dun Laoghaire at Monkstown end.

Dun Laoghaire · Roly @ The Pavilion

Restaurant · 8 The Pavilion Dun Laoghaire Co. Dublin
Tel: 01 2360 286 Fax: 01 2360 288

Roly Saul's purpose-built restaurant just across the railway line from the Royal St George Yacht Club is full of light, with gleaming contemporary decor balanced by some traditional gilded mirrors and leather upholstery in white and a shade that now looks black but (appropriately enough) will age to a deep burgundy; different levels and a mixture of banquettes and high-back chairs are used to break the area up and give it interest and semi-private areas. A youthful kitchen team, who relish the international cuisine, produce starters like rare tuna with ginger risotto spring roll & shitake broth, tian of crabmeat with guacamole & chilled gazpacho and mains of organic salmon, mussels, leek and dicedpotato stew or roast rump of lamb with chilli polenta chips, ratatouille & thyme jus. True to his philosophy of offering an accessible wine list and real value, Roly has managed to keep the (French) house wines - Fox Mountain Chardonnay/Sauvignon Blanc and Jean-Louis Chancel Vin de Pays de Vaucluse - to just €12.70 (£10) and the list has many other good bottles at fair prices. Outside eating area. No-smoking area; air conditioning. Not Suitable for children under 7 after 7 pm. **Seats 100**. L&D daily. Closed 25-27 Dec, Good Fri. Amex, MasterCard, Visa, Laser. **Directions:** Opposite Railway Station. ◇

Dun Laoghaire · Southbank Restaurant

Ⓝ Restaurant · 1 Martello Terrace Sandycove Road Dun Laoghaire Co. Dublin
Tel: 01 280 8788

On the Dun Laoghaire seafront in an attractive semi-basement house with good views of the sea, this welcoming neighbourhood restaurant has a loyal local following who enjoy the relaxed atmosphere and no-nonsense good food. The dining room is not large, but pleasant and quietly atmospheric, with simple decor, some interesting pictures and inviting tables laid with good white linen and crockery, and promising plain wine glasses. Well-made breads are served with olives and dips while you consider menus (changed regularly) which offer about 6-8 choices on each course, plus daily specials - a mixture of classic and more contemporary dishes, with fish a speciality. Starters might include sautéed chicken livers (perfectly cooked with a hint of shallot and brandy and served with a small pool of rich butter jus) or kidneys (served pink in a rich wine sauce), while main course special might be prawns, wrapped in sole fillets, served simply in a creamy white sauce, with wine and herbs. Simple, perfectly cooked vegetables too, and classic desserts (lemon curd tart, perhaps) to round off the meal. Not cutting edge stuff, but very good cooking - and value for money. Booking essential. Visa, MasterCard. **Directions:** Seafront beyond the People's Park - corner of Sandycover Road and Islington Road. ◇

Glencullen — Johnnie Fox's Pub

 Pub

Glencullen Co. Dublin **Tel: 01 295 5647** Fax: 01 295 8911
Email: 7nights@johnniefoxs.com Web: johnniefoxs.com

Nestling in an attractive wooded hamlet in the Dublin Mountains, south of Dublin city, this popular pub has numerous claims to fame, including the fact that it is one of the oldest, with a history going back to the eighteenth century. Daniel O'Connell, who lived in Glencullen at one time, was a regular apparently, and it's "undoubtedly" the highest pub in the land. Whatever about that, it's a warm, friendly and generally well run place just about equally famous for its food – the "Famous Seafood Kitchen" – and its music – "Famous Hooley Nights" (booking advisable). Unlike so many superficially similar pubs that have popped up all over the world recently, it's also real. Kitsch, perhaps, but real nonetheless – the rickety old furniture is real, the dust is real and you certainly won't find a gas fire here – there's a lovely turf or log fire at every turn. It's a pleasant place to drop into at quieter times too, if you're walking in the hills or just loafing around and Dubliners find it an amusing place to take visitors from abroad. Reservations recommended for food. Own parking. Children welcome (under supervision). Traditional Irish music and dancing. **Seats 350** (private room, 150). Open all day (12-10, Sun 1-10); all food à la carte, house wine €18.50. No SC. Closed 25 Dec & Good Fri. Amex, Diners, MasterCard, Visa, Laser. **Directions:** In Dublin Mountains, 30 minutes drive from Dublin city centre.

Howth — Abbey Tavern

Restaurant/Pub

Abbey Street Howth Co. Dublin
Tel: 01 839 0307 / 8322006 Fax: 01 839 0284
Email: info@abbeytavern.ie Web: www.abbeytavern.ie

Just 50 yards up from the harbour, part of this famous pub dates back to the 15th century, when it was built as a seminary for the local monks (as an addition to the 12th century Chapter House next door). Currently owned by James and Eithne Scott-Lennon - James' grandfather bought it in 1945 - the entire establishment was refurbished in 1998 but this well-run and immaculately maintained pub retains features that have always made the Abbey special - open turf fires, original stone walls, flagged floors and gas lights. In 1960 the Abbey started to lay on entertainment and this, more than anything else, has brought the tavern its fame: it can cater for groups of anything between two and 200 and the format, which now runs like clockwork, is a traditional 5-course dinner followed by traditional Irish music. It's on every night but booking is essential, especially in high season. Bar food such as Howth seafood chowder, smoked salmon with home-made brown bread, a hot traditional dish such as corned beef and cabbage, and ploughman's salad is available at lunchtime.
Restaurant: The first floor restaurant, The Abbot, is entered through the bar or separate entrance from the street, a wide carpeted staircase leads to a series of semi open-plan rooms on slightly different levels, with open turf fires and decor which has been gently updated (muslin drapes, gentle wall lights, a soothing scheme of cream and dark green paint) and white-clothed tables set up in classic style - a welcoming sight. A new chef, Stéphane Lemercier, joined the Abbey shortly before the guide went to press and has introduced a much briefer à la carte menu, with perhaps six choices on each course; this, together with confidently simplified cooking, has made a great improvement. Dishes such as baked goats cheese in a sesame crust (served on a well-dressed little mixed leaf salad) or shredded duck & vegetable spring rolls are not original but have real flavour and perfectly cooked main courses of Dublin Bay prawns in garlic butter or sirloin steak, with a dish of mixed vegetables on the table to share, are pleasingly simple and very enjoyable. **Seats 75.** D only, Mon-Sat, 7.-10.30. A la carte. House wine €18. Restaurant closed Sun. Banqueting for 200. Amex, Diners, MasterCard, Visa. **Directions:** 9 miles from Dublin, in the centre of Howth. ◇

Howth — Aqua Restaurant

Restaurant

1 West Pier Howth Co. Dublin **Tel: 01 832 0690** Fax: 01 832 0687
Email: dine@aqua.ie Web: www.aqua.ie

In a stunning sea and harbourside location at the end of the west pier, overlooking the island of Ireland's Eye and with views west towards Portmarnock and Malahide, this building was previously a yacht club and has been senstively converted by the current owners to make a fine contemporary restaurant with plenty of window tables. Behind a glass screen, head chef Brian Daly and his team provide entertainment as well as zesty cooking of colourful food that is thoughtfully presented without the overhandling that has beset so many restaurants lately. What was once a snooker room is now a characterful bar - with an open fire and comfortable seating, it has retained a cosy, clubby atmosphere. Brian Daly, who joined the team in June 2001, was previously at the well-known Dublin restaurant Cooke's Café and has clearly brought that influence with him. His lively modern cooking strongly favours seafood, notably lobster, but dry aged sirloin steak - with grilled peppers, roasted baby potatoes, balsamic vinegar and extra virgin olive oil, perhaps - is also a speciality. The waterside location, well-sourced ingredients, skilful cooking and solicitous service all make dining at Aqua a pleasure. Although prices on the à la carte menu are high, vegetables are charged extra, a small meanness which attracts unnecessary negative comment. On the other hand, well-balanced set menus (early dinner, lunch and the popular Sunday jazz brunch), offer good value. **Seats 100.** D Tue-Sat, early D Tue-Fri (5-7 pm), L Sun only, 12.30-6.30. Early D €26.95, Set Sun L €25. A la carte also available. House wine €19. SC discretionary. Closed D Sun, all Mon, 25 Dec, 3 days at Christmas, bank hols. Amex, MasterCard, Visa, Laser. **Directions:** Left along pier after Howth Dart Station.

Howth   Casa Pasta

Restaurant   12 Harbour Road Howth Co. Dublin **Tel: 01 839 3823** Fax: 01 839 3104

Atmosphere in spades is what sets this first floor restaurant overlooking Howth harbour apart, and although this was partly due to its tiny size, doubling it in 1998 didn't diminish its appeal - it's still notoriously hard to get into, especially at weekends. The secret of Casa Pasta's success is in its universal appeal for all age groups - it's the ideal place for family outings - swift, good humoured young servers and blackboard menus featuring youthful international food (lots of pastas and salads) that is neither over-ambitious nor over-priced - although cooking standards might improve if the choice were reduced. Regulars that locals happily order without even consulting the menu include runny deep-fried brie with spicy chutney, big Caesar salads (possibly with slivers of chicken breast), home-made tagliatelle with mixed seafood in a creamy wine sauce - and desserts like gooey, boozy tiramisu and sticky banoffi pie. Wines are not quite as cheap and cheerful as might be hoped given the style of food and surroundings. Open daily D 6-11, L Sun only 12-6). A la carte, SC discretionary. Children welcome. Open all year. Amex, MasterCard, Visa. **Directions:** Harbour front, overlooking Howth Yacht Club. ◇ *Also at:*

55 Clontarf Road, Dublin 3. Tel/Fax: 01 833 1402

Eirpage House, Donnybrook, Dublin 4. Tel: 01 2608108.

Howth   Deer Park Hotel & Golf Courses

Hotel/Restaurant   Howth Co. Dublin
                    Tel: 01 832 2624 Fax: 01 839 2405 Email: sales@deerpark.iol.ie

Set high up on the Hill of Howth, in the midst of Ireland's largest golf complex, the Deerpark Hotel enjoys wonderful views across Howth demesne (of which it is part) to the islands of Ireland's Eye and Lambay - and, on a clear day, right up the coast to the distant Mournes. Golf breaks are a particular attraction, especially in summer, and that guarantees that the hotel is always busy - also, perhaps, why it is so well-worn. However, although far from sumptuous, the hotel makes a comfortable base for anyone visiting the area. Swimming pool, sauna, steam room, all-weather tennis courts. Conference/banqueting (95/100). Parking. Children welcome (under 12s free in parents' room; cots available). Wheelchair accessible. No pets. **Rooms 80** (all en-suite) B&B about €100.

Howth   King Sitric Fish Restaurant & Accommodation

féile bia Restaurant/Guesthouse   East Pier Howth Co. Dublin **Tel: 01 832 5235** Fax: 01 839 2442
                                    Email: info@kingsitric.ie Web: www.kingsitric.com

Aidan and Joan MacManus' striking harbourside restaurant is named after an 11th century Norse King of Dublin. who had close links with Howth and was a cousin of the legendary Brian Boru. It is one of Dublin's longest established fine dining restaurants - and, from its East Pier site, chef-patron Aidan MacManus can keep an eye on his lobster pots in Balscadden Bay on one side and the fishing boats coming into harbour on the other. Recently completely re-built, this traditional restaurant has blossomed into a fine contemporary space, with first floor dining to take full advantage of the views (notably at lunch, which is especially good value too). Aidan's reputation for cooking seafood (and the excellent sauces that accompany) is of course what brings most people to The King Sitric, and lovers of game also wend their way here in winter, when it is likely to feature on both lunch and dinner menus. Always interested in using the best of local produce, informative notes on menu

covers state the restaurant's commitment to local producers, some of whom are named, and gives a listing of Irish fish in six languages. Less well known seafood, such as locally fished razor shell clams in garlic butter, share the menu with classics like sole meunière and Dublin lawyer (lobster with whiskey sauce) - and make sure you leave room for their speciality dessert, meringue Sitric. But wine interests Aidan MacManus every bit as much as food and he has long had one of the country's finest wine lists, with an especially fine selection of Chablis, magnificent burgundies and a special love of the wine of Alsace. Hence a very special feature of the King Sitric: a temperature controlled wine cellar on the ground floor, where tastings are held. It is cleverly incorporated into the reception area, with only a glass door between them so diners can enjoy the ambience while having aperitifs, or spill over to use stools around the table in the cellar area if the restaurant is very busy. The house wine, Pinot Blanc Cuvée Les Amours Hugel (a special reserve for the King Sitric) is outstanding for both quality and value. The King Sitric received the guide's Wine List of the Year Award in 2001 and the restaurant operates a Food & Wine Club off-season. Banqueting (75). **Seats 70** (private room, 30). No smoking area; air conditioning. L Mon-Fri,12.30-2.15; D Mon-Sat, 6.30-10.30. Set L from €24 set D from €45; also à la carte; house wine from €20; SC discretionary. Toilets wheelchair accessible. Closed L Sat, all Sun, bank hols, last 2 weeks Jan.
Accommodation: There are eight lovely rooms, all with sea views and individually designed bathrooms. **Rooms 8** (all no-smoking). B&B from €63 pps (penthouse, €92.25), ss€26.
Amex, MasterCard, Visa, Laser, Switch. **Directions:** Far end of the harbour front, facing the east pier.

Howth — The Waterside & The Wheelhouse Restaurant

Restaurant/Pub   Harbour Road Howth Co. Dublin **Tel: 01 839 0555** Fax: 01 839 3632

The ground floor of this attractive premises overlooking the harbourfront is one of the pleasantest bars in the area - well-run, comfortable and full of character.
Wheelhouse Restaurant: On the first floor over the Waterside, this is a friendly and welcoming restaurant, with a cosy ambience and moderately priced middle-of-the-road food. They offer a wide choice on menus that naturally include a large selection of local fish dishes - but they're also known for good steaks and meat dishes; specialities include rack of Kildare lamb with honey & mustard crust, so non-fish eaters will be well looked after too. Main course dishes are consistently reliable.
Seats 60. Air conditioning. D only (in restaurant) 6.30-10 daily. Bar Food served daily 12-8.30. Children welcome. Car parking nearby. Closed 25 Dec, Good Fri. Amex, Diners, MasterCard, Visa.
Directions: On Howth harbour front. ◇

Killiney — Fitzpatrick Castle Dublin

Hotel   Killiney Co. Dublin **Tel: 01 230 5400** Fax: 01 230 5466
Email: dublin@fitzpatricks.com Web: www.fitzpatrickshotels.com

Located in the fashionable suburb of Killiney, this imposing castellated mansion overlooking Dublin Bay dates back to 1741. It is surrounded by landscaped gardens and, despite its size and grand style, has a relaxed atmosphere. Spacious bedrooms combine old-world charm with modern facilities and have recently been refurbished as part of a major programme that has also seen upgrading of some public areas, function and conference rooms - and, most recently, the Health & Fitness area, which now has a 22 metre pool, jacuzzi, spa and relaxation deck. Although perhaps best known as a leading conference and function venue, Fitzpatrick's also caters especially well for business guests and The 'Crown Club', on the 5th floor functions as a 'hotel within a hotel', offering pre-arranged private transfer from the airport, private check-in and check-out, private Club lounge and a wide range of facilities for business guests including business support systems, ISDN lines, private email and internet facilities, voice-mail and hands-free phones, interactive digital TV and entertainment system. Five championship golf courses, including Druid's Glen, are nearby. Conferences/banqueting (400/350). Secretarial services. Business centre. Leisure centre; swimming pool. Disco. Children welcome (under 12s free in parents' room; cots available free of charge; crèche), but not in restaurant after 7.30. No pets. Garden. Lift. **Rooms 113** (7 suites, 2 junior suites, 38 executive rooms, 36 no-smoking). B&B €120 pps, ss €30; (room-only rate €140). Closed 24-28 Dec. Amex, Diners, MasterCard, Visa, Laser. **Directions:** Take M50 from the airport, follow signs for Dun Laoghaire ferry port; south to Dalkey - top of Killiney hill.

Leixlip — Becketts Country House Hotel

Hotel/Restaurant   Cooldrinagh House Leixlip Co. Dublin
Tel: 01 624 7040 Fax: 01 624 7072

A handsome house on the Co. Dublin side of the river that divides Leixlip, Becketts is an unusual country house offering a special kind of service aimed specifically at business guests: from the moment you arrive a butler looks after all your needs, whether it be dining, laundry, limousine facilities or specific requirements for meetings or conferences. Imaginatively converted to its present use, luxurious accommodation includes four boardroom suites and six executive suites, all furnished to a high standard in a lively contemporary style. All have a workstation equipped for computers, including modem/internet connection and audio visual equipment, private fax machines etc are also available on request. Public areas, including a bar and a stylish modern restaurant, have a far less business-like atmosphere. Cooldrinagh House overlooks the Eddie Hackett-designed Leixlip golf course, for which golf tee off times may be booked in advance. Conference/banqueting (350/250) Business centre/secretarial services. Wheelchair accessible. No pets. **Rooms 10** (4 suites, 6 executive rooms) B&B about €70. Open all year. **Directions:** Take N4, turn off at Spa Hotel, next left after Springfield Hotel. Amex, Diners, MasterCard, Visa. ◇

Lucan — Finnstown Country House Hotel

Hotel   Newcastle Road Lucan Co. Dublin **Tel: 01 601 0700** Fax: 01 628 1088
Email: manager@finnstown-hotel.ie Web: www.finnstown-hotel.ie

Very much the hub of local activities, this fine old manor house set in 45 acres of woodland is impressive, but also full of charm. An open fire in the foyer sets a welcoming tone and all of the large, well-proportioned reception rooms - drawing room, restaurant, bar - are elegantly furnished in a traditional style well-suited to the house. Although quite grand, there is a comfortable lived-in feeling throughout. Bedrooms include studio suites, with a small fridge and toaster in addition to the standard tea/coffee making facilities, and all rooms have good facilities including full bathrooms (with bath and shower). Residential golf breaks are a speciality. Conference/banqueting (200) Business centre. Leisure centre. Swimming pool. Tennis. Children welcome (Under 3s free in parents' room; cots available). Pets permitted by arrangement. Own parking. Wheelchair accessible. **Rooms 51** (28 suites, 10 no-smoking, 1 for disabled) B&B about €102. Open all year. Amex, Diners, MasterCard, Visa, Laser. **Directions:** Off main Dublin-Galway Road (N4): take exit for Newcastle off dual carriageway.

Malahide — Beanos

Restaurant   1-3 The Green Malahide Co. Dublin **Tel: 01 806 1880** Fax: 01 806 1881

This contemporary bar and restaurant opened in the late summer of 2001 and, although it may look like an office block from the road, the split level interior is pleasing - not least, perhaps, due to a good impression created by speedy and welcoming staff, but also because of the warmth given to minimalist decor by a deep red used selectively in lights, carpet and a feature wall. Some tables have views over the marina - those at the front of the upper level are best - and there's a long bar. Menus are simple and appealingly informal, with sections given over to appetisers, pizza & pasta, main courses - and a whole section on burgers - but this doesn't do the food justice: Beano's pizza, for example, is on a thin, crisp base topped with prawn tails, capers, red onion & tomato, while the mains are mainly seared dishes - tuna, salmon, fillet steak, chicken breast - attractively presented with roasted vegetables and interesting salads. Desserts tend towards the rich classics, like crème brulée, or there's an Irish cheese board to finish. Despite key personnel changes taking place in the first year, high standards of food and service at Beanos have been maintained. Average main course about €18-22, but pizzas and burgers much less. No smoking area; air conditioning. Not suitable for children after 8 pm. **Seats 135** (private room, 90). Open all day (12-10.30); short bar lunch menu 12-5; evening à la carte 5-10.30. House wine from €18.50. SC discretionary. Closed 25 Dec. Amex, MasterCard, Visa, Laser. **Directions:** Facing the marina in Malahide Village.

Malahide — Bon Appetit

féile ☆ Restaurant   9 St James Terrace Malahide Co. Dublin **Tel: 01 845 0314**
bia   Fax: 01 845 0314 Email: info@bonappetit.ie Web: www.bonappetit.ie

In a Georgian terrace near the marina, Patsy McGuirk's highly-regarded basement restaurant is attractively decorated in shades of deep blue and creamy yellows enhanced by a collection of local watercolours - and there's a welcome emphasis on comfort. Patsy McGuirk is a very fine chef in the classic French style, sometimes tempered by Mediterranean and modern Irish influences; many years in the kitchen have resulted in a long list of specialities, each as tempting as the next, although if a choice had to be made it is probably his fish cookery that would top the bill - seafood, mostly from nearby Howth, predominates on menus although steaks, Wicklow lamb, farmyard duckling and ostrich, which is farmed nearby, also feature. Fresh prawn bisque with cognac is a regular and a long-established house speciality is Sole Creation McGuirk (a whole boned black sole, filled with turbot and prawns, in a beurre blanc sauce - now a classic) while simple sole on the bone is presented whole at the table, then re-presented bone-free and neatly reassembled. Roast crispy duckling Grand Marnier on a potato & herb stuffing is another speciality, also ostrich - medallions, perhaps, served on champ with onion marmalade and port wine jus. It's worth leaving room for pretty desserts: fresh strawberries in a crisp filo basket, sliced and sprinkled with Grand Marnier is typical, or there's an Irish cheese platter - and petits fours with your coffee. A fine wine list has its heart in France; there are helpful tasting notes and a special selection, as well as six fairly priced house wines. While not inexpensive, prices have held steady at the Bon Appetit (which is one of the few not to round up a few notches when converting to the Euro); the set lunch menu is particularly good value. Not suitable for children under 12. Booking essential, especially for dinner. **Seats 60** (private room, 20) No smoking area; air conditioning. L Mon-Fri.12.30-2, D Mon-Sat 7-10; Set L €22.85, Set D €44, also à la carte; house wine from €17; sc discretionary. Closed Sun, bank hols & Christmas week. Amex, Diners, MasterCard, Visa, Laser. **Directions:** Coming from Dublin go through the lights and turn left into St James's Terrace at Malahide Garda Station.

Malahide — Cruzzo Bar & Restaurant

féile bia Restaurant   The Marina Malahide Co. Dublin
Tel: 01 845 0599 Fax: 01 845 0602 Email: info@cruzzo.ie Web: www.cruzzo.ie

Built on a platform over the water, this attractive bar and restaurant is large, Florida style, with views over the marina. The interior is dashing, with a bar on the lower floor and a rather grand staircase rising to the main dining areas above, which are comfortable and well-appointed, with well-spaced tables in interesting groupings. Chef Tom Meenaghan, previously executive chef at Conran's Mezzo in London, presents contemporary menus of which grilled red mullet with shaved fennel, orange & watercress salad or penne with herbs, cherry tomatoes & parmesan crackling are typical starters while main courses might include a couple of imaginative vegetarian choices, seared tuna with pepper ragoût & basil aioli and fillet steak with black bean sauce, pickled ginger & spring onion salad; vegetables are charged extra on the à la carte. Uneven service has bedevilled this attractive restaurant for some time, unfortunately, and there is a feeling that it is not always reaching its potential; beware of having an aperitif in the downstairs bar on arrival - they do not appear to liaise with the restaurant staff and will not add drinks to your bill. Although prices have risen quite steeply, set menus remain good value, especially the early dinner menu. **Seats 220.** A la carte L Mon-Fri & Sun,12.30-2.30 (Sun to 4); D Mon-Sat 6-10. early D Mon-Fri from €18 (6-7pm), set D from €30, D also à la carte. (Tue, special musical night, dinner & show €30.47 pp). House wine from €15. SC discretionary. Closed L Sat, L Sun, 25 Dec. Amex, Diners, MasterCard. **Directions:** From Malahide Village through arch into Marina.

Malahide — Grand Hotel

Hotel   Malahide Co. Dublin **Tel: 01 845 0000** Fax: 01 816 8025
Email: info@thegrand.ie Web: www.thegrand.ie

Just 8 miles from Dublin airport in one of Ireland's most attractive coastal towns, The Grand Hotel is well-situated for business and pleasure; set in six acres of gardens, the orginal building at the heart of this large hotel dates back to 1835, which gives it a certain gravitas. Recent additions have included an excellent leisure centre and extensive conference and banqueting facilities. Many of the bedrooms have sea views, the beach (a tidal estuary) is just across the road, there are numerous golf courses nearby - also numerous other activities, including equestrian, fishing and watersports - and there is much of interest within walking distance in the town. Special breaks offered. Conference/banqueting (500/350) Business centre. Leisure centre (21 metre swimming pool, jacuzzi, gym). Tennis, golf and fishing nearby. Own parking. Wheelchair accessible. Children welcome (under 12s free in parents' room; cots available). No pets. **Rooms 150** (7 suites, 2 junior suites, 39 executive rooms, 15 shower only, 25 no-smoking, 1 for disabled). Lift. B&B about €210 pps. Closed 25-27 Dec. Amex, Diners, MasterCard, Visa, Laser. **Directions:** Centre of Malahide; near Dublin Airport and about 30 mins from Dublin city centre.

Malahide — Le Restaurant 12A

Restaurant   12A New Street Malahide Co. Dublin
Tel: 01 806 1928 Email: jasonmccabe@ireland.com

This chic little restaurant in the centre of Malahide opened in 2001, a welcome newcomer to the growing cluster of interesting eating places in the town. Although not French-owned, it is in the contemporary French style - clean-lined, with crisp linen and fine modern crystal - with a menu in the window to entice you in. The menu is sensibly limited to a choice of around five to seven dishes on each course, which might typically include starters like rillette of pork & caramelised apple and marinated brochette of Dublin Bay prawns with a lime & rocket salad and main courses such as fresh loin of yellow fin tuna with niçoise salad and chargrilled fillet of beef bourguignonne style, with vegetables charged extra, which makes the bill mount up very quickly. Tempting desserts might include a simple crumble like apple & blueberry, with vanilla ice cream or summer puding with fromage frais, or there's a European cheeseboad. Accurate cooking, attractive presentation and friendly, willing service make for an enjoyable occasion, although the pricing structure makes it quite an expensive outing - a competitively priced early dinner menu would be an attraction. **Seats 46**. D only, Tue-Sun 6-10. A la carte. House wine about €16. SC discretionary. Closed Mon, 3 weeks Jan. Amex, MasterCard, Visa, Laser. **Directions:** Opposite Gibneys Public House, Malahide. ◇

Malahide | Siam Thai Restaurant

Restaurant — Gas Lane Malahide Co. Dublin **Tel: 01 845 4698** Fax: 01 845 7178
Email: siames@eircom.net Web: www.siamthai.ie

Handily located in a laneway close to the marina, this large restaurant was one of Dublin's earlier Thai restaurants and still regularly fills its tightly-packed tables. Suracheto Yoodsang, head chef since 1996, presents menus that offer many of the Thai classics on an extensive à la carte as well as the set menus and, although perhaps blanded down a bit for local tastes, there's a willingness to vary the spiciness according to personal preference. Siam Combination Appetizers (including chicken satay, spring rolls, special coated prawns, marinated pork ribs, prawns wrapped in ham and bags of golden wonton with plum sauce) usually make a good beginning, followed by main courses like Ghung Phad Phong Garee (Tiger prawns with scallions, mushrooms and basil leaves and a spicy sauce) and Ped Makham (boneless crisp-skinned duck with crispy noodles and plum sauce). Cooking is perhaps less consistent than formerly, but staff are friendly, knowledgable and efficient No monosodium glutamate is used. Children welcome. No-smoking area; air conditioning. **Seats 105**. D 6-11.30 daily, Sun 5-10.30. Set D from €26; à la carte available, house wine €17.50, SC 10%. Closed 25-26 Dec & Good Fri. Amex, Diners, MasterCard, Visa, Laser. **Directions:** In Malahide village, near marina; turn left at Church to end of road.

Malahide | Silks

Restaurant — 5 The Mall Malahide Co. Dublin **Tel: 01 845 3331**

This smart Chinese restaurant is spacious, modern and airy, with cheerful decor and staff who are friendly and helpful to match. Although the long menu offers no major surprises, the food is well above average and can show imagination and flair. Sizzlers and sweet & sours are there, but they are expertly done using quality ingredients, especially the seafood. Excellent crispy Peking duck with pancakes or a light, delicately spiced chicken and mushroom broth make good starters followed, perhaps, by fresh-flavoured main courses of crunchy salt & chilli squid and prawns with ginger and spring onions. Cantonese-style chicken is a speciality - tender slices of chicken in a light, fruit-based sauce with just a hint of spiciness - and desserts are unsurprising: banana fritters with an above average vanilla ice cream, perhaps, or a simple bowl of lychees. Reservations are essential as this restaurant has a loyal following and is busy every night of the week. **Seats 90** (private room 20). No-smoking area; air conditioning. D only, Mon-Sat 6-12.30; Sun 5-11. A la carte. ◇

Monkstown | Empress Restaurant

Restaurant — Clifton Avenue Monkstown Co. Dublin **Tel: 01 284 3200** Fax: 01 284 3188

Since opening in 1992 owner-chef Burt Tsang has built up a strong local following for this pleasant first-floor restaurant just off Monkstown Crescent. A warm welcome and charming, efficient service compliment regional Chinese dishes - Sichuan, Shandong and Beijing - plus Thai and Vietnamese cuisine, offered in set dinners for varying numbers in addition to an à la carte. Specialities include Beijing duck, carved at the table and served with fresh vegetables and hoi sin sauce on pancakes, which requires 24 hours notice. Thai dishes may may seem to have been blanded down for local tastes but cooking overall is consistently good, presentation attractive and prices reasonable; a good choice of vegetarian options is always available, typically Thai vegetable curries. No smoking area. D 6-12 Mon-Sat; Sun open from 3pm. MasterCard, Visa. **Directions:** Just off the Crescent. ◇

Monkstown | The Purty Kitchen

Pub/Restaurant — Old Dunleary Road Monkstown Co. Dublin **Tel: 01 284 3576**
Fax: 01 284 3576 Email: c-cm@iol.ie Web: purtykitchen.com

Established in 1728 - making it the second oldest pub in Dublin (after The Brazen Head) and the oldest in Dun Laoghaire - this attractive old pub has seen some changes recently, but its essential character remains and it's well set up for enjoyment of the bar food for which it has earned a good reputation (and membership of the BIM Seafood Circle). Ballymaloe-trained chef Sheenagh Toal took over as head chef in January 2001 and is now well established so, although the old favourites like the famous Purty Kitchen seafood chowder and Purty Seafood Platter are still there, there's also creative cooking to be found here. Menu combinations are geared to suit to every time of day or occasion so you'll find the smart little menus offering contemporary dishes like cous cous salad with black olives, peppers, sundried tomatoes and melted mozzarella alongside the more traditional bar food; more substantial dishes include 'all day breakfast', home-made beef burgers with salad and baked black sole, on or off the bone, all at reasonable prices. Bar food 12 noon-10pm daily. Amex, Diners, MasterCard, Visa, Laser.

Portmarnock — Portmarnock Hotel & Golf Links

☆🏨 Hotel/Restaurant

Strand Road Portmarnock Co. Dublin
Tel: 01 846 0611 Fax: 01 846 2442
Email: marketing@portmarnock.com Web: www.portmarnock.com

Originally owned by the Jameson family, Portmarnock Hotel and Golf Links enjoys a wonderful beachside position overlooking the islands of Lambay and Ireland's Eye. Very close to the airport, and only eleven miles from Dublin city centre, the hotel seems to offer the best of every world - the peace and convenience of the location and a magnificent 18 hole Bernhard Langer-designed links course. Public areas, including an impressive foyer, are bright and spacious, with elegant modern decor and a relaxed atmosphere.

The Jameson Bar, in the old house, has character and there's also an informal Links Bar and Restaurant next to the golf shop (open 12-9.30 daily). Accommodation is imaginatively designed so that all rooms have sea or golf course views. Sixty rooms have recently been refurbished and all - including some in the original house which are furnished with antiques, two suites with four-posters and private sitting rooms and executive rooms with balconies or bay windows - are furnished to a very high standard of comfort and have excellent bathrooms. Conference/banqueting (350/220) Business centre. Golf (18); Garden. Children under 3 free in parents' room, cots available without charge. **Rooms 103** (2 suites, 16 executive, 15 no-smoking, 6 for disabled). Lift. B&B €140pps, ss €70. Open all year.

The Osborne Restaurant: Named after the artist Walter Osborne, who painted many of his most famous pictures in the area including the view from the Jameson house, the restaurant has been a major addition to the north Dublin dining scene since the hotel opened in 1996. Stefan Matz, a renowned chef and previous co-owner of a highly-regarded hotel in Connemara, joined the hotel as executive chef in May 2001 and has proved a great asset - although, on the Guide's most recent visit, there was no sign of the wonderful signature dishes brought from Connemara, such as saddle of mountain lamb with roast garlic and fines herbes and fillet of beef freshly smoked on turf. However, although the style is now less individual, Stefan is a master of contemporary cooking and his menus are constructed with the discerning international traveller in mind, making full use of the best quality ingredients available - especially seafood from the nearby fishing port of Howth. menus ofered include a tempting 7-course Tasting Menu, a short Seafood Menu and an extensive à la carte. Luscious desserts include hot soufflés - lemon, perhaps, with dark chocolate ice cream - and an irresistible Dessert Suprise. No smoking area; air conditioning. **Seats 80** (private room, 20). D only Tue-Sat, 7-10. Set D from €44.50, Tasting Menu €70. A la carte available; house wine from €18.75; SC discretionary. Closed Sun, Mon. Amex, Diners, MasterCard, Visa, Laser. **Directions:** On the coast in Portmarnock.

Saggart — Citywest Hotel Conference Leisure & Golf Resort

féile bia Hotel

Saggart Co. Dublin **Tel: 01 4010 500** Fax: 01 4588 756
Email: sales@citywesthotel.com Web: www.citywesthotel.com

Only about 25 minutes from the city centre and Dublin airport (traffic permitting), this impressive big hotel was planned with the needs of the rapidly expanding western edge of the capital in mind and provides excellent conference and leisure facilities. It is set in its own estate, which includes tw 18-hole golf courses and a comprehensive leisure centre with a large deck level swimming pool and a wide range of health and beauty facilities. The other big attraction is the hotel's banqueting, conference and meeting facilities, which include a new state of the art convention centre catering for 6,500 delegates, making Citywest one of the largest venues in the country. All this, plus ommitted staff, a high standard of accommodation and a steady hand in the kitchen make the hotel fine amenity for west Dublin. Conference/banqueting (6,500/2,200); secretarial services, video-onferencing. Leisure centre, swimming pool. Hairdressing/beauty salon. Children welcome (under s free in parents' room, cots available free of charge). **Rooms 400** (13 suites, 6 junior suites, 3 xecutive rooms, 82 no smoking). Lift. B&B from €73pps, ss €47.

errace Room: Well-appointed large restaurant serving above-average food at fair prices. **Seats 110.** o smoking area; air conditoning. Children welcome. L Mon-Fri, D daily. Set D €40, house wine €18.40. Amex, MasterCard, Visa, Laser. **Directions:** Off Naas Road - N7 (from Dublin, take left after ndependent printers & follow road for about a mile.

Skerries — Red Bank House & Restaurant

féile bia Restaurant/Guesthouse
5-7 Church Street Skerries Co. Dublin **Tel: 01 849 1005**
Fax: 01 849 1598 Email: redbank@eircom.net Web: www.redbank.ie

here's a double-entendre to the name of Terry and Margaret McCoy's restaurant - not only is there sandbank of the same name nearby, but it's also in a converted banking premises, which makes a estaurant of character and practicality - even the old vault has its uses: as a wine cellar. Margaret provides a warm welcome, serving aperitifs and crudités in a comfortable bar/reception area and overseeing service in the traditional restaurant (where smoking is only allowed if a private party takes over a room). One of the great characters of contemporary Irish cooking, Terry is an avid upporter of local produce and suppliers and fresh seafood from Skerries harbour provides the backbone of his menus, but without limiting the vision - this is a man who goes out at dawn with a bucket to gather young nettles for soup. Dishes conceived and cooked with generosity have names of local relevance - thus, for example, grilled goats cheese St Patrick is a reminder that the saint once lived on Church Island off Skerries. The dessert trolley is legendary (perhaps the traditional adjective 'groaning' should apply to the diners - a large space should be left if pudding is to be part of your meal). Plainly cooked food is provided on request and dishes suitable for vegetarians are marked on the menu. No smoking area. **Seats 50** (private room,12). D Mon-Sat, 7-9.45; L Sun only, 12.30-4.30. Set D from €38, Set Sun L €26. A la carte also available. House wine €20; sc discretionary. Children welcome. Closed D Sun, 24-25 Dec

Accommodation: As well as comfortably furnished bedrooms, there are facilities for small conferences/banqueting (25/50). Gourmet golf breaks are a speciality. Children under 3 free in parents' room (cots available free of charge). **Rooms 12** (8 shower only, 7 no-smoking). B&B €55 pps, ss €10. Amex, Diners, MasterCard, Visa, Laser. **Directions:** Opposite AIB Bank in Skerries.

Stillorgan — Beaufield Mews Restaurant & Gardens

Restaurant
Woodlands Avenue Stillorgan Co. Dublin **Tel: 01 288 0375** Fax: 01 288 6945
Email: beaumews@iol.ie Web: www.beaufieldmews.com

Dublin's oldest restaurant is located in a characterful 18th century coachhouse and stables - and, as the name implies, it is surrounded by beautiful mature gardens. The effect in a built-up area is quite startling, as you are just a few hundred yards off one of Dublin's busiest roads and yet, with its mature trees, spacious surroundings and old-fashioned feeling in both the buildings and gardens, you could be forgiven for thinking you have been mysteriously transported to the country - there's even an antique shop where guests are encouraged to have a browse before dining. Atmosphere is the trump card at this legendary restaurant and the cooking style and courteous service are in tune with the old-fashioned surroundings. Good wine list. Meals: D Tue-Sat, f6.30-10; L Sun only, 12.30-5. Closed Mon, bank hols. Amex, Diners, MasterCard, Visa. **Directions:** 4 miles from city centre, off Stillorgan dual carriageway.

Stillorgan — China-Sichuan Restaurant

Restaurant
4 Lower Kilmacud Road Stillorgan Co. Dublin
Tel: 01 288 4817 Fax: 01 288 0882

David Hui's unique restaurant runs in co-operation with the cultural exchange programme of the state-run China Sichuan Catering Service Company, which supplies chefs and special spices direct from Sichuan province. Since 1986 their refusal to 'bland-down' the style to suit local tastes has earned the restaurant widespread recognition for authenticity. Spicy and chilli-hot dishes are identified on menus - 'Bon Bon Chicken' for example, is a dish of cold chicken shreds in a hot and spicy sauce - but spicing can be varied to suit individual tastes. While set menus are relatively limited (especially at lunch time), the à la carte offers plenty to tempt the most jaded palate including a wide range of seafood dishes and a particularly strong vegetarian section. Children welcome. **Seats 60.** Air conditioning. L Mon-Fri 12.30-2.30, L Sun (& bank hols) 1-2.30. D daily 6-11. Set L about €12, Set

D about €27.30, à la carte available; house wine about €15; sc 10%. Toilets wheelchair accessibl Closed L Sat, 25-27 Dec & Good Fri. Amex, MasterCard, Visa, Laser. **Directions:** 5 miles south fro city, through Stillorgan main road, turn right from Lower Kilmacud Road.

Stillorgan   Stillorgan Park Hote

féile bia Hotel   Stillorgan Road Stillorgan Co. Dublin **Tel: 01 288 1621** Fax: 01 283 161
Email: sales@stillorganpark.com Web: www.stillorganpark.co

This hotel on the Stillorgan dual carriageway is notable for great improvements made in recent yea and is furnished in a dashing modern style throughout. Public areas include the stylish receptio and lounge areas and bedrooms - some with views of Dublin Bay - are spacious, attractive decorated in a bright contemporary style, with well-finished bathrooms. Ample free parking is a attraction and good facilities for business guests include work space and fax/modem lines in room Conference/banqueting (500/350), business centre, secretarial services. Children welcome (under 4 free in parents' room, cots available without charge). Pets permitted by arrangement. **Rooms 12** (4 suites, 125 executive rooms, 50 no-smoking, 4 for disabled) Lift. B&B €80 pps, ss €70. No SC **The Purple Sage Restaurant:** An attractive, informal restaurant with seating in several areas, th Purple Sage has a welcoming staff and menus are appealing in a fairly contemporary style - crisp duck with caramelised orange sauce, for example, or steamed fillet of seabsss with an olive crust basil purée, red pepper beurre blanc. Imaginative vegetarian cooking has always been a feature an the hotel regularly runs special themed dining weeks, including one when 'healthy options' ar highlighted on the menu. Good food and service with fair pricing adds up to good value. Childre welcome. **Seats 50.** No smoking area. Air conditioning. L & D daily, 12-2.30 & 5.45-9.30. Set L €22 SetSun L €21.50; à la carte D available; house wine €19.50; no SC. Amex, Diners, MasterCard, Visa Laser. **Directions:** Situated on main N11 dual Carriageway.

Swords   Old Schoolhouse Restaurant

Restaurant   Church Road Swords Co. Dubli
Tel: 01 840 2846 Fax: 01 840 5060 Email: sincater@gofree.indigo.i

In a quiet riverside site close to the Northern Cross motorway, and only a short drive from th airport, this 18th century stone school building has been restored by the Sinclair family to make attractive country-style restaurant. Major renovations recently saw the dining room restored to it original 20' height, and the garden and conservatory upgraded for al fresco dining. Personal service and good home cooking are the aims; all ingredients are locally sourced and fresh every day, whic allows for a seasonal à la carte and table d'hôte menus (plus daily blackboard specials which include a lot of seafood). A la carte menus offer starters such as baked crab and an unusual Old Schoolhouse style chowder, with big chunks of fish, whole crab claws and generous juices rather than soup. Mair courses include plenty of seafood and some less usual options like ostrich medallions (farmed locally) and wild boar (panfried with Madeira and figs), plus several vegetarian dishes. Children welcome. **Seats 80** (private room, 20) No smoking area; air conditioning. L Sun-Fri, 12.30-2.30 (Sun 1-3.30) D Mon-Sat 6.30-10.30. Set L €19.25 (Set Sun L €25). Early D €30 (Mon-Fri, 6.30-7.30); Set D €45; à la carte also available; house wine €22.50; sc discretionary. Closed L Sat, D Sun, Christmas/New Year,bank hols. Amex, Diners, MasterCard, Visa, Laser. **Directions:** Coming from Dublin, turn left after Lord Mayor's Pub.

Swords   Paparazzi Café

Ⓝ Restaurant   Mainscourt Main Street Swords Co. Dublin **Tel: 01 890 4233**

In a pedestrianised laneway just off the main street in Swords, this smart little contemporary restaurant offers modern menus all day. Friendly staff, pleasant surroundings and a snappy menu that offers plenty of good quality informal fare: salads, baguettes, panini, pasta, pizza, home-made burgers & 'Headliners', ie more substantial - or more grown-up - main courses like meaty ribs, salmon en croûte or roast half duck with orange sauce. Nice little drinks menu includes good coffees. A good choice for families as the menu has plenty to please all age groups, all good of its type and the place has a bit of style - a useful restaurant to know about before going to the airport, perhaps. Tables outside. Children welcome. Open from 10am daily; L menu 12-5, D menu 5-11.30 (Sun to 10.30). A la carte (from about €5.50-€15.50.) House wine €17.50. Amex, MasterCard, Visa, Laser. **Directions:** Behind Bank of Ireland, Main Street.

COUNTY CARLOW

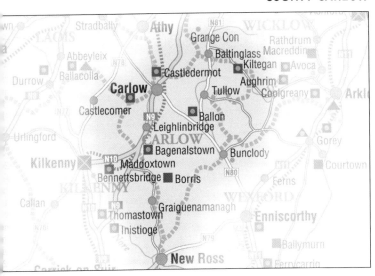

Although it is Ireland's second smallest county, Carlow confidently incorporates such wonderful varieties of scenery that it has been memorably commented that the Creator was in fine form when He made this enchanting place. Whether you're lingering along the gentle meanderings of the waterway of the River Barrow, or enjoying the upper valley of the River Slaney while savouring the soaring lines of the Blackstairs Mountains as they sweep upwards to the 793 m peak of Mount Leinster, this gallant little area will soon have you in thrall.

There's history a-plenty if you wish to seek it out. But for those who prefer to live in the present, the county town of Carlow itself - named as Ireland's "most litter-free town" at the end of August 2002 - fairly buzzes with student life and the energetic trade of a market centre, while a more leisurely pace can be enjoyed at riverside villages such as Leighlinbridge and Bagenalstown. Leighlinbridge - pronounced "Lochlinbridge" - was Barrowside's most community-conscious village for many years, but as we go into 2003 there are also welcome improvements taking place to fulfill Bagenalstown's potential as a proper miniature river port.

Local Attractions and Information

Carlow town Tourist Information	0503 31554
Carlow county Carlow Rural Tourism	0503 30411/30446
Carlow Craft Brewery Micro-brewery	0503 34356
Tullow Altamont Gardens	0503 59128

Bagenalstown **Kilgraney House**

Country House   Borris Road Bagenalstown Co Carlow **Tel: 0503 75283**   Fax: 0503 75595
Email: info@kilgraneyhouse.com   Web: www.kilgraneyhouse.com

Halfway between Carlow and Kilkenny, Bryan Leech and Martin Marley's charming late Georgian house - which (encouragingly) takes its name from the Irish 'cill greine', meaning 'sunny hill or wood' - is in a lovely site overlooking the Barrow Valley. Set in extensive wooded grounds that feature - amongst many other delights - a croquet lawn, fine cut-stone outbuildings (currently under renovation) and the kitchen garden that provides much that Bryan and Martin will transform into delicious dinners, in a contemporary style that also makes good use of other local and artisan produce. A typical summer menu might include baked St Tola goats cheese with a sun-dried tomato pesto and basil served with pecan & buttermilk dressing, Bloody Mary soup, roast loin of pork stuffed with mango & chilli, a seasonal dessert such as roast plums with bay leaf custard or farmhouse cheeses - and your breakfast next morning will be worth allowing time to enjoy. But it is for the sheer sense of style pervading the house that it is most famous - the enjoyment that

Bryan and Martin have derived from their dedication to its restoration and furnishing is abundantly clear: elegant, yes, but with a great sense of fun too. Dinner is normally served at a communal table; private dining on request. Self-catering accommodation is also available, in two courtyard suites and the gate lodge. Small conferences (a helipad is to be ready for the 2003 season, along with more self-catering accommodation.) Not suitable for children under 12. **Rooms 8** (2 suites, 3 shower only, all no smoking). No dogs. B&B €57.50, ss €12.50. Residents' D, 8 pm. Set 6-course D, €40. (Vegetarian meals or other special dietary requirements on request.) Wine €19-68. Closed 1 Nov-1 Mar. Amex, MasterCard, Visa, Laser. **Directions:** Just off the R705, halfway between Bagenalstown and Borris.

Bagenalstown — Lorum Old Rectory

Country House · · · Kilgraney Bagenalstown Co. Carlow **Tel: 0503 75282** Fax: 0503 75455
Email: reservations@lorum.com Web: www.lorum.com

This historic country house is close to many places of interest, including medieval Kilkenny, Altamont Gardens, New Ross (where river cruises are available), Kildare's National Stud and Japanese Gardens. Also close by is Gowran Park racecourse and activities such as golf and a riding school (offering both outdoor and indoor tuition). Elegant and spacious, there's a lovely drawing room for guests and accommodation includes a bedroom with a four-poster- all are very comfortable, with big beds, phones and tea/coffee trays. But it is Don and Bobbie Smith's hospitality that keeps bringing guests back: Euro-Toques member Bobbie prepares good home cooking (rack of lamb, perhaps, with honey, rosemary & garlic sauce) based mainly on organic ingredients - dinner for residents is served at a long mahogany table (book by 3 pm). This relaxed place was the guide's Pet Friendly Establishment for 2000 and there are many interesting resident animals - so it is hardly surprising that this is a place where guests are welcome to bring their own dogs too, by arrangement. Not suitable for children. Private parties/small conferences (10). Own parking. **Rooms 5** (all en-suite). B&B €60 pps, ss €20. Dinner available for residents (except Sunday). Closed 15 Dec-1 Jan. Amex, MasterCard, Visa, Laser. **Directions:** Midway between Borris & Bagenalstown on the R705.

Ballon — Sherwood Park House

féile bia Country House · · · Kilbride Ballon Co. Carlow **Tel: 0503 59117** Fax: 0503 59355
Email: info@sherwoodparkhouse.ie Web: www.sherwoodparkhse.ie

Patrick and Maureen Owens, who have run this delightful Georgian farmhouse next to the famous Altamont Gardens since 1970, accurately describe it as "an accessible country retreat for anyone who enjoys candlelit dinners, brass and canopy beds and the relaxing experience of eating out while staying in". Spacious accommodation is furnished in period style and thoughtful in the details that count - and Maureen takes pride in offering guests real home cooking based on the best of local produce. Dinner for residents is served at 8 pm and guests are welcome to bring their own wine. There's a lovely garden, Altamont Gardens are nearby and it's a good area for walking - and fishing the Slaney. Golf nearby. Private parties (max 14). **Rooms 4**, all en-suite & no-smoking. B&B €45, ss €10. Residents D €35 (must be booked ahead). Open all year except Christmas Day. Amex, MasterCard, Visa **Directions:** Drive is Junction N80/N81. Signed from there.

Borris — The Step House

Guesthouse · · · 66 Main Street Borris Co. Carlow
Tel: 0503 73209 Fax: 0503 73395

James and Cait Coady's attractive old house has undergone extensive renovation and has been stylishly decorated and furnished in period style, with antiques throughout. Well-proportioned reception rooms include a fine dining room (used for breakfast); a matching drawing room that overlooks the back garden (which is still being developed) and a putting green. Comfortable, elegant bedrooms include one with a four-poster and all are furnished to a high standard with smart shower rooms, TV and tea/coffee facilities. A great deal of commitment is evident in the ongoing renovation and upgrading of this fine old house, including the recent conversion of the whole of the lower ground floor making a magnificently characterful kitchen and living room area with direct access to the garden - and new decking beside the dining room means guests can now enjoy breakfast outdoors on fine mornings. The Coadys also own the bar next door and also one of Ireland's finest classic pubs, Tynans Bridge Bar, in Kilkenny city. NB - there are several flights of stairs, including steps up to the front door. Not suitable for children. Pets permitted in some areas by arrangement. Fishing, walking, garden. Own secure parking. **Rooms 5** (all no-smoking, 4 shower only). B&B €39pps, ss10. Closed 20 Dec-16 Mar. MasterCard, Visa. **Directions:** From main Carlow-Kilkenny road, take turning to Bagenalstown.

Carlow   Barrowville Townhouse

Guesthouse   Kilkenny Road Carlow Co. Carlow
        Tel: 0503 43324 Fax: 0503 41953 Web: www.barrowvillehouse.com

Ex-hoteliers Marie and Randal Dempsey have run this exceptionally comfortable and well-managed
guesthouse just a few minutes walk from the town centre for over ten years. Although immaculately
maintained the house is old, so bedrooms vary, but all are comfortable and attractively furnished with
a mixture of antiques and fitted furniture, plus direct dial phones, tea/coffee trays and TV. Good
housekeeping and generous, thoughtfully designed and well-finished bathrooms contribute greatly to
a generally high standard of comfort. Marie Dempsey is renowned for excellent breakfasts served in a
handsome conservatory (complete with a large vine) overlooking the lovely back garden. There is also
a particularly pleasant and comfortable residents' drawing room, with an open fire, grand piano and
plenty to read. Barrowville was the guide's Guesthouse of the Year for 2000. Private parking. Not
suitable for children under 15. No pets. **Rooms 7** (2 shower only, all no-smoking). B&B €37.50 pps,
ss €12. Open all year. Amex, MasterCard, Visa. **Directions:** Southside of Carlow Town on the N9.

Carlow   The Beams Restaurant

féile bia Restaurant   59 Dublin Street Carlow Co. Carlow
                                                     Tel: 0503 31824

Originally a coaching inn, this characterful building was restored by Betty and Peter O'Gorman, who
opened it as a restaurant in 1986. Massive wooden beams create a warm atmosphere and are a
reminder of the building's long history (it has held a full licence since 1760) and, although there are
some eccentricities about the restaurant and the way it is run, the essentials are right and many of
the country's trendy young restaurateurs would do well to come and learn some basics here. Classic
French cuisine is the speciality of French chef Romain Chall, who has been at The Beams since it
opened and was deservedly described by the late Peter O'Gorman as a "master craftsman". He has
established a reputation for fine fare, including game in season and fish cooked with admirable
simplicity. Vegetarian dishes regularly feature on the menu (seasonal vegetables, many of them home
grown, are a delight) and any special dietary requirements can be met at a day's notice. **Seats 40.** D
Tue-Sat 7.30-9.30 pm (Sat to 10 pm); D €36; no s.c. Closed Sun & Mon, bank hols, Christmas wk &
1 wk July. MasterCard, Visa **Directions:** Town centre, on main street.

Carlow   Lennon's Café Bar

féile bia Pub/Café   121 Tullow Street Carlow Co. Carlow
                                                     Tel: 0503 31575

HAPPY HEART EAT OUT

Sinéad Byrne, runs this attractive modern café-bar with her husband,
Liam, and their stylish contemporary design and deliciously healthy,
reasonably priced food has clearly been a hit with both local business
professionals and visitors to the town. In a manner reminiscent of that
great Kerry speciality, the pub that gradually develops into a
restaurant at the back without actually having a dedicated restaurant
area, the design of the bar- which has a striking metal spiral staircase
at the back - helps the atmosphere to shift into café gear as you move
through it. Simple, uncluttered tables and speedy service of jugs of
iced water bode well for menus that include a host of wholesome
dishes: delicious home-made soups; open sandwiches (on freshly-
baked home-made bread); ciabattas (bacon, avocado, tomato &
Carrigbyrne brie cheese); wraps, (cold cajun chicken with lettuce,
onion, tomato & Cashel Blue cheese mayo); some very tempting salads
(fresh salmon with homemade fresh herb mayo) and a range of hot
specials like steak & kidney pie topped with pastry & served with
champ. There are lots of must-have mainstream dishes that are highlighted as suitable for vegetarians,
eg couscous with roasted Mediterranean veg served with homemade bread or aubergine, courgette &
tomato cheese bake with tossed salad. Everything is freshly made to order from top quality ingredients
(some local sources are named on the menu, which is always encouraging) and really wholesome, - all
this and good value too: with main courses averaging around €8-9, prices are very accessible, so it's
a winning formula. Leave room for delicious home-made desserts - hazelnut meringue roulade with
raspberry sauce, perhaps, or hot apple crumble. This is well-balanced good home cooking and a worthy
winner of the Happy Heart Eat Out Award for 2003. L Mon-Fri,12-3 & Sat 12-4 (also on Sun for 2003
season). Toilets wheelchair accessible. **Directions:** At Junction of Tullow Street & Potato Market.

COUNTY CAVAN

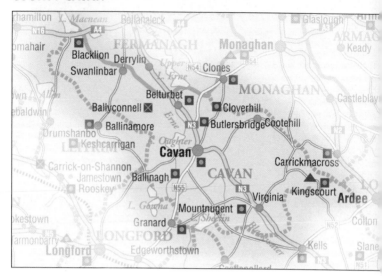

In its quiet way, lake-studded Cavan is one of Ireland's most watery counties. This is classic drumlin country, almost with more water than they know what to do with. But the very fact that the meandering waterways dictate the way of the roads means that much of Cavan is hidden. In 2003 this is a virtue. It is a place best discovered by the discerning visitor. Much of it has quiet and utterly rural charm, seemingly remote - yet it isn't so very far from Dublin or Belfast.

So if you take your time wandering through this green and silver land - particularly if travelling at the leisurely pace of the deservedly renowned Shannon-Erne Waterway which has joined Ireland's two greatest lake and river systems - then you'll become aware that this is a place of rewardingly gentle pleasures. And you'll have time to discover that it does have its own mountain, or at least it shares the 667 m peak of Cuilcagh with neighbouring Fermanagh. No ordinary mountain, this - it has underground streams which eventually become the headwaters of the lordly River Shannon.

In fact, Cavan is much more extensive than is popularly imagined, for in the northeast it has Shercock with its own miniature lake district, while in its southeast it takes in all of Lough Ramor at the charming lakeside village of Virginia. It also shares Lough Sheelin, that place of legend for the angler, with Westmeath and Meath, and always throughout its drumlin heartlands you can find many little Cavan lakes which, should the fancy take you, can be called your own at least for the day that's in it.

Local Attractions and Information

Bailieboro Tourism Information	042 9666666
Ballyjamesduff Cavan County Museum	049 8544070
Ballyjamesduff International Pork Festival (June)	049 8544242
Belturbet Tourist Office	049 9522044
Cavan Town Cavan Crystal	049 4331800
Cavan Town Tourist Information	049 4331942
Cootehill Maudabawn Cultural Centre	049 5559504
Killykeen Equestrian Centre	049 4361707
Mullagh Lakeview Gardens	046 42480
Shannon-Erne Waterway (Ballinamore-Ballyconnell)	078 45124

Ballinagh — Lacken Mill House & Gardens

Guesthouse

Lacken Lower Ballinagh Co. Cavan
Tel: 049 433 7592 Fax: 049 433 7592
Email: info@lackenmillhouse.com Web: www.lackenmillhouse.com

This restored Victorian millhouse is set in gloriously unspoilt rolling countryside in a little known area about seven miles from Cavan town. To say that the restoration of the house - and, even more so perhaps, the gardens and woodland areas alongside the river - has been a labour of love for Dubliners Eamon O'Donoghue and Naomi Brennan since they purchased the property several years ago is, if anything, an understatement. Their achievement is remarkable, especially as they not only remain sane but are relaxed and hospitable hosts to those lucky enough to find their home. Welcoming log fires are a feature of this warm and comfortable house (fuel is not in short supply) and the dining room, where both breakfast and evening meals are served, opens onto a patio and gardens: magic in fine weather. Expect good home cooking based on fresh produce and you will not be disappointed. Spacious individually decorated bedrooms have well-finished shower rooms (there is also a luxurious bathroom, which any guest may use) tea/coffee trays, direct dial phones and TV (fax facility and iron available on request). Behind the house, the ruins of a corn and flax mill are still standing and awaiting restoration, but extensive areas of woodland have already been cleared to make long walks (there are even hammocks dotted around, should you feel the need of a rest) and the river and its wildlife provide endless interest. Many guests never feel the need to wander, but restless souls will find plenty of other activities nearby, including fishing, golf and horseriding. Children welcome (under 2s free in parents' room, cot available without charge). Dogs allowed in some areas. **Rooms 5** (all shower only); room service available on request. B&B €38.50pps, ss €11.50. Closed 19-28 Dec. MasterCard, Visa. **Directions:** N3 to Cavan, N55 to Ballinagh & follow signs.

Ballyconnell — Angler's Rest

féile bia Pub/Restaurant/B&B

Main Street Ballyconnell Co. Cavan
Tel: 049 952 6391 Email: bycl@iol.ie

Golf, fishing, walking and cycling are among the pursuits that attract visitors to this lovely lakeland area and Francis McGoldrick's characterful pub makes an inexpensive and welcoming base for a relaxing stay. Modest accommodation is comfortable, staff hospitable and the bar has spirit - a real inn, in fact. There's a pleasantly informal restaurant at the back of the bar and, as the proprietor is also the chef, you can be sure of consistency in the kitchen. Live music some evenings (inquire for further details.) Children welcome; under 6s free in parents' room, cot available free of charge. Garden. **Rooms 8** (all with en-suite shower) B&B about €30 pps, ss about €10. Bar Food served 6-9 daily, L Sun 12.30-2.30 pm. Closed 25 Dec & Good Fri. MasterCard, Visa **Directions:** On N3 Main Street in Ballyconnell Village. ◇

Ballyconnell — Polo D Restaurant

Restaurant

Main Street Ballyconnell Co. Cavan
Tel: 049 952 6228

Owner-chef Paul O'Dowd's cottagey little restaurant consists of two small rooms on two floors with the country character of stripped pine, old brick and stonework - all of which suit its daytime persona, when informal light meals are served. But Paul's talents really come into play at dinner time, when he presents imaginative contemporary menus - typically a trio of seafood with prawn & vermouth sauce, crispy duck with mango & peach sauce and an accomplished dessert selection - all cooked with a flair and confidence. Low-key surroundings (quite a squeeze and cutlery wrapped in paper napkins) are more than offset by reasonable prices, and friendly, helpful service, making this a very welcome addition to dining options in the area. Children welcome. Wheelchair accessible. **Seats 40**. Light meals all day; L 12-3pm, D 6-10pm Mon-Sat. Set D aabout €32, early menu about €20 (5-7pm), also à la carte; house wine about €16. Closed Sun. MasterCard, Visa **Directions:** On main street of Ballyconnell village. ◇

Ballyconnell — Slieve Russell Hotel & Country Club

Hotel

Ballyconnell Co. Cavan **Tel: 049 952 6444**
Fax: 049 952 6474 Email: slieve-russell@quinn-hotels.com

Close to the attractive town of Ballyconnell, this striking flagship of the Sean Quinn Group is named after a nearby mountain and set amongst 300 acres of landscaped gardens and grounds, including 50 acres of lakes. Everything is on a generous scale - and it's very much the social and business centre of the area. In the foyer, generous seating areas are arranged around the marble colonnades and a grand central staircase, flanked by a large bar on one side and two restaurants at the other. All bedrooms have pleasant country views, extra large beds and spacious marble bathrooms as well as the usual amenities (direct dial, phone tea/coffee tray, TV, trouser press). Excellent conference and business facilities are matched by leisure facilities in the Golf and Country Club - their championship golf course, is one of the top golfing venues in Ireland and there's a putting green, practice area and nine hole, par 3 course. Off-season value breaks. Children under 3 free in parents' room, cot available free of charge; crèche. Conference/banqueting (800/500); video-conferencing. Leisure centre. Golf, tennis, snooker, garden. Hairdresser. No pets. Lift. **Rooms 159** (10 suites, 3 mini-suites, 3 for disabled) B&B from about €95 pps, ss about €25. Open all year. Amex, Diners, MasterCard, Visa. **Directions:** take N3 from Dublin to Cavan, go to Belturbet and Ballyconnell. ◇

Belturbet   Erne Bistro

Restaurant/Pub   The Lawn Belturbet Co. Cavan **Tel: 049 952 2443**

This well established restaurant and lounge bar is near the bridge over the River Erne and handy to the Emerald Star marina. Past a welcoming reception area with fresh flowers, there's a door to the comfortable bar and another takes you through to the restaurant, which is in two connecting rooms. Busy decor and friendly staff give it a warm ambience and it's an idea to order an aperitif quickly to allow the time required to consider an exceptionally long à la carte menu reminiscent of the '70s and early '80s, which may send out warning signals as short menus tend to be a good sign. But this is the exception that proves the rule, as everything is very well done in classic style - for example, a random choice from a selection of no less than seven soups offered showed that the basics are in place, and good home-made bread is served with it. Salads are well-dressed,with generous quantities of crab, prawns, or whatever and home-made paté arrives with both warm toast and brown bread. Ingredients are well-sourced and main course specialities include old favourites - tournedos chasseur, darne of salmon on a bed of fresh spinach, roast duckling and black sole and are all typical. Christmas Day Luncheon (2 sittings) and New Year Gala Dinner are much in demand. Special menus are available for private parties. Taxi service available. Live music (occasional). No-smoking restaurant. Not suitable for children after 8pm. **Seats 80** (private room, 40). D daily in summer, 7-11(Sun to 10), L Sun only 1-3. All à la carte. Closed Mon off-season (Oct-Mar). MasterCard, Visa, Laser. **Directions:** At Bottom of Bridge Street Belturbet. ◇

Belturbet   International Fishing Centre

Restaurant/Guesthouse   Loughdooley Belturbet Co. Cavan **Tel: 049 952 2616** Fax: 049 952 2616
Email: michelneville@eircom.net Web: www.angling.holidays

At this lovely waterside location, Michel and Yvette Neuville offer residential fishing holidays, mainly for continental guests although B&B is available when there is room and there's also a restaurant which is open to non-residents. The centre is like a little corner of France, with all signage in French, and neatly manicured lawns sweeping down to the river where, with in typical French style, the menu is clearly displayed. When the weather allows, tables are set out on the terrace. As well as attracting local diners, the restaurant provides an excellent facility for holidaymakers on river cruises, as there are pontoons at the bottom of the garden. A very French set menu is accompanied by a much longer wine selection - and a refreshingly reasonable bill. No children under 10. **Seats 80** Max preferred table size 8, (Private Room, 30). Set D 6-10pm daily.
Accommodation: Rooms 16 (all en-suite). No pets. about €35 pps, svce incl; no ss. Open all year. MasterCard, Visa. ◇

Blacklion   MacNean House & Bistro

féile bia ☆ Restaurant/B&B   Main Street Blacklion Co. Cavan
Tel: 072 53022 Fax: 072 53404

Nearby attractions include Marble Arch Caves and Florence Court, golf, fishing and hill walking - but it is Neven Maguire's cooking that has put this little border town firmly on the culinary map. Since winning the Baileys Euro-Toques Young Chef competition in 1994 - with a prize giving him experience in a famous Luxembourg restaurant - Neven's cooking moved into the international class, culminating in his selection to represent Ireland at the world's most prestigious cooking competition, the Bocuse d'Or, in 2001. Here, in a small family restaurant - recently refurbished to provide a more appropriate setting for cooking that reflects international trends rather than local preferences - the range of menus offered is amazing: in addition to a fine table d'hôte and an extensive à la carte, Neven offers a number of others including an 8-course 'surprise' tasting menu and a vegetarian menu. Sourcing is meticulous - Neven is a strong advocate of local and artisan producers - and his absolute dedication comes through in cooking of the highest order and, although presentation can sometimes be a little over-worked - reflecting, perhaps, the demands of competitions - a simpler, more mature style was noted on the Guide's most recent visit. Examples from a Dinner Menu: hand-dived scallops with a crab risotto & crispy spring roll; Eden Plants salad (organic leaves); roast loin of lamb with the confit of shoulder, organic spinach & rosemary jus. Desserts have always been a particular passion for Neven and it's a must to leave a little room for one of his skilfully crafted confections - the grand finale is just that in this case. Sunday lunch somehow combines elements of the traditional meal with more adventurous choices - and very good value at €22. Service, by family members, is friendly and efficient. No-smoking restaurant. **Seats 40**. D Wed/Thu-Sun 6-10pm (Sun to 9.30); L Sun only, 12.30-3.30. Set D, €50, Vegetarian Menu €32; other menus available, also à la carte. House wine from €15. Service discretionary. Accommodation: **Rooms 5** (all en-suite, 2 shower only). €33 pps, ss€3. Direct-dial phone, tea/coffee tray & TV in all rooms. Children under 3 free in parents' room; cot available free of charge. No pets. Establishment closed Mon, Tue in summer, also Wed in winter, 5 days Christmas. MasterCard, Visa **Directions:** On N17, main Belfast-Sligo road.

Cavan — Oak Room

 Ⓝ Restaurant

Cavan Crystal Building Dublin Road Cavan Co. Cavan
Tel: 049 436 0099 / 436 2748 Fax: 049 433 2927

Norbert Neylon, a previous winner of the Baileys Young Chef competition (in 1997) runs The Oak Room restaurant at Cavan Crystal as proprietor-chef. Large, well-proportioned and stylish, this is an impressive restaurant with a vibrant colour scheme in deep oranges and reds, big mirrors, a dramatic floral centrepiece, plenty of natural materials - and classy, simple table settings with just a strip of white linen, plain glasses, restrained cutlery and white china. A well-planned bar area has plenty of comfortable seating and arriving guests are welcomed well, with menus and aperitifs speedily offered. Ambitious menus offer a wide choice and the pricing structure is user-friendly: à la carte but you can choose anything to make up a 5-course dinner menu (€38), with only a couple of supplements (on shellfish, such as warm salad of pan-fried scallops with a citrus dressing) or there's a 7-course Surprise Menu for complete tables, at €55. Variations on familiar dishes include warm terrine of Clonakilty black and white pudding on a compôte of apples & raisins and confit of duck leg with honey and sesame on puy lentils - the repertoire is well-rehearsed and none the worse for that. Home-baked bread, well-made salads, carefully cooked vegetables and gorgeous puddings are all impressive details - also the classic petits fours that arrive with coffee. Excellent food, fairly priced and served with charm: this is a restaurant that deserves to succeed. **Seats 75**. No smoking area; air conditioning. Toilets wheelchair accessible. D Tue-Sun, 6.30-10; L Sun only 12.30-3. Set D €38, Surprise Menu €55, Set L €18.50. D also à la carte. House wine €17.50. SC discretionary. Closed D Mon, 25-26 Dec. MasterCard, Visa, Laser. **Directions:** At Cavan Crystal Show rooms.

Cloverhill — The Olde Post Inn

Restaurant/Accommodation

Cloverhill Co. Cavan **Tel: 047 55555** Fax: 047 55111
Email: oldepostinn@eircom.ie

This old stone building in a neatly landscaped garden served as a post office until 1974 and now makes an attractive inn. As the guide was going to press, news broke that Gearoid Lynch - a talented chef and previous winner of the Baileys Young Chef Competition - has taken over the premises; after giving immediate attention to the restaurant, he plans to upgrade the accommodation, which is reasonably comfortable, although not as luxurious as the brochure implies. Ample parking. Wheelchair access (restaurant/ground floor only). Children welcome. Restaurant **Seats 80** (private room 25); no smoking restaurant; toilets wheelchair accessible. D Wed-Sat, 6.30-9.30, à la carte. L Sun only, 12.30-3, Set L €22.50.
Accommodation: Rooms 7 (all en-suite, 2 shower only), B&B €38 pps, ss about €6.50. 1 family room; children free in parents' room up to 3. No pets. Closed D Sun, Mon & Tue.*A phone call to check times and prices is recommended. Amex, Diners, MasterCard, Visa, Laser, Switch. **Directions:** N3 from Dublin, N54 from Butlersbridge - 3 miles.

Kingscourt — Cabra Castle Hotel & Golf Club

Hotel   Kingscourt Co. Cavan **Tel: 042 966 7030** Fax: 042 966 7039
                          Email: cabrach@iol.ie Web: www.cabracastle.com

Formerly known as Cormey Castle and renamed Cabra Castle in the early 19th century, this impressive hotel is set amidst 100 acres of garden and parkland, with lovely views over the Cavan countryside, famous for its lakes and fine fishing. (The nearby Dun A Ri Forest has many walks and nature trails on land once part of the Cabra estate.) Although initially imposing, with its large public rooms and antique furnishings, the atmosphere at Cabra Castle is relaxing. Due to the age of the building, the bedrooms vary in size and outlook, but all are comfortable and individually decorated. Accommodation includes some ground floor rooms suitable for less able guests and, in addition to rooms in the main building, the newer rooms in an extension are particularly suitable for families. There are also some romantic beamed rooms, in a courtyard that has been converted to provide modern comforts without sacrificing character. The combination of formal background and easy ambience make this a good venue for private and business functions; it is popular for both weddings and conferences. Conferences/banqueting (200/350). Garden, golf (9), fishing. Off-season value breaks. Children welcome (under 3s free in parents' room, cots available without charge); pets permitted by arrangement. **Rooms 80** (2 suites, 2 junior suites, 8 executive rooms, 2 for disabled). B&B about €89pps, ss about €19. Closed 24-26 Dec. Amex, MasterCard, Visa, Laser. **Directions:** Dublin - N2 - Navan - R162 - Kingscourt. ◇

Kingscourt — Gartlans Pub

Pub   Main Street Kingscourt Co. Cavan **Tel: 042 966 7003**

This pretty thatched pub is a delightfully unspoilt example of the kind of grocery/pub that used to be so typical of Ireland, especially in country areas. Few enough of them remain, now that the theme pub has moved in, but this one is real, with plenty of local news items around the walls, a serving hatch where simple groceries can be bought, all served with genuine warmth and hospitality. The Gartlans have been here since 1911 and they have achieved the remarkable feat of appearing to make time stand still. Closed 25 Dec & Good Fri. ◇

Mountnugent — Ross House & Castle

Farmhouse   Mountnugent Co. Cavan **Tel: 049 854 0218** Fax: 049 854 0218
                          Email: rosshouse@eircom.net Web: www.rosshouse.com

In mature grounds on the shores of Lough Sheelin, Peter and Ulla Harkort's old manor house enjoys a very lovely location and offers a good standard of accommodation at a modest price. Bedrooms, which are distinctly continental in style, have telephone, TV and tea/coffee trays and some unusual features: three have their own conservatories, four have fireplaces (help yourself to logs from the shed) and most have unusual continental style showers. Peace and relaxation are the great attraction, and there's a fine choice of activities at hand: a pier offers boats (and engines) for fishermen to explore the lake, there's safe bathing from a sandy beach, tennis and a sauna. An equestrian centre at Ross House has 35 horses stabled, and offers hacking and trekking as well as instruction and schooling on the cross-country course. At the castle nearby, Peter and Ulla's daughter Benita Walker provides most unusual accommodation (it is a very real castle). Ulla cooks for everyone, making packed lunches, sandwiches and High Tea (€4/14) and a 4-course dinner (€20). Equestrian, fishing, tennis. Children and pets welcome. **Rooms 6** (all en-suite, 5 shower only). B&B from €35 pps, ss €13. Open all year. MasterCard, Visa **Directions:** 5Km from Mountnugent, signposted.

COUNTY CLARE

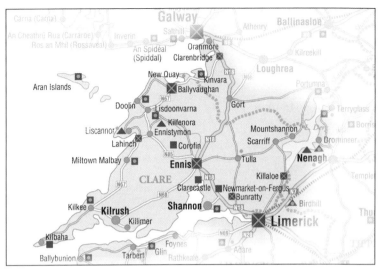

Clare is a larger-than-life county which is bounded by the Atlantic to the west, Galway Bay to the north, the Shannon and Lough Derg to the east, and the Shannon Estuary to the south. And it's typical of Clare that, even with its boundaries marked on such a grand scale, there is always something extra added. Thus the Atlantic coasts include not only the astonishing and majestic Cliffs of Moher, but also one of Ireland's greatest surfing beaches at Lahinch on Liscannor Bay. As for that Galway Bay coastline, it is where The Burren, the fantastical North Clare moonscape of limestone which is home to so much unexpectedly exotic flora, comes plunging spectacularly towards the sea around the attractive village of Ballyvaughan.

To the eastward, Lough Derg is one of Ireland's most handsome lakes, but even amidst its generous beauty, we find that Clare has claimed one of the most scenic lake coastlines of all. As for the Shannon Estuary, well, Ireland may have many estuaries, but needless to say the lordly Shannon has far and away the biggest estuary of all. Along its northern shore on the Fergus Estuary, Clare's county town of Ennis has cause for celebration in 2003. On September 8th 2002, it was declared Ireland's tidiest large town in the annual Tidy Towns competition.

"The Banner County" of sporting legend, Clare is somewhere special to call home - in the survey of 1996-2002, its population increased by 9.9%, above the national average of 8%. It has many attractions, in recent years becoming the leading county for the study of dolphin life - the hundred-plus colony of bottle-nose dolphins which make the Shannon Estuary their summer home are monitored from the increasingly busy recreational port of Kilrush, while Doolin in the north of the county has its own exceptionally friendly dolphin.

Other places like Ennistimon, Milltown Malbay, Corofin and Mountshannon - they all have a very human and friendly dimension. For this is a county where the human spirit defines itself as being very human indeed, in the midst of scenic effects which at times seem to border on the supernatural.

Local Attractions and Information

Ballyvaughan Aillwee Cave	065 7077036
Bunratty Bunratty Castle & Folk Park	061 360788
Cliffs of Moher Tourist Information	065 7081171
Corofin Clare Heritage Centre	065 6837955
Ennis Tourist Centre	065 6828366
Killimer Killimer-Tarbert Ferry	065 53124
Kilrush Kilrush Heritage Centre	065 9051577
Kilrush Scattery Island Interpretive Centre	065 9052139
Kilrush Vandeleur Walled Garden	065 9051760
Quin Craggaunowen (Celts & Living Past)	061 360788
Quin Knappogue Castle	061 360788
Shannon Airport Tourist Information	061 471664

Ballyvaughan — Aillwee Cave

Café · Ballyvaughan Co. Clare **Tel: 065 707 7036** Fax: 065 707 7107
Email: aillwee@eircom.net Web: www.aillweecave.ie

Visitors to this 2-million-year-old cave will see more than the amazing illuminated tunnels and waterfalls, for there is much of interest to foodlovers as well. Driving up to the entrance, look out for the sign to the cheese-making demonstrations - for it is here that the local Burren Gold cheese is made. Even if the process is in a quiet phase at the time of a visit, there is still plenty to see - and buy - as the cheesemaking takes place alongside a well-stocked food shop. A themed potato bar café serves inexpensive, wholesome fare - typically baked potatoes with Burren Gold cheese. Fast food (coffee, paninis etc) also available outside - and a new mountain trail "guaranteed to work up an appetite". The Liscannor Rock Shop is a sister enterprise (see entry) - and it also provides wholesome, inexpensive food in its little café (and goodies, such as home-made preserves, to take home too). Children welcome. Cafe **Seats 80**. No-smoking area. Meals all day Mon-Sun (9.30-6.30). Closed 22-27 Dec. MasterCard, Visa **Directions:** 2 miles south of Ballyvaughan.

Ballyvaughan — An Fear Gorta (Tea & Garden Rooms)

Café · Ballyvaughan Co. Clare
Tel: 065 707 7157 Fax: 065 707 7127

Approached from the harbour front through a lovely front garden, Katherine O'Donoghue's delightful old stone restaurant dates back to 1790, when it was built as a residence for 'coast security officers'. Having been rebuilt by the present owners in 1981, it is now just the spot for a light bite to eat. In fine weather the beautiful back garden or the conservatory can be idyllic; otherwise the homely dining room offers comfort and shelter, with its informal arrangement of old furniture and a tempting display of home-baked fare. This is the speciality of the house - all laid out on an old cast-iron range and very reasonably priced - beginning at only €1.50 for scone, butter & home-made jam. Speciality teas are available as well as savoury choices including farmhouse cheeses, home-baked ham and Tea Room Specials including Open Smoked Salmon Sandwich on Brown Bread. 2-3 course lunch specials are available at around €10 and there's home-made jam and marmalade to take away. Open Jun-Sep, Mon-Sat:11-5.30 (L 12-4.30). Closed Oct-May. **No Credit Cards. Directions:** On the harbour front in Ballyvaughan.

Ballyvaughan — Drumcreehy House

Ⓝ Guesthouse · Ballyvaughan Co. Clare **Tel: 065 707 7377** Fax: 065 707 7379
Email: b&b@drumcreehyhouse.com Web: www.drumcreehyhouse.com

Just along the road beyond the Whitethorn restaurant and craftshop, Armin and Bernadette Moloney-Grefkes' purpose-built guesthouse makes a comfortable and moderately-priced base for a break in this lovely area. The furnishing style is a mixture of old and new with antiques and newer country furnishings blending well; front bedrooms have sea views across Galway Bay while those at the back have a pleasant outlook over the Burren - and all have phones and television. There's also a comfortable sitting room with an open fire available for guests' use. Extensive breakfast menu (order the night before); 3-course evening meals are available by arrangement. Banqueting (40). Beach nearby (10 minute walk). Garden. **Rooms 10** (all en-suite & no smoking). Children welcome (under 3s free in parents' room, cot available without charge. B&B €38pps, ss16. D by arrangement at 7pm, €22. Wine licence. MasterCard, Visa, Laser. **Directions:** N67 to Ballyvaughan, at Hylands Hotel turn right. Continue for 1 mile, Drumcreehy House on the right.

Ballyvaughan — Gregans Castle Hotel

Hotel/Restaurant · Ballyvaughan Co. Clare **Tel: 065 707 7005** Fax: 065 707 7111
Email: res@gregans.ie Web: www.gregans.ie

Gregans Castle has a long and interesting history, going back to a tower house, or small castle, which was built by the O'Loughlen clan (the region's principal tribe) between the 10th and 17th centuries and is still intact. The present house dates from the late 18th century and has been continuously added to, up to the present day. The owners, Peter and Moira Haden, opened Gregans Castle as a country house hotel in 1976 and (true to the traditions of the house) have continued to evelop and improve it, recently with their son Simon who is now Manager. The exterior is grey and tark, in keeping with the lunar landscape of the surrounding Burren, serving only to heighten the ontrast between first impressions and the warmth, comfort and hospitality to be found within. pacious accommodation is furnished to a very high standard and rooms all have excellent athrooms and lovely countryside views. Peace and quiet are the dominant themes - the otherwise uxurious rooms are deliberately left without the worldly interference of television. Yet this luxurious otel is not too formal or at all intimidating; non-residents are welcome to drop in for lunch or fternoon tea in the Corkscrew Bar - named after a nearby hill which, incidentally, provides the most cenic approach to Ballyvaughan. In fine weather guests can sit out beside the Celtic Cross rose arden and watch patches of sun and shade chasing across the hills. In the morning, allow time to njoy an excellent breakfast. Children welcome (no concessions, but cot available,€15). No pets. All ay room service. **Rooms 22** (4 suites, 2 junior suites) B&B €99 pps; ss€79. No service charge.

he Dining Room: The restaurant, which was greatly improved by a recently added bay window area, s decorated in a rich country house style and elegantly furnished in keeping with the rest of the ouse. Most tables have lovely views over the Burren (which on fine summer evenings enjoys very pecial light effects as the sun sets over Galway Bay) and dinner is often gently accompanied by a ianist or harpist. Head chef Regis Herviaux cooks fine meals in the modern Irish style with some rench influence, offering a wide choice of dishes based on the best of local produce: oysters and obster from nearby New Quay and Doolin, lamb from Chris O'Flaherty's farm at Belharbour (a roast eg, perhaps, with an Irish whiskey & oregano sauce), Burren smoked trout and organic goats cheese alad are all typical. There is always a fine selection of local cheeses, with homemade biscuits - and here's a growing emphasis on organic produce on all menus, including breakfast (organic eggs from Hans & Ute Krewer in the East Burren, for example). Dinner is a treat at Gregans castle, but they lso offer an attractive short à la carte lunch menu (served in The Corkscrew Bar) and delicious Afternoon Teas too. **Seats 50** (Private Room, 30). No smoking restaurant. Well-behaved children welcome (not under 10 after 7.30). Toilets wheelchair accessible. D 7-8.30, 5-course D €50, any 2 ourses €33. House wines from €20. Service discretionary. Short à la carte lunch is available in the orkscrew Bar, 12-3 daily. Hotel closed 18 Nov-13 Feb. Amex, MasterCard, Visa, Laser. **Directions:** On N67, 3 miles South of Ballyvaughan.

Ballyvaughan — Hyland's Burren Hotel

otel

Ballyvaughan Co. Clare
Tel: 065 707 7037 Fax: 065 707 7131
Email: hylandsburren@eircom.net Web: www.hylandsburren.com

After eight generations in the Hyland family this much-loved 18th century hotel changed hands in 2002 but, judging by recent visits, it so far remains reassuringly unchanged except for some efurbishment and the addition of a new bar. Open fires in public areas still create the welcoming tmosphere for which the hotel is famous - and a modern bedroom wing at the back offers comfortable accommodation with good amenities (direct dial phone, tea/coffee tray, TV). Restaurant meals are available in the evening and an extensive bar menu, which includes a range of dishes ased on local seafood, is offered all day (12.30-9.30). Banqueting (70). Secretarial services vailable. Off-season breaks. Walking, fishing, cycling. **Rooms 30** (all en-suite, 12 no smoking). hildren welcome (under 4s free in parents' room; cot avilable without charge). B&B €65 pps, s€25. Closed 22-26 Dec. Amex, Diners, MasterCard, Visa, Laser. **Directions:** In centre of 3allyvaughan, beside the harbour.

Ballyvaughan — Monks Bar & Restaurant

ub/Restaurant

The Quay Ballyvaughan Co. Clare
Tel: 065 7077059 Fax: 065 707 0330
Email: monkspub@eircom.net Web: www.monkspub.com

This famous pub has been drawing people along to the pier at Ballyvaughan since 1981. It's an nformal, cottagey kind of a place with several small bars, open fires and a reputation for informal ervice of fresh seafood, especially crab: crab claws in garlic butter, open crab sandwiches, seafood howder, poached local mussels and seafood platters are all typical. This isn't really the place for anyone who doesn't like seafood, although there's always a vegetarian dish of the day and a chef's pecial. Live music (Wed & Sat, from 10pm). **Seats 80** (private room 28). No smoking area. Toilets wheelchair accessible. Food served 12 noon-8 pm daily. A la carte. Closed 25 Dec, Good Fri. Diners, MasterCard, Visa, Laser. **Directions:** In Ballyvaughan Village, next to pier.

Ballyvaughan — Rusheen Lodge

Guesthouse · Knocknagrough Ballyvaughan Co. Clare **Tel: 065 707 7092** Fax: 065 707 715
Email: rusheen@iol.ie Web: www.rusheenlodge.co

Karen McGann took over the reins at Rusheen Lodge in 2001 and maintains the reputation f
hospitality earned by her parents John and Rita McGann - who are not far away, should occasion
help be required, as they swapped houses with Karen and live next door. Fresh flowers in both th
house and garden create a riot of colour in contrast to the overall green-greyness of the surroundin
Burren, suggesting an oasis in a wilderness - which is just what Rusheen Lodge provides. Existin
private accommodation was converted to make a new 3-room executive suite in 2002 and all of th
generously proportioned, well-appointed bedrooms have phones, tea/coffee trays, TV, trouser pres
and good bathrooms; there are also spacious public rooms, making this a very comfortable place
stay. All this, plus good food and warm hospitality, make Rusheen Lodge (which was the guide
Guesthouse of the Year for 2001) outstanding. While evening meals are not provided, the pubs ar
restaurants of Ballyvaughan are only a few minutes' walk and breakfast - whether traditional Iris
or continental - is a major feature of a stay. It was John McGann's father, Jacko McGann, wh
discovered the Aillwee Cave, an immense network of caverns and waterfalls under the Burren whic
is now a major attraction in the area. Children welcome (under 3s free in parents' room, cot availab
without charge). No pets. **Rooms 9** (3 suites, 6 executive rooms, 1 for disabled, all no-smoking
B&B €45pps, ss€20. Off-season breaks available. Closed mid Nov-mid Feb. MasterCard, Visa, Lase
Directions: 3/4 Km from village on the N67.

Ballyvaughan — Whitethorn Restaurant

Restaurant · Ballyvaughan Co. Clare **Tel: 065 707 7044** Fax: 065 707 715
Email: whitethorne@eircom.net Web: thewhitethorn.co

Sarah and John McDonnell's restaurant is beautifully located on the sea side of the road and the
also run a fine craft shop and a visitor centre, "Burren Exposure", where visitors learn (in fou
languages) about the formation of the Burren rockscape, its history and the amazing diversity o
flora which brings so many visitors to the region in early summer. The restaurant has magnificer
sea views and offers excellent home-made buffet-style fare throughout the day (which visitors ca
take indoors or out depending on the weather and inclination): home-made soups including chowde
and a daily special - tomato & basil perhaps, baked cod with a pesto crust & sundried tomato sauc
and aubergine charlotte are typical. Meals 9.30-6 daily, average saters €3-5, main courses €8-1C
Seats 120. House wine €16.50. Closed Nov-Mar. MasterCard, Visa, Laser **Directions:** 1/4 mi
outside Ballyvaughanon Main Galway Rd.

Bunratty — Bunratty Castle Hotel

Hotel · Bunratty Co. Clare **Tel: 061 478700** Fax: 061 36489
Email: info@bunrattycastlehotel.com Web: www.bunrattycastle.cor

This modern hotel on a rise just beside Bunratty Castle and overlooking Bunratty Castle and Fol
Park is attractively designed to reflect its Georgian origins. Public seating areas are spacious an
comfortable, while traditionally furnished rooms have all the modern comforts, including a
conditioning and satellite TV - and bathrooms with both (tiny) bath and good overbath showe
executive rooms are more luxurious, with extras including ISDN facilities and two-line phones. I
addition to food and entertainment offered by the hotel (including the unique 'new Medieval bar')
the pubs and restaurants of Bunratty village are all close by. Excellent shopping opportunities exis
at quality shops situated within the hotel grounds. Good business facilities for small to mediur
meetings (max 150). Business centre. Ample parking. Children welcome; pets allowed in some areas
Rooms 80. B&B €82.50pps. Closed 25 Dec. Amex, Diners, MasterCard, Visa, Laser. **Directions:** 5 mi
drive from Shannon Airport.

Bunratty — Bunratty View Guesthouse

Guesthouse · Cratloe Bunratty Co. Clar
Tel: 061 357 352 Fax: 061 357 491 Email: bunrattyview@eircom.ne

Ideally located for the visitor arriving to or leaving from Shannon Airport, Joe and Maura Brodie'
modern house just a mile from the famous Bunratty Castle and Folk Park provides comfortable
spacious accommodation and is well-placed as a base for touring. There are many other attraction
nearby, including Cragganowen Bronze Age Lake Dwelling and places of interest near enough for da
trips include the Burren, Cliffs of Moher and The Burren. Rooms have double and single beds, phone

tea/coffee facilities, satellite TV and hairdryers - and there's a comfortable residents' lounge with an open fire for guests' use. Joe and Maura are fine hosts offering relaxed comfort at a very reasonable price, also good breakfasts which are served in a bright dining room with pleasant rural views over the Shannon River and Cratloe Hills. Transport available to and from the Banquets at Bunratty Castle. Golf, walking, fishing, horseriding, pony trekking all nearby. Children welcome (under 4s free in parents' room, cot available without charge). **Rooms 6** (4 no-smoking, 2 suitable for less able guests); B&B €30 pps, ss €10. Open all year. MasterCard, Visa. **Directions:** First off the N18 coming from Bunratty to Limerick.

Bunratty — Durty Nelly's

Pub — Bunratty Co. Clare **Tel: 061 364861** Web: www.durtynellys.ie

Although often seriously over-crowded with tourists in summer, this famous and genuinely characterful old pub in the shadow of Bunratty Castle somehow manages to provide cheerful service and above-average food to the great numbers who pass through its doors. All-day fare is served downstairs in the Oyster Restaurant daily, upstairs there is a more exclusive restaurant, The Loft, open in the evening only (Mon-Sat, 6-10). Both areas offer à la carte menus. Closed 25 Dec, Good Fri. Amex, Diners, MasterCard, Visa. **Directions:** Beside Bunratty Castle.

Bunratty — Fitzpatrick Bunratty Hotel

féile bia Hotel — Bunratty Co. Clare **Tel: 061 361177** Fax: 061 364863
Email: reservations@bunratty.fitzpatricks.com Web: www.fitzpatrickhotels.com

Conveniently located just ten minutes from both Shannon International Airport and Limerick city, Fitzpatrick Bunratty is in wooded grounds beside Bunratty Castle and Folk Park and offers good facilities for business and leisure guests. The style of the building is typical of many hotels established in the 1960s and is still a disadvantage, making the hotel seem dated in some areas, although the Fitzpatrick Hotel Group have been energetic in their efforts to upgrade facilities. Public areas are quite impressive, as are recent additions, including a new gallery lounge and PJ's restaurant as well as a fine fitness centre with 20 metre swimming pool and an excellent conference & banqueting centre with state-of-the-art facilities. Thirty new bedrooms have recently been added but, although the older ones have been refurbished, they still seem dated; however, they are well-equipped, with the usual facilities. Off season breaks offer good value. Conference/banqueting (1000/500); video-conferencing; business centre; secretarial services. Leisure centre. Hair & beauty salon. Courtesy coach available. Garden. Children welcome (under 12s free in parents room; cots available without charge; crèche). No pets. Wheelchair accessible. **Rooms 115** (11 suites, 13 executive rooms, 6 no-smoking rooms). B&B €75 pps, ss €32. Closed 24-25 Dec. Amex, Diners, MasterCard, Visa, Laser. **Directions:** Just off N18 Limerick-Galway road, beside Bunratty Castle.

Bunratty — Muses Restaurant

Restaurant — Bunratty House Mews Bunratty Co. Clare
Tel: 061 364 082 Fax: 061 364 350
Email: muses@oceanfree.net Web: www.musesrestaurant.com

Aidan McGrath's basement restaurant at the back of the Bunratty estate is all warmth and welcome: a small hall leads to a lovely bar area overlooking Bunratty Park and castle, with a proper counter and deep sofa to relax in while enjoying a promptly served aperitif and consulting helpful staff about the menu, a well-balanced offering that promises well, especially in unusually imaginative use of vegetables which are planned as an integral part of each dish and make mouth-watering reading. Seafood and local organic produce are much in evidence, also wild game in season. The dining rooms consists of three small rooms, with well-appointed tables and lovely flowers, prints and bric-à-brac creating a soothing, restful atmosphere. High quality ingredients, skilful cooking and caring service should make for a memorable experience here. Each dish has its own complementary vegetable garnish: a starter of flash-fried smoked salmon comes with asparagus, rocket, lemon & tarragon butter for example, or there's an organic leaf salad tossed with marinated feta cheese, black olives and air-dried ham while a main course of grilled fillet of beef is served with sautéed spinach & scallions and cracked pepper sauce; a platter of more unusual vegetables is also served as a side dish, without extra charge - and, at an average of around €22 for a main course, prices are not unreasonable for the quality offered. Luscious desserts (caramelised apple tart with vanilla ice cream perhaps) and a well-chosen, fairly priced wine list will also add to the pleasure. Private parties and small weddings can be catered for. Group lunch bookings accepted any day, also group dinner bookings Sun/Mon. Not suitable for children under 10 after 7.30 pm. No smoking area. **Seats 45** (private room 14). D Tue-Sat,last orders 9.30; à la carte. House wines from about €21.50; sc discretionary. Closed Sun, Mon, Christmas, all Jan. Amex, MasterCard, Visa, Laser. **Directions** Bearing left at the village green, turn sharp left up the hill road for 100 metres, restaurant's space are on the right hand side.

Clarecastle   Carnelly House

🏛 Country House   Clarecastle Co. Clare **Tel: 065 682 8442** Fax: 065 682 9222
Email: info@carnelly-house.com Web: www.carnelly-house.com

Conveniently located for Shannon airport and for touring the west of Ireland, Dermott and Rosemarie Gleeson's fine redbrick Georgian house is set on 100 acres of farm and woodland and offers discerning guests very special accommodation. Reception rooms include an impressive drawing room with Corinthian pillars, Francini ceiling, grand piano and a striking panelled dining room where communal dinners are taken at 7.30 pm. (Residents only, except groups for lunch or dinner by arrangement.) Bedrooms are large and furnished to a high standard, with antiques, canopied king size or twin beds and luxurious private bathrooms. Yet the grandeur is not at all daunting and Carnelly - which is well-placed for a wide range of country pursuits, including many of the country's most famous hunts - has been described as "one of the warmest, friendliest and most entertaining houses in Ireland". Children welcome (cot available free of charge). There is also a gate lodge, which is available by the night, week or month. Conferences/banqueting (25/25). Pets permitted by arrangement. Garden, walks. **Rooms 5** (all executive, 4 no -smoking); limited room service. €115 pps, ss€75. D by arrangement, €45. licensed. SC discretionary. Open all year. Amex, MasterCard, Visa, Laser. **Directions:** One mile south of Clarecastle on Limerick Road N18.

Corofin   Clifden House

Country House   Corofin Co. Clare **Tel: 065 683 7692** Fax: 065 683 7692
Email: clifdenhousecountyclare@eircom.net Web: www.clifdenhouse-countyclare.ie

This unusual early Georgian manor on the shore of Lough Inchiquin was found "slipping gracefully into ruin" 25 years ago by Jim and Bernadette Robson who, while conceding that "the work is not yet finished nor will it be twenty years hence", have gone a considerable way towards restoration "following the criteria of respecting its tradition of hospitality and the comfort of our friends and guests". Bedrooms are highly individualistic (one bathroom in particular even more so), stylish and comfortable - do not be concerned that certain areas may be only partially restored. Hospitality is king here and the Robsons enjoy their food, in every sense of the word - organic meats come from a nearby farm, fish and game are also local and organic vegetables and fruit from their own lovely walled garden - Bernadette enjoys cooking (ask to see her collection of old cookery books) and everybody enjoys the results. There is a short wine list and guests are also welcome to bring their own. Accommodation is also offered in two 3- and 4-bedroom holiday houses in a stable wing, with cobbled yard and riverside lawn; they can be either self-catering or serviced. Gardens, walking fishing (boats available). Children welcome (cot available, no charge). No pets. **Rooms 4** (1 shower only).€65 pps, ss€25. Communal dinner at 8 pm, €35. Closed Oct-Mar. Amex, MasterCard, Visa, Laser. **Directions:** Going north out of Corofin turn left at Grotto take 2nd right then 1st right.

Corofin   Fergus View

Farmhouse   Kilnaboy Corofin Co. Clare
Tel: 065 683 7606 Fax: 065 683 7606 Email: deckell@indigo.ie

Mary Kelleher runs a very hospitable house and the care taken to ensure guests enjoy their visit to the full is shown in details like the the information packs on the area compiled by her and left in each bedroom - and interesting breakfasts that include home-made yogurt, freshly squeezed juice, home-made muesli, local cheese and a wide range of teas as well as cooked breakfasts with free range eggs. Rooms are comfortable although a little on the small side, as often happens when family homes are converted to include en-suite facilities. Refurbishment is an ongoing business - last year traditional wooden windows were installed throughout the house and a new entrance conservatory built, which opens onto the garden and has extensive views; this year it was replacement of the soft furnishings in all the bedrooms. Every time the guide visits there is something else in progress - and there's also a lovely stone cottage next door, Tigh Eamon, which has been charmingly converted for self-catering accommodation. Children welcome (cot available). No pets. **Rooms 6** (5 en-suite with shower only,1 with private bathroom, all no-smoking). B&B €30.50pps ; ss €13.50-16.50. D by arrangement, 6.30 Mon-Thu, €23.50; wine licence. No D Fri-Sun; closed mid Oct-1 Apr. **No Credit Cards. Directions:** 2 miles north of Corofin on Kilfenora Road.

Doolin — Aran View House Hotel

Hotel   Coast Road Doolin Co. Clare **Tel: 065 707 4061** Fax: 065 707 4540
Email: bookings@aranview.com Web: www.aranview.com

Just outside Doolin, and commanding dramatic sea views across to the islands, the Linnanes' family-run hotel makes a good base for a family holiday - it is only a mile to a good beach, there is sea-angling and golf nearby and, of course, there is the traditional music for which Doolin is world famous. Public rooms include a comfortable bar for all weathers - it has a sea view and an open fire. Bedrooms vary considerably in size and outlook due to the age and nature of the building: rooms at the front are most desirable - several at the back have no view, but are otherwise pleasant. There are two extra large ones and two singles; all have phones, tea/coffee trays and TV (local stations). Children are welcome - outdoor play area and children's menu provided. The restaurant, which is open to non-residents, offers reasonably priced set menus (lunch, €15-18; dinner, €20-35) as well as an à la carte featuring local produce, possibly including lobster. **Rooms 19** (2 superior, some shower only, 6 no smoking, 2 for disabled); B&B €60 pps, ss €12. Closed 31 Oct-15 Apr. Amex, Diners, MasterCard, Visa, Laser. **Directions:** N67 exit off near Lisdoonvarna to Doolin.

Doolin — Ballinalacken Castle Country House & Restaurant

Hotel   Doolin Co. Clare **Tel: 065 707 4025** Fax: 065 707 4025
Email: ballinalackencastle@eircom.net Web: ballinalackencastle.com

Well away from the bustle of Lisdoonvarna, and with wonderful views of the Atlantic, Aran Islands, Cliffs of Moher and the distant hills of Connemara, Ballinalacken is easily identified by the 15th century castle still standing beside the hotel. In the O'Callaghan family ownership since opening in 1940, and currently managed by Marian O'Callaghan, Ballinalacken has retained a Victorian country house atmosphere with its welcoming fire in the hall and well-proportioned public rooms comfortably furnished with antiques. Public rooms and some bedrooms enjoy magnificent views and recent renovations have resulted in a major upgrade of accommodation, which now includes two suites - one with panoramic views, the other an historic room with a fireplace and luxurious bathroom. The grounds - which include a lovely big field as well as planted areas nearer the house - are being improved on an ongoing basis. Children welcome (under 4s free in parents' room, cot available without charge). Pets permitted by arrangement. **Rooms 12** (2 suites,1 room shower only; all no-smoking). B&B €63pps, ss€50.

Restaurant: The restaurant offers lovely views from window tables and provides a fitting setting for Frank Sheedy's modern cooking, which is based firmly on the best local produce although the style is international. Good home-made breads - traditional brown, walnut, tomato - set the tone and a choice of half a dozen starters might include local seafood, a tian of fresh crabmeat on pickled vegetables, with peanut pesto & sweet chilli dressing perhaps, two soups and a vegetarian option such as a Mediterranean salad, or goat cheese fritters. Well-balanced flavours and accurate cooking are evident throughout, making the most of prime ingredients like lobster and Burren lamb. Good coffee, served at the table or in the drawing room, rounds off the evening nicely and refills are automatically offered. Open to non-residents. D daily, 6.45-9. A la carte. Service discretionary. Closed Oct-Apr. Amex, MasterCard, Visa. **Directions:** Coast road, R477 North of Doolin Village.

Doolin — Cullinans Seafood Restaurant & Guesthouse

Restaurant/Guesthouse   Doolin Co. Clare **Tel: 065 707 4183** Fax: 065 707 4239
Email: cullinans@eircom.net Web: www.cullinansdoolin.com

Music may be Doolin's major attraction, but people also travel here specially to eat at Cullinans. James Cullinan is the chef and Carol looks after service in an unpretentious, comfortable dining room overlooking the Aille river at the back of the house. Menus include a very nice early dinner, with three or four choices on each course (including vegetarian dishes) and an à la carte which is available at any time from opening. Local produce - including Burren smoked salmon, Inagh goats cheese, Doolin crabmeat and Aran scallops - is credited on the menu, providing a sound base for fairly modern Irish cooking with some French influence, as in specialities like tian of Burren smoked salmon & Doolin crab and monkfish on curried lentils. Tempting desserts - caramel mousse brulée with home-churned ice creams perhaps - or farmhouse cheeses to finish. Children welcome. No smoking restaurant. **Seats 25** D Thu-Tue, 6-9. A la carte; early D €25 (6-7pm). House wines 16-17.50. Closed Wed & Oct-Easter.
Accommodation: Warm hospitality, comfortable beds and a good breakfast make this a good place to stay. Cheerful modern rooms have all the necessities, including phones and tea/coffee trays - at a reasonable price. Children welcome (under 3s free in parents' room, cot available without charge).

No pets. **Rooms 6** (all shower only & no-smoking, 1 for disabled). B&B €40 ss €30
Accommodation is open all year. MasterCard, Visa, Laser. **Directions:** Centre of Doolin between
McGanns & O'Connors Pub.

Doolin — Flagship Restaurant/Doolin Crafts Gallery

Restaurant/Café   Ballyvoe Doolin Co. Clare **Tel: 065 707 4309** Fax: 065 707 451
Email: marygray@doolinscrafts.com

Matthew O'Connell and Mary Gray's delightful shop could keep you happily occupied for longer than
you think: it's jam-packed with terrific, quality crafts and clothing - some of them exclusively
available here - and the Flagship Restaurant will tempt you to linger over what is, with unusual
accuracy, described as "simple home cooking, using local produce, and home baking": grilled local
goats cheese with pesto on garden salad, Lisdoonvarna smoked salmon plate, fresh salmon
mayonnaise on brown bread, Kerry apple pie. The home-made jams, chutneys and dressings used in
the restaurant are also for sale. The garden is quite charming too, and very typical of Clare. **Seats
40** (+ 20 in garden) No-smoking restaurant. Open 10-5.45 daily. Closed 1 Oct-Good Fri. A la carte
Wine licence (house wine €16.80). Service charge discretionary. Amex, MasterCard, Visa, Laser
Directions: Beside the cemetery, just outside Doolin.

Ennis — Hal Pino's Restaurant

féile bia Ⓝ Restaurant   7 High Street Ennis Co. Clare **Tel: 065 684 0011** Fax: 065 684 002
Email: halpinsrestaurant@eircom.net Web: www.halpins.com

Derek Halpin's first floor restaurant is up a staircase over a bar in the town centre and has succeeded
in making its mark as one of the area's most popular eating places since opening in 2001. You can
have an aperitif and place orders from a sensibly restricted menu in the comfortable reception/bar
before going to your table (simply appointed but generous and well-spaced); the decor may not make
very much impact, depending on the style of paintings exhibited all around the walls at the time
anyway the most noticeable feature is likely to be the buzz of lots of people enjoying themselves
Prawns in filo pastry, duck breast with blackberry jus (pink, tender with a welcome bit of bite in the
sauce), Burren lamb with a herb crust are all typical of the food - also lovely Clare potatoes
imaginative seasonal vegetables and well-dressed side salads. Accurate cooking, excellent flavour and
appetising presentation go a long way towards making a meal enjoyable, and a good atmosphere can
make it memorable; uneven service makes a visit here something of a lottery, however. (In the Guide's
experience service has varied from very poor to excellent; a consistent standard somewhere in the
middle would be more acceptable.) The early dinner menu offers good value. **Seats 70.** No smoking
area; air conditioning. Not suitable for children under 8 after 7pm. D daily, 5-10.30 (Sun to 10). L Fri
only, by arrangement. Set D from €27; early D €15-19 (5-7pm). House wine €17. SC discretionary
Amex, MasterCard, Visa, Laser. **Directions:** Just off Main Town Square.

Ennis — Newpark House

Farmhouse   Ennis Co. Clare **Tel: 065 6821233** Fax: 065 682123
Email: newparkhouse.ennis@eircom.net Web: http://homepagetinet.ie/~newparkhouse

Strange as it may seem to find a genuine farmhouse in a country setting within easy walking
distance of the pubs and restaurants of Ennis, the Barron family home is the exception that defies
easy description. It's an old house of great historic interest with large homely rooms, furnished with
old family furniture and an hospitable, relaxing atmosphere. Bedrooms vary in size and character, as
old houses do, but are comfortable and full of interest. Children welcome (under 3s free in parents
room, cot available); pets permitted by arrangement. Communal dinner about €22 at 6.30, please
book by 3 pm. Bring your own wine. **Rooms 6** (all en-suite; 4 triple rooms, 1 family room). B&B
€40-50pps, ss €10. Closed Oct-Easter. **Directions:** R352, turn right at Roselevan Arms.

Ennis — Old Ground Hotel

Hotel   O'Connell Street Ennis Co. Clare **Tel: 065 6828127** Fax: 065 6828112
Email: oghotel@iol.ie Web: www.flynnhotels.com

This ivy-clad former manor house dates back to the 18th century and, set in its own gardens, creates
an oasis of calm in the centre of Ennis. One of the country's best-loved hotels, the Old Ground was
bought by the Flynn family in 1995 and has been imaginatively extended and renovated by them in
a way that is commendably sensitive to the age and importance of the building. Despite the
difficulties of dealing with very thick walls in an old building, major improvements were made to
existing banqueting/conference facilities in the mid '90s, then an extra storey was added to provide

new rooms. Again, was a sensitive development and, as the famous ivy-clad frontage continues to thrive, the external changes are barely noticeable to the casual observer. Major refurbishment has also taken place throughout the interior of the hotel, including all bedrooms - which have good amenities and well-designed bathrooms - the O'Brien Room restaurant and a traditional style bar, Poet's Corner (bar menu 12-9) features traditional music on some nights.* Town Hall Café (see entry), an informal contemporary restaurant in an historic building adjacent to the hotel, opened in 2001. Children welcome (free cot available). Conference/banqueting (max 200). No pets. Garden. **Rooms 83** (8 suites, 20 executive rooms, 5 no-smoking, 2 disabled.) Lift. All day room service. B&B €70pps; ss €40 Closed 25-26 Dec.

O'Brien Room Restaurant: The hotel's formal dining room is at the front of the hotel and has great character. Head chef Gerry Walsh, who has been with the hotel since 1980, takes pride in using local produce in imaginatively presented dishes such as roast rack of Burren lamb with rosemary & honey glaze or fillets of turbot with lemon & chive beurre blanc. **Seats 65** (private room, 70) Toilets wheelchair accessible. No smoking area; air conditioning. L&D daily: L12-2.30, D 6.30-9. Set L €15.50, Set D €29.50. House wine €16.50. SC discretionary. Closed 25-26 Dec. Amex, Diners, MasterCard, Visa, Laser. **Directions:** Town Centre.

Ennis — Temple Gate Hotel

féile bia Hotel

The Square Ennis Co. Clare **Tel: 065 682 3300** Fax: 065 682 3322
Email: info@templegatehotel.com Web: wwwtemplegatehotel.com

Built in the centre of Ennis town, to a clever design that makes the best possible use of the site, this family-owned hotel opened to some acclaim in 1996. While retaining the older features (including a church which was first used as a pub and is now the Great Hall Banqueting/Conference room), existing Gothic themes have also been successfully blended into the new, creating a striking modern building which has relevance to its surroundings in the heart of a medieval town. Since then it has succeeded in providing the comfort and convenience expected by today's travellers at a reasonable price. In 1998, 40 new deluxe rooms and state-of-the-art syndicate/conference rooms for up to 100 people were added and the newer "Preachers Bar" replaced the original one in the church. The restaurant has since been extended and redesigned to the same theme as Preachers Bar. Conference/banqueting (220/265); business centre, secretarial services, ISDN lines. Children under 10 free in parents' room; cot available without charge. No pets. Garden. **Rooms 70** (2 suites, 2 junior suites, 11 non-smoking, 1 for disabled). B&B about €70 pps, ss about €28. Closed 25 Dec. Amex, Diners, MasterCard, Visa, Laser, Switch. **Directions:** In Ennis, follow signs to tourist office hotel: hotel is beside it. ◇

Ennis — Town Hall Café

Café/Restaurant

O'Connell Street Ennis Co. Clare **Tel: 065 682 8127** Fax: 065 682 8112
Email: oghotel@iol.ie Web: www.flynnhotels.com

Adjacent to (and part of) The Old Ground Hotel, the Town Hall Café has a separate street entrance and this contemporary space in no way feels like a 'hotel restaurant'. The old town hall has been well restored and the restaurant is in an impressive high-ceilinged room with sensitively spare decor - large art works which will be loved or loathed, big pots and simple table settings allow the room to speak for itself. Daytime menus are limited but varied, a mixture of modern bistro-style dishes (eg chargrilled tandoori chicken salad with homemade hazelnut dressing), daily specials, and tea-room fare - just what people need to re-charge during a day's shopping it seems, as the cooking is good, service swift and value excellent. In the evening it all moves up a notch or two, when a shortish à la carte menu comes on stream, offering about half a dozen choice per course. Starters (average €6) might include country style terrine with spicy Indian chutney and classic Mediterranean fish soup with garlic bread, followed by main courses (average €18) like butter baked tranche of salmon with a citrus jus or prime 10oz sirloin steak with a grain mustard & Irish whiskey sauce. Desserts from a daily selection. Not fine dining, but great at the price. **Seats 80.** Open 10-5 (coffee 10-12, L 12-5, teas 4-5) & D 6-10. Closed 24-26 Dec. Amex, Diners, MasterCard, Visa. **Directions:** Main street Ennis town.

Ennis — West County Conference & Leisure Hotel

Hotel

Clare Road Ennis Co. Clare **Tel: 065 6828421** Fax: 065 6828801
Email: westcounty@lynchotels.com Web: www.lynchhotels.com

Recently extended and refurbished, this modern hotel 5 minutes walk from the centre of Ennis town is not only a well-located and comfortable base for holidaymakers but also renowned for its exceptional business and conference facilities, earning Lynch Hotels the guide's 2000 Business Hotel Award. The hotel's Island Convention Centre can seat 1,650 delegates in a range of four conference rooms and five meeting rooms that are almost infinitely variable. There is also video-conferencing, full business/office support services and an impressive Health and Leisure Club in which to wind down or shape up. Bedrooms include interconnecting rooms, mini-suites, family rooms and 43 recently added Premier standard rooms with ISDN lines. This very busy hotel offers a range of dining options for different times and occasions, the latest being Café West, a contemporary café offering gourmet sandwiches, cakes & speciality coffees. Off-season value breaks. Children welcome (under 3 years free in parents' room; cots available free of charge; playroom, crèche.) Leisure centre, swimming pool; beauty salon. No pets. **Rooms 152** (1 suite, 3 executive, 17 non-smoking, 2 for disabled). Lift. 24 hour room service. B&B €82.53 pps, ss €25.40. Open all year. Amex, Diners, MasterCard, Visa. **Directions:** N18 main Limerick-Galway road. Ten minutes walk from Ennis Town.

Ennis — Woodstock Hotel & Golf Club

féile bia Hotel/Restaurant

Shanaway Road Ennis Co. Clare
Tel: 065 684 6600 Fax: 065 684 6611
Email: info@woodstockhotel.com Web: www.woodstockhotel.com

This sister hotel to the Hibernian Hotel, Dublin and McCausland Hotel, Belfast is built around a 19th century manor house on 200 acres, now mostly utilised by the golf course. It opened in May 2000 and, although it has settled down somewhat since opening, initial impressions may still be mixed: it is not especially attractive from the road, but generous parking space, an impressive foyer and a welcoming fire burning in the grate create a more positive mood. Spacious public areas are furnished with style and large, luxurious bedrooms have equally luxurious bathrooms and also ISDN lines in addition to the more usual amenities. Golf is the major attraction (championship course on site, residents' rates available) and there's a health and fitness club on the premises, also an equestrian centre half a mile away. Children are welcome (free in parents' room up to 2; cots available free of charge). Conferences/banqueting (200); business centre, secretarial services; video conferencing on request. Golf (18); leisure centre (gym, swimming pool, sauna, jacuzzi). Walking; garden; no pets. **Rooms 67** (12 junior suites, 47 no-smoking, 3 disabled). Lift. B&B €115 pp. Closed 24-26 Dec.
Restaurant: High-ceilinged, with cool blue-grey decor (a little too) reminiscent of the Clare skies and stylish classic table settings, with white linen and fresh flowers, the dining room has a formal atmosphere at odds with its title. Head chef Anthony Duggan's moderately priced Table d'Hôte and A la Carte menus are, perhaps, designed with golfers in mind and offer quite substantial fare alongside contemporary dishes. Local seafood such as scallops and Atlantic prawns feature, also seafood from more distant seas, as in a speciality of roasted pavé of seabass with shrimp & herb couscous, sauce vierge. Red meats are always popular with golfers - roast Kerry lamb, perhaps - and vegetarians are always well looked after. **Seats 100**. D 7-9.30pm daily, L Sun only, 12.30-2.30pm. Set D from €39, Set Sun L €25. House wine from €19.95.(*Bar food also available 12.30-7.30 daily, in Spikes Bar). Restaurant closed L Mon-Sat; 24-26 Dec. Amex, Diners, MasterCard, Visa, Laser, Switch. **Directions:** From Ennis, take main road, N18; at the first roundabout take N85 to Lahinch for 1 km, then turn left and continue 1 km to hotel.

Ennistymon — Byrne's Restaurant & Townhouse

Restaurant

Main Street Ennistymon Co. Clare **Tel: 065 707 1080**
Fax: 065 707 2103 Email: byrnesennistymon@eircom.net

Located in a fine period house at the top of this old market town, Byrne's has views of Ennistymon's famous cascading river from the restaurant and terrace at the back of the building. Contemporary style, immaculate cleanliness, genuine hospitality and ambitious standards of food and cooking are the hallmarks. Menus are in the modern mode - prawns in filo with spiced tomato chutney & crisp salad, baked goats cheese, roast crispy duckling with tarragon & fig stuffing, smoked garlic jus. No smoking area; air conditioning. Not suitable for children after 8 pm. **Seats 55**. D only, Mon-Sat 6.30-9.30pm; à la carte; early D, Mon-Fri 6.30-7, €22. House wines from €17.50. Closed Sun (except bank hol weekends), mid Feb-mid Mar. (*2002 saw the opening of six superior rooms (not yet viewed by the Guide). B&B €65 pps, ss € 25.) Amex, Diners, MasterCard, Visa, Laser. **Directions:** Large prominent building overlooking Main Street. ◇

Kilbaha — Anvil Farm Guesthouse

Accomodation

Kilbaha Loop Head Co. Clare
Tel: 065 905 8018 Fax: 065 905 8331

In a house beside the family's clifftop farm at the end of the Loop Head peninsula, Maura Keating provides comfortable accommodation in one of the country's most remote and unspoilt areas. Rugged cliff scenery, angling, diving, bird watching and walking are some of the attractions that bring visitors to this wild and windblown beauty spot - the perfect antidote to city life. There is plenty to visit in the area too - Maura has all the details for her guests - and good local food for dinner, including Aberdeen Angus beef from their own farm, locally caught Atlantic salmon and local Inagh and Cratloe cheeses. Visitors may also visit the farm, which has a variety of animals and a special interest in Irish sport horse breeding. **Rooms 5** (all en-suite, 4 shower-only) B&B about €25, ss about €7. D for residents by arrangement. Closed Nov-Mar. **Directions:** Take Loop Head road from Kilkee; Anvil Farm is 2 miles after Cross village. ◇

Kilfenora — Vaughan's Pub

Pub   Kilfenora Co. Clare **Tel: 065 708 8004**
Fax: 065 708 8144 Web: www.vaughanspub.com

One of the most famous music centres in the west of Ireland, traditional Irish music and set dancing at Vaughan's pub and (previously thatched) barn attract visitors from all over the world. In the family since about 1800, John and Kay Vaughan have worked hard since the mid-70s to ensure that visitors to this attractive old pub have the best possible time. It is warm and homely, with an open fire in the front bar and a garden set up with tables at the back. Kay still personally supervises the food, which has become an important part of the operation over the years: traditional Irish menus (bacon & cabbage, beef & Guinness casserole) are based on good local ingredients, including organic meats, seafood and North Clare cheese and (like everywhere else it seems) some oriental influences have crept in. **Seats 50.** Food served 10-9 daily. Closed 25 Dec & Good Fri. MasterCard, Visa, Laser. **Directions:** 18 miles from Ennis on the main street of Kilfenora, next to the church.

Kilkee — Halpins Townhouse Hotel

Hotel   Erin Street Kilkee Co. Clare **Tel: 065 905 6032** Fax: 065 905 6317
Email: halpins@iol.ie Web: www.halpinsprivatehotels.com

Adapting the original Victorian building of the Halpin family's small townhouse hotel to provide en-suite bathrooms has meant that bedrooms are neat rather than spacious, but they are comfortable and well-appointed with direct-dial phone, TV, hospitality tray with mineral water as well as tea/coffee-making facilities and a laundry service. There's a characterful basement bar with an open fire where visitors, including the many who come to play the adjacent Kilkee Golf Course get together after dinner at the hotel's restaurant, Vittles. In common ownership with Aberdeen Lodge and Merrion Hall (see Dublin entries.) Conference/banqueting (50). Own parking. Off-season value breaks. Children welcome (cots available). **Rooms 12** (2 suites, 4 non-smoking) B&B €45 pps, ss €25. Bar food available 11-4 daily, D 6,30-9. Closed 15 Nov-15 Mar. Amex, Diners, MasterCard, Visa. **Directions:** Centre of Kilkee.

Killaloe — Cherry Tree Restaurant

Restaurant   Lakeside Ballina Killaloe Co. Clare
Tel: 061 375 688 Fax: 061 375 689

Proprietor/chef Harry McKeogh's impressive purpose-built restaurant makes the most of its lovely waterside location and this attractive building - specifically its striking interior - makes a fine setting for Harry's cool contemporary cooking. Carefully sourced ingredients provide the basis for a wide range of admirably simple dishes, including great salads, based on locally grown organic produce. Specialities include warm asparagus bundles with truffle oil, fresh crab salad- and superb sirloin of beef, which is cut to order and cooked as requested then served with thickly sliced, golden brown potato crisps - and a classic béarnaise sauce, perhaps: an admirably simple dish that was a very worthy winner of the guide's Irish Beef Award in 2001. Although the exact origins of ingredients may not be mentioned on menus, there is a clear commitment to quality ingredients, especially organic produce. **Seats 60** (private room, 12). Toilets wheelchair accessible. No smoking area. Children over 7 welcome. D 6-10 Tue-Sat. A la carte except Set Vegetarian Menu €36. House wine about €17.45. Closed Sun (except bank hol weekends), Mon; 24-26 Dec; last week Jan, 1st week Feb. Amex, MasterCard, Visa, Laser. **Directions:** At Molly's Pub in Ballina turn down towards the Lakeside Hotel, you will find The Cherry Tree restaurant by The Lakeside Hotel.

Killaoe — Kincora Hall Hotel

Ⓝ Hotel   Killaloe Co. Clare **Tel: 061 376000** Fax: 061 376665
Email: info@kincorahall.com Web:www. kincorahall.com

This friendly and well-maintained family-run hotel is beautifully located overlooking its own marina and the Shannon. The bar and restaurant take full advantage of the location, both have river views and there's a sheltered patio off the bar for al fresco dining in fine weather, and there's a peaceful lounge with plenty of comfortable seating on the other side of the building. Non-residents are welcome at any time (including breakfast) and accommodation is very comfortable, with all the facilities expected of a modern hotel. **Rooms 30.** B&B about €65. Amex, Diners, MasterCard, Visa. **Directions:** Shoreside location west of the bridge.

Killaloe   Waterman's Lodge Hotel

Hotel   Ballina Killaloe Co. Clare **Tel: 061 376333** Fax: 061 375445
                                    Email: info@watermanslodge.ie Web: www.watermanslodge.com

Views down to Killaloe and across the Shannon are among the pleasant features of this appealing country house hotel and restaurant. It changed hands late in 1998 and has since been undergoing systematic refurbishment. Small weddings and private parties are a speciality. Golf, fishing, horse riding and pony trekking are all available nearby. Wheelchair accessible (including toilets). No pets. **Rooms 10** (5 superior, 1 shower only); B&B about €160. Wheelchair accessible. Bar menu, 12.30-7.30 daily. Restaurant **Seats 50**. D daily, 7-9.30; L Sun only, 12.30. Set D about €32-42; à la carte available; house wine about €19.90; sc discretionary. Bar L 12.30-2.30; Closed 23-28 Dec. Restaurant Amex, MasterCard, Visa, Laser. **Directions:** N7 to Birdhill turn left 500yds after the bridge.

Lahinch   Barrtra Seafood Restaurant

Restaurant   Lahinch Co. Clare
                                    Tel: 065 708 1280 Email: barrtra@hotmail.com

Paul and Theresa O'Brien have been providing fine food and hospitality at their traditional, whitewashed restaurant on the cliffs just outside Lahinch for over a decade. A conservatory added to the side of the original cottagey building made it lighter and brighter, opening up the whole area to make a more spacious atmosphere. Reception can be the weak point of this otherwise admirable restaurant - the room itself is rather small and it is sometimes necessary to wait there for an uncomfortably long time before being seated. Once into the restaurant itself, however, things immediately take a turn for the better and the sound of lots of people enjoying their meals and having a good time is infectious. The decor is appealingly simple and the views of Liscannor Bay - which can be magic from window tables on a fine evening - are the visual highlight. But local seafood is the star attraction and Theresa's excellent, unfussy cooking makes the most of a wide range of fish, while also offering a choice for those with other preferences, including a vegetarian menu. Paul, meanwhile, provides warm and easy hospitality and maintains good service. Main courses include lobster, when available, as well as the day's selection of other local seafood - and all at the kind of prices that many restaurants claim to be "impossible" these days. Richly flavoured chowders, glorious crab salads with home-made mayonnaise and breads, perfectly cooked fish with excellent sauces; exact timing and perfect judgement of flavourings enhances while always allowing the fish to be "itself". Vegetables are also a strong point, served on a platter which might include beautiful Clare potatoes, wilted spinach, flavoursome flaked carrot - and some warm ratatouille as well. An interesting and keenly priced wine list, good cheeseboard, home-baked breads and aromatic cafetière coffee show an attention to detail in tune with an overall high standard which we have found consistently enjoyable over the years. Children welcome before 7pm. The early dinner menu is exceptionally good value. Barrtra was our Seafood Restaurant of the Year for 2002. **Seats 32** D only Tue-Sun 5-10, Set D €35; Early D 5-6.30, €20; also à la carte. House wines from €13. s.c. discretionary. Closed Mon (except Jul-Aug) & Jan-Mar. Phone to check opening hours off season. Amex, MasterCard, Visa, Laser. **Directions:** 3.5 miles south of Lahinch N67.

Lahinch   The Conch Shell

 Restaurant   Lahinch Co. Clare
                                                                        Tel: 065 708 1888

Gordon (front of house) and Suzanne (the chef) Lightbourne moved their Liscannor restaurant into larger premises at The Aberdeen Arms Hotel in Lahinch in 2002. The cooking style remains the same - a shortish menu that favours seafood, but also offers other popular dishes, notably steak, and a couple of vegetarian dishes. Ingredients in dishes such as crabmeat tartlet, ragout of seafood and turbot with rösti crust are clearly well-sourced, very fresh and well cooked - and main courses come with a generous vegetable platter, including delicious local potatoes. Desserts include refreshing seasonal fruit - in a rhubarb crème brulée, perhaps - and home-made icecreams. Children welcome. **Seats 60**. D daily, 6-10. A la carte. House wine €16-17. SC discretionary. Amex, MasterCard, Visa, Laser. **Directions:** Main Street - Aberdeen Arms Hotel.

Lahinch — Moy House

Country House

Lahinch Co. Clare **Tel: 065 708 2800** Fax: 065 708 2500
Email: moyhouse@eircom.net Web: www.moyhouse.com

COUNTRY HOUSE OF THE YEAR

This stunning house just outside Lahinch has been open for several year now and is superbly well-run in admirably hands-on style by manager Bernie Merrie - yet it's still a surprisingly well-kept secret. The house is on a 15 acre site on the river Moy which also includes areas of mature woodland, and enjoys a commanding position overlooking Lahinch Bay. Set on a hill, with clear coastal views, the house has recently been renovated and decorated to an exceptionally high standard: combining the best materials with an inspired sense of design has created one of Ireland's most appealing (and luxurious) country houses, greatly enhanced by Bernie's genuine hospitality and great attention to detail. Although it appears to be quite a small, low building as you approach, the scale is larger than at first appears and its hillside position allows for a lower floor on the sea side - there is a side entrance below with direct access to the dining room and lower bedrooms (useful for anyone who might have difficulty with the narrow spiral staircase which joins the two floors internally). On the main entrance level there are four bedrooms and also a large, elegant drawing room with an open fire and honesty bar, where guests are free to enjoy aperitifs before going down to dine, or to relax with coffee (or tea or herbal/fruit tea) and petits fours after dinner. The decor throughout is in rich country house tones, with rugs and beautiful heavy fabrics used to great advantage - antique furniture is lovely but it is the inspired use of fabrics which is memorable. Bedrooms, which all have sea views, are wonderfully spacious and luxuriously appointed, as are the bathrooms (with underfloor heating so tiles are always warm on bare feet). Dinner - which is mainly for residents, although bookings may be taken from non-residents if there is room - and breakfast are served at separate tables in a dining room which is elegant yet also cosy, which would be reassuring in wild weather. Dining here is a treat. The 4-course dinner menu offers three or four well-balanced choices on each course so you might start with deep-fried crab and vegetable spring roll, follow with one of a choice of soups or a refresher such as strawberry & aniseed granita, then maybe a house speciality of honey roast duckling with an orange sauce and lemon polenta cake with crème fraîche and summer berries; farmhouse cheeses are also offered and there's a short but interesting wine list (house wines are currently from California, but Europe is also well-represented). All round, this lovely house offers a unique experience and is worth a special trip. **Rooms 9** (3 shower only) B&B about €115 pps, ss€46. D7-8.15, €45. House wine €21. Closed Christmas &1-14 Jan. Amex, MasterCard, Visa, Laser. **Directions:** On the sea side of the Miltown Malbay road outside Lahinch.

Liscannor — Liscannor Rock Shop Café

 Café

Derreen Liscannor Co. Clare
Tel: 065 708 1930 Fax: 065 708 1944

A useful place for anyone touring Clare to know about, the café is on the premises of the Liscannor Stone Story and The Rock Shop which are both extremely interesting and worth allowing some time to visit (especially if the weather is poor). It's a sister operation to the Aillwee Cave at Ballyvaughan (see entry) and, here too, it's a good place to factor in a bite to eat - not a major meal, perhaps, but a light lunch or a tea or coffee break. The café, which overlooks the stones and the hills, has a terrace outside for fine weather; it's quite simply set up with a servery display area, but everything is freshly home-made on the premises, giving dishes like cottage pie, Irish stew and (vegetarian) lasagne very much more appeal - home-made ravioli is a speciality and there's a blackboard menu offering the day's home-made soup, various salads (served with French bread), a range of hot dishes (poached salmon, honey coated bacon with cabbage & jacket potatoes), a range of hot dishes (poached salmon, honey coated bacon with cabbage & jacket potatoes). Home-made scones, cakes (well-displayed and tempting by the slice) and desserts are lovely for morning or afternoon breaks - and you can also buy their home-made preserves to take home. **Seats 75.** Self service. Open daily 10.30-5.30 (Sun from 11.30). Closed Nov-Mar. MasterCard, Visa, Laser. **Directions:** On road from Liscannor to Cliffs of Moher.

Liscannor — Vaughans Anchor Inn

ⓝ Pub

Main Street Liscannor Co. Clare
Tel: 065 7081548 Web: www.vaughansanchorinn.com

A naturally characterful traditional bar, with lots of memorabilia and a newer restaurant area beyond the main bar, this is the place for some seriously good seafood at fair prices. Although famed locally for their seafood platters there's much more to it than that: all cooking is to order patience is quite reasonably requested on this score, as it gets very busy and everything really is fresh - the menu may even be changed in mid-stream because there's something new coming up off the boats. However, you don't have to eat seafood to eat well here - vegetarian options are offered and they do excellent steaks too. Cooking combines old-fashioned generosity with some contemporary twists: succulent fresh salmon, for example, may be a good thick darne, grilled and served on a bed of just-cooked fennel, with a delicious creamy samphire sauce, while perfectly seared scallops may come on a brilliant bed of crisp-fried smoked haddock & scallion mash with a frothy white wine sauce. Understandably very popular and they don't take bookings so, if you want to have a reasonably quiet dinner without a long wait, get there before seven o'clock. Children welcome. **Seats 100.** Food served 12-9.30 daily. Toilets wheelchair accessible. Accommodation also available (not viewed by the Guide). Closed 25 Dec. (Open Good Fri for food, but bar closed.) MasterCard, Visa. **Directions:** 2.5 miles from Lahinch on Cliffs of Moher route. ◇

Lisdoonvarna — Sheedy's Country House Hotel

🏛 Hotel/Restaurant

Lisdoonvarna Co. Clare **Tel: 065 707 4026** Fax: 065 707 4555
Email: enquries@sheedys.com Web: www.sheedys.com

John and Martina Sheedy's fine hotel has undergone major redevelopment over the last couple of years and now offers some of the best accommodation as well as the finest food in the area - but it still has the warm ambience (in every sense - the sunny foyer has a comfortable seating area and an open fire for chillier days) and friendly hands-on management, which make Sheedy's one of the west of Ireland's best loved small hotels. All the bedrooms are spacious and individually designed to a high standard with quality materials and elegant, quietly soothing colours; comfort is the priority, so bathrooms have power showers as well as full baths and there are CD music systems in addition to TV and the usual room facilities. Good food and warm hospitality remain constant qualities however - and the latest idea will enhance the exterior in a way that is as practical as it is pleasing to the eye: the gardens are gradually being developed to include a potager (formal vegetable and herb garden) plus other similarly specialised areas, including an orchard and a rose garden: magic! Not suitable for children. No pets. **Rooms 11** (1 suite, 2 junior suites, 1 for disabled, all no smoking). B&B €60pps, ss €30. Closed mid Oct-mid Mar. **Sheedys Restaurant:** The restaurant - and, specifically, John Sheedy's cooking - is a major attraction and, in the setting of a stylishly subdued olive-grey, curtainless dining room with plain candle-lit tables, he presents confident modern Irish cooking based on the best local ingredients. A local cheddar style cheese, Mount Callan, may be used in a delicious twice-baked soufflé, or Burren smoked salmon served warm with asparagus in an imaginative risotto, with curry oil and crème fraîche, for example. Roast rump of Burren lamb is naturally a favourite main course choice and may be given a contemporary twist by serving it with a spicy dressing as well as its own gravy - and served with a generous platter of perfectly cooked seasonal vegetables. Hospitality and service are exemplary and prices reasonable for the high standard offered, making this a regular treat for a growing number of devotees. No smoking restaurant. Not suitable for children under 10. **Seats 28.** D daily, 6.45-8.30. A la carte. House wine €17.50. SC discretionary. Closed mid-Oct to mid-Mar. MasterCard, Visa, Laser. **Directions:** 200 metres from square of town on road to Sulphur Wells.

Miltown Malbay — Berry Lodge

Restaurant/B&B

Annagh Miltown Malbay Co. Clare
Tel: 065 708 7022 Fax: 065 708 7011
Email: info@berrylodge.com Web: www.berrylodge.com

Near the coast of west Clare, between Kilkee and Lahinch, this Victorian country house is the family home of Rita Meade, who has run it as a restaurant with accommodation since 1994 and cookery

classes - given by Rita in her own kitchen - are a special feature of Berry Lodge. (Information, including a short breaks brochure, is available on request and cookery weekends can be worked out individually.) The house can seem a little uninviting on arrival, especially as there is no real reception area; however the restaurant is set up welcomingly in an informal country style with pine furniture and is quite extensive, with a newer conservatory area at the back of the house, overlooking the garden. Menus are interesting, food quality is very high and the cooking is sound - a combination which makes for an enjoyable dining experience. Wide-ranging menus offer local seafood of course but meats, from a local butcher, are exceptional and, in the hands of a good cook, a simple dish like roast best end of lamb can be memorable; poultry is another strength - an updated classic of slow roast spiced duckling with Guinness honey & orange sauce & red onion marmalade is a speciality. **Seats** 45. D6.30-9.30. Early D €25 (6-7pm); otherwise Set D €32; also à la carte. House wines €15-16.50. SC discretionary. Open daily Jul-Aug, otherwise advance booking required.
Accommodation: Neat bedrooms, each with its own little shower room, are furnished with an attractive country mixture of old and new, including Irish craft items. Children welcome. No pets. **Rooms** 5 (all shower only,1 suitable for disabled guests). B&B about €30 pps, ss about €13. MasterCard, Visa. **Directions:** N87 from Ennis to Enagh, R460 to Milltown Malbay, N67 to Berry Lodge over Annagh Bridge, second left first right to Berry Lodge.

Miltown Malbay   Black Oak

Restaurant   Rineen Miltown Malbay Co. Clare **Tel: 065 708 4408**

Set on a hillside with views over Liscannor Bay, this large modern house may not look like a restaurant (and the sign at the gate is small, although it is well-signed from Lahinch), but it is well-established and very comfortable, with plenty of sofas and chairs in a smallish reception area - a policy of seating guests quickly and taking orders from the table prevents overcrowding. The dining room is decorated in warm tones, with well-spaced, well-appointed tables - fresh flowers, good linen and glasses, comfortable chairs - setting a positive tone ahead of the meal. While not especially innovative, moderately priced menus offer a very fair choice, with starters like St Tola goat cheese, crab in filo pastry and mussels in wine then main courses such as rack of lamb and Seafood Pot (a house speciality - a generous and perfectly cooked selection of fish cooked in a tomato, leek, saffron & garlic sauce and served in its own pot), well-presented with a selection of side vegetables. Desserts tend towards the classics - lemon tarte, variations on crème brûlée. This restaurant delivers what it promises: good fresh food, with a high level of comfort and service at reasonable prices. Air conditioning. **Seats** 65 (Max table size, 10). D Wed-Mon,5.30-9.30 pm.; early D 5.30-6pm about €20; Set D about €28 from 6.30pm. House wines from about €13. Closed Tue & Christmas-April. MasterCard, Visa. **Directions:** 7 km outside Lahinch village on the Miltown road. ◇

Mountshannon   An Cupán Caifé

féile bia Restaurant   Main Street Mountshannon Co. Clare
             Tel: 061 927275 Fax: 061 927275 Email: bistrodago@eircom.net

Dagmar Hilty's little restaurant on the main street only seats about 20, but there are also tables for nearly as many again outside in fine weather. Better still, perhaps, there's a welcoming fire on cold days - and a range of about a dozen wines on the mantlepiece for perusal, with a short description hanging from the bottle neck: a novel idea that adds to the atmosphere - and you're also welcome to bring your own. Rather dashing menus offer a series of choices from breakfast (extensive menu including scrambled egg with smoked salmon, served until noon), lunch (just chowder with home-made brown bread or a range of homely dishes, 12-3.30) and dinner (more extensive à la carte; includes vegetarian and children's choices, 6-9). Daily specials go up on a board. Everything is based on fresh local produce (organic wherever possible) and the emphasis is on freshness and wholesome good cooking; excellent side salads, lovely home-made cakes. BYO wine also allowed (no corkage charge). High season (May-Aug), open 10.30am-9.30pm every day except Wed; low season (Mar/Apr & Sep/Oct), open 12-9 Fri-Tue, also D Thu, 5-9. Closed all Wed, also L Thu off season. MasterCard, Visa, Laser. **Directions:** On main street, Mountshannon village.

Newmarket-on-Fergus   Clare Inn Golf & Leisure Hotel

Hotel   Dromoland Newmarket-on-Fergus Co. Clare **Tel: 061 368161** Fax: 061 368622
                         Email: cro@lynchotels.com Web: www.lynchhotels.com

Built in the grounds of Dromoland Castle, this 1960s hotel overlooks the Shannon estuary and shares the Castle's golf course. Like the other Lynch hotels (group recipients of the guide's Business Hotel Award in 2000), facilities for conferences and business guests are good, with back-up secretarial services, a business centre and video-conferencing. As well as golf, there's a leisure centre with 17-

metre pool, gymnasium and sauna, so the combination of business and leisure facilities make this a popular conference venue. However, the hotel is also a favourite destination for families and the management seem unable to keep up with the resulting wear and tear. Maintenance in public areas left a lot to be desired on recent visits and, although bedrooms are generally quite large and well-appointed, including extra features like free movies, ISDN lines and an in-room safe, maintenance and refurbishment are not always up to standard. Breakfast, although adequate, is a depressing experience, served in a large canteen-like room. However, facilities are good, staff are pleasant and helpful and rates are very reasonable for the area. Conference/banqueting 400/350; business centre, video conferencing. Children welcome (under 3s free in parents' room, cot available without charge; play centre, crèche. No pets. **Rooms 183** (1 suite, 32 executive,1 disabled). B&B €56pps, ss€26. Room-only €99 (max 3). Open all year. Amex, Diners, MasterCard, Visa, Laser. **Directions:** Located on the Dromoland Estate, 10 minutes drive from Ennis Town & Shannon Airport.

Newmarket-on-Fergus — Dromoland Castle Hotel

 Hotel/Restaurant Newmarket-on-Fergus Co. Clare **Tel: 061 368144** Fax: 061 363355
Email: sales@dromoland.ie Web: www.dromoland.ie

Dromoland is one of Ireland's grandest hotels, and also one of the best-loved. The ancestral home of the O'Briens, barons of Inchiquin and direct descendants of Brian Boru, High King of Ireland, it is one of the few Irish estates tracing its history back to Gaelic royal families. Today, the visitor is keenly aware of this sense of history, but will not find it daunting. Under the warm and thoughtful management of Mark Nolan, who has been General Manager since 1989, Dromoland is a very relaxing hotel, where the grandeur of the surroundings - the castle itself, its lakes and parkland and magnificent furnishings - does not overpower but rather enhances the pleasure for guests. It is an enchanting place, where wide corridors lined with oak panelling are hung with ancient portraits and scented with the haunting aroma of woodsmoke. Public areas are very grand, with all the crystal chandeliers and massive antiques to be expected in a real Irish Castle, but the atmosphere suggests that a lot of fun is to be had here too. Bedrooms are all furnished to a very high standard, with luxurious bathrooms. The Brian Boru International Centre brought a new dimension to the Castle's activities a few years ago and can accommodate almost any type of business gathering, including exhibitions, conferences and banquets. A new wing, also built to blend in with the castle, was recently completed. Child under 12 free in parents' room (cot available free of charge). No pets. **Rooms 100** (6 suites, 15 junior suites, 50 executive, 10 no smoking, 2 disabled). Lift. Room rate €370 (max 2 guests), SC 12.5%

★ **Earl of Thomond Restaurant:** The most beautiful room in the castle, the Earl of Thomond Dining Room is magnificent, with crystal, gilding and rich fabrics - and has a lovely view over the lake and golf course. Guests ease into the experience of dinner with an aperitif in the Library Bar, overlooking the eighteenth green, before moving through to beautifully presented tables and gentle background music provided by a traditional Irish harpist. In the evening a wide choice includes a table d'hôte menu, vegetarian menu and an à la carte offering a wonderful selection of luxurious dishes. The table d'hôte is more down-to-earth - a little less glamorous than the carte but with the same quality of ingredients and cooking. Although the style is basically classic French (with some of the current international influences) some dishes highlight local ingredients and are more Irish in tone: terrine of Kinvara smoked eel and salmon 'en gelée' with onion, gherkin, capers, watercress & egg salad, for example, and roast rack of Burren lamb with colcannon potatoes, courgettes, tomato, glazed shallots & thyme sauce. Executive head chef David McCann's cooking is invariably superb, all the little niceties of a very special meal are observed and service, under restaurant manager Tony Frisby, is excellent. The wine list - about 250 wines, predominantly French - is under the constant review of sommelier Pascal Playon, winner of our Sommelier of the Year Award in 2000, who is not only knowledgeable, but an exceptionally thoughtful and helpful wine host.(House wines from €24). A 15% service charge is added to all prices. **Seats 76**. No smoking Restaurant. D daily, 7.30-9.30, L Sun only 12.30-1.30; L&D set menus offered, à la carte also available.*The Gallery Menu offers a lighter choice of less formal dishes throughout the day (12-7), including Afternoon Tea. *Beside the castle, the Dromoland Golf and Country Club incorporates an 18-hole parkland course, a gym, a Health Clinic offering specialist treatments, also the Green Room Bar and Fig Tree Restaurant, which provide informal alternatives to facilities in the castle, including excellent food. Open all year. Amex, Diners, MasterCard, Visa, Laser. **Directions:** Located on N18,17 miles from Limerick, 8 miles from Shannon.

Shannon | Great Southern Hotel

 Hotel   Shannon Airport Shannon Co. Clare **Tel: 061 471122** Fax: 061 471982
Email: res@shannon-gsh.ie Web: www.gshotels.com

In an lovely location overlooking the estuary with sea views and rather gracious atmosphere, this hotel retains a little of the old romance of flight. The hotel is fully sound-proofed and bedrooms, all of which have been recently refurbished and upgraded, are spacious and comfortable, with all the amenities expected of a good modern hotel, including ISDN lines. Snooker; mini-gym; golf and horseriding nearby. Conference/banqueting (250/200); business centre; secretarial services. Children welcome (under 2s free in parents' room, cot available without charge). **Rooms 115.** (1 suite, 56 executive rooms, 29 no-smoking rooms). Lift, limited room service. Room Rate €150 (up to 3 guests) Closed 24-26 Dec. Amex, Diners, MasterCard, Visa, Laser. **Directions:** Situated within airport complex.

Shannon | Oakwood Arms Hotel

Hotel   Shannon Co. Clare **Tel: 061 361500** Fax: 061 361414
Email: manager@oakwoodarms.com Web: www.oakwoodarms.com

John and Josephine O'Sullivan opened this mock-Tudor red brick hotel in 1991 and it created a good impression from the start, with its high standard of maintenance and neatly laid-out flower beds. The lounge bar and function room both have aviation themes: the bar honours the memory of the pioneer female pilot Sophie Pearse, who came from the area, and the restaurant is named after The Spruce Goose, Howard Hughes' famous flying boat. Public areas are quite spacious and comfortably furnished and although not individually decorated, rooms have all the necessary comforts and are double-glazed with air conditioning, ISDN lines, hospitality trays, ironing facilities and TV. Conference/banqueting (300/250) facilities are good, with video-conferencing and back-up secretarial services available. Children welcome. No pets. **Rooms 101** (4 suites, 4 junior suites, 23 executive rooms, 37 no-smoking). B&B about €75 pps, ss about €33. No SC Closed 24-26 Dec. Amex, Diners, MasterCard, Visa, Laser. **Directions:** Located on the N19, 2 kms from Shannon Airport. ◇

Shannon | Quality Hotel Shannon

Hotel   Ballycasey Shannon Co. Clare **Tel: 061 364 588** Fax: 061 364 045
Email: sales@qualityshannon.com Web: www.choicehotelsireland.ie

A recent addition to the choice of accommodation at Shannon airport, the Quality Hotel offers modern comforts at a reasonable price. Rooms all have multi-channel TV and modem points and the hotel is geared for the convenience of guests who are meeting or seeing off relatives, or want somewhere for a quick business meeting before heading off to another destination. Wholesome fare is served in the informal hotel restaurant, Lannigans. Conferences/banqueting (20/60). Ample parking. Children under 12 free in parents' room. No pets. **Rooms 54** (10 no-smoking, 3 for disabled).Lift. B&B about €65 pps, ss about €20. Amex, Diners, MasterCard, Visa. **Directions:** On N19 coming to Shannon Town. ◇

Tulla | Flappers Restaurant

Restaurant   Tulla Co. Clare **Tel: 065 35711**

Jim and Patricia McInerney's simple little split-level restaurant (the lower part is non-smoking) is refreshingly free of decoration, except for a pair of striking pictures and fresh flowers on the tables. Lunchtime sees the emphasis on fairly hearty food and good value but, although the menu is limited, you can easily work up to a rather smart 3-course meal if you wish: organic mixed greens with honey mustard dressing to start, perhaps, lemon peppered chicken (breast of chicken grilled with a light lemon pepper sauce) and a home-made dessert such as fresh fruit meringues with banana cream. In the evening the mood changes and, in addition to a set 2 or 3-course menu, there's a more ambitious à la carte offering the likes of spicy crab cakes with basil aioli and leek and wild mushroom puff pastry tartlet, followed by main courses like roast rack of lamb with creamy flageolet beans and redcurrant sauce or grilled salmon on a bed of roasted peppers and courgettes with lemon & chive cream sauce. Vegetarian options are imaginative and desserts like flourless chocolate cake with frangelico ice cream are equally tempting. There's a well-chosen and very fairly priced wine list too- and even a take-away service, which must be a boon for holidaymakers self-catering in the area as well as locals. Not suitable for children after 8pm. **Seats 40** No-smoking area; air conditioning. Wheelchair access to toilets. L 12-3, D 7-10. (Shorter hours in winter - please phone for details) A la carte. House wine about €16. SC discretionary (except 10% on groups of 8+). Closed all Sun, D Mon, bank hols and first 2 weeks Nov. MasterCard, Visa, Laser. **Directions:** Main streetTulla village, 10 miles from Ennis. ◇

CORK CITY

There's a new buzz to Cork in 2003, with major refurbishment of the city centre under way, and interesting developments shaping up in suburban areas. Cork's designation as the European City of Culture for 2005 has given added impetus to the new vitality. But in fact the sympathetic re-shaping of this ancient city port - which is located on many islands among the several channels of the River Lee - had been steadily gathering momentum in recent years.

It is Cork, of all Ireland's cities, which most warmly gives the impression of being a place at comfort with itself through being set in the midst of a land flowing in milk and honey. Cork is all about the good things in life. While it may be stretching things a little to assert that the southern capital has a Mediterranean atmosphere, there's no doubting its Continental and cosmopolitan flavour, and the Cork people's relaxed enjoyment of it all.

Cork's special qualities, and its people's appreciation of the pleasant commodities of life, make it a special destination for connoisseurs. Trading in life's more agreeable commodities has always been what Cork and its famous "merchant princes" are all about. At one time, the city was known as "the butter capital of Europe", and it continues to be unrivalled for the ready availability of the very best in fresh produce.

The way in which sea and land intertwine throughout the wonderfully sheltered natural harbour, and through the lively old city itself, has encouraged waterborne trade and a sea-minded outlook. Thus today Cork is at the heart of Ireland's most dynamically nautical area, a place world-renowned for its energetic interaction with the sea, whether for business or pleasure.

In the city itself, we find two Irish stouts being brewed - Murphy's and Beamish. Each has its own distinctive flavour, each in turn is different from Dublin's Guinness, and it is one of life's pleasures - in a characterful Cork pub - to discuss and compare their merits while savouring the Cork people's delightful line in deflationary and quirky humour.

Local Attractions and Information

Cork Airport	021 431 3031
Cork Arts Society	021 427 7749
Cork City Gaol	021 430 5022
Cork Tourist Information	021 427 3251
Guinness Cork Jazz Festival (late October)	021 427 8979
Cork International Choral Festival (April/May)	021 430 8308
Cork International Film Festival (October)	021 427 1711
Cork Public Museum	021 427 0679
Crawford Gallery, Emmett Place	021 427 3377
English Market (covered, speciality food stalls Mon-Sat), corner between Grand Parade & Patrick Street	
Firkin Crane Dance Centre Shandon	021 450 7487
Opera House	021 427 0022
Railway Station	021 450 4888
Triskel Arts Centre Tobin Street off South Main Street	021 427 2022

Cork | **A Taste of Thailand**

Restaurant | 8 Bridge Street Cork

Tel: 021 450 5404 Fax: 021 450 5404 Email: maryann@iol.ie

This authentic Thai restaurant has earned a strong following, giving it a lively atmosphere, even early in the week. Wide-ranging menus offer plenty of choice, including vegetarian options (Thai food caters well for vegetarians) and the familiar set menus ('banquets') for groups of various sizes, as well as an à la carte which has a more interesting selection of dishes. All the well known Thai styles are represented and there are always a few appealing specials offered - Thai style ducking, for example: half a farmyard duckling - crispy style and boneless - served on a bed of Thai spicy soft noodles. Fresh ingredients (all irish except for exotics), making everything to order, sound cooking and attractive presentation add up to an appealing package: good food, service and value explain this restaurant's popularity - booking is advisable and, if you are not having the early menu it might be wise to allow plenty of time for the first sitting to finish, as arrivals for the popular 8 o'clock slot may have to wait or tables and there is nowhere to do so in comfort. A small European menu is also offered. **Seats 60** (private room 12). D daily, 6-11; Early D €16 (6-7 pm); Set menus from €21.50, otherwise à la carte. House wine from €13.85 (beers, including Thai beers, available and BYO also allowed). Amex, MasterCard, Visa, Laser. **Directions:** 1 minute from city centre, just across St Patrick's Bridge.

Cork — Amicus

Restaurant   14A French Church Street Cork
Tel: 021 427 6455 Fax: 021 422 3547

Tucked into a small space in Cork's Huguenot district, Ursula and Robert Hales' restaurant has a few tables for street dining while indoors you can enjoy Robert's well-prepared food in a bistro-style environment. This tiny restaurant, almost cramped with tables, comprises one small, bustling room, which has been fitted out with cool creams, wood, large mirrors and a few choice canvasses. Starters include fresh, flavoursome salads (typically including Parma ham with peach & mint leaves and roasted peppers salad). Main courses offer a choice of gourmet hamburgers as well as seafood, pasta and chargrilled chicken. Service, under Ursula's direction is smart and friendly, with children made especially welcome. But the main attraction is the availability of real food at affordable prices. A short, but well chosen wine list complements the uncomplicated food, which Robert presents with flair. **Seats 38**. Open through the day Mon-Sat; house wine about €14. MasterCard, Visa, Laser. ◇

Cork — Bodega / Café Bar Deli

Café/Pub   Cornmarket Street Cork
Tel: 021 427 2878 Fax: 021 427 2897 Email: bodega@indigo.ie

Cork's coolest eating place is attached to the youthful Bodega bar, which is beautiful but can get very noisy with its stone walls and wooden floors accentuating loud music and conversation - in contrast to the Café, which has a more relaxing atmosphere for eating. Housed in an old limestone warehouse building, the restaurant is informal in the best contemporary style and has recently adopted the Café-Bar-Deli format that has proved such a success in the Dublin sister restaurant. Sourcing of quality local foods is a high priority: imaginative salads are packed with colourful, flavoursome treats in the modern idiom - rocket, parmesan, anchovies, baby spinach, goat's cheese, hazelnuts, chickpeas, couscous, tapenade are the vocabulary of this menu - with pizza and pasta menus continuing in the same tone. The ten or so pizzas offered include a Café Bar Deli special, changed daily, as do the pastas - and there are also family sized bowls available. Vegetarian options are particularly appealing, the wine list is sensibly limited but well chosen to combine quality and style (sparkling and dessert wines included) with value, service is friendly and efficient and prices remarkably moderate - a winning formula. The place has great style, staff are attentive, friendly and very professional, cooking is excellent - and it's good value for the high standard of food and service (2-course meal averages about €15). Lunch menu available in Bodega, also weekend brunches. Parking in the area is not difficult after 6.30pm. No smoking area. **Seats 60** (private room, 50). D Wed-Sun 5 -10.30. A la carte. House wine €15. *Daytime food available at Bodega, Mon-Sat 12-5 (L12-3); also Sat & Sun brunch. Café-Bar-Deli closed Mon,Tue. Establishment closed 25 Dec, Good Fri. Amex, MasterCard, Visa, Laser. **Directions:** Travelling west from Patricks Bridge, turn left in Cornmarket Street from Coal Quay.

Cork — Bully's Restaurant

Restaurant   40 Paul Street Cork **Tel: 021 273555**

A small, buzzy and inexpensive restaurant in one of the busiest little shopping streets in the city centre, Bully's has built up a strong reputation over the years for good food at reasonable prices. A speciality is pizzas, which had ultra light, crisp bases long before they began to show up in fashionable restaurants; the dough is made on the premises every day using Italian flour. But their No.10 pizza is a Cork Special, with ham, sausage, black and white pudding as well as tomatoes and mozzarella. They serve lots of other things too - freshly made burgers, steaks, omelettes, chicken dishes and pasta - and there's a short, reasonably priced wine list. Pavement seating outside the restaurant for fine weather. No smoking restaurant. **Seats 35** Open Mon-Sat 8am-11.15, Sun 9am-11pm (Open for breakfast in Paul Street only.) A la carte. House wine about €16. Closed 25-26 Dec & 1 Jan.
Also at: 7 Douglas Village East, Douglas, Cork (021-4892415) Mon-Sat, 12-11, Sun 1-10; Open 1 Jan in Douglas only. Amex, MasterCard, Visa, Laser. **Directions:** In Cork city centre, next to Paul Street Shopping Centre. ◇

Cork — Café Gusto

Café

3 Washington Street Cork **Tel: 021 4254446** Fax: 021 4254446
Email: info@cafegusto.com Web: www.cafegusto.com

Big ideas are evident in this little designer coffee bar near Singer's Corner, which specialises in gourmet rolls, wraps and salads, either to go or eat on the premises. The brainchild of Marianne Delaney, previous manager of The Exchange on George's Quay, and her Ballymaloe-trained partner Denis O'Mullane, Café Gusto came to our attention when a reader praised their "exemplary sourcing" - and small is indeed beautiful here, where coffee is made by baristas trained to master standard, using 100% arabica beans from the Java Roasting Company. The same philosophy applies to the food in this tiny café, in a short menu ranging from Simply Cheddar (freshly baked Italian bread filled with with beef tomato, white onion & relish) to The Flying Bacon (filled with chicken, bacon, Emmenthal, honey Dijon, lettuce & tomato). Food prices are not much more than supermarket sandwiches and the extensive selection of coffees, teas, herbal teas etc are good value too. No smoking area; air conditioning. **Seats 20**. Open Mon-Sat, 11 am-5pm. **Directions:** Across from Capitol Cinema. ◇

Cork — Café Paradiso

☆ Restaurant

16 Lancaster Quay Western Road Cork
Tel: 021 4277 939 Fax: 021 4274973
Email: info@cafeparadiso.ie Web: www.cafeparadiso.ie

Even the most committed carnivores love every mouthful at Denis Cotter and Bridget Healy's ground-breaking vegetarian restaurant, which has earned a well-deserved national reputation for exciting mainstream cooking and great service. House specialities that people cross the country for include a delicious goats' cheese, pinenut and oven-roasted tomato charlotte, served with wilted greens and puy lentils in basil oil - which was selected as the guide's Vegetarian Dish of the Year in 2000 and is an excellent example of the cooking style at this colourful little restaurant, It's a lively place with a busy atmosphere and the staff, under the direction of Bridget Healy, are not only friendly and helpful but obviously enthusiastic about their work. Seasonal menus based on the best organic produce available are topped up by daily specials, might include a modish starter like vegetable sushi with tempura of cauliflower & aubergine, pickled ginger, wasabi and a dipping sauce and a broad beans salad with grilled haloumi, crispbreads, wild garlic and a lemon thyme oil.

Irresistible desserts too - gooseberry and almond tartlet with amaretto custard, perhaps, or strawberry baked alaska with summer berry sauce - and some organic wines on a well-priced global list. Significantly, in this era of "cheffy" food and big egos, the creator of this wonderful food decribes himself simply as "owner cook". Many of his creations are featured in the acclaimed Café Paradiso and devotees will be glad to hear that a new book, Café Paradiso Seasons, is due out in early summer 2003. Café Paradiso may be small, but it packs a mighty punch. **Seats 45**. No Smoking area. Toilets wheelchair accessible. LTue-Sat, 12.30-3, D Tue-Sat 6.30-10.30. A la carte. House wines from €12. Service discretionary. Closed Sun, Mon, Christmas, last 2 weeks Aug. MasterCard, Visa, Laser. **Directions:** On Western Road, opposite Jurys Hotel.

Cork — Citrus Restaurant

Ⓝ Restaurant

Barrycourt House East Douglas Village Cork
Tel: 021 4361613 Fax: 021 4361613

Harold Lynch and Beth Haughton already had a strong following from their previous restaurant, Harolds - which was just around the corner - when they opened Citrus in 2002, in spanking new premises which suit the style perfectly. It's a lovely bright space, with windows on two sides and simple uncluttered tables - not a lot to absorb the sound of lots of happy people enjoying Harold's fine cooking but there's a good buzz. The style is international but as much as possible is based on local produce: meats and fish come from the famous butchers, O'Flynns, and fishmongers, O'Connells, for example, both at the English Market. Menus read simply enough but they're full of things you'd just love to try - so why not start with an excellent home-made soup, served with superb breads impeccably sourced from Declan Ryan's Arbutus bakery. On the other hand, you might not be able to resist a baby spinach, goats cheese & walnut salad with walnut dressing - or grilled calamari with chilli, lemon & olive oil...there's a practical middle section of dishes which can go either way - a scrumptious Clonakilty black pudding salad with bacon & rustic potatoes, for example, can be a starter (€6.50) or main course (€11,50) according to your mood - and there's a fair sprinkling of highly tempting vegetarian dishes (tagliatelle with roasted vegetables, pesto & pinenuts, for example) and updated classics such fish & chips with mint pea purée & tartare sauce. Accomplished cooking allows the goodness of excellent raw materials to speak for itself, this is confident, colourful food with great flavours, presented simply to its best advantage. Desserts tend to be variations on favourite themes - meringue roulade with mango & passionfruit sauce is typically delicious - and the wine list is short but sweet. Service, under Beth's supervision, is charming and efficient. **Seats 55.** No smoking area. Toilets wheelchair accessible. Children welcome before 8pm. Open Mon-Sat 10am-10pm (L&D menus), Sun 5.30-9. House wine €12.50. SC discretionary. Amex, MasterCard, Visa, Laser.

Cork — Crawford Gallery Café

Restaurant/Café
Emmet Place Cork
Tel: 021 427 4415 Fax: 021 465 2021 Web: www.ballymaloe.ie

This fine 1724 building houses an excellent collection of 18th- and 19th-century landscapes and has recently has a large new extension added. It is also home to the Crawford Gallery Café, one of Cork city's favourite informal eating places, which is managed by Isaac Allen, son of Darina & Tim Allen, who run the famous Ballymaloe Cookery School, and grandson of Myrtle and Ivan Allen, founders of Ballymaloe House - and, by a remarkable coincidence, also descendant of Arthur Hill, architect of a previous extension to the gallery, completed in 1884. Head chef Keith Woods' menus reflect the Ballymaloe philosophy that food is precious and should be handled carefully, that meals should be happy and convivial and that cooking is an art, so the Gallery Café serves freshly prepared dishes made from natural local ingredients and offers Ballymaloe breads and many of the other dishes familiar to Ballymaloe fans. The menu changes weekly, but the style - a judicious mixture of timeless country house fare and contemporary international dishes featuring carefully sourced meats, fish from Ballycotton and the freshest of seasonal vegetables - remains reassuringly constant. Home-made pickles, relishes, chutneys and preserves are delicious details. A short well-balanced wine list offers a good choice of half and quarter bottles. **Seats 70.** No smoking area. Toilets wheelchair accessible. Open Mon-Sat, 10am-5pm, B'fst 10-12, L 12.30-2.30 (Sat to 3). Set L €18; also à la carte. House wine €16.50. No S. Closed Sun, 24 Dec (after lunch)- early Jan, bank hols. MasterCard, Visa, Laser. **Directions:** City centre, next to Opera House.

Cork — The Crows Nest Bar & Restaurant

Pub/Restaurant
Victoria Cross Cork **Tel: 021 454 3330**
Email: thecrowsnestbarandrestaurant@eircom.net

This large, friendly pub is enormously popular in the locality. Both the bar and upstairs restaurant are bright and colourful in a contemporary (but emphatically not minimalist) style and the selection of past awards collected by the proprietor-chef indicates an encouraging commitment to good food. The restaurant menu is imaginative, with the provenance of some ingredients given, which is confidence-inspiring: steaks are a speciality, for example, and the local butcher who supplies them is credited on the menu. The standard of food and cooking is above average, although longish menus and a busy pub downstairs may make service a little slow noticeably as the pub downstairs fills up with the evening rush. An informative, well-priced wine list includes some lesser-known choices and a fair number of half bottles Not suitable for children after 7 pm. Bar meals 12.30-9 daily (carvery lunch & short à la carte afternoon menu). A large free carpark, on the Carrigrohane Road, is directly opposite. Restaurant **Seats 60.** Air conditioning. Toilets wheelchair accessible. Not suitable for children under 16 after 6pm. Food all day (12-10, Sun from 12.30). D 6-10pm daily (Sun to 9). Set Sun L €19; also à la carte; SC discretionary. House wine €19. Closed 25-26 Dec & Good Fri. Amex, MasterCard, Visa, Diners, Laser, Switch. **Directions:** One mile from City Centre via Western road.

Cork — Dan Lowrey's Tavern

Pub
13 Mc Curtain Street Cork **Tel: 021 4505071**

This characterful pub just across the road from Isaacs was established in 1875 and has been run by Anthony and Catherine O'Riordan since 1995. Long before the arrival of the "theme pub", Lowrey's was famous for having windows which originated from Kilkenny Cathedral, but it also has many of its own original features, including a fine mahogany bar. Catherine O'Riordan herself oversees the kitchen, so it's a good place for an inexpensive home-cooked meal - popular dishes like home-made quiche or lasagne served with salad or fries, for example, or seafood bake, filled with salmon, monkfish & cod, topped with creamed potatoes and toasted breadcrumbs. There's also a nice little quarter-bottle wine list representing Chile, California, Italy and Portugal, all at €3.90 L Mon-Fri, 12.30-3; D daily 7.30-9.30. Closed 25 Dec & Good Fri. **No Credit Cards. Directions:** Next to Metropole Gresham Hotel.

Cork — The Douglas Hide

Pub/Restaurant

63 Douglas Street Cork

Tel: 020 4315695 Email: douglashide@eircom.net

Tadhg and Aoife O'Donovan's narrow little bar is bright and cheerful, with two smallish dining areas behind it, making for a friendly, informal ambience. Despite its small size, it's quite comfortable, with wooden bench seats running along the walls and a young clientele creating a lively atmosphere. Some modern paintings and background music (not too obtrusive) complete the scene, but it's the food that makes this a destination bar. Careful sourcing of ingredients provide the building blocks for good cooking: local meat and fish come from O'Flynns butchers and O'Connells seafood at the English Market, also olives from the Real Olive Co, and smoked fish from Sally Barnes. Sensibly short menus change as the day progresses - imaginative soups, sandwiches, pastas and lightish bites for lunch include some tempting vegetarian options (Durrus cheese and tomato and homemade chutney on ciabatta, for example) while more substantial dinner menus offer tasty starters like dressed crab with a lime & ginger coulis, served with home-made brioche and mains like chicken in a spicy Moroccan sauce with couscous or fish specials (based on market availability). Specialities include O'Flynn's spicy handmade sausages and mash; there's also a Sunday Brunch menu. Outside meal times, it operates as a normal pub, with pub opening times. The standard of food and cooking is high, the service friendly and attentive. **Seats 45**. Toilets wheelchair accessible. No-smoking area. Not suitable for children after 8pm. L daily12-3 (Sun from 12.30), D Tue-Sun 6-10 (Sun to 9); all à la carte; house wines from €15.90. SC discretionary. Closed D Mon, 25 Dec & Good Fri. MasterCard, Visa, Laser. **Directions:** Opposite South Presentation Convent.

Cork — ECO Douglas

Restaurant

1 Eastville Douglas Cork **Tel: 021 4892522** Fax: 021-4895354
Email: mail@eco.ie Web: www.eco.ie

This busy, contemporary restaurant is understandably popular, as it combines interesting menus with good cooking and reasonable prices - a winning formula by any standards, so booking ahead is wise. Space is limited and the decor on the dark side, but the lively buzz compensates for lack of natural light and tables are reasonably spaced, although the small reception area can be a problem if your table isn't ready on arrival: service is usually friendly and helpful, but delays do occur. Perhaps the choice offered - on an interesting international menu with vegetarian dishes considerably highlighted in green - is a bit over-ambitious and it might be wise to opt for specialities such as cajun salmon or stir fries at busy times. Good wine list - over 80 reasonably priced wines from all over the world, including Argentina and Uruguay. Children welcome. Parking can be difficult. **Seats 75** No-smoking area; air conditioning. Open Mon-Sat 12-11, Sun & bank hols D only, 5-11pm. Evening menu from 5 pm. A la carte. House wine about €15. Service discretionary except on parties over 7 (10%). Closed Good Fri, 25-26 Dec. Amex, MasterCard, Visa. **Directions:** In Douglas village - 3 miles out from city centre, 1 mile from airport. ◇

Cork — The Exchange Bar

Pub

1 Buckingham Place Georges Quay Cork

Tel: 021 431 1786 Fax: 021 489 3391 Web: www.theexchangebar.com

Gary & Katie O'Donovan breathed new life into this fine old quayside building when they opened it as a wine bar ("Cork's first wine focused licensed premises"). You'll find oodles of wines by the glass (or bottle) and Ballymaloe-trained chef Mary-Clare Horgan offers a range of wholesome lunchtime food: in addition to daily specials and desserts from a board, a compact menu offers informal fare like home-made soup served with health loaf or olive and tomato bread; salads - typically chicken with roasted peppers, spring onion, balsamic vinaigrette with roasted pinenuts & parmesan shavings - and gourmet sandwiches. Vegetarian dishes are highlighted and there's a range of coffees, teas and hot chocolate (also available in the morning). Unnecessarily loud music can make conversation difficult. **Seats 70**. Bar Food served Mon-Sat 10.30-3 1(Sat 11-3), L menu 12-3. No food serve on Sun. Wine by the glass, from €3.49. MasterCard, Visa, Laser. **Directions:** Waterfront, City Centre. ◇

Cork — Farmgate Café

féile bia Restaurant/Café

Old English Market Cork

Tel: 021 4278134 Fax: 021 4278134

A sister restaurant to the Farmgate Country Store and Restaurant in Midleton, Kay Harte's Farmgate Café shares the same commitment to serving fresh food - and, as it is located above the English

Market, where ingredients are purchased daily, it doesn't come much fresher than this. They serve traditional food, including some famous old Cork dishes with a special market connection - tripe & drisheen and corned beef & champ with green cabbage. Another speciality is "the freshest of fish". All this and home-baked cakes and breads too. Moderately priced meals daytime Mon-Sat. Amex, Diners, MasterCard, Visa, Laser. **Directions:** English Market - off Oliver Plunkett Street & Grand Parade.

Cork — Fenns Quay Restaurant

féile bia Restaurant

5 Fenns Quay Sheares Street Cork
Tel: 021 427 9527 Fax: 021 4279526

Situated in a 250-year old listed building, this is a bright, busy restaurant with a welcoming atmosphere and simple decor enlivened by striking modern paintings. Both lunch and dinner menus offer plenty of interesting choices, with several vegetarian options and daily specials, including seafood sourced daily from the nearby English Market. Carefully sourced ingredients are local where possible (including meat from the owners' own business, which is a point of pride) presented in a contemporary style based on classical cooking; typical examples include honey-blackened duck salad with sweet & sour veg & toasted pumpkin seeds (from a range available as starters or main courses) and fillet steak "Welly style" with sauté potatoes, which is a house speciality. Lunch menus include some informal food, like open sandwich of the day and desserts are all coeliac friendly. The wine list offers variety at reasonable prices, with several by the glass - good value is a feature of both food and drink. The age of the building has made it difficult to provide wheelchair access. *Major expansion and refurbishments were ongoing at the time of going to press. **Seats 60.** Children welcome. On street parking can be difficult during the day but is easy to find after 6.30. No-smoking area; air conditioning. Open all day Mon-Sat 10-10; L 12.30-3, D 6.30-10. A la carte; average L €12, D €25. House wine €16.50. Service discretionary. Closed Sun, 25 Dec, bank hols. Amex, MasterCard, Visa, Laser. **Directions:** Central city - 2 minutes from the Courthouse.

Cork — Flemings

Restaurant/Accommodation

Silver Grange House Tivoli Cork **Tel: 021 482 1621**
Fax: 021 482 1800 Email: flemings@iolfree.ie

Clearly signed off the main Cork-Dublin road, this large Georgian family house is set in well-maintained grounds, including a kitchen garden which provides most of the fruit, vegetables and herbs required for the restaurant during the summer. The light, airy double dining room is decorated in an elegant low-key style that highlights its fine proportions, while well-appointed linen-clad tables provide a fine setting for Michael Fleming's classical cooking. Seasonal table d'hôte and à la carte menus offer a good selection of classics, slightly influenced by current international trends but, even where local ingredients feature strongly, the main thrust of the cooking style is classical French - as in a modern classic starter of foie gras de canard with Timoleague black pudding & Calvados apple. Vegetables are imaginative in selection and presentation, while desserts may include a beautiful tasting plate. Banqueting (80). **Seats 80** (private room 35). No smoking area. Children welcome before 8pm. Lunch and dinner are served every day.
Accommodation: There are four spacious en-suite rooms, comfortably furnished in a style appropriate to the age of the house (B&B €50 pps, ss€20). Closed 24-27 Dec. Amex, Diners, MasterCard, Visa, Laser. **Directions:** Main Cork-Dublin route, 3 km from city centre.

Cork — G's Restaurant

Restaurant

Grafton Mall Grand Parade Cork **Tel: 021 4276430**

Gina Casey's informal café-style restaurant is open through the day and its situation in the Grafton shopping Mall (beside the multi-storey carpark) makes it an ideal meeting place. Gina - whose previous experience includes working at Longueville House and with Michael Clifford - sources ingredients with care and offers a concise menu that varies through the day, beginning with breakfast (from 9 am) and finishing with teas in the afternoon. A sensibly limited range of hot dishes includes a fish of the day, regular main courses might include a tasty vegetarian dish like warm char-grilled salad served on a basil potato cake and topped with vegetable crisps & balsamic dressing - and there's a warning that hot food takes 15-20 minutes to prepare, which is reassuring if you value freshly cooked food. 'Special sambos' like bacon, cheese & tomato melt with relish in a pitta pocket are quicker and old favourites like meringue roulade and chocolate biscuit cake with caramel sauce are equally good as a snack with tea or coffee. A short wine list includes a couple of quarter bottles, but no halves. Children welcome. **Seats 107.** No smoking area; air conditioning. Open Mon-Sat, 9-4.30; L 12-3.30, (average main course about €10). House wine about €118. Closed Sun, bank hols, Christmas. MasterCard, Visa, Laser.

Cork — Great Southern Hotel Cork Airport

Hotel   Cork Airport Cork **Tel: 021 494 7500** Fax: 021 494 750?
Email: res@corkairport-gsh.com Web: www.gshotels.com

This brand new hotel opened in spring 2001 and is very handily located, within walking distance o
the terminal. Ideal for a first or last night's stay, it's also a useful meeting place and is well equippe
for business guests. Rooms have voice mail, fax/modem lines, desk space and TV with in-house
movie channel as well as more usual facilities like radio, hair dryer, tea/coffee trays and trouse
press. There's a business centre with secretarial services and extensive conference/banqueting
facilities (200/100); business centre, secretarial services. Gym, jacuzzi, sauna. Children welcome
(under 2s free in parents room, cot available without charge). Ample free parking. **Rooms 81** (78
executive, 27 no smoking, 4 for disabled). Room rate €150 (max 3 guests). Closed 24-26 Dec. Amex
Diners, MasterCard, Visa, Laser. **Directions:** Situated within Airport Complex.

Cork — Gresham Metropole

 Hotel   MacCurtain Street Cork **Tel: 021 4508122** Fax: 021 450645C
Email: info@gresham-metropolehotel.com Web: www.gresham-hotels.com

This imposing city-centre hotel next door to the Everyman Palace and backing on to the River Lee
celebrated its centenary in 1998. Many of the original features remain, such as the marble facade
outside carved stonework and plaster ceilings inside. Always popular with those connected with the
arts and entertainment industry, there are many displays (photos and press cuttings) of stars pas
and present in the public areas and the atmospheric, traditionally-styled Met Tavern. Recent
refurbishment has greatly improved the bedrooms, most of which now combine a period feel with
modern facilities, and care has been taken to bring previously neglected areas back to their forme
elegance by, for example, correcting ceiling heights which had been changed in previous
'improvements'. Unusually for an old city-centre hotel, there's a splendid leisure club with a large
(and unconventionally shaped) indoor swimming pool, overlooked by the Waterside Café (where
breakfast is served) and also a gym. State of the art conference and meeting facilities have an
conditioining and natural daylight. (400/300). Children under 2 free in parents' room, cots available.
Rooms 113 (2 suites, 18 shower only, 10 no-smoking, 1 for disabled). B&B €100, ss €40. Open al
year. Amex, Diners, MasterCard, Visa, Laser. **Directions:** City centre hotel.

Cork — Hayfield Manor Hotel

Hotel/Restaurant   Perrott Avenue College Road Cork
Tel: 021 4315900 Fax: 021 4316839 Web: www.hayfieldmanor.ie

Set in two acres of gardens next door to University College Cork,
Hayfield Manor Hotel provides every comfort and a remarkable
level of privacy and seclusion just a mile from the city centre.
Although quite new - it only opened in 1996 - it has the genuine
feel of a large period house. Conference rooms of varying sizes
include a library/boardroom beside the drawing room that
doubles as a private dining room. Spacious bedrooms vary in
decor, are beautifully furnished to a very high standard with
antiques and have generous marbled bathrooms with individual
tiling, heated towel rails and quality toiletries. Conference
facilities for up to 120 delegates; secretarial services. Tennis,
golf and fishing nearby. Beauty and massage therapies by
arrangement. Under 5s free in parents' room (cots available). No
pets. **Rooms 87** (5 suites, 12 junior suites, 70 executive rooms;
15 no-smoking, 6 for disabled). B&B about €175 pps, ss about
€75. Open all year.

The Manor Room: As there is no dedicated reception area or cocktail bar attached to the restaurant,
aperitifs must be taken in the bar (which can be noisy), at the table - or, perhaps, in the lobby -
which is not an ideal way to begin a fine dining experience. However, once inside this well-
appointed, traditional dining room, the view over the walled garden at the back of the hotel is
soothing, giving it the quiet, serene atmosphere that head chef Philippe Farineau's fine cooking
deserves. He joined the hotel in 2002, and makes good use of local produce, in impressive classica
cuisine that may have an occasional contemporary twist; he is not afraid of simplicity and, given
the qulity of ingredients and skilful cooking, this is great strength. Service has greatly improved
since the Guide's previous visit, so the combination of accomplished cooking and caring service

should ensure an enjoyable dining experience. Ensure that you are offered the full wine list if taking an aperitif in the bar, as the bar list is very limited. **Seats 90** L12.30-2, D 7-10 (Sun to 9.30). Set L €32. Set D about €55; à la carte also available. House wine about €32. Service discretionary (10% on parties of 8+). *Informal meals are also available in the bar, 11am-8pm daily. Amex, Diners, MasterCard, Visa, Laser.

Cork — Hotel Isaacs

Hotel   48 MacCurtain Street Cork **Tel: 021 450 0011** Fax: 021 450 6355
Email: cork@isaacs.ie Web: www.isaacs.ie/cork

Opposite the theatre and approached through a cobbled courtyard, this attractive hotel offers comfort in spacious rooms at a reasonable price. The bedrooms have attractive polished stripped wood floor, free-standing pine furniture and the usual amenities; some rooms over the street might be noisy, although renovations planned at the time of the Guide's most recent visit (summer 2002) included improving sound insulation as well as opening new rooms and upgrading the existing accommodation. Car park nearby. Lift. **Rooms 36** (all en-suite, some shower-only, some no-smoking, 2 for disabled) B&B about €80pps. Closed 23-26 Dec. Greene's Restaurant. Despite being next door to the well-known Isaacs restaurant (with the confusion of the hotel's similar name) Greene's Restaurant has established itself successfully and is clearly prospering. The atmosphere is more like an independent restaurant than an hotel dining room and the style lively and international; prices are quite reasonable. **Seats 100**. Food served from 7.30 am. Closed 24 Dec(from 3pm) - 28 Dec. Despite being next door to the well-known Isaacs restaurant (with the confusion of the hotel's similar name) Greene's Restaurant has established itself successfully and is clearly prospering. The atmosphere is more like an independent restaurant than an hotel dining room and the style lively and international; prices are quite reasonable. **Seats 100**. Food served from 7.30 am. Closed 24 Dec(from 3pm) - 28 Dec. Diners, MasterCard, Visa. **Directions:** Halfway along MacCurtain Street, opposite Dan Lowrey's Pub. ◇

Cork — Idaho.Café

féile bia Ⓝ Café   19 Caroline Street Cork
Tel: 021 4276376

Baby sister to Jacobs on the Mall, this friendly and exceptionally well-located little café is hitting the spot for discerning shoppers, who appreciate Mairead Jacob's hearty food - this is good home cooking based on the best of ingredients and all the better for that. Belgian waffles with organic maple syrup, crispy duck and brie quesadillas and sheperdess's pie (using organic beef) are all typical of treats in store here. Baking is a speciality, which is just ideal for that quick morning coffee or afternoon tea break - the coeliac friendly 'orange almond' cake has developed quite a following, and gluten free hot drinks are also available. **Seats 30**. No smoking area. Toilets wheelchair accessible. Children welcome. Open Mon-Sat, 8.30-6 (to 5 in summer); L 12-4.30. Licensed: house wine €3.30 (glass). Closed Sun, 24-26 Dec, bank hols. **No Credit Cards. Directions:** Directly behind Brown Thomas, Cork.

Cork — Imperial Hotel

Hotel   South Mall Cork **Tel: 021 427 4040** Fax: 021 427 4040
Email: info@imperialhotelcork.ie Web: www.imperialhotelcork.ie

This thriving hotel in Cork's main commercial and banking centre was taken over by the Flynn family in 1998. It dates back to 1813 and has a colourful history - Michael Collins spent his last night here, no less, and that suite now bears his name. However, it's the convenient location, near the river and just a couple of minutes walk from the Patrick Street shopping area - that makes this hotel so popular for business and pleasure - also the free car parking available for residents. Rooms are all en-suite, with a mixture of furnishings, and there are attractive weekend and off-season rates. Conference/banqueting (300). Private car park. Children welcome; under 12s free in parents' room, cots available. No pets. **Rooms 88** (all en-suite, 5 shower-only). Room rate about €115(max 3 guests) Closed 24-27 Dec. Amex, Diners, MasterCard, Visa, Laser. **Directions:** City centrel ocation. ◇

Cork — Isaacs Restaurant

féile bia Restaurant   48 MacCurtain Street Cork
Tel: 021 450 3805 Fax: 021 455 1348 Email: isaacs@iol.ie

This large, atmospheric modern restaurant in an 18th-century warehouse has been one of the great restaurant success stories, not just in Cork but throughout the country. The co-owners, Michael and Catherine Ryan together with partner/head chef Canice Sharkey, make a great team. Canice cooks tempting, colourful dishes which cleverly combine sunny Mediterranean influences and reassuring Irish traditions - a welcome introduction enjoyed on a recent visit by the Guide was a tapas plate (€8.25), which can be shared and is often just what's needed with a glass of wine, while a number of dishes are offered in a choice of sizes - salmon & potato cake, for example, come with chive mayonnaise & tossed green salad at €7.45/13.65 depending whether it's a starter or main course. Although it has been done in a quiet, low-key way, this restaurant has played a leading role in Ireland's culinary revolution. Isaacs' exciting blend of Irish and international themes, together with a policy of providing great food and good value in an informal, relaxed ambience has proved irresistible since they opened and was way ahead of the current fashion. **Seats 120**. L Mon-Sat 12.30-2.30, D daily 6.30-10.30 (Sun to 9). Short à la carte and daily blackboard specials; vegetarian dishes highlighted. House wine from €16. Service discretionary (10% on parties of 8+). Closed Christmas week. Amex, Diners, MasterCard, Visa, Laser, Switch. **Directions:** Opposite Dan Lowrey's Pub.

Cork — The Ivory Tower

Restaurant   The Exchange Buildings Princes Street Cork **Tel: 021 4274665**

Seamus O'Connell, one of Ireland's most original culinary talents, runs this unusual restaurant upstairs in an early Victorian commercial building. The street entrance (to dowdy office buildings) can be off-putting, also the slightly faded decor of a high-ceilinged dining room without soft furnishings to absorb noise. But tables are comfortable and well-spaced - and what you're here for is Seamus O'Connell's cooking, which is always interesting and often inspired. Very best quality ingredients (all local and organic or wild, including game in season), creative menus and excellent details like delicious home-baked breads and imaginative presentation are the hallmarks of The Ivory Tower - and vegetarian dishes interesting enough to tempt hardened carnivores are always a feature. Menus start off with a "surprise taster" to set the mood and examples from a high summer menu that show the style include a starter of organic globe artichoke with vanilla & lemon beurre blanc, which might be followed by an oyster bloody mary or a little granita, then, from a choice of about nine dishes, perhaps wild salmon hot smoked to order over oak, on a samphire bed & water cress 'chlorophyl'. Desserts are equally unconventional, so why not finish with aphrodisiac of tropical fruits? A shortish wine list includes a number of rare treats, including some organic wines. Children welcome (by prior arrangement). **Seats 40** D Thu-Sun (possibly Wed-Sun in 2003 - phone for details), 6.30-9.30. Set 5-course D €50. 9-course Menu Dégustaton €70; also à la carte. House wine €18-20. SC discretionary. Closed 15-30 Nov. Amex, Diners, MasterCard, Visa, Laser, Switch. **Directions:** Corner of Princes/Oliver Plunkett streets.

Cork — Jacobs On The Mall

féile bia ☆ Restaurant

30A South Mall Cork
Tel: 021 4251530 Fax: 021 4251531

Its location in the former Turkish baths has created a highly unusual and atmospheric contemporary dining space for one of Cork's leading restaurants (possibly the leader; the restaurant hierarchy in Cork city has never been the same since Declan Ryan sold Arbutus Lodge and took up baking). Mercy Fenton returned from abroad to take up the position of head chef here when the restaurant opened in 1998 and she has done a consistently superb job. Modern European cooking is the promise and, with close attention to sourcing the best ingredients allied to outstanding cooking skills, the results are commendably simple and never less than exceptional in terms of balance and flavour. Details like home-made breads are excellent - try the unusual black pepper soda bread - and fresh local and organic produce makes its mark in the simplest of dishes, like delicious mixed leaf salads. Reflecting the availability of local produce, lunch and dinner menus change daily and are sensibly brief - offering a choice of around five to seven dishes on each course, notably seafood and vegetables in season: a simple meal of teamed Kinsale asparagus with lemon butter and seared scallops with potato and chive dressing could be memorable, for example. Creativity with deliciously wholesome and colourful ingredients, accurate cooking, stylish presentation and efficient yet relaxed service all add up to an outstanding dining experience. Finish on a high note - with a Jacobs Dessert plate, perhaps, or farmhouse cheeses, which are always so good in Cork, served here with homemade digestive biscuits and oatcakes. Pianist on some evenings. Children welcome. Special diets willingly accommodated with advance notice. **Seats 130** (Private room, 25, with own bar). No smoking area; air conditioning. Toilets wheelchair accessible. L Mon-

at 12.30-2.30, D Mon-Sat 6.30-10pm. A la carte. House wines €18-22; s.c.10%. Closed Sun, 25-26
, L on bank hols. Amex, Diners, MasterCard, Visa, Laser, Switch. **Directions:** Beside Bank of Ireland,
t the Grand Parade end of the South Mall.

Jacques Restaurant

ork

☆ Restaurant

Phoenix Street Cork **Tel: 021 427 7387**
Fax: 021 427 0634 Email: jacquesrestaurant@eircom.net

An integral part of Cork life since 1982, sisters Eithne and Jacqueline Barry's delightful restaurant has changed with the years, evolving from quite a traditional place to the dashing Mediterranean-toned bistro it is today. There is always a personal welcome and, together with Eileen Carey, who has been head chef since 1989, they are known for putting a high value on the provenance and quality of the food that provides the basic building blocks for their delicious meals. Menus have always been based on carefully sourced ingredients from a network of suppliers built up over many years and this care, together with skill and judgment in the kitchen, shows particularly in having the confidence to keep things simple and allow the food to speak for itself. Menus are refreshingly short, allowing this skilled team to concentrate on the delicious cooking that is their forte - in sun-filled starters such as Spanish salad of chick peas, spinach, roast tomatoes & Serrano ham and main courses including, perhaps, an updated classic of roast stuffed pork on 'Italian' potatoes with with apple sauce & green vegetables. Desserts could be polenta lemon tart & almond cake with rhubarb & mascarpone cheese and nice details include the offer of a half botle of manzanilla sherry with nuts and olives - a delicious and sociable way to start a meal. Consistently good cooking in stylish, relaxed surroundings and service which is unfailingly helpful and attentive have led to Jacques' present position as one of Cork's leading restaurants - and it's excellent value too, especially the early dinner. **Seats 50**. No-smoking area; air conditioning. An interesting, fairly priced wine list includes some organic wines and about ten half bottles. L Mon-Sat 12-3, D Tue-Sat 6-10.30. Early D €16.50 (6-7pm), otherwise à la carte. House wine €16.50. SC discretionary. Closed L Sat, all Sun, D Mon, bank hols & 24 Dec-2 Jan. Amex, MasterCard, Visa, Laser. **Directions:** Rear of Q.P.O, off Pembroke Street.

Jurys Inn Cork

Cork

téile Hotel
bia

Anderson's Quay Cork **Tel: 021 427 6444** Fax: 021 427 6144
Email: julieann_brennan@jurysdoyle.com Web: www.jurysdoyle.com

In a fine central riverside site, this budget hotel has all the features that Jurys Inns have now become well known for: room prices include accommodation for up to four (including a sofa bed) and there is space for a cot (which can be supplied by arrangement). No room service. Limited parking (22 spaces), plus arrangement with nearby car park. **Rooms 133** (7 suitable for disabled guests). Room rate from €75 (max 3 guests). Café/restaurant 7-10am, 6-9.30pm. The Inn Pub bar serves lunch every day and there's a late bar (residents only) every night. (Bar closed on Good Friday). Closed 25 Dec. Amex, Diners, MasterCard, Visa.

The Kingsley Hotel

Cork

Hotel

Victoria Cross Cork
Tel: 021 480 0500 Fax: 021 480 0526
Email: res@kingsleyhotel.com Web: www.kingsleyhotel.com

Conveniently situated in an attractive location alongside the River Lee, just minutes from both Cork airport and the city centre, this modern hotel has been built and furnished to a high standard and is especially attractive for business visitors. The large, comfortably furnished foyer, and an informal restaurant area a few steps up from it (and overlooking the weir), both make good meeting places and accommodation is personally decorated and well-planned to make a good base away from home. Spacious rooms offer traditional comfort and are designed with care: air conditioning, desk space, ISDN lines, interactive TV with message facilities, safes, trouser press with ironing board and same day laundry service all increase the hotel's appeal for business guests - and these details are matched by excellent conference, business and leisure facilities. In addition to the attractive restaurant, private dining facilities are also available, in rooms catering for 16-80 guests. Conference/banqueting (95/80); business centre, secretarial services; video conferencing on request;

24 hour room service. Leisure centre, swimming pool; treatment rooms. Children welcome (under 15 free in parents' room, cot available without charge). Garden. Riverside walks. Pets permitted by arrangement. Parking. Helipad. **Rooms 69** (2 suites, 2 junior suites, 30 no-smoking, 4 for disabled). Lift. B&B about €130pps, ss about €45. Open all year.

Otters at The Kingsley: Set up in contemporary bistro style, with darkwood furniture, comfortably upholstered chairs and uncluttered table settings, this restaurant appeals to non-residents as well as hotel guests. International menus offer plenty of choice without being overlong, typically including Bandon smoked salmon with horesradish cream and 'The Kingsley crispy duck', served on colcannon, with a coriander & mustard seed sauce, or pan-fried West Cork fillet steak, with Lyonnaise potatoes and a thyme & red wine sauce. Service is friendly and professional. **Seats 100** (function room 140). L daily12.30-2.30, D 6-10 (Sun from 6.30). Set L from €21. Also à la carte. House wine from €16.50. SC discretionary. *Lounge and bar food also available through the day. Amex, MasterCard, Visa, Laser. **Directions:** On main N22 Killarney Road by Victoria Cross.

Cork — Lancaster Lodge

Guesthouse

Lancaster Quay Western Road Cork
Tel: 021 425 1125 Fax: 021 425 1126
Email: info@lancasterlodge.com Web: lancasterlodge.com

This guesthouse opened in 1999 and it was built with vision, to offer hotel quality accommodation with personal supervision, at a moderate price. Spacious rooms are furnished to quite a high standard (with ISDN lines, safes, 12 channel TV, trouser press, tea/coffee facilities and room service as well as the more usual facilities) and well-designed bathrooms (two with jacuzzi baths). Good breakfasts are served in a contemporary dining room, or in your room. Maintenance seemed to have slipped a little on a recent visit by the Guide (summer 2002), but this remains a useful address and offers better value for money than many hotels. Children welcome (under 5s free in parents' room, cot available). Parking. 24 hr reception. **Rooms 39** (2 junior suites, 3 shower only, 2 for disabled). Lift. B&B about €75 pps. Closed 23-25 Dec. Amex, Diners, MasterCard, Visa. **Directions:** located alongside Jury's Hotel on Cork's Western Road. ◇

Cork — Lotamore House

Accommodation

Tivoli Cork **Tel: 021 482 2344**
Fax: 021 482 2219 Email: lotamore@iol.ie

This large period house is set in mature gardens and, although not grand, it was built on a generous scale. Big, airy rooms have air conditioning, phones, TV and trouser press (tea/coffee trays on request), and they're comfortably furnished to sleep three, with room for an extra bed or cot and full bathrooms. A large drawing room has plenty of armchairs and an open fire and, although only breakfast and light meals are offered, Fleming's Restaurant (see entry) is next door. Children welcome (Under 5s free in parents' room, cots available, baby-sitting by arrangement; over 5s sharing parents room, 50% discount). Wheelchair access. Own parking. **Rooms 20** (5 no-smoking, 1 for disabled). Garden. Pets permitted. B&B €45pps, ss €10. Closed 20 Dec-7 Jan. Amex, MasterCard, Visa. **Directions:** On N8, 5 minutes drive from Cork City.

Cork — Lovetts Restaurant & Brasserie

Restaurant

Churchyard Lane off Well Road Douglas Cork
Tel: 021 429 4909 Email: lovetts@utvinternet.com

Home to both the restaurant and the Lovett family since 1977, this fine restaurant is in a late Georgian house situated in mature grounds. Ownership is now in the capable hands of Niamh Lovett jointly with head chef Marie Harding, a talented and creative cook who has been at Lovetts since 1991 who is committed to serious cooking, using the best of fresh, free range and local products. Marie's treasured suppliers are credited - duck's from Barry's of Fermoy, for example, smoked salmon and eel from Cresswells of Ummera and so on - on a number of menus: a refreshingly concise à la carte, a good value Brasserie menu and a 2-course vegetarian option. Menus demonstrate her interest in developing modern Irish dishes which sometimes acknowledge world influences: roast rack of spring lamb, for example, may be served with a lovage & bacon jus & Serrano ham potato cake; fish dishes depend on daily availability and are given as specials. There's a fully licensed bar (the extensive wine list is Niamh's father Dermod Lovett's particular passion) and private dining is available in the 'Wine Geese' Room. Accomplished and consistently interesting cooking and warmly professional service, under Niamh's supervision, ensure a loyal following. **Seats 60.** (Private room 6-24). No-smoking restaurant (smoking allowed in the bar). Vegetarian Menu €20, otherwise à la carte. House wine from about €18. Service discretionary. Brasserie & Restaurant: DTue-Sat, 6.30-10. Closed Sun,

Mon, bank hols, Christmas week, 1 week Aug. Amex, Diners, MasterCard, Visa, Laser. **Directions:** Close to south Cork city: from Douglas Road take turning to Mahon and Blackrock and go through a roundabout. Take the fourth turn on the left, Wells Road; Lovetts is off it in Churchyard Lane.

Cork — Maryborough House Hotel

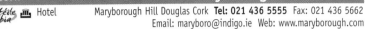

féile bia ⛰ Hotel   Maryborough Hill Douglas Cork **Tel: 021 436 5555**   Fax: 021 436 5662
Email: maryboro@indigo.ie Web: www.maryborough.com

The Maryborough House Hotel has at its heart a fine country house set in its own grounds and gardens and has been developed with sensitivity. The original house, which is beautifully proportioned, has many fine features, restored with care and furnished in period style with antiques. The main entrance is via the original flight of steps up to the old front door and, as there is no conventional reception area, guests check in at the desk just inside the front door. The new section of the hotel, which is modern and blends comfortably with the trees and gardens surrounding it, includes excellent leisure facilities and well-designed accommodation: simple, modern and bright, utilising Irish crafts. Generously-sized rooms have a pleasant outlook, good amenities and extras including complimentary mineral water; bathrooms are well-finished and well-lit, with plenty of marbled shelf space, and a robe; they have environmentally friendly toiletries and suggestions on saving water by avoiding unnecessary laundry - which may explain why baths and towels are both uncomfortably small. Extensive conference and banqueting facilities have a separate entrance; three new meeting rooms have recently been added. Conference/banqueting (500/350). Leisure centre, swimming pool. Snooker. Children welcome (under 2s free in parents room, cots available). No pets. Garden. **Rooms 79** (2 suites, 3 junior suites, 74 executive rooms, 10 no-smoking, 8 for disabled). Lift. B&B €80, ss €65. Closed 24-26 Dec.]

Zings Restaurant: This contemporary dining area is now more logically located next to the bar, which has been moved up from its original position on the lower ground floor; it is cleverly designed to create several areas without physical divisions, partly through use of lighting - and the tables of lone diners who wish to read are considerably spotlit. Gerry Allen, who has been head chef since the hotel opened in 1997, offers European cuisine with traditional and Mediterranean flavours - a speciality based on local produce that sums up the style neatly is rack of lamb with garlic, provençal vegtables & rosemary jus. While not exceptional, menus offer plenty of choice and staff are helpful. Not suitable for children after 7pm. **Seats 140.** No smoking area; air conditioning. L daily 12.30-2.30, D 6.30-9.30. Set L €22; D à la carte. House wine from €20. SC discretionary. * Bar meals also available every day, 9.30am-9.30pm. Amex, Diners, MasterCard, Visa, Laser. **Directions:** Near Douglas village; signed from roundabout where Rochestown Road meets Carrigaline Road.

Cork — Milano

🅝 Restaurant   8 Oliver Plunkett Street Cork
Tel: 021 4273106 Fax: 021 4273107

This spacious modern restaurant is one of a small chain operated in Ireland by the UK company PizzaExpress. Like its sister restaurants (see Dublin) it specialises in providing good moderately priced Italian food - mainly, but not exclusively, authentic pizzas and pastas - in stylish surroundings. Consistency and good service are their strong points and they're happy to cater for large parties, drinks receptions and so on. Live jazz on Wednesady nights. **Seats 120.** No smoking area; air conditioning. Toilets wheelchair accessible. Children welcome. Open daily, noon-midnight (Sun to 11); à la carte. House wine €16.60. Closed 25-26 Dec. Amex, Diners, MasterCard, Visa, Laser. **Directions:** City centre.

Cork — Nakon Thai Restaurant

Restaurant   Tramway House Douglas Village Cork
Tel: 021 436 9900 Fax: 021 488 8002
Email: nakonthai@eircom.net Web: www.nakonthai.com

Efficient reception gets guest off to a good start at this smart new restaurant in Douglas village. Authenticity is to be expected as the chef, Samai Singkham, was previously head chef at the Dusit Thani in Bangkok and the aim is to provide traditional Thai cuisine in a relaxed and friendly atmosphere, although the flavours typical of Thai cuisine - coriander, lime, chilli, saltiness - seem to have been tamed somewhat, presumably to meet local demand. Several set menus are offered and a à la carte that may seem overlong, but there is considerable overlap between dishes that are basical similar and everything is freshly cooked, without any artificial flavourings or MSG. If in doubt try som of the house specialities such as hot & sour prawn soup, or a sizzling dish of fried beef with chill onion, pepper, garlic & spring onions. A limited dessert selection includes exotic Thai fruit salad fc a refreshing finish. Informative fairly priced wine list, also imported Thai beers. Not suitable fc children after 7pm. **Seats 42.** No smoking area. Air conditioning. D daily 5.30-11. Set menus fro €24.75; à la carte also available. House wine from €14.95. PSC discretionary. Closed 3 day Christmas. Amex, Diners, MasterCard, Visa, Laser. **Directions:** Douglas Village opposite Rugby Club.

Cork   Pí Restaurant

Restaurant   Courthouse Chambers Washington Street Cor
                                                     Tel: 021 4222 860 Fax: 021 4273 72

Most of the produce is local and comes from the nearby English Market, but contempora international food for all is the aim at this large, bright modern restaurant, which is especially popula with families. Reception is friendly and there's seating at the bar as well as a sizeable seating are to have a drink and wait comfortably for your table. Pizzas are the main speciality, but there's also shortish à la carte of more 'grown-up' dishes - about ten on each course, typically starting with duc confit salad and progressing to dishes including a perfectly cooked fillet steak with 3-peppercorn wild mushroom sauce, or tapenade roast hake, with spring onion & basil beurre blanc. Vegetaria dishes are marked up and there are lots of gooey desserts and icecreams (yes, including 'Pi Scream') An extensive, unusual and wide-ranging wine list includes a large selection available by the glass Good cooking, good service and good value in a fun atmosphere keep people coming back for more Children welcome. **Seats 100+.** Air conditioning. Open daily 12-11: L 12-5, D 6-11. À la carte. Hous wine about €18 (glass, about €4.50). SC discretionary. Amex, MasterCard, Visa, Laser. **Directions** Across from the Courthouse on Washington Street. ◇

Cork   Proby's Bistro

Restaurant/Accommodation   Proby's Quay Crosses Green Cor
                                                     Tel: 021 431 6531 Fax: 021 497588
                              Email: info@probysbistro.com Web: www.probysbistro.cor

Handier to the city centre than it first appears, this is a pleasant spot for a bite to eat during the day (tables outside for fine weather) as well as in the evening, when a piano bar is an adde attraction. The style - established before the current wave and competently executed - is globa cuisine, with an emphasis on things Mediterranean. Menus - which include a fast lunch and early dinner as well as à la carte choices - offer lively fare with an international tone yet plenty of loca produce; West Cork black pudding is a favourite starter (served with grainy mustard sauce & colcannon), and duck confit (with red wine jus, crushed baby potatoes with chives & sautéed julienne of fresh potatoes) is a speciality main course. Specials change daily and there's a special seafood nigh on Wednesdays (Set D €25). Piano some evenings. Children welcome. **Seats 120** (private room 40) Air conditioning, no-smoking area. Open Mon-Sat, 10 am - midnight: L 12-5, D 6-10 (Fri & Sat to 11) Early D EIR13.95 (6-7.30), otherwise à la carte; SC discretionary (except 12% on parties of 8+). House wine €15.50. Closed Sun, bank hols, 3-4 days at Christmas. Amex, MasterCard, Visa, Laser. **Directions** Adjacent to St. Finbarre's Cathedral and Beamish & Crawford brewery.

Cork   Rochestown Park Hotel

féile bia Hotel   Rochestown Road Douglas Cork **Tel: 021 489 0800** Fax: 021 489 2178
                              Email: info@rochestownpark.com Web: www.rochestownpark.com

Formerly a home of the Lord Mayors of Cork, this attractive hotel stands in lovely grounds and the original parts of the building feature gracious, well-proportioned public rooms. Since opening ir 1989 the hotel has seen many changes under the watchful eye of General Manager Liam Lally. Rooms are furnished to a high standard with all the comforts - including air conditioning, ISDN lines, fax and safe in executive rooms, as well as the more usual conveniences like tea/coffee trays, multi-channel TV and trouser press, all of which make this a popular base for business guests, who are well looked after in an executive wing. Facilities include a fine leisure centre with a Roman style 20-metre swimming pool, sauna, steam room and computerised gymnasium, as well as a Thalasso Therapy centre which pre-dates the current fashion for spas by a good few years: seaweed baths, seaweed wraps, hydrojets, therapeutic pools and massage aim to provide relaxation and renewal for both body and mind. They also offer reflexology and beauty treatments including Yonka facials. Conference and meeting facilities are amongst the best in the country. Conference/banqueting (700/500); video conferencing on request. Children welcome (under 5s free in parents' room; cots

vailable). Leisure centre, indoor swimming pool, beauty salon. Garden. Parking. No pets. **Rooms 62** (1 suite, 10 junior suites, 90 executive rooms, 3 for disabled). Lift. 24 hour room service. B&B rom €65pps, ss about €30. SC 12.5%. Short breaks offered. Closed 24-26 Dec.
Gallery Restaurant: The restaurant is in a pleasant position overlooking the hotel gardens; the mbience and service are both good and head chef Gerry Kirwin ensures that the food goes beyond the xpectations of a hotel dining room, making dining-in a positive option for residents. Menus, which hange monthly, are well-balanced and always include some strong vegetarian options in starters like oasted beetroot & orange salad or a main course of polenta, spinach & goats cheese with roasted pine ernels, tomato & herb vinaigrette; prime Irish beef is a speciality and there's always a choice of local eafood. Set menus are good value. L&D daily. SC 12.5%. Amex, Diners, MasterCard, Visa, Laser. **Directions:** Adjacent to South ring road which links all main routes into Cork city.

Cork   Seven North Mall

Accommodation   7 North Mall Cork **Tel: 021 4397191**
                                    Fax: 021 4300811 Email: sevennorthmall@eircom.net

Angela Hegarty runs one of the city's most pleasant guesthouses, on a tree-lined south-facing mall overlooking the River Lee. Rooms in this 1750s townhouse are all spacious, individually furnished in keeping with the house (with bathrooms skilfully built in) and good amenities. Some rooms have river views and there is a ground floor room specially designed for disabled guests. Excellent breakfasts. Many of the city's best restaurants, pubs, museums, galleries and theatres are within a short walk. Not suitable for children under 12. **Rooms 7** (1 shower only,1 for disabled). B&B €60 pps, ss €25. Closed 21 Dec-6 Jan. MasterCard, Visa, Laser. **Directions:** Near North Gate Bridge, city centre.

Cork   Silver Springs Moran Hotel

féile bia Hotel   Tivoli Cork **Tel: 021 450 7533** Fax: 021 455 2466
                        Email: silver@morangroup.ie Web: www.silverspringhotel.ie

This well-known hotel, situated in 25 acres of landscaped gardens about five minutes drive from the city centre, is a modern tower block overlooking the River Lee and has an eye-catching external glass lift; spacious bedrooms are furnished to a high standard, with safe and fax available on request in addition to the usual facilities; they have good bathrooms and some share the view. A self-contained convention centre has conference/banqueting facilities for 1400/1000 guests respectively; secretarial service available Mon-Fri; video-conferencing. A well-equipped leisure centre is a short walk uphill. Pool table. Garden, tennis, walking. **Rooms 109** (2 suites, 3 junior suites, 16 no-smoking rooms, 5 disabled). B&B €90 pps, ss€25. Amex, Diners, MasterCard, Visa, Laser. **Directions:** At the Tivoli flyover above the main Cork Dublin road and clearly signed off it. (From Cork, take first left then right at the flyover.)

Cork   Table 8

N Restaurant   8/9 Careys Lane Cork **Tel: 021 4270725** Fax: 021 4270694

Husband and wife team Chris and Eleanor O'Brien took over this bright, modern restaurant in a characterful area of the city early in 2002. Eleanor is the restaurant manager while Chris, who trained at Ballymaloe House, offers moderately priced menus with strong Mediterranean and some modern Irish influences - as in starters like Greek salad or Mediterranean salad with goats cheese, and main courses such as roast cod with prawn colcannon & chive velouté and chargrilled chicken with roast flat mushrooms and tomato & basil sauce. Chris bakes all the breads on the premises and desserts - vanilla ice cream with rhubarb & strawberry compôte - are also home-made. Ground floor wheelchair accessible. **Seats 100.** L Mon-Sat, 12-3.30; D Mon-Sat, 5.30-"late". Early D €20 (5.30-7.30), otherwise à la carte. Closed Sun, bank hols, 25-26 Dec. Diners, MasterCard, Visa, Laser. **Directions:** On Carey's Lane, pedestrian street between Patrick St & Paul Street in the centre of Cork.

Cork   The Wine Vault

Pub   Lancaster Quay Western Road Cork **Tel: 021 275751**

Situated just across the road from the entrance to Jurys Hotel, Reidy's Wine Vault makes a convenient meeting place and can be a good choice for a quick bite to eat. Originally a wine warehouse, it has been imaginatively converted to its present use, with a high vaulted ceiling and an attractive mixture of old and new fixtures and furnishings. Noelle Reidy supervises the food personally and early visitors will be greeted by the aroma of bread baking at the back, shortly followed by soups, pies and casseroles (shepherd's pie, Irish stew) for lunch, all marked up on the blackboard as they come on stream; don't overlook the home-cooked Cork spiced beef, which is a local speciality. Closed 25 Dec, Good Fri. Amex, Diners, MasterCard, Visa. **Directions:** Western Road, opposite Jurys Hotel. ◇

COUNTY CORK

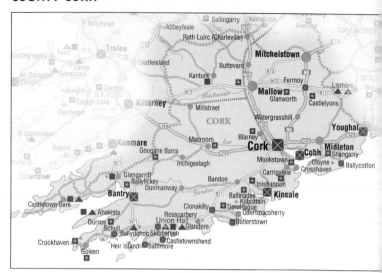

Cork is Ireland's largest county, and its individualistic people take pride in this distinction as they savour the variety of their territory, which ranges from the rich farmlands of East Cork, away westward to the handsome coastline of West Cork where the mighty light of the famous Fastnet Rock swings across tumbling ocean and spray-tossed headland.

The county's many towns and villages have their own distinctive character. Midleton in East Cork is home to the Jameson Heritage Centre, where the fascinating story of whiskey is entertainingly told in a town which is also the locality for Irish Distillers' manufacturing headquarters, producing Jameson, Power's and Paddy whiskeys together with many variants, as well as Huzzar Vodka and Cork Dry Gin.

At the far end of East Cork, 2003 sees the opening of the by-pass around the ancient port of Youghal, an intriguing place which is re-discovering itself now that the blight of excessive through traffic has been removed. The spectacularly located township of Cobh - facing south over Cork Harbour - is also asserting its own identity, with a renewed sense of its remarkable maritime heritage being expressed through events such as a Sea Shanty Festival, while the town's direct link with the Titanic is celebrated in many ways.

The county is a repository of the good things of life, a treasure chest of the finest farm produce, and the very best of seafood, brought to market by skilled specialists. But it isn't all work by any means. As Ireland's most southerly county, Cork enjoys the mildest climate of all, and it's a place where they work to live, rather than live to work. The arts of living, in fact, are probably seen at their most skilled in County Cork, and they are practised in a huge territory of such variety that it is difficult to grasp it all, even if you devote your entire vacation to this one county.

Local Attractions and Information

Ballydehob Nature Art Centre	028 37323
Bantry Bantry House	027 50047
Bantry Murphy's International Mussel Fair (May)	027 50360
Bantry Tourism Information	027 50229
Blarney Blarney Castle	021 438 5252
Cape Clear Island International Storytelling Festival (early September)	028 39157
Carrigtwohill Fota Estate (Wildlife Park, Arboretum)	021 481 2728
Castletownroche Annes Grove (gardens)	022 26145
Clonakilty Lisselan Estate Gardens	023 33249
Cobh The Queenstown Story	021 481 3591
Cobh Sirius Arts Centre	021 481 3790
Cork Airport	021 431 3131
Glanmire Dunkathel House	021 482 1014
Glanmire Riverstown House	021 482 1205

lengarriff Garinish Island | 027 63040
insale Gourmet Festival (October) | 021 477 2234
insale Charles Fort | 021 477 2263
insale Desmond Castle | 021 477 4855
insale Tourism Information | 021 477 2234
lacroom Brierly Gap Cultural Centre | 026 42421
lallow Cork Racecourse | 022 50207
lidleton Jameson Heritage Centre | 021 461 3594
lillstreet Country Park | 029 71810
lizen Head Mizen Vision Signal Station | 028 35591
hanagarry Ballymaloe Cookery School Gardens | 021 464 6785
chull Ferries to Sherkin, Cape Clear and Fastnet | 028 28278
chull Schull Planetarium | 028 28552
kibbereen Creagh Gardens | 028 22121
kibbereen Tourism Information | 028 21766
kibbereen West Cork Arts Centre | 028 22090
oughal Myrtle Grove | 024 92274

Ahakista — Ahakista Bar

ub — Ahakista Durrus Co. Cork **Tel: 027 67203**

Anthony and Margaret Whooley run one of the most relaxed bars in the country: known affectionately as "the tin pub" because of its corrugated iron roof, it has a lovely rambling country garden going down to the water at the back, where children are very welcome to burn off excess energy. It's been in the family for two generations now and, although finally succumbing to the telephone after years of resistance, it's a place that just doesn't change. Normal pub hours don't apply in this part of the world, but they're open from 12 noon and evenings all year, except 25 Dec & Good Fri. **Directions:** Sheeps Head, round from Durrus. ◇

Ahakista — Hillcrest House

Farmhouse — Ahakista Durrus Co. Cork **Tel: 027 67045**
Email: hillcrestfarm@ahakista.com Web: www.ahakista.com

Agnes Hegarty's traditional farmhouse attracts many types of visitor, including walkers, who revel in the 55 mile "Sheep's Head Way" - and hospitality comes first at this working farm overlooking Dunmanus Bay, where guests are welcomed with a cup of tea and home-baked scones on arrival. The bedrooms were all refurbished in 2002, and have power showers, very comfortable beds, tea/coffee making facilities and clock radios. The dining room is furnished with antiques and moderately priced evening meals are offered to guests as well as fine cooked-to-order breakfasts; guests also have the use of a comfortable sitting room with an open fore and television - and, for families, there's a large games room, a swing and a donkey on the farm. Although beautifully situated, with wonderful views over Dunmanus Bay, Hillcrest House is not as remote as it feels, and it's only a short walk to the beach, or to the shops and pubs in the village. Hillcrest was our Farmhouse of the Year in 2001. **Rooms 4**. B&B €34 pps (Under 2s free in parents' room, cot available without charge.) Evening meals by arrangement (7 pm; €22); light meals also available. Closed 1 Nov-1 Apr. Visa. **No Credit Cards. Directions:** 3 km from Bantry, take turn for Durrus.

Ballinadee — Glebe House

Country House — Ballinadee nr Kinsale Co Cork **Tel: 021 477 8294** Fax: 021 477 8456
Email: glebehse@indigo.ie Web: http://indigo.ie/~ glebehse/

Church records provide interesting detail about this charming old rectory near Kinsale which dates back to 1690 (when it was built for £250; repairs and alterations followed at various dates, and records show completion of the present house in 1857 at a cost of £1,160). More recently, under the hospitable ownership of Gill Good, this classically proportioned house has been providing a restful retreat for guests since 1989. The house, which is set in beautiful, well-tended gardens (including a productive kitchen garden) has spacious reception rooms and large, stylishly decorated bedrooms with phone and tea/coffee making facilities. The Rose Room is on the ground floor, with french doors to the garden. A 4-course candle-lit dinner for residents, much of it supplied by the garden, is served at a communal table (please book by noon). Although unlicensed, guests are encouraged to bring their own wine. The whole house may be rented by parties by arrangement and several self-catering apartments are also available. Children welcome (cot available). Pets permitted. **Rooms 4** (2 shower only, all no-smoking), B&B €45 pps, ss €12. Residents' D €30, at 8 pm. Closed Christmas & New

Year. MasterCard, Visa, Diners. **Directions:** Take N71 west from Cork to Innishannon Bridge, go ove
bridge and take a sharp left. Travel 6 miles. After village sign, 1st on right.

Ballycotton   Bayview Hotel

Restaurant/Hotel   Ballycotton Co Cork **Tel: 021 464 6746** Fax: 021 464 607
                                               Email: info@bayviewhotel.net Web: www.bayviewhotel.ne

Overlooking Ballycotton Harbour, Bayview Hotel enjoys a magnificent location on the sea side of th
road and with a path to the beach through its own gardens. Since 1971 the hotel has been owne
by John and Carmel O'Brien, who completely rebuilt it - fairly low, and sympathetic to the tradition
style and scale of the surrounding buildings and harbour - in the early 1990s. Comfortable, home
public areas are complemented by spacious well-furnished bedrooms with good bathrooms; the
open on to small balconies and include two corner suites (with jacuzzi) and some particularly cos
top floor rooms. Small conferences/banqueting (40/80). Children under 12 free in parents' room (cc
available without charge). No pets. **Rooms 35** (2 suites, 3 no-smoking rooms, 5 wheelchai
accessible) B&B €107pps, ss €32. Closed 30 Oct-17 Apr.
Capricho at the Bayview: Head chef Ciaran Scully has been at the Bayview since 1996 and his creativ
daily menus are modern Irish, developed from a classic French base. This talented chef promises a
interesting and satisfying dining experience, especially when complemented by an elegantly appointe
restaurant with lovely sea and harbour views and good service. His menus offer less usual dishes suc
as honey & mustard pigs cheek with a purée of swede turnip & caramelised crispy cabbage and braise
crubeen with sweetbreads & wood mushrooms in addition to a wide selection of better known loca
seafood, meats and interesting vegetarian dishes. Desserts include classics like tangy lemon tart, serve
with poached rhubarb & vanilla ice cream, or there's a farmhouse cheese selection - served with a glas
of port. In fine weather, light meals may be served in the garden. An extensive wine list includes
good choice of half bottles. **Seats 65** (private room 36). Toilets wheelchair accessible. No smokin
area. D 7-9 daily, L 12.30-6 (Sun 1-2). Set D €45; also à la carte. Wine from about €25. (Bar meal
available 12.30-5.30 daily). Amex, Diners, MasterCard, Visa, Laser. **Directions:** At Castlemarty on th
N25 turn onto the R632 in the direction of Garryroe.

Ballycotton   Grapefruit Moon

🅝 Restaurant   Main Street Ballycotton Co Cork **Tel: 021 464 664**

Ivan Allen - previously a teacher at Ballymaloe Cookery School and chef at Ballymaloe House- an
Jean Manning opened this little restaurant in the spring of 2002 and word of it quickly spread aroun
the county. The large banner proclaiming the name would be hard to miss (in daylight anyway)
inside it's bright and cheerful with white walls, modern art, comfortable seats and a livel
atmosphere - and promising well-appointed tables, with white linen and fresh flowers. Daily menus
while not over-extensive, are adventurous and wide-ranging: for example, you might find an
unusual starter of wakame seaweed with pickled ginger, pine nuts and smoked seafood (eel, mussel
& salmon) and main courses like Shanghai fried noodles with crispy duck, spring onions, chilli
garlic, ginger, mangetout & pak choi. Seafood (all from Ballycotton harbour) features strongly
(poached monkfish with red pepper sauce, perhaps) and vegetarian dishes are always particularl
appealing. Classic desserts include old favourites like strawberry meringue roulade and bread &
butter pudding, with butterscotch sauce & vanilla ice cream - or Irish farmhouse cheese, of course
Friendly and attentive staff, interesting and accomplished cooking and a good atmosphere add u
to a winning formula: this attractive and interesting restaurant has found a niche in an area well
served by good restaurants and looks set to succeed. Short but varied wine list is to be expanded
Seats 40. No smoking area. Children welcome. D Tue-Sat, 6.30-10. A la carte (average main course
about €19). House wine €15. SC discretionary. Closed Christmas, 1 week Jan, 2 weeks Nov.
Directions: In the middle of the village.

Ballycotton   Spanish Point Seafood Restaurant

Restaurant/Accommodation   Ballycotton Co Cork **Tel: 021 4646177**
                                               Fax: 021 4646179 Email: spanish@indigo.ie

Halfway through the village of Ballycotton you suddenly come upon the entrance to Spanish Point
an attractive old building on the seaward side of the road with a clear view across the bay. John
and Mary Tattan have been running this relaxed seafood restaurant since 1991 and have built up a
considerable reputation locally. The Tattans take pride in using local produce, especially fish from
the family's two trawlers, and the arrival of head chef Frederic Desormeaux in 1999 has eased Mary's
work in the kitchen and introduced new dishes to menus that are interesting without being over
complicated: dishes like goujons of lemon sole with a basil & lime mayonnaise, or filo parcels of

resh crab with a chive butter sauce are typical of the new style. Aperitifs are served and orders taken in a little lounge/bar at the back or the sun lounge; menus change weekly and majoring on local seafood, of course, but also plenty of other choices, including vegetarian dishes. The restaurant is in two rooms (one a conservatory) overlooking the harbour or, weather permitting, outside on a sun deck - a lovely setting for good food, cooked and presented with care, and with service to match. The wine list includes an interesting house selection. Small conferences/banqueting (30/60) by arrangement. **Seats 60** (private room 20). No smoking area. L&D daily: L 12.30-2.30, D 6.30-9.30; Set L €22, early D €30 (6.30-7), Set D €30-40. House wine about €16.50. A la carte also offered. Service discretionary. Low season open weekends only - phone for details.
Accommodation: Comfortable, well-furnished bedrooms all have sea views and good amenities including phone, TV and tea/coffee trays. Children welcome (cot available without charge). Pets permitted. **Rooms 5** (all shower only & no smoking) B&B €40 pps, ss €10. Closed Nov-Apr. MasterCard, Visa, Laser. **Directions:** Off the N25.

Ballydehob — Annie's Restaurant

Restaurant   Main Street Ballydehob Co Cork **Tel: 028 37292**

Anne and Dano Barrie have been running their cottagey restaurant for 20 years - and, for many, a visit to West Cork is unthinkable without a meal here; quality, value and personal service are the key to their success and people return year after year. Despite recent enlargement and refurbishments, this is the same old Annies - she is a great host, welcoming everybody personally, handing out menus - and then sending guests over to Levis' pub across the road for an aperitif. Then she comes over, takes orders and returns to collect people when their meals are ready - a famous arrangement that works extremely well. As to the food at Annie's, everything is freshly made on the day, using local ingredients - fish is delivered every night, meat comes from the local butcher (who kills his own meat), farmhouse cheeses are local (including one of Ireland's most renowned cheeses, Gubeen, which is made by Annie's sister-in-law Giana Ferguson) and all the breads, ice creams and desserts for the restaurant - and for 'Clara' (see below) - are made on the premises. Dano's cooking is magnificently simple - and he cooks fish like a dream. This place is magic. Children welcome, but not after 9 pm. Street parking only. **Seats 40.** Toilets wheelchair accessible. No smoking area; air conditioning. Children welcome - but not after 9pm. D Tue-Sat 6.30-10, Set D € 42; à la carte also offered. House wine €16. SC discretionary. Closed Sun & Mon, all Oct-Nov & 24-27 Dec. *Café Clara, Annie's sister restaurant up the road is a cafe/bookshop and is, in Annie's own true words: "Cheep & cheerful - honest to god soups, sandwiches and daily specials". Open Mon-Sat, 10.30-5 all year. Closed Sun, bank hols. MasterCard, Visa **Directions:** Centre of village.

Ballydehob — Levis' Bar

Pub   Corner House Main Street Ballydehob Co Cork **Tel: 028 37118**

Julia and Nell Levis have run this 150-year-old bar and grocery for as long as anyone can remember. It is a characterful and delightfully friendly place, whether you are just in for a casual drink or using the pub as the unofficial 'reception' area for Annie's restaurant across the road (see entry for Annie's above). Closed 25 Dec & Good Fri. **Directions:** Centre of village.

Ballylickey — Ballylickey Manor House

Country House   Ballylickey Co Cork **Tel: 027 50071** Fax: 027 50124
Email: ballymh@eircom.net Web: homepage.eircomnet/~ballymh

Built some 300 years ago by Lord Kenmare as a shooting lodge and home to the Franco-Irish Graves family for four generations, Ballylickey Manor enjoys a stunning, romantic setting overlooking Bantry Bay, with moors and hills behind. There are ten acres of gardens, through which the Ouvane river (trout and salmon fishing) flows. Choose between the elegant and grand bedrooms in the Manor, all lavishly furnished, or more rustic accommodation in the garden - cottages and chalets, some grouped around the outside swimming pool. Dinner for residents is served in a lovely period dining room. Garden, outdoor heated swimming pool. Family accommodation "on application" (cot available, about €25). No pets. Private parking. **Rooms 12** (7 suites, 5 en-suite) B&B about €130 pps. Closed Nov-Mar. Amex, Diners, MasterCard, Visa. **Directions:** On N71 between Bantry & Glengariff. ◇

Ballylickey — Larchwood House Restaurant

Restaurant   Pearsons Bridge Ballylickey Co Cork **Tel: 027 66181**

The gardens are a special point of interest here, complementing the restaurant, which is in a relatively modern house with both the traditionally-furnished lounge and dining room enjoying lovely views. Sheila Vaughan, a Euro-Toques chef, presents seasonal dinner menus: smoked salmon with citrus salad, an unusual soup such as nettle & apple, loin of lamb with lemon and mint, and crème caramel with rhubarb coulis - good cooking, although a meal can take longer than might be expected. The garden setting is a treat though - there are acres to explore, river boulders to cross and nothing prettier than the wild bluebell wood in spring. (B&B accommodation is also offered). **Seats 25**. D Mon-Sat, 7-9.30. Set D €38. House wine €20. SC discretionary. Closed Sun & Christmas week. Amex, Diners, MasterCard, Visa. **Directions:** Take the Kealkil Road off N71 at Ballylickey; after 2 miles signed just before the bridge.

Ballylickey — Seaview House Hotel

 Hotel/Restaurant   Ballylickey Co Cork **Tel:** 027 50462 Fax: 027 5155
Email: info@seaviewhousehotel.com Web: www.seaviewhousehotel.com

Personal supervision and warmth of welcome are the hallmarks of Kathleen O'Sullivan's restorative country house hotel close to Ballylickey Bridge. Spacious, well-proportioned public rooms include a graciously decorated drawing room, a library, cocktail bar and television room, while generously-sized bedrooms - some in a fine new wing and many with sea views - are all individually decorated with good bathrooms. Family furniture and antiques enhance the hotel and standards of maintenance and housekeeping are consistently high. Children welcome (free in parents' room under 4, cot available without charge). Pets permitted by arrangement. **Rooms 25** (some junior suites, 2 rooms suitable for less able guests.) B&B from about €65pps, ss about €30.
Restaurant: Overlooking the garden, with views over Bantry Bay, the restaurant is elegant and well-appointed with antiques, fresh flowers and plenty of privacy. Set five-course dinner menus change daily and offer a wide choice on all courses, with the emphasis firmly on local produce, especially seafood, in dishes like simple Irish oak smoked salmon, bacon & spinach salad or lemon sorbet sorbet, brill in a light wine sauce or roast stuffed duckling with port & orange sauce. Choose from classic desserts - glazed lemon tart, fresh peach Melba - or local cheeses to finish. Tea or coffee and petits fours may be served out of doors on fine summer evenings. **Seats 50**. No-smoking restaurant. Toilets wheelchair accessible. No music. D 7-9 daily, L Sun only 12.45-2; Set D about €36, Set Sun L about €20. House wines from about €16.50. SC 10%. Hotel closed mid Nov-mid Mar. Amex, MasterCard, Visa, Laser. **Directions:** 10 mins drive from Bantry, on N71 to Glengarriff.

Baltimore — Baltimore Bay Guest House & La Jolie Brise

Restaurant/Guesthouse   The Waterfront Baltimore Co Cork **Tel:** 028 20600 Fax: 028 20495
Email: youenjabcob@youenjabcob.com Web: baltimorebay@youenjacob.com

It is hard to say whether this is a restaurant with rooms, or a guesthouse serving food. Taking the food first, La Jolie Brise quite literally brings a breath of fresh air to eating out in Baltimore. Run by Youen Jacob the younger, this cheerful continental-style café spills out on to the pavement and provides holiday-makers with good, inexpensive meals to be washed down with moderately priced wines. Breakfast menus include regular continental and full Irish breakfast and several fish choices including hot smoked salmon, plus a range of drinks including hot chocolate. Generous, well-made pizzas (also to take away) and pastas are available and for lunch and dinner there are "European & Irish" specialities like traditional mussels & chips and char-grilled sirloin steaks with salad & chips - all youthful, contemporary use of local ingredients. The only downside to this great little place is that it can get very crowded in summer and it's hard to keep pristine. **Seats 50**. Smoking unrestricted. Open 8am-11 pm daily; à la carte & special menus. House wine about €13. SC discretionary.
Accommodation: Above the restaurant, the Jacobs have eight very attractive, well-equipped bedrooms in their guesthouse overlooking the harbour. Everything in it is big - the rooms, the beds, the bathrooms. Amenities are good - direct-dial phones, tea/coffee-making facilities, TV with video. Furniture is modern, with a light sprinkling of Georgian and Victorian pieces and, in addition to a good sitting area in each room, there's a comfortable residents' lounge. Children up to 4 free in parents' room (cot available). Pets permitted. No private parking. **Rooms 8** (1 shower only for wheelchairs). B&B about €50pps, ss about €15. Open all year. Amex, MasterCard, Visa, Diners, Laser. **Directions:** The Square, Baltimore. ◇

Baltimore — Baltimore Harbour Resort Hotel & Leisure Centre

 Hotel

Baltimore Co Cork
Tel: 028 20361 Fax: 028 20466 Email: info@bhrhotel.ie

Since the Cullinane family took over this old hotel, they have done a prodigious amount of work, including the fairly recent addition of suites (incorporating the traditional arch which now leads through to the carpark) and a new leisure centre, which has a wide range of facilities including a 16-metre swimming pool and gymnasium. The hotel enjoys a lovely position overlooking Roaring Water Bay and is well located for deep sea fishing and visits to nearby islands, including Sherkin and Cape Clear. Modern furnishings, with plenty of light wood and pastel colours, create a sense of space in public areas and the accommodation includes family rooms, junior suites and the new suites. All rooms are comfortably furnished, with neat bathrooms and sea views, and the larger ones have double and single beds. Public areas include a bar that can be reversed to serve the Sherkin Room (banqueting/conferences for 140) and a bright semi-conservatory Garden Room for informal meals and drinks. Children are well looked after - there's a playroom, a children's club in school holidays and under 3s are free in parents' room (cots available). Off-season breaks are good value. No pets. Lift. **Rooms 64** (12 suites, 1 mini-suite). B&B about €80pps, ss about €25. Closed Jan. Amex, Diners, MasterCard, Visa. **Directions:** Signposted on the right as you enter Baltimore on the R595 from Skibbereen. ◇

Baltimore — Bushe's Bar

 Pub/B&B

The Square Baltimore Co. Cork **Tel: 028 20125** Fax: 028 20596
Email: tombushe@eircom.net Web: www.bushesbar.com

Everyone, especially visiting and local sailors, feels at home in this famous old bar. It's choc-a-bloc with genuine maritime artefacts such as charts, tide tables, ships' clocks, compasses, lanterns, pennants et al - but it's the Bushe family's hospitality that makes it really special. Since Richard and Eileen took on the bar in 1973 it's been "home from home" for regular visitors to Baltimore, for whom a late morning call is de rigeur (in order to collect the ordered newspapers that are rolled up and stacked in the bar window each day). Now there's a new generation of Bushes involved with the business, so all is humming nicely. Simple, homely bar food starts early in the day with tea and coffee from 9.30, moving on to home-made soups and a range of sandwiches including home-cooked meats (ham, roast beef, corned beef), salmon, smoked mackerel or - the most popular by far - open crab sandwiches, served with home-baked brown bread. And all under eight euro. This is a terrific pub, at any time of year, and was a very worthy recipient of our Jameson Pub of the Year Award in 2000. Not suitable for children under 10. Bar food served 9.30am-9pm daily.
Accommodation: Over the bar, there are some big, comfortable bedrooms, all with a double and single bed, bath & shower, TV and a kitchenette with all that is needed to make your own continental breakfast. There are also showers provided for the use of sailors and fishermen. **Rooms 3.** B&B €22.50-27.50 pps (depending on room), ss €12.50. Bar closed 25 Dec & Good Fri. Amex, MasterCard, Visa, Laser. **Directions:** In the middle of Baltimore, on the square overlooking the harbour.

Baltimore — Casey's of Baltimore

Hotel/Restaurant

Baltimore Co Cork **Tel: 028 20197** Fax: 028 20509
Email: caseys@eircom.net Web: www.caseysofbaltimore.com

With dramatic views over Roaring Water Bay to the islands beyond, this attractively developed hotel has grown from the immaculately maintained bar/restaurant that the Caseys had run for twenty years. The old back bar and restaurant have been ingeniously developed to extend the ground floor public areas and make best use of the view, and bedrooms are spacious and well-furnished, with good facilities (phone, TV, tea/coffee tray, trouser press) neat bathrooms and views. The staff are always friendly and helpful, there's a relaxed atmosphere and there are well-organised outdoor eating areas for bar food in fine weather. On less favoured days, the open fires are very welcome - and there's traditional music at weekends. Although best known for their seafood - an extensive selection of local fish and shellfish is offered, including mixed seafood platters - a good choice of other food is available, including vegetarian dishes. Children are welcome (cots available without charge), but not in public areas after 7 pm. No pets. **Rooms 14** (13 en-suite,1 shower only) B&B €77.50 pps, ss €25.

Restaurant open for L&D daily; Set L €19, Set D €40; also à la carte. Bar meals daily 12.30-2.30 & 6.30-9. Closed 28 Feb-6 Mar, 10 -17 Oct, 19-25 Dec.

Casey's of Baltimore Restaurant: A comfortable informal dining room overlooking the bay provides just the setting for good, unpretentious food. Baltimore seafood naturally takes pride of place - crab and lobster are specialities and there will always be other fish of the day on the blackboard. Dinner menus may well begin with the local version of smokies (creamed smoked mackerel, topped with cheese and served hot) and soups will certainly include the Casey's chowder - and Roaring Water Bay mussels are served as a main course, steamed in the shell with white wine, garlic and onion. Steaks (served with pepper sauce or garlic butter) are almost as popular and there's always a vegetarian option, such as a vegetable stir-fry. Friendly, relaxed service adds to the enjoyment. **Seats 65:** L 12.30-2.30, D 6.30-9.30 daily. Set L (Sun) €17, Set D €32. House wine from €15.24; à la carte also available; service discretionary. Amex, Diners, MasterCard, Visa, Laser. **Directions:** From Cork take the N71 to Skibereen & then R595 to Baltimore.

Baltimore   Chez Youen

Restaurant   Baltimore Co Cork **Tel: 028 20136** Fax: 028 20495
                          Email: chezyouen@youenjacob.com Web: www.youenjacob.com

Since 1979, Youen Jacob's Breton restaurant has been a major feature in Baltimore. Although other eating places have sprung up around him, Youen is still doing what he does best: simple but dramatic presentation of seafood in the shell. Lobster is very much a speciality and available all year round, while the Shellfish Platter is a sight to behold: a complete meal of Dublin Bay Prawns, crab and often velvet crab as well as lobster - all served in shell. Only minor concessions are made to non-fish eaters - starters of leek and potato soup or melon with port and, correspondingly, half a duck with wild mushroom sauce or steak with green peppercorn sauce for main course, although vegetarians are willingly catered for. **Seats 40.** No smoking area. D daily 6-10. Set D from about €35; Shellfish Platter about €45; à la carte also offered. House wine from about €20. Service 10%. Closed Nov & Feb. Amex, Diners, MasterCard, Visa, Laser. **Directions:** The Square, Baltimore. ◇

Baltimore   Customs House Restaurant

☆ Restaurant   Baltimore Co Cork **Tel: 028 20200**

Susan Holland and Ian Parr's uncluttered contemporary restaurant has made a lot of friends over the last few years and it's easy to see why. They don't take credit cards, do Sunday lunch or allow young children. But they do use only the freshest of local produce in season and they do great daily menus - short menus that highlight local seafood, especially, which is cooked by Susan with flair, served by Ian with unflappability - and give outstanding value for money. The couple, who are Australian, have been running the Customs House as a seasonal restaurant since 1995, then use the winter months to travel, They have worked in some very distinguished kitchens indeed and, between them, have 60 years experience in hospitality, in half a dozen countries - and, each summer, visitors to the little town of Baltimore are the fortunate beneficiaries of all this talent and commitment. Superb ingredients are presented with deceptive simplicity, mostly in classic French and Italian dishes served with organic salads, or simple, perfectly cooked organic side vegetables like new potatoes and spinach. You may well begin with a wonderful tapas plate, typically of of langoustine (Dublin Bay prawns), john dory, salt cod (brandade of) and red mullet, each with its own dressing or garnish; alternatively there might be a rocket salad zinging with vitality, with parmesan, pine nuts & balsamic vinaigrette - and perhaps one or two 'unofficial' ingredients added, like semi-dried tomatoes and puy lentils; thoroughly satisfying. Main courses depend on the catch but three of four main courses will probably be fish - including a classic sole meunière perhaps, and grilled monkfish with rösti potatoes and saffron & langoustine sauce. Then there are those unbeatable timeless desserts - rich chocolate fondant with house lavender ice cream, tarte tatin with house cinnamon ice cream, or farmhouse cheese - Cooleeney, Ardagh, Carraig goat - in perfect condition. All this is complemented by an interesting, highly informative and keenly-priced wine list and Ian Parr's efficient, refreshingly low-key service. **Seats 30.** No smoking area. D Wed/Thu-Sat (sometimes Sun), 7-9.30; Set D €22 (3-course, 1 choice on main course only) & €32 (3-course, more choices); house wines €13. Vegetarian dishes on request; not suitable for children under 12. Closed Mon, Tue. Some Sundays, some Wednesdays; Oct-Apr. (Cheques, incl sterling cheques, accepted). **No Credit Cards. Directions:** Beside the Garda Station 50 Metres from Pier.

Baltimore — The Mews

Restaurant   Baltimore Co Cork **Tel: 028 20390** Fax: 028 20390

Owner-chef Lucia Carey runs this well-appointed restaurant on the ground floor and adjacent conservatory of an attractive stone building. Menus are contemporary and the cooking combines the admirable qualities of generosity and lightness. Meals start off with freshly-baked breads and tapenade and prompt service means that starters like baked goats cheese or prawn, crab and coriander filo parcels will not be far behind. Main courses could include a variation on traditional themes such as rack of lamb served on olive potatoes and drizzled with home-made mint pesto while a typical vegetarian dish might be filo tartlet filled with seasonal vegetables in a blue cheese sauce, all served with imaginative and well-cooked vegetables. Good home-made ices are likely desserts, or you could finish with a local cheese plate and freshly brewed coffee. A short wine list is expensive when compared with the good value available locally. **Seats 30**. No smoking area. D Tue-Sun, 6-10; à la carte (average main course about €25); house wine about €20. Closed Mon & Oct-May. **Directions:** In Village of Baltimore. ◇

Baltimore — Rolf's Restaurant "Café Art" & Wine Bar

Ⓝ Restaurant/Café   Baltimore Co Cork **Tel: 028 20289**
Fax: 028 20930 Web: www.rolfsholidays.com

Although it is a bit of a trek up from the village if you are on foot, a visit to Rolf's is well worth the effort. The Haffner family have been here for 20 years and, although part of the business is still a holiday hostel, it's a hostel with a difference; the complex has been extensively renovated and sensitively developed over the last few years, to include self-catering accommodation of some character - and the restaurant and wine bar, which is attracting a loyal following, particularly of discerning locals who appreciate both the food and the fact that it remains open after the summer visitors have left. For the casual visitor, the café is open all day and serves an à la carte lunch as well as excellent light food with morning coffee or afternoon tea and, in the evening, a more extensive dinner menu is served in the Restaurant 'Café Art' which has views over Baltimore harbour - and is named after the contemporary art exhibitions held in the restaurant. Euro-Toques chef Johannes Haffner uses as much home-grown, organic and local produce as possible and all pastries, desserts and breads are home-made; his wide-ranging contemporary menus include quite a few classics - starters like house paté with cranberry sauce & toast and smoked salmon with crusty brown bread for example, sit easily beside updated dishes such as steamed mussels with lemongrass and fresh ginger (starter or main course); vegetarians do well (dishes highlighted on the menu) and local seafood is prominent, of course, but there's also a better choice than in most other restaurants in the area for carnivores. Desserts include some continental treats - Flemish apple tart, "Linzer" almond tart - and coffees are delicious. A new wine bar - with an open fire - opened in 2002 and is just the place for a drink before (or after) dinner; many wines not given on the wine list are available here by the glass. Garden terrace and seaview terrace available for fine weather. **Seats 50**. Toilets wheelchair accessible. Open daily in summer, 8.30am-9.30pm (B'fst 8-9.30, L 1-4, D 6-9.30). Closed Mon & Tue off season. MasterCard, Visa, Laser.

Baltimore — The Slipway

B&B   The Cove Baltimore Co Cork **Tel: 028 20134** Fax: 028 20134
Email: theslipway@hotmail.com Web: www.theslipway.com

Quietly located just beyond the bustle around the square, Wilmie Owen's delightful house has uninterrupted views of the harbour and distant seascape from all the bedrooms and the lovely first floor breakfast room, which has a balcony. This unusual and imaginatively designed house and now also has a charming oyster bar in a converted outbuilding; very much intended for residents, it is only open when Wilmie's husband Dave is not away on his travels. Not suitable for children; no pets. **Rooms 4** (all shower only & no-smoking). B&B €33 pps, ss €17. Closed Nov-Mar officially, but phone to check. **No Credit Cards. Directions:** Through Baltimore village, to the Cove, 500 metres.

Baltimore Area — The Islander's Rest

Ⓝ Hotel   Sherkin Island Baltimore Co Cork **Tel: 028 20116** Fax: 028 20360
Email: info@islandersrest.ie Web: www.islandersrest.ie

Just a 10 minute ferry trip from Baltimore harbour, Sherkin is a small island about 3.5 miles long by 1.5 miles wide with a population of only a hundred or so and three lovely safe beaches. This newly-built hotel would make a comfortable base for a break and is understandably becoming a popular place for weddings - it may not have a great deal of character (as yet) but the island location is highly romantic. Large bedrooms include some family rooms with four beds and most have stunning views; all have good quality pine beds and soft furnishings, television, phone and ensuite bathroom. There's a large breakfast room for guests as well as a sitting room with open fire place - still sparsely furnished in the summer of 2002, but pictures had yet to go up and plants be put in position. Food served in the bar offers a good choice of dishes like : poached monkfish with brandy and peppercorn sauce, warm goats' cheese salad with honey and pear dressing and steak with garlic butter and chips, all under €15. Pleasant service by staff and owner. Conference/banqueting (30/110). Fishing, walking, garden. No pets. **Rooms 21** (all en-suite). Children welcome (under 3s free in parents' bedroom, cot available). B&B €55pps, ss €12.50. SC discretionary. Open all year but a phone call is essential in winter. MasterCard, Visa, Laser. **Directions:** 1 hr 30 mins from Cork City, 10 mins by boat from Baltimore.

Baltimore Area   Windhoek

Ⓝ Guesthouse

Sherkin Island Baltimore Co Cork
Tel: 028 20275 Fax: 028 20275 Email: windhoel@esatclear.ie

The front garden of Dutch-born Ingrid van Maarle and Peter van de Ruenen's beautiful renovated farmhouse reaches down to the waterfront and, across a narrow strip of land, it is flanked to the rear by two deserted beaches. Accommodation is in two rooms in the main house and three studio apartments, situated around a central paved herb garden; roof windows bring in extra light and a pretty, Scandinavian-style greyish-blue and white colour scheme is used to great effect throughout – a veritable showcase for Ingrid and Peter's respective talents in interior design and building restoration. Rooms are comfortably and stylishly furnished, with TV and tea/coffee-making facilities provided. Meals are available by arrangement and, although primarily self-catering, breakfast can also be provided for guests taking the apartments. The couple organise seminars and courses, and Windhoek is available for corporate hospitality (10-16 guests). **Rooms 5** (3 with private bathroom, 2 with shared bathroom, 2 no smoking). Children welcome (under 4s free in parents' room, cot available). B&B in house €30 pps, ss€5; studio apartment €70 (€35pps), also available for short and long lets. **Directions:** Cork - Skibbereen - Baltimore- 10 min ferry to Sherkin.

Bantry   O'Connor's Seafood Restaurant

féile bia Restaurant

The Square Bantry Co Cork **Tel: 027 50221** Fax: 027 50221
Email: oconnorseafood@eircom.net Web: www.oconnorseafood.com

O'Connor's long-established seafood restaurant is right on the main square (site of the annual early May mussel festival) and, after 34 years in the family, the business is now in the capable hands of Matt & Ann's son, Mark. A lobster and oyster fish tank by the entrance sends all the right messages and, beyond the front room, there are booths and a seated bar (full bar facilities include beers on draft) in the back, all decorated in a nautical theme. Bantry Bay mussels, cooked all ways, are a speciality - a starter of them grilled with herbs and lemon butter fits the bill perfectly, followed perhaps by fresh scallops and salmon mornay in shells, served with an abundance of vegetables, or else mussels marinière with a fish pie as a main course. There are some non-fish dishes available, all using local produce - fillet steak is another speciality. At lunchtime you can have soup and a sandwich in the bar or daily-changing dishes off the blackboard. No children after 7 pm. **Seats 50**. Toilets wheelchair accessible. No smoking area; air conditioning. Open 12.15-9.30 daily, L 12.30-3, D6-9.30. Set L from about €8, Set D from about €27. A la carte. House wine €17.50, SC. discretionary. Open all year. MasterCard, Visa, Laser. **Directions:** Town Centre. Promient location on square.

Bantry   The Snug Bar

féile bia **Ⓝ** Pub

The Quay Bantry Co Cork
Tel: 027 50057

Maurice and Colette O'Donovan's well-named bar is a cosy and welcoming place, bustling with life and ideal for a wholesome bite at moderate prices. Maurice is the chef and takes pride in using local produce and giving value for money; his menus feature a wide range of popular dishes, many of which are in the house style. At lunch time, home-made soups - chicken & leek, perhaps, or carrot & coriander - top the bill and are followed by other equally good things like fresh whiting goujons, traditional Irish stew, home-made beefsteak & onion pie and lasagne "house style" (which is available with meat or for vegetarians). More extensive evening menus offer dressier dishes as well, including starters like Bantry Bay prawn cocktail or oak smoked salmon salad, and a good choice of main courses like steaks, home-made beefburgers and farmyard duckling with orange sauce as well as a number fish dishes - including Bantry Bay mussels, of course. This wholesome fare is good value (lunch main courses about €8, evening all except steaks €13 or less). Children welcome. Food served daily, 10.30am-9pm. MasterCard, Visa, Laser. **Directions:** Beside Garda Station, near the Harbour.

Blarney — Blairs Inn

féile bia Pub/Restaurant

Cloghroe Blarney Co Cork **Tel: 021 438 1470**
Email: blair@eircom.net Web: http://homepage.eircom.net/~blair

John and Anne Blair's riverside pub is in a quiet, wooded setting just outside Blarney yet, sitting in the garden in summer, you might see trout rising in the Owennageara river (or see a heron out fishing), while winter offers welcoming open fires in this comfortingly traditional country pub. There's traditional music on Monday nights (and ballads on Sundays) from April to October - and the Blairs have built up a special reputation for their food. Anne supervises the kitchen personally, and care and commitment are evident in menus offering a wide (but not over-extensive) range of interesting but fairly traditional dishes including seafood (from Kenmare and Dingle); old favourites like corned beef with champ & cabbage & parsley sauce, casserole of lamb & stout and Irish stew sit easily alongside some fancier fare and make a pleasing change from international menus; there's always a vegetarian dish on, and game in season too. A la carte menus are available in the bar from lunchtime onwards; lunch and dinner can be booked in the candlelit Snug or Pantry dining areas. Children welcome, but not after 7 pm. **Seats 40/50** (restaurant/bar) & 60 in garden. No-smoking area. Bar menu 12.30-9.30 daily. Restaurant L 12.30-3.30, D 6.30-9.30. A la carte. House wine €17.75. Service discretionary. Closed 25 Dec & Good Fri. Amex, Diners, MasterCard, Visa, Laser. **Directions:** 5 minutes from Blarney village, on the R579.

Blarney — Blarney Park Hotel

Hotel

Blarney Co Cork **Tel: 021 438 5281** Fax: 021 438 1506
Email: info@blarneypark.com Web: blarneypark.com

Blarney may be best known for its castle (and the famous Blarney Stone) but there is always something going on at Blarney Park and its excellent facilities for both conferences and leisure are put to full use. Close proximity to Cork city (just half an hour on the Limerick road) makes this a very convenient location for business and families love the leisure centre, which has a 40-metre water slide and 20-metre pool among its attractions; there are also two all-weather tennis courts on site. Conference/banqueting (270/250); business centre, secretarial services, video-conferencing. Children welcome; supervised playroom. **Rooms 91** (11 shower only; 1 junior suite, 14 executive rooms, 2 no-smoking, 2 disabled). Lift. B&B about €90 pps, ss about €25. Closed 23-26 Dec. Amex, MasterCard, Visa, Diners. **Directions:** In centre of Blarney, on left on entering town from Cork. ◇

Butlerstown — Atlantic Sunset

Accommodation/B&B

Dunworley Butlerstown Co Cork **Tel: 023 40115**

Mary Holland provides comfortable accommodation and a genuinely warm welcome in her neat modern house with views down to the sea at Dunworley. The house is wheelchair accessible and the ground floor rooms are suitable for less able guests. The breakfast room and some bedroom windows have sea views and, weather permitting, the sight of the sun setting over the Atlantic can indeed be magnificent. Sandy beaches and coastal walk nearby. **Rooms 4** (2 en-suite, shower only). B&B about €23pps (about€25 en-suite). Closed Christmas period. **Directions:** From Bandon Road R602 to Timoleague, then Butlerstown Village, Atlantic Sunset 1 km. ◇

Butlerstown — O'Neill's

Pub

Butlerstown Co Cork **Tel: 023 40228**

Butlerstown is a pretty pastel-painted village, with lovely views across farmland to Dunworley and the sea beyond. Dermot and Mary O'Neill's unspoilt pub is as pleasant and hospitable a place as could be found to enjoy the view - or to admire the traditional mahogany bar and pictures that make old pubs like this such a pleasure to be in. O'Neill's is now a popular stopping off point for the newly opened "Seven Heads Millennium Coastal Walk" so it may be useful to know that children (and well-behaved pets) are welcome. *A point of historical interest: the anchor from the S.S. Cardiff Hall, which sank off the nearby coast in 1925, was unveiled on a platform beside the pub in April 2002. Closed 25 Dec & Good Fri. **No Credit Cards. Directions:** On the Courtmacsherry - Clonakilty Coast Road.

Butlerstown — Otto's Creative Catering - O.C.C.

Restaurant/B&B

Dunworley Butlerstown Co Cork **Tel: 023 40461**
Email: ottokunze@eircom.net Web: www.ottoscreativecatering.com

With the help of their talented son who lives nearby and is a creative and practical woodworker, Hilde and Otto Kunze have created a dream of a place here, very close to the spot where they

originally started the famous Dunworley Cottage restaurant many years ago. The house is a little unusual from the outside, but only reveals its true personality once you are inside; words cannot do it justice, so you must go and see it for yourself. Deeply committed to the organic philosophy, their vegetable gardens provide a beautiful and satisfying view from the dining room, where meals of wonderful simplicity cooked by Otto are presented by Hilde. Take time to marvel at the sheer originality and ingenuity of their home over a drink (brought with you, as they have no licence) in the sitting room, while also pondering a dinner menu that offers several choices on each course. Typically you will start with a vegetarian salad platter, with organic leaves and several dips or, perhaps, a fish plate of Anthony Cresswell's smoked wild salmon and Frank Hederman's eel and mussels, again with organic leaves. Freshly baked breads and butter will be left temptingly close by on the table - try to resist trying everything as there are still marvellous soups (most likely based on whatever vegetable is most prolific at the time), before you even reach main courses of, perhaps, wild salmon caught off the Seven Heads, panfried and served with a dill & white wine cream or a Balkan speciality such as 'Chevap', of lean minced lamb, spiced with paprika, pepper and garlic, fried and served with a garlic cream. A magnificent selection of vegetables, with potatoes and rice, accompanies the main course. Then there are desserts - apfelstrudel with vanilla ice cream, perhaps, or home-grown strawberries with cream. Or, if you are very lucky, there might be freshly picked top fruit, warm from the trees in the growing tunnels - cherries, plums, apricots, white peaches... This wonderful food needs no embellishment, it is extraordinarily good value for the quality given - and it clearly gives Otto and Hilde great satisfaction to see their guests' appreciation. This place is a must for any food lover travelling in west Cork. Organic farm: pork and eggs are home-produced as well as fruit and vegetables; cookery school (please inquire for details). **Seats 30** (max table size 14). Toilet wheelchair accessible. Smoking restricted. D €45, 7-9pm, by reservation (24 hours notice if possible), also Sun L, 1 pm, Set Sun L €25. Bring your own wine (no corkage). Restaurant closed Mon & Tue.
Accommodation: Bedrooms with wonderful sea and garden views share the fresh originality of the rest of the house and are furnished in a simple artistic style which, like the cleverly designed shower rooms, is intensely practical. And, of course, you will wake up in a most beautiful place - and have more of that superb food to look forward to, at a breakfast that counts home-made sausages and home-produced rashers among its gems. B&B €50 pps, ss 20. Closed Nov & Feb. MasterCard, Visa, Laser. **Directions:** Bandon to Timoleague to Dunworley.

Butlerstown — Sea Court

Country House — Butlerstown Co Cork **Tel: 023 40151** / 40218
Email: seacourt-inn@yahoo.com Web: www.tourismresources.ie/cht/seacort.htm

Set in 10 acres of beautiful parkland (source of the fallen trees used in the construction of Otto's Creative Catering, nearby) Sea Court is at the heart of an unspoilt wonderland for bird-watchers and walkers - and a restful retreat for any discerning traveller. Since 1985, David Elder - an American academic who spends his summers in Ireland - has devoted his energies to restoring this gracious Georgian mansion and, while the task is nowhere near completion, the achievement is remarkable - and ongoing. The improvements planned for this year - upgrading bathrooms, restoring sash windows and "eliminating the rattles in windy weather" have been completed, although the search for Victorian roll-top baths continues. On the Guide's last annual visit a bath rescued from a field had been resurfaced and installed - if readers notice any others in the locality, a phone call to David might give it a new lease of life. Meanwhile, the grounds and exterior generally are always a credit to him and, while it is wise not to expect too much luxury, what Sea Court has to offer guests is comfortable and very reasonably priced accommodation in a real and much-loved country house; bedrooms are, for the most part, elegantly proportioned with bathrooms that are already adequate and gradually being upgraded. Breakfast, cooked by David himself, is served at a long dining table, where dinner is also available if there are reservations for at least four people - and there is a drawing room where guests can chat around the fire after dinner. The house is also available for small conferences (12-16 people) and for rental off-season. **Rooms 6** (5 en-suite, 1 with private bathroom). B&B €40, no s.s. D 8pm, €32 (by arrangement, except Sun - min 4 persons). Closed 21 Aug-7 June. **No Credit Cards. Directions:** Butlerstown is signposted from Timoleague.

Carrigaline — Carrigaline Court Hotel & Leisure Centre

Hotel — Main Street Carrigaline Co Cork
Tel: 021 485 2100 Fax: 021 437 1103
Email: carrigcourt@eircom.net Web: www.carrigcourt.com

The spacious foyer of this modern hotel creates a good first impression and it has attractive features throughout, with interesting contemporary furniture in both public areas and bedrooms, which are stylishly decorated and well-equipped for business guests with work desks, ISDN lines and safes as well as the more usual amenities (TV, tea/coffee making, trouser press); suites also have queen size beds, and marbled bathrooms are quite luxurious, with good quality toiletries. Friendly staff are very pleasant and helpful. Conference/banqueting facilities (350/250), also smaller meeting rooms; secretarial services. Leisure centre; swimming pool. Children welcome (under 4s free in parents' room, cot available without charge). Weekend breaks available all year. No pets. **Rooms 50** (2 suites). Lift. B&B from €85 pps, ss about €25. Closed 25 Dec. Amex, MasterCard, Visa, Diners, Laser. **Directions:** Follow South Link Road and then follow signs for Carrigaline.

Carrigaline — Glenwood House

Guesthouse

Ballinrea Road Carrigaline Co Cork
Tel: 021 4373 878 Fax: 021 4373 878
Email: glenwoodhouse@eircom.net Web: www.glenhotel.com

This well-respected guesthouse is in purpose-built premises, very conveniently located for Cork Airport and the ferry and set in gardens, where guests can relax in fine weather. Comfortable, well-furnished rooms (including one designed for disabled guests) have all the amenities normally expected of hotels, including ISDN lines, TV with video channel, trouser press/iron, tea/coffee facilities and well-designed bathrooms. Breakfast has always been a strong point - fresh fruits and juices, cheeses, home-made breads and preserves as well as hot dishes (available from 7am for business guests, until 10 am for those taking a leisurely break). A guest sitting room with open fire makes a cosy retreat on dark winter evenings.* Glenwood came into new ownership in 2002 but there are no immediate changes. Under 10s free in parents' room. **Rooms 16** (all en-suite). B&B about €45pps, ss about €13. Closed 25-31 Dec. MasterCard, Visa. **Directions:** Entering Carrigaline from Cork, turn right at Ballinrea Road roundabout; house signed on left.

Carrigaline — Gregory's Restaurant

féile bia Restaurant

Main Street Carrigaline Co Cork
Tel: 021 437 1512

Owner-chef Gregory Dawson and his partner and restaurant manager Rachelle Harley opened here in 1994 and it's bright, comfortable and friendly, with plenty of buzz. Sensibly short à la carte menus based on local produce change monthly and the cooking style is fairly classical, sometimes with a modern twist. Dishes like Clonakilty black pudding & asparagus bruschetta with homemade tomato preserve, or stuffed fillet of pork with basil & pinenuts, provençal sauce are typical and there's always an Irish cheese plate as well as a selection of classic desserts. Good details include home-baked breads and excellent coffee and service is friendly and helpful. Vegetarian options available on request. **Seats 40.** No-smoking area. Air conditioning. Toilets wheelchair accessible. Children welcome. D Wed-Sat 6.30-10, L Sun only 12.30-3; D à la carte, Sun L €20.95. House wine €16.95. Closed D Sun, all Mon & Tue, bank hols, 3 weeks hols (dates TBC), Christmas. Amex, Diners, MasterCard, Visa, Laser. **Directions:** On main street, opposite Bank of Ireland.

Castlelyons — Ballyvolane House

Country House

Castlelyons Fermoy Co Cork **Tel: 025 36349** Fax: 025 36781
Email: ballyvol@iol.ie Web: www.ballyvolanehouse.ie

Jeremy and Merrie Greene's gracious mansion is surrounded by its own farmland, magnificent wooded grounds, a recently restored trout lake and formal terraced gardens, all carefully managed and maintained to a high standard - a major replanting of 400 rhododendrons, azaleas and specimen trees is the current project. The Italianate style of the present house - including a remarkable pillared hall with a baby grand piano and open fire - dates from the mid 19th century when modifications were made to the original house of 1728. This is a very lovely house, elegantly furnished and extremely comfortable, with central heating and big log fires; bedrooms are varied, but all are roomy and, like the rest of the house, are furnished with family antiques and look out over attractive gardens and grounds. Ballyvolane has private salmon fishing on 8km of the renowned River Blackwater, with a wide variety of spring and summer beats. Fishing is Merrie's special enthusiasm (a brochure is available outlining the fishing services she provides) and she's also a great cook, providing guests with delicious country house dinners which are served in style around a long mahogany table (no smoking in the dining room). A typical menu might be smoked salmon pancakes with crème fraîche, roast sirloin of beef with new potatoes & fresh vegetables, a selection of luscious desserts (strawberries, meringues, loganberry fool) and cheeses; everything is based on local produce, notably Blackwater salmon and farmhouse cheeses which come from a number of valued suppliers including Midleton country market. There is much of interest in the area - the beautiful Blackwater Valley has many gardens and historic sites, and Lismore, the Rock of Cashel and Waterford Crystal can easily be visited. The standard of hospitality, comfort and food at Ballyvolane are all exceptional, making this an excellent base for a peaceful and very relaxing break. French is spoken. Children welcome (cot available, €7). No pets. Garden; croquet; fishing; walking. **Rooms 6** (1 shower only, 1 for disabled). B&B €80pps ss €20. Residents D €37 at 8pm, book by 10am (no-smoking dining room); menu changes daily. House wine from €18. Closed 23-31 Dec. Amex, MasterCard, Visa, Laser. **Directions:** From Cork, turn right off N8. Following house signs on to R628.

Castlemartyr — Old Parochial House

Country House — Castlemartyr Middleton Co Cork **Tel: 021 466 7454** Fax: 021 466 7429
Email: enquires@oldparochail.com Web: www.oldparochial.com

Kathy Sheehy will have tea and home-made scones for you on arrival at this warm and welcoming period house in the village of Castlemartyr. Conveniently situated for many activities and places of interest, including the Jameson Heritage Centre, Fota Wildlife Park & Arboretum, golf, beaches and wonderful cliff and woodland walks, this lovely house would make a perfect base for a restful and interesting break. Fresh flowers throughout the house set a caring tone, not only in the fine well-proportioned drawing room and dining rooms (which both have log fires) but also in bedrooms that are elegantly furnished with antiques and have bathrooms cleverly designed to maintain the architectural harmony of the old house. Unexpected little luxuries include a turn down service at night and home-made biscuits and Irish chocolates in each bedroom, as well as the convenience of tea/coffee trays, ironing facility and TV. There's even a complimentary drink offered by the fire each evening before retiring - a truly hospitable touch. Children welcome (under 5s free in parents' room, cot available free of charge). Garden. No pets. **Rooms 3** (1 shower only, all no smoking). B&B €50-60, no ss. Closed 1 Nov-31 Jan. MasterCard, Visa. **Directions:** Midleton area. Take N25 to Castlemartyr. At bridge turn for Garryvoe & Shangarry. House first on left hand side.

Castletownbere — MacCarthy's

Pub — The Square Castletownbere Co Cork
Tel: 027 70014 Email: adrimac22@yahoo.com

Dating back to the 1870s, and currently run by Adrienne MacCarthy, this famous old pub and grocery store really is the genuine article. Fortunately, it shows no signs of changing. Atmosphere and live traditional music are the most obvious attractions, but the grocery is real and provisions the local fishing boats. Simple bar food - seafood chowder, open seafood sandwiches - is available all day. Closed 25 Dec & Good Fri. **No Credit Cards. Directions:** In town square.

Castletownbere — The Old Presbytery

Accommodation/B&B — Brandy Hall House Castletownbere Co Cork
Tel: 027 70424 Fax: 027 70420
Email: marywrigley@eircom.net Web: midnet.ie/oldpresbytery/index.htm

On the edge of Castletownbere and well-signposted from the road, this very pleasant old house on 4 acres is in a magnificent position - on a little point with the sea on two sides and clear views of Berehaven Harbour. The house dates back to the late 1700s and has been sensitively restored by the current owners, David and Mary Wrigley. The five bedrooms vary in size and outlook but all have phone, tea/coffee tray and TV and are furnished to a high standard, in keeping with the character of the house. Breakfast - which includes a vegetarian menu - is served in a pleasant conservatory overlooking the sea. Children welcome (under 5s free in parents' room, cot available); pets permitted by arrangement. **Rooms 5** (all en-suite, 4 shower only). B&B about €32, ss about €13. MasterCard, Visa. **Directions:** Turn left as the road narrows by Brandy Hall bridge and follow the sign. ◇

Castletownshend — Bow Hall

B&B — Main Street Castletownshend Co Cork
Tel: 028 36114 Email: dvickbowhall@eircom.net

Castletownshend is one of west Cork's prettiest villages and this very comfortable 17th century house on the hill is a wonderful place to stay. With a pleasant outlook over beautiful well-tended gardens to the sea, excellent home-cooking and a warm welcome by enthusiastic hosts, Dick and Barbara Vickery, a visit to this lovely home is a memorable experience. The house is full of interest but its most outstanding feature is perhaps the food, which is not only imaginative but much of it is home-grown too. Residents' dinner is available by reservation and this treat will be a truly seasonal menu, based on their own produce fresh from the garden - potatoes, courgettes, swiss chard, salads, fresh herbs and fruit - picked just before serving with other local specialities such as fresh crab or salmon. Menus, which change daily, might include treats like potato & smoky bacon soup, wild salmon fillets & creamy lime sauce on a bed of colcannon (with gingered carrots, courgette fritters and red cabbage) followed by Fresh rhubarb pie & Dick;s vanilla ice cream... and breakfasts are also a highlight, with home-baked breads and muffins, home-made sausages, home-made preserves among the delights. Non-smoking house. No pets. **Rooms 3** (1 en-suite, 2 with private bathrooms, all no smoking), B&B €45, ss €5; min 2 night stay preferred. Advance bookings essential, especially in winter; D 8 pm, by reservation; €32 (no wine licence). Closed last 2 weeks Nov & Christmas week. **No Credit Cards. Directions:** 5 miles from Skibbereen.

Castletownshend — Mary Ann's Bar & Restaurant

Pub/Restaurant

Castletownshend Co. Cork
Tel: 028 36146 Fax: 028 36377 Email: maryanns@eircom.net

Mention Castletownshend and the chances are that the next words will be 'Mary Ann's', as this welcoming landmark has been the source of happy memories for many a visitor to this picturesque west Cork village over the years. (For those who have come up the hill from the little quay with a real sailor's appetite, the sight of its gleaming bar seen through the open door is one to treasure.) The pub is as old as it looks, going back to 1846, and has been in the energetic and hospitable ownership of Fergus and Patricia O'Mahony since 1988. Any refurbishments at Mary Ann's have left its original character intact. The O'Mahonys have built up a great reputation for food at the bar and in the restaurant, which is split between an upstairs dining room and The Vine Room at the back, which can be used for private parties. Seafood is the star, of course, and comes in many guises, usually along with some of the lovely home-baked brown bread which is one of the house specialities. Another is the Platter of Castlehaven Bay Shellfish and Seafood - a sight to behold, and usually including langoustine, crab meat, crab claws, and both fresh and smoked salmon; taking this extravaganza one stage further, there's a Supreme Platter, which also includes a whole lobster and, not surprisingly, costs a king's ransome (€50.95 to be precise). Much of the menu depends on the catch of the day, although there are also good steaks and roasts, served with delicious local potatoes and seasonal vegetables. Desserts are good too, but local West Cork cheeses are an excellent option.* A Wine Club was started at Mary Ann's in September 2001 and is proving a great success. Restaurant **Seats 30** (private room 20). Toilets wheelchair accessible. Children welcome D 6-9; L Sun only in winter, 12-2.30. A la carte House wine from €15.25. SC discretionary. *Bar food 12-2.30 & 6-9 daily. Closed Mon, from Nov-Mar; 25 Dec, Good Fri & 12 Jan-3 Feb. MasterCard, Visa, Laser. **Directions:** Five miles from Skibbereen.

Clonakilty — An Sugan

Restaurant/Pub

Wolfe Tone Street Clonakilty Co Cork
Tel: 023 33498 Email: sineadcrowley@hotmail.com

The O'Crowley family has owned An Sugan since 1980 and they have done a great job: it's always been a really friendly, well-run place and their reputation for good food is well-deserved. This year saw a new extension to the traditional bar, providing more space for bar meals - and a no smoking area. Meanwhile, at the back of the main bar, a contemporary café bar provides a contrast to the old bar and restaurant and has outside seating in a sheltered courtyard at the back. Food served in the new area is lighter and more modern, but the older bar and restaurant remain equally popular and have kept their character. Menus changes daily and remain very strong on seafood - fish specials could include a choice of ten, ranging from cod on a bed of champ to lobster salad. Options like chicken liver paté and Parma ham & roasted tomato tagliatelle give a choice if you're not in the mood for seafood. No private parking. Restaurant **seats 48**. Food served 12.30-10 daily. A la carte. House wine €15-16. No SC. Closed 25 Dec & Good Fri. MasterCard, Visa, Laser. **Directions:** From Corkon the left hand side as you enter Clonakilty.

Clonakilty — Dunmore House Hotel

féile bia Hotel   Muckross Clonakilty Co Cork **Tel: 023 33352** Fax: 023 34686
Email: dunmorehousehotel@eircom.net Web: www.dunmorehousehotel.com

The magnificent coastal location of Jeremiah and Mary O'Donovan's family-owned and managed hotel has been used to advantage to provide sea views for all bedrooms and to allow guests access to their own stretch of foreshore. Comfortable public areas include a bar and lounges; bedrooms are furnished to a high standard and the numerous leisure activities in the area include angling and golf - green fees are free to residents on the hotel's own (highly scenic) nine hole golf course - cycling, horse-riding and watersports; packed lunches are provided on request. Hands-on owner-management, a high standard of maintenance and housekeeping (down to the fresh flowers ordered for the hotel on a weekly basis) and a professional and exceptionally friendly and helpful staff make this a hotel that guests return to again and again. Conference/banqueting 250; secretarial services. Wheelchair accessible. Children welcome (under 4s free in parents' room, cot available without charge; junior evening meal 5.30-6.30). Golf, fishing, walking. Pets permitted by arrangement. **Rooms 23** (2 junior suites, 4 shower only, 1 for disabled). B&B €70pps, ss€20. Food available all day (12-8.30). Restaurant **Seats 80**. Toilets wheelchair accessible. Air conditioning D daily, 7-8.30 (€40), L Sun only, 1-2.30. Closed 4 days Christmas and 19 Jan- 6 Mar. Amex, Diners, MasterCard, Visa, Laser. **Directions:** 4 km from Clonakilty Town, well signed.

Clonakilty — Emmet Hotel

féile bia Hotel/Restaurant   Emmet Square Clonakilty Co Cork **Tel: 023 33394** Fax: 023 35058
Email: emmethotel@eircom.net Web: www.emmethotel.com

The Emmet Hotel is hidden away in the centre of Clonakilty on a lovely serene Georgian square that contrasts unexpectedly with the hustle and bustle of the nearby streets; it's a most attractive location, although parking is likely to be difficult. Rooms vary a little due to the age of the building, but all are comfortable and have phone, air conditioning, TV and Tea/coffee making facilities. The standard of furnishing and comfort is high throughout, with management in the capable hands of Tony and Marie O'Keeffe (who run a separate restaurant next door, see below). Conference/banqueting (40/55). Children welcome (under 3s free; cots available without charge). Pets permitted by arrangement. **Rooms 20** (2 executive). B&B €60pps. Open all year.

O'Keeffe's of Clonakilty: Although located in separate premises next door, O'Keeffe's also has direct access from the hotel and bookings are made through the hotel. Overlooking Emmet Square, the restaurant is creatively decorated in a colourful style that is most unexpected in an old house and allows a complete change of atmosphere. Marie O'Keeffe's cooking is based on the best of seasonal local produce, much of it organic, and her reputation for creative modern cooking was already well known, helping the restaurant to achieve its present success. A short, moderately priced à la carte menu offers four or five choices on each course plus half a dozen specials. Although there are some very strong alternative choices, seafood takes the starring role and typical starters might include garlic breaded mussels or lobster cocktail, followed by main courses like Ballycotton brill simple panfried in butter with sea asparagus - or loin of lamb with a rosemary & red wine jus is a likely alternative. Vegetarian dishes are offered (ask if necessary) and there is an awareness of special dietary requirements in, for example, a dessert of non-dairy citrus mousse with organic Irish strawberries & a peach coulis. Friendly, helpful staff enhance a visit to either hotel or restaurant. D 6.30-10 daily; L 12.30-2.30 (in The Bistro at the hotel); Set D €32-36. House wine from €15.20. SC discretionary. Restaurant closed 25 Dec. Amex, Diners, MasterCard, Visa, Laser, Switch. **Directions:** In the centre of Clonakilty - turn left into Emmet Square at the Catholic Church.

Clonakilty — The Lodge & Spa at Inchydoney Island

Hotel   Inchydoney Island Clonakilty Co Cork **Tel: 023 33143** Fax: 023 35229
Email: administration@inchydoneyisland.com Web: www.inchydoneyisland.com

Although architecturally uninspired, this hotel enjoys fine views over the two 'Blue Flag' beaches at Inchidoney and it has proved a great success, Once inside the hotel (as opposed to the Dunes Pub, which has a more down to earth atmosphere), that pampered feeling soon takes over. Public areas are spacious and impressive, notably a large, comfortably furnished first-floor residents' lounge and library, with a piano and extensive sea views. Bedrooms are all furnished and decorated in an uncluttered contemporary style and most have wonderful views. Outstanding health and leisure facilities include a superb Thalassotherapy Spa, which offers a range of special treatments and makes Inchidoney a particularly attractive venue off-season. However, even without taking up any of the these amenities, there is something in the air that makes this a very relaxing place. Special breaks are a major attraction - fishing, equestrian, golf, therapies or simply an off-season weekend away. Conferences/banqueting (300/250); business centre; secretarial service, video-conferencing (by arrangement). Thalassotherapy spa (24 treatment rooms/beauty treatments); leisure centre; swimming pool; equestrian; snooker. Children welcome (under 12s free in parents' room; cots available, €12). Pets permitted in some areas. **Rooms 63** (3 suites, 1 junior suite, all executive rooms; 17 no smoking; 2 for disabled). Lift. 24 hour room service. B&B €82.50. SC10%. Closed 25-26 Dec.

Gulfstream Restaurant: Located on the first floor, with panoramic sea views from the (rather few) window tables, this elegant restaurant offers fine dining in a broadly Mediterranean style, utilising organic produce where possible. Menus change monthly, include vegetarian options and willingly cater for special dietary requirements. **Seats 80** (private room 70). Not suitable for children under 5, or after 8.30pm. Toilets wheelchair accessible. No smoking area; air conditioning. D 6-10, early D €15, Set D €50. House wine from €16. SC10%. [*Informal/ bar meals also available 12-9 daily.] Restaurant closed Sun. Amex, Diners, MasterCard, Visa, Laser. **Directions:** N71 from Cork to Clonakilty, then Causeway to Inchydoney.

Clonakilty — Randles Clonakilty Hotel

Ⓝ Hotel — Wolfe Tone Street Clonakilty Co Cork **Tel: 023 34749** Fax: 023 35035
Email: clonakilty@randleshotels.com

This new sister hotel to the Randles hotels in Killarney opened in 2002 after complete renovation to create its new personality as a boutique hotel. The public face is impressive - deep carpets, elegant furnishings - and accommodation has been upgraded to match. The Ballymaloe trained head chef, Michelle O'Regan, is responsible for food in both restaurants and the bar. Conferences (50); secretarial services. Leisure centre (indoor swimming pool). Own parking. **Rooms 31** (5 no smoking, 2 disabled). Lift. Children welcome (under 5s free in parents' room, cot available). B&B €70 pps, ss €35. No SC. Food available 12.30-3 (bar); 6.30-9 (Kingfisher brasseries & Maxwells restaurant). Closed Christmas. Amex, Diners, MasterCard, Visa, Laser. **Directions:** Town centre, beside An Sugan.

Cloyne — Barnabrow Country House

téile bia Country House/Restaurant — Barnabrow Cloyne Co. Cork
Tel: 021 465 2534 Fax: 021 465 2534
Email: barnabrow@eircom.net Web: www.barnabrowhouse.com

John and Geraldine O'Brien's sensitive conversion of an imposing seventeenth century house makes good use of its stunning views of Ballycotton, and the decoration is commendably restrained. Innovative African wooden furniture (among items for sale in an on-site shop) is a point of interest and spacious bedrooms are stylishly decorated and comfortable (although only two have a bath). Some bedrooms are in converted buildings at the back of the house, but (good) breakfasts are served in the main dining room, at a communal table. Recent developments have increased the dining capacity at Barnabrow, so they can now cater for weddings and other functions (up to 150) as well as normal private dining; word has clearly got out to discerning would-be-weds that weddings at Barnabrow are conducted with style and personal interest, as this is now an important (and growing) side of the business. Head chef Eamon Harty is Ballymaloe trained and brings to Barnabrow's Trinity Rooms Restaurant and catering operations the philosophy and cooking style that has earned such acclaim (Shanagarry smoked salmon and gratin of cod with Imokilly cheese & mustard topping are typical specialities.) Children welcome (cots available, €6.50). Pets permitted by arrangement. **Rooms 19** (17 shower only, 2 with private bathrooms, all no smoking). B&B €50pps, ss €13. D 7-9 Tue-Sat, L Sun Only 12.30-3; D à la carte; Set Sun L €21. House wine €18; service discretionary. Closed 24-28 Dec. Diners, MasterCard, Visa, Laser. **Directions:** From Cork N25 to Midleton roundabout, right for Cloyne, then 2 miles on to Ballycotton road.

Cloyne — The Cross of Cloyne

Pub/Restaurant — Cloyne Co Cork **Tel: 021 465 2401**

The long narrow bar of this traditional, pub has been sensitively renovated, with an open fire at the far end for colder times and interesting music some nights. The restaurant is accessed by two entrances - through the pub, or directly into the restaurant which is in a renovated terrace on the left; in either case, the welcome is warm and you may be shown to a small reception area to consider the menu, or go straight to attractively set up tables discreetly well-lit by spotlights that also pick up modern oils on the walls. Anyone who remembers Colm Falvey's previous restaurants - The Clean Slate in Midleton, The Earl of Orrery in Youghal - will have high expectations of the food and is not likely to be disappointed. The hallmarks are here - a menu based on local ingredients and not over-extensive, a tempting selection of imaginative dishes, with the emphasis on fish but not to the exclusion of well-balanced choices. Ballycotton seafood chowder is predictable, perhaps, but very good; panfried fishcake comes with a fresh tarragon mayonnaise dressing and main courses of fillet of hake with a fresh crab and herb crust and roast rack of lamb with chargrilled Mediterranean vegetables and a red wine jus are all excellent choices. Accomplished cooking, generous portions and attractive presentation are all good points but, best of all, are the flavours - and service, which is friendly and efficient, the better to enjoy this fine fare. Imaginative desserts too - walnut & armagnac tart, for example, with crème anglaise - and a short but well-chosen wine list. **Seats 60.** D Mon-Sat high season (Jun-Aug), otherwise Wed-Sat, 6-9.30; Sun 4-9.30, all year. A la carte (average main course €20). Smoking area. Closed Mon & Tue except Jun-Aug, 25 Dec & Good Fri. Diners, MasterCard, Visa, Laser. **Directions:** Approaching from Midleton, straight through cross in centre of town (Ballycotton is indicated to the left); pub/restaurant 50 yards on left. ◇

Cobh   Mansworth's Bar (Est 1895)

Pub   Midleton Street Cobh Co Cork **Tel: 021 481 1965**

Cobh's oldest established family-owned bar dates back to at least 1895 and is currently in the capable hands of John Mansworth, who is a great promoter of the town and a knowledgeable provider of local information. Bar snacks are available but it's really as a character pub that Mansworth's is most appealing. It's a bit of a climb up the hill to reach it but well worth the effort, especially for anyone with an interest in the history of Cobh as a naval port - the photographs and memorabilia on display here will provide hours of pleasure. Not suitable for children after 7 pm. Pets permitted. Open from 10.30 am. Closed 25 Dec & Good Fri. **Directions:** Above St. Colman's Cathedral.

Cobh   Robin Hill House & Restaurant

féile bia Restaurant/Guesthouse   Lake Road Rushbrooke Cobh Co Cork
                                        Tel: 021 481 1395 Fax: 021 481 4681
            Email: robinhillhouse@eircom.net Web: www.robinhillhouse.com

A neat driveway leads up to Colin and Teresa Pielow's freshly-painted Victorian rectory and the whole interior has also been renovated since they came here in 1999. The dining operation is so central to this house that it feels like a restaurant with rooms. There's a comfortable reception area (with a real fire) and, alongside it, a stylishly bright restaurant with high-back chairs and handsomely-laid tables in the modern idiom with very fine glasses - all overlooking a terrace and gardens to the sea beyond. Well-made freshly-baked breads, bowls of butter and jugs of iced water arrive immediately along with an exceptional wine list. (Colin has also set up a tasting room in his wine cellar.) Seasonal menus offer about four choices on each course plus daily specials and include some especially tempting and unusual dishes, including game in season. Starters like carpaccio of Irish beef with parmesan shavings, lemon juice and black pepper, or three cheese & spinach tart with a salad of baby spinach leaves might be followed by roast loin of of rabbit with a chasseur sauce or Dublin Bay prawns or scallops with chilli, basil or garlic butter. Desserts include classics like fresh raspberry sablé and there's an Irish & continental cheese selection. Some dishes - daily specials and the cheeseboard, for example - attract a supplement, which could be as much as €10. Banqueting (50). **Seats 50.** Toilets wheelchair accessible. Not suitable for children under 12. D Tue-sat, 7.30-9.30; L Sun only 12.45-2.15. Set D €40, Set Sun L €22. House wines from €18; SC. discretionary. Restaurant closed D Sun, all Mon
Accommodation: En-suite accommodation is offered in rooms imaginatively furnished in a somewhat minimalist style; they have specially made furniture in different woods - hence the Beech Room, the Sycamore Room, the Cherry Room and so forth. (The same craftsman also made a magnificent cigar humidor which is an exceptional piece of work.) Rooms all have phones, TV and tea/coffee-making facilities. Garden. **Rooms 6** (all en-suite & no smoking) B&B €60, ss€15. Off-season offer (Sep 02-Apr 03): Tue-Thu 1DB&B €150 per couple, Fri/Sat €165 per couple. Establishment closed 25-27 Dec & 7 Jan -7 Feb. MasterCard, Visa, Laser. **Directions:** Over the bridge past Fota, take right turn right for Cobh 4 miles past the Statoil garage, next turn left, 300 yards on the left.

Cobh   WatersEdge Hotel

Hotel   Yacht Club Quay Cobh Co Cork **Tel: 021 481 5566** Fax: 021 481 2011
                    Email: watersedge@eircom.net Web: www.watersedgehotel.ie

The name says it all at Michael and Margaret Whelan's hotel, which is neatly slotted between the road and the harbour, taking full advantage of its unique waterside setting. There's a carpark underneath the hotel and public areas include an impressive foyer, while the spacious bedrooms -

some of which have French windows opening onto a verandah, most have a sea view - include a suite which is designed to be used for small conferences as well as accommodation. Children welcome (under 2s free in parents' room, cot available without charge). Pets permitted by arrangement. **Rooms 19** (1 suite, 1 for disabled, 5 no-smoking). B&B about €50-127pps, ss about €26. Closed 23-28 Dec.

Jacob's Ladder: Michael Whelan has been in the tugboat business for many years (there may well be a tug berthed alongside the hotel when you visit) and the restaurant name has particular maritime relevance. The restaurant is well-located within the hotel, with large windows affording views across the harbour, and well-appointed tables are arranged brasserie style, creating a light, bright atmosphere. Local seafood is, of course, the star here - including Rossmore oysters and Shanagarry smoked salmon as well as sea fish landed nearby, but vegetarians are not overlooked and red meats (including Wicklow lamb), duck and pigeon feature regularly too. L&D daily. House wine about €18; sc discretionary. Amex, Diners, MasterCard, Visa, Laser. **Directions:** R624 off the N25. Follow signs for Cobh Heritage Centre. ◇

Crookhaven   O'Sullivans

Pub   Crookhaven Co Cork
Tel: 028 35319 Fax: 028 35319 Email: osullivans@crookhaven.ie

This long-established family-run bar is in an attractive location right on the harbour at Crookhaven, with tables beside the water - when it's not too busy, it can be heaven on a sunny day. Angela O'Sullivan personally supervises all the food served in the bar - home-made soups and chowders, shrimps (in summer only), local fresh crab, smoked and fresh salmon open sandwiches, home-baked bread, scones and desserts - all good homely fare. Bar food daily 10.30-8.30 (a little earlier in winter). Closed 25 Dec & Good Fri. Visa. **Directions:** From Cork, take the N71 and turn left on to the R591 just before Bantry.

Durrus   Blairs Cove House

☆ Restaurant/Accommodation   Durrus Co. Cork
Tel: 027 61127 Fax: 027 61481 Email: blairscove@eircom.net

ATMOSPHERIC RESTAURANT OF YEAR

Philippe and Sabine de Mey's beautiful property enjoys a stunning waterside location at the head of Dunmanus Bay. Although additions over the years have enlarged the restaurant considerably - including an elegant conservatory overlooking a courtyard garden - the original room at this remarkable restaurant is lofty, stone-walled and black-beamed: but, although characterful, any tendency to rusticity is immediately offset by the choice of a magnificent chandelier as a central feature, gilt-framed family portraits on the walls, generous use of candles and the superb insouciance of using their famous grand piano to display an irresistible array of desserts. They have things down to a fine art at Blairs Cove - and what a formula: an enormous central buffet groans under the weight of the legendary hors d'oeuvre display, a speciality that is unrivalled in Ireland. Main course specialities of local seafood or the best of meat and poultry are char-grilled at a special wood-fired grill right in the restaurant and, in addition to those desserts, full justice is done to the ever-growing selection of local farmhouse cheese for which West Cork is rightly renowned. The food is terrific, service friendly and efficient and the atmosphere memorable: this place is truly an original. **Seats 80.** D 7.30-9.30 Tue-Sat. Set D €48; house wine €19, SC discretionary. Closed Sun & Mon (Sun only in Jul & Aug) &1 Nov-16 Mar.

Accommodation: 3 Suites. Three small apartments, offered for self-catering or B&B, are furnished in very different but equally dashing styles and there is also a cottage in the grounds. Children welcome, cot available. B&B €110 pps, ss€20; SC incl. Diners, MasterCard, Visa, Laser. **Directions:** 1.5 miles outside Durrus on Mizen Head Road, blue gate on right hand side.

Farran   Farran House

🏛 Ⓝ Country House   Farran Co Cork **Tel: 021 733 1215** Fax: 021 733 1450
Email: info@farranhouse.com Web: www.farranhouse.com

Set in 12 acres of mature beech woodland and rhododendron gardens in the rolling hills of the Lee valley, this impressive house was built in the mid 18th century, although its present elegant Italianate style only dates back to 1863. Its position allows views over the medieval castle and abbey of Kilcrea and its location 10 miles west of Cork city makes it a good base for exploring Cork and Kerry. In the present energetic and caring ownership of Patricia Wiese and John Kehely, the house has been carefully restored and, although there are some contemporary touches as well as antiques, none of its original charm has been lost. Despite its considerable size, there are just four bedrooms - both they and their adjoining bathrooms are exceptionally spacious and decorated with style and comfort adding greatly to the sense of luxury that the house imparts. There's a fine drawing room for guests use (complete with grand piano) and a billiard room with full size table. Golf nearby (six 18 hole courses within 20 km). Children welcome (under 12s free in parents' room, cot available without charge). No pets. Garden. B&B €90 pps, ss €30 (advance bookings only); residents D €32 (24 hours notice; not available Sun or Mon, but nearby pub does good meals). House also available for self-catering (groups of 8-9, from €2,900). Closed 1Nov-1 Apr. MasterCard, Visa, Laser. **Directions:** Take N22 west, 5 miles after Ballincollig, turn right to Farran Village, up hill, 1st gate on left.

Fermoy — Castlehyde Hotel

Hotel/Restaurant — Castlehyde Fermoy Co Cork **Tel:** 025 31865 Fax: 025 31485 Email: cashyde@iol.ie Web: castlehydehotel.com

In a lovely unspoilt area only a short drive from Cork, this would make a soothing base for exploring north Cork. Erik and Helen Speekenbrink's delightful hotel is retained within the original buildings of a beautifully restored 18th century courtyard, with all the original features preserved. Warm hospitality, gracious surroundings, open fires and a high level of comfort combined with the character of the old buildings and courtyard make this an unusually appealing hotel. Bedrooms, which are individually furnished to a high standard with antiques, have a great style and the feeling of a private home; ground floor rooms along a courtyard verandah are more suitable for guests with limited mobility. Small conferences (35). Heated outdoor swimming pool. Children welcome (under 10s free in parents' room, cot available free of charge). No pets. **Rooms 14** (5 cottage suites, 10 no-smoking, 1 for disabled). B&B about €95pps, ss about €35. Open all year.
Mermaids Restaurant: A conservatory extension helps make the most of the restaurant's pleasant situation, overlooking a lawn and mature woodland. Lunch and dinner menus in a creative Irish international style offer some unusual choices - a wild boar terrine with toast brioche perhaps - and, given the lengthy descriptions on many current menus, are refreshingly brief and to the point. **Seats 65**. (Private room, 14). L only 12.30-2.30 (Sun to 3), D 6.30-9; Set Sun L about €22, D à la carte. House wine about €18. Service discretionary; air conditioning. Toilets wheelchair accessible. *Light meals also available during the day, 11-5. Amex, Diners, MasterCard, Visa. **Directions:** At Fermoy, turn off the N8 and take the N72 (Mallow direction) for about 2 miles. ◇

Fermoy — La Bigoudenne

Restaurant — 28 MacCurtain Street Fermoy Co Cork **Tel:** 025 32832

At this little piece of France in the main street of a County Cork town, Noelle and Rodolphe Semeria's hospitality is matched only by their food, which specialises in Breton dishes, especially crêpes - both savoury (made with buckwheat flour) and sweet (with wheat flour). They run a special pancake evening once a month or so, on a Saturday night. But they do all sorts of other things too, like salads that you only seem to get in France, soup of the day served with 1/4 baguette & butter, a plat du jour and lovely French pastries. **Seats 18**. D Tue-Sun, 5.45-10. Early D Tue-Thu about €16.50 (5.45-7.15); otherwise Set D about €25; Fri & Sat D €32; Sun Set D €25, also à la carte. House Wine about €16. Closed Mon & Jan. Amex, MasterCard, Visa. **Directions:** On the main street, opposite ESB. ◇

Glandore — Hayes' Bar

 Pub — The Square Glandore Co Cork **Tel:** 028 33214 Email: dchayes@tinet.ie

Hayes Bar overlooks the harbour, has outdoor tables - and Ada Hayes' famous bar food. The soup reminds you of the kind your granny used to make and the sandwiches are stupendous. Everything that goes to make Hayes' special - including the wines and crockery collected on Declan and Ada's frequent trips to France (which also affect the menu, inspiring the likes of Croque Monsieur) - has to be seen to be believed. Just order a simple cup of coffee and see what you get for about €1.75.

Wine is Declan's particular passion and Hayes' offers some unexpected treats, by the glass as well as the bottle, at refreshingly reasonable prices. Great reading too, including a lot of background on the wines in stock - and you can now see some of Declan's pictures exhibited, from June to August. By any standards, Hayes' is an outstanding bar. Meals 12-6, Jun-Aug; weekends only off-season. Closed weekdays Sep-May except Christmas & Easter. **No Credit Cards. Directions:** The square Glandore.

Glanmire — The Barn Restaurant

Restaurant   Glanmire Co Cork **Tel: 021 486 6211** Fax: 021 486 6525

At Glanmire, on the edge of Cork city on the old Youghal road, the Leahy family have been running his traditional restaurant since 1980 and they have earned a loyal clientèle who appreciate the consistently good cooking and professional service. Food with a real home-cooked flavour is based on the best of local ingredients and herbs from the restaurant's own herb garden. Jean-Francois Bernard, who has been head chef since 1990, combines French and Irish influences in well-balanced menus that offer French specialities like baked Burgundy snails with parsley & garlic butter alongside Clonakilty black & white pudding "Barn Style" - and main courses include many old favourites like steak Diane and crisp roast farmyard duckling with port & orange sauce. Finish off with a treat from the traditional dessert trolley. Car park. D daily, 6.30-9.30, L Sun only 12.30-2.30. Set D €37, Set Sun L about €22. Amex, Diners, MasterCard, Visa, Laser, Switch. **Directions:** Old Youghal Road (from Cork city).

Glanworth — Glanworth Mill Country Inn

Guesthouse   Glanworth Co Cork **Tel: 025 38555** Fax: 025 38560
                              Email: glanworth@iol.ie Web: www.glanworthmill.com

Beside a Norman castle on the banks of the River Funcheon, set in landscaped riverside gardens, this imaginatively converted stone mill - complete with the old mill wheel which has been restored, encased in glass and worked into the interior design - makes an unusual place to stay. Bedrooms - all have good en-suite bathrooms, phones, complimentary water and fruit. A leisure garden, with giant chess, maze, boules and deck was added in 2002. Small conferences/private parties(46). Fishing. No pets. **Rooms 10** (1 junior suite, all no-smoking). B&B €69pps, ss €20. Children welcome; cot available without charge. Informal meals are served (12 noon-9.30 pm). [*It is possible that the inn may change hands during 2003, although there is no definite information available at the time of going to press.] Restricted hours in winter - please phone for details. Amex, Diners, MasterCard, Visa, Laser. **Directions:** 5 miles off N8 between Mitchelstown and Fermoy.

Glengarriff — Glengarriff Eccles Hotel

 N Hotel   Glengarriff Co Cork **Tel: 027 63003** Fax: 027 63319
                              Email: eccleshotel@iol.ie Web: www.eccleshotel.com

Eccles Hotel was established in 1745, when it was known as the Glengarriff Inn, and is one of the oldest hotels in Ireland. The warming influence of the Gulf Stream has made this corner of Ireland very special and the hotel - which has panoramic views of Bantry Bay - is just opposite Garinish Island, world famous for its stunning semi-tropical Italianate gardens. Its mild climate made Glengarriff popular as a health resort in the nineteenth and early twentieth centuries and Eccles Hotel was used as a spa; the hotel earned a reputation for its hospitality and many famous people stayed here, including Yeats, Thackeray and Shaw. The current owners, brothers Carl and Gerard Hanratty, took over the hotel in a sad state of disrepair in 2000 and have breathed new life into it: fires burn cheerfully in the foyer once again and there is a sense of real hospitality. While not luxurious, accommodation is very comfortable and fairly priced - and many of the rooms enjoy panoramic views of the bay and Garinish Island. Familes are made very welcome, there are many activities in the area and this could make a good base to explore the Beara Peninsula and beyond - it's on the cusp of west Cork and south Kerry, so well-placed for touring. Conference/banqueting (500/300). No pets. **Rooms 66** (3 junior suites, 12 shower only, 1 disabled). Lift. Room service (limited hours). Children under 3 free in parents' room, cot available without charge. B&B €75pps, ss €20. Amex, MasterCard, Visa, Laser. **Directions:** 17 km from Bantry/ 90 km from Cork City.

Goleen — Fortview House

Farmhouse   Gurtyowen Toormore Goleen Co Cork **Tel: 028 35324** Fax: 028 35324
                              Email: fortviewhousegoleen@eircom.net
                    Web: http://homepage.eircom.net/~fortviewhousegoleen/

Violet & Richard Connell's remarkable farmhouse in the hills behind Goleen is immaculate. It is beautifully furnished, with country pine and antiques, brass and iron beds in en-suite bedrooms (all individually decorated) and with all sorts of thoughtful little details to surprise and delight. Richard is a magic man when it comes to building - a recent creation was the lovely conservatory dining room, which he completed with great attention to detail. For her part, Violet loves cooking, and she provides residents' dinners, to the great delight of her guests - who also wake up to a fantastic array at breakfast. The choice includes a range of fresh fruit and vegetable juices, home-made muesli, home-made pancakes & maple syrup, hot potato cakes with crème fraîche, local farmhouse cheeses (Giana Ferguson's Gubbeen is made nearby), full Irish breakfast and a whole range of dishes made with their own freshly-laid eggs - it would be a wise plan to take one of the many long walks in the area afterwards. A self-catering cottage is also available. **Rooms 5** (all en-suite). B&B €40pps. Set D served at 8pm, €25. Please book by noon. Closed 1 Nov-1 Mar. **Directions:** 2 km from Toormore on main Durrus-Bantry road (R591).

Goleen Harbour   The Heron's Cove

Restaurant/Accommodation   Harbour Road Goleen Co. Cork
Tel: 028 35225 Fax: 028 35422
Email: suehill@eircom.net Web: www.heronscove.com

When the tide is in and the sun is out there can be few prettier locations than Sue Hill's restaurant overlooking Goleen harbour. Delicious desserts - tangy lemon tart or a wicked chocolate gateau - are also available with afternoon tea or freshly brewed coffee. The Heron's Cove philosophy is to use only the best of fresh, local ingredients - typically in wholesome starters like fisherman's broth or warm duckling salad and main courses such as Goleen lamb cutlets with a redcurrant sauce, and prices are refreshingly reasonable. An unusual Wine on the Rack system offers a great selection of interesting, well-priced wines that change through the season - they are listed but the idea is that you can browse through the bottles and make your own selection. Children welcome at discretion of the management. **Seats 30** D daily in summer 6.30-9.30 (bookings only out of season), L Sun 1.30-3. D à la carte. Closed Christmas & New Year.
Accommodation: Good-sized en-suite rooms have bathrooms, satellite TV, phones, tea/coffee-making facilities and hair dryers. The three doubles have private balconies with sea views and two smaller rooms have a woodland view. Garden. **Rooms 5** (all en-suite & no smoking). B&B €35pps, ss about €8. Open for dinner, bed & breakfast all year except Christmas week, but it is always advisable to book, especially off-season. Amex, Diners, MasterCard, Visa, Laser. **Directions:** Turn left in middle of Goleen to the Harbour, 300m fom village.

Gougane Barra   Gougane Barra Hotel

Hotel   Gougane Barra Co. Cork **Tel: 026 47069** Fax: 026 47226
Email: gouganebarrahotel@eircom.net Web: www.gouganebarra.com

In one of the most peaceful and beautiful locations in Ireland, this delightfully old-fashioned family-run hotel is set in a Forest Park overlooking Gougane Barra Lake (famous for its monastic settlements). The Lucey family has run the hotel since 1937, offering simple, comfortable accommodation as a restful base for walking holidays. Rooms are comfortable but not over-modernised, all looking out on to the lake or mountain. There are quiet public rooms where guests often like to read; breakfast is served in the lakeside dining room. No weddings or other functions are accepted. Children welcome. No pets. Fishing, walking. **Rooms 27** (all en-suite). B&B €68pps, ss €17. Closed 13 Oct-14 Apr. Amex, Diners, MasterCard, Visa, Laser. **Directions:** Situated midway between Macroom and Bantry, in Gougane Barra National Forest (which is well signposted).

Heir Island   Island Cottage

Restaurant   Heir Island Co. Cork **Tel: 028 38102** Fax: 028 38102
Email: ef@islandcottage.com Web: www.islandcottage.com

Just a short ferry ride from the mainland (near Skibbereen) yet light years away from the "real" world, this place is unique. Hardly a likely location for a restaurant run by two people who have trained and worked in some of Europe's most prestigious establishments - but, since 1990, that is exactly what John Desmond and Ellmary Fenton have been doing at Island Cottage. Everything about it is different from other restaurants and the no-choice 5-course menu (€30) depends entirely on the availability of the fresh local, organic (where possible) and wild island ingredients of that day. (A vegetarian dish can be accommodated with advance notice). An early autumn menu will give an idea of John's attachment to the island and the kind of meal to expect: roast duck leg with a béarnaise sauce, sweet red pepper salsa & little roast potatoes (using hand-reared ducks "of exceptional quality" from Ballydehob), turbot with shrimp sauce on a bed of sea beet or spinach (the shrimp is caught by local fishermen; sea beet is a wild foreshore vegetable, rather like spinach) and a classic terrine of vanilla ce cream with meringue served with a blackberry sauce, using berries picked by children holidaying on the island. [Cookery courses: 2-day off-season cookery courses available for 2 people, with overnight stay; also intensive 1-week course Jul-Aug; also speciality courses, eg duck, followed by lunch; off season demonstrations can be arranged on the mainland, also private dinner parties (Oct-May).] **Seats 24** (max table size 10; be prepared to share a table). No smoking restaurant. D Wed-Sun, 8.15-11.45 pm; one sitting served at group pace. D €30 approx. L off-season for groups of 16+. Closed Mon & Tue and 16 Sep-14 May. No credit cards. **No Credit Cards. Directions:** From Skibbereen, on Ballydehob road, turn left at Church Cross, signposted Hare Island and Cunnamore. Narrow winding road, past school, church, Minihan's Bar. Continue to end of road, Cunnamore car park. Ferry departs Cunnamore pier at 7.55 returns at 11.55 (journey: 4 minutes.)

Innishannon   Innishannon House Hotel

 Hotel

Innishannon Co Cork

Tel: 021 477 5121 Fax: 021 477 5609 Email: inishannon@tinet.ie

This lovely house was built in 1720 in the 'petit chateau' style and both it and the riverside location and gardens have great charm. Public rooms include a residents' bar and sitting room, and bedrooms vary in shape and character; the best rooms have river views, while others overlook the lovely gardens and all have original wooden shutters. After many years as a family-run business, the hotel changed hands in 2001 and is currently operated by a consortium, who have plans for major upgrading and a new bedroom block. So far everything seems much the same, but changes are likely in the near future. Garden, fishing, boating. **Rooms 13** (1 suite). B&B about €95. Closed 24-27 Dec.. **Directions:** Off Cork-Bandon road, north of Kinsale. ◇

Kanturk   Assolas Country House

 Country House

Kanturk Co Cork **Tel: 029 50015** Fax: 029 50795
Email: assolas@eircom.net Web: www.assolas.com

Home to the Bourke family for generations and currently managed by Joe and Hazel Bourke, this gracious 17th century manor house is famous for generous, thoughtful hospitality, impeccable housekeeping and wonderful food. Hazel, who was the winner of the guide's Euro-Toques Natural Food Award in 2000, is a Euro-Toques chef and renowned for imaginative and skilled use of organic produce from their own garden and the surrounding area, offered in a daily residents' dinner menu which documents in detail the produce used in their kitchen and the people who supply it. Memorable dinners for residents are served in a lovely dining room - high-ceilinged and elegantly proportioned with deep red walls, antique furniture and crisp white linen - which is not over-decorated, providing an appropriate setting for food that is refreshingly natural in style as well as substance: specialities like warm salad of garden potatoes with Kenmare mussels, Hazel's white yeast rolls and garden fruit compôte with buttermilk pudding tell the tale. Bedrooms vary according to their position in this lovely old house - some are very spacious and overlook the garden and river, and there are some courtyard rooms which are especially suitable for families. A lovingly maintained walled kitchen garden, a little river with tame swans and a couple of boats for guests to potter about in all add to the charm - even boots kept beside the front door for the use of anyone who may feel like looking up the local otters at dusk. The wine list concentrates on European wine, notably Maison Guigal, which has supplied the house wines since 1983. Small conferences/banqueting (18/20). Fishing, garden, tennis, walking. Pets permitted by arrangement. **Rooms 9** (all en-suite). B&B €95 pps, ss €16. Children welcome (under 4s free in parents' room, cot available without charge), but not in the dining room after 7pm. Dining Room **Seats 20** (max table size 14). D, for residents only, €48, 7-8 pm; house wine €21. Service is included in prices and tipping is discouraged. Closed 1 Nov-14 Mar. MasterCard, Visa, Laser. **Directions:** Signposted off N72, 8 miles West of Mallow.

Kanturk   The Vintage

Pub/Restaurant

O'Brien Street Kanturk Co Cork **Tel: 029 50549** Fax: 029 51209

Stephen Bowles has been running this fine pub since 1985, and it's a consistently well-run establishment: the attractive, well-maintained exterior draws people in and, once through the door, the comfortable, pleasingly traditional interior keeps them there. Be sure to stay for a pint or a quick bite of bar food, even if it's only a bowl of home-made soup. Other regulars include steaks done various ways, fish of the day, eg fillet of lemon sole with tartare sauce and something special fo vegetarians, as well as freshly prepared sandwiches. Meals 12.30-10 Mon-Sat, 6-10 Sun. Closed 2! Dec & Good Fri. MasterCard, Visa. **Directions:** In a terrace of houses, alongside the river.

Kilbrittain   Casino House

féile bia ☆ Restaurant

Coolmain Bay Kilbrittain Co Cork
Tel: 023 49944 Fax: 023 49945 Email: chouse@eircom.net

While Kerrin and Michael Relja's delightful restaurant is just a few miles west of Kinsale, it has been one of the country's best kept secrets for a long time and is only now achieving well-deserved recognition. The couple's cool continental style makes a pleasing contrast to their lovely old house, and the warmth of Kerrin's hospitality is consistently matched by the excellence of Michael's food. He cooks with verve and confidence, offering imaginative, wide-ranging menus based on the finest seasonal ingredients - and with clear respect for local produce. Ummera smoked organic salmon, for example, is produced nearby and appears regularly - typically in a crème fraîche roulade, served with a green summer salad - and fresh seafood from nearby fishing ports features in many dishes including a wonderful speciality lobster risotto which is offered as a starter but a variation with mixed seafood is also available as a main course. Local duck is another speciality and appears in many forms - roast breast of Ballydehob duck is served on a lentil potato cake with a honey & port sauce (house style is rare - ask if you prefer it cooked longer) and a '3 variation' duck terrine is made with the remaining parts - foie gras, confit and some breast - served with warm brioche& a pineapple chutney. Vegetarian dishes are not only tempting, but listed ahead of the other main courses - tagliatelle with a sun-dried tomato & pinenut pesto and parmesan is typical - which often include less usual dishes like saddle of rabbit; saddle of lamb is another speciality (on a courgette & roasted garlic sugo, for example) and nightly specials will include extra seafood dishes, all with ndividual vegetable garnishes and deliciously simple seasonal side vegetables. The Reljas' attention to detail is outstanding and their perfectionism in every aspect of the restaurant is admirable. Local cheeses are handled with particular respect, earning the restaurant this guide's Farmhouse Cheese Award in 1999.*Casino Cottage: sleeps two €58 per night, everything provided except breakfast - which can be supplied if needed. Weekly & winter rates available. **Seats 35** (private room 22). D Mon-Tue & Thu-Sun, 7-9, L Sun only,1-3; all à la carte; house wine about €17; sc discretionary. Closed Wed and 1 Jan-17 Mar. MasterCard, Visa, Laser, Switch. **Directions:** On R600 between Kinsale and Timoleague.

Kinsale   Actons Hotel

féile bia Hotel

Pier Road Kinsale Co Cork **Tel: 021 4772135** Fax: 021 4772231
Email: info@actonshotelkinsale.com Web: www.actonshotelkinsale.com

Overlooking the harbour and standing in its own grounds, this attractive quayside establishment is Kinsale's most famous hotel, dating back to 1946 when it was created from several substantial period houses. It has recently undergone extensive renovations - bedrooms and public areas were refurbished in 2001 and, following this, a new Health & Fitness Club has been completed; it now offers a brand new swimming pool with separate children's pool, hot tub, sauna, steam room and whirlpool spa; there's also a gym (with Technogym equipment), aerobics room, solarium and treatment facilities. Good conference/banqueting facilities too (300/250). Children welcome (under 4s free in parents' room, cots available without charge.) No pets. Wheelchair access. Lift. **Rooms 76** (3 junior suites, 14 executive, 1 shower only, 2 for disabled). B&B €98pps, ss €40 (wide range of special breaks available). Captain's Table Restaurant, L&D daily (speciality: the 'Derek Davis' steamed local seafood platter). Bar food available daily, 12-9. Closed 24-26 Dec, 5-31 Jan. Amex, Diners, MasterCard, Visa, Laser. **Directions:** On the waterfront, short walk from town centre.

Kinsale   Blindgate House

Guesthouse

Blindgate Kinsale Co Cork **Tel: 021 4777858** Fax: 021 4777868
Email: info@blindgatehouse.com Web: www.blindgatehouse.com

Maeve Coakley's fine modern guesthouse is set in its own developing garden high up over the town and has brought a contemporary element to the range of accommodation offered in Kinsale. With pacious rooms, uncluttered lines and a generally modern, bright and airy atmosphere, Blindgate makes a refreshing contrast to the more traditional styles that prevail locally. All bedrooms are carefully furnished with elegant modern simplicity, have full en-suite bathrooms and good facilities including fax/modem sockets as well as phones, satellite TV, tea/coffee trays and trouser press. Maeve is a hospitable host - and well-known in Kinsale for her skills in the kitchen, so breakfast here is a high priority: there's a buffet displaying all sorts of good things including organic muesli, fresh fruits and juices, farmhouse cheese and yogurts, as well as a menu of hot dishes featuring, of course, the full Irish Breakfast alongside catch of the day and other specialities - so make sure you allow time to enjoy this treat to the full. Private parking. Not suitable for children under 8. No pets. **Rooms 11** (1 superior, all no smoking). B&B €75pps. Closed 23 Dec-1 Mar. Amex, Diners, MasterCard, Visa, Laser, Switch. **Directions:** 300 m after St Multose Church on left hand side.

Kinsale — The Blue Haven Hotel

féile bia Hotel   3 Pearse Street Kinsale Co Cork **Tel: 021 477 2209** Fax: 021 4774268
Email: bluhaven@iol.ie Web: www.bluehavenkinsale.com

Due to the nature of the building, public areas in this attractive hotel at the heart of Kinsale are quite compact, but the lounge/lobby and the bar areas are well-planned and comfortable. A major refurbishment programme and the addition of eight superior bedrooms was recently completed, so all the bedrooms are new or redone, with double glazing offsetting the street noise that is inevitable in a central location. However, although both the well-appointed rooms and their neat bathrooms make up in thoughtful planning anything they lack in spaciousness, there are plans to reduce the number of rooms in order to create more space; currently the smaller rooms have shower only and are charged at a lower rate. Café Blue, a small evening wine bar adjacent to the lobby, doubles as an off-licence, and a gourmet coffee shop was also opened in summer 2002. Not very suitable for children, but cots are available without charge. No pets. Street parking. **Rooms 17** (8 superior, 4 shower only). B&B (standard/superior) €90/110pps, ss €37/68. Restaurant: **Seats 60** (private room, 22) D 7-9.30 daily, Set D €50, à la carte available. House wine from €18; SC discretionary. Closed 24-26 Dec. Amex, Diners, MasterCard, Visa, Laser, Switch. **Directions:** In the centre of town.

Kinsale — The Bulman

Restaurant/Pub   Summercove Kinsale Co Cork
Tel: 021 477 2131 Fax: 021 477 3359

The Bulman bar is characterful and maritime (though this is definitely not a theme pub) and a great place to be in fine weather, when you can wander out to the seafront and sit on the wall beside the carpark. The first floor restaurant specialises in locally caught seafood. Wheelchair access. Own carpark. **Seats 50.** (Phone for food service times). Closed 25 Dec & Good Fri. MasterCard, Visa. **Directions:** Beside Charles Fort, short distance from Kinsale. ◇

Kinsale — Chart House

B&B   6 Denis Quay Kinsale Co Cork **Tel: 021 477 4568** Fax: 021477 7907
Email: charthouse@eircom.net Web: www.charthouse-kinsale.com

Billy and Mary O'Connor took over this delightful 200 year old house in 1999 and completely renovated it with commendable attention to period details, opening their luxurious accommodation in spring 2000. Beautifully furnished bedrooms have orthopaedic mattresses, phone, TV, hair dryer and a trouser press with iron; tea and coffee are served by the fire in a cosy reception/sitting room. An imaginative breakfast menu is served communally on a fine William IV dining room suite. Not suitable for children. No pets. **Rooms 4.** (2 suites with jacuzzi baths, 2 shower only, all no-smoking). B&B (depending on room) €52-76, ss €15, ss €33. Closed Christmas week. Amex, MasterCard, Visa, Laser. **Directions:** On Pier Road between Actons and Trident Hotels, turn right after Actons, last house on right.

Kinsale — Crackpots Restaurant

féile bia Restaurant   3 Cork Street Kinsale Co Cork **Tel: 021 477 2847** Fax: 021 477 3517
Email: crackpots@iol.ie Web: www.crackpots.ie

Carole Norman's attractive and unusual restaurant has a lot going for it - not only can you drop in for a glass of wine at the bar as well as the usual meals but all the pottery used in the restaurant is made on the premises so, if you take a fancy to the tableware, you can buy that too. Menus are imaginative and considerate, with plenty for vegetarians and, although many of the s specialities are fish (seafood platter, for example), the range of dishes offered provides some contrast in an area that naturally focusses strongly on seafood. International influences are at work - Mediterranean salad, crispy roast duckling with a pickled ginger, lime & soy sauce and Thai chicken might share the menu with simple Oysterhaven oysters served o the shell - and that's all part of the fun. An interesting wine list features some "Wine Geese" labels (a visit to nearby Desmond Castle will tel you all about this) and some organic wines. Children welcome. **Seats 50**. No smoking area; ai conditioning. D daily 6-10. Early D €18.50 (6.30-7.30pm); otherwise à la carte, house wine €15.50 Closed Nov. Amex, MasterCard, Visa, Switch. **Directions:** Between Garda Station and Wine Museum.

Kinsale — Fishy Fishy Café @ The Gourmet Store

Restaurant   Guardwell Kinsale Co. Cork **Tel: 021 477 4453**

Martin and Marie Shanahan's delightful fish shop, delicatessen and restaurant is a mecca fo gourmets in and around Kinsale and was our Seafood Restaurant of the Year in 2001. The café, which has tables both indoors, alongside the shop, and outside under an awning, sports trendy little aluminium chairs and an agreeably continental air. Although all sorts of other delicacies are on offer, seafood is the serious business here - and, as well as the range of dishes offered on the menu and specials board, you can ask Martin to cook any of the fresh fish on display to your liking. Not tha you'd feel the need to stray beyond the menu, in fact, as it makes up in interest and quality anything it might lack in length - and you can have anything you like from seafood chowder or smoked salmon sandwich to grilled whole prawns with lemon garlic & sweet chilli sauce or fresh lobster, crayfish o crab. All the seafood at Fishy Fishy is caught locally by one-day boats so it is really fresh. Children welcome. **Seats 36**. No smoking restaurant; air conditioning. Toilets wheelchair accessible. L daily 12-3.45 (Mon-Sat only off season); à la carte; house wines from about €18. No reservations, so ge there early or be prepared to queue. Closed Sun from Oct to Mar. **No Credit Cards**. **Directions:** Opposite St Multose church, next to Garda station.

Kinsale — Harbour Lodge

Guesthouse   Scilly Kinsale Co Cork **Tel: 021 477 2376**
Email: relax@harbourlodge.com Web: www.harbourlodge.com

This guesthouse has one of the best locations in the area, with 180° views over Kinsale harbour and, before opening in summer 2001, Raoul and Seiko de Gendre refurbished it throughout with new carpets, top of the range beds and bedding and upgraded bathrooms, which are now luxurious, with the largest, thickest possible towels and bathrobes - and in-house laundry to take care of them. The position, away from the bustle of the town centre is lovely and peaceful; most bedrooms have balconies and there's a large conservatory "orangerie" (where breakfast is served), for the leisurely observation of comings and goings in the harbour and a sitting room with an open fire for chilly days. A high level of personal attention and service is the aim: guests are offered a welcoming glass of champagne on arrival and complimentary afternoon tea is served in the Orangerie. Bedrooms are very comfortably appointed, with complimentary mineral water and tea/coffee facilities - and a full turndown service. Simple meals are available on request - salads, sandwiches, soup, steaks, moules marinière - and there's a limited laundry and pressing service. Walking, cycling. Golf and many other activities nearby. Special breaks offered. **Rooms 8** (1 suite, all no smoking). B&B €82.50pps, ss €82.50 (child or other 3rd person sharing room €50). Open all year. Amex, Diners, MasterCard, Visa, Laser. **Directions:** 0.5 mile from Town Centre, beside the Spinnaker.

Kinsale — Jean Marc's Chow House

Restaurant   7 Pearse Street Kinsale Co Cork **Tel: 021 477 7117**
Fax: 021 477 8929 Email: thechowhouse@msr.com

Jean-Marc Tsai is no stranger to Kinsale - many will remember his exquisite combination of classical French and Chinese cooking in his previous restaurant, Chez Jean Marc. But this little place is something different; very Asian and very accessible with average prices for a meal only around €27.70 (with wine). Jean Marc's combination of Chinese, Thai and Vietnamese cuisines has gone down a treat with the area's discerning diners, who now cite the Chow House as a favourite evening destination. It's bright and modern, with comfortable seating and a lively atmosphere - a patio at the back has been turned into a covered 'Monsoon Garden', which increases the seating significantly. Many dishes on the fairly extensive menu may sound familiar - including specialities like Vietnamese spring rolls, hot & sticky ribs and Pad Thai - but they're different in the hands of a master like Jean-Marc. Although specialist ingredients must obviously be imported, Jean-Marc uses a lot of fresh local produce and everything is authentic, colourful, attractively presented and fresh-flavoured - all this with friendly, helpful service and terrific value for money makes for a thoroughly enjoyable experience - truly a winning combination. Unusually for an Asian restaurant, desserts are home-made on the premises - and here we catch a glimpse of Jean-Marc in his classic French mode: crêpes suzettes and crème brulée are typical. also raspberry cheesecake and apple fritters; not Asian, but very nice thank you. Not suitable for children after 8.30. **Seats 64** (private room 25). Toilets wheelchair accessible. No smoking area. D daily, 7-10. House wine €17 (Chinese & Thai beers to be available "shortly"). Closed 31 Dec -17 Mar. MasterCard, Visa, Laser. **Directions:** Next door to A.I.B Bank.

Kinsale — Man Friday

féile bia Restaurant

Scilly Kinsale Co. Cork
Tel: 021 477 2260 Fax: 021 477 2262

High up over the harbour, Philip Horgan's popular, characterful restaurant is housed in a series of rooms. It has a garden terrace which makes a nice spot for drinks and coffee in fine weather. Martin Fox, who has been head chef since 1998, presents seasonal à la carte menus that major on seafood but offer plenty else besides, including several vegetarian choices and duck, steak and lamb. While geared to fairly traditional tastes - specialities include crab au gratin and hot Kinsale seafood platter - the cooking is sound and can include imaginative ideas. Simple, well-made desserts include good ice creams. Service is cheerful and efficient and, unlike many other restaurants in the area which are seasonal, Man Friday is open in the winter. **Seats 130** (private room, 35). Toilets wheelchair accessible. No smoking area; air conditioning. D Mon-Sat 6.45-10.15; à la carte, house wine €19; SC discretionary. Closed Sun, Dec 24-26. Amex, MasterCard, Visa, Laser. **Directions:** Overlooking the harbour, at Scilly.

Kinsale — Max's Wine Bar

Restaurant

48 Main Street Kinsale Co. Cork
Tel: 021 477 2443 Fax: 021 4772443

Max's is run by a young couple, Anne Marie Galvin, who supervises front of house, and chef-owner Olivier Queva, who have earned a loyal following in the locality. It's a characterful little place with stone walls at the bar end, varnished wooden tables and an attractive conservatory area at the back. They offer a light snack lunch and a short menu that's available at lunch or in the early evening, as well as the main dinner menu. Olivier's seasonal menus change regularly (some seasonal, others daily) and offer a balance of meats and poultry, as well as the seafood from the pier - langoustines, oysters, mussels, black sole, salmon, ray and so on - which is always so much in demand. Roast rack of Irish lamb is a consistent favourite - served with a fashionable lavender sauce, perhaps - and imaginative vegetarian dishes are always offered too: crispy galette of Durrus and Ardrahan cheeses with sweet & sour carrot is typical. A wide selection of wines is now available by the glass. Not suitable for children under 5 after 8pm. **Seats 32.** No smoking area. L Wed-Mon,12.30-2.45 (Sun 1-3), D Wed-Mon, 6.30-10.30 (Sun to 10). Set L/Early D €17 (6.30-7.30), à la carte available; house wine €15.50, SC discretionary. Closed 1 Nov-1 Mar. Amex, MasterCard, Visa, Laser, Switch. **Directions:** Street behind the petrol station on pier.

Kinsale — The Old Bank House

féile bia Guesthouse

11 Pearse Street Kinsale Co. Cork **Tel: 021 477 4075** Fax: 021 477 4296
Email: oldbank@indigo.ie Web: www.oldbankhousekinsale.com

Marie and Michael Riese's townhouse in the middle of Kinsale has earned a high reputation for quality of accommodation and service - it has an elegant residents' sitting room, a well-appointed breakfast room and comfortable country house-style bedrooms with good amenities, antiques and quality materials. In 1999, the Old Bank House expanded into the Post Office next door, to include a further seven bedrooms and - this is a major improvement - they installed a lift. All rooms are furnished and decorated to the same high standard, with lovely bathrooms, phone, TV all-day (8am-10pm) room service for coffee, tea, wine, mineral water etc (which may also be served in the sitting room) ISDN line and safe available at reception. No smoking in public areas. Babies up to 1 year free in parents' room; cot €15. Golf-friendly: tee-off times, hire of clubs, transport to course, golf tuition can all be arranged; golf storage room. **Rooms 17** (1 suite, 3 junior suites). Lift. B&B €170 per room (max 2 guests). Closed 23-26 Dec. Amex, MasterCard, Visa, Laser, Switch. **Directions:** On right hand side at start of Kinsale, next to the post office.

Kinsale — The Old Presbytery

Accommodation

43 Cork Street Kinsale Co. Cork **Tel: 021 277 2027** Fax: 021 477 2166
Email: info@oldpres.com Web: www.oldpres.com

This old house in the centre of the town has provided excellent accommodation for many years and the current owners, Philip and Noreen McEvoy, have added three new self-catering suites, each with two en-suite bedrooms, sitting room, kitchenette and an extra bathroom. The new rooms are well-proportioned and furnished in the same style and to the same high standard as the original refurbished bedrooms (with stripped pine country furniture and antique beds); they can be taken on a nightly basis, sleeping up to six adults. The top suite has an additional lounge area leading from a spiral staircase, with magnificent views over the town and harbour. Children welcome; cot available without charge. No pets. **Rooms 6** (3 suites, 3 shower only, all no-smoking). B&B €115pps, ss €25. Closed 1 Dec-14 Feb. Amex, MasterCard, Visa, Laser, Switch. **Directions:** Follow signs for Desmond Castle - in same street.

Kinsale — Perryville House

Accommodation — Long Quay Kinsale Co. Cork **Tel: 021 477 2731** Fax: 021 477 2298
Email: sales@perryville.iol.ie Web: www.perryvillehouse.com

One of the prettiest houses in Kinsale, Laura Corcoran's characterful house on the harbour front has been renovated to a high standard and provides excellent accommodation only 15 minutes from the Old Head of Kinsale golf links. Gracious public rooms are beautifully furnished, as if for a private home. Spacious, individually decorated bedrooms vary in size and outlook (ones at the front are most appealing, but the back is quieter) and all have extra large beds and thoughtful extras such as fresh flowers, complimentary mineral water, quality toiletries, robes and slippers. The suites, have exceptionally luxurious bathrooms although all are well-appointed. Breakfasts include home-baked breads and local cheeses; morning coffee and afternoon tea are available to residents in the drawing room and there is a wine licence. No smoking establishment. Own parking. Not suitable for children under 12. No pets. **Rooms 26** (6 junior suites,8 superior, all no-smoking). B&B €100 pps, SC discretionary. Closed 1 Nov-1 Apr. Amex, Diners, MasterCard, Visa. **Directions:** Central location, on right as you enter Kinsale from Cork, overlooking marina.

Kinsale — The Spaniard Inn

Pub — Scilly Kinsale Co Cork **Tel: 021 477 2436**
Fax: 021 477 3303 Email: thespaniard@eircom.net

Who could fail to be charmed by The Spaniard, that characterful and friendly old pub perched high up above Scilly? Although probably best known for music (nightly), it offers bar food all year round and there's a restaurant in season. Since changing hands in 2001, the fairly traditional fare (Spaniard seafood chowder, smoked salmon platter, moules marinières) for which it is well known continues to be served informally in the bar alongside a wide range of more contemporary dishes such as warm goats cheese tartlet, Thai noodles (with chicken or beef) and a range of gourmets sandwiches. Evening restaurant meals (Dublin By prawns, fillet of lamb, roast monkfish) are more extensive and ambitious. Bar meals: 12.30-5.30 (average main dish about €10); evening meals: 6.30-10 (main courses €21.25-€24.50). House wine €18. Closed 25 Dec & Good Fri. Amex, MasterCard, Visa, Laser.

Kinsale — Toddies

Restaurant/Accommodation — Eastern Road Kinsale Co. Cork **Tel: 021 477 7769**
Email: toddies@eircom.net Web: www.toddieskinsale.com

Together with his wife Mary, this new restaurant with rooms is run by Pearse O'Sullivan, son of Conal and Vera O'Sullivan - until recently proprietors of the lovely Innishannon House Hotel - and grandson of the legendary hotelier Toddie O'Sullivan, hence the name. Facing south-westwards over Kinsale harbour, it's one of the best locations in the area - easy to find yet secluded, with views across the water from the restaurant. Commitment, hard work - and that magic ingredient of great delight - have clearly gone into converting the house and furnishing it in a pleasingly personal contemporary style enhanced by interesting art. Aperitifs are served and ambitious menus presented in a cosy little sitting room at the back, while the well-appointed restaurant has harbour views and a lively atmosphere. A wide choice of starters range from soup (cream of potato and watercress, perhaps) to sophisticated dishes like home-made ravioli of langoustines & spinach with a cherry tomato butter sauce & shaved parmesan, while main courses range from an imaginative vegetarian dish (like a strudel of spinach, wild mushrooms and ricotta with asparagus spears, pine nuts & a roasted pepper coulis) to prime fish such as Dover sole (simply meunière). Seafood, including lobster, is dominant and other choices include a choice of steaks (sirloin, fillet and entrecôte) with various sauces, eg fillet of Angus beef with potato rösti, green asparagus spears & roasted shallot jus. Finish with mainly classic desserts, or farmhouse cheeses. A wide-ranging and informative wine list includes an interesting Sommelier's Choice selection. Banqueting (30). Children welcome. **Seats 30**. D Tue-Sun, 6.30-10. A la carte.(Starters about €6-15; main courses about €20-30.50.) House wine €18.50. SC discretionary. Closed Mon & 15 Jan-15 Mar. **Accommodation:** Although the accommodation offered is in three lovely generous guest rooms, rather than suites as described, they have luxurious bathrooms and harbour views. Amenities include phone/ISDN line,TV & tea/coffee-making facilities, with secretarial services available on request. Children welcome. Pets permitted by arrangement. Garden. **Rooms, 3** (all superior & no smoking). B&B €72.50pps, ss €26.50, (Room only rate €145, max 2 guests). Amex, MasterCard, Visa, Laser. **Directions:** 4th house on left hand side past Texaco Station as you enter Kinsale.

Kinsale — Trident Hotel

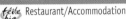 Hotel   World's End Kinsale Co. Cork **Tel: 021 477 2301** Fax: 021 477 4173
Email: info@tridenthotel.com Web: www.tridenthotel.com

This blocky, concrete-and-glass 1960s waterfront building enjoys one of Kinsale's finest locations and, under the excellent management of Hal McElroy, is a well-run, hospitable and comfortable place to stay. The genuinely pubby Wharf Tavern is a good meeting place and Gerry O'Connor, head chef for the main restaurant, also has responsibility for the bar food (12-9 daily). Bedrooms include two suites, with private balconies directly overlooking the harbour and all bedrooms are spacious and comfortable, with phone, TV and tea/coffee trays (iron and board available on request). Conference/banqueting (220); secretarial services, video-conferencing on request. Children welcome. No pets. **Rooms 58** (2 suites, 2 wheelchair accessible). Lift. B&B €95 pps, ss €33. Closed 24-26 Dec. **Savannah Waterfront Restaurant:** While it is difficult for a hotel restaurant to compete with the exceptional number and variety of restaurants in Kinsale, the Savannah - which is named after the first steam-powered vessel to cross the Atlantic from west to east - does a good job. The restaurant, well-located on the first floor with views over the harbour - which also makes it an exceptionally pleasant room for breakfast - has plenty of atmosphere. The food is good and especially welcome in winter, when many of the smaller restaurants are closed **Seats 80**. D daily, 7- 9, L Sun only 12.30-2. Set L from €20; D à la carte. House wine from €18. SC discretionary. Toilets wheelchair accessible. Amex, MasterCard, Visa, Laser. **Directions:** Take the R600 from Cork to Kinsale - the Hotel is at the end of the Pier Road.

Kinsale — Vintage Restaurant

féile bia Restaurant/Accommodation   50 Main Street Kinsale Co. Cork
Tel: 021 477 2502 Fax: 021 477 4828
Email: info@vintagerestaurant.ie Web: www.vintagerestaurant.ie

Raoul and Seiko de Gendre have been running the cottagey Vintage restaurant successfully since 1994. Frederic Pastorino, who has been head chef since January 2000, has the kitchen running sweetly and specialises in 'continental cuisine with an Irish accent'. The best of Irish ingredients are used in dishes that tend towards the classical and wide-ranging à la carte menus are especially strong on seafood in summer and game in the winter - examples that indicate the style include a speciality hors d'oeuvre of home-smoked wild fish and seafood from Irish waters, duck foie gras and tempura of Dublin Bay prawns in Guinness batter; many of the main course choices are luxurious: Dublin lawyer (lobster with a rich whiskey sauce), scallops, sole, turbot and game (venison, wild duck) all feature in season. Details are good - tasty little amuse-bouches are served with aperitifs, tables are beautifully appointed, service professional. Wine appreciation evenings and other special events are held regularly off-season (i.e. mid-Feb-Easter and mid Oct-early Jan). **Seats 56**. Private dining room available (25). No-smoking area; air conditioning D Tue-Sat 6.30-10; à la carte. House wine €25. SC discretionary. Open 7 days Easter-15 Oct; Closed 1 Jan-13 Feb, also Sun & Mon off season except for festive Sundays.
Accommodation: Raoul and Seiko de Gendre operate Harbour Lodge, a well-located guesthouse in the Scilly area of Kinsale, which overlooks the marina. (See separate entry). Amex, Diners, MasterCard, Visa, Laser. **Directions:** From the Post Office, turn left at the Bank of Ireland - restaurant is on the right.

Macroom — The Castle Hotel & Leisure Centre

féile bia Hotel   Main Street Macroom Co. Cork **Tel: 026 41074** Fax: 026 41505
Email: castlehotel@eircom.net Web: www.castlehotel.ie

In the ownership of the Buckley family for 50 years, this well-managed hotel is ideally located for touring the scenic south-west. Major developments which have been taking place over the last couple of years include the addition of superior rooms, an extensive new foyer and reception area, a new bar and two attractive dining areas. Impressive leisure facilities include a fine swimming pool (with children's pool, spa and massage pool), steam room, solarium and gym and new bedrooms above it. Conferences/banqueting (60). Special breaks are offered, including golf specials (tee times reserved at macroom's 18-hole Parklands course). Children welcome (under 4s free in parents' room, cots available without charge; playroom). No pets. **Rooms 60**. B&B €77.50 pps, ss €25. Food available 11am-9pm. Closed 24-28 Dec. Amex, MasterCard, Visa, Laser. **Directions:** On N22, midway between Cork & Killarney.

Macroom | The Mills Inn

Pub/Accommodation   Ballyvourney Macroom Co. Cork **Tel: 026 45237** Fax: 026 45454
Email: millinn@eircom.net Web: www.millinn.ie

One of Ireland's oldest inns, The Mills Inn is in a Gaeltacht (Irish-speaking) area and dates back to 1755. It was traditionally used to break the journey from Cork to Killarney - and still makes a useful stopping place as it has old-world charm (despite the regrettable conversion of real fires to gas) and the food is home cooked. Toilets wheelchair accessible. L&D daily. Closed 25 Dec.
Accommodation: Rooms vary considerably due to the age of the building, but all are comfortably furnished with neat bathrooms and good amenities. Superior rooms have jacuzzi baths, and there is a large, well-planned ground-floor room suitable for less able guests (who can use the residents' car park right at the door - in a courtyard shared with a vintage car and an agricultural museum). Room service is available for drinks and meals. Small conferences/banqueting (20/60), secretarial services. Off season value breaks. Children welcome; cots available. Pets permitted. **Rooms 13** (7 executive rooms, 3 shower only, 1 for disabled. B&B about €45pps. Wheelchair access. Amex, Diners, MasterCard, Visa, Laser. **Directions:** on N22, 20 minutes from Killarney.

Mallow | Longueville House Hotel

🏛 Country House/Restaurant   Mallow Co. Cork **Tel: 022 47156** Fax: 022 47459
Email: info@longuevillehouse.ie Web: www.longuevillehouse.ie

IRISH BREAKFAST AWARD - MUNSTER AND NATIONAL WINNER

When Longueville House opened its doors to guests in 1967, it was one of the first Irish country houses to do so. Its history is wonderfully romantic, "the history of Ireland in miniature", and it is a story with a happy ending. Having lost their lands in the Cromwellian Confiscation (1652-57), the O'Callaghans took up ownership again some 300 years later. The present house, a particularly elegant Georgian mansion of pleasingly human proportions, dates from 1720, (with wings added in 1800 and the lovely Turner conservatory - which has been completely renovated - in 1862), overlooks the ruins of their original home, Dromineen Castle. Many things make Longueville special, most importantly the warm, informal hospitality and charm of the O'Callaghans themselves - Michael and Jane, their son (and talented chef) William and his wife Aisling. The location, overlooking the famous River Blackwater, is lovely. The river, farm and garden supply fresh salmon in season, the famous Longueville lamb and all the fruit and vegetables. In years when the weather is kind, the estate's crowning glory (and Michael O'Callaghan's great enthusiasm) is their own house wine, a light refreshing white, "Coisreal Longueville". Graciously proportioned reception rooms include a bar and drawing room both elegantly furnished with beautiful fabrics and family antiques. Accommodation is equally sumptuous and bedrooms are spacious, superbly comfortable and stylishly decorated to the highest standards (under the personal supervision of Jane O'Callaghan) - and, after a good night's sleep, a Longueville breakfast is a treat to be cherished: in addition to a wide range of more usual choices, you can have delicious pressed apple juice and seasonal compôtes from the walled garden, then there's home-mixed muesli, natural yogurt, farmhouse cheeses and slices off a mustard glazed baked ham. Then there are all the home-bakes - soda breads, scones, pain au chocolat and croissants - and house preserves, marmalade and Longueville honey. And that's all from the buffet - there's still a cooked breakfast menu to follow, including porridge and fish of the day as well as a superb rendition of the traditional cooked breakfast. Of all the breakfasts sampled by the Guide during the last year, Longueville's was the best: a clear winner of our Denny Irish Breafast Awards, for Munster and all Ireland. Worth dropping in for even if you can't stay overnight - what a way to break a journey! As well as being one of the finest leisure destinations in the country, the large cellar/basement area of the house has been developed as a conference centre with back-up services available. The house is also available for small residential weddings throughout the year. Conference/banqueting (50/110). Children welcome (under 2s free in parents' room, cots available without charge). Pets permitted in some areas (by arrangement). **Rooms 21**. (2 suites, 5 junior suites, 14 superior rooms, 10 no-smoking). B&B €95pps. Closed Christmas and all Feb (but may open for groups of 20+ excl. Christmas/New Year. Shooting weekends available Nov, Dec, Jan; telephone for details).

★ **Presidents' Restaurant:** Named after the family collection of specially commissioned portraits of all Ireland's past presidents, which made for a seriously masculine collection until Ireland's first woman president, Mary Robinson, broke the pattern, this is the main dining room and opens into the renovated conservatory; there is a smaller room for those who wish to smoke and also the Chinese Room, which is suitable for private parties. William O'Callaghan is a highly accomplished chef and home- and locally-produced food is at the heart of all his cooking. His well-balanced dinner menus are not over-extensive, offering a choice of four or five dishes on each course, plus an intriguing 8-courseTasting Menu for complete parties. Local ingredients star, in a starter of house smoked salmon with a garden salad, for example, followed by rack of Longueville lamb - with rosemary sauce and roasted garden vegetables, perhaps - or home reared pork loin or duck, all worked into creative dishes which sound simple enough on the menu but can be complex. Home produce influences the dessert menu too, as in gooseberry tart with elderflower ice cream (a magic combination) and it is hard to resist the local farmhouse cheeses. Delicious home-made chocolates and petits fours come with the coffee and service, under Jane or Aisling O'Callaghan's direction, is invariably excellent. A fine wine list includes many wines imported directly by Michael O'Callaghan. **Seats 110** (private room 22).. D daily, 6.30-9.30, Set D €47, light meals 1-5 daily (set L for groups of 20+). House wine €23, sc discretionary (10% on parties of 8+). Annual closures as above. Amex, Diners, MasterCard, Visa, Laser. **Directions:** 3 miles west of Mallow via N72 to Killarney.

Midleton	Farmgate

féile bia Restaurant

The Coolbawn Midleton Co. Cork
Tel: 021 463 2771 Fax: 021 463 2771

This unique shop and restaurant has been drawing people to Midleton in growing numbers since 1985 and it's a great credit to sisters Marog O'Brien and Kay Harte. Kay now runs the younger version at the English Market in Cork, while Marog looks after Midleton. The shop at the front is full of wonderful local produce - organic fruit and vegetables, cheeses, honey - and their own super home baking, while the evocatively decorated, comfortable restaurant at the back, with its old pine furniture and modern sculpture, is regularly transformed from bustling daytime café to sophisticated late-week evening restaurant complete with a talented pianist, Donal Casey. Typically wonderful food on seasonal menus includes starters like fresh local crab salad and roast Portobello mushroom with Cashel Blue & rocket pesto bruschetta, at least five varieties of fish, plus free range poultry and local meats. A different vegetarian dish is offered each week and there's a choice of superb classic deserts (pannacotta with blackberries,for example) or an Irish farmhouse cheeseboard. Marog O'Brien is a founder and stallholder of the very successful Midleton Farmers Market, which is held on Saturday mornings. Meals 10-5 Mon-Sat (L 12-4); D Thu-Sat 6.30-9.45. Closed Sun, bank hols. MasterCard, Visa, Laser.

Midleton	Finins

Pub

75 Main Street Midleton Co. Cork
Tel: 021 4631878 Fax: 021 4633847

Finin O'Sullivan's thriving bar in the centre of the town has long been a popular place for locals to meet for a drink and to eat some good wholesome food. It's an attractive, no-nonsense sort of a place, and the owner-chef specialises in local produce, notably steaks, seafood and duck; bar menus are available all day. Open Mon-Sat, all day: 10.30am to midnight. L & D daily. Closed Sun, 25-26 Dec. Amex, Diners, MasterCard, Visa. **Directions:** Town centre. ◇

Midleton	Glenview House

Country House

Midleton Co. Cork **Tel: 021 4631680** Fax: 021 4634680
Email: glenviewhouse@esatclear.ie Web: www.dragnet-systems.ie/dira/glenview

When Ken & Beth Sherrard acquired their lovely Georgian house near Midleton in 1963 it was virtually derelict. Two years later, Ken bought the entire contents of the Dublin Georgian buildings infamously demolished to make way for the new ESB offices - and today this well-tended, comfortable and elegantly furnished house is the richer for that act of courage. Now, with a welcoming fire in the hall and two well-proportioned reception rooms on either side, it's hard to imagine it any other way. Except for one adapted for wheelchair users, bedrooms in the main house are on the first floor, all comfortably furnished with en-suite bathrooms (one has an old bath with a highly original - and practical - shower arrangement built in), hair dryers and tea/coffee-making facilities. The latest phase of restoration has created some delightful self-catering accommodation in converted outbuildings - with the agreeable arrangement of dinner in the main house as an option. Dinner is cooked by Beth and served at a communal table (8pm, usually residents only; book by noon). There is much to do in the area: the heritage sites at Cobh and Midleton are nearby, also

Fota House and Wildlife Park, Arboretum & Golf, wonderful walks and much else besides. Midleton Market (every Saturday) is a must for foodlovers. Garden, terrace, croquet, lawn tennis, forest walks, cycling. Children welcome. **Rooms 7** (4 in main house, 3 in converted coach house, 2 suites, 4 shower-only 2 for disabled). B&B €63.50 pps ss €15.24. Room Rate €127 (2 guests). Open all year. Amex, MasterCard, Visa, Laser. **Directions:** Take L35 from Midleton to Fermoy for 2.5 miles, take left for Watergrasshill and then immediately right. Glenview is signposted from the road.

Midleton — Loughcarrig House

Country House   Midleton Co. Cork **Tel: 021 463 1952** Fax: 021 461 3707
Email: info@loughcarrig.com Web: www.loughcarrig.com

Bird-watching and sea angling are major interests at this relaxed and quietly situated country house, which is in a beautiful shoreside location. Small conferences (20; max capacity sitdown meal 10). Children welcome (free in parents' room under 2, cot available without charge). **Rooms 4** (all en-suite, shower only & no smoking). Closed Christmas/New Year. B&B €32 pps, ss €8. **No Credit Cards.** **Directions:** Take Whitegate Road, 2 miles from roundabout on N25.

Midleton — Midleton Park Hotel & Spa

féile bia Hotel   Old Cork Road Midleton Co. Cork **Tel: 021 4635100** Fax: 021 4635101
Email: anthony@midletonpark.com Web: www.midletonpark.com

This pleasant hotel situated in the town of Midleton, close to the Old Midleton Distillery, has been completely refurbished and upgraded. Renovations include a new bar and restaurant and an impressive leisure centre with 18-metre deck level swimming pool, gymnasium, outdoor Canadian hot tub and much else besides - including a Wellness Centre and Spa, with a wide range of treatments including seaweed wraps, Indian head massage and reflexology as well as Yonka revitalising beauty treatments. Comfortable en-suite bedrooms - which are all furnished to a high standard with interactive TV with video and movie channel, phone/ISDN line, trouser press & ironing facilities, hairdryer and tea/coffee facilities - include some suitable for disabled guests and some non-smoking rooms as well as a 'presidential suite' for visiting VIPs. Although it is used a lot by the business community, the hotel also makes a good base for touring east Cork - Fota Island wildlife park, Cobh harbour (last port of call for the Titanic) are nearby and golf packages are arranged. Banqueting/conferences (300). Secretarial services. Children welcome. Wheelchair access. Ample parking. Garden, walking. No pets. **Rooms 80** (2 suites, 2 no smoking, 3 disabled). Lift. B&B €62.50pps, ss €22.50. Closed 25 Dec. Amex, Diners, MasterCard, Visa, Laser. **Directions:** 12 miles east of Cork city, off N25.

Midleton — Old Midleton Distillery

Café/Restaurant   Midleton Co. Cork **Tel: 021 4613594** Fax: 021 4613 642
Email: davidbyrne@iol.ie Web: www.irish-whiskey-trail.com

The Old Midleton Distillery is a fascinating place to visit - that such visiting can be thirsty work is acknowledged at the door (a whiskey tasting is part of the tour) but it can also be hungry work. Sensibly, the Centre has a pleasant restaurant where you can get a wide range of dishes, including simple fare like Irish stew, shepherd's pie and lasagne - and there's always a good selection of home-made cakes. **Seats 120.** Toilets wheelchair accessible. Air conditioning. Food available 10-5 daily. Closed Christmas period & Good Fri. Amex, Diners, MasterCard, Visa, Laser. **Directions:** 15 miles east of Cork on main Waterford (N25) road.

Midleton — Rathcoursey House

Country House/Restaurant   Ballinacurra Midleton Co. Cork
Tel: 021 461 3418 Fax: 021 461 3393
Email: beth@rathcoursey.com Web: rathcoursey.com

Set in 35 acres of woodland above an inlet of Cork Harbour, this peaceful small Georgian manor was opened to guests in 1999 by the food writer and former restaurateur Beth Hallinan - since moving here she has not only renovated the whole house, but planted 2,000 trees, a herb garden and also a children's garden. Beth's renowned 4-course dinner is available for residents, by arrangement - book well ahead, as this has become a favourite destination for discerning travellers in the know. Children welcome (children's garden with sandpit & stage; babies free in parents' room, cot available); pets permitted by arrangement. **Rooms 6** (1 junior suite, 1 shower only, 1 suitable for disabled guests). B&B about €70pps, ss about €15. Residents' dinner about €35, house wine about €15. Open all year. MasterCard, Visa. **Directions:** At Midleton roundabout take Whitegate road. After 4km turn right for East Ferry, then small village of Rathcoursey and follow green arrows to the left. ◇

Mitchelstown — O'Callaghan's Delicatessen, Bakery & Café

féile bia Café/Restaurant

19/20 Lower Cork Street Mitchelstown Co Cork
Tel: 025 24657 Fax: 025 24657 Email: ocalhansdeli@eircom.net

The ideal place to break a journey, O'Callaghans have an impressive deli and bakery as well as tasty fare for a snack or full meal in the café, where lovely things to look forward to include steak sandwiches, goats cheese on a crouton, salmon & potato cakes and Mediterranean sandwich. If you're going home to an empty house, this is the place to stock up with delicious home-baked breads and cakes, home-made jams and chutneys - and, best of all perhaps, there's a range of home-made frozen meals. And if you have a wedding coming up in the family, ask about their wedding confectionery, made to order... The only downside to this life-saving stopping place is that it's closed on Sundays. To avoid the busy main street, park around the corner on the road to the creamery - or, coming from Dublin, parking is also available on the New Square (on right after second set of lights); but remember the square is not available for parking on Thursday - market day. Restaurant **Seats 120**. Food served Mon-Sat, 8.30 am-5.30 pm; L 12.3-2.30. Closed Sun, 25-26 dec, 1 Jan, 17 Mar, bank hols. Amex, MasterCard, Visa, Laser. **Directions:** From Dublin after traffic lights on left halfway to next set of lights.

Monkstown — The Bosun

Pub/Restaurant/Accommodation

The Pier Monkstown Co. Cork
Tel: 021 484 2172 Fax: 021 484 2008

Nicky and Patricia Moynihan's waterside establishment close to the Cobh car ferry, has grown a lot over the years, with the restaurant and accommodation growing fast and becoming an increasingly important part of the enterprise. Bar food is still taken seriously, however; seafood takes pride of place and the afternoon/evening bar menu includes everything from chowder or garlic mussels through to real scampi and chips, although serious main courses for carnivores such as rack of lamb and beef stroganoff are also available. Next to the bar, a well-appointed restaurant provides a more formal setting for wide-ranging dinner and à la carte menus - and also Sunday lunch, which is especially popular. Again seafood is the speciality, ranging from popular starters such as crab claws or oysters worked into imaginative dishes, and main courses that include steaks and roast duckling as well as seafood every which way, from grilled sole on the bone to medallions of marinated monkfish or a cold seafood platter. There's always a choice for vegetarians and vegetables are generous and carefully cooked. Finish with home-made ices, perhaps, or a selection of Irish farmhouse cheeses. Not suitable for children after 7pm. Restaurant **Seats 80** (max table size 12). No-smoking area; air conditioning. D daily 6.30-9.30 (Sun to 9), L Sun 12-2.30, Set D €36, Set Sun L €22; à la carte also available; house wine €18.50, sc discretionary. Bar food available daily 12-9.30 (L12-2.30, D 6.30-9.30). Closed 24-26 Dec.
Accommodation: Bedrooms are quite simple but have everything required (phone, TV, tea/coffee trays); those at the front have harbour views but are shower only, while those at the back have the advantage of a full bathroom and are quieter. Guests tend to be working in the area and resident all week, with weekends bringing more leisure visitors. Fota Island Golf Course is only 12 minutes away, also Fota House and Wildlife Centre. **Rooms 15** (9 shower only). Lift. B&B €46pps, ss €7. Children welcome (under 5s free in parents' room, cot available without charge). No pets. Closed 24-26 Dec. Amex, Diners, MasterCard, Visa, Laser. **Directions:** On sea front, beside the Cobh ferry.

Oysterhaven — Oz-Haven

Restaurant

Oysterhaven Co Cork **Tel: 021 477 0974**

In a delightful waterside location at the head of Oysterhaven creek, Australian Paul Greer has transformed what was once a cosy cottage restaurant into something very different. The stone walls and open fires are still there, but the whole place has been done over in a highly idiosyncratic, colourful modern style - there's a great sense of fun about the whole approach and, despite its modernism, it works suprisingly well with the old building. Well-spaced tables in three separate areas have comfortable high-back carver chairs and are simply laid in quality contemporary style, with generous wine glasses and white plates decorated only with the restaurant logo. Interesting, quite ambitious weekly-changing menus offer world cuisine through a choice of six starters and main courses; typical examples include a special of lobster done four ways; Thai red curry with tiger prawns & squid flavoured with "all the tastes from the east"; and satay chicken strips coated in "the rich peanut flavours of the orient". Interesting, well-cooked and attractively presented (if quite expensive) food and friendly attentive service in entertaining surroundings. **Seats 50** (private room 30). Toilets wheelchair accessible. No smoking area. Children welcome. D We-Sun, 7-10; L Sun only 1-5. D à la carte, Set Sun L €24.95. House wine €17.95. Open all year except Christmas. Amex, MasterCard, Visa, Laser. **Directions:** 30 Min from Cork City; turn for Oysterhaven just before Kinsale.

Oysterhaven — Walton Court

Ⓝ Country House/Restaurant — Oysterhaven Co Cork **Tel: 021 4770878** Fax: 021 4770932
Email: waltoncourt@eircom.net Web: www.waltoncourt.com

Walton Court dates back to 1645, and when Paul and Janis Rafferty took it over on their return from Kenya in 1996, it was derelict. Five years of restoration work brought this listed building back to its former glory and the courtyard has been converted to stylish bedrooms and self-contained cottages, each with its own personality. There is also a small conference room (ISDN, video & lecture facilities), a bar with an open fireplace where guests can have a drink before dinner, and a restaurant in a plant-filled courtyard conservatory at the back of the main house, which is not yet fully open - the restored Georgian dining room is used instead, for residents dinners. This unusual place will please those who value character above the hotel conveniences (television, room service) and it helps to like animals as you will certainly be greeted by the dogs as well as their owners, and quite probably cats and other household animals too. Small conferences (30). Indoor exercise pool and sauna. Private berthing facilities for visiting sailors planned for spring 2003. **Rooms 6** (all en-suite & no smoking). B&B €54-85. Not suitable for children under 15, except in self-catering cottages. MasterCard, Visa, Laser. **Directions:** 6 miles from Kinsale towards Cork.

Rosscarbery — Celtic Ross Hotel, Conference and Leisure Centre

féile bia Hotel — Rosscarbery Co. Cork **Tel: 023 48722** Fax: 023 48723
Email: info@celticrosshotel.com Web: www.celticrosshotel.com

Opened in 1997, this contemporary hotel is close to the sea, overlooking Rosscarbery Bay (although not on the sea side of the road). It's an attractive modern building with an unusual tower feature containing a bog oak, which is quite dramatic. Well placed as a base for touring west Cork, the facilities in the leisure centre offer alternative activities if the weather should disappoint. Public areas are spacious, the restaurant looks over the road to the sea, as do many of the bedrooms, which are well-equipped with phones, tea/coffee trays and TV. Shortage of accommodation in the area means this hotel is always busy and recent visits indicate that the necessary care and maintenance systems may not be adequate. Children welcome (under 12s free in their parents' room; cots available without charge). Conference/banqueting (250/220). Short breaks, golf packages and themed breaks (bird watching, bridge, murder mystery) available, mainly off season. **Rooms 66** (1 suite, 3 for disabled). Wheelchair access. Lift. 24 hour room service. B&B about €90pps, ss €25. Open all year except Christmas. Amex, Diners, MasterCard, Visa, Laser. **Directions:** Take N71 from Cork City, 10 miles west of Clonakilty.

Rosscarbery — O'Callaghan-Walshe

Restaurant — The Square Rosscarbery Co. Cork
Tel: 023 48125 Fax: 023 48125 Email: funfish@indigo.ie

This unique restaurant on the square of the old village (well off the busy main West Cork road) has a previous commercial history that's almost tangible - and the atmosphere is well-matched by both proprietor-host Sean Kearney's larger-than-life personality and the exceptional freshness and quality of the seafood, although steaks share the billing. Menus change daily but specialities to look out for include a superb Fruits de Mer platter (available as small or large but, in the guide's experience, the small one is very large indeed with an exceptional range and quality of fish and shellfish included). The famous Rosscarbery Pacific oysters feature, of course, also char-grilled prime fish such as turbot, steamed lobster with lemon butter, whole Dover sole - nine of eleven main courses may well be seafood, the others classic meat dishes like cannon of lamb with Madeira sauce and grilled fillet steak with a choice of sauces. Ultra-freshness, attention to detail in breads and accompaniments, all add up to make this place a delight. Vegetarians may well have several attractive starter options, but main courses are likely to be prepared on request. Not suitable for children after 8 pm. **Seats 40** D 6.30-9.15 Tue-Sun, all à la carte (average main course about €25), house wine €17.70. SC discretionary. Closed Sun; open weekends only in winter (phone ahead to check). MasterCard, Visa, Laser. **Directions:** Main square in Rosscarbery.

Schull — Adèle's

Restaurant/Café Main Street Schull Co. Cork **Tel: 028 28459** Fax: 028 28865
Email: adeles@oceanfree.net Web: adelesrestaurant.com

Adèle Connor's bakery and coffee shop in Schull works like a magnet - if you happen to be in Schull early in the morning, you'll find it hard to squeeze in to buy some of her wonderful home bakes, never mind trying to find a table for a cup of coffee and a home-baked scone. There are delicious savoury things too, such as ciabatta specials served with small tossed salads - traditional and smoked Gubbeen with chutney perhaps - or an omelette with roasted red pepper and garlic. In the evening Simon Connor presents a different kind of menu in the first floor restaurant; a set menu might include a scallop soup and a smooth duck liver mousse then main courses like a bowl of mussels with a spicy tomato & lime sauce tossed salad or whole prawns with butter and garlic, with saffron potatoes followed by petit pot au chocolat or blueberry muffin with vanilla ice cream - taken with a glass of dessert wine perhaps. Times of opening vary according to the season; bookings advised. Children welcome. No wheelchair access. **Seats 40.** Open daily from 9.30, D 7.30-10.30, Sun L 11-5, Set L about €10, Set D about €25, à la carte available, house wine about €15, sc discretionary. Closed Nov-Christmas/Jan-Easter. Amex, MasterCard, Visa. **Directions:** Turn off N71 at Ballydehob for Schull - in town centre. ◇

Schull — Grove House

Guesthouse Colla Road Schull Co. Cork
Tel: 028 28067 Fax: 028 28069 Web: www.grovehouseschull.com

Overlooking Schull Harbour, just a few minutes walk from the main street, this beautifully restored period house is a much-needed addition to the accommodation in the area. Many period features have been retained and the large bedrooms have individual character; the outlook from them has improved over the last year as landscaping is maturing. A lovely dining room is used for breakfast - featuring local foods such as Gubbeen smoked bacon or Sally Barnes smoked fish - and there's a sitting room and panelled reading room available to guests. No smoking house. Not suitable for children. No pets. **Rooms 5** (4 shower only, all no smoking); B&B €60, ss €15. Closed 1 Nov-28 Feb. Amex, MasterCard, Visa, Laser. **Directions:** On right beyond C/ Ireland Colla Road, 4 mins walk from village.

Schull — La Coquille - Restaurant Francais

Restaurant Main Street Schull Co. Cork **Tel: 028 28642**

Jean-Michel Cahier's little restaurant is situated in the main street, convenient to the harbour. Like the restaurant itself, the à la carte menu appears to have remained more or less the same since it opened, which is perhaps unsurprising as competently handled classics are the main feature, typically duck paté, onion soup, half roast duck with orange sauce and scallops with a brandy cream. It offers more red meats and poultry than most places in the area but the menu in the window doesn't do it justice as there is also a blackboard brought to the table with the day's specials (mostly fish). Desserts, also classic, usually include tarte tatin and meringue suisse. A mixture of French and local staff provide service that ranges from aloof professionalism to friendly competence. **Seats 35.** No smoking area. D 7-9.30. Set D from about €35, also à la carte. House wine from about €16. SC10%. Opening hours appear to be erratic, a phone call to check would be wise, especially off-season. Amex, Diners, MasterCard, Visa. **Directions:** In the village, across from the church. ◇

Schull — Lasair Choille

B&B Ardmanagh Schull Co Cork **Tel: 028 27982**
Email: venita@gofree.indigo.ie Web: www.lasair-choille.com

A mile or so outside Schull, at the foot of Mount Gabriel, Venita and David Galvin's newly-built guesthouse offers modern, clean-lined accommodation in an area of natural beauty. It's furnished to a high standard in contemporary style, with a large lounge with communal tea/coffee making facilities and television and spruce en-suite bedrooms. It would make a good base for the many activity holidays in the area - walking (several short or long routes of 2-10 miles, also maps for serious hill walkers), horse riding, angling, diving, canoeing and so on - or simply touring the area. Packed lunches available (€5), also residents' dinner on request, based on local foods and organic produce from the garden. (€15). Children welcome (under 2s free in parents' room but no cot available). Small conferences (10). No pets. Garden (incomplete when visited). B&B €32, ss €8. Open all year except Christmas. **No Credit Cards. Directions:** Turn right at bank on Main Street, then right at T. Junction.

Schull — Stanley House

Accommodation/Country House

Schull Co. Cork **Tel: 028 28425** Fax: 028 27887
Email: stanleyhouse@eircom.net Web: www.stanley-house.net

Nancy Brosnan's modern guesthouse provides a west Cork home from home for her many returning guests. Compact bedrooms are comfortably furnished with TV and tea/coffee making facilities and there's a pleasant conservatory running along the back of the house, with wonderful sea views over a field where guests can watch Nancy's growing herd of deer and sometimes see foxes come out to play at dusk. Good breakfasts too. Children welcome (under 3s free in parents' room, cots available without charge). No pets. **Rooms 4** (all shower only, all no-smoking). B&B €30 pps, ss€12.50. Closed 31 Oct- 28 Feb. MasterCard, Visa. **Directions:** At top of main street, follow signs for Stanley House.

Schull — T J Newman's

Pub

Main Street Schull Co Cork **Tel: 028 27776**

Just up the hill from the harbour, this characterful and delightfully old-fashioned little pub has been a special home-from-home for regular visitors, especially sailors up from the harbour, as long as anyone can remember. The premises was sold in 2000 but, although Kitty Newman is missed, there is very little obvious change. Closed 25 Dec & Good Fri. **Directions:** Main West Cork route to Mizen Head.

Shanagarry — Ballymaloe House

féile bia 🏛 Country House/Restaurant

Shanagarry Co. Cork
Tel: 021 465 2531 Fax: 021 465 2021
Email: res@ballymaloe.ie Web: www.ballymaloe.ie

Ireland's most famous country house hotel, Ballymaloe was one of the first country houses to open its doors to guests when Myrtle and her husband, the late Ivan Allen, opened The Yeats Room restaurant in 1964. Accommodation followed in 1967 and since then a unique network of family enterprises has developed around Ballymaloe House - including not only the farmlands and gardens that supply so much of the kitchen produce, but also a craft and kitchenware shop, a company producing chutneys and sauce, the Crawford Gallery Café in Cork city and, of course, Tim and Darina Allen's internationally acclaimed Cookery School. Yet, despite the fame, Ballymaloe is still most remarkable for its unspoilt charm: Myrtle - now rightly receiving international recognition for a lifetime's work "recapturing forgotten flavours, and preserving those that may soon die"- is ably assisted by her children and now their families too. The house, modestly described in its Blue Book (Irish Country House & Restaurants Association) entry as "a large family farmhouse" is in the middle of the family's 400 acre farm, but the description fails to do justice to the gracious nature of the original house, or the sensitively designed later additions. The intensely restorative atmosphere of Ballymaloe is still as strong as ever; there are few greater pleasures than a fine Ballymaloe dinner followed by the relaxed comforts provided by a delightful, thoughtfully furnished (but not over decorated) country bedroom. Groundfloor courtyard rooms are suitable for wheelchairs. Children welcome. Special winter breaks offered. **Rooms 33.** B&B from €100pps, ss€20. Service discretionary.

★ **Restaurant:** The restaurant is in a series of domestic-sized dining rooms (some for non-smokers) and guests are called to their tables from the conservatory or drawing room, where aperitifs are served. A food philosophy centred on using only the highest quality ingredients is central to everything done at Ballymaloe, where much of the produce comes from their own farm and gardens. The rest, including seafood from Ballycotton and Kenmare, comes from leading local producers. Rory O'Connell (who is Darina Allen's brother) has been head chef at Ballymaloe since 1995 and presents a daily 7-course dinner menu, with vegetarian dishes given a leaf symbol. He is doing an inspired job in the kitchen, creating generous, beautiful, daringly simple meals: Ballymaloe brown bread, cruditées with garlic mayonnaise, Ballymaloe Cheddar cheese fondue, roast free range epork with aubergines, Irish farmhouse cheeses with home-made biscuits and a dessert trolley that included rhubarb compôte and vanilla ice cream are typical of the truly impressive yet homely dishes that leave guests lost in admiration and, as if a 7-course dinner isn't enough, they even offer second helpings of the main course! The teamwork at Ballymaloe is a sight to behold: this is, quite simply, as good as it gets. Finish with coffee or tea and home-made petits fours, served in the drawing room - and perhaps a drink from the small bar before retiring contentedly to bed. Children welcome at lunchtime, but the restaurant is not suitable for children after 7pm. (Children's high tea is served at 5.30.) Buffet meals only on Sundays. **Seats 120** (private room 25). L daily 1-1.15, D daily 7-9.15; Set D €55; set L €27-35. House wine from €21. SC discretionary. Reservations essential. House closed 23-26 Dec. Amex, Diners, MasterCard, Visa, Laser. **Directions:** Take signs to Ballycotton from N 25 Situated between Cloyn & Shangarry.

Shanagarry — Ballymaloe Shop Café

 Café   Ballymaloe House Shanagarry Co Cork **Tel: 021 465 2032**

At the back of Wendy Whelan's magnificent crafts and gift shop at Ballymaloe, there is a very nice little family-run café selling wholesome home-bakes and just the kind of light, nourishing fare that is needed to sustain you through a shopping expedition that may well be taking longer than you had planned. So take the weight off your feet, settle down with an aromatic cup of coffee and a slice of quiche and organic salad leaves (or why not an almond slice or some hazelnut meringue cake?). Open shop hours. **Directions:** Beside Ballymaloe House. ◇

Skibbereen — Kalbo's Bistro

Restaurant   48 North Street Skibbereen Co. Cork
Tel: 028 21515 Email: kalbo@eircom.ie

Siobhán O'Callaghan and Anthony Boyle are doing a great job at this bright, buzzy town-centre restaurant. It's informal but there has always been an air of quality about it - staff are quick and helpful and Siobhán's simple food is wholesome and flavoursome in a light contemporary style - good soups, pastas, bruschettas and salads at lunchtime and more serious dishes of local seafood, rack of lamb, steaks and so on in the evening. Delicious home-made burgers come with a choice of toppings and vegetarian options (highlighted on the menu) are imaginative. They have a shop jsut across the road too. **Seats 45**. Open daily, L 11.30-4.30 (Sun 12-2.30), D 6.30-9.30. A la carte; house wine about €15, sc discretionary. Closed Christmas & Good Fri. Amex, MasterCard, Visa, Diners. **Directions:** In town centre. ◇

Skibbereen — Ty Ar Mor Seafood Restaurant

féile bia Restaurant   46 Bridge Street Skibbereen Co. Cork
Tel: 028 22100 Email: tyarmor@iol.ie Web: www.tyarmor.com

SEAFOOD RESTAURANT OF THE YEAR

Chef Michel Philippot and front-of-house manager Rosaleen O'Shea's delightful little Breton restaurant in the centre of Skibbereen has a lively maritime theme and offers exceptionally high quality of ingredients, cooking and service - and at very moderate prices for seafood. The Menu Gastronomique offers great value at €40 (£31.50), with the only supplements for lobster starters and main courses, €8.50/€17 respectively, and there's also a Menu Touristique with two choices on each course, at only €30 (£23.63). Begin, perhaps, with a traditional Breton fish soup with rouille and croûtons, half a dozen Rossmore oysters with shallot sauce and lemon or a cassolette of prawns & squid in lobster & Armagnac sauce: the ingredients are all local, but this is real Breton cooking - just close your eyes and taste it. Outstanding main courses might include classics like black sole on the bone with garlic butter and grilled fillet of turbot beurre blanc (either of which would cost the price of the entire menu in many east coast restaurants) alongside more contemporary renditions such as fillet of John Dory with lime & ginger. In the unlikely event that you're not in the mood for seafood, there are one or two excellent meat choices, like chargrilled rack of spring lamb with grain mustard sauce or chargrilled fillet steak sauce poivrade. Side vegetables are invariably interesting and desserts will not disappoint: there's a rich gateau maison made with chocolate and Grand Mariner, while other classics such as île flottante, pears poached in red wine & cinnamon or a wonderful caramelised tarte tatin would all make a memorable end to a magnificent meal. And, if you can find the appetite to appreciate them, local farmhouse cheeses are beautifully presented, French style, with a walnut salad. The value for money is exceptional and professional service under Rosaleen's supervision, from mostly French staff, matches the food: this place is a little gem. Not suitable for children under 12. **Seats 30** (Max table size, 10). D Wed-Mon, 6.30-9.15 (Sun to 9). (D daily in Jul-Aug, closed Mon-Tue in winter and Tue in spring & autumn.) Restaurant closed end Sep-mid Nov & mid-Feb to mid-Mar) Set D from €30, Menu Gastronomique

€40; s.c 10%. House wine €18.50-20. D daily in Jul-Aug, closed Tue in spring & autumn, Mon & Tue in winter. Closed end Sep-mid Nov & mid-Feb to mid-Mar. MasterCard, Visa, Laser. **Directions:** Skibbereen town centre, towards road to Schull.

Skibbereen   The West Cork Hotel

Hotel   Ilen Street Skibbereen Co Cork **Tel: 028 21277** Fax: 028 22333
                                Email: info@westcorkhotel.com Web: www.westcorkhotel.com

John Murphy's welcoming family-run hotel enjoys a pleasant riverside site beside the bridge, on the western side of the town, and recent refurbishment has been completed with style. The entrance is quite small, but the hotel opens up behind the foyer, to reveal a bright and airy bar along the river side of the hotel, and a pleasant modern restaurant, where breakfast is served to residents, as well as main meals. Bedrooms are not especially large, but they are comfortably furnished in a gently contemporary style and have all the necessary amenities (phone, tea/coffee tray, TV) and neat, well-designed en-suite bathrooms - this would make a good base from which to explore this beautiful area. Rooms at the back are quieter and have a pleasant outlook over trees and river. Conference/banqueting (250). Children welcome (under 6s free in parents' room, cot available without charge). Pets permitted by arrangement. Garden. Private parking. **Rooms 30.** (3 suites, 4 junior suites, 23 superior rooms). B&B €80, ss 6. Food available in restaurant and bar: 12.30-2.30 & 6-9.30. Closed 22-27 Dec. Amex, Diners, MasterCard, Visa, Laser, Switch. **Directions:** Follow signs N71 to Bantry through Skibbereen.

Timoleague   Dillon's

Restaurant   Mill Street Timoleague Co Cork **Tel: 023 46390**

On the main road to West Cork, Dillons was one of the first café-bars and has always laid the emphasis on good food. Although still very much involved, times have changed since Isabelle Dillon did all of the cooking herself - she now has a creative American chef, so you're less likely to find dishes inspired by her native Brittany than vibrant international food, on menus that change daily. All à la carte, average main course around €20. Open daily in summer, 6.30-9.30; closed Mon in Oct; closed Mon & Tue, Nov-17 Mar. No bookings. **No Credit Cards. Directions:** On main Street of village. On M71. ◇

Timoleague   Lettercollum House

Country House   Timoleague Co. Cork **Tel: 023 46251** Fax: 023 46216
                                                        Email: info@lettercollum.ie

Con McLoughlin and Karen Austin no longer run the famous restaurant in the Chapel of their Victorian house but they still offer accommodation. The very roomy bedrooms have phones and tea/coffee making facilities and are furnished and decorated in a homely way which is ideal for families - who will have great fun at Lettercollum. The best bedroom has the only bath. Any food served is based on carefully sourced ingredients including organic produce from their own walled garden as well as the best of local meats and seafood. Children up to 3 are free in parents' room; cots available. Banqueting (50). Garden, walking. No pets. **Rooms 9** (8 shower only). B&B €40pps, ss €10. Closed Christmas. MasterCard, Visa. **Directions:** Drive through village of Timoleague, 1st right on the Clonaklty Road.

Union Hall   Casey's

🄽 Pub   Union Hall Co cork **Tel: 028 33590**
                                Email: caseysbar@tinet.ie Web: http://web.ukonline.co.ukcaseybar

This friendly traditional family-run pub has the best location in Union Hall, by far, with a walled outside seating area on the sea side of the building for the better enjoyment of Martha Casey's food on fine days. Seafood is the speciality here, available seven days a week for six months a year. No food in winter. Closed 25 Dec-6 Jan. **Directions:** N71 from Cork City.

Union Hall   Shearwater

B&B   Keelbeg Pier Union Hall Co. Cork **Tel: 028 33178**
                                Fax: 028 34020 Email: shearwater@esatclear.ie

Adela Nugent's B&B is located close to Keelbeg pier, on an elevated site overlooking Glandore harbour and the surrounding countryside. All bedrooms are good-sized and comfortably furnished with en-suite facilities (only one with bath); most rooms overlook the harbour. The breakfast room and TV room also have views, and there's a patio for guests' use in fine weather. Children welcome (under 2s free in parents' room). No pets. **Rooms 4** (3 shower only; all no smoking). B&B about 30pps, ss about €13. Closed 31 Oct-1 Apr. Amex, Diners, MasterCard, Visa. **Directions:** Off N71 between Clonakilty and Skibbereen. ◇

Youghal — Aherne's Seafood Restaurant & Accommodation

Restaurant/Pub
🏛 Accommodation

163 North Main Street Youghal Co. Cork
Tel: 024 92424 Fax: 024 93633
Email: ahernes@eircom.net Web: www.ahernes.com

Now in its third generation of family ownership, one of the most remarkable features of Aherne's is the warmth of the FitzGibbon family's hospitality and their enormous enthusiasm for the business which, since 1993, has included seriously luxurious accommodation. It is for its food - and, especially, the ultra-fresh seafood that comes straight from the fishing boats in Youghal harbour - that Aherne's is best known, however. While John FitzGibbon supervises the front of house, his brother David reigns over a busy kitchen. Bar food tends pleasingly towards simplicity - oysters, chowder, smoked salmon (all served with the renowned moist dark brown yeast bread) - its sheer freshness tells the story. Restaurant meals are naturally more ambitious and include some token meat dishes - rack of lamb with a rosemary jus or mint sauce, char-grilled fillet steak with mushrooms and shallot jus or pepper sauce - although seafood is still the undisputed star of the show and David is not afraid of simplicity when it is merited. Specialities like prawns cooked in garlic butter or fresh crab salad can make memorable starters, for example, and hot buttered Youghal Bay lobster are all, in a sense, simple dishes yet they have plenty of glamour too. A wine list strong on classic French regions offers a fair selection of half bottles and half a dozen champagnes. **Seats 60**. Toilets wheelchair accessible. No smoking area. D 6.30-9.15 daily, Set D €38; also à la carte; house wine €18.50, sc discretionary. *Bar food daily, 12-10.

Accommodation: The stylish rooms at Aherne's are generously sized and individually decorated to a very high standard; all are furnished with antiques and have luxurious, beautifully finished bathrooms. Housekeeping is exemplary and excellent breakfasts are served in a warm and elegantly furnished residents' dining room. Rooms more recently added are equipped to give the option of self-catering if required. Conference room (30); banqueting (60). Children under 5 free in parents' room (cot available without charge). No pets. **Rooms 13** (5 junior suites,6 no smoking, 3 for disabled). B&B €90pps, ss €20. Wheelchair access. Closed 5 days at Christmas. Amex, Diners, MasterCard, Visa, Laser. **Directions:** on N25, main route from Cork-Waterford.

Youghal — Ballymakeigh House & Brownes Restaurant

féile bia Farmhouse/Restaurant

Killeagh Youghal Co. Cork **Tel: 024 91373** Fax: 024 95370
Email: ballymakeigh@eircom.net Web: www.ballymakeighhouse.ie

Winner of our Farmhouse of the Year Award in 1999, Ballymakeigh House provides a high standard of comfort, food and hospitality in one of the most outstanding establishments of its type in Ireland. Set at the heart of an east Cork dairy farm, this attractive old house is immaculately maintained and run by Margaret Browne, who is a Euro-Toques chef and author of a successful cookery book. The house is warm and homely with plenty of space for guests, who are welcome to use the garden and visit the farmyard. The individually decorated bedrooms are full of character and equally comfortable and Margaret's hospitality is matched only by her energetic pursuit of excellence - ongoing improvements and developments are a constant characteristic of Ballymakeigh. Equestrian centre, tennis, garden, children's playground. Off-season value breaks. Children welcome (under 3s free in parents' room, cots available). Pets allowed in some areas. **Rooms 5** (all en-suite & no smoking). B&B €50pps, ss €15. House closed 1 Nov-14 Feb.

Brownes Restaurant: Margaret and her team have earned an excellent reputation at Ballymakeigh House over the years, for a personal blend of traditional and new Irish cuisine with international influences, all based on the very best of fresh local ingredients. So, when the Brownes planned an equestrian centre nearby, it was natural to build on that success by incorporating a restaurant into the new development - hence the fine big country-style restaurant just along the road, which they now operate during the day at weekends and five evenings a week. Good home cooking of local ingredients is a speciality - crisp honey roast duck on a bed of apple purée, baked ham with Jameson whiskey sauce - and home baking is also a strong point. Children welcome; vegetarian menu available. Banqueting (90). **Seats 90** (private room, 90) L Sat & Sun,12-4, D Wed-Sun 5.30-9.30 (Sun to 8.30), Set Sun L €25; Set D €25 - €40. House wine from €18, sc discretionary. Closed L Mon-Sat, D Mon & Tue. Restaurant closed 1 Jan-14 Feb. MasterCard, Visa. **Directions:** Located on N25 between Youghal & Killeagh.

Youghal — Old Imperial Hotel

Hotel/Restaurant/Pub

27 Main Street Youghal Co Cork
Tel: 024 92435 Fax: 024 90268

James and Mary Browne's new hotel presents an attractive, sprucely-painted face to the world. There's a separate entrance to the hotel off the street, but it would be a pity to miss the downstairs bar, which incorporates the wonderful old-world bar previously known as D. McCarthy ("A lovely little low-ceilinged bar of great character with an open fire and a long history to tell...") as well as the much larger new bar area which has just been added. The limitations of the site have resulted in a shortage of space in the hotel, which is on three rather steep floors, with no lift and no space for a residents' sitting room or separate reception area for the first-floor restaurant (where breakfast is also served). Bedrooms also tend to be on the small side, although there are two quite impressive junior suites and all rooms are furnished and fitted to a high standard with all the usual amenities including trouser press with steam iron.

Restaurant: Menus show individuality and an impressive freshness of approach: seven starters on the à la carte dinner menu might include a warm salad of farmhouse cheese with garlic croûtons, pine nuts and walnut oil dressing or sautéed wild mushrooms on a rosemary & garlic potato cake with truffle cream sauce - and a choice of eight or nine courses will include several dishes featuring local seafood well-balanced by a fair selection of meats and poultry - and at least one imaginative vegetarian dish. Carefully sourced ingredients, accurate cooking and simple, attractive presentation add up to a satisfying dining experience. Service is friendly. **Seats 40**. No smoking area; air conditioning. D daily, 6.15-9.15. * Bar meals served daily, 12.30-9; L12.30-3.30 (Sat 1-2.30); D 6.30-9. Diners, MasterCard, Visa, Laser. **Directions:** On the N25 - 30 miles from Cork Airport. ◇

COUNTY DONEGAL

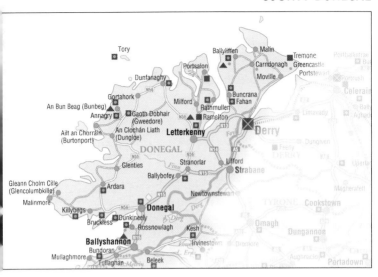

In 2003, Donegal is literally taking flight. The spectacular Glenveagh National Park in the northern part of the county has been selected for the re-introduction of the golden eagle to Ireland. Almost a century after the species became extinct, the first six golden eagle chicks were released at Glenveagh in June 2001. Over a five year period, 50 birds are being released, and there are high expectations of success for the programme.

Travel at sea level is also an increasingly significant element in visits to Donegal, one of Ireland's most spectacularly beautiful countries. It is much-indented by the sea, but the introduction of car ferry services is shortening journeys and adding interest. The new ferry between Greencastle and Magilligan across the narrow entrance to Lough Foyle has been very popular since starting in June 2002, and 2003 will see another car ferry - between Buncrana and Rathmullan across Lough Swilly - adding to the travel options.

For many folk, particularly those from Northern Ireland, Donegal is the holiday county par excellence. But in recent years, despite the international fluctuations of trading conditions, there has been development of modern industries and the strengthening of the fishing, particularly at the hugely busy harbour of Killybegs, home port of the world's largest fishing vessel, the Atlantic Dawn. This entrepreneurial spirit has led to a more balanced economy, with the pace being set by the county town of Letterkenny, where the population has increased by 50% since 1991.

But much and all as Donegal county is increasingly a place where people live and make a living, nevertheless it is still a place of nature on the grand scale, a place assaulted by the winds and weather of the Atlantic Ocean if given the slighest chance. Yet at communities like Bundoran and Rossnowlagh, where splendid beaches face straight into the Atlantic, enthusiastic surfers have demonstrated that even the most demanding weather can have its sporting uses.

For most folk, however, it is the contrast between raw nature and homely comfort which is central to Donegal's enduring attraction. For here, in some of Ireland's most rugged territory, you will find many sheltered and hospitable places whose amenities are emphasised by the challenging nature of their broader environment. And needless to say, that environment is simply startlingly utterly beautiful as well.

Local Attractions and Information

Arranmore Ferry Burtonport-Arranmore	075 20532
Ballintra Ballymagroarty Heritage Centre	073 34966
Buncrana National Knitting Centre	077 62355
Bundoran Tourism Information	072 41350
Burt Grianan of Aileach Centre	077 68512

Churchill Glebe House & Gallery (Derek Hill)	074 37071
Donegal Airport Carrickfin	075 48232
Donegal Highlands Hillwalking/Irish language (adults)	073 30248
Donegal town Donegal Castle	073 22405
Donegal town Tourism information	073 21148
Donegal town Waterbus Cruises	073 21148
Dunfanaghy Workhouse Visitor Centre	074 36504
Dungloe Mary from Dungloe Int. Festival (July/August)	
Dungloe Tourism Information	075 21297
Glencolumbcille Folk Museum	073 30017
Glencolumbcille Tourism Information	073 30017
Glenties Patrick Mac Gill Summer School (August)	
Glenveagh National Park (Castle, gardens, parkland)	074 37088
Greencastle Lough Foyle Ferry	077 81901
Greencastle Maritime Museum	077 81363
Inishowen Inishowen Tourism (Carndonagh)	077 74933
Letterkenny An Grianan Theatre	074 20771
Letterkenny Arts Centre	074 29186
Letterkenny County Museum	074 24613
Letterkenny Newmills watermill	074 25115
Letterkenny North West Tourism	074 21160
Lifford Cavanacor Historic House	074 41143
Tory Island Ferry	075 31320

Annagry — Danny Minnie's Restaurant

Restaurant/Accomodation   Annagry Co. Donegal **Tel: 075 48201** Fax: 075 48201

The O'Donnell family has run Danny Minnie's since 1962, and a visit is always a special treat. There's nothing about the exterior as seen from the road to prepare first-time visitors for the atmosphere of this remarkable restaurant: hidden behind a frontage of overgrown creepers a surprise awaits when, after a warm welcome from Terri O'Donnell, guests are suddenly surrounded by antiques and elegantly appointed candle-lit tables. The menu is presented in both Irish and English and Brian O'Donnell's cooking is a good match for the surroundings - fine, with imaginative saucing, but not at all pompous. On a wide-ranging à la carte menu, seafood stars in the main courses - lobster and other shellfish, availability permitting - and there is also a strong selection of meats including Donegal mountain lamb, typically served with caramelized onions, blackcurrant & mint jus and Donegal beef, served various ways including classic Beef Wellington. Vegetables are a strength and gorgeous desserts such as crêpes suzette with orange and Grand Marnier can be relied on to create an appropriately dramatic finale. Under Terri's direction, helpful service from attentive waitresses is another bonus. There's nowhere quite like Danny Minnie', our winner of the guide's Atmospheric Restaurant of the Year in 2000. **Seats 80** (private room, 30). No smoking area; air conditioning. D daily in summer, 6.30-9.30. Set D about €32, also à la carte; house wine about €16; sc10%. (Phone ahead to check opening hours, especially for possible lunch, off peak season) Closed Christmas & Sun/Mon off season. [Accommodation is also offered in eight non-smoking rooms, five of them en-suite and one suitable for disabled guests]. Diners, MasterCard, Visa. **Directions:** R259 off N56 - follow Airport signs. ◇

Ardara — The Green Gate

B&B   Ardvally Ardara Co. Donegal **Tel: 075 41546**

Paul Chatenoud's amazing little B&B is a one-off. Above Adara, up a steep and twisting boreen (follow his unique signing system) that will reward you with a stunning view on arrival, Paul offers simple but comfortable accommodation in his unspoilt traditional cottage and converted outbuildings. It's a far cry from the Parisian bookshop he once ran, but this little place is magic. In the morning (or whenever you wake up - he will be working around his lovely garden and is happy to stop at any time it suits his guests), he cooks up breakfast while you take in the laid-back homeliness of his cosy cottage sitting room. If the morning is fine he may serve breakfast in the garden (just where is that beautiful music coming from?) while he regales you with stories of famous people who have fallen in love with The Green Gate. Just be glad you found it, because he's probably right - it may well be "the most beautiful place anywhere in Ireland". Children welcome (Under 10s free in parents' room, cot available). Pets permitted. **Rooms 4** (all en-suite). B&B €30pps, ss €10. Open all year. **Directions:** One mile on the hill from Ardara.

Nancy's Bar
Ardara
Pub — Front Street Ardara Co. Donegal **Tel: 075 41187**

This famous pub, in the village renowned for its tweeds and handknits, is a cosy, welcoming place, with five or six small rooms packed with bric à brac and plenty of tables and chairs for the comfortable consumption of good home-made food, especially seafood. Famous for their chowder - maybe try it with a "Louis Armstrong" (smoked salmon on brown bread topped with grilled cheese) and finish with an Irish coffee. Live music too. Bar food served daily 12-9.30, from Easter to September. Wheelchair access. Closed 25 Dec & Good Fri. **No Credit Cards. Directions:** Half mile from Donegal Town. ◇

Woodhill House
Ardara
Guesthouse/Restaurant/Bar — Woodhill Ardara Co. Donegal **Tel: 075 41112** Fax: 075 41516
Email: yates@iol.ie Web: www.woodhillhouse.com

Formerly the home of Ireland's last commercial whaling family, John and Nancy Yates' large country house is set in its own grounds overlooking the Donegal Highlands and the hard restoration work they have put in over more than a decade is now bearing fruit. This hospitable house has a full bar where light lunches are served and unusual accommodation in the main house and nearby converted outbuildings - rooms are all en-suite but vary greatly in position, size and character so it is worth spending a few minutes discussing your preferences when booking. There's also a restaurant (booking recommended as it's very popular locally) offering quite traditional food based on local ingredients at reasonable prices: specialities include oysters, Donegal mountain lamb, duck off the bone and carrageen pudding. Gradually restoring the garden is perhaps Nancy's greatest challenge and it's turning out beautifully, not only on the kitchen garden side but as a pleasure garden too. Renovations, on both the main house and some fine outbuildings, continue on an ongoing basis. Small conferences (15). Children welcome (free in parents' room up to 6). Pets permitted by arrangement. **Rooms 9** (all en-suite, 6 shower-only). B&B €52 pps, ss €30. Restaurant: **Seats 40** (private room, 15). No smoking area. D 6.30-10 daily, Set D€34, house wine €14; sc discretionary. * Bar lunch available 1-2 pm daily. House closed 24-27 Dec. Amex, Diners, MasterCard, Visa, Laser. **Directions:** 1/4 mile from Ardara.

Jackson's Hotel
Ballybofey
Hotel — Ballybofey Co. Donegal **Tel: 074 31021** Fax: 074 31096
Email: bjackson@iol.ie Web: www.jacksons-hotel.ie

Although it has a town centre location, this attractive family-run hotel is set in its own gardens and enjoys a tranquil position alongside the River Finn. The spacious, elegantly furnished foyer (with open fire) creates a good first impression and this is followed through in other public areas including the restaurant, which overlooks the garden. Bedrooms, all recently refurbished to a high standard, are very comfortable with direct-dial phones, tea/coffee trays and TV with video channel, and the best have river views. Conference/banqueting (400/600); business centre, ISDN lines, secretarial services. Leisure centre (22m pool). Children welcome (under 2s free in parents' room, cots available). Bank Holiday Special Breaks throughout the year offer particularly good value. Horse-riding, golf, fishing and bike hire all nearby. Pets permitted in some areas. **Rooms 87** (2 suites, 4 executive rooms). B&B about €67 pps, ss about €20 Wheelchair access. Lift. Open all year. Amex, Diners, MasterCard, Visa. **Directions:** Beside the river, in the centre of town. ◇

Kee's Hotel
Ballybofey
Hotel/Restaurant — Stranorlar Ballybofey Co. Donegal **Tel: 074 31018** Fax: 074 31917
Email: info@keeshotel.ie Web: www.keeshotel.ie

This centrally located, all-year hotel has an unusually long line of continuous family ownership, having been in the Kee family since 1892. Public areas have recently undergone radical renovations, including a new foyer, meeting rooms and a lift. Bedrooms are regularly refurbished and have good bathrooms; those at the back of the hotel, with views of the Blue Stack Mountains, are most desirable and avoid the problems caused by through traffic which may be disturbing at the front. Residents have direct access from the hotel to the excellent leisure facilities. Golf and fishing nearby. Conference/banqueting (150/250). Children welcome, under 3s free in their parents' room; cots and high chairs available. Special breaks offered by the hotel include a novel "Post Christmas Recovery Break". **Rooms 53** (1 junior suite, 31 executive rooms,1 for disabled). Limited room service. B&B €80pps, ss €15. Lift. Open all year.

The Looking Glass: Hand-worked tapestries decorate this pleasant warm-toned restaurant, which is in two areas with plenty of alcoves for privacy. Head chef Frank Pasquier's daily menus offer balanced Table d'Hôte, in addition to quite an ambitious à la carte. A typical menu might include roast goats cheese on a bed of Mediterranean terrine with split tomato dressing, a soup (smoked haddock chowder perhaps) and main courses like best end of lamb with red cabbage confit and garlic cream or pan-fried cod with courgette & sweet potato mousseline and saffron butter. Vegetarian dishes are offered on request. Dessert specialities include warm apple tart (cooked to order) and there's an Irish farmhouse cheese trolley. No smoking area. **Seats 75** (private room, 60). D 6.30-9.30 daily, Sun 12.30-3, Set Sun L about €20; Set D €40, à la carte available; house wine €15.50. sc discretionary [Informal meals also available in the Old Gallery, 12.30-3 and 5.30-9.30 daily.] Amex, Diners, MasterCard, Visa, Laser. **Directions:** On the Main Street in the village of Stranorlar.

Ballyliffin   Rossaor House

Accommodation   Ballyliffin Inishowen Co. Donegal **Tel: 077 76498** Fax: 077 76498
                                 Email: rossaor@gofree.indigo.ie Web: www.ballyliffin.com/rossaor.htm

Brian and Anne Harkin's very pleasant and hospitable house is in a beautiful area that deserves to be better known and it has amazing views down over two golf courses to Pollen Strand and Malin Head. Bedrooms are furnished to a high standard (generous beds, direct dial phone, tea/coffee facilities and TV) and luxuriously decorated - an aspect of the business in which Anne clearly takes particular pleasure. Spacious, comfortably furnished public rooms include a large sitting room, which takes full advantage of the view, and a conservatory (considerately situated overlooking the lovely front garden and away from the full blast of morning sunshine) where excellent breakfasts are served with commendable efficiency. There is also self-catering accommodation on the property - details from the Harkins. Children welcome (cot available). No pets. **Rooms 4** (all en-suite). B&B €40pps, ss €10. Closed 23 Dec-2 Jan. MasterCard, Visa. **Directions:** Take signs to Buncrana, to Clonmany to Ballyliffin (R238).

Bruckless   Bruckless House

Farmhouse   Bruckless Co. Donegal **Tel: 073 37071** Fax: 073 37070
                                 Email: bruc@bruckless.com Web: www.iol.ie/~bruc/bruckless.htm

Clive and Joan Evans' lovely 18th-century house and Connemara pony stud farm is set in 19 acres of woodland and gardens overlooking Bruckless Bay - an ideal place for people who enjoy quiet countryside and pursuits like walking, horse-riding and fishing. The gardens are not too formal but beautifully designed, extensive and well-maintained - they really enhance a visit here, as does the sea: guests have direct access to the foreshore at the bottom of the garden. Family furniture collected through a Hong Kong connection add an unexpected dimension to the elegant reception rooms and generous, comfortably furnished bedrooms. Bedrooms include two single rooms and there is a shared bathroom. Pets permitted by arrangement. **Rooms 5** (2 en-suite, 1 shower only, all no-smoking) B&B €45-50pps, no ss. Closed 1 Oct-31Mar. Amex, MasterCard, Visa **Directions:** On N56, 12 miles West of Donegal.

Bunbeg   Ostan Gweedore Hotel & Leisure Centre

Hotel   Bunbeg Co. Donegal **Tel: 075 31177** Fax: 075 31726
                                 Email: reservations@ostangweedore.com Web: www.ostangweedore.com

Although its architectural style may not be to today's taste, Ostan Gweedore was built to make the most of the view - and this it does very well. Most of the comfortable if a little dated bedrooms (plus three suites) and all the public areas, including the recently refurbished restaurant and the Library Bar ("the most westerly reading room on the Atlantic seaboard") have superb views over the shoreline and Mount Errigal. It's ideal for families, with its wonderful beach and outdoor activities, including tennis, pitch & putt and day visits to nearby Tory Island. Wet days are looked after too, with indoor leisure facilities, including a 19-metre swimming pool, jacuzzi and gym, all supervised by qualified staff. Fishing and golf (9 hole) available locally. This romantic setting means weddings are popular (conferences/banqueting up to 300). Under 5s free in parents' room (cot available, free of charge). No pets. **Rooms 39** (3 suites). B&B €77pps, ss€13. Closed 4 Nov-14 Feb. Amex, MasterCard, Visa, Laser. **Directions:** From Letterkenny, take coast road past hospital.

Bundoran   Brennan's

N Pub   Main Street Bundoran Co. Galway **Tel: 072 41810**

The discerning drinker visiting this part of the country should make a point of calling in at this delightful pub in the centre of Bundoran town - it's as fine an unspoilt Irish pub as you'll find

nywhere in the country: " no television, just conversation". Friendly, welcoming, just 'itself': magic.
losed 25 Dec & Good Fri. **Directions:** Town centre.

Bundoran · Le Chateaubrianne

Restaurant   Sligo Road Bundoran Co. Donegal **Tel:** 072 42160 Fax: 072 42160

Since opening here in 1993, Brian and Anne Loughlin have established this welcoming and very
professionally run establishment as the leading restaurant in the area. Brian's cooking is classic
french with modern Irish and international overtones and he is a strong supporter of local produce.
Imaginative dinner menus offer a well-balanced selection with local seafood well represented (crab
profiteroles are a typical starter), also game in season, with interesting vegetarian options available.
Sunday lunch provides something for everyone by offering a well-judged combination of traditional
roasts and more adventurous fare; the same high standard of cooking applies and the meal will be
nicely finished off with coffee and petits fours. **Seats 56** (private room, 20). No-smoking restaurant.
D Tue-Sat 6.30-9.30, L Sun only 12.30-3, Set Sun about L €22, Set D from about €30; house wine
about €17 sc discretionary. Closed Mon, 24-25 Dec, 3 wks Jan & bank hols. Amex, MasterCard, Visa
Directions: On Left entering Bundoran from Sligo. ◇

Carndonagh · Corncrake Restaurant

Restaurant   Millbrae Carndonagh Co. Donegal **Tel:** 077 74534

Brid McCartney and Noreen Lynch made a decision to live and work in this lovely (and, so far,
unspoilt) part of the country some years ago, when they established the original Corncrake in its old
'downtown' premises. It became one of the hottest addresses in Donegal for foodlovers not least
because of the off-season residential cookery courses they have run for some years at the restaurant,
together with Rossaor House (see entry) who provide the accommodation element. A recent move
to larger premises on the edge of the town has allowed for a dedicated reception area as well as
more spacious dining - and will enable them to run the cookery courses with greater comfort and,
perhaps, slightly larger numbers. Meanwhile, they continue to relish the area and take pleasure in
its produce which appears typically in a fresh crab bake with chilli & fresh coriander or main courses
(about €16-20) like roast rack of Donegal mountain lamb with rosemary & redcurrant gravy -or one
of several seafood dishes. Vegetarian dishes are available on request. No children after 8 pm. **Seats
26.** No smoking area. D Wed-Sun, 6-9 (approx); à la carte; house wine €14; sc discretionary. Closed
Mon & Tue; Christmas-17 Mar. **No Credit Cards. Directions:** Derry road as you enter the town.

Clonmany · Glen House

B&B   Straid Clonmany Co. Donegal **Tel:** 077 76745

Doris Russo's charming period house is beautifully located with an ocean view and would make a most
comfortable and hospitable base for any of the many activities this lovely area offers - including
visiting the nearby waterfall, which has recently been opened to the public. Rooms are appealing
decorated in a genuinely country style which will take many guests back to their childhood. Several
hill walks start at Glen House, which is also handy to a beach and has two golf courses nearby, while
festivals in June, July and August highlight music and culture of the area. Children welcome (under
5s free in parents' room, cot available without charge). **Rooms 3** (2 en-suite & shower only, all no
smoking). B&B €30, ss 10. Open all year. MasterCard, Visa, **Directions:** From Derry N1, A2 to
Buncrana, right sign to Clonmany. Through village, left over bridge, signed to house, .5 mile.

Culdaff · McGrory's of Culdaff

Pub/Restaurant/Guesthouse   Culdaff Inishowen Co. Donegal
Tel: 077 79104 Fax: 077 79235
Email: mcgr@eircom.net Web: www.mcgrorys.ie

In an area that has so much to offer, in terms of natural beauty and activities like golf, angling and
walking, McGrory's would make an ideal base. An inn in the true sense of the word, offering rest and
refreshment to travellers, this north-western institution was established in 1924 and remains in the
active care of the McGrory family. It has recently undergone a major makeover, resulting in a pleasing
combination of old and new which is easy on the eye and includes a new restaurant as well as an
overhaul of the whole premises. Comfortable bedrooms vary in size and outlook but are attractively
furnished in a classic contemporary style that is both practical and appropriate; all have well-
planned bathrooms and all the necessary amenities (phone, tea/coffee tray, TV), although there were
signs of wear and tear on the Guide's most recent visit. For anyone touring the Inishowen peninsula
this is a logical place to take a break, as popular bar food is available throughout the day. But it is

probably for music that McGrory's is most famous - as well as traditional sessions in The Front Ba
on Tuesday and Friday nights, Mac's Backroom Bar (constructed on the site of the old outhouses c
McGrory's shop) is a major venue for live shows featuring international names. (Live musi
Wednesday and Saturday; events listings on the web.) Conference/banqueting (100). Specia
interest/off season breaks. **Rooms 10** (all with full en-suite bathrooms). Children welcome (unde
12s free in parents' room; cot available free of charge). No pets. B&B €45, ss €10. Restaurant:
Tue-Sun, L Sun. Bar meals daily, 12.30-8. Restaurant closed Mon; establishment closed 24-27 De
Amex, MasterCard, Visa, Laser. **Directions:** On R238 around Inishowen Peninsula.

Donegal — St. Ernan's House Hotel

Country House/Hotel — Donegal Co. Donegal **Tel: 073 21065** Fax: 073 2209.
Email: info@sainternans.com Web: www.sainternans.con

Set on its own wooded island connected to the mainland by a causeway, tranquillity is the mai
characteristic of Brian and Carmel O'Dowd's unique country house hotel. Spacious public rooms hav
log fires and antique furniture and, while they vary in size and outlook, the individually decorate
bedrooms are furnished to a high standard and have good amenities including (surprisingly perhaps
television, while most also have lovely views. Children under 6 not catered for. No pets. Garden
Rooms 10 (2 suites, 3 superior, 1 shower only) B&B €135pps.
Restaurant: The dining room is mainly for resident guests, but reservations may be taken from non
residents if there is room. Daily 5-course country house-style dinner menus based on local produce
vegetarian dishes on request. No smoking restaurant. **Seats 22**. D 6.30-8.30 daily, D from about €2
(semi-à la carte, priced by course); house wine from €19. Closed end Oct-Easter. MasterCard, Visa
Laser. **Directions:** 1.5 mile south of Donegal Town.

Dunfanaghy — The Mill Restaurant & Accommodation

Restaurant/B&B — Figart Dunfanagh Co. Donegal **Tel: 074 36985** Fax: 074 3698!
Email: themillrestaurant@oceanfree.net Web: www.themillrestaurant.con

Beautifully located on the shore of the New Lake, which is a special area of conservation, the mil
was the home of Susan Alcorn's grandfather and, as they are a family of accomplished painters, th
walls are hung with wonderful watercolours. Susan and her husband Derek, who is the chef, have ru
this remarkable place as a restaurant with rooms since March 2000 and, not surprisingly, it ha
already acquired a dedicated following as the location is superb, the welcome warm and the cooking
both imaginative and assured. The dining room is on two levels, with plenty of windows framing the
views, fresh flowers on the tables, soft lighting and some well-placed antiques - a room of characte
and atmosphere. Menus are based firmly on the best ingredients, local where possible, and change
every 6 weeks. While based on the classics, the house style is quite contemporary: purée o
asparagus and pea soup with parmesan is nothing short of a revelation, while roast rack of new
season lamb with spiced aubergine & garlic mash seems a very comfortable combination. Delicious
classic desserts might include a seasonal rhubarb trifle with gooseberry ice cream, or there's a good
Irish cheese plate. (Lovely breakfasts too.) No-smoking restaurant; air conditioning. Children
welcome. **Seats 45**. D Tue-Sat 7-9pm, Set D €33; house wine €13.25; sc discretionary. Closed Mon
mid-week Nov-Dec; Jan-Feb).
Accommodation is offered in six individually decorated rooms, which have opened gradually as they
have been finished. The decor is simple but stylish, with good new beds and some antique pieces,
and there's also a lovely little sitting room off the dining room, with comfy big chairs and sofas to
relax in. Children welcome (under 5s free in parents' room, cot available without charge). **Rooms 6**
(all en-suite & no-smoking, 2 shower only). B&B €38 pps, ss €7. Closed midweek Nov-Dec; Jan-Feb.
Amex, MasterCard, Visa, Laser. **Directions:** N56 from Letterkenny to Dunfanaghy. 1/2 mile outside
Dunfanaghy on Falcarragh Rd on right hand side at the mill.

Dunkineely — Castle Murray House Hotel

Hotel/Restaurant — St. John's Point Dunkineely Co. Donegal **Tel: 073 37022** Fax: 073 37330
Email: castlemurray@eircom.net Web: www.castlemurray.com

This beautifully located clifftop hotel has wonderful sea and coastal views over the ruined castle after
which it is named. It is a comfortable and relaxing place to stay, with a little bar, a residents' sitting
room and a large verandah that can be covered with an awning in a good summer, so meals can be
served outside. The hotel changed hands in 2002, when it was acquired by Martin and Marguerite
Howley, previously of The Fleet Inn in nearby Killybegs, but it is to their credit that no immediate
changes have been made: many people who have been coming here for some time like it just the way
it is. Bedrooms are perhaps a little dated but are individually decorated with a mixture of modern and

ieces that give each room its own character; most have sea views and all are quite large with a double and single bed, good bathrooms (most with full bath) and facilities including digital TV as well s phone and tea/coffee trays. A sun area on the sheltered flat roof at the back of the building has direct access from some bedrooms. Good breakfasts are served in in the restaurant, or in bedrooms on request. Banqueting (45. Pets permitted by arrangement. Children welcome; cots available without charge. Off-season value breaks. **Rooms 10** (all en-suite). B&B €62pps, ss €23. Closed 25-25 Dec, 31 Dec, mid Jan-mid Feb.

Restaurant: The restaurant is on the seaward corner of the hotel and maximises the impact of the dramatic view, including the castle (which is floodlit at night). Heavy curtains and an open fire make for real warmth in this exposed location, even in winter. Remy Dupuis, who has been head chef since 1994 now works alongside Marguerite Howley and there is no obvious change of style: :ulti-choice menus (basically 3-course, plus options of soup and sorbet), are sensibly priced according to the hoice of main course and offer a wide choice, including vegetarian dishes. Seafood is the speciality of the house in the summer months; in winter there are more red meats, poultry and game. **Seats 65**. No smoking restaurant. D daily 7-9.30, L Sun only 1.30-3.30; D from €36 (depending on choice of main course); Set Sun L €22.50; house wine about €19; SC discretionary. Closed 25-26 Dec, 31 Dec, 14Jan-14 Feb as above but phone to check restaurant opening in low season, which may vary according to demand. MasterCard, Visa, Laser. **Directions:** Situated on the N56 .8km from Killybegs,20 m Donegal Towm on the coast road to St Johns Point. Take first left outside Dunkineely Village.

Fahan — St. John's Country House & Restaurant

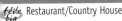

Restaurant/Country House

Fahan Inishowen Co. Donegal **Tel: 077 60289**
Fax: 077 60612 Email: stjohnsrestaurant@eircom.net
Web: homepage.eircom.net/~stjohnscountryhouse

BREKFAST AWARD WINNER - ULSTER

In this substantial period house overlooking Lough Swilly, Reggie Ryan and Phil McAfee have run Restaurant St John's to growing acclaim since 1980. It's one of the most hospitable houses in Ireland - Reggie has a way with guests (and there's many an international figure among them) which must be pretty well unrivalled, making each one feel especially welcome so the whole occasion is relaxed and fun. A conservatory extension allows lough views in addition to the original cosy inside rooms, all a fit setting for Phil's cooking, which combines a respect for tradition and understanding of the value of simplicity with a willingness to experiment, ensuring that the many guests who regularly return always have a meal that is both stimulating and relaxing. Given the location, seafood is very popular (a delicious house speciality is baked turbot on a creamy casserole of butterbeans, sweetcorn, smoked bacon & chives) but Phil's menus are based on a wide range of local ingredients, including game in winter. Donegal mountain lamb, which she cooks in many different ways is an established favourite(another excellent speciality is "Rack of Donegal Mountain Lamb with Rosemary and Mascarpone Risotto"), and her crispy roast duckling is also a real treat. Vegetarian dishes are on the regular menu. A carefully selected wine list includes nine house wines, a special seasonal selection and a good choice of half bottles. **Seats 70** (private room, 25) No smoking restaurant; air conditioning. D Tue-Sun 7.30-9.30, Set D€38; L Sun only, 12.30-3.30pm, Set Sun L €18. house wines from €16.50; SC discretionary. Restaurant closed Mon; bank hols.

Accommodation: The five stylish, comfortable rooms are beautifully furnished with antiques and have many thoughtful details to make a stay more enjoyable, including well-finished bathrooms; rooms at the front also have lovely lough views. Breakfasts are a real treat, composed by Reggie for the maximum enjoyment of guests, who can have anything from the very best of fare in a traditional cooked breakfast to a house speciality 'Health Breakfast' composed of a stunning assortment of fresh fruits - pineapple, melon, plums, pears, apples, soft fruit - raspberries, strawberries, loganberries, blackberries, blueberries, cherries; you name it, if it's in season and in prime condition, Reggie will work it into a work of early morning art. Delicious freshly-baked breads, home-baked breads and a pot of tea or cafetière coffee accompany: after this the word can do you no wrong. Children welcome (under 3s free in parents' room, cot available). No pets. **Rooms 5** (1 junior suite, 2 shower only, all no-smoking) B&B €56 pps, ss €5.60. Closed Jan-Feb. Amex, MasterCard, Visa, Laser, Switch.
Directions: In Fahan village on R238 Derry-Buncrana road.

Greencastle — Kealys Seafood Bar

Restaurant/Pub

The Harbour Greencastle Co. Donegal
Tel: 077 81010 Fax: 077 81010 Email: kealys@iol.i

Under-stated quality remains a fair description of the tone of James and Tricia Kealy's excellent seafood restaurant, which has always valued simplicity. Since 1989 the restaurant has been a key establishment in a major fishing port and still retains the original bar at its heart. Until the arrival of the new ferry between Greencastle and Magilligan Point in Northern Ireland in 2002, Greencastle seemed quite emote but the ferry has brought many new visitors to the area - and to Kealys, who have responded to this sudden increase in demand by increasing their opening hours. Even if it' just to pop in for a bowl of Greencastle chowder and some home-baked bread, don't miss the opportunity of a visit to Kealys- although simple, this place is really special. James takes a creative and balanced approach to seafood, presenting this precious resource as a component in complete dishes which are modern in tone but also often echo traditional Irish themes. House specialities demonstrating this healthy and (ecologically sound) philosophy include a starter of spinach wrapped seafood terrine with a tomato and chilli coulis and main courses like pan fried fillet of cod with parsley sauce on a chive and garlic champ and baked Atlantic salmon with a wholegrain mustard crust served on Irish spring cabbage and bacon. James also bakes a variety of breads and uses local organic vegetables (from Greencastle organic farm) and farmhouse cheeses - typically Gubbeen, St Killian, Boilie and Cashel Blue. Not suitable for children after 8 pm. **Seats 70**. No smoking area. 12.30-3pm (Sun1-3), D 7-9.30 (Sun to 8.30); Set Sun L €30, also à la carte, house wine about €12. Closed Mon, 2 weeks Nov. Amex, MasterCard, Visa, Laser. **Directions:** On the harbour at Greencastle 20 miles north of Derry City.

Gweedore — An Chuirt

Ⓝ Hotel

Gweedore Co. Donegal **Tel: 075 32900** Fax: 075 3292
Email: anchuirt@eircom.net Web: www.anchuirt-hotel.i

This immaculate family-run hotel is beautifully situated in the heart of the Donegal Gaeltacht and provides a very comfortable base for exploring the area, at a reasonable price. There has been a hotel here for many years - quotations from the Visitors Book go back as a far as 1845 - but it has been rebuilt under the present ownership, re-opening in 1999. Past and present are brought together neatly - not only in the hotel, which is furnished in a traditional style throughout - but in an impressive heritage centre and art gallery alongside, which is run by the hotel and also used for conferences and banqueting. Hotel restaurant open evenings only (except Sunday), but bar food is available every day. Conference/banqueting 60/100. Children welcome (under 4s free in parents' room, cot available without charge). Garden, walking. **Rooms 19** (2 junior suites, 1 disabled, all no smoking). B&B €65, ss €25. MasterCard, Visa, Laser. **Directions:** N56 main road from Letterkenny to Gweedore.

Killybegs — Bay View Hotel

Hotel

Main Street Killybegs Co. Donegal **Tel: 073 31950** Fax: 073 3185
Email: bvhotel@iol.ie Web: www.bayviewhotel@iol.ie

This friendly hotel on the harbour front is a great addition to the accommodation and facilities of the area, for leisure and business. Public areas include a cocktail bar adjacent to the first floor restaurant as well as the main Wheel House Bar at street level and good leisure facilities will appeal to business guests and make this a good 'weather proof' base for a family holiday - there's a 16 metre swimming pool, plus sauna, jacuzzi, steam room and gym. Comfortable bedrooms have full bathrooms and all the necessary facilities (phone, TV, tea/coffee tray and trouser press), while executive rooms also have mini-bar, fax/modem line and access to a lounge with boardroom table, many overlook the harbour, although those at the back may be quieter, especially at weekends when there is live music in the main bar. Leisure centre, swimming pool. Conference/banqueting (300/280). Children welcome, cot available free of charge. **Rooms 40** (4 executive, 4 for disabled). Lift. B&B €63pps, ss €32. Closed 24-26 Dec. Amex, Diners, MasterCard, Visa, Laser. **Directions:** 25 km from Donegal Town.

Kincasslagh — Iggy's Bar

Pub

Kincasslagh Co. Donegal **Tel: 075 43112**

Just a short walk up from the harbour - it's also called the Atlantic Bar - Ann and Iggy Murray have run this delightfully unspoilt pub since 1986 and it's an all year home-from-home for many a visitor. The television isn't usually on unless there's a match and Ann makes lovely simple food for the bar,

hainly seafood - home-made soups, delicious crab sandwiches and Rombouts coffee. No children after
pm. Light food available 10.30-12.30 Mon-Sat. No food on Sundays. Closed 25 Dec & Good Friday.
o Credit Cards. **Directions:** On the corner of the Main Street, where the road turns off to the harbour.

aghey   Coxtown Manor

estaurant/Country House   Laghey Co. Donegal **Tel:** 073 34574 Fax: 073 34576
                         Email: coxtownmanor@oceanfree.net Web: www.coxtownmanor.com

ust a short drive from Donegal town, this late Georgian house set in its own parkland is in a lovely,
eaceful area close to Donegal Bay. It's an exceptionally friendly, welcoming place and Belgian
roprietor, Edward Dewael - who fell for the property a year or two ago and is still in the process of
pgrading it - personally ensures that everything possible is done to make guests feel at home.
ublic areas include a very pleasant wood-panelled bar with an open fire - well-stocked, notably with
elgian beers and a great selection of digestifs to accompany your after dinner coffee - and an
legant period dining room, which is the heart of the operation and, like the style of food
resentation, attractive without being too formal. Dining at Coxtown is a very pleasant experience
ndeed, not least because of the positive, relaxing tone of staff who settle guests in with the prompt
ffer of aperitifs and presentation of menus which are sensibly priced for any two or three courses;
here are a few supplements but pricing overall is moderate. Among the choice of seven starters
ou'll find a good home-made soup of the day or bisque and probably mussels of some sort and duck
ver paté with toast and onion marmalade (€3 supplement), while typical main courses from a
hoice of nine would be veal escalopes with mushrooms, muscat & honey sauce and John Dory a
'Ostendaise (pan fried and served with prawns). The aim is to serve (mostly) local produce in a
elgian way and they're offering a different experience from other dining options in the area, with
high standard of cooking and good value. Belgian chocolate features every which way on the
essert menu (Dame blanche, a speciality of home-made vanilla ice cream with hot chocolate sauce
nd cream is worth leaving room for) but fresh fruit salad (with or without champagne mousse) is
refreshing option. Banqueting (55). Not suitable for children after 8pm. **Seats 55** (private room
4). No smoking area. D 7-9 (daily in summer), L Sun only 12.30-5. Set Sun L about €22, Set D
rom about €25. House wine €18. Restaurant closed Mon-Tue off season.

ccommodation: The atmosphere is more restaurant with rooms than country house: bedrooms, while
ot luxurious, are large, well-proportioned and comfortable (some with countryside views and open
ireplaces). Breakfast buffet 8-10am; cooked options include delicious Fermanagh dry-cured black
acon. Children welcome (under 5s free in parents'room, cot available without charge). **Rooms 5** (4
n-suite, 1 with private bathroom). B&B about €50 pps, ss €19. Establishment closed 18 Feb-21 Mar.
lasterCard, Visa, Laser. **Directions:** Main sign on N15 between Ballyshannon & Donegal Town. ◇

etterkenny   Castle Grove Country House Hotel

ountry House/Restaurant   Letterkenny Co. Donegal **Tel:** 074 51118 Fax: 074 51384
                         Email: marytsweeney@hotmail.com Web: www.castlegrove.com

arkland designed by "Capability" Brown in the mid 18th-century creates a wonderful setting for
aymond and Mary Sweeney's lovely period house overlooking the lough. Castlegrove is undoubtedly
he first choice for discerning visitors to the area, especially executives with business in Letterkenny.
onstant improvement is the policy and the last few years have seen major changes, including a new
onservatory, a larger new restaurant and, most recently, the adjoining coach house has been
eveloped to make seven lovely bedrooms - all carefully designed and furnished with antiques to feel
ike part of the main house - and a small conference room (max 25). The original walled garden is
lso under restoration as part of an ongoing development of the gardens which will continue for
everal years. Bedrooms are spacious and elegantly furnished to a high standard, and bathrooms are
radually being upgraded where practical, to provide walk-in showers as well as full bath. Good
reakfasts include a choice of fish as well as traditional Irish breakfast, home-made breads and
reserves. Mary Sweeney's personal supervision enures an exceptionally high standard of maintenance
nd housekeeping and staff are friendly and helpful. Two boats belonging to the house are available
or fishing on Lough Swilly and there is a special arrangement with three nearby golf clubs.
onference/banqueting (25/50). Not suitable for children under 12. No pets. **Rooms 14** (1 suite, 2
unior suites, 4 shower only,3 disabled all no-smoking) B&B €80pps, ss €10. Closed 22-28 Dec.
Restaurant: Pascal Desnet has been head chef at Castle Grove since 1998. He offers several menus
 table d'hôte, à la carte and vegetarian - at dinner, plus 2 or 3-course set lunch menus, in a style
s that combines classic French and modern Irish with international overtones. Local ingredients, are
he sound base for his cuisine, including home grown herbs, vegetables and soft fruit, as well as
ocal seafood such as wild salmon and Swilly oysters; local meats are not overlooked either, and a
peciality dish of pan fried fillet of beef with grilled horseradish polenta and caramelized chicory

illustrates the style well. Not suitable for children under 12. No smoking restaurant. **Seats 5** (private room, 18) L 12.30-2 Mon-Sat, D 6.30-9 daily, Set L from €18, Set D €30-45, also à la carte house wines €14-18; sc discretionary. Closed 22-28 Dec. (Restaurant also closed Sun off-season) Amex, Diners, MasterCard, Visa, Laser. **Directions:** N 245 off Main Road to Letterkenny.

Lough Eske — Ardnamona House

Country House   Lough Eske Donegal Co. Donegal **Tel: 073 22650** Fax: 073 2281
Email: info@ardnamona.com Web: www.ardnamona.com

The glorious gardens, which were first planted by Sir Arthur Wallace in the 1880s, are central to the special atmosphere of Kieran and Annabel Clarke's secluded Victorian house overlooking Lough Eske and it's hard to credit that it's only a few miles from Donegal town. It's a gentle, hospitable house and draws people who value its peace and beauty. Front rooms have lovely views over the Lough to the mountains beyond, but all are individualistic with private bathrooms (and a peaceful outlook through rhododendrons and azaleas which have received international acclaim). Gardeners will enjoy doing the garden trail (guide leaflet provided and all plants labelled) and special interest groups are welcome to visit the gardens by arrangement. There are also miles of walks through ancient oak forests full of mosses and ferns and private boating and fishing on the Lough. Except on Sunday, communal dinner is available for residents, by reservation. Children welcome (under 8s free in parents' room, cot available without charge; playground, playroom); under 5s not allowed in dining room after 7pm. Dogs allowed in some areas. Cycling. **Rooms 5** (all with en-suite or private bathrooms). Limited room service provided. B&B €70, ss €15. D by reservation at 8.30pm. (D €32) house wines €18-40). SC discretionary. No D on Sun; closed Christmas. MasterCard, Visa. **Directions** From Donegal, follow signs to Harveys Point.

Lough Eske — Harvey's Point Country Hotel

Hotel   Lough Eske Donegal Co. Donegal **Tel: 073 22208** Fax: 073 2235
Email: info@harveyspoint.com Web: www.harveyspoint.com

In a stunning location on the shores of Lough Eske, this unusual hotel has a distinctly alpine atmosphere, with chalet-style buildings, pergolas and covered walkways joining the residential area to the main bars and restaurant. Maintenance is immaculate and the atmosphere can be deeply peaceful. Rooms, which are based on a Swiss design with show-wood furniture and four-posters, have all been refurbished recently; generally they have good amenities and direct access to verandah and gardens, although some are shower-only (and of continental design, ie without shower cubicle, which can be messy). A further 30 new rooms (all suites) are due to come on stream for 2003. Conferences/banqueting (200/300). Dinner dances and special breaks are often offered; telephone for details. Not suitable for children under 12 years after 6pm. Pets permitted. **Rooms 30** (6 suites, junior suites, 16 executive rooms, 6 food disabled, all no smoking, some shower only). B&B €99 pps ss €25. Open all year, but Nov-Mar closed Sun, Mon & Tue.
Restaurant: The restaurant extendsright down to the shores of Lough Eske, taking advantage of the beautiful view. Service has always been attentive and professional; the wine list includes a range of 'everyday easy drinking' wines (all under €25) and a good selection of half bottles. A new head chef, Martin Lynch, took over the kitchens just before the guide went to press. **Seats 100** (private room, 20). No smoking restaurant; air conditioning. Toilets wheelchair accessible. D 6-9.30 daily in summer (Nov-Mar open only Wed D-Sun L)),Set D €45; Sun L 12-5, Set Sun L €19.95; house wine from €18.50; no sc. Closed Sun, Mon & Tue off season.. Amex, Diners, MasterCard, Visa, Laser. **Directions:** 6km from Donegal town.

Lough Eske — Rhu - Gorse

B&B   Lough Eske Co. Donegal
Tel: 073 21685 Fax: 073 21685 Email: rhugorse@iol.ie

Beautifully located, with stunning views over Lough Eske (and windows built to take full advantage of them), Grainne McGettigan's modern house may not be architecturally outstanding but it has some very special attributes, notably the warmth and hospitality of Grainne herself. Bedrooms and bathrooms are all ship-shape and residents can have afternoon tea as well as breakfast, although not evening meals (however Harveys Point is very close, see entry, and Donegal town is also nearby). Animals are central to Rhu Gorse, which is named after a much-loved pedigree dog bred by Grainne's father-in-law (a descendant now follows her around everywhere), and one of her special interests is breeding horses: not your average B&B, but a comfortable, hospitable and very interesting base for a walking holiday or touring the area. **Rooms 3** (2 en-suite, 1 shower only); B&B about €38, ss about €13. Closed 1 Nov-Easter. MasterCard, Visa, Laser. **Directions:** Take N15 /N56 from Donegal Town. Take signs for Logheske & Harveys Point Hotel. Pick up signs for Rhu-Gorse.

Portsalon — Croaghross

Accommodation

Portsalon Letterkenny Co. Donegal **Tel: 074 59548** Fax: 074 59548
Email: jkdeane@croaghross.com Web: www.croaghross.com

John and Kay Deane's latter-day country house enjoys a lovely location on the Fanad peninsula, overlooking Lough Swilly. It's within 5 minutes walk of a great beach - and the renowned 100-year old Portsalon Golf Course - and very convenient to Glenveagh National Park. Three bedrooms open onto a sun terrace, while the two side rooms overlook a landscaped rock garden - one is especially suitable for wheelchair users, who can park beside it. Residents' dinner is, like breakfast, based on local ingredients and 'good Irish cuisine', with home-made breads and farmhouse cheeses always available (please book ahead; very reasonably priced short wine list offered). Barbecues are sometimes arranged when the weather is favourable and, although officially closed in winter, bookings can be made by arrangement. This is an attractive option for a group, as the house is centrally heated throughout and the living room has a big open fire. The Deanes also have a 3-bedroom self-catering cottage available nearby. Children welcome (cot available without charge). Pets permitted. garden. **Rooms 5** (all en-suite & no smoking, 1 for disabled). B&B from €35pps, ss €6.50. Residents D 7.30 pm, from €27.50; wines from €13.50. Closed 1 Nov-15 Mar. MasterCard, Visa, Laser. **Directions:** Letterkenny - Ramelton- R246 (Milford Direction) through Kerrykeel to Portsalon; opposite golf course turn up hill.

Ramelton — Ardeen

B&B

Ramelton Co. Donegal **Tel: 074 51243** Fax: 074 51243
Email: ardeenbandb2@eircom.net Web: www.ardeenhouse.com

Overlooking Lough Swilly, set in its own grounds on the edge of the characterful town of Ramelton and well-located for touring Donegal and Glenveagh National Park, Anne Campbell's mid-nineteenth century house is not too grand and has the comfortable atmosphere of a family home. Individually decorated bedrooms with views over the Lough or nearby hills all have their own character and are charmingly furnished (Anne is very handy with a sewing machine and time available in the winter is well used for guests' comfort). The drawing room and dining room are both furnished with antiques and have open fires, making this a very warm and comfortable place to return to after a day out. No dinners, but there are some good pubs and restaurants nearby (eg The Bridge Bar, which is within walking distance in fine weather). Children welcome (under 2s free in parents' room, cots available free of charge). Garden, tennis. Self-catering cottage also available. **Rooms 5** (4 en-suite, 1 twin has private bathroom, all no smoking). B&B €35, ss €10. Open all year (Oct-Easter by prior arrangement only). MasterCard, Visa **Directions:** Follow river to Town Hall,turn right 1st house on right.

Ramelton — Frewin

Country House

Ramelton Co. Donegal **Tel: 074 51246** Fax: 074 51246
Email: flaxmill@indigo.ie Web: accommodationdonegal.net

Thomas and Regina Coyle have restored this unspoilt Victorian house with the greatest attention to period detail and guests have the opportunity to drink in the atmosphere on arrival while having a cup of tea in the little book-lined library, where the old parish safe is still set in the wall. Beautifully furnished bedrooms have snowy white bedlinen and a robe provided in case of night-time forays along the corridor and a delicious breakfast, including freshly baked breads warm from the oven, is taken communally at a long polished table - at night lit only by candlelight. This beautiful house is most unusual, notably because Thomas Coyle specialises in restoring old buildings and is a collector by nature - much of his collection finds a place in the house, some is for sale in an outbuilding at the back. Not suitable for children under 8. No dogs. No smoking except in sitting room & library. **Rooms 4** (3 en-suite, 1 with private bath). B&B from €50, ss €20. D €35 (by arrangement). Closed 24-25 Dec. MasterCard, Visa. **Directions:** Take R245 from Letterkenny. Travel 7 miles approx and take right turn on approach to Ramelton.Located 400 yards on right.

Rathmullan — Fort Royal Hotel

Hotel/Restaurant

Rathmullan Co. Donegal **Tel: 074 58100** Fax: 074 58103
Email: fortroyal@eircom.net Web: www.fortroyalhotel.com

Overlooking the sea, and with direct access to a sandy beach, the Fletcher family's attractive Victorian hotel is set in 19 acres of lawn and woodland above Lough Swilly. It's a good base for family holidays or visiting places of local interest, including Glenveagh National Park and Glebe House, the artist Derek Hill's former home, which has a museum and gallery next door. Public rooms, which include a recently refurbished bar, are spacious, well-proportioned and comfortably furnished in country house style, with big armchairs and open fires. Well-appointed bedrooms (all en-suite, most with bath and shower, a few bath only) are designed for relaxation and enjoy a pleasant outlook over wooded grounds. Croquet, tennis, golf, pitch & putt are available on the premises and activities such as riding and fishing nearby. Special interest breaks offered. Children welcome (under 4s free in parents' room, cot available without charge). Pets permitted. **Rooms 15**. B&B €85pps, ss €25. Closed 1 Nov-1 Apr.

Restaurant: This attractive traditional dining room overlooking lawns and woodland is well appointed with crisp white linen and fresh flowers - just the right setting for good country house cooking. Much of the food at Fort Royal comes from the hotel's own walled gardens (although this is not mentioned on menus, which is a pity) and is cooked by Robin and Ann Fletcher's son, Timothy, who has been head chef since 1995 and is establishing a growing reputation for the hotel's food. He offers nightly dinner menus with about five choices on each course, considerably priced to allow two- or three-course options. Typical examples from a summer menu include a starter of smoked salmon rolls with mixed leaves & chive mayonnaise; sole meunière (and vegetable selection) and crème brulée with raspberry compôte. Tea or coffee is served in the lounge afterwards - or, on fine evenings, you could take it outside and enjoy the view down over the lough. Staff are very pleasant and helpful, although it can be unclear who is in charge. **Seats 50**. No smoking restaurant; not suitable for children under 10 after 7pm. D daily, 7.30-8.30 (last orders). Set D from €30. *Light lunches are also served in the bar or at tables in the garden, 12-2 daily. Phone ahead to check availability. Amex, Diners, MasterCard, Visa, Laser. **Directions:** Ramelton Road from Letterkenny, straight on to Rathmullan.

Rathmullan   Rathmullan House

Country House/Restaurant   Rathmullan Co. Donegal **Tel:** 074 58188 Fax: 074 58200
Email: info@rathmullanhouse.com   Web: www.rathmullanhouse.com

Built as a summer house by the Batt banking family of Belfast in the 1800s, Rathmullan has been run as a country house hotel since 1961 by Bob and Robin Wheeler who have now semi-retired and it's currently managed by their sons William and Mark and daughter-in-law Mary. Set in lovely gardens on the shores of Lough Swilly, this gracious early nineteenth century house is fairly grand with public areas which include three elegant drawing rooms, but it's not too formal - and there's a cellar bar which can be very relaxed. Bedrooms vary in decor, facilities and cost to suit different requirements and budgets - there are luxurious garden suites (close to the swimming pool and leisure facilities) as well as the unpretentious old-fashioned comforts of family rooms at the top of the house, which many guests like best. Donegal has an other-worldliness that is increasingly hard to capture in the traditional family holiday areas, and the laid-back charm of Rathmullan House - albeit given invisible backbone by the professionalism of the Wheeler family and their staff - somehow symbolises that special sense of place. Small conferences (15-20); banqueting (100). Swimming pool, steam room, tennis. Children welcome; cot €10. Pets permitted by arrangement. **Rooms 24** (11 suites, 2 room for disabled). B&B €105pps, ss €20.

Pavilion Dinning Room: The dining room with its unusual tented ceiling (designed by the late Liam McCormick, well known for his striking Donegal churches) makes the most of the garden outlook and provides a fine setting for Seamus Douglas's country house cooking as well as the tremendous breakfasts for which Rathmullan is justly famous. Cooking here is upbeat traditional - a speciality is Rathmullan loin of lamb on colcannon mash, with buttered cabbage & rosemary jus and desserts like compôte of garden fruit with carrageen moss pudding convey the style. The carrageen is equally at home at breakfast too - each morning a tremendous buffet is laid out, offering a huge variety of juices, fresh and poached fruits with yogurt and carrageen pudding to go with them, cooked ham, smoked salmon and farmhouse cheeses, plus home-baked breads, scones and preserves from the garden - and all this before anything from the menu of hot dishes is even contemplated. (Rathmullan was the 2002 winner of our Denny Irish Breakfast Awards for the Ulster region). **Seats 70**. No smoking restaurant. daily D 7.30-8.45, Set D €47.50; house wine from €17.50; sc 10%. Closed 6 Jan -14 Feb. Amex, Diners, MasterCard, Visa. **Directions:** Letterkenny to Ramelton - turn right to Rathmullan at the bridge, through village and turn right to hotel.

Rossnowlagh   Sand House Hotel

Hotel/Restaurant   Rossnowlagh Co. Donegal **Tel: 072 51777** Fax: 072 52100
Email: info@sandhouse-hotel.ie   Web: www.sandhouse-hotel.ie

Perched on the edge of a stunning sandy beach two miles long, Mary and Brian Britton's famous hotel lost its trademark crenellated roof-line in major renovations over the winter of 2001/2 and has emerged with an extra storey and an elegant new look, reminiscent of a French chateau. The wonderful sea views and easy access to the beach have always been the great attractions of the Sand House, which started life as a fishing lodge in the 1830s and has now completed it latest metamorphosis with a new floor of bedrooms, a panoramic lift (who will bother with the stairs when the lift has the best view in the house?), a new boardroom and a marine spa, where seaweed products are used for a range of exclusive body and skincare treatments. Existing bedrooms were also refurbished and upgraded and many have a superb outlook; all are very comfortable, with excellent bathrooms - and everyone can enjoy the view from the sun lounge (known as the Atlantic Conservatory), which is designed as a comfortable retreat from which to soak in the sea view. Things that haven't changed at the Sand House include the ever-burning welcoming fire in the foyer- and the hospitality of the Britton family and staff (not to mention Mary Britton's reputation for exceptional housekeeping), which is the real appeal of this remarkable hotel. Jacuzzi, steam room, balneo bath, beauty salon. Fishing, cycling, tennis, walking, tennis on site; golf, horse riding, boating and many other activities available nearby. Conference/banqueting (90). Children welcome under 5s free in parents' room; cots available). Pets permitted in some areas by arrangement. **Rooms 55** (2 suites, 2 junior suites, 4 shower only, 10 no-smoking, 1 disabled). All day room service. B&B €120pps, ss €20. Closed Dec.

Seashell Restaurant: The restaurant is rather unexpectedly at the front of the hotel (and therefore faces inland) but is well-appointed, in keeping with the rest of the hotel. Sid Davis, Head Chef since 1994, presents seasonal 5-course dinner menus that change daily. The style is traditional, with plenty of choice offered on all courses; meals finish well with a choice of Irish cheeses or classic desserts. **Seats 70**. No smoking restaurant. D daily 7-9, L Sun only, 1-2.30. Set D €40, Set Sun L €22.50; house wines €17-25. Amex, Diners, MasterCard, Visa, Laser. **Directions:** Coast road from Ballyshannon to Donegal Town.

Tory Island — Ostan Thoraig (Hotel Tory)

Hotel

West End Tory Island Co. Donegal
Tel: 074 35920 Fax: 074 35613 Email: hoteltory@tinet.ie

The Gaeltacht (Irish-speaking) island of Tory lies eight miles off the north-west corner of Donegal and, in spite of its exposed position, has been inhabited for four thousand years. Perhaps not surprisingly, this other-worldly island managed quite well without an hotel until recently, but once Patrick and Berney Doohan's Ostan Thoraig was built in 1994 it quickly became the centre of the island's social activities - or, to be more precise, The People's Bar in the hotel quickly became the centre. The hotel is beside the little harbour where the ferries bring in visitors from mainland ports. Although simple, it provides comfortable en-suite accommodation with telephone and television. A special feature of the island is its 'school' of primitive art (founded with the support of well-known artist Derek Hill of nearby Glebe House and Gallery, Church Hill). It even has a king as a founder member: the present King of the Tory is Patsy Dan Rogers, who has exhibited his colourful primitive paintings of the island throughout the British Isles and in America. A tiny gallery on Tory provides exhibition space for the current group of island artists. Small conferences. Children welcome (cot available, small charge). Pets permitted by arrangement. **Rooms 14** (1 for disabled) B&B about €40pps, ss about €13. Wheelchair access. Closed Oct-Easter. [NB: Current data not confirmed at time of going to press; a phone call ahead is strongly advised.] MasterCard, Visa. **Directions:** Tory is accessible by ferry (subject to weather conditions) from several mainland ports: telephone 075-31320 for details, or ask at the hotel. ◇

Tremone — Trean House

Ⓝ Farmhouse

Tremone Lecamy Inishowen Co. Donegal **Tel: 077 67121** Fax: 077 67227
Email: treanhouse@oceanfree.net Web: www.treanhouse.com

Way out on the Inishowen peninsula, Joyce and Mervyn Norris's farmhouse is tucked into a sheltered corner in stonewalled countryside beside the sea. Surrounded by a large garden with mature trees and welcoming flowers, it is a substantial house and offers a comfortable base for a a relaxing holiday in a homely atmosphere. Guests have the use of a cosy sitting room with an open fire and simple country bedrooms have everything that is needed - the only room without an en-suite shower room has a private bathroom nearby - and, if any other guest prefers a bath, it can be used by arrangement. Joyce's home cooking is another attraction - breakfasts to set you up for the day, evening meals by arrangement. **Rooms 4** (3 en-suite, 3 shower only, all no smoking). B&B €27.50. No SC. Open all year except Christmas. MasterCard, Visa **Directions:** From Moville follow R238 5kms, turn right & follow house signs.

COUNTY GALWAY

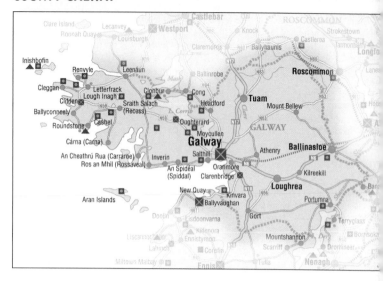

Galway can more than match any other Irish county for the variety and charm of its many scenic routes. But it also has more to offer than any other Irish county in the way of slightly offbeat expeditions and experiences, in addition to all the usual visual attractions of Ireland's Atlantic seaboard.

Visiting the Aran Islands, for instance, can be done by air as well as by sea. Then, too, there are many coastal boat trips, including an informative seaborne tour from Killary Harbour, Ireland's only genuine fjord, while Lough Corrib is also served by miniature cruise liners. As for sport ashore, the Galway Races at the end of July have developed into a six day meeting which is firmly established as Ireland's premier summer horse racing event, while the Ballinasloe International Horse Fair in the Autumn is simply unique. It dates back more than 280 years, and the Fair of 2002 (from September 26th to 29th) was reckoned the best yet.

This has to be Ireland's most generous county, for in effect you get two counties for the price of one. They're neatly divided by the handsome sweep of island-studded Lough Corrib, with the big country of many mountains to the west, and rolling farmland to the east. As a bonus, where the Corrib tumbles into Galway Bay, we find one of Ireland's - indeed, one of Europe's - most vibrant cities. Galway is a bustling place which cheerfully sees itself as being linked to Spain and the great world beyond the Atlantic.

The theme of double value asserts itself in other ways. As Autumn ripeness makes its presence felt, the county and city provide not one, but two, Oyster Festivals. Once September has ushered in the traditional oyster season, Galway's long and distinguished connection with the splendid bivalve mollusc is celebrated first with the Clarenbridge Oyster Festival on the southeast shore of Galway Bay, and then a week or so later with the Galway Oyster Festival itself, right in the heart of the city.

Lough Corrib is both a geographical and psychological divide. East of it, there's flatter country, home to hunting packs of mythic lore. West of the Corrib - which used itself to be a major throughway, and is now as ever place of angling renown - you're very quickly into the high ground and moorland which sweep up to the Twelve Bens and other splendid peaks, wonderful mountains which enthusiasts would claim as the most beautiful in all Ireland.

Their heavily indented coastline means this region is Connemara, the Land of the Sea, where earth, rock and ocean intermix in one of Ireland's most extraordinary landscapes. Beyond, to the south, the Aran Islands are a place apart, yet they too are part of the Galway mix in this fantastical county which has its own magical light coming in over the sea. And yet all its remarkable variety happens within very manageable distances.

Local Attractions and Information

GALWAY CITY

Arts Centre 47 Dominick St	091 565886
Galway Airport	091 752874
Galway Arts Festival (July)	091 565886
Galway Crystal Heritage Centre	091 757311
Galway Races (late July/early August, Sept & Oct)	091 753870
Galway Oyster Festival (late September)	091 527282/522066
Kenny's Bookshops & Art Galleries High Street	091 562739
O'Brien Shipping (Aran Island Ferries)	091 563081
Tourist Information	091 563081
Town Hall Theatre	091 569755

CO GALWAY

Aran Islands Heritage Centre	099 61355
Aran Islands Ferries from Rossaveal	091 568903/561767
Aran Islands Flights from Inverin Airport	091 593034
Aughrim Battle of Aughrim Centre	0905 73939
Ballinasloe International Horse Fair (Sept/Oct)	0905 43453
Clarenbridge Oyster Festival (September)	091 796342
Clifden Connemara Pony Show (mid August)	095 21863
Clifden Connemara Safari - Walking & Islands	095 21071
Gort Thoor Ballylee (Yeats' Tower)	091 631436
Inishbofin Arts Festival (Biennial, September)	095 45909
Inishbofin Ferries (Cleggan)	095 44642
Inisheer Duchas Inis Oirr (Arts Centre)	099 735576
Killary Cruises on Connemara Lady	091 566736
Kinvara Dungaire Castle	061 360788
Letterfrack Connemara Bog Week (May)	095 43443
Letterfrack Connemara Sea Week (October)	095 43443
Letterfrack Kylemore Abbey & Gardens	095 41146
Loughrea Dartfield Horse Museum	091 843968
Roundstone Roundstone Arts Week (July)	095 35834
Roundstone Traditional bodhran makers	095 35808
Tuam Little Mill (last intact cornmill in area)	093 25486

GALWAY CITY

Galway City — Ardawn House

Guesthouse

College Road Galway Co. Galway
Tel: 091 568 833 Fax: 091 563 454
Email: ardawn@iol.ie Web: www.galway.net/page/ardawn-house/

Mike and Breda Guilfoyle's hospitable guesthouse is easily found, just a few minutes walk from Eyre Square. Accommodation is all en-suite and rooms are comfortably furnished, with good amenities. But it's Mike and Breda who make Ardawn House special - they take great pride in every aspect of the business, (including an extensive breakfast) and also help guests to get the very best out of their visit to Galway. Children welcome. Pets permitted by arrangement. **Rooms 8** (all shower only & no-smoking). B&B €60pps. Closed 21-27 Dec. Amex, MasterCard, Visa, Laser. **Directions:** Off N6, take city east exit; follow signs to city centre. First house on right after greyhound track.

Galway City — Ardilaun House Hotel

féile bia Hotel/Restaurant

Taylors Hill Galway Co. Galway **Tel: 091 521 433** Fax: 091 521 546
Email: ardilaun@iol.ie Web: www.ardilaunhousehotel.ie

Ardilaun House Hotel has an interesting history - it dates back to about 1840, when it was built as a townhouse for prominent members of Galway society, the Persse family (Augusta Persse became Lady Grogory, co-founder of the Abbey Theatre) - and recently celebrated 40 years in the ownership of the Ryan family, who opened it as an hotel in 1962. While convenient to the city, its wooded grounds give it a country feeling. Friendly, helpful staff make a good impression on arrival and everything about the hotel - which has recently been extensively renovated, extended and refurbished - confirms the feeling of a well-run establishment. Public areas are spacious, elegantly furnished and some - notably the dining room - overlook gardens at the back. Bedrooms are traditionally furnished to a high standard (and have modem lines as well as the usual amenities) and in-house leisure facilities include snooker and a new leisure centre with indoor swimming pool, gym, solarium, beauty salon and treatment rooms. Purpose-built conference facilities offer a wide range of options for large and small groups (max 400), with back-up business services, including video conferencing on request. An attractive banqueting room is especially suitable for weddings (up to 270 guests). Children welcome (under 3s free in parents' room, cots available without charge). Pets permitted. **Rooms 89** (1 suite, 2 junior suites, 9 executive rooms, 6 shower only, 8 no-smoking, 2 for disabled). Lift. B&B €110 pps, ss €25. Closed 21-27 Dec.

Camilaun Restaurant: The restaurant is in a fine old-fashioned hotel dining room with crystal chandeliers and bay windows overlooking a colourful garden, traditional white-clothed tables, warm decor and a welcome emphasis on comfort - and friendly staff make guests feel welcome. Head chef John Kelly has been with the hotel since 1985 and knows his market well, using the best of ingredients in a traditional style with a light sprinkling of words like balsamic, red onion marmalade and lemongrass on the menu, giving the tiniest nod to fashion here and there. Menus offer a predictably wide choice of prime meats and fish - the house speciality is chateaubriand, closely followed by rack of lamb and a medley of scallops and prawns - competently cooked and attractively served with an exceptional variety of side vegetables - perhaps as many as seven or eight - all perfectly cooked. The grande finale is an excellent traditional dessert trolley - sherry trifle, tiramisu, charlotte royale, apple tart - and an invitation to double up on the sweets reinforces the overall feeling of being generously treated in pleasant, formal surroundings that is the essential pleasure of dining here. Good coffee to finish. Extensive wine list, although wine service is a little amateur. **Seats 140.** No smoking restaurant. L&D daily: L1-2.15, D 7-9.15. Set L €18. Early D €17 (7-8pm) Set D from €18 (5-course Set D €35), D also à la carte. House wine €16.50. SC 10%. Amex, Diners, MasterCard, Visa, Laser. **Directions:** 1 mile from City Centre, Take signposts for Salthill.

Galway City · Brennan's Yard Hotel

Hotel · Lower Merchants Road Galway Co. Galway **Tel: 091 568 166** Fax: 091 568 262
Email: info@brennansyardhotel.com Web: brennansyardhotel.com

In an old stone building close to Spanish Arch, this hotel first opened in 1992 - all rooms were individually designed with country pine antiques and Irish craft items, which gives them character. A major expansion and renovation programme saw 25 new rooms added in 1999; original rooms were refurbished to the same standard, the restaurant was also redecorated, a new bar built and, finally, a long-promised new reception and lobby area completed. Prices are moderate and, providing maintenance programmes are kept up, this will remain an interesting choice for city centre accommodation. Children welcome; cots available. **Rooms 45** (10 no-smoking). Lift. B&B €66.50 pps, ss €16.50. Closed 24-28 Dec. Amex, Diners, MasterCard, Visa, Laser. **Directions:** In Galway city centre, beside Spanish Arch.

Galway City · Corrib Great Southern Hotel

 Hotel · Renmore Galway Co. Galway **Tel: 091 755 281** Fax: 091 751 390
Email: res@corrib-gsh.ie Web: www.greatsouthernhotels.com

Extensive conference/banqueting and leisure facilities are the outstanding feature of this large modern hotel overlooking Galway Bay. It offers good facilities for both business guests and family holidays (ask about their Weekend Specials); in summer evening entertainment and crèche facilities are laid on. Bedrooms vary considerably; the best are spacious and well-planned, with stylish bathrooms and sea views, but all have TV with video channel, tea/coffee trays etc. Children welcome; under 2s free in parents' room, cots available without charge, children's teas (5-6pm); playroom, crèche. Leisure centre; swimming pool. Conference/banqueting 750/550. Business centre, secretarial service. No pets. **Rooms 180** (4 suites, 46 executive, 20 no-smoking, 2 disabled). Lift. 24 hour room service. B&B €135 pps, ss €30. Closed 24-26 Dec. Amex, Diners, MasterCard, Visa, Laser. **Directions:** On main Dublin Road into Galway city.

Galway City · Devondell

B&B · 47 Devon Park Lr. Salthill Galway Co. Galway
Tel: 091 528 306 Email: devondel@iol.ie Web: www.devondell.com

Although quite unremarkable from the road, Berna Kelly's immaculate house has won many admirers and it's easy to see why: a warm welcome, pretty bedrooms with crisp white linen and many homely touches and Berna's special breakfasts served in a fine dining room overlooking the back garden, are just a few of the reasons guests keep coming back. It's a little difficult to find on the first visit, but well worth the effort. **Rooms 4** (all en-suite & no smoking, 3 shower only). B&B €38 pps, no ss. Closed Nov-Mar. **No Credit Cards. Directions:** Fr Griffin Road to T Junction-take left after 400 - 500 yds, Take right at Devon Park House, go to fork 100 yds up, take left and sharp left.

Galway City — Galway Bay Hotel

féile bia Hotel   The Promenade Salthill Galway Co. Galway **Tel: 091 520 520** Fax: 091 520 530
Email: info@galwaybayhotel.net Web: www.galwaybayhotel.net

This well-named hotel has clear views over Galway Bay to the distant hills of County Clare from public rooms on the ground floor as well as many of the spacious, well-equipped bedrooms. The large marbled foyer and adjacent public areas are very spacious and facilities for both business and leisure are particularly impressive. A good choice for business guests as well as the usual facilities, all rooms have modem points and interactive TV for messages, internet and preview of the bill. Conference/banqueting (1000/600), video-conferencing. Leisure centre, swimming pool, gym; beauty salon. Children welcome (free in parents room under 2, cot available; playroom). Rooftop garden. Parking (inc underground). No pets. **Rooms 153** (4 suites, 7 executive, 24 no smoking, 5 for disabled). Lifts. B&B €153 pps. Open all year. Amex, Diners, MasterCard, Visa. **Directions:** Located on Salthill Road beside Leisureland overlooking Galway Bay.

Galway City — Glenlo Abbey Hotel

Hotel   Bushypark Galway Co. Galway **Tel: 091 526 666** Fax: 091 527 800
Email: glenlo@iol.ie Web: www.glenlo.com

Originally an eighteenth century residence, Glenlo Abbey is just two and a half miles from Galway city yet offers all the advantages of the country - the hotel is on a 138-acre estate, with its own golf course and Pavilion. It enjoys views over Lough Corrib and the surrounding countryside. The scale of the hotel is generous throughout, public rooms are impressive and bedrooms are well-furnished with good amenities and marbled bathrooms. The old Abbey has been restored to provide privacy for meetings and private dining, and there is a fully equipped business service bureau to back up seminars, conferences and presentations; (conference/banqueting 250/170). For indoor relaxation there's the Oak Cellar bar (where light food is served) and, in addition to the classical River Room restaurant, the hotel operates an historic Pullman train carriage as a restaurant in the hotel grounds - it's in beautiful order, has a great atmosphere and, needless to say, makes a meal here a memorable event. No pets. Own parking. **Rooms 46** (4 suites, 17 no-smoking, 2 for disabled). Wheelchair access. Lift. Room rate from about €150. Open all year. Amex, Diners, MasterCard, Visa. **Directions:** 2.5 miles from Galway on N59 in the Clifden direction. ◇

Galway City — Goya's

Café   2/3 Kirwans Lane Galway Co. Galway
Tel: 091 567010 Email: goyas@eircom.net Web: www.goyas.ie

If only for a cup of cappuccino or hot chocolate and a wedge of chocolate cake or a slice of quiche, a restorative visit to this delightful contemporary bakery and café is a must on any visit to Galway. There's something very promising about the cardboard cake boxes stacked up in preparation near the door, the staff are super, there's a great buzz and the food is simply terrific. What's more, you don't even have to be in Galway to enjoy Emer Murray's terrific baking - contact Goya's for her seasonal mail-order catalogues "Fabulous Festive Fancies"(Christmas cakes, plum pudding, mince pies etc) and "Easter Delights" (simnel cake and others); wedding cakes also available. If you're wondering where to start, why not try a speciality: Goyas 3-layer chocolate gateau cake. Open all day Mon-Sat. MasterCard, Visa, Laser. **Directions:** Behind McDonaghs Fish Shop off Quay Street.

Galway City — Great Southern Hotel

féile bia Hotel   Eyre Square Galway Co. Galway **Tel: 091 564 041** Fax: 091 566 704
Email: res@galway.gsh.ie Web: www.gshotels.com

Overlooking Eyre Square right in the heart of Galway, this historic railway hotel was built in 1845 and has retained many of its original features and old-world charm which mixes easily with modern facilities. Public rooms - notably the foyer - are quite grand and there's a pleasant country style bar, O'Flahertys Pub, down in the basement (with access from the Square or the hotel) in addition to the hotel cocktail lounge. Exciting news for 2003: as we go to press the hotel is closing for a total revamp on the same lines as the stunning refurbishment of their Killarney hotel; it will include a dedicated floor of new suites, executive rooms plus a refurbished conference venue and public areas. Conference/banqueting (350/300); business centre, secretarial services. Leisure centre, indoor swimming pool. Children under 2 free in parents' room, cots available without charge. No pets. Arrangement with nearby carpark. **Rooms 99** (11 suites, 45 executive,30 no-smoking, 2 for disabled). Lift. B&B €140 pps, ss €30 (Room only rate: €250, max 3 guests). Re-opening March 2003. Amex, Diners, MasterCard, Visa, Laser. **Directions:** In heart of the city overlooking Eyre Square.

Galway City   Harbour Hotel

Ⓝ Hotel/Restaurant   The Harbour Galway Co. Galway **Tel:** 091 569466 Fax: 091 569455
                                Email: info@galwayharbour.com Web: www.galwayharbourhotel.com

This contemporary style hotel is conveniently situated at the heart of the city and offers comfortable, moderately priced accommodation with secure parking adjacent. Functional bedrooms with all the usual facilities (TV, trouser press) and well-fitted bathrooms are already scheduled for refurbishment although the hotel only opened in spring 2001 - a clear indication of Galway's current popularity as a holiday destination.
Krusoes Restaurant: (Tel: 091 539115) is entered directly from the hotel lobby and bar but run as a separate operation by well-known local restaurateur Michael O'Grady (who also provides breakfast and bar lunches). Chic and trendy, with colourful big paintings and a large mirror at one end giving a sense of depth, it has minimalist shiny black table tops and paper napkins. Background jazz is pleasant and the food style is, predictably, contemporary international; although cooking and presentation are both a little uneven but it 's above-average as an hotel restaurant. Open for lunch and dinner daily. Amex, Diners, MasterCard, Visa. **Directions:** City centre waterfront, near Spanish Arch. ◇

Galway City   Jurys Galway Inn

féile bia Hotel   Quay St. Galway Co. Galway
                                                     Tel: 091 566 444 Fax: 091 568 415

Jurys Galway Inn is magnificently sited to make the most of both the river - which rushes past almost all the bedroom windows - and the great buzz of the Spanish Arch area of the city (just outside the door). Like the other Jurys room-only 'inns', the hotel offers a fair standard of basic accommodation without frills. Rooms are large (sleeping up to four people) and well finished, with everything required for comfort and convenience - ample well-lit work/shelf space, neat en-suite bathroom, TV, phone - but no extras. Beds are generous, with good-quality bedding, and open wardrobes are more than adequate. Neat tea/coffee-making facilities are built into the design, but there is no room service. Public areas include an impressive, well-designed foyer with seating areas, a pubby bar with good atmosphere and self-service cafeteria. Arrangement with next door car park. **Rooms 128.** Room Rate €94 (max 3 adults; 2 rooms for disabled). Closed 24-26 Dec. Amex, Diners, MasterCard, Visa. **Directions:** City centre, beside Spanish Arch, overlooking the bridge. ◇

Galway City   K C Blakes

Restaurant   10 Quay Street Galway Co. Galway
                                                 Tel: 091 561826 Fax: 091 561829

K C Blakes is named after a stone Tower House, of a type built sometime between 1440 and 1640, which stands as a typical example of the medieval stone architecture of the ancient city of Galway. The Caseys' restaurant, with all its sleek black designer style and contemporary chic could not present a stronger contrast to such a building. Proprietor-chef John Casey sources ingredients for K C Blakes with care and cooks with skill to produce dishes ranging from traditional Irish (beef and Guinness stew), modern Irish (black pudding croquettes with pear & cranberry sauce), classical French (sole meunière) to global cuisine (a huge choice here - let's say chicken fajita) and creative dishes based on the new deep-sea varieties of fish such as siki shark. It's a remarkable operation, aimed at a wide market and fairly priced. Closed 25 Dec. Amex, MasterCard, Visa. **Directions:** City centre, near Spanish Arch. ◇

Galway   Kilkenny Café

Ⓝ Café   6-7 High Street Galway Co. Galway **Tel:** 091 566110

At the top floor of the new 3-storey Kilkenny store in Galway city, this bright modern café is run on similar lines to the successful Dublin operation. Wholesome, flavourful, good-home-cooking style self-service food is available throughout the day; breakfast and lunch menus are offered, otherwise a tempting selection of panini, wraps and sandwiches plus the home-bakes for which Kilkenny is well-known (scones with butter, preserves and cream, pear & almond tart) are available all day. The drinks menu includes a range of Java Republic coffees and a short wine list (a house wine available by the bottle and a couple of quarter bottles) as well as juices, smoothies and other soft drinks. Vegetarian and gluten-free options are highlighted on the menu. This is a welcome addition to informal dining options in Galway and is sure to very popular when word gets out. The only disadvantage is its location within the building (no lift). Open: Shop hours. Breakfast, 9-11.30; Lunch, 11.30-3. Closed 25-26 Dec. Amex, Diners, MasterCard, Visa, Laser. **Directions:** City centre.

Galway City — Killeen House

🏠 Country House   Bushy Park Galway Co. Galway **Tel: 091 524 179** Fax: 091 528 065
Email: killeenhouse@ireland.com Web: www.killeenhousegalway.com

GUESTHOUSE OF THE YEAR

Catherine Doyle's delightful house really has the best of both worlds. It's on the Clifden Road just on the edge of Galway city and yet, with 25 acres of private grounds and gardens reaching right down to the shores of Lough Corrib, it offers all the advantages of the country, too. Catherine has been welcoming guests to Killeen House for a decade and her quiet, thoughtful hospitality and high standards make a stay here very special, beginning with tea on arrival, properly served on a beautifully arranged tray with fine linen and polished silver - a house speciality extending to the tray provided in your bedroom, which manages to bring real class to that most practical of facilities. The house was built in 1840 and has all the features of a more leisurely era, when space was plentiful - not only in the reception rooms, which include a guest drawing room and an elegant dining room overlooking the gardens (where delicious breakfasts are served in style), but also the bedrooms. These are luxuriously and individually furnished, each in a different period, e.g. Regency, Edwardian and (most fun this one) Art Nouveau; the bedding is exquisite and they have lovely bathrooms too - again, highly individual in style and with every possible comfort provided. As in all the very best guesthouses, your hostess seems to have thought of all the little things that make people feel at home (and some of the bigger ones too, like comfortable armchairs and flat screen TV); her attention to detail is an object lesson in how to do things right: there are fresh flowers everywhere (including the bathroom), there's a turn-down service (and fresh towels in the bathroom while you're out for dinner) and, although the menu is not especially extensive, breakfast is a delight - lots of fresh juice and aromatic coffee, free range eggs - and little details like a separate toast rack and butter dish for each guest - delicious home-made preserves too. Just lovely. Not suitable for children under 12. Garden. No pets. **Rooms 5** (1 shower only). Lift. B&B €70pps, ss €30. Closed 23-27 Dec. Amex, Diners, MasterCard, Visa.
Directions: On N59 between Galway city and Moycullen village.

Galway City — Kirbys of Cross Street

Restaurant   Cross Street Galway Co. Galway **Tel: 091 569404** Fax: 091 569403
Web: www.kirbysrestaurant.com

One of a trio of establishments situated on the corner of Cross Street and Kirwan's Lane (the others are two of Galway's leading pubs, Busker Browne's and The Slate House), this pleasantly informal two-storey restaurant offers everything from Irish stew to lobster, with a wide range of popular and international dishes in between, including a good selection for vegetarians. No-smoking area; air conditioning. Children over 7 welcome. No parking. **Seats 80.** L&D daily. Closed 24-25 Dec. Amex, Diners, MasterCard, Visa, Laser. **Directions:** City centre - on corner of Cross Street and Kirwan's Lane.

Galway City — Kirwan's Lane Restaurant

Restaurant   Kirwans Lane Galway Co. Galway
Tel: 091 568 266 Fax: 091 561645

This well-known contemporary restaurant is in a laneway just beside the Hotel Spanish Arch. When it opened in 1996, it was Galway's first cutting-edge restaurant - and such a success that it was extended to double the capacity less than three years later. Today, things are slightly different; the formula has been changed from contemporary fine dining to a more informal bistro style, offering extensive international menus (Asian influences, quite a lot of grills, popular desserts like tiramisu) at relatively moderate prices and, at the time of the Guide's most recent visit (just before going to press), this slick modern restaurant had not quite settled down to its new format, so it is a question of watch this space. Good fish cookery, a decent (if rather expensive) wine list and piano playing by Ciaran Duffy that adds to the atmosphere at weekends are all plus points. No parking (multi-storey carpark nearby). **Seats 100** (private room 50). No smoking area; air conditioning. L & D daily: L12.30-2.30, D 6-10.30; Set L €17.95, Set D €20-32, also à la carte; house wine about €18; sc discretionary. Closed 24-30 Dec. Amex, MasterCard, Visa, Laser, Switch. **Directions:** Just off Cross St and Quay St.

Galway City — The Malt House

Restaurant   High Street Galway City Co. Galway **Tel: 091 567 866** Fax: 091 563 993
Email: info@malt-house.com Web: www.malt-house.com

The Cunninghams' welcoming old restaurant and bar in a quiet cul-de-sac laneway off High Street has great character and a friendly attitude. There's a lunchtime bar menu with soups and salads, served with good home-made bread, classic starters and light dishes like duck liver paté with Cumberland sauce or deep-fried camembert with pear sauce & salad, popular hot seafood dishes - baked garlic mussels, panfried crab claws - steaks and vegetarian dishes. Dinner menus are more formal but the emphasis is still on fairly traditional dishes - and none the worse for that. This is one of Galway's most consistent restaurants and its cosy atmosphere and comfortingly familiar food make a welcome alternative to contemporary fare served in hard-edged minimalist surroundings. Multi-storey carpark nearby. **Seats 50** (private room, 20). No smoking restaurant; air conditioning. L & D Mon-Sat: L12.30-2.30, D 6-10. Bar Food also available. Set L€20, Early D €19.60 (6-7pm), Set D €35, à la carte L&D available, house wine €18; no SC. Closed Sun & 25 Dec-2 Jan. Amex, Diners, MasterCard, Visa, Laser. **Directions:** Located in Courtyard just off High Street.

Galway City — McDonagh's Seafood House

Restaurant   22 Quay Street Galway Co. Galway**Tel: 091 565 001** Fax: 091 562 246
Email: mcdonagh@tinet.ie Web: www.mcdonaghs.net

This unusual restaurant is a fish shop during the day - whole catches bought from local fishermen are on sale in the shop within a couple of hours of leaving the boat - buying the whole catch guarantees the wide variety that has made the shop famous. Then, when it comes to the cooking, there's the fish & chips operation - select your variety and see it cooked in front of you. On the other side of the shop is the Seafood Bar, a more formal restaurant where an extensive range of dishes is offered, including McDonagh's shellfish platter (half lobster, scallops, mussels, crab claws, prawns) and Clarinbridge oysters. They even do their own smoking on the premises and fish caught by anglers can be brought in and smoked to take home - and they do party food, too. The Bill of Fare is informative on the characteristics and eating quality of mainstream fish and shellfish - variety and good value are the key points here. The family also owns the Hotel Spanish Arch (091 569600) nearby and a wine bar across the street. Carpark nearby. **Seats 42.** No smoking area; air conditioning. Open all day. L 12-2.30 daily, D 5-10 Mon-Sat, Set L about €12, Set D from about €20, à la carte available; house wine €14; sc discretionary. Closed 24-25 Dec & 1 Jan. Amex, Diners, MasterCard, Visa, Laser. **Directions:** Bottom of Quay Sreet, near Jury's Inn and The Spanish Arch.

Galway City — Milano

Ⓝ Restaurant   The Cornstore Middle Street Galway Co. Galway
Tel: 091 568488 Fax: 091 568497

This spacious modern restaurant is one of a small chain operated in Ireland by the UK company PizzaExpress. Like its sister restaurants (see Dublin entries) it specialises in providing good moderately priced Italian food - mainly but not exclusively authentic pizzas and pastas - in stylish surroundings. Consistency and good service are their strong points and they're happy to cater for large parties, drinks receptions and so on. It's a popular place for an afternoon tea or coffee - and there's a resident pianist on Wednesday and Thursday nights. **Seats 120** (private room 30). No smoking area; air conditioning. Toilets wheelchair accessible. Children welcome. Open daily, noon-11pm; à la carte. House wine €16.60. Closed 25-26 Dec. Amex, Diners, MasterCard, Visa, Laser. **Directions:** Just off Shoppe Street on the quays.

Galway — Nimmo's Restaurant & Wine Bar

Ⓝ Restaurant/Wine Bar   Spanish Arch Galway Co. Galway
Tel: 091 561114

Good food and a friendly, bustling atmosphere have made Harriet Leander's first floor restaurant in a characterful old stone building on the water's edge one of Galway's most popular dining places. Pleasant staff meet and seat guests efficiently, presenting short but balanced à la carte menus with about half a dozen choices on each course. The style is fairly modern but there is no question of presentation taking precedence over flavour and texture: dishes relished on a recent visit included fresh-tasting salmon & chive terrine wrapped in smoked salmon and served with horseradish cream and perfectly cooked canon of lamb with red roast peppers, spring onion mash and asparagus; plentiful side vegetables, although not especially appealing, made up in flavour anything missing in presentation and the overall impression is of excellent ingredients in safe hands. Desserts are bought-in and their provenance is impeccable (from Goya's, see entry) but a couple of home-made ones would add a welcome dimension. Good coffee - refilled without charge - and a good wine list too. Prices may seem a little steep for the surroundings (quite basic furnishings and table settings), but this is offset by good cooking - and the ambience has the happy informality of a busy French bistro. Open Tue-Sun, 7-10pm. Closed Sun. No bookings.

Nimmo's Wine Bar, downstairs, is a sister to the first floor restaurant and, although much more informal, offers delicious food at reasonable prices. It has a bit of style - flowers in wine buckets, lots of prints and memorabilia on the walls - and you can get delicious things not often found elsewhere like coq au vin (made by a Frenchman and served by one too, in the Guide's experience). Other treats in store might include light dishes like a warm salade du jour or smoked salmon & crab and informal hot dishes like frittata or steak sandwich. L Tue-Sat, 12,30-3, D Tue-Sun 7-10 (live music Sun, 6.30-9.30). Closed Mon. MasterCard, Visa. **Directions:** Harbour front, beside Spanish Arch. ◇

Galway City — Norman Villa

Guesthouse   86 Lower Salthill Salthill Galway Co. Galway
Tel: 091 521131 Fax: 091 521131
Email: normanvilla@oceanfree.net Web: www.normanvilla.com

Dee and Mark Keogh's guesthouse is exquisite. It's a lovely old house, immaculately maintained and imaginatively converted to make the most of every inch, ensuring guest comfort without spoiling the interior proportions. Dee and Mark are dedicated hosts and their home is dashingly decorated, with lovely rich colours and a great collection of modern paintings looks especially magnificent juxtaposed with antique furniture. Bedrooms have neat shower rooms ingeniously fitted into tiny spaces and also phones and tea/coffee-making facilities, while a converted coach house at the end of the lovely little back garden makes an unusual self-contained suite. Children welcome (under 2s free in parents' room). No pets. **Rooms 6** (all shower only & no-smoking). B&B €50-55 pps, ss €10. Closed Nov-Feb. MasterCard, Visa. **Directions:** Follow signs from Galway city centre to Salthill, then Lower Salthill - house is beside P.J. Flaherty's Pub.

Galway City — Park House Hotel

 Hotel   Forster St. Eyre Square Galway Co. Galway **Tel: 091 564 924** Fax: 091 569 219
Email: parkhousehotel@eircom.net Web: www.parkhousehotel.ie

It would be hard to beat the location of this attractive and welcoming owner-run hotel just off Eyre Square - and it is furnished to a high standard and warmly decorated throughout. Rooms are spacious and cosily furnished, with all the comforts that make you feel at home when travelling, including good bathrooms. Providing a high level of personal service is a particular point of pride, making this an especially comfortable base for visitors on business or leisure. There are facilities for small conferences and banqueting (40/50) and one of the hotel's greatest assets in this busy city is a private residents' car park. Park Room Restaurant (D daily & L Sun); bar food L&D daily. Children welcome (under 12s free in parents' room, cots available). No pets. **Rooms 57** (2 junior suites, 1 for disabled). Lift. 24 hour room service. B&B €150pps, ss €65. Closed 24-26 Dec. Amex, Diners, MasterCard, Visa, Laser. **Directions:** Located adjacent to Eyre Square.

Galway City — Radisson SAS Hotel

féile bia 🏨 Hotel   Lough Atalia Road Galway Co. Galway **Tel: 091 538300** Fax: 091 538380
Email: sales@radissonsas.com Web: www.radissonsas.com

Ideally situated on the waterfront, overlooking Lough Atalia, this dashing new hotel is much more central than its scenic location might suggest, as the railway and bus stations are very close and the shops and restaurants of Eyre Square are only a few minutes walk. A high, airy foyer with satellite reception desk, unusual sculptures, audacious greenery and a glass-walled lift is designed to impress and lift the spirits, a feeling confirmed by the atmosphere in adjacent public areas, including a very pleasant big lounge area a few steps up, in a sunny position looking over the Roman-style leisure centre to Lough Atalia, and the cosier Backstage Bar. Bedrooms are designed in three distinct styles - Scandinavian, Maritime or Classic - all furnished to a high standard, with excellent bathrooms and facilities (air conditioning, phone/voice mail & modem, safe, TV with video channel as well as the more mundane but necessary tea/coffee making and trouser press); all of this plus 3-hour express laundry and 24 hour room service make this the ideal business accommodation. Facilities for conferences and meetings are excellent: the main conference room (appropriately named Inis Mór) can seat 1,000 delegates, and there are also five boardrooms and six meetings rooms (all named after the Tribes of Galway), with cutting edge equipment and business support services available. The hotel restaurant, Marinas, is a large split-level room with decor in blues and browns inspired by Lough Atalia, and works equally well for formal dining (where Galway seafood features strongly) and as a place to make the most of the famous Scandinavian buffet breakfast. Conference/banqueting (750/570). Video-conferencing, business centre, secretarial services. Leisure centre (17m pool, children's pool, gym, sauna, steam bath, jacuzzi, outdoor hot tub). Pitch & putt. No pets. **Rooms 204** (3 suites, 10 junior suites, 138 no smoking, 10 for disabled.) Lift. Children welcome (under 10s free in parents' room, cot available without charge) B&B €185, ss €90, no SC. Amex, Diners, MasterCard, Visa, Laser. **Directions:** Beside Lough Atalia, 200m from Bus & Train Station.

Galway City — Tigh Neachtain

Pub

Cross Street Galway Co. Galway
Tel: 091 592189 Fax: 091 563940

Tigh Neachtain is one of Galway's oldest pubs - the origins of the building are medieval and it has been in the same family for a century - the interior has remained unchanged since 1894. Quite unspoilt, it has great charm, an open fire and a friendly atmosphere - and the pint is good too. Simple bar food (sandwiches and a variety of coffees) are available but perhaps the nicest thing of all is the way an impromptu traditional music session can get going at the drop of a hat. Closed 25 Dec & Good Fri. **No credit cards. Directions:** Situated on crossroads Quay Street/Cross Street/High Street.

Galway City — Westwood House Hotel

Hotel

Dangan Upper Newcastle Galway Co. Galway **Tel: 091 521 442** Fax: 091 521 400
Email: info@westwoodhousehotel.com Web: www.westwoodhousehotel.com

A sister hotel to The Schoolhouse Hotel in Dublin and the Station House Hotel, Clifden, Westwood House is well located, on the edge of Galway. Convenient to both the city and Connemara, it's set well back from the road and offers a high standard of accommodation for business and leisure at fairly reasonable prices. Air-conditioned throughout, the hotel has good conference/banqueting facilities (350/275) with back-up services and fax/ISDN lines in bedrooms. A range of 2-3 night leisure breaks offers particularly good value. No pets. **Rooms 58** (6 junior suites, 8 executive, 17 no smoking, 3 for disabled). Lift. B&B €99.50pps, ss €25. Closed 24-25 Dec. Amex, Diners, MasterCard, Visa, Laser. **Directions:** 1.5 km from Eyre Square (N59 for Clifden).

COUNTY GALWAY

Aran Islands — Kilmurvey House

Guesthouse

Kilronan Aran Islands Co. Galway **Tel: 099 61218** Fax: 099 61397
Email: kilmurveyhouse@eircom.net Web: wwww.kilmurveyhouse.com

Right at the foot of the island's most famous attraction, Dun Aengus fort (and beside the visitor centre), this 150 year old stone house is within walking distance of beaches, pubs and restaurants. It has been extended to provide extra en-suite accommodation, but that is completely in line with the habit of organic development in a family home that includes furnishings accumulated from the early 20th century (or beyond), to this day - an interesting record of changing interior fashions through a century or more. But it's the scrupulous cleanliness and Treasa Joyce's warm and chatty personality that make this an ideal place to stay for a cycling or walking holiday, or just to relax. Children welcome (under 5s free in parents' room, cots available free of charge). **Rooms 12** (all en-suite and no smoking), B&B €38, ss €15. Closed 31 Oct-1 Apr. MasterCard, Visa, Laser. **Directions:** 4.5 miles from Kilronan.

Aran Islands | Man Of Aran Cottages

Restaurant/B&B

Kilmurvey Inishmore Aran Islands Co. Galway
Tel: 099 61301 Fax: 099 61324
Email: manofaran@eircom.net Web: http:homepage.eircom.net/~manofaran

Despite its fame - this is where the film Man of Aran was made - Joe and Maura Wolfe make visiting their home a genuine and personal experience. The cottage is right beside the sea, surrounded by wild flowers, and Joe has somehow managed to create a successful organic garden in this exposed location, so their meals usually include his vegetables (even artichokes and asparagus), salads, nasturtium flowers and young nettle leaves as well as Maura's home-made soups, stews and freshly-baked bread and cakes. In summer they're open for lunch (soups, sandwiches, desserts)and you can eat in the little restaurant or, on fine days, take your food out to benches in the garden with stunning views across the sea towards the mountains. Packed lunches are available too. Maura and Joe also cook almost every night during the summer; occasionally, they make arrangements for guests staying with them to go to Teach Nan Phaidi (5 minutes walk, see separate entry). Private parties (40). **Seats 40.** No smoking restaurant. L 12.30-3 (Sun from 12); D 7.30. Set D from €28; house wine from €15-18. SC discretionary (10% at D)
Accommodation: The three little bedrooms are basic but full of quaint, cottagey charm and they're very comfortable, although only one is en-suite. Breakfast will probably be a well cooked full-Irish - made special by Joe's beautifully sweet home-grown cherry tomatoes if you are lucky - although they'll do something different if you like. Garden, walking. No pets. **Rooms 3** (1 en-suite, all no smoking). B&B €35, ss €9. Closed Nov-Mar. **Directions:** Mini bus or cycle from Kilronan, 4 miles.

Aran Islands | Pier House Restaurant & Guest House

Restaurant/Guesthouse

Kilronan Inishmore Aran Islands Co. Galway
Tel: 099 61417 Fax: 099 61122 Email: pierhouse@iol.ie

In a new building, right on the pier where the boats arrive, Maura & Padraig Joyce's house incorporates a restaurant where Ballymaloe-trained Aine Maguire cooks. The accommodation is smartly decorated and comfortable, with more facilities than most island accommodation - there's a large residents' lounge and bedrooms (all with views) have TV and phones as well as communal tea/coffee making facilities downstairs to use at any time. It is perhaps less characterful than some of the older houses, but very comfortable and well-run. Self-catering cottage also available. **Rooms 12** (all en-suite & no smoking). B&B about €35, ss about €16.50.
Restaurant: Aine Maguire has brought the Ballymaloe philosophy to Kilronan and is serving wonderful food, with the emphasis on good ingredients and clean, modern cooking. Local seaweeds gathered from the shores are used as other cooks use herbs, especially in pasta sauces. Other house specialities include clam chowder, local fish, such as ray with herbed yogurt & caramelised butter and monkfish with smoked butter hollandaise & salsa verde - butter is smoked by the same local smoker, Gearoid de Brun, who does other produce, including smoked salmon and tuna. Seafood tends to dominate, but they also do great steaks and sometimes get organic beef from Inis Oirr - where possible Aine uses organic and free range products, including local eggs. A wide selection of yeast, sourdough and soda breads is served, also home-made ices. It's quite an expensive restaurant and if there is a criticism, it would be that pricing can be inconsistent (eg stuffed mackerel may not be much less than steak), but to find food of this quality on an island is a blessing. Gourmet pizza night, Tue. **Seats 46.** No smoking restaurant. Children welcome (from 6-7.30). D Tue-Sun, 6-10. A la carte. House wine about €16, sc discretionary. Closed Nov-Mar. MasterCard, Visa, Laser.
Directions: Galway to Rosamhil then Ferry, 30 minutes to Island. ◇

Aran Islands | Teach Nan Phaidai

Restaurant

Chill Mhiurbhigh Aran Islands Co. Galway
Tel: 099 61330 Fax: 099 61330

Just around the corner from Man of Aran Cottage, this quaint little thatched restaurant is whitewashed in traditional fashion with cheerful yellow windows. Inside, it's clean and fresh with a huge open fireplace providing ventilation as well as warmth - a charming setting for good food, which is served all day. Snacks are available morning and afternoon, while the lunch menu offers more substantial fare - Teach nan Phaidi chowder, whiskey cured Aran smoked salmon to start, perhaps, then pan fried fillet of hake, a small sirloin steak or vegetable korma and a selection of desserts. Evening menus overlap with lunch but are more formal and offer a wider choice, including roast crispy half duckling with a honey citrus sauce, perhaps, and seared king scallops with bacon and a white wine and butter sauce - served with island-grown, seaweed nurtured potatoes. Desserts include lovely home-made ice cream. It's popular with locals as well as visitors, as there's a great buzz, the cooking's good (chefs tend to change at island restaurants, but the standard here seems to be consistent) and service, by charming well-informed staff, is excellent. An efficient bus-service will collect and drop-off people from all B&B's throughout the island. **Seats 60**. Children welcome. Open 11 am-9pm daily; L 11-3.30, D 7-9. Average main course about €19; house wine about €18. Closed Christmas week. MasterCard, Visa. ◇

Ballinasloe — Haydens Gateway Business & Leisure Hotel

Hotel

Ballinasloe Co. Galway **Tel: 0905 42347** Fax: 0905 42895
Email: cro@lynchhotels.com Web: www.lynchhotels.com

Now in the ownership of the Lynch family (who have a group of hotels in the west of Ireland), this long-established hotel is the centre of local activities in and around Ballinasloe - conference facilities are good, there's a pleasant banqueting room overlooking the courtyard garden at the back and prices are moderate. As it's about halfway between Dublin and Galway, with refreshments available all day, it's a handy place to break the journey although, on several recent visits, the standard of tidiness in public areas has been less than satisfactory. Conference/banqueting (300/350), Special breaks (golf etc). Children welcome. No pets. **Rooms 48** (7 executive rooms, 1 for disabled). Lift. B&B €46pps, ss €22 (room-only rate: €79). Bar/coffee shop 12.30-10 daily; buffet. Open all year. Amex, Diners, MasterCard, Visa, Laser. **Directions:** N6 Galway-Dublin road, on main street of Ballinasloe.

Ballinasloe — Tohers Bar & Restaurant

féile bia Restaurant/Pub

18 Dunlo Street Ballinasloe Co. Galway
Tel: 0905 44848 Fax: 0905 44848

This family-run pub on the main street is very attractive, with a traditional style bar on the ground floor and the restaurant in three separate dining rooms upstairs. A tempting bar lunch menu offers simple but tasty fare: a choice of soups with home-baked bread, a range of freshly-baked baguettes with various fillings (roast marinated chicken breast with curry mayonnaise, for example, or BLT), smoked salmon & cream cheese bagel or chicken salad - plus daily hot specials like home-made burger and chicken fajitas. If you can hit Ballinasloe at the right time, this is the spot to be and it's only a short walk up from the new marina too. Restaurant meals offer a wide choice of interesting international dishes, typically in starters like spring roll of gingered crab with a marinated carrot & fennel salad, lemon aioli & grilled pepper salsa or a trio of local smoked & cured organic fish. Main courses lead off with an imaginative vegetarian dish - grilled & baked aubergines, stuffed with basil, pinenuts & parmesan, served in a tomato sauce with chargrilled polenta & mozzarella cheese, perhaps - and, as well as regulars like steaks and fish dish of the evening, may offer unusual dishes like slow cooked Moroccan spiced lamb shank with lemon & garlic couscous steaks - and there's game in season too. Lots of tempting desserts or a cheese plate to finish. Outside catering service available; gourmet nights on request. Bar meals Mon-Sat, 12-3 & 6.30-9.30. Restaurant: **Seats 64**. D Tue-Sat 6.30-10. Set D €32 (on request, for parties only), otherwise à la carte; house wine €17.14. SC discretionary. No food on Sun, restaurant also D Mon. Establishment closed 2 weeks mid Oct. MasterCard, Visa, Laser. **Directions:** Town centre, just off market square.

Barna — O'Grady's on the Pier

Restaurant

Sea Point Barna Co. Galway
Tel: 091 592223 Fax: 091 590677

In a stunning position, with views over the harbour and beach to distant mountains, Michael O'Grady's charming seafood restaurant has attracted a loyal clientèle since opening in 2000. There are some contemporary elements (specially on the first floor) but tradition has also been allowed its place - the old fireplace has been kept, for example, which bodes well for cosy sessions in wild weather - and Michael's aim is for his seafood to be "simply prepared and very fresh as my father did it years ago". This he is doing very well, although world cuisine is certainly allowed a little space too, notably among the daily blackboard specials which might include dishes like filo wrapped cod with lemongrass cream or baked seabass with sweet chilli glaze alongside the ultimate classic, grilled whole black sole with lemon butter. Three or four popular dishes on each course are offered for non seafood eaters too. Always innovative, Michael joint winner of the Guide's Creative Seafood Dish Award in 2001 (together with Cathal Reynolds of Cré-na-Cille, Tuam). Michael's dish - sautéed baby shark on bok choi with sweet chili & scallion butter - demonstrated just how appealing this little-known variety can be when cooked simply but imaginatively in the contemporary idiom. Children welcome. **Seats 85** (max table size 10, private room 22). No smoking area, air-conditioning. D daily 5-10, L Sun only 12.30-2.45. Set Sun L €21, also à la carte L&D; house wine €17.50. Closed 23-27 Dec. MasterCard, Visa, Amex, Laser, Switch. **Directions:** West of Galway City Spiddal Road. Barna is 4 miles from Galway City.

Cashel — Cashel House Hotel

🏨 Hotel/Restaurant   Cashel Co. Galway **Tel:** 095 31001   Fax: 095 31077
Email: info@cashel-house-hotel.com   Web: www.cashel-house-hotel.com

HOTEL OF THE YEAR

Dermot and Kay McEvilly were among the pioneers of the Irish country house movement when, as founder members of the Irish Country Houses and Restaurants Association (now known as The Blue Book) they opened Cashel House as an hotel in 1968. The following year General and Madame de Gaulle chose to stay for two weeks, an historic visit of which the McEvilly's are justly proud - look out for the photographs and other memorabilia in the hall. The de Gaulle visit meant immediate recognition for the hotel, but it did even more for Ireland by putting the Gallic seal of approval on Irish hospitality and food. Comfort abounds here, even luxury, yet it's tempered by common sense, a love of gardening and the genuine sense of hospitality that ensures each guest will benefit as much as possible from their stay. The gardens, which run down to their own private beach, contribute greatly to the atmosphere, and the accommodation includes especially comfortable ground floor garden suites, which are also suitable for less able guests (wheelchair accessible but no special grab rails etc in bathrooms). Relaxed hospitality combined with professionalism have earned an international reputation for this outstanding hotel and its qualities are perhaps best seen in details - log fires that burn throughout the year, day rooms furnished with antiques and filled with fresh flowers from the garden, rooms that are individually decorated with many thoughtful touches. Service (with all day room service, including all meals) is impeccable and superb breakfasts include a wonderful buffet display of home-made and local produce, including everything from soda bread and marmalade to black pudding in addition to hot dishes cooked from the breakfast menu. (Cashel House was the Connaught winner of the Guide's Denny Breakfast in 2001.) Not suitable for children under 5, although cots are available for young babies (€15). Pets permitted. **Rooms 32** (13 suites, 9 superior rooms, 1 shower only, 16 no-smoking, 4 suitable for less-able guests). B&B €110pps, no ss; SC 12.5%.

Dining Room: A large conservatory extension (completely revamped in 2001) enhances this well-appointed split-level restaurant. Although assisted by head chef Florent Foulard since 2000, Dermot McEvilly has overseen the kitchen personally since the hotel opened, providing a rare consistency of style in five-course dinners that make imaginative use of local produce and seafood - lobster, oysters, fresh and home-smoked wild salmon, mussels, turbot, monkfish - is a great strength. Connemara lamb regularly stars and another, more unusual, speciality is roast stuffed crown of pork. Garden produce is also a welcome presence throughout, in soups, salads, side dishes, fine vegetarian dishes and desserts, such as rhubarb tart or strawberries and cream. Farmhouse cheeses come with home-baked biscuits and a choice of coffees and infusions is offered to finish. Service, under the personal supervision of Kay McEvilly and restaurant manager Ray Doorley, is excellent. An interesting wine list includes four House Wines (€21.50). An attractive little à la carte bar lunch menu offers interesting snacks and sandwiches, but also hot meals, including lobster if you want it; afternoon teas are also served daily in the bar (L12.30-2.30, Afternoon Tea 2-5). Dining Room **Seats 70**. No smoking restaurant. D daily 7-8.45 (Sun to 8.30). Set D €45; à la carte. 12.5% s.c. added to bills. Closed 10 Jan-10 Feb. Amex, MasterCard, Visa, Laser, Switch. **Directions:** South off N59 (Galway-Clifden road) 1 mile west of Recess.

Cashel — Zetland Country House

Hotel/Restaurant   Cashel Bay Cashel Co. Galway **Tel:** 095 31111   Fax: 095 31117
Email: zetland@iol.ie   Web: www.zetland.com

Originally built as a sporting lodge in the early 19th century, Zetland House is on an elevated site, with views over Cashel Bay and still makes a good base for fishing holidays. This is a charming house, with a light and airy atmosphere and an elegance bordering on luxury, in both its spacious antique-furnished public areas and bedrooms. The latter are individually decorated in a relaxed country house style. The gardens surrounding the house are very lovely too, greatly enhancing the peaceful atmosphere of the house. Its unusual name dates from the time when the Shetland Islands were under Norwegian rule and known as the Zetlands - the Earl of Zetland (Lord Viceroy 1888-1890) was a frequent visitor here, hence the name. Small conferences/banqueting (20/65). Special breaks. Garden, tennis, cycling, walking, billiards, pool table. Children welcome (cot available). Pets permitted by arrangement in some areas. **Rooms 19** (9 junior suites, 4 executive rooms, 8 no smoking). B&B €95pps, ss €35; SC 12.5%. Wheelchair access.

Restaurant: Like the rest of this lovely hotel, the dining room is bright, spacious and elegant. Decorated in soft, pretty shades of pale yellow and peach that contrast well with antique furniture - including a fine sideboard where plates and silver are displayed - the restaurant is in a prime position for taking full advantage of the view and makes a wonderful place to watch the light fading over the mountains and the sea. A warm welcome and quietly efficient service from staff who are clearly happy in their work greatly enhances the pleasure of dining - and the quality of food and head chef Jason Le Gear's cooking (in an appropriate country house style) are both very high. Excellent breakfasts are also served in the restaurant - home-made preserves are an especially delicious feature. Children welcome. **Seats 45.** No smoking restaurant. D 7.30-9 daily. Set D €47.50 house wine €24. Closed Dec-Mar. Amex, Diners, MasterCard, Visa, Laser. **Directions:** N59 from Galway. Turn left after Recess.

Clarenbridge — Oyster Manor Hotel

Hotel   Clarenbridge Co. Galway **Tel: 091 796777** Fax: 091 796770
Email: reservations@oystermanorhotel.com Web: oystermanorhotel.com

Family-owned by Ned and Julianne Forde, this modern hotel on the edge of Clarenbridge is popular for conferences and family celebrations (800/350 respectively) and the large bar at the back makes a focal point, with live music most nights. Rooms have all the necessary amenities and are comfortably furnished with modern facilities. Children free in parents' room up to 10; cot available without charge. No pets. **Rooms 26** (1 suite, 3 executive rooms, 3 no-smoking). B&B about €90pps. Wheelchair access. Closed 24-26 Dec. Amex, Diners, MasterCard, Visa. **Directions:** Main Limerick road, South East of Galway city. ◇

Clarenbridge — Paddy Burkes

Restaurant/Pub   Clarenbridge Co. Galway
Tel: 091 796226 Fax: 091 796016

Established in 1650 and still going strong, Paddy Burkes' internationally famous pub and seafood bar has been home to the Clarenbridge Oyster Festival for nearly half a century. The festival goes back to 1954, when a total of thirty four people attended, mostly Dubliners. Since then it has become an international event attracting over 10,000 visitors from Ireland and abroad - to consume over 50,000 oysters! The visitors book, which was started in 1959, reads like a Who's Who - an unbelievable array of the rich and famous. And that's not including the ones who "prefer not to be named". *The pub changed hands in 2000, but no significant changes have so far been made by the new owners. Bar Meals 12-10 daily. No smoking area; air conditioning; wheelchair access. Closed 24-25 Dec & Good Fri. Amex, MasterCard, Visa, Laser. **Directions:** Seven miles south of Galway city on Limerick Road.

Clarinbridge — The Old School House Restaurant

féile bia **N** Restaurant   Clarinbridge Co. Galway
Tel: 091 796898 Fax: 091 796117 Email: kenc@iol.ie

Kenneth Connolly's refurbished schoolhouse just off the Galway/Limerick road gives a good first impression, with its own garden (and parking) and the fine old stonework typical of the era giving it character. It's a bright, tall-windowed room with simple varnished tables lifted by quality china and linen napkins - and a warm welcome from friendly staff makes a good start. Menus are offered promptly, in the bar/reception area or at your table, and the range of dishes is wide - perhaps a dozen starters and as many as fifteen main course choices, with salads predominating in the first courses and fish main courses especially strong, although there will also be some attractive meat and poultry dishes (stuffed fillet of pork with apple compôte, sage & rosemary jus / breast of corn-fed chicken with roast vegetables & thyme) and a couple of vegetarian options. While not especially adventurous this is a restaurant steering a well-judged line between the all-year local market and summer visitors. Head chef Daire Hanrahan's skilful cooking makes the most of carefully sourced quality Irish produce (some local products, including oysters and black pudding, are highlighted on the menu) and classic dishes like black sole - beautifully fresh and served off the bone with butter, lemon & capers - are perfectly executed. Salad garnishes may be a little over-generous at times (perhaps because of an abundance in their own organic garden) but otherwise presentation is like the cooking, really good; service, from knowledgeable and attentive staff deserves special praise. The only disappointment is likely to be desserts, which can be very ordinary - perhaps the Irish cheeseboard (served with pear & raisin chutney) would be a better bet. **Seats 60** (private room 20), No smoking area. Toilets wheelchair accessible. Pianist some evenings. Not suitable for children after

3pm. D Tue-Sun, 6.30-10.30; L Sun lonly 12.30-2.30. Set D €37, Set Sun L €20 (à la carte L also available). House wine €17.50. Closed Mon, except bank hols; closed 1 Jan-14 Feb. Amex, MasterCard, Visa, Laser, Switch. **Directions:** 6 miles from Galway City, on N18.

Clifden — Abbeyglen Castle

Hotel   Sky Road Clifden Co. Galway **Tel:** 095 21201 Fax: 095 21797
Email: info@abbeyglen.ie Web: abbeyglen.ie

Set romantically in its own parkland valley overlooking Clifden and the sea, Abbeyglen is family-owned and run in a very hands-on fashion by Paul and Brian Hughes. It's a place that has won a lot of friends over the years and it's easy to see why: it's big and comfortable and laid-back - and there's a generosity of spirit about the place which is very charming. Complimentary afternoon tea for residents is a particularly hospitable speciality, served in a spacious drawing room or in front of an open peat fire in the relaxing, pubby bar, where many a late night is spent. Bedrooms (all with good bathrooms) are quite big and have been recently refurbished, as part of an ongoing improvement programme. Helipad. Garden. Pitch & putt. Snooker. Outdoor swimming pool. Pets permitted. Not suitable for children. Wheelchair accessible. **Rooms 38** (9 superior, 20 standard, all en-suite) Lift. B&B from about €80pps, ss about €30. Closed 6 Jan-1 Feb. Amex, Diners, MasterCard, Visa. **Directions:** About 300 yards out of Clifden on the Sky road, on the left. ◇

Clifden — Ardagh Hotel & Restaurant

féile bia Hotel   Ballyconneely Road Clifden Co. Galway **Tel:** 095 21384 Fax: 095 21314
Email: ardaghhotel@eircom.net Web: www.ardaghhotel.com

Beautifully located, overlooking Ardbear Bay, Stephane and Monique Bauvet's family-run hotel is well known for hospitality, comfort and good food. Public areas have style, too, in a gentle sort of way - not "decorated" but furnished in a homely style with good fabrics and classic country colours. Turf fires, comfortable armchairs and a plant-filled conservatory area upstairs all indicate that peaceful relaxation is the aim here. Bedrooms vary according to their position but are all well-furnished in a relaxed style with all the amenities required for a comfortable stay, and have been recently renovated. (Not all have sea views - single rooms are at the back with a pleasant countryside outlook, and have shower only). Bedrooms include some extra large rooms, especially suitable for families. Children welcome (under 5s free in parents' room, cot available without charge); pets permitted by arrangement. **Rooms 17** (3 suites, 4 shower only, all no smoking). B&B €82.50pps, ss €25.
Restaurant: The well-appointed restaurant is on the first floor and set up to take full advantage of the view, providing an appropriate setting for Monique's fine cooking, which specialises in local seafood. She makes imaginative use of local ingredients, including organic vegetables, in à la carte or nightly 5-course dinner menu offering plenty of choice - typically in a starter such as house marinated fresh wild salmon gravlax with a mustard & dill sauce, followed by a soup - Ardagh's fresh mussel chowder perhaps - and main course of Connemara lamb (with roasted celeriac wedges, perhaps, and red wine jus with rosemary & thyme) or lobster, various ways (€11.50 supplement). The dinner menu includes the choice of tea/herbal tea/coffees with home-made petits fours and is good value. A fairly priced wine list strong on old world wines, especially Bordeaux and Burgundy, offers a good choice of half bottles and a selection of magnums. **Seats 50**. No smoking area. (Light bar food, 11-5 daily. D 7.15-9.30 daily, Set D €45, à la carte also available; house wine €18; sc discretionary. Closed Nov-Mar. Amex, Diners, MasterCard, Visa, Laser. **Directions:** 2 km outside Clifden on Ballyconneely Road.

Clifden — Dolphin Beach Country House

Country House   Lower Sky Road Clifden Co. Galway **Tel:** 095 21204 Fax: 095 22935
Email: dolphinbeach@iolfree.ie Web: www.connermara.net/dolphinsbeachhouse

IRISH BREAKFAST AWARD - CONNAUGHT

Billy and Barbara Foyle's stunning beachside house is set in 14 acres of wilderness, which only serves to emphasise the style and comfort within. It started as an early 19th century farmhouse, now totally renovated and extended to include new bedrooms. Those familiar with the old Foyle magic will find it much in evidence here: Billy is brother to Paddy, of The Quay House and Eddie, who has been running the original family hotel in Clifden for many years and recently acquired Rosleague House at

Letterfrack from their sister Anne... Something they have in common is a talent for creating original interiors and, in this case, an example is Billy's unusual woodwork - bedheads, mirror frames, anything that takes his fancy - which is an important characteristic of the fresh style at Dolphin Beach. The have also spared no cost to ensure that the best materials are used throughout which creates wonderful feeling of quality: bedrooms are finished to a very high standard, with antique furniture pristine bedlinen, lovely bathrooms and underfloor heating. They grow their own organic vegetable too, and these, together with other local produce, notably seafood and Connemara lamb, are used fc residents' dinners which are served in a dining room overlooking the beach (ask about dinner whe booking your room). Their outstanding Breakfasts follow the same philosophy - you can even collec your own free-range eggs. Not suitable for children. No pets. Walking, garden. **Rooms 8** (4 showe only, all no smoking). B&B €44.44 pps, ss €20. Residents dinner 7.15-8pm, €37 (booking essential) MasterCard, Visa, Laser. **Directions:** Left off Skye Road from Clifden, approx 3 miles.

Clifden   Fire & Ice
Restaurant   Station House Courtyard Clifden Co. Galwa
        Tel: 095 22946 Email: fireandice@eircom.net Web: www.fireandice-food.cor

Gary Masterson and Winnie Lynch's attractive contemporary restaurant in the Station House Hote complex is now well-established as the most exciting restaurant in the area. While not a particularl large room, it is high-ceilinged, with big windows giving it an air of spaciousness, while lots of warr wood tones and colourful high-backed chairs combine to create a stylish backdrop for what the accurately call "fine dining without the formality and pretentiousness". Both are experienced anc well-travelled chefs, so the world cuisine they offer is especially appropriate and the cooking has ring of authenticity not always found in Irish restaurants following this style. Carefully source ingredients include a high proportion of specialist local produce and reflect a wide range o influences, in specialities like mussels with chilli, ginger, lemongrass, lime leaves & coconut mil and crispy duck with stirfry noodles, plum jus and sweet chilli sauce. Everything is cooked to order so service may sometimes seem a little slow (a note on the menu asks guests to say if they are ii a hurry before ordering). But their Sunday Brunch is the meal everone is talking about: fresh juice and smoothies, home-made pastries, traditional breakfast treats like eggs benedict or florentine anc a whole raft of dishes that are more lunch than breakfast - ploughman's lunch of Cashel Blue & cheddar with pickled red cabbage & onions with crusty bread and salad; minute steak sandwich or fresh ciabatta, with onion marmalade & home fries, pan-fried fish cakes with sweet chill mayonnaise. Quiet a few dishes, including a speciality dessert of warm chocolate cake with vanilla ice cream & orange sauce, are carried over from the evening menu. Brunch is good value (the mos expensive dish is only about €16, most are far less) and has built up a great following. A short bu interesting wine list includes some organic wines and several half bottles. **Seats 49**. No smoking restaurant; air conditioning. D Tue-Sat (also Sun in Aug), Sun Brunch 11.30-3.30. A la carte (average starter €7, average main course €18.50). House wine from €15. SC discretionary. Closed Mon, 2 wks Oct, Feb. Amex, Diners, MasterCard, Visa, Laser. **Directions:** Above Old Station House Bar, two minutes walk from town.

Clifden   Fogerty's
Ⓝ Restaurant   Market Street Clifden Co. Galway **Tel: 095 21427** Fax: 095 21427
                                                         Email: fogertys@irisheguide.com

This pretty thatched cottage is one of the most attractive little restaurants in Clifden, acting as a kind of magnet on a highly competitive street - which must be a big plus for chef Kieran Shaughnessy, who took over the lease last season. It's as pretty inside as out, with dining areas on three floors and happy, busy atmosphere. Menus offer a balanced selection of fairly traditional fare - steamed mussels, chicken liver paté and chowder are typical starters and Irish stew; steaks and seafood platter among the main courses - and are none the worse for that. Cooking can be a little variable, but there is a welcome generosity about the food, service is cheerful and capable - and visitors clearly enjoy both the ambience and the style of cooking, which offer a contrast to the contemporary scene. The shorter Early Bird dinner offers good value. **Seats 48** (private room 16). No smoking area. Toilets wheelchair accessible. Children welcome. D daily, 5.30-10. Early D €25 (5.30-7), otherwise à la carte. house wine €16.50. Closed Jan. Amex, MasterCard, Visa, Laser. **Directions:** Clifden town centre.

Clifden   Mitchell's
féile bia Restaurant   Market Street Clifden Co. Galway
                                                      Tel: 095 21867 Fax: 095 21770

This attractive and well-managed family-run restaurant offers efficient, welcoming service and very agreeable "good home cooking" all day, every day throughout a long season - and they have been doing so, with admirable consistency, since 1991. An all-day snack menu offers a wide range of lightish fare - everything from sandwiches and wraps to seafood chowder seafood tagliatelle; the international flavours are there (in snacks like Cajun chicken pannini and Thai chicken wrap, for example) but how refreshing it is to find old friends like deep-fried Gubbeen cheese and bacon & cabbage there amongst the home-made spicy fishcakes and fresh crab salad with home-made brown bread. There's some overlap onto an à la carte menu, which offers a judicious selection from the snack menu but a wider choice of main dishes, including traditional Irish stew and a range of seafood. This is a very fair place, offering honest food at honest prices: half dozen local oysters at €9, for example, and a main course of pan-seared scallops with spinach & mornay sauce, €21.50. **Seats 70.** No smoking area; air conditioning. Not suitable for children after 6 pm. Open daily, 12-10; L 12-6, D 6-10. A la carte. House wine €16. Closed Nov-Feb. Amex, MasterCard, Laser. **Directions:** Next to SuperValu Supermarket.

Clifden — O'Grady's

Restaurant · Market Street Clifden Co. Galway **Tel: 095 21450** Fax: 095 21976
Email: info@sunnybankhouse.com

O'Grady's was the first place to create a reputation for Clifden as a good food town and was one of Ireland's foremost seafood restaurants for many years. It is currently run by Shane O'Grady, who gave it a makeover in 2002, with a completely new pared-down interior to match a more contemporary menu - and provide a bright, uncluttered backdrop for the work of local artists who display their oil paintings, prints and sculptures here throughout the season. Head chef Niazi Lahdri has brought a very cosmopolitan look to menus which still offer plenty of seafood (mussels with coconut milk, garlic, sweet chilli and spring onions is their most popular dish and there are always daily fish specials) but also provides more alternatives - try the honey and soya pot-roast duckling with red cabbage, rôsti and redcurrant sauce, for example. Their aim is to do imaginative but basically simple, judiciously flavoured food and keep the atmosphere relaxed and informal - this they seem to be doing very well, backed up by friendly, efficient service under the supervision of restaurant manager Alice Coyle. Not suitable for children under 7. **Seats 55** (private room, 20). No smoking area. D Mon-Sat, 5.30-10.30; all à la carte, house wine from €16.50; sc discretionary. Closed Sun & Nov-Mar. Amex, MasterCard, Visa. **Directions:** While driving on one-way system, it's on the right hand side.

Clifden — Quay House

Accommodation · Beach Road Clifden Co. Galway **Tel: 095 21369**
Fax: 095 21608 Email: thequay@iol.ie Web: www.thequayhouse.com

In a lovely location - the house is right on the harbour, with pretty water views when the tide is in - The Quay House was built around 1820. It has the distinction of being the oldest building in Clifden and has also had a surprisingly varied usage: it was originally the harbourmaster's house, then a convent, then a monastery, was converted into a hotel at the turn of the century and finally, since 1993, has been enjoying its most recent incarnation as specialist accommodation in the incomparable hands of long-time hoteliers, Paddy and Julia Foyle. Airy, wittily decorated and sumptuously comfortable rooms include not only two wheelchair-friendly rooms but a whole new development alongside the original house - seven stunning studio rooms with small fitted kitchens and balconies overlooking the harbour. As in the older rooms, excellent bathrooms all have full bath and shower. Breakfast, including delicious freshly-baked breads and scones straight from the Aga, is served in the conservatory. Although officially closed in winter it is always worth inquiring. Children under 12 free in parents' room (cots available). No pets. **Rooms 14** (all with full bathrooms, 2 for disabled). B&B €77.50pps, ss €7.50. Closed Nov-mid Mar. Amex, MasterCard, Visa, Laser. **Directions:** 2 minutes from town centre, overlooking Clifden harbour - follow signs to the Beach Road.

Clifden — Rock Glen Country House Hotel

Hotel/Restaurant · Clifden Co. Galway **Tel: 095 21035** Fax: 095 21737
Email: rockglen@iol.ie Web: www.connemara-net/rockglen-hotel

Beautifully situated in quiet grounds well away from the road, Rock Glen was built in 1815 as a shooting lodge for Clifden Castle and enjoys views over a sheltered anchorage. Since 1973 it has been run by the Roche family as a delightful hotel in which the public rooms and some of the bedrooms have the full advantage of the view - indeed the whole hotel is very restful and comfortable, with a pleasing outlook from all windows. Rooms are furnished in country house style with good bathrooms (all have a full bath and over-bath shower) and amenities - some, such a tea/coffee trays, are not in the rooms but available on request. In addition to local activities fishing, pony trekking, golf - there's a putting green on site, also all-weather tennis and croquet indoors there are plenty of places to read quietly and a full size snooker table. Special interest shor breaks available, notably tutored painting holidays. Children welcome (under 3s free in parents room, cots available without charge). Pets permitted by arrangement, in some areas. **Rooms 26** (' suite, 2 junior suites). Wheelchair access. B&B €95pps, ss€40; sc 12.5%. Closed end Oct-mid Feb **Restaurant:** Traditionally furnished in country house style, the emphasis in this pleasant restauran is on comfort and relaxation. Five-course dinner menus are considerately also available a individually priced courses, making it semi à la carte - any starter chosen separately is €11, fo example, any main course €25); local ingredients, especially seafood, play a major role in a updated country house style and dishes like herb crusted roast rack of Connemara lamb with re cabbage, buttered spinach, glazed carrot& shallots with mint jus or pan-fried fresh king scallop with scallion mash and tomato & butter sauce are typical. Finish with tempting desserts - Irish strawberries in an almond tuile gratinated with sauternes sabayon, perhaps - or Irish farmhouse cheese & biscuits. Service is friendly and efficient and an excellent breakfast is served in the restaurant. **Seats 60:** No-smoking restaurant. D 7-9 daily; Set D €44.50, also à la carte; house win about €18; sc 12.5%. Toilets wheelchair accessible. Closed end Oct-mid Feb. Amex, MasterCard, Visa Laser. **Directions:** 1.5 miles from town of Clifden on Ballyconneely road.

Clifden   Seaview House

B&B   Clifden Co. Galway **Tel: 095 2144**
                  Email: sgriffin@eircom.net Web: www.connemara.net/seaview

Sheila Griffin's attractive house was built in 1825, using local quarried stone. Major renovation undertaken over the last four years have retained its character while adding modern comforts allowing her to offer stylish and comfortable accommodation. The most recent improvement ha been the addition of a conservatory, which provides a spacious room overlooking the garden, where guests can relax - and fruit from the garden is used in spiced fruit compôtes and preserves which appear at breakfast along with home-made breads, American-style pancakes with fresh fruit salsa and scrambled eggs with smoked salmon. A private carpark (5 spaces) is to be ready for the 200 season. **Rooms 6** (all shower only & no-smoking). B&B €42pps, ss €15. Closed Christmas week MasterCard, Visa. **Directions:** Left at square and a little down on right.

Clifden   Station House Hotel

Hotel   Clifden Co. Galway **Tel: 095 21699** Fax: 095 2166
                  Email: info@stationhousehotel.com Web: www.stationhousehotel.com

Built on the site of the late lamented railway station this large new hotel comes complete with leisure centre and conference/banqueting facilities 250/150). Public areas are impressively spacious and modern, while bedrooms are a good size, contemporary in style and comfortably furnished with ISDN lines as well as more usual amenities such as direct-dial phones, tea/coffee making and TV. The old Station House has become a themed bar and restaurant, run separately (see separate entry, Fire & Ice) and the complex includes an upmarket range of shops and boutiques. Leisure centre, indoor swimming pool, beauty salon. Children welcome (under 2s free in parents' room; cots available without charge; playroom). No pets. **Rooms 78** (2 junior suites, 8 executive, 48 no-smoking, 4 for disabled). Lift. B&B €100pps, ss €20. Closed 25 Dec. **Restaurant** - see separate entry: Fire & Ice. Amex, Diners, MasterCard, Visa, Laser. **Directions:** Follow N59 from Galway city 80 km.

Clifden   Sunnybank House

Guesthouse   Clifden Co. Galway **Tel: 095 21437** Fax: 095 21976
                  Email: info@sunnybankhouse.com Web: www.sunnybankhouse.com

Set in its own mature gardens, with panoramic views, Sunnybank is owned and run by the O'Grady family, of O'Grady's restaurant and has recently been refurbished throughout. At a reasonable price they offer very comfortably appointed en-suite bedrooms with good facilities (phone, tea/coffee-making, iron/trouser press and TV) and day rooms for guests' use. This comfortable and peaceful base also has lovely gardens, a heated outdoor swimming pool, sauna and tennis court. Not suitable for children under 7; no pets. **Rooms 8** (1 suite, 4 shower only, all no-smoking). B&B €55 pps, ss 15. Closed Nov-Mar. MasterCard, Visa, Laser. **Directions:** from Galway - right at Esso station & first left, house 200 m on right.

Clonbur — Ballykine House

Farmhouse   Clonbur Co. Galway **Tel: 092 46150** Fax: 092 46150
Email: ballykine@eircom.net Web: www.dirl.com

Comfortable accommodation and Ann Lambe's warm hospitality make this an appealing base for a peaceful holiday. There are guided forest walks from the house, angling on Lough Corrib, an equestrian centre (at nearby Ashford Castle) and bikes for hire locally. It's also well-placed for touring Connemara. Moderately priced rooms have TV, tea/coffee making facilities and hairdryers. No evening meals but the pubs and restaurants of Clonbur - including Burke's pub (Tel: 092-46175), which is renowned for its food (and music) - are all within walking distance. There's plenty of comfortable seating in the sitting room and conservatory for lounging and chatting, also a pool table - and a drying room for anglers. Garden. **Rooms 5** (4 with en-suite shower; 1 with private bath, restricted use), B&B €30, ss €10. Closed Nov-Apr.

Costello — Fermoyle Lodge

Country House   Costello Co. Galway **Tel: 091 786 111** Fax: 091 786 154
Email: fermoylelodge@eircom.net Web: www.ermoylelodge.com

One of Ireland's best-kept secrets, Nicola Stronach's delightful sporting lodge seems to enjoy the best of all possible worlds. Although only 29 miles from Galway (and six miles from the ferry to the Aran Islands), it's hidden from the road in one of the wildest and most remote parts of Connemara. Protected by mature woodland and shrubs, it has stunning lake and mountain views, with both salmon and sea trout fishing on the doorstep. All this and creature comforts too. The spacious, well-proportioned house has been sensitively renovated and beautifully furnished and decorated. Nicola has used the best of materials wisely, in a warm, low-key style that allows for every comfort without detracting from the wonderful setting that is its greatest attribute. Bedrooms are all very comfortable, with private bathrooms - and Nicola has yet another ace up her sleeve in the form of her French husband, Jean-Pierre Maire, who's a wizard in the kitchen as well as on the lough. A set dinner changes nightly - lemon sole en cocotte, quail on a bed of celery with wild mushrooms and poached pears with blackcurrant coulis & chantilly cream is a typical menu - is served for residents at 7.30pm; 24 hour notice is required and any particular dislikes or allergies should be mentioned on booking. Not suitable for children. Pets permitted in certain areas. Fishing, garden, walking. **Rooms 6** (all en-suite & no smoking). B&B €85pps, ss €25. D €35. No sc. Closed Nov-Mar. MasterCard, Visa. **Directions:** From Galway, take Clifden road (N59). At Oughterard turn left by Bridge Restaurant; Lodge is 10 miles along this road on right.

Craughwell — Raftery's, The Blazers Bar

Pub   Craughwell Co. Galway **Tel: 091 846708** Fax: 091 846004
Email: rafterys@eircom.net

Donald and Therese Raftery's famous family-run establishment (now in its third generation) is on the main Galway-Dublin road and is the meeting place for the well-known Galway Blazers Hunt, who are kennelled close by. It was completely refurbished in 2000 - and can make a handy stopping place: popular bar food is served every day 10 am-4.30pm. Bar Food:10.30-7.30 in winter (to 8.30 in summer), Sun 12.30-6. Set 3-course Menu, €14.50. Closed 25 Dec & Good Fri. MasterCard, Visa, Laser. **Directions:** On N6 between Loughrea and Galway.

Furbo — Connemara Coast Hotel

féile bia Hotel   Furbo Co. Galway **Tel: 091 592 108** Fax: 091 592 065
Email: sinnott@iol.ie Web: www.sinnotthotels.com

Like the other Sinnott hotels - Connemara Gateway and Brooks Hotel in Dublin - this beautifully located hotel is an attractive building which makes the best possible use of the site without intruding on the surroundings. Set on the sea side of the road, in its own extensive grounds, it is hard to credit that Galway city is only a 10 minute drive away. An impressive foyer decorated with fresh flowers sets the tone on entering, public areas are spacious and facilities are particularly good - a fine bar, two restaurants, a children's playroom and a leisure centre (which has a Canadian hot tub) among them. A policy of constant refurbishment and upgrading of facilities ensures that the hotel has a warm, well-cared for atmosphere. Conference/banqueting facilities (450/400) with secretarial back-up. A range of special breaks is available. Children under 3 free in parents' room cots available. No pets. **Rooms 112** (1 suite, 9 executive rooms). B&B from about €60pps, ss €32 Restaurant open 7-9.15 pm; bar food also available. Open all year. Amex, Diners, MasterCard, Visa Laser. **Directions:** 6 miles from Galway city on Spiddal Road. ◇

Headford — Lisdonagh House

Country House — Caherlistrane Headford Co. Galway **Tel: 093 31163** Fax: 093 3152€
Email: cooke@lisdonagh.com Web: www.lisdonagh.com

Situated about 15 minutes drive north of Galway city in the heart of hunting and fishing country Lisdonagh House is on an elevated site with beautiful views overlooking Lake Hackett. It is a lovely property, with large well-proportioned reception rooms, a fine staircase and luxurious bedrooms, furnished with antiques and decorated in period style, with marbled bathrooms to match. D €40, 7-9pm. House wine €20. Children welcome (under 2s free in parents' room, cots available without charge). Pets permitted in some areas. Equestrian, fishing, walking, cycling. **Rooms 10** (7 executive rooms, 3 shower only, 5 no-smoking, 2 for disabled) B&B €120 pps, ss €30. Wheelchair access. Closed end Oct-Easter. Amex, MasterCard, Visa, Laser, Switch. **Directions:** N17 to within 4 mles of Tuam, R33 to Caherlistrane.

Inishbofin — Day's Inishbofin House Hotel

Hotel — The Quay Inishbofin Co. Galway
Tel: 091 45809 / 095 45809 Fax: 095 45803

This hospitable family-run hotel beside the harbour has been first (and last) port of call for many visitors to the island over the years. Very extensive renovations were required and, at the time of going to press it is being re-built and expects to re-open June/July 2003. Visa, Laser. **Directions** Ferries to the island run regularly from Cleggan, with ticket offices in Clifden (regular buses between Clifden and Cleggan) and also at Kings of Cleggan. For bookings and enquiries, phone: 095 44642 or 095 21520. Credit card bookings are accepted.

Inishbofin — The Dolphin Restaurant

Restaurant — Middle Quarter Inishbofin Co. Galway **Tel: 095 45991** / 2
Fax: 045 45992 Email: inishshark@hotmail.com

Menus change throughout the day at Pat and Catherine Coyne's versatile little island restaurant which is a great asset to the island. At lunchtime - which considerately runs all afternoon - there's a range of drinks to comfort or refresh, depending on the weather, home-bakes (including hot waffles with maple syrup and cream) and made to order club or open sandwiches or simple hot meals, some with special child appeal. Evening menus are more substantial - lamb cutlets with boulangère potatoes and honey & rosemary jus, perhaps, or baked Connemara salmon with julienne of leek & butter sauce. **Seats 43.** No smoking restaurant. Toilets wheelchair accessible. Children welcome. L12.30-4.30; D 7-9. A la carte. Wines from €16.50. No sc. Closed Oct-Apr. MasterCard, Visa.

Kilcolgan — Moran's Oyster Cottage

🌱 Restaurant/Pub — The Weir Kilcolgan Co. Galway **Tel: 091 796 113** Fax: 091 796 503
Email: moranstheweir@eircom.net Web: www.moransoystercottage.com

This is just the kind of Irish pub that people everywhere dream about. It's as pretty as a picture, with a well-kept thatched roof and a lovely waterside location (with plenty of seats outside where you can while away the time and watch the swans floating by). It's also brilliantly well-run by the Moran family - and so it should be, after all they've had six generations to practise. They're famed throughout the country for their wonderful local seafood, including lobster, but especially the native oysters (from their own oyster beds) which are in season from September to April. Willie Moran is an ace oyster opener, a regular champion in the famous annual competitions held in the locality. Farmed Gigas oysters are on the menu all year. Then there's chowder and smoked salmon and seafood cocktail and mussels, delicious crab salads - and lobster, with boiled potatoes & garlic butter. Private conference room. Morans was the guide's 1999 Seafood Pub of the Year. **Seats 120** (privates rooms, 6 and 8) Meals

12 noon -10pm daily. House wine €17. Closed 24-26 Dec & Good Fri. Amex, MasterCard, Visa, Laser.
Directions: Just off the Galway-Limerick road, signed between Clarenbridge and Kilcolgan.

Kinvara   The Pier Head Bar & Restaurant

Pub/Restaurant   The Quay Kinvara Co. Galway **Tel: 091 638188**

Mike Burke took over this well-known harbourside establishment in the picturesque village of
Kinvara in 2000 and, with the help of an excellent Belgian chef Philippe de la Roux, has rapidly
built up and retained a reputation for serving the best food in the area. Seafood is, of course, the
main speciality - especially lobster - served in the shell with garlic butter and a side salad it makes
a meal for €33 - and the other thing they take pride in doing well is top of the range steak, using
local beef (totally traceable) which is slaughtered and butchered specially. As well as good food,
there's also music, all year: bands on on Friday & Saturday nights, usually also traditional on Sunday
afternoon. Children welcome. **Seats 100** (private room 50). No smoking area. Food served daily in
summer, 5-10 (Sun 12-8); off-season 5-8 (end Oct-May). A la carte. Closed 25 Dec & Good Fri.
Diners, MasterCard, Visa, Laser. **Directions:** Kinvara harbour front. ◇

Kinvara   Tully's

Pub   Kinvara Co. Galway **Tel: 091 637146**

Definitely a spot for traditional music, this is a real local pub in the old tradition, with a little
grocery shop at the front and stone-floored bar at the back. Tully's has a fine old stove in the bar
for cosy winter sessions, which is always a good sign (They also have a small enclosed garden with
a few parasoled tables for fine weather). Not a food place, although sandwiches, teas and coffees
are always available. Normal pub hours. Closed 25 Dec & Good Fri. **No credit cards**.

Leenane   Blackberry Café & Coffee Shop

Café   Leenane Co. Galway **Tel: 095 42240**

Sean and Mary Hamilton's lovely little restaurant is just what the weary traveller hopes to happen
on when touring or walking in this beautiful area. They're open through the afternoon and evening
every day during the summer, serving home-made soups and chowders (from about €3) with home-
baked bread, substantial snacks such as fish cakes and mussels (from about €8.75-€11.50) and
delicious desserts like rhubarb tart and lemon meringue pie with cream (all €3.75). Extra dishes like
hot smoked trout and a chicken main course might be added to the menu in the evening, but the
secret of the Blackberry Café's appeal is that they don't try to do too much at once and everything
is freshly made each day. **Seats 40**. Open 12-9 daily in high season. A la carte. House wine €13.97
(also 1/4 bottles, €3.75). Closed Tue in shoulder seasons. Closed 30 Sep-Good Fri. Visa, Laser,
Switch. **Directions:** On main street, opposite car park.

Leenane   Delphi Lodge

Country House   Leenane Co. Galway **Tel: 095 42222** Fax: 095 42296
                                        Email: delfish@iol.ie Web: www.delphilodge.ie

One of Ireland's most famous sporting lodges, Delphi Lodge was built in the early 19th-century by
the Marquis of Sligo. It is beautifully located in an unspoilt valley, surrounded by the region's highest
mountains (with the high rainfall dear to fisherfolk). Owned since 1986 by Peter Mantle - who has
restored and extended the original building in period style - the lodge is large and impressive in an
informal, understated way, with antiques, fishing gear and a catholic selection of reading matter
creating a stylish yet relaxed atmosphere. The dozen guest rooms are all quite different, but they
are en-suite (to be upgraded for 2003 season) and very comfortably furnished (with lovely lake and
mountain views). Dinner, for residents only, is taken at a long oak table. It is cooked by Cliodhna
Prendergast, who has "a range of dishes that is vast and eclectic" - some traditional, some 'nouveau',
some oriental. (To illustrate the point; home made game sausages are a speciality, also nephrops
from Killary Bay, with warmed rocket butter; reading the menu is a mouth-watering exercise.) The
famous Delphi Fishery is the main attraction, but people come for other country pursuits, painting,
or just peace and quiet. A billiard table, the library and a serious wine list (great bottles at a very
modest mark-up) can get visitors through a lot of wet days. Just across the road, four restored
cottages offer self-catering accommodation. Small conferences/banqueting (20/28). Not suitable for
children under 15. No pets. Garden, fishing, walking.* Wild game & fine wine weekends held in
winter (Oct/Nov). **Rooms 12** (all executive standard). B&B €90 pps, ss €45. Meals 1 pm and 8pm.
Residents L €15, D €45; House wine €19; SC discretionary Closed 20 Dec-10 Jan. MasterCard, Visa.
Directions: 8 miles northwest of Leenane on the Louisburgh road.

Leenane — Delphi Mountain Resort & Spa

🅝 Hotel — Delphi Leenane Co. Galway **Tel: 095 42208** Fax: 095 42303
Email: delphigy@iol.ie Web: www.delphiscape.com

Stunningly located on a 300-acre estate in one of the most beautiful and unspoilt areas of the west of Ireland, this luxurious retreat offers a wide range of health and fitness programmes designed as an antidote to the stresses of contemporary life - or, visited as an hotel, simply a place to relax and unwind - and it is extremely impressive at many levels. The building (which is to have a grass roof by 2003) is inspired by and designed to reflect the natural beauty and materials of the area: a big turf fire is lit in the reception area every morning, ensuring a warm welcome for newcomers and setting the tone for the whole enterprise. Storm-felled timber and local stone is used throughout, incorporating traditional craftsmanship and modern detailing - curving corridors echo ring forts, luxurious contemporary bedrooms are wood-themed (beech room, oak room etc), with complementary natural fabrics and furnishings underpinning the organic philosophy behind every aspect of this extraordinary place. Considered simply as an hotel offering understated luxury in uniquely beautiful surroundings, it has a great deal to offer. The bedrooms (especially those at the back) have beautiful views and all have either a window balcony or patio; furnished to a very high standard in a simple, clean-lined style and neutral colours, with central heating, direct dial phone, hair dryer, tea/coffee making trays, neat bathrooms and good contemporary paintings and pottery - and the suites have a loft bedroom over a downstairs living room. Normal hotel facilities include a full bar and fine dining restaurant on the first floor (open to non-residents), with big windows to take full advantage of the mountain view; good food is a major part of the plan - Canadian head chef Jeff McCourt is committed to using the best of local produce, including organic whenever possible (they have started to grow their own in a poly-tunnel in the grounds); short menus are strongly seasonal and the cooking style is contemporary Irish with some Canadian and occasional oriental influences; there's nothing at all penitential about dining here - there's no sense of the old-fashioned 'health farm' ethos of denial here, indeed enjoyment and relaxation are the aim. A light lunch (soup, salads, open sandwiches) is also available. Booking would be essential for dinner and a phone call to check availability/times for lunch would be wise. A brochure detailing the very wide range of facilities and therapies offered (both residential and day programmes) is available from the hotel; children can be accommodated at the adventure centre next door, providing an unusual choice for a family holiday, with much to offer different age groups. It is also an interesting and well-equipped centre for conferences and team building. Conference/banqueting (200/70). Equestrian, fishing, cycling, walking; beauty salon. **Rooms 22** (8 suites, 2 for disabled, all no smoking.) B&B €109, ss €44. Closed 16 Dec-16 Jan. Amex, MasterCard, Visa, Laser. **Directions:** From Galway take the N59 to Leenane - then 7 miles to Delphi.

Leenane — Killary Lodge

Accommodation — Leenane Co. Galway **Tel: 095 42276** Fax: 095 42314
Email: lodge@killary.com Web: www.killary.com

Situated on the shores of Killary harbour, Jamie and Mary Young's former hunting lodge has been renovated in a relaxed modern style and now offers a very comfortable place to stay in a beautiful location. Those with an interest in outdoor pursuits will get particular enjoyment from the many activities operating from here, but it also makes an excellent, moderately priced base for touring Connemara. Friendly staff, an informal atmosphere and home cooked evening meals are all part of the attraction and there is plenty of walking - and other activities such as water-skiing and kayaking, available on site - for the energetic. Conferences and corporate training are among the many programmes offered at this unusual establishment - contact the manager, Kathy Evans, for further details. Garden, tennis, walking, cycling. **Rooms 21** (12 shower only, 2 for disabled). B&B €53 pps, no ss. Residents D €25; house wine €16. Closed Dec-Jan. MasterCard, Visa, Laser. **Directions:** Off the N59, 3 miles outside the village of Leenane on theClifden Road.

Leenane — Portfinn Lodge

Restaurant/Accommodation — Leenane Co. Galway **Tel: 095 42265** Fax: 095 42315
Email: rorydaly@anu.ie Web: www.portfinn.com

There are few views in Ireland to beat the sight of the sun sinking behind the mountains over Killary Harbour. On a good evening that's something you can look forward to at Rory and Brid Daly's seafood restaurant, Portfinn Lodge. The dining area is in a room of the main house and an adjoining conservatory. The lobster tank at the entrance bodes well for a good meal - a high proportion of the menu is likely to be seafood: prawns, salmon, brill, turbot and many of their cousins make a nightly appearance. Rory's cooking style is classic: examples from a selection of specialities that are changed weekly include roast monk tail mode du patron (monkfish tail roasted whole in herbs, served with a mushroom & white wine sauce) and traditional roast half duckling à l'orange (half a Cavan ducklin, roasted & served with a port & orange sauce); there is also at least one vegetarian dish daily. Cooking is consistently good and portions generous, including a selection of side vegetables. Good brown bread comes with country butter, which is quite a feature in these parts, and there's always an Irish cheeseboard. Not suitable for children under 12. **Seats 35**. No smoking area. D 6.30-9 daily. A la carte; house wine from €17.50; sc discretionary. Closed 1 Nov-1 Apr.

Rooms: Modest but comfortable accommodation is offered in eight neat purpose-built en-suite rooms, all sleeping three and one with four beds; one room has wheelchair access. Pets permitted by arrangement. Fishing, walking. **Rooms 8** (all en-suite). B&B €35pps, ss €30, 10% sc. MasterCard, Visa. **Directions:** Midway between Westport and Clifden (N59).

Letterfrack — Kylemore Abbey Restaurant & Tea House

Restaurant   Kylemore Letterfracy Co. Galway **Tel: 095 41146** Fax: 095 41368
Email: info@kylemoreabbey.ie Web: www.kylemoreabbey.ie

Kylemore Abbey, with its stunning mountain and waterside setting, would make a dramatic location for any enterprise. But what the Benedictine nuns are doing here is truly astonishing. The abbey is not only home for the nuns but is also run as an international girls' boarding school. In addition, the nuns run a farm and a restored walled garden, which is open to the public. A short walk further along the wooded shore leads to the Gothic church, a miniature replica of Norwich cathedral. In a neat modern building beside the carpark is one of the country's best craft shops - and an excellent restaurant. Everything at this daytime self-service restaurant is made on the premises, and the range of wholesome offerings includes a good selection of hot and cold savoury dishes, including traditional beef & Guinness casserole, Irish stew and several vegetarian options - typically black eye bean casserole or vegetarian lasagne. Home baking is a special strength and big bowls of the nuns' renowned home-made jams are set up at the till, for visitors to help themselves. Beside them are neatly labelled jars to buy and take home. **Seats 240**. Meals daily 9.30-5.30. Closed Christmas week & Good Fri. (The Garden Tea House, in the restored walled garden, is open Easter-Hallowe'en, 10.30-5, using produce from the garden.) MasterCard, Visa, Amex, Laser. **Directions:** 2 miles from Letterfrack, on the N59 from Galway. ◇

Letterfrack — Oceans Restaurant

Ⓝ Restaurant   Derryinver Letterfrack Co. Galway **Tel: 095 43842**

The Curran family's pretty little restaurant close to Derryinver harbour is a useful place to know about if you're staying in the area or, if you are touring or walking nearby during the day, it's a pleasant place to break a journey. A short lunch menu offers a choice of soups - chowder perhaps, with home-baked brown bread - and a range of open sandwiches, including wild smoked salmon and fresh crabmeat (both about €7.50). Ordinary sandwiches too, plain or toasted, a few hot dishes, including Irish Stew (about €7.25), plus several desserts (chocolate fudge cake, about €3.50). A much wider range is offered in the evening, when the emphasis is understandably on seafood (Connemara crab with avocado & mango, fillet of cod with bacon & scallion mash) but there's also a choice of meats and poultry (including roast rack of lamb with rosemary & garlic, perhaps), served by hospitable and obliging staff. The early dinner menu is particularly good value. [Opening times not confirmed at time of going to press, please phone for details.] MasterCard, Visa. **Directions:** Overlooking Derryinver Bay, beside Oceans Alive sea life centre. ◇

Letterfrack — Pangur Bán

Ⓝ Restaurant   Letterfrack Co. Galway **Tel: 095 41243**
Email: pban@indigo.ie Web: www.pangurban.com

This simple, whitewashed roadside cottage has a tiny front garden and large carpark at the back; you enter directly into the larger of the two rooms used for the restaurant, which is unexpectedly bright and airy, with a raised wooden ceiling and plenty of light from the cottage door as well as windows. With whitewashed walls and an old fireplace its natural cottagey character remains, however, and table settings are appropriately simple. A relaxing evening with good home cooking and caring service is the aim and this they seem to achieve well. Cooking can be a little uneven, but dishes enjoyed on a recent visit included a very good rack of lamb (€23.50), perfectly cooked, and a vibrant side dish of stir-fried vegetables. But desserts are what Pangur Bán does best, so leave some room for a little indulgence from a choice of about ten, ranging from homemade icecreams and rhubarb fool through fresh fruit and ricotta sponge, chocolate pudding, fresh strawberries in balsamic vinegar and, perhaps, a tangy lime & lemon cheesecake. *Cookery classes available off-season. **Seats 50**. No smoking room D 6-9.30/10; daily in high season (Jul-Aug); 6 nights in shoulder seasons(Mar-May & Sep-Oct) close Mon; 5 nights low season (Nov-Dec) closed Sun & Mon. (A phone call to check opening times ar time except high season is advised.) A la carte. House wine about €14.50. Closed 24-25 Dec, 6 Jar 17 Mar. MasterCard, Visa. **Directions:** In Letterfrack village. ◇

Letterfrack   Rosleague Manor Hotel

Country House/Restaurant   Letterfrack Co. Galway **Tel:** 095 41101 Fax: 095 4116
Email: rosleaguemanor@eircom.net Web: www.rosleague.co

A lovely pink-washed Regency house of gracious proportions and sensitively handled modernisatior Rosleague looks out over a tidal inlet through gardens planted with rare shrubs and plants. Althoug the area offers plenty of activity for the energetic, there is a deep sense of peace and it's hard t imagine anywhere better to recharge the soul. The hotel recently changed hands within the Foyl family and is now run by Anne Foyle's nephew, Mark Foyle; considerable refurbishment wa completed before the hotel re-opened in spring 2001 and renovations are continuing on an ongoin basis. Childen welcome (cot available, €10; not under 4 in restaurant.) Garden, tennis, fishin walking. Pets permitted. **Rooms 20** (4 junior suites). B&B €95pps, ss €25. Food available all da from 9.30am. D 7.30-9.30 daily; Set D €42. House wine €18. Wheelchair access. Closed 1 Nov-1 Mar. Amex, MasterCard, Visa. **Directions:** On N59 main road, 7 miles north of Clifden.

Moyard   Rose Cottage

Farmhouse/B&B   Rockfield Moyard Co. Galway **Tel:** 095 4108.
Email: info@connemaratourism.or

This long-established farmhouse is situated on a working farm in a scenic location surrounded b the Twelve Bens mountains. John O'Toole, who is a qualified chef, took over management in 200 (with his mother Mary, who ran the business for many years, still lending a hand when necessary) There's a sitting room with an open turf fire and comfortable bedrooms have tea/coffee making tray and hair dryers. John uses local produce, including lamb from the farm and herbs and vegetable from their own garden in both lunch and dinner menus, which are open to non-residents. Childre welcome. No pets. **Rooms 6** (all en-suite, shower only). B&B €26pps, no ss. Early D €19.50 (5 6pm), otherwise Set D €35, also à la carte. L à la carte. House wine €15. Open all year. Visa MasterCard. **Directions:** Main Westport Rd,6 miles from Clifden.

Moycullen   Moycullen House & Restaurant

féile bia Country House/Restaurant   Moycullen Co. Galway **Tel:** 091 555621 Fax: 091 555 56
Email: info@moycullen.com Web: www.moycullen.cor

Overlooking Lough Corrib, and set peacefully in 30 acres of rhododendrons and azaleas, Moyculle House was built as a sporting lodge in the arts and crafts style at the beginning of the century an has been run as a country house for some years by the Casburn family. When Richard and Louise Casburn decided to open this very professionally run restaurant in the house in 1998, they added a new name to the list of must-visits in the area. A great deal of thought and work went into gettin the changes right, and the effort has paid off handsomely. Louise looks after front-of-hous beautifully and Richard is the chef - his menus are ambitious but he offers a sensibly short à la cart with daily extras, including seafood. Having worked with Gerry Galvin at nearby Drimcong House i its heyday and been influenced by its philosophy, Richard seeks out quality ingredients, which he treats with due respect and very pleasing results. The style is fairly modern but based on classics Well-balanced and fairly priced menus could include starters of sautéd scallops & Parma ham sala and grilled goats cheese on a garlic & tomato brioche while typical main courses could include turbo as one of the daily specials and, from the carte, roast loin of Connemara lamb with roasted shallots spinach and potato - simply delicious. (Moycullen was selected for the Bord Bia Irish Lamb Awarc in 2001). Presentation is not overworked and cooking is consistently excellent. Banqueting (45) **Seats 40**. D Thur-Tue 6.30-9.30; L Sun only, 4-5.30 pm. D à la carte; Set Sun L from €21. Hous wine €18. SC discretionary. Restaurant not suitable for children after 7pm. Closed Wed.

Accommodation: Large bedrooms furnished with antiques all have private baths and there's a spacious residents' sitting room with an open log fire. Children welcome; under 5s free in parents room, cot/extra bed available without charge; baby-sitting by arrangement. No pets. Garden, walking. **Rooms 3** (1 superior room, all no-smoking). B&B €45.50 pps, ss€15. House closec Christmas & 8 Jan-10 Mar. Amex, MasterCard, Visa, Laser. **Directions:** N59 Galway to Moycullen; a Cross Roads, take left turn onto Spiddal Road, signed on left after about 1.5km.

Moycullen   White Gables Restaurant

féile bia Restaurant   Moycullen Co. Galway **Tel: 091 555 744** Fax: 091 556 004
     Email: info@whitegables.com Web: www.whitegables.com

Kevin and Ann Dunne have been running this attractive cottagey restaurant on the main street of Moycullen since 1991 and it's now on many a regular diner's list of favourites. Open stonework, low lighting and candlelight (even at lunch time) create a soothing away-from-it-all atmosphere. Kevin sources ingredients with care and offers weekly-changing dinner and à la carte menus and a set Sunday lunch (which is enormously popular and has two sittings). Cooking is consistently good in a refreshingly traditional style and, while there is much else to choose from - roast half duckling with orange sauce is one of their most popular dishes - fresh fish is the main speciality, including lobster (served thermidor, perhaps) from their own tank and other classics like sole on the bone, scallops mornay, monfish panfried in garlic butter and poached turbot in martini sauce. Well-cooked seasonal vegetables are always particularly enjoyable at this fine restaurant and their roast beef, as served for Sunday lunch, is like no other. Good desserts, including home-made ices, and friendly, efficient service all help make this one of the area's finest restaurants. **Seats 45**. Children welcome. No smoking area; air conditioning. D 7-10 (daily in high season), L Sun only, 12.30-3. Set D €35, also à la carte; Set Sun L €21. House wine about €18; sc discretionary. Closed Mon, except Jul-Aug; 24 Dec-14 Feb. Amex, MasterCard, Visa, Laser. **Directions:** On N59 in Moycullen village, 8 miles from Galway city.

Oranmore   Galway Bay Golf & Country Club Hotel

Hotel   Oranmore Co. Galway **Tel: 091 790 500** Fax: 091 790 510
     Email: cro@lynchotels.com Web: www.lynchotels.com

This rather handsome modern hotel, just eight miles from Galway city, looks out over an 18-hole championship golf course (designed by Christy O'Connor Jnr.) towards Galway Bay ; the location is lovely, it has a wide range of facilities for both business and leisure and is potentially one of the pleasantest hotels in the area. Public areas include an impressively spacious lobby, large bar and a well-appointed restaurant with imaginative decor - all have views. Generous-sized bedrooms, which include six for wheelchair users and a high proportion of executive suites, are comfortably furnished with all the necessary facilities and many have lovely views across the bay, although maintenance and routine refurbishment is not always up to standard. However, prices are quite moderate and special packages, especially, give good value on both golf and non-golfing breaks. Conference/banqueting (275/250); business centre. Children welcome. No pets. **Rooms 92** (53 suites, 6 rooms for disabled). B&B £75 pps, ss £26. Golf (18), garden, walking Open all year. Amex, Diners, MasterCard, Visa, Laser. **Directions:** Turn left in Oranmore off main Galway - Limerick road (N18). Hotel is signposted.

Oughterard   Corrib Wave Guesthouse

Guesthouse   Portcarron Oughterard Co. Galway **Tel: 091 552147** Fax: 091 552736
     Email: ewh@gofree.indigo.ie Web: www.corribwave.com

A fisherman's dream, Michael and Maria Healy's unpretentious waterside guesthouse offers warm family hospitality, comfortable accommodation, an open turf fire to relax by and real home cooking. All rooms have phone, tea/coffee-making, TV, radio and a double and single bed; some are suitable for families. Best of all at Corrib Wave is the location - utter peace and tranquillity. Golf and horseriding nearby and everything to do with fishing organised for you. **Rooms 10** (all en-suite). B&B €35. Closed 20 Dec-2 Jan. MasterCard, Visa. **Directions:** From Galway, signed from N59, 1 km before Oughterard.

Oughterard   Currarevagh House

Country House   Oughterard Co. Galway **Tel: 091 552312** Fax: 091 552731
     Email: currarevagh@ireland.com Web: www.currarevagh.com

Tranquillity, trout and tea in the drawing room - these are the things that draw guests back to the Hodgson family's gracious, but not luxurious early Victorian manor overlooking Lough Corrib. Currarevagh, which was built in 1846 as a wedding present for Harry Hodgson's great, great, great grandfather, is set in 150 acres of woodlands and gardens with sporting rights over 5,000 acres. Guests have been welcomed here for over half a century and the present owners, Harry and June Hodgson, are founder members of the Irish Country Houses and Restaurants Association (known as the Blue Book). Yet, while the emphasis is on old-fashioned service and hospitality, they are adamant that the atmosphere should be more like a private house party than an hotel, and their restful rituals underline the differences: the day begins with a breakfast worthy of its Edwardian origins, laid out on the sideboard in the dining room; lunch may be one of the renowned picnic hampers required by sporting folk. Then there's afternoon tea, followed by a leisurely dinner. Fishing is the ruling passion, of course - notably brown trout, pike, perch and salmon - but there are plenty of other country pursuits to assist in building up an appetite for June's good home cooking, all based on fresh local produce. Not suitable for children. Garden, walking, tennis. **Rooms 15** (all en-suite). B&B about €88, ss about €32. SC10%. Residents D €35, at 8pm. Wines from €15. Closed 20 Oct-1 Apr. MasterCard, Visa, Laser. **Directions:** Take N59 to Oughterard. Turn right in village square and follow Glann Road for 4 miles.

Oughterard — River Run Lodge

Restaurant/Guesthouse | Glann Road Oughterard Co. Galway **Tel: 091 552697** Fax: 091 55669
Email: riverrun@indigo.ie Web: www.connemara.net/riverrunlodge

Tom and Anne Little's modern guesthouse and restaurant is quietly located in landscaped gardens just outside the village of Oughterard, on the banks of the Owenriff River. A welcoming fire in the reception area sets a caring note that is evident throughout the house, especially in the thoughtful planning of spacious bedrooms which all have exceptional facilities including minibar, hospitality tray, satellite television, radio, trouser press with iron and writing desk - there's even a suite, The Corrib overlooking the back garden, it has a double and single bed, comfortable chairs, a separate dressing room and separate bath and shower. A ground floor room beside the front door has less privacy than others. **Rooms 8** (1 suite, 3 shower only, all no smoking). B&B about €50pps. Closed Nov-Jan.
Restaurant: The well-appointed restaurant is in the prime spot, towards the back of the house and overlooking maturing gardens and the little river - and dinner is likely to be the highlight of your visit. Ingredients are carefully sourced and everything is freshly prepared and cooked to order. There's a shortish à la carte menu, with half a dozen choices on each course and the style is modern international. Delicious starters typically include crispy duck wontons with spring onions, cucumber & hoi sin sauce and crab claws & chilli butter served with linguini, followed perhaps by medallions of prime Irish beef with boxty & wild mushroom gratin or duo of hake and cod with nutmeg-scented spinach & tomato ragoût. Finish with a special dessert such as crème brulée with rum & raisin ice cream, perhaps, or an Irish coffee. Not surprisingly this little gem is popular with locals as well as resident guests, so booking is required. **Seats 32.** D Mon-Sat, 6-9. A la carte. House wine from €17. Closed Sun. MasterCard, Visa, Amex, Diners, Laser. **Directions:** In Oughterard village take turning for Glann Road - it's a few hundred yards down on the right.

Oughterard — Sweeney's Oughterard House

Hotel | Oughterard Co. Galway **Tel: 091 552207**
Fax: 091 552161 Email: phiggins@iol.ie

The Sweeney-Higgins family have owned and run this attractive creeper-clad old hotel for several generations. Prettily situated opposite the river and surrounded by mature trees (on the Clifden side of the town), it is genuinely old-fashioned with comfortable, cottagey public rooms furnished with antiques - a very pleasant place to break a journey. (Very acceptable light food is served in the bar during the day.) Bedrooms vary considerably - some have four-posters. Fishing is the main attraction, but there are plenty of other outdoor pursuits including the gentle pleasure of taking tea on the lawn. Closed about 22 Dec-mid-Jan. **Directions:** From Galway : through Oughterard, across river, on right. ◇

Portumna — Shannon Oaks Hotel & Country Club

féile bia Hotel | St. Josephs Rd Portumna Co. Galway **Tel: 0509 41777** Fax: 0509 41357
Email: sales@shannonoaks.ie Web: www.shannonoaks.ie

Situated near the shores of Lough Derg and adjacent to the 17th century Portumna Castle and estate (with recently restored gardens), this attractive, privately-owned hotel opened in 1997. The interior is spacious - a large lobby is quite impressive, with polished wooden floor, faux-marble pillaring featuring a winter treescape and ample (if clearly well-used) seating in contemporary style, while other public rooms include a warm-toned restaurant, which can be opened out in summer, and a cosy, pub-like bar. It's a good choice for business and corporate events - bedrooms have air conditioning and fax/modem lines as standard, conference and meeting facilities are designed for groups of all sizes, with full back-up services. Off-duty delegates will find plenty to do too, a fine leisure centre on-site has an air-conditioned gymnasium as well as a swimming pool and ancillary services and nearby activities include river cruising, fishing, golf, horseriding, cycling and clay pigeon shooting. Conference/banqueting(600/350). Children welcome (under 5s free in parents' room). No pets. **Rooms 63** (3 suites, 4 no smoking, 2 for disabled). B&B from about €73 pps ss about €25. Open all year. Amex, Diners, MasterCard, Visa, Laser. **Directions:** Situated on St Joseph Road, Portuma. ◇

Recess — Ballynahinch Castle Hotel

Hotel

Recess Co. Galway **Tel: 095 31006** Fax: 095 31085
Email: bhinch@iol.ie Web: www.ballynahinch-castle.com

Renowned as a fishing hotel, this crenellated Victorian mansion enjoys a most romantic position in ancient woodland on the banks of the Ballynahinch River. It is impressive in scale and relaxed in atmosphere - a magic combination which, with a high level of comfort and friendliness (and an invigorating mixture of residents and locals in the bar at night) all combine to bring people back. Renovations and extensions have recently been undertaken, with great attention to period detail, a policy also carried through successfully in furnishing both public areas and bedrooms. Views over the river make a lovely setting for head chef Robert Webster's fine meals based on the produce of the area - including excellent breakfasts to give you a good start ahead of a day's fishing or touring the area. (Ballynahinch was the Connaught winner of Guide's Denny Irish Breakfast Awards in 2002.) The bar food is consistently good too - a great place to drop into for a bite when touring Connemara. Facilities for small conferences (24); Fishing, cycling, walking; garden, tennis. Children welcome (under 3s free in parents' room; cots available without charge). No pets. **Rooms 40** (3 suites, 4 no smoking). B&B from €95 pps, ss €26. Restaurant open daily, D only 6.30-9 (Set D €42), house wine €20. Bar meals 12.30-3 & 6.30-9 daily. SC 10%. Closed Christmas & Feb. Amex, Diners, Visa. **Directions:** N59 from Galway left after Recess (Roundstone Rd), 2 km.

Recess — Lough Inagh Lodge

Hotel

Recess Co. Galway **Tel: 095 34706** Fax: 095 34708
Email: inagh@iol.ie Web: www.loughinaghhotel.ie

Maire O'Connor's former sporting lodge on the shores of Lough Inagh makes a delightful small hotel with a country house atmosphere. It has large, well-proportioned rooms, interesting period detail and lovely fireplaces with welcoming log fires, plus all the modern comforts. Public areas include two drawing rooms, each with an open fire, a lovely dining room - the Finnisglen Room) with deep green walls and graceful spoonback Victorian mahogany chairs (non-residents welcome when there is room)- and a very appealing bar with a big turf fire and its own back door and tiled floor for wet fishing gear. Bedrooms, some with four-posters, are all well-appointed and unusually spacious, with views of lake and countryside. Walk-in dressing rooms lead to well-planned bathrooms and tea/coffee-making facilities are available in rooms on request. While it has special appeal to sportsmen, Lough Inagh is only 42 miles from Galway and makes a good base for touring Connemara. Walking, cycling, golf and pony trekking all nearby; garden. Off-season breaks offer especially good value. Small conferences (15). Children welcome (under 4s free in parents' room, cots available without charge). Pets permitted. **Rooms 12** (5 junior suites, 7 executive); B&B €107 pps, ss €20. Restaurant open daily 7-9 (reservations required), Set D €38; house wine €20; Bar meals 12.30-4 & 7-9 daily. SC10%. Closed mid Dec-mid Mar. Amex, Diners, MasterCard, Visa. **Directions:** From Galway city travel on N59 for 40 miles. Take Right N344 in Recess. Right for Lough Inagh Lodge.

Renvyle — Renvyle House Hotel

féile bia Hotel/Restaurant

Renvyle Co. Galway **Tel: 095 43511** Fax: 095 43515
Email: renvyle@iol.ie Web: www.renvyle.com

In one of the country's most appealingly remote and beautiful areas, this famous Lutyens-esque house has a romantic and fascinating history, having been home to people as diverse as a Gaelic chieftan and Oliver St John Gogarty - and becoming one of Ireland's earliest country house hotels in 1883. Although it was in a state of decline for some time, recent (and continuing) investment is gradually bringing this magic place back to its old self. It is approached via a stunning scenic drive along a mountain road with views down into a blue-green sea of unparalleled clarity. However, once reached, the hotel seems to be snuggling down for shelter and has only limited views. This sheltered feeling is reinforced by the cosy atmosphere of the original building, with its dark beams, rug strewn floors and open fires - and a snug conservatory where guests can survey the garden and landscape beyond from a comfortable vantage point. Photographs and mementoes recording visits from the many famous people who have stayed here - Augustus John, Lady Gregory, Yeats and Churchill among them - keep guests happily occupied for hours, but there is plenty to distract you from this enjoyable activity. There's a heated outdoor swimming pool and other on-site activities include tennis, trout fishing, golf (9 hole) and croquet - while the surrounding area offers more challenging activities including archaeolgical expeditions, horse riding, hill walking, scuba diving and sea fishing. Just loafing around is perhaps what guests are best at here, however, and there's little need to do much else. Head chef Tim O'Sullivan looks after the inner man admirably in lovely dinners featuring local seafood and Connemara produce, including Renvyle rack of lamb, local lobster and game in season - and the hotel's bar food is also excellent. All this, plus the scent of a turf fire and a comfortable armchair, can be magic. Continuing refurbishment and improvements have now brought all bedrooms up to a high standard and three new suites were opened in 2002. Special breaks (midweek, weekend and bank holiday are very good value and Renvyle makes an excellent conference venue. (conference/banqueting 150/180); business centre, secretarial services. Children welcome (cots available; crèche, playroom, children's playground, children's tea). Archery, all-weather tennis court, clay pigeon shooting, croquet, lawn bowls, snooker. **Rooms 68** (5 suites, 1 junior suite, 3 executive, 10 no smoking, 3 for disabled). B&B about €95, ss about €32, SC 10%. Restaurant open 7-9.30 daily (Set D €40). Bar lunch, 12-3. Closed Jan. Amex, Diners, MasterCard, Visa, Laser. **Directions:** 12 miles north of Clifden.

Roundstone   O'Dowd's

Pub
Roundstone Co. Galway **Tel: 095 35809**
Fax: 095 35907 Email: odowds@indigo.ie

The O'Dowd family have been welcoming visitors to this much-loved pub overlooking the harbour for longer than most people care to remember - and, although there are some new developments from time to time, the old bar is always the same. It's one of those simple places, with the comfort of an open fire and good pint, where people congregate in total relaxation. A reasonably priced bar menu majoring in seafood offers sustenance or, for more formal meals, the restaurant next door does the honours. All day food also available at the adjacent family-run coffee shop. Own parking. Meals 11.30-9.30 daily. Closed 25 Dec, 3-6pm in winter & some bank hols. [Times not confirmed at time of going to press.] Amex, MasterCard, Visa. **Directions:** On harbour front in Roundstone village. ◇

Tuam   Cré-na-Cille

 Restaurant
High Street Tuam Co. Galway **Tel: 093 28232**
Fax: 093 28232 Email: crenacille@hotmail.com

Cathal and Sally Reynolds' consistently excellent restaurant in Tuam makes a fine stopping place en-route to Galway city or Connemara but, as it is deservedly popular with the locals both at lunchtime and in the evening, booking is strongly advised. Evenings are a little more formal and the setting softer, but the common link is Euro-Toques chef Cathal Reynolds' confident use of local ingredients in generous food at remarkably keen prices. Wide-ranging menus - set lunch, early evening special, set dinner and à la carte - offer a wide range of seafood, meats, poultry and game in season: delicious specialities regularly on the menu include a starter of John Begley's black pudding with apple and onion in a balsamic sauce, and main course of herb-crusted rack of Connemara mountain lamb in a light red wine sauce, while vegetarian dishes might include a roast vegetable & pasta bake with mozzarella in a spicy tomato & nut sauce. Lunchtime menus, which are particularly good value, include a 2-course light lunch such as chowder & brown bread folowed by courgette & mushroom quiche with side salad - just right for a busy weekday. Always an inventive chef, Cathal was the joint winner of the Guide's 2001 Creative Seafood Dish Award (together with Mike O'Grady of O'Grady's on the Pier, Barna). Another nice feature of the restaurant is a customer-friendly wine/drinks list, which offers an exceptional range of whiskeys and after-dinner drinks, including nearly thirty Irish whiskeys. Arrangement with nearby carpark. Children welcome to 7.30 pm. **Seats 45** (private room 30). No-smoking area; air conditioning. L&D Mon-Sat, Early D (5.45-6.30pm). À la carte available at L&D. House wine from about €15.25. No SC. Closed Sun, 24-28 Dec & all bank hols. Amex, Diners, MasterCard, Visa, Switch. **Directions:** 1200 mtrs from square, opposite old churchyard.

Tuam   Finns Bar & Restaurant

 Pub
Milltown Tuam Co. Galway
Tel: 093 51327 Email: johnfinn.indigo.ie

John and Lucy Finn's restaurant is on the river, in a charming little award-wining tidy town a few miles north of Tuam - a welcome sight for hungry travellers between Galway and Sligo. John cooks an eclectic mix of international (Caesar salad, chicken korma, tagliatelle house style) and traditional (prawn cocktail, steaks, honey roasted duck) dishes - reasonably priced and served in a relaxed atmosphere. The cooking is sound, it's good value for money and the small village setting - where everyone seems to know someone at another table - makes a welcome change from busy towns. Children welcome, but not after 7 pm. **Seats 60** (Private room 24); no smoking area, air conditioning. DTue-Sun, 5-9pm. A la carte, house wines from €13.33. Service discretionary. Closed Mon, 25 Dec & Good Fri. Children welcome. [?Times not confirmed at time of going to press.] Visa, Laser. **Directions:** 8 miles from Tuam, Main N17 to Sligo. ◇

COUNTY KERRY

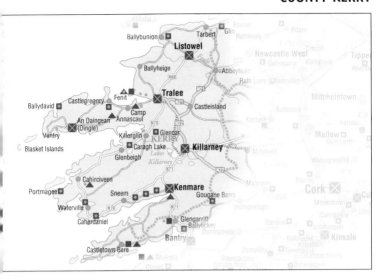

It's not easy, being Kerry. This magnificent county in the far southwest has Ireland's highest mountains, and certain favoured areas also have our longest-lived citizens. Then, too, it's a region which has long been a global pioneer in the hospitality and tourism business. So visitors inevitably arrive with high expectations.

Kerry, however, can face the challenge. This magnificent county really is the Kingdom of Kerry. Everything is king size. For not only has Kerry mountains galore - more than anywhere else in Ireland - but there's a special quality to Carrantuohill, the highest of all.

By international standards, this loftiest peak of MacGillicuddy's Reeks (try pronouncing it "mackil-cuddy") may not seem notable at just 1038 m. But when you sense its mysterious heights in the clouds above a countryside of astonishing beauty, its relative elevation is definitely world league.

And that beauty of the lower countryside sweeps out into Kerry's fabulous coastline, and up into Kerry's mountains as well. They're beautiful, and remarkably varied with it. So, in the upland stakes, Kerry has quantity and quality.

But these days, spectacular scenery isn't enough on its own. Like other leading visitor destinations, Kerry is well aware of the need to provide accessible entertainment and an increasing choice of places with cultural and historical interest. A pace setter in this is the Kerry County Museum in Tralee, which literally scaled new heights in 2002 by persuading Sir Edmund Hillary, the conqueror of Everest, to visit Ireland to officially open an exhibition about local man Tom Crean, who played a leading role in Shackleton's expedition to the Antarctic in 1914.

That Kerry should have produced someone of the calibre of Tom Crean tells us much about the place. He came from the little village of Annascaul, and when he had finished with adventuring, he returned to Annascaul and opened the South Pole Inn.

Local Attractions and Information

Beaufort Hotel Dunloe Castle Gardens	064 44583
Castleisland Crag Cave	066 41244
Dingle Ocean World	066 52111
Dunquin Great Blasket Centre	066 9156444/9156371
Farranfore Kerry International Airport	066 9764644
Glencar Into the Wilderness Walking Tours (May-Sep)	066 60104
Kenmare Walking Festivals	064 41034
Kenmare Heritage Centre	064 41233
Killarney Muckross House, Gardens & Traditional Farm	064 31440
Killarney Tourism Information	064 31633

Killorglin Kerry Woollen Mills	064 44122
Killorglin Puck Fair (ancient festival), mid-August	066 9762366
Lauragh Dereen Gardens	064 83103
Listowel St John's Art Centre	068 22566
Listowel Writers' Week (June)	068 21074
Tralee Kerry County Museum	066 7127777
Tralee Rose of Tralee Festival (late August)	066 7123227
Tralee Siamsa Tire Arts Centre	066 7123055
Valentia Island The Skellig Experience	066 9476306

Annascaul   The South Pole Inn

Pub   Annascaul Co. Kerry **Tel: 066 57388** / 57477

Annascaul, on the Dingle peninsula, is one of the most-photographed villages in Ireland – mainly because of the brilliantly colourful and humorous frontage painted onto his pub by the late Dan Foley (which is still a fine pub). Nearby, The South Pole, which is down at the lower end of the street is equally interesting - the name becomes clear when you realise there is a connection with the great Irish explorer Tom Crean. As well as being a delightful, well-run pub, The South Pole is full of fascinating Shackleton/Crean memorabilia. Closed 25 Dec & Good Fri. ◇

Ballybunion   Harty - Costello Townhouse Bar & Restaurant

Guesthouse   Main St. Ballybunion Co. Kerry **Tel: 068 27129** Fax: 068 27489
                                    Email: hartycostello@eircom.net Web: www.hartycostello.com

Although styled a townhouse in the contemporary mode, Davnet and Jackie Hourigan's welcoming town centre establishment is really an inn, encompassing all the elements of hospitality within its neatly painted and flower bedecked yellow walls, albeit at different times of day. Spacious, well-maintained bedrooms have not only television, direct dial phones, tea & coffee-making facilities and hair dryer, but also comfortable chairs and curtains thoughtfully fitted with blackout linings to keep out intrusively early summer light. There's also a pleasant lounging area between the accommodation and the evening restaurant (also on the first floor) and a choice of no less than three bars in which to unwind. Seafood is the speciality in the restaurant, where both table d'hôte and à la carte menus are offered, complemented by an extensive wine list. It all adds up to a relaxing and hospitable base for a golfing holiday, or for touring the south-west. Children welcome (under 12s free in parents' room). No pets. **Rooms 8** (all en-suite & no-smoking). B&B €65pps, ss €15. Bar meals, Mon-Sat, 12-6.30. No food on Sun; establishment closed end Oct-Apr. Amex, MasterCard, Visa, Laser. **Directions:** 50 miles from Limerick N69 40 miles from Killarney.

Ballybunion   Iragh Ti Connor

Hotel   Main Street Ballybunion Co. Kerry **Tel: 068 27112** Fax: 068 27787
                                    Email: iraghticonnor@eircom.net Web: www.golfballybunion.com

The name, which translates as "the inheritance of O'Connor", says it all: what John and Joan O'Connor inherited was a 19th century pub with potential and, thanks to their scrupulous attention to detail when planning and sourcing materials like real slates and wooden windows for its transformation, their inheritance has now been transformed into a fine establishment with exceptionally large, comfortable bedrooms. All rooms have been carefully refurbished and furnished with antiques to complement the convenience of satellite television, direct dial phones and generous bathrooms with cast-iron tubs and power showers - and many rooms even have working fireplaces, where fires can be lit on request. Public areas, which include the original public bar, a lounge bar and a fine dining restaurant with a baby grand to add to the atmosphere, are also generous in scale, and furnished with style and individuality. Golfing holidays are a serious attraction here and Iragh Ti Connor is fast establishing a reputation as one of the best places to stay on the discerning golfers' circuits. Food available daily, from 5.30. **Rooms 17** (3 junior suites, 14 superior rooms, all no-smoking). B&B €95 pps, ss €55. Closed 23-26 Dec. Amex, MasterCard, Visa. **Directions:** Opposite statue of Bill Clinton.

Ballybunion   Teach de Broc

Guesthouse   Links Road Ballybunion Co. Kerry **Tel: 068 27581** Fax: 068 27919
                                    Email: teachdebroc@eircom.net Web: www.ballybuniongolf.com

You don't have to play golf to appreciate this highly popular guesthouse, but it certainly must help as it is almost within the boundaries of the famous Ballybunion links. Aoife and Seamus Brock offer a high standard of comfort, with direct dial phones, TV and tea/coffee-making in all rooms and there is a commitment to constant upgrading and improvement: plans for 2003 include not only a new sitting room, dining room and another four new bedrooms (in addition to the four added last year, but also a lift. But, however comfortable and well-located this exceptional guesthouse may be, it's the laid-back and genuinely hospitable atmosphere that really gets them coming back for more. Internet for guests' use. Horse riding available nearby. Own parking. Garden. Not suitable for children. Wine licence. **Rooms 10** (all en-suite & no-smoking, 1 for disabled). B&B €65pps, ss €25. Closed Dec-Feb. MasterCard, Visa, Laser. **Directions:** Directly opposite entrance to Ballybunion Golf Club.

Caherdaniel — Derrynane Hotel

 Hotel/Restaurant

Caherdaniel Co. Kerry **Tel: 066 947 5136** Fax: 066 947 5160
Email: info@derrynane.com Web: www.derrynane.com

If only for its superb location – on the seaward side of the Ring of Kerry road – this unassuming 1960s-style hotel would be well worth a visit, but there is much more to it than the view, or even its waterside position. The accommodation is quite modest but very comfortable, the food is good and, under the excellent management of Mary O'Connor and her well-trained staff, this hospitable, family-friendly place provides a welcome home from home for many a contented guest. Activity holidays are a big draw - there are beautiful beaches, excellent fishing with local fisherman Michael Fenton (who supplies all necessary equipment and has a fully licensed boat), Waterville Golf Course offers special rates at certain times - and the hotel has published its own walking brochure. Don't leave the area without visiting Daniel O'Connell's beautiful house at Derrynane – or the amazing Ballinskelligs chocolate factory. Children welcome (under 4s free in parents' room, cots available without charge; playroom) Heated outdoor swimming pool, tennis, pool table. Well-behaved small dogs with their own beds may stay with their owners. Garden. **Rooms 74** (all en-suite, 10 no smoking). B&B About €70pps, ss about €20.
Restaurant: Beautifully located, overlooking the heated outdoor swimming pool and the hotel's gardens (which reach down to the shore), the restaurant enjoys stunning sea views on a good day and the best of local ingredients are used in imaginative, very fairly priced four-course dinner menus. **Seats 80.** D 7-9 daily, Set D €35, sc discretionary. House wine €16. No smoking restaurant; air conditioning. Hotel closed Oct-Easter. Amex, Diners, MasterCard, Visa, Laser. **Directions:** Midway on Ring of Kerry.

Caherdaniel — Iskeroon

B&B

Bunavalla Caherdaniel Co. Kerry **Tel: 066 947 5119** Fax: 066 947 5488
Email: info@iskeroon.com Web: www.iskeroon.com

Geraldine and David Hare's beautiful old house is in a secluded position overlooking Derrynane Harbour. The effort taken to get there makes it all the more restful once settled in. All three of the comfortable and interestingly decorated bedrooms overlook the harbour – and the islands of Deenish and Scarriff – and each has its own private bathroom just across a corridor. The private pier at the bottom of the garden joins an old Mass Path which, by a happy chance, leads not only to the beach but also to Keating's pub (known as Bridie's) where a bit of banter and some good seafood is also to be had in the evenings, although it's wise to check on this beforehand. Unsuitable for children. No pets. Fishing, walking, garden. *Self-catering apartment for two also available. **Rooms 3** (all with private bathrooms, all no smoking). B&B €50pps, ss ss€20. Closed 30 Sep-1 May. MasterCard, Visa. **Directions:** Between Caherdaniel and Waterville (N70), turn off at the Scariff Inn, signed to Bunavalla Pier. Bearing left at each bend, go to the pier and left through "private" gate; cross beach and enter through white gate posts.

Caherciveen — O'Neills "The Point Bar"

 Pub

Renard Point Cahirciveen Co. Kerry
Tel: 066 947 2165 Fax: 066 947 2165

In the same family for 150 years, Michael and Bridie O'Neill's pub, The Point Bar, is beside the Valentia Island car ferry. Renovated in true character by the present owners, it's always neat and makes an appealing place to drop into for a quick one while you're waiting for the ferry – but even better to stay awhile and make the most of their super fresh seafood, served during the summer. The menu covers everything from a whole range of salads and open sandwiches on brown bread – fresh and smoked wild salmon, smoked mackerel, crabmeat, crab claws – to hot dishes like deep-fried squid and a couple of hake and monkfish dishes with garlic and olive oil. Not very suitable for children. The Valentia Island ferry runs continuously – i.e. not to a time table – from April-September inclusive. L Mon-Sat, D daily. Closed L Sun. Food available only from April to October (Phone to check off season) **No credit cards.** ◇

Cahirciveen — QC's Seafood Bar & Restaurant

Restaurant   3 Main St. Cahirciveen Co. Kerry **Tel: 066 947 2244** Fax: 066 947 2244
Email: kquinlan@oceanfree.net Web: www.qcbar.net

Kate and Andrew Cooke renovated this old building with style and sensitivity - introducing a pleasingly continental tone (Spanish to be precise) while retaining interesting and characterful features such as the original stone wall and a big fireplace that must be a great draw on cold winter days. The bar counter is also over a century old and there are numerous nautical antiques and pictures of local interest. Although there are plenty of other things on the menu, local fish is the main feature - supplied by the family company, Quinlan's Kerry Fish at Renard's Point - cooked Basque-style on a charcoal grill specially imported from Spain, so expect delicious chargrills, with lots of olive oil and garlic. Wild Kerry salmon, smoked in the family factory, is another speciality, served simply with leaves or as part of a Nordic platter, which also includes crab, prawns and marinated herrings. The wine list is almost exclusively Spanish (house wine €16.50). Children welcome. **Seats 48.** L Jun-Sep, 12-3; D Apr-Sep, 6-9.30 (Sun from 5); D Oct-Mar (excl Jan), Thu-Sun only. Closed Sun until 5pm, L Oct-May, D Mon-Wed Oct Mar, 25 Dec, Good Fri; annual closure. 8 Jan-8 Feb. The minimum transaction for credit cards is €25. MasterCard, Visa, Laser. **Directions:** In the centre of Cahirciveen.

Cahirciveen — The Quarry Restaurant

Restaurant   Kells Post Office Cahirciveen Co. Kerry **Tel: 066 9477601** Fax: 066 9477660
Email: patscraftshop@eircom.net Web: www.patscraftshop.com

Pat Golden's family-run "one stop shop" on the Ring of Kerry is extremely useful to know about - not only will you get good home cooking here, but there's a post office and foodstore, filling station, tourist information point and bureau de change. Aside from these practical points, there are more interesting aspects to this many-sided venture as it also includes a fine craft shop, with quality Irish clothing and gift items and a unique attraction in the shape of 'The Golden Mile Nature Walk' up behind the quarry, which is just the place to walk off your lunch. The restaurant is on the first floor with large windows to take advantage of panoramic views over Kells Bay to the Dingle Peninsula and - another surprise - the cooking style includes genuine Mediterranean influences as well as Irish dishes as head chef Elena Stavri is a Greek Cypriot and "cooks with the heart". So you'll find real home-made Greek food like moussaka, hummous, tzatziki and baklava sitting happily alongside Irish stew and wild Dingle Bay salmon. The pricing is reasonable (most main courses around €9; top price, for sirloin steak, about €16) and, best of all perhaps, this is somewhere you can get a decent bite to eat during the day on a Sunday, when most of our recommendations in the area are closed. *On alternate Friday nights in July & August Greek mezza style banquets are held - ring the restaurant for information and booking. **Seats 86.** No smoking area; air conditioning. Children welcome. Open daily 9am-6pm, Easter-Oct. A la carte; house wine about €13.95. Closed Nov-Easter. Amex, Diners, MasterCard, Visa, Laser. **Directions:** Midway Between Glenbeigh & Cahirciveen.

Camp — Barnagh Bridge Country House

Guesthouse   Cappaclough Camp Co. Kerry **Tel: 066 713 0145** Fax: 066 713 0299
Email: bbguest@eircom.net Web: www.barnaghbridge.com

Snuggled into the hillside overlooking Tralee Bay, Heather Williams' unusual architect-designed guesthouse is in extensive grounds between the mountains and the sea. Attractive and comfortable, it was purpose-built, with five individually furnished guest bedrooms (decor themed on local wild flowers), all with en-suite shower rooms. In the dining room guests can drink in the view of Tralee Bay while doing justice to Heather's breakfasts – fresh juices, newly baked breads and scones, locally made preserves, and Dingle smoked salmon and scrambled eggs or a traditional fry (in addition to daily specials such as kippers or French toast). The stylishly decorated guest drawing room opens onto a patio overlooking the Maharees islands and their spectacular sunsets, and the latest improvement is a conservatory, which extends the reception area and dining room - and maximises still further on the wonderful view. Garden, fishing, walking. Not suitable for children under 10. No pets. **Rooms 5** (all shower only & non-smoking). B&B €40 pps, ss €10. Closed 31 Oct-1 March. Amex, MasterCard, Visa, Laser. **Directions:** Take N86 from Tralee for 10 miles, then R560 for 1 mile.

Camp — The Cottage Restaurant

Restaurant

Camp Co. Kerry **Tel: 066 713 0022** / 713 0176
Web: www.irelandview.com

Although quite newly built, both the design and materials of Frank & Gretta Wyles' bright, airy restaurant are in the local idiom so it fits in well and is maturing gracefully. Local ingredients feature in wholesome, quite traditional fare (west coast chowder, boxty, roast stuffed loin of Kerry lamb, with colcannon mash and garlic & rosemary sauce). Seafood is a speciality (pan-fried sole on the bone with butter & parsley, daily specials) and also steaks, various ways; vegetarian dishes - typically an aubergine stack of grilled aubergine filled with goats cheese and semidried tomato, baked & finished with chunky tomato sauce - are always on the main menu. Pleasant service and reasonable prices too. Ample parking; children welcome. **Seats 60**. (private room, 14). Separate smoking room. D 6-10 daily, L12-3.30; à la carte; house wine from € 13.35; SC discretionary. Closed Mon & Tue off season. Establishment closed Jan-Mar. Amex, MasterCard, Visa, Laser. **Directions:** On the Tralee-Castlegregory-Conor Pass-Dingle road (10 miles from Tralee).

Camp — James Ashe

Pub

Camp Co. Kerry **Tel: 066 413 0133**

This fine old pub just off the Tralee-Dingle road has been in the family for 200 years and the present owners Rory and Gertie Duffin, intend to keep things pretty much the way they've been, at least in the recent past. It's a delightful place, full of genuine character and hospitality - ideal for a drink and a chat. Closed 25 Dec & Good Fri. Phone ahead to check opening times off season. Amex, Diners, MasterCard, Visa. **Directions:** On the main Tralee-Dingle road, 10 miles from Tralee. ◇

Camp — Suan Na Mara

B&B

Lisnagree Castlegregory Rd Camp Co. Kerry **Tel: 066 713 9258** Fax: 066 713 9258
Email: suanmara@eircom.net Web: www.kerryweb.ie/suanmara

Fionnula Fitzgerald's welcoming modern B&B near the sea is set well back from the road in spacious grounds and even has its own pitch & putt course in an adjoining field. It's a relaxed and very pleasant place to stay, with a comfortable sitting rooms for guests and bedrooms that are a little on the small side but well-equipped, with hair dryer, TV, radio and tea/coffee making facilities and neat bathrooms. Maintenance is immaculate, hospitality genuine - and breakfast will be a treat. Garden, pitch & putt, walking. **Rooms 6** (all en-suite & no smoking). B&B €33 pps, ss€33 (high season). Children welcome (cot available, €8). Closed 31 Oct-1 Mar. MasterCard, Visa. **Directions:** Take N86 to Camp Junction and then R560 for approx 5 Km.

Caragh Lake — Caragh Lodge

🏛 Country House
Restaurant

Caragh Lake Co. Kerry
Tel: 066 976 9115 Fax: 066 976 9316
Email: caraghl@iol.ie Web: www.caraghlodge.com

Less than a mile from the Ring of Kerry, Mary Gaunt's lovely Victorian house and gardens nestling on the shores of the startlingly beautiful Caragh Lake is an idyllic place, with views of Ireland's highest mountains, the McGillicuddy Reeks. The house - which is elegantly furnished with antiques but not too formal - makes a cool, restful retreat. Bedrooms include some newer garden rooms with wonderful views, their own entrance and sitting room (complete with open log fire), and are all sumptuously furnished with lovely bathrooms.

Salmon and trout fishing, boating and swimming are all available at the bottom of the garden. Not suitable for children under 12. No pets. Banqueting (50). **Rooms 15** (1 suite, 8 junior suites, 6 superior). B&B €80, ss €30. Closed 1 Jan-24 Apr & 13 Oct-31 Dec.
Restaurant: In the elegant dining room overlooking the lake (open to non-residents by reservation), Mary's real love of cooking shines through. Local produce (such as freshly caught seafood, often including wild salmon from Caragh Lake, Kerry lamb and home-grown vegetables) takes pride of place. Wide-ranging menus tempt with starters like warm carpaccio of wild salmon with a lemongrass infused cream, followed by soup or sorbet of the day and main courses including specialities such

as Caragh Lodge crispy half duck with plum sauce or noisette of Kerry lamb niçoise. Baking is a particular strength, not only in delicious home-baked breads, but also baked desserts and treats for afternoon tea - including recipes handed down by Mary's family through the generations. D 7-8.30; about €40 (average, à la carte). House wine €22. sc discretionary. Establishment closed mid Oct-24 April. Amex, Diners, MasterCard, Visa. **Directions:** From Killorglin on N70, Glenbeigh direction, take second road signed Caragh Lake; at end of road go left again. The house is on the right.

Caragh Lake — Carrig House Country House & Restaurant

Restaurant/Country House

Caragh Lake Killorglin Co. Kerry
Tel: 066 976 9100 Fax: 066 976 9166
Email: info@carrighouse.com Web: www.carrighouse.com

At the heart of Frank and Mary Slattery's sensitively extended Victorian house lies a hunting lodge once owned by Lord Brocket - and he chose well, as it is very atttractive and handsomely set in fine gardens with the lake and mountains providing a dramatic backdrop. The house is welcoming and well-maintained, with friendly staff (Frank himself carries the luggage to your room) and a very relaxed atmosphere, notably in a series of sitting rooms where you can chat beside the fire or have a drink before dinner. Individually decorated bedrooms furnished with antiques (some with their own patio) are large, high-ceilinged and airy, with generous, well-designed bathrooms. The gardens are extensive and a laminated map is available, naming the various areas - Waterfall Garden, Pond Garden, Rock Walk etc - and the main plantings in each; a more detailed list is available on request. Not suitable for children under 8 except small babies (under 1 free of charge, cot available). Dogs allowed in some areas. Swimming (lake), fishing (ghilly & boat available), walking, garden, croquet. **Rooms 16** (1 suite, 1 junior suite, 12 superior, 2 no smoking) B&B about €75pps, ss about €31. Closed Dec-Feb inc.
Restaurant: Situated in a prime position overlooking the lake, the restaurant is open to non-residents (booking essential). An extensive à carte menu based on local ingredients is offered - notably seafood and Kerry lamb - with organic vegetables, herbs and fruit supplied by their own walled kitchen garden. Vegetarian dishes are always available. **Seats 50.** No smoking restaurant. D daily, 6.30-9. A la carte. House wine about €22. SC discretionary. Establishment closed Dec-Feb. MasterCard, Visa, Laser, Switch. **Directions:** left after 2.5 miles on Killorglin/Glenbeigh Road N70 (Ring of Kerry). ◇

Caragh Lake — Hotel Ard-na-Sidhe

Hotel

Caragh Lake Co. Kerry **Tel: 066 976 9105** Fax: 066 976 9282
Email: sales@kih.liebherr.com Web: www.iol.ie/khl

Set in woodland and among award-winning gardens, this peaceful Victorian retreat is in a beautiful mountain location overlooking Caragh Lake. Decorated throughout in a soothing country house style, very comfortable antique-filled day rooms provide plenty of lounging space for quiet indoor relaxation and a terrace for fine weather – all with wonderful views. Bedrooms – shared between the main house and some with private patios in the garden house – are spacious and elegantly furnished in traditional style, with excellent en-suite bathrooms. This is a sister hotel to the Hotel Europe and Dunloe Castle (see entries), whose leisure facilities are also available to guests. Dooks, Waterville, Killeen and Mahony's Point golf courses are all within easy reach. Not very suitable for children, although concessions are given (under 12s free in parents' room; cots available). No pets. **Rooms 20** (5 no smoking). B&B Room Rate from about €215 (max 2 guests), SC included. 24 hr room service. Closed 1 Oct-1 May. Amex, Diners, MasterCard, Visa, Laser. **Directions:** Off N70 Ring of Kerry road, signed 5 km west of Killorglin. ◇

Castlegregory — Spillanes

Pub

Fahamore Maharees Castlegregory Co. Kerry
Tel: 066 713 9125 Fax: 066 713 9538

It's a long way down from the main road to reach the Maharees, but well worth it for many reasons, not least a visit to Marilyn and Michael Spillane's great traditional pub - they work hard at both the food and hospitality and have earned a well-deserved loyal following as a result. There's a tempting display of salads and desserts to choose from and seafood stars on the menu - mussels grilled with garlic breadcrumbs, crabclaws served in shell with brown bread and a cocktail dipping sauce, fresh and wild salmon in salads and open sandwiches, scampi made from Dingle prawns. There's plenty for meat-lovers, such as chargrilled steaks, several chicken dishes (in the evening), some vegetarian dishes and some with child-appeal too. Meals daily in high season (Jun-Sep), 1-9.30 (Sun 2-9). No food Nov-mid March. MasterCard, Visa, Laser. **Directions:** Dingle Peninsula, 3.5 miles north of Castlegregory, between Bandon and Tralee bays.

Dingle — Bambury's Guesthouse

Guesthouse

Mail Road Dingle Co. Kerry **Tel: 066 915 1244** Fax: 066 915 1786
Email: info@bamburysguesthouse.com Web: www.@bamburyguesthouse.com

Just a couple of minutes walk from the centre of Dingle, Jimmy and Bernie Bambury's well-run, purpose-built guesthouse has spacious rooms (including three suitable for disabled guests) with tea/coffee trays, phone, satellite TV, hair dryer and complimentary mineral water. Bernie Bambury's breakfasts include griddle cakes with fresh fruit and honey – a house speciality – and vegetarian breakfasts are offered by arrangement. Not suitable for children under 4; no pets. Own parking. **Rooms 12** (all shower only & no smoking, 4 for disabled) B&B €50, ss €20. Open all year. MasterCard, Visa. **Directions:** On N86, on the left after the Shell garage, on entering Dingle.

Dingle — Beginish Restaurant

Restaurant

Green Street Dingle Co. Kerry **Tel: 066 915 1321** Fax: 066 915 1321
Email: dunlavin@gofree.indigo.ie Web: www.beginish.restaurant.com

Ronan and Denise Kane have been running this famous restaurant since March 2000 - and, not not only do both the food and service continue to please devotees of the previous régime, but they now have a well-earned reputation independent of the establishment's illustrious past. Unusually for cottagey Dingle, the restaurant is high-ceilinged and elegant, with a conservatory at the back overlooking the garden – lovely at night, when it is floodlit. Seafood is naturally very much in evidence, but Ronan's well-balanced menus offer a wide choice, including Kerry mountain lamb and a vegetarian dish of the day. The style includes classics alongside contemporary dishes: Glenbeigh oysters served with lemon on a bed of ice, crispy seafood springroll with a balsamic & ginger butter sauce, poached Dingle Bay lobster (Thermidor, or served simply with garlic or melted butter) and honey glazed duck breast & leg conift with apple & Calvados sauce are all typical. Classic desserts or Irish cheeses with a glass of port to finish. Caring service from staff who really want guests to enjoy their visit. **Seats 52.** No smoking area, air conditioning. D only, Tues-Sun, 6-9.30; Set D €29.50, also à la carte. House wine about €20; SC discretionary. Closed Mon & 3 weeks over Christmas. MasterCard, Visa, Laser. **Directions:** Below the Catholic Church, on the opposite side of the street.

Dingle — Benners Hotel

Hotel

Main Street Dingle Co. Kerry **Tel: 066 915 1638** Fax: 066 915 1412
Email: benners@eircom.net Web: bennershotel.com

Major refurbishment and the addition of spacious new rooms at the back have greatly improved this 300 year old centrally-located hotel. Public areas include a streetside bar which has more character than expected of an hotel (food available 6.30-9.30 daily) and a large, bright, dining room towards the back of the building. Bedrooms in the older part of the hotel have more character (some have four-posters), but the new back bedrooms are quieter. Private parking. Children welcome (under 4s free in parents' room, cot available without charge). Pets by arrangement. **Rooms 51** (4 junior suites, disabled 2). Lift. B&B about €102pps, ss about €20. Closed 25-26 Dec. Amex, Diners, MasterCard, Visa. **Directions:** In centre of town, beside The Lord Baker's. ◇

Dingle — Captains House

Guesthouse

The Mall Dingle Co. Kerry **Tel: 066 915 1531** Fax: 066 915 1079
Email: captigh@eircom.net Web: homepage.eircom.net/ncaptigh/

When Jim, a retired sea captain, and Mary Milhench bought this guesthouse in the late 80s they were renewing a seafaring tradition going back to the original captain, Tom Williams, who first took lodgers here in 1886. Today this charming house is as relaxed and hospitable a place as could be wished for: approached via a little bridge over the Mall river then through a lovely garden, it has been renovated and furnished with the antiques and curios collected by Jim on his voyages. The age and nature of the building - which extends into the next door premises - has created a higgledy-piggledy arrangement of rooms that adds to the charm; rooms vary considerably, as would be expected, but all have comfort (orthodpaedic beds, phones, satelllite TV, hospitality trays, plenty of hot water) as well as character. A welcoming turf fire in the reception area encourages guests to linger over tea, or with a book, and breakfast - which is a very special feature of a stay here - is served in the conservatory. Not suitable for children. No pets. **Rooms 9** (1 suite, 7 shower only, all no smoking). B&B €45pps, ss €5. Closed 1 Dec-16 Mar. MasterCard, Visa. **Directions:** Turn right at town entrance roundabout and Captains House is 100 metres up on left.

Dingle — The Chart House

féile bia Restaurant

The Mall Dingle Co. Kerry **Tel: 066 915 2255**
Email: charthse@iol.ie Web: www.charthousedingle.com

HOST OF THE YEAR - *(see page 32)*

Informal in furnishing style and general approach, Jim McCarthy's purpose-built restaurant brought a new element to Dingle's dining scene when it opened in 1997 and it quickly became established as one of the leading restaurants in an area exceptionally well-endowed with good eating places. It's attractively built in local stone to a low-key design that matches the proportions of the town well and seems always to have been there; there's a smart little bar just inside the door - and Jim McCarthy, the perfect host, who always seems to be there meeting, seating and seamlessly ensuring that everyone is well looked after and generally having a good time. And he has a good kitchen team to match his warm professionalism: while based mainly on local ingredients, notably seafood, head chef Gary Fitzgerald's well-judged menus are international in tone - a superb speciality starter of Annascaul black pudding, for example, is accompanied by gingered apples (or pear chutney) then wrapped in filo pastry and served with a bacon jus and, similarly, a main course of pan-fried brill comes with warm gazpacho salad and cilantro tartare sauce. But there are some themes from closer to home too: roast rack of Kerry lamb, for instance - supplied by Ashe's butchers in Annascaul - is served with mint & garlic polenta and redcurrant jus - a nod to fashion with the polenta, but the combination of flavours is very traditional; high quality ingredients and accurate, confident cooking make this an excellent dish and a large selection - perhaps as many as 6-8 different ones - of simple, perfectly cooked side vegetables complement it well. Meat- and fish-free dishes - probably two or more on each course - offer mainstream contemporary cooking of the same high standard and are equally appealing to non-vegetarians. Desserts include classics like a basket of home-made ice creams or intriguing variations on familiar themes such as apple & clove tartlet topped with ginger nut crumble, served with a Calvados – but the smart money is on the Irish cheeses, which are cannily offered, at €14, with a glass of vintage port (Dows '88) and served with delicious home-made oat biscuits and two varieties of grapes. Prices are fairly moderate (starters around €8.50, main courses average €20). An interesting wine list has helpful tasting notes as well as a clear layout of country of origin as well as vintages - and, of course, there's always a Chateau MacCarthy in stock. [An additional selection imported directly from South Africa is now available) **Seats 45**. No smoking area, air conditioning. D Wed-Mon, 6.30-10; à la carte. House wine €16.75. Closed Tue & 7 Jan-13 Feb. MasterCard, Visa, Laser. **Directions:** Left at the roundabout as you enter the town.

Dingle — Cleevaun Country House

féile bia Guesthouse

Lady's Cross Milltown Dingle Co. Kerry **Tel: 066 915 1108**
Fax: 066 915 2228 Email: cleevaun@iol.ie Web: www.cleevaun.com

A cup of tea or coffee and a slice of home-made porter cake welcomes guests to Charlotte and Sean Cluskey's well-run, recently renovated guesthouse just outside the town. Set in an acre of landscaped gardens overlooking Dingle Bay, it's near enough to Dingle to be handy and far enough away to enjoy the peace that the peninsula promises. Furnishing throughout is in a pleasant country pine style: bedrooms are all non-smoking, have good facilities and are well organised, with quality beds, quilted bedspreads and well-finished en-suite bathrooms; one bedroom has a separate dressing room. Charlotte's breakfasts – served in a large south-facing dining room overlooking Dingle Bay – are quite a speciality and she is a most hospitable hostess. **Rooms 8**. B&B €46, ss €19. Closed mid-Nov-mid-Mar. MasterCard, Visa, Laser. **Directions:** Just outside the town, on the Slea Head/Ventry scenic route R559.

Dingle — Dick Mack's

Pub

Green Lane Dingle Co. Kerry **Tel: 066 915 1960**

Once a cobbler's, this old shop-bar still sells an eclectic mixture of modern leather items, wellington boots and patent hangover cures. It's run by Dick's son, Oliver J MacDonnell, who has had the wisdom to leave well alone. Seating is basic, there's an old gas fire for cold evenings and the cashier's booth is put to good use as a snug. Definitely not a food place but open over lunchtime (12-2.30) and evenings (4-11). **Directions:** A few doors up the street from the Beginish restaurant.

Dingle — Dingle Skellig Hotel

 Hotel   Dingle Co. Kerry **Tel: 066 915 0200** Fax: 066 915 1501
Email: dsk@iol.ie Web: www.dingleskellig.com

It may be modest-looking from the road, but this 1960s hotel enjoys a shoreside location on the edge of the town and has won many friends over the years. It is a particularly well-run, family-friendly hotel, with organised entertainment for children and an excellent leisure centre. Roomy public areas are comfortably furnished with a fair degree of style and good use is made of sea views throughout, especially in the conservatory restaurant, which has special anti-glare glass. Bedrooms are reasonably large, are regularly refurbished and have small but neat bathrooms; the third floor is to be completely refurbished during the winter of 2002/3. Although best known as a holiday destination, the Dingle Skellig also has excellent conference and business meeting facilities, with back-up services including French and German translation on request. Conference/banqueting 250/230); business centre, secretarial services. Children under 3 free in parents' bedrooms; cots available free of charge; all year crèche, playroom, children's playground. Garden, fishing, leisure centre, swimming pool. New health & beauty centre due to open March 2003. [*Benner's Hotel (see entry) is in the same ownership, also the Dingle Marina Cottages.] **Rooms 112** (3 suites, 36 executive,10 no-smoking). B&B €120, ss €19. Restaurant: D daily 7-9.30 (cl Sun & Mon Nov & Jan-Feb); bar meals 12.30-9 all year. Hotel closed Christmas week. Amex, Diners, MasterCard, Visa, Laser.
Directions: On the sea side of the road as you approach Dingle from Tralee & Killarney.

Dingle — Doyle's Seafood Restaurant & Townhouse

féile bia Restaurant/Guesthouse   John Street Dingle Co. Kerry **Tel: 066 915 1174**
Fax: 066 915 1618 Email: cdoyles@iol.ie Web: www.doylesofdingle.com

In the good hands of Sean Cluskey and his wife Charlotte (who runs Cleevaun guesthouse), flagstone floors and old furniture give this restaurant lots of character. Local seafood is the main attraction - nightly specials depend on the day's landings - and lobster, selected from a tank in the bar, is a speciality. Aside from lobster, speciality seafood dishes include hot oysters with smoked Gubbeen cheese, an Atlantic platter and fish stew provençale - which is a meal in a (large) soup bowl. There are, however, concessions to non-seafood eaters, such as a duo of Kerry mountain lamb (roast rack and leg with braised puy lentils, roast garlic & thyme jus) and traditional beef & Guinness stew - and vegetarian dishes typically including crispy provençal strudel with basil, olives and tomato butter sauce. Puddings are nice and traditional or there's a plated selection of farmhouse cheeses from the Munster region to finish. **Seats 45**. No-smoking area; air conditioning. D only, Mon-Sat 6-10. A la carte; house wine from €19; sc 10%. Closed Sun.
Accommodation: Quality accommodation includes a residents' sitting room as well as eight spacious bedrooms with well-designed en-suite bathrooms. B&B €67 pps, ss €62. Establishment closed mid Dec-mid Mar. Diners, MasterCard, Visa, Amex, Laser. **Directions:** On entering Dingle, take third exit from roundabout into The Mall; turn right into John Street.

Dingle — Emlagh House

Country House   Dingle Co. Kerry **Tel: 066 915 2345** Fax: 066 915 2369
Email: info@emlaghhouse.com Web: www.emlaghhouse.com

Michael and Marion Kavanagh's luxurious country house style guesthouse is tucked into a site close to the Dingle Skellig Hotel, on the sea side of the road; it has been built with exceptional attention to detail and will age gracefully as the landscaping matures. The style throughout the house is gracious, in large, well-proportioned rooms furnished in traditional country house style but with a contemporary streak that gives it a great lightness of touch. Bedrooms (most of which have harbour views) are elegant and extremely comfortable, with fresh flowers, fruit and chocolates to greet guests on arrival and many features, including individually controlled heating/air conditioning, trouser press with iron, direct dial phone with modem, satellite TV, video, radio & CD - the latter wired to lovely marbled bathrooms with underfloor heating, separate shower and bath, double basins, heated mirror and towel rails and thick bathrobes. Some interconnecting rooms are available to provide private accommodation for groups. Hosts Marion and Grainne Kavanagh do everything possible to make guests comfortable, and their attention to detail includes an evening turndown service. Delicious breakfasts are served in a stylish dining room with contemporary influences in the decor alongside the antiques. Many activities (golf, fishing, sailing, equestrian) available nearby. Not suitable for children under 8. No pets. Own parking. **Rooms 10** (all no smoking, 1 for disabled). Lift. B&B €120pps, ss €40. Closed 10 Jan-1 Mar. MasterCard, Visa, Laser. **Directions:** Upon entering Dingle take first left after Shell Service Station.

Dingle Area — Gorman's Clifftop House & Restaurant

Restaurant/Guesthouse

Glaise Bheag Ballydavid Dingle Peninsula Co. Kerry
Tel: 066 915 5162 Fax: 066 915 5162 Email: gormans@eircom.net

Beautifully situated near Smerwick Harbour on the Slea Head scenic drive and Dingle way walking route, Sile and Vincent Gorman's guesthouse is, as they say themselves "just a great place to relax and unwind". It's also a very comfortable place to do this, as the whole premises has recently been virtually rebuilt and upgraded to a high standard. Natural materials and warm colours are a feature throughout the house and open fires, newspapers and books in two generous lounging areas (and a lot of pottery from the nearby Louis Mulcahy workshops) create a welcoming laid-back atmosphere. Bedrooms, which include some on the ground floor with easy access from the parking area, are not luxurious but very comfortable and attractively furnished in country style with thoughtfully finished bathrooms as well as phones and TV. The Gormans are knowledgeable and helpful hosts too, giving personal advice where it's needed in addition to the interesting information about the area provided at reception. Breakfast - an excellent buffet with home-baked breads, freshly squeezed juices, fruits, cheeses and cold meats as well as hot dishes cooked to order - is a treat and will set you up well for the day. Gorman's was the Guide's Guesthouse of the Year in 2002. Children welcome (under 3s free in parents' room, cot available free of charge). No pets. Garden, tennis, fishing, cycling, walking. **Rooms 9** (all en-suite & no smoking, 2 superior, 1 for disabled, shower only). B&B €60 pps, ss€30. **Restaurant:** The restaurant - which is open to non-residents - is on the sea side of the house, with large windows commanding superb sea views and, on fine evenings, spectacular sunsets. Vincent Gorman is the chef and Sile, who is a warm and solicitous host, supervises front of house; it's a good team, ensuring service that is both friendly and efficient. Vincent offers a couple of soups - fresh salmon chowder or carrot & courgette, perhaps - and four or five other starters, such as potato cake & black pudding sandwich with mushroom & bacon sauce (attractively presented and lighter than it sounds) and a pretty smoked Irish salmon with cream cheese & chives. Well-balanced main courses include several seafood dishes and the ever-popular sirloin steak (with mushroom & brandy sauce perhaps); vegetarian choices are always given - a main course of grilled aubergine and spinach mille feuille is typical - and copious dishes of delicious vegetables are left on the table. But don't forget to leave a little room, as desserts are a strong point: home-made ice creams, chocolate fondants and tiramisu Irish style (with Baileys) are just a few of the temptations on offer, or you can finish with a cheese plate. Tea or coffee can be served in the lounge, which smokers will prefer as the dining room is no smoking. **Seats 35.** D daily, 6-9. Set D €35. House wine from €16.50. Closed Nov-Mar except by reservation. MasterCard, Visa, Laser. **Directions:** 8 miles from roundabout west of Dingle Town - Sign posted An Fheothanach. Keep left at V.

Dingle — Greenmount House

Guesthouse

Upper John Street Dingle Co. Kerry **Tel: 066 915 1414** Fax: 066 915 1974
Email: mary@greenmounthouse.com Web: www.greenmounthouse.com

Just five minutes walk from the centre of Dingle, John and Mary Curran have run one of Ireland's finest guesthouses since the mid-70s. It's an exceptionally comfortable place to stay, quietly located on the hillside, with private parking and uninterrupted views across the town and harbour to the mountains across the bay. The spacious, well-appointed bedrooms are mainly junior suites with generous seating areas and particularly good amenities, including fridges as well as tea/coffee-making trays, phone and TV (and, in most cases, also their own entrance and balcony). There's also a comfortable residents' sitting room with an open fire and a conservatory overlooking the harbour, where breakfast - which has always been a special feature of Greenmount and won the Guide's Denny Breakfast Award (Munster Region) in 2001 - is served. The buffet - laden down with all kinds of fresh and poached fruits, juices, yogurts, cheeses, freshly baked breads - is augmented by an extensive choice of hot dishes, including the traditional full Irish breakfast. Home baking is a speciality and all the preserves are home-made too - the wonder is that anyone ever leaves this place of a morning at all. Not suitable for children under 8. No pets. Garden. Parking. **Rooms 9** (7 junior suites, 1 shower only, all no smoking). Room rate €125 (2 guests), SC discretionary. Closed 20-27 Dec. MasterCard, Visa, Laser. **Directions:** Turn right and right again on entering Dingle.

Dingle — The Half Door

Restaurant

John Street Dingle Co. Kerry
Tel: 066 915 1600 Fax: 066 915 1883 Web: halfdoor@iol.ie

Since 1991 chef-proprietor Denis O'Connor and his team have been preparing great seafood at the cottagey Dingle restaurant he runs with his wife, Teresa. Menus go with the seasons but whatever is available is perfectly cooked and generously served without over-presentation. An outstanding speciality of the house is the seafood platter, available hot or cold as either a starter or main course with (depending on availability of individual items) lobster, oysters, Dublin Bay prawns, scallops, crab claws and mussels (attractively presented with garlic or lemon butter). Good traditional puddings or Irish farmhouse cheeses to follow. **Seats 50.** No smoking area; air conditioning. D Mon-Sat, 6-10. Early D 6-6.30 only; later, à la carte. Closed Sun; several days at Christmas. [Times not confirmed at time of going to press.] MasterCard, Visa. **Directions:** On entering Dingle, turn right onto The Mall at roundabout, then right onto John St. ◇

Dingle — Heatons House

Guesthouse The Wood Dingle Co. Kerry **Tel: 066 915 2288** Fax: 066 915 2324
Email: heatons@iol.ie Web: www.heatonsdingle.com

Cameron and Nuala Heaton's fine purpose-built guesthouse is set in well-maintained gardens just across the road from the water and, although convenient to the town, it's beyond the hustle and bustle of the busy streets. An impressive foyer-lounge area sets the tone on arrival and spacious bedrooms confirm first impressions: all have bathrooms finished to a very high standard and phones, TV and hospitality trays - and the two new junior suites and three superior rooms added this year are not only luxurious but very stylish in a refreshingly contemporary idiom. Getting guests off to a good start each day is a point of honour and breakfast includes an extensive buffet (everything from fresh juices to cold meats and Irish cheeses) as well as a full hot breakfast menu. Fishing, walking, garden. **Rooms 16** (2 junior suites, 3 superior, all no smoking). B&B €59 pps, ss €36. Closed Christmas week. MasterCard, Visa, Laser. **Directions:** 600 yards beyond marina, at front of town.

Dingle — James Flahive

Pub The Quay Dingle Co. Kerry **Tel: 066 915 1634**

They don't make them like this any more - James Flahive's welcoming, friendly old pub has been a home from home for many a regular visitor for over 30 years. It's hard to imagine any call for a tailor's shop in Dingle these days, but that's how it started off in the 1890s; more recently it's long been a special favourite of sailing people and has had some very distinguished visitors and photos of many of them adorn the walls - along with several of Dingle's best-loved resident, Fungie the dolphin. No food, but a good pint and good company. Opening hours are irregular.

Dingle — Lord Baker's Restaurant & Bar

féile bia Pub/Restaurant Dingle Co. Kerry **Tel: 066 915 1277** Fax: 066 915 1274
Email: lordbakers@tinet.ie

Believed to be the oldest pub in Dingle, this business was established in 1890 by a Tom Baker. A popular businessman in the area, a colourful orator, member of Kerry County Council and a director of the Tralee-Dingle Railway, he was known locally as "Lord Baker" and as such is now immortalised in John Moriarty's excellent pub and restaurant in the centre of Dingle. A welcoming turf fire burns in the front bar, where bar food such as chowder and home-baked bread or crab claws in garlic butter is served. At the back, there's a much more sophisticated dining set-up in the restaurant proper (and, beyond it, a walled garden). Seafood (notably lobster from their own tank) stars, of course, and speciality dishes include monkfish wrapped in bacon, with garlic cream sauce and classic seafood mornay; but there's also a good choice of other dishes – local lamb (roast rack or braised shank, perhaps), also Kerry beef, chicken and local duckling – all well-cooked and served in an atmosphere of great hospitality. In addition to the main menu there are chef's specials each evening - and an unusual house speciality features on the dessert menu: traditional plum pudding with brandy sauce! Sunday lunch in the restaurant is a particularly popular event and very well done (booking strongly advised); on other days the lunchtime bar menu, plus one or two daily specials such as a roast, can be taken in the restaurant. An informative wine list includes a Connoisseur's Selection of ten wines. John is an excellent host, caring and watchful - no detail escapes his notice, ensuring that every guest in Dingle's largest restaurant will leave contented. **Seats 120.** L Fri-Wed 12.30-2; D Fri-Wed, 6-9.45. Set D menus & à la carte; light 2-course D €21.20. No smoking area. Closed Thurs, 24-25 Dec & Good Fri. Amex, MasterCard, Visa, Laser. **Directions:** Town centre.

Dingle — Milltown House

Guesthouse Dingle Co. Kerry **Tel: 066 915 1372** Fax: 066 915 1095
Email: millhouse@indigo.ie Web: www.indigo.ie/~milltown/

Mark and Anne Kerry's attractive guesthouse on the western side of Dingle, is set in immaculate gardens running down to the water's edge and enjoys beautiful views of the harbour and distant mountains. Day rooms include an informal reception room, a comfortably furnished sitting room and a conservatory breakfast room overlooking the garden - breakfast is quite an event, offering everything from fresh juices and fruit, through cold meats and cheeses, freshly baked breads and an extensive cooked breakfast menu. The bedrooms – all very comfortable and thoughtfully furnished with phone, TV with video channel, tea/coffee making facilities and iron/trouser press - include two with private patios. Constant upgrading is the policy here: a number of rooms have recently been increased in size and a new lounge, with sea and mountain views, has been added to the front of the house. Some room service available. Not suitable for children. No pets. Garden. **Rooms 10** (3 junior suites, all en suite and no smoking). Closed Dec & Jan. Amex, MasterCard, Visa, Laser. **Directions:** West through Dingle town, 0.75 miles from town centre.

Dingle   Pax Guest House
Guesthouse   Upper John Street Dingle Co. Kerry **Tel: 066 915 1518** Fax: 066 915 2461
Email: paxhouse@iol.ie Web: www.pax-house.com

Just half a mile out of Dingle, this modern house enjoys what may well be the finest view in the area – and, thanks to the exceptional hospitality and high standards of the owners, Joan Brosnan and Ron Wright, is also one of the most comfortable and relaxing places to stay. The furnishing style is daringly bright and fresh and thoughtfully furnished bedrooms have every amenity (including little fridges as well as phone, TV, tea/coffee making facilities and iron/trouser press) and well-finished bathrooms, most with full bath. Two suites have their own terraces where guests can lounge around and enjoy that stupendous view. Breakfast is a major event, featuring fresh Dingle Bay seafood as well as an exceptional range of meats and cheeses. Children welcome (under 2s free in parents' room; cots available, €10). Pets permitted by arrangement. **Rooms 13** (1 junior suite, 2 superior, 3 shower only, all no-smoking). B&B €60 pps, no ss. Wine licence. Closed 1 Dec-31 Jan. MasterCard, Visa, Laser. **Directions:** Turn off at sign on N86.

Fenit   The Tankard
Restaurant/Pub   Kilfenora Fenit Co. Kerry **Tel: 066 713 6164** Fax: 066 713 6516
Email: sulladn@compuserve.com Web: adlib.ie.eaterie/tankard

Easily spotted on the seaward side of the road from Tralee, this bright yellow pub and restaurant has built up a great reputation, especially for seafood. An imaginative bar menu is available from lunchtime to late evening (1-9) serving the likes of "smokeys" and boxty, warm chicken salad and vegetarian choices like mushroom & mozzarella salad.
Restaurant: Except on Sunday this is an evening restaurant, although lunch is available by arrangement. A phone call is worthwhile to get the best of seafood cooking, which can be exceptional: although bar menus give a passing nod to current trends, the restaurant style is quite traditional and beyond fashion - simple well-cooked food, based on the finest local ingredients with excellent saucing and unfussy presentation makes a refreshing change from the ubiquitous 'world cuisine'. Beyond seafood there's quite a wide choice, especially steaks in various guises, duckling, Kerry lamb and some strong vegetarian options. There are sea and mountain views from the restaurant, which has recently been extended and opened out to make the most of its location, with a patio area and a path down to the sea. **Seats 100**. D daily 6-10, à la carte; L Sun only 12.30-2, Set Sun L about €20 House wines from about €18; sc discretionary Closed 25 Dec & Good Fri. Amex, Diners, MasterCard, Visa. **Directions:** 5 miles from Tralee on Spa/Fenit road. ◇

Fenit   West End Bar & Restaurant
Pub/Restaurant/B&B   Fenit Co. Kerry **Tel: 066 713 6246** Fax: 066 713 6599

The O'Keeffes' family-run pub is exactly seven minutes walk from the marina. Good food is available in both the bar and the restaurant, which has earned a sound reputation in the area and has fairly recently been extended to include a conservatory. Head chef Bryan O'Keeffe is a member of the Panel of Chefs of Ireland and his style is "classic French with Irish popular cuisine", with seafood and meats billed equally as specialities. Expect starters ranging from Atlantic fisherman's chowder with brown bread, through local 'Cromane' mussels with bay leaves, garlic & cream (also available as a main course), to deep-fried 'Roulet Brie' pieces. Main courses include old favourites - sirloin steak, half roast duckling - and a range of seafood dishes including sole on the bone (with lemon butter) and strips of monkfish deep fried in beer batter, at quite reasonable prices. Simple, moderately priced accommodation is offered in ten en-suite rooms (B&B €30, no ss). Bar/restaurant Meals 5.30-10 daily Apr-Oct. A la carte; house wine from €13. Phone ahead to check food service off-season. Bar closed 25 Dec & Good Fri. MasterCard, Visa, Laser. **Directions:** 7 miles from Tralee, in village.

Kenmare — An Leath Phingin

Restaurant   35 Main Street Kenmare Co. Kerry **Tel: 064 41559**

As the ground floor is cosy in a traditional Irish way, visitors may be surprised to find that Cornelius Guerin's long-established restaurant specialises in northern Italian food. All is revealed as soon as the menu appears, however, or when going up to the first floor which is more stylish and arty, with Italian posters. Cornelius takes pride in sourcing the best of local ingredients - organic green salads from Gilly Clifford, Kenmare smoked salmon for risotto, meats from the local "A Taste of Kerry" butcher - and interpreting Italian dishes with a certain amount of artistic chef's licence, which should not be seen as a criticism, as this is passionate cooking, well-executed and none the worse for some untraditional twists. Choices range from old favourites like salad Caprese, through home-made pork sausages flavoured with fennel and bruschetta, to a range of interesting home-made pastas (tortellini, perhaps, with spinach, ricotta and parmesan), risotto (typically with smoked salmon) and half a dozen pizzas. Reasonable prices (main courses in the €15-18 region) and friendly, helpful service add to the enduring appeal of this attractive restaurant. D only Thur-Mon. A la carte. House wine about €16. Closed Wed; mid Nov-mid Dec. MasterCard, Visa. **Directions:** Town centre. ◇

Kenmare Area — Avoca Handweavers

Café   Moll's Gap Kenmare Co. Kerry **Tel: 064 34720** Fax: 064 35742
Email: info@avoca.ie Web: www.avoca.ie

High up at a famous viewing point on the Ring of Kerry, this outpost of the County Wicklow weaving company sells its fine range of clothing and crafts - and offers wholesome, home-made fare to sustain the weary sightseer. Restaurant seats 80. No-smoking area. Food service all day 10-5. Closed 20 Nov -10 Mar. Amex, Diners, MasterCard, Visa. **Directions:** on Ring of Kerry, 14 miles from Killarney, 5 from Kenmare at famous panoramic crossroads.

Kenmare — d'Arcys

Restaurant/B&B   Main Street Kenmare Co. Kerry **Tel: 064 41889** Fax: 064 41889
Email: info@darcys-kenmare.com Web: www.darcys-kenmare.com

Formerly a bank – you can still make out where the vault used to be – Pat Gath has been running this well-known restaurant with rooms since 1998. Head chef Brendan Byrne joined the team in 2001 bringing with him experience in some other fine establishments and quickly put his mark on the cooking through well-balanced contemporary menus which also work with the established house style, where seasonal local ingredients are integrated in dishes with a global flavour. Start, perhaps, with local crab & smoked salmon cakes or home made beef sausages with glazed apples and move on to seared scallops with roast forest mushrooms or breast of Skeaghanore Duck with confit leg meat and roast Jerusalem artichoke; there is real creativity at work here, notably in the imaginative use of vegetables to make interesting and well-balanced dishes. Finish with farmhouse cheeses (with an optional glass of vintage port) or delicious desserts such as refreshing strawberries in kir jelly with lemon & basil sorbet. A good wine list, home-made breads, and pleasant, efficient service all add to the appeal of this pleasantly cosmopolitan and fairly priced restaurant. No smoking area. Not suitable for children under 2 after 7 pm. **Seats 40.** D daily in summer, 6-10 (phone to check opening off season); Early D from €21 (Sun-Fri, 6.30-7.30), also à la carte. House wine €15.87; sc discretionary. Closed Christmas & mid-Jan/Feb.
Accommodation: The five bedrooms are all pleasantly decorated with neat new shower rooms and further upgrading is planned shortly. B&B €30; ss €5. MasterCard, Visa, Laser, Switch. **Directions:** Top of Main Street on left.

Kenmare — Dromquinna Manor Hotel

Hotel   Blackwater Bridge PO Kenmare Co. Kerry
Tel: 064 41657 Fax: 064 41791

Built in 1850 in an idyllic location – the hotel is set in 42 acres of wooded grounds and has three quarters of a mile of sheltered south-facing sea frontage – Dromquinna Manor has a number of unusual features including a romantic tree house (a 2-bedroom suite with four-poster and balcony, 15ft up a tree), a safe little sandy beach (beside the informal Boat House Bistro) and a 34ft Nelson Sport Angler with professional skipper for fishing parties and scenic cruises. The interior of the house features an original oak-panelled Great Hall, a traditional drawing room complete with concert grand piano, a panelled bar, pool room and table tennis room. Bedrooms are all individually decorated to specific themes, with good bathrooms; a new ground floor suite is wheelchair friendly. The hotel is popular for weddings. Conference/banqueting (40/150). Children welcome (playroom, playground) Garden. Walking. Tennis. Boating. Pets permitted. **Rooms 29** (1 suite, 2 mini-suites, 2 shower only B&B from about €70 pps, ss about €26. Closed 31 Oct-1 Mar. Amex, Diners, MasterCard, Visa **Directions:** 3 miles outside Kenmare on the Sneem Road. ◇

Kenmare   The Horseshoe

Restaurant/Pub
3 Main St. Kenmare Co. Kerry
Tel: 064 41553 Fax: 064 4250?

Chef-proprietor Irma Weeland's pleasingly old-fashioned bar and restaurant is cosy and well-run - and the good home cooking she offers in the informal oil-cloth-tabled restaurant at the back, with its open fire and original cattle stall divisions, is unpretentious and wholesome. Soups, chowders chicken goujons, burgers and pies will all be home-made, as will the chips (a rare enough event these days). Seafood and steaks are the key players on evening menus, but there's plenty else to choose from, including strong vegetarian options. Classic puddings – apple pie, chocolate tart – and a short but adequate wine list. No children after 8.30. **Seats 45.** L Mon-Sat 12-4, D daily 5-10.30 (Sun to 11.30); à la carte. House wine about €16; sc dicretionary. Closed L Sun, 25 Dec, Good Fri. Open weekends only Jan-Mar. MasterCard, Visa. **Directions:** Centre of Kenmare. ◇

Kenmare   Jam

Café
6 Henry St Kenmare Co. Kerry **Tel: 064 41591** Fax: 064 4079C
Email: james@jam-kenmare.com Web: www.jam-kenmare.com

James Mulchrone - previously head chef at D'Arcy's Restaurant - opened this delightful bakery and café in March 2001 and, unlikely as this may seem in the town that has the highest concentration of good eating places in Ireland, it brought something new and very welcome. Affordable prices, friendly service and an in-house bakery have proved a winning combination; everything is made on the premises using the best of local produce and you can pop into the self-service café for a bite at any time all day. To give a little flavour of the wide range offered, lovely main course choices include salmon baked in pastry with spinach, bacon, onion & cheddar & bacon quiche or, among the many tempting options for vegetarians, lentil & nut parcel with tomato. This is the place to visit if you are planning a fine day out as they have all you could want for a delicious picnic, including a wide range of sandwiches and salads, quiches, terrines and all sorts of irresistible cakes and biscuits. The café menu changes daily and party platters and celebration cakes are made to order; more choices for special diets, eg gluten-free and fat-free dishes, will shortly be introduced. The stated aim is "to provide fresh, quality, imaginative food t affordable prices in nice surroundings"; this they seem to be doing very well. **Seats 50.** No smoking area; air conditioning. Open Mon-Sat, 8am-6pm. Closed Sun, 4 days Christmas week. **No Credit Cards. Directions:** Lower Henry St on the left.

Kenmare   The Lime Tree Restaurant

☆ Restaurant
Shelburne Street Kenmare Co. Kerry **Tel: 064 41225** Fax: 064 41839
Email: benchmark@iol.ie Web: www.limetreerestaurant.com

Built in 1832, Tony and Alex Daly's restaurant is an attractive cut stone building set well back from the road. An open log fire, exposed stone walls, original wall panelling and a minstrels' gallery (which provides an upper eating area) all give character to the interior and, as it fills up, there's always a real buzz. Menus change with the seasons, and there are always daily specials, including several imaginative vegetarian options - typically a starter of wild mushroom linguini carbonara and main course of baked goat's cheese roulade (cheese layered with sliced potato & pesto, baked & served with seasonal salad, aged balsamic dressing). Cooking is very sound and local produce – Sneem black pudding, local free-range duck and Kerry lamb (oven-roasted, with sweet mint pesto perhaps) – is highly valued; local seafood such as Killmakillogue mussels appear in delicious specialities like seafood potpourri "en papillotte". Finish, perhaps, with a traditional pudding like warm blackberry and pear fruit crumble. Warm hospitality and excellent service add greatly to the enjoyment of the dining experience - and you can have more than a good meal here too, as part of the first floor has been given over to an impressive contemporary art gallery (open daily from 4pm until the restaurant closes). It might be wise to budget a little extra for dinner here - you could be taking home a modern masterpiece. Toilet wheelchair accessible. No-smoking area; air conditioning. Not suitable for children after 7 pm. **Seats 60.** D daily 6.30-10; à la carte (average main course about €20). House wine €20; sc discretionary. Closed-Nov-Mar. MasterCard, Visa, Laser. **Directions:** top of town next to Park Hotel.

Kenmare   The Lodge

Guesthouse   Killowen Road Kenmare Co. Kerry **Tel:** 064 41512 Fax: 064 42724
                              Email: thelodgekenmare@eircom.net Web: www.thelodge.com

In a town where good accommodation can be hard to find at short notice, this large, purpose-built guesthouse just 3 minutes walk from the centre, is a welcome addition. It offers hotel-style accommodation in spacious rooms which have everything you could possibly need - including phone, TV, safe, iron/trouser press and tea/coffee facilities, as well as well-finished bathrooms - at guesthouse prices. Children welcome (under 2s free, cot available without charge). 24 hour room service. No pets. Garden. **Rooms 11** (all en-suite & no smoking, 1 disabled). B&B €54 pps, ss€46. Closed 7 Nov-17 Mar. MasterCard, Visa. **Directions:** On the Cork road opposite the golf course.

Kenmare   Mickey Neds

Ⓝ Pub/Restaurant   The Square Kenmare Co. Kerry **Tel:** 064 40200 Fax: 064 40222
                              Email: info@mickeyneds.com Web: www.mickeyneds.com

Owned by former Kerry All-Ireland winning football captain Mickey Ned O'Sullivan and his wife Marian - who are both friendly and efficient hosts - this recently renovated pub and restaurant is in a quiet corner of Kenmare, overlooking the square. The original building dates back to 1795 and Mickey Ned was born here; today, while the exterior has clearly undergone some renovation, there is little about it to prepare the first-time visitor for the ambitiously re-designed and modernised interior, which is stylishly and refreshingly modern in a town that is known for its quaint, old world style – a spacious and airy mixture of concrete, dark wood, plain white walls and mirrors, cubed seats, leather sofas and low dark oak tables. Fresh flowers on every table, warm lighting effects and old photographs alongside some pieces of modern art emphasise the aim to create a stimulating contemporary environment which is also cosy and reflects traditional local values - this it clearly does very successfully and it has gone down a treat with the locals, particularly at lunch time. Menus read well and the food on the plate follows through - really fresh ingredients (some of which come straight from the farmers' market outside) are used in contemporary dishes served in generous amounts on modern large white plates; there's quite a lot of overlap between dishes on the bar menu and those served in the evening restaurant upstairs (a starter dish of warm slivers of smoked salmon with potato salad, for example, and main course of roast chicken fillet with tomato & basil potatoes and herb pesto) - so you can have a full meal or just a really delicious snack (like home-made seafood chowder, with a selection of gorgeous breads) to make a very good value lunch The wine list includes half a dozen sold by the glass or by quarter bottles. Music at weekends (traditional; jazz). Restaurant **Seats 60** (private room, 40). No smoking restaurant. Toilets wheelchair accessible. Children welcome. D Tue-Sat, 6-9; L Sun,12-4. D, à la carte; Set L from €14; house wine €15. SC discretionary. Bar Meals daily, 11.30-9 (Sun from 12 noon). Closed 25 Dec, Good Fri. Diners, MasterCard, Visa, Laser. **Directions:** Next to Tourist Office and Heritage Centre in Square.

Kenmare   Mulcahys

Restaurant   16 Henry Street Kenmare Co. Kerry **Tel:** 064 42383 · 087 2364449

The decor at Bruce Mulcahy's wacky restaurant is definitely different, with all sorts of influences jumbled up; it's funky but warm, fairly comfortable and sympathetically lit - and it certainly gives people something to talk about while waiting to eat. Menus offer fashionable fare such as a starter of sushi & sashimi (Japanese nori sheets filled with local seafood and served with wasabi, pickled ginger & mirin dip) and main courses like salmon on chive mash with fennel confit & brown sage butter or pan-fried loin of Kerry lamb with cep powder & pistachio nut crust (along with many other things). Vegetarians are offered a daily special and, while the menu is a bit wordy, there's genuine enthusiasm here both in the cooking and front of house, and a mainly youthful clientèle makes for an enjoyably lively atmosphere. Children welcome. Smoking unrestricted. **Seats 30.** D Wed-Mon, 6-10. A la carte. Set D €38, also à la carte. House wines from €17. SC discretionary. Closed Tue, 24-26 Dec, 10-30 Jan. MasterCard, Visa, Laser. **Directions:** Halfway down Henry Street, on the left hand side.

Kenmare   Muxnaw Lodge

Country House/B&B   Castletownberehaven Road Kenmare Co. Kerry **Tel:** 064 41252

Within walking distance from town (first right past the double-arched bridge towards Bantry), Mrs Hannah Boland's wonderfully cosy and homely house was built in 1801 and enjoys spectacular views across Kenmare Bay. Disregard any imperfections in the rather steep driveway or cobwebs around the door - this is very much a home where you can relax in the TV lounge or outside in the sloping gardens (you can even play tennis on the all-weather court). Bedrooms are tranquil, all en suite and with cleverly hidden tea/coffee-making facilities, and are individually furnished with free-standing period pieces and pleasant fabrics. Notice is required by noon if you would like dinner – a typical meal cooked in and on the Aga might be carrot soup, oven-baked salmon and apple pie, but guests are always asked beforehand what they like. **Rooms 5** (all en-suite & no-smoking). B&B €30-35. Residents D about €20. Closed 25 Dec. Visa. **Directions:** 2 minutes drive from Kenmare Town.

Kenmare   P F McCarthy

 Pub

14 Main Street Kenmare Co. Kerry **Tel: 064 4151€**
Fax: 064 42766 Email: failtebar@eircom.ne

This fine establishment has been in the McCarthy family since 1913 and may be remembered by visitors familiar with Kenmare as the Failte Bar, which was run Maureen McCarthy and her late husband Florry until 2000. Maureen and her daughter Margaret then renovated the premises and re-opened under its new name: it is now stylishly and spaciously designed to bring natural light into bright rooms, with a dining area separated from the bar by low cream-coloured, tongue-in-groove partitions, topped by wine bottles for privacy. Everyone loves it, whether for a drink to meet friends during the day, for the craic in the evening, or for a snack lunch or more leisurely dinner. Head chef P.J. Reidy cooks modern food with an underlying classical French influence - at lunchtime there are excellent home-made soups, salads (organic leaves & herbs) and light international snacks - bruschetta, melts, ciabatta pizza, enchiladas - and a wide range of regular and hot sandwiches; evening menus are more extensive: starters might include seared Parma ham wrapped goats cheese with Parmesan and balsamic vinaigrette or one of their speciality salads, while main courses include char-grilled steaks and a well-balanced choice of lively meat and fish dishes, plus a daily vegetarian special. There's a great buzz (without overcrowding), a friendly atmosphere and a very efficient service. Craft-brewed draught beers stocked, from Dwan microbrewery in Thurles, Co Tipperary. *An enclosed beer garden, with seating under the shade of a mature tree, is planned for 2003. **Seats 36.** Toilets wheelchair accessible. Children welcome. L Mon-Sat 12-3. D Mon-Sat 6-10. No food on Sun. A la carte; house wine from €15; SC discretionary. Closed 25 Dec, Good Fri. MasterCard, Visa, Laser. **Directions:** First Pub/Restaurant on the right hand side as you travel up Main Street.

Kenmare   Packie's

☆ Restaurant

Henry Street Kenmare Co. Kerry
Tel: 064 41508 Fax: 064 42135

CHEF OF THE YEAR

Tom and Maura Foley's buzzy little restaurant is stylish but unpretentious, with small tables and a big heart. Great local ingredients, especially organic produce and seafood, mingle with imports from sunnier climes and, in Maura's skilful hands, result in imaginative Ireland-meets-the-Med food that is memorable for its simplicity and intense flavouring. First impressions are of world cuisine and there's a clear awareness of international trends, but the cooking here is far above the influence of fashion. Maura modestly describes her food as "simple, with an emphasis on local ingredients" but what makes it special is her sure judgement of complementary food combinations. Many of these are traditional and that is why they have lasted - crab cake with tartare sauce, for example, or rack of lamb with mint & redcurrant sauce for example - while others, like pan-fried fillet of plaice with coriander, lime & orange butter sound modern but are actually based on a time-honoured combination of flavours. Close examination of menus will probably reveal more dishes that have stood the test of time than new ones, but what is impressive is the sheer quality of both food – especially local seafood – and cooking, also that new flavours will only be introduced because they make genuinely good partnerships. Puddings include good ices and a real traditional sherry trifle with Harvey's Bristol Cream – or there are Irish farmhouse cheeses to finish. Interesting and well-priced wine list. "Faites simple" was the famous (and, alas, largely ignored) dictum of the great Escoffier: Maura Foley is one of the few chefs with the confidence to do just that and the result is invariably memorable. **Seats 35.** D only Tue-Sat, 6-10; à la carte. House wine about €16.60; sc discretionary. Closed Sun & Mon and 15 Nov-15 Mar. Amex, MasterCard, Visa, **Directions:** Town centre.

Kenmare — Park Hotel Kenmare

Kenmare

Hotel

Park Hotel Kenmare

Kenmare Co. Kerry **Tel: 064 41200** Fax: 064 41402
Email: info@parkkenmare.com Web: www.parkkenmare.com

In a lovely location adjoining Kenmare town, with views over sloping gardens to the ever-changing mountains across the bay, this renowned hotel was built in 1897 by the Great Southern and Western Railway Company as an overnight stop for passengers travelling to Parknasilla, 17 miles away. Since 1985, when Francis Brennan became proprietor, Park Hotel Kenmare has earned international acclaim for exceptional standards of service, comfort and cuisine. Once inside the granite Victorian building, a warm welcome and the ever-burning fire in the hall begin weaving the Park's special magic: any tendency to formality in the antique furnishings is offset by amusing quirks of taste and, despite the constant quest for perfection, it is surprisingly relaxed. Public rooms are not overpoweringly grand and several open onto a verandah overlooking river and gardens. Luxurious, spacious bedrooms have excellent bathrooms and are furnished to exceptional standards of comfort with all the pampering extras expected of top hotels – fresh flowers, fruit, mineral water, robes, quality toiletries – and some newer ones, including hi-fi systems. A constant programme of renovation and upgrading ensures that accomodation is always of the highest international standard. But the most outstanding feature of the Park Hotel is its staff. The exceptional standard of training overseen by Francis Brennan through the years has had a very significant effect on standards not only in the hotel, but also throughout the country (and beyond) as those trained under his management have moved on to other positions. In acknowledgment of this contribution, the Guide awarded Francis Brennan a Skills Development Award in 2000. Golf club adjacent. Garden, tennis, cycling, walking, snooker. **Rooms 47** (9 suites, 23 superior, 14 no smoking, 3 for disabled). Lift. Children welcome (under 4s free in parents' room, cots available without charge). No pets; kennels available nearby. B&B €223pps, (single occupancy €233). *A very special spa facility is to be ready for the 2003 season.
★ **Restaurant:** Service in this elegant dining room is unfailingly outstanding and the views from window tables are simply lovely – a fitting setting for very fine food. A stylishly restrained classicism has characterised this distinguished kitchen under several famous head chefs. Joe Ryan, who has been head chef since 1999, offers seasonal à la carte and daily set dinner menus - and has clearly been on top form on the Guide's most recent visits. There is an understandable leaning towards local seafood, including lobster (try the house selection of Kenmare Bay seafood with leeks, lemon beurre blanc) but Kerry lamb and local Skeaghanore duck are also specialities: a treat of dish for two people is roast Skeaghanore duck with sautéed mouli & pomme paille with Kenmare honey & vinegar reduction. There are always some interesting vegetarian choices available on the à la carte and Joe Ryan's admirably disciplined dinner menus offer just three dishes on each course, making up in quality and flavour anything they lack in length. Superb attention to detail - from the first trio of nibbles offered with aperitifs in the bar, through an intriguing amuse-bouche served at the table (a tiny brandade of salt cod with beetroot perhaps), well-made breads, punctilious wine service and finally the theatrical little Irish coffee ritual and petits fours at the end of the meal - all this contributes to a dining experience that is exceptional. The wine list, although geared towards the deep-pocketed guest, offers a fair selection in the €30-40 bracket and includes a wine suitable for diabetics. Service, under the direction of restaurant manager John O'Sullivan since 1990, is immaculate. A short à la carte lounge menu is available, 11am-6pm. Not suitable for children under 8 after 8 pm. No smoking area. **Seats 80** (private room, 60). D only, 7-9 daily; Set D menus €48-64, also à la carte. House wine from €25; sc discretionary. Hotel closed 2 Jan-18 April & late Oct-23 Dec. Amex, Diners, MasterCard, Visa, Laser. **Directions:** Top of town.

Kenmare — The Purple Heather

Kenmare

Pub/Restaurant

The Purple Heather

Henry Street Kenmare Co. Kerry **Tel: 064 41016**

Daytime sister restaurant to Packie's, Grainne O'Connell's traditional darkwood and burgundy bar gradually develops into an informal restaurant at the rear. Run by the O'Connell family since the mid-1970s, The Purple Heather was among the first to establish a reputation for good food in Kenmare. What they aim for – and achieve, with commendable consistency – is good, simple, home-cooked food. Start with refreshing freshly squeezed orange juice, well-made soups that come with home-baked breads or salad made of organic greens with balsamic dressing. Main courses include a number

of seafood salads, vegetarian salads (cold and warm), pâtés – including a delicious smoked salmo
pâté– plus a range of omelettes, sandwiches and open sandwiches (Cashel Blue cheese and walut
perhaps, or crabmet with salad) or Irish farmhouse cheeses (with a glass of L.B.V Offley port if yo
like). **Seats 40.** Bar open 10.45-7; food served Mon-Sat, 11.45-5. Closed Sun, Christmas, Good Fri
No Credit Cards. Directions: Town centre. ◇

Kenmare — Sallyport House

Country House
Kenmare Co. Kerry **Tel: 064 42066** Fax: 064 4206
Email: port@iol.ie Web: www.sallyporthouse.con

The Arthur family's renovated country house on the edge of Kenmare is in a quiet and convenien
location overlooking the harbour, with fine garden and mountain views at the rear. It is spaciou
throughout, from the large entrance hall (with welcoming fire) to bedrooms that are thoughtfull
furnished with a mixture of antique and good quality reproduction furniture, plus orthopaedic beds
TV, phone and (still unusual enough to merit mention) lights and mirrors correctly placed for thei
function. All rooms have practical, fully-tiled bathrooms with powerful over-bath showers and built
in hair dryers. Under Janie Arthur's eagle eye, housekeeping is outstanding - and delicious breakfast
are served in a sunny dining room overlooking the garden. Not suitable for children. No pets. **Room**
5 (all en-suite & no-smoking). B&B €70, ss €25. Closed 1 Nov- 1 Apr. **No Credit Cards. Directions**
South of town on N71, between town and bridge.

Kenmare — Sea Shore Farm Guest House

Ⓝ Guesthouse
Tubrid Kenmare Co. Kerry **Tel: 064 41270** Fax: 064 4127(
Email: seashore@eircom.net Web: http://homepage.eircom.net/~seashore

The O'Sullivans' well-named farm guesthouse is beautifully situated overlooking the Beara peninsula
with field walks through farmland down to the shore - and, despite its peace and privacy, it's alsc
exceptionally conveniently located, just a mile from Kenmare town. Mary Patricia O'Sullivan provides
old-fashioned Irish hospitality at its best, with friendly, welcoming and efficient reception anc
spotlessly clean accommodation. A pleasant lounge for guests has stunning views and plenty o
tourist information and Irish heritage books - and Mary Patricia is herself a veritable mine of loca
information who obviously delights in her job of telling guests about it. Spacious, comfortably
furnished bedrooms have the considerate small touches that make all the difference to the comfort
of a stay such as a hairdryer that is placed conveniently in front of a mirror, shelves beside the
washbasin for toiletries and a chaise-longue in front of a huge window so you can make the most
of those unforgettable views. No dinner, but breakfast is a feast of fruit salads, yoghurt, cereals etc
as well as a choice of scrambled eggs draped with locally smoked salmon, pancakes or traditional
Irish. Garden, walking. *Glen Inchaquin Park is nearby and should not be missed. **Rooms 6** (all en-
suite & no smoking, 2 for disabled). B&B €60pps, ss €15. Closed 10 Nov-1 Mar. MasterCard, Visa.
Directions: Off Ring of Kerry N70 Kenmare/Sneem road.

Kenmare — Sheen Falls Lodge

🏬🏬 Hotel
Kenmare Co. Kerry **Tel: 064 41600** Fax: 064 41386
Email: info@sheenfallslodge.ie Web: www.sheenfallslodge.ie

Set in a 300-acre estate just across the river from
Kenmare town, this stunning hotel made an
immediate impact from the day it opened in April
1991; it has continued to develop and mature most
impressively since. The waterside location is
beautiful and welcoming fires always burn in the
elegant foyer and in several of the spacious,
elegantly furnished reception rooms, including a
lounge bar area overlooking the tumbling waterfall.
Decor throughout is contemporary classic., offering
traditional luxury with a modern lightness of touch
and a tendency to understatement that adds up to great style and accommodation in spacious suites
and bedrooms is luxurious - all have superb amenities, including video recorders and CD players,
beautiful marbled bathrooms and views of the cascading river or Kenmare Bay. Outstanding facilities
for both business and private guests include state-of-the-art conference facilities, a fine library
(with computer/internet), an equestrian centre (treks around the 300 acre estate) and The Queen's
Walk (named after Queen Victoria), which takes you through lush woodland. A Health & Fitness Spa
includes a pretty 15 metre pool (and an extensive range of treatments including seaweed wraps and

romatherapy massages) and, alongside it, there's an informal evening bar and bistro, "Oscars", which has its own separate entrance as well as direct access from the hotel. But it is the staff, under the guidance of the exceptionally warm and hospitable General Manager, Adriaan Bartels, who make this luxurious and stylish international hotel the home from home that it quickly becomes for each new guest. Two luxuriously appointed self-contained two-bedroomed thatched cottages, Little Hay Cottage and Garden Cottage, are also available to rent, singly or together. Conference/banqueting 120); Business centre, secretarial services, video-conferencing. Health & Fitness Spa (swimming pool, jacuzzi, sauna, steam room, treatments), snooker, equestrian, walking, fishing, gardens, tennis, cycling. Children welcome (cots avilable, €30; playground). **Rooms 61** (9 suites, 8 junior suites,10 no-smoking bedrooms, 1 disabled). Room rate €395 (1 or 2 guests).

★ **La Cascade:** This beautifully appointed restaurant is arranged in tiers to take full advantage of the waterfalls – floodlit at night and providing a dramatic backdrop for Chris Farrell's modern Irish cooking, with the backing of faultless service under restaurant manager Johnny Le Poel. An admirably concise table d'hôte offers about seven choices on each course - perhaps three seafood, one vegetarian and a balanced selection of meats and poultry. Cooking is consistently impressive and the range of dishes offered often includes variations on a number of specialities: carpaccio of beef, for example, may be served with with caramelised walnuts, smoked tomato, globe artichoke, anchovy, lemon & rosemary, and pigeon, rabbit and scallops or crab from Castletownbere are all likely to feature amongst the starters. Main courses are in a similar vein – Kerry lamb is almost de rigeur, of course, and predictably delicious (typically it might be a roast rack with aubergine purée, ravioli of lamb shank, lamb jus) and there may be wild salmon from the estate, perhaps served with lobster risotto, mussels and clams alongside a summer vegetable nage. Speciality desserts include updated classics like hot soufflés (apricot with almond & amaretto ice cream, perhaps) and farmhouse cheeses, served with scrumptious parmesan biscuits. The hotel's atmospheric wine cellar is a particular point of pride and guests can choose their own bottle from nearly 950 wines - and port can also be served in the cellar after dinner. The hotel's Chef du Sommelier, Alain Bras, was the Guide's Sommelier of the Year for 2001 and has seemingly limitless knowledge of wines from all over the world. Like other exceptional sommeliers, Alain wears his knowledge lightly and is supremely accessible and warmly enthusiastic in his manner when assisting guests towards the best wine for their menu choices. *Light lunches (smoked salmon, club sandwiches etc) and afternoon tea are available in the sun lounge, 12-6 daily, and the informal Oscar's Bistro offers an extensive à la carte dinner menu every night, 6-10pm. Restaurant **Seats 120** (private room, 24). D daily 7-9.30. Set D €65 House wines from €33. SC discretionary. Hotel closed Jan. Amex, Diners, MasterCard, Visa, Laser. **Directions:** Take N71 from Kenmare to Glengariff, take 1st left at Riversdale Hotel.

Kenmare · Shelburne Lodge

🏨 Accommodation

Cork Road Kenmare Co. Kerry
Tel: 064 41013 Fax: 064 42135

Shelburne Lodge is the oldest house in Kenmare and has all the style and attention to detail that would be expected from Tom and Maura Foley, proprietors of the dashing Kenmare restaurant, Packies. A fine stone house on the edge of the town, the lodge is set back from the road in its own grounds and lovely gardens. Spacious day rooms include an elegant, comfortable drawing room and a large, well-appointed dining room where excellent breakfasts are served. Accommodation, in seven rooms individually decorated to a high standard, is extremely comfortable and everything (especially beds and bedding) is of the highest quality; individual decoration extends to the excellent bathrooms – all with full bath except the more informal conversion at the back of the house, which is especially suitable for families and has neat shower rooms. No evening meals are served, but residents are directed to the family's restaurant, Packies. Garden, tennis. Own parking. No pets. **Rooms 9** (2 shower-only). B&B €65, ss €15. Closed 15 Dec-28 Feb. MasterCard, Visa. **Directions:** 500 yards from town centre, on the Cork road R569.

Killarney · Aghadoe Heights Hotel

Hotel/Restaurant

Killarney Co. Kerry
Tel: 064 31766 Fax: 064 31345
Email: aghadeeheights@eircom.net Web: aghadoeheights.com

A few miles out of town, this famous low-rise hotel, built in the '60s, enjoys stunning views of the lakes and the mountains beyond and also overlooks Killarney's two 18-hole championship golf courses. Major refurbishment of the hotel was undertaken in the winter of 1999/2000 and, while the controversial exterior was still undergoing modifications in summer 2002, the renovation of the interior is complete. The new rooms - junior suites and a Presidential Suite - have superb views and balconies and are equipped and furnished to a high standard in a contemporary style. The whole hotel is luxuriously furnished and decorated, with lots of marble, antiques and good paintings, and the famous first-floor restaurant, Fredrick's, has been extended and incorporated into an open-plan lounge area, where traditional Afternoon Tea is served (2-5.30pm). Conference/banqueting facilities have also been increased and upgraded (150/80); business centre. Leisure centre, swimming pool beauty salon, garden, tennis. Children welcome (Under 2s free in parents' room; cot available, €19). No pets. Garden. **Rooms 69** (2 suites, 7 junior suites, 36 superior rooms, 2 for disabled). Lift. B&B about €199 pps, ss about €45. Open all year.

Fredrick's: The restaurant itself may have changed somewhat - while still on the first floor it is now part of an open plan area - but the same team is still in place: head chef Robin Suter has been with the hotel since 1990 and restaurant manager John Doyle's history goes back even further, to 1986 and the classic style of food and service for which the hotel is famous remains the same. A la carte menus (considerably priced by course for those not requiring the full five-course dinner) offer updated variations on well-loved dishes - fresh seafood cakes may come with a tomato chilli salsa for example, and roast loin of lamb with girolles & rösti potatoes - but there's no messing about with the great classics like grilled chateaubriand sauce béarnaise and sole meunière. Piano 7-11pm. Not suitable for children under 10 after 7 pm. **Seats 120** (private room 40). D daily, 6.30-9.30; L Sun only, 12.30-2. Set D about €55 (also semi-à la carte); house wine from about €25, sc discretionary. Amex Diners, MasterCard, Visa. **Directions:** Two miles west of Killarney; signposted off N22. ◇

Killarney Area — The Beaufort Bar & Restaurant

 Pub/Restaurant   Beaufort Killarney Co. Kerry **Tel: 064 44032** Fax: 064 44390
Email: beaurest@eircom.net Web: www.beaufortbar.com

In the fourth generation of family ownership, Padraig O'Sullivan's immaculate establishment near the Gap of Dunloe is an absolute delight. Recent major renovations have seen the old tree at the front left safely in place which, together with features like the stonework and an open fire in the bar for winter, all contribute to the genuine character that can easily be lost in refurbishments. The pride taken by the family in running this fine pub is palpable and the upstairs restaurant (which can be reached through the bar or by a separate entrance from the carpark) is a logical extension of the existing business. Head chef Tim Brosnan, who joined the team in 1999, presents quite extensive, well-balanced à la carte dinner menus with a generous, traditional tone (seafood cocktail, chilled galia melon with a seasonal fruits & a strawberry sorbet, chicken liver paté; roast rack of Kerry lamb or duckling, sole meunière) plus a few more international dishes. There's a pleasingly local feel to some dishes - Aghadoe black pudding is singled out for mention; finish with classic desserts or farmhouse cheeses. Pricing is fairly moderate (main courses about €12.50-30) and Sunday lunch is especially good value. Children welcome. Restaurant **Seats 56**. No smoking area. D Tue-Sat, 6.30-9.30, à la carte; L Sun only, 1-3; Set Sun L €17. House wine €17. SC discretionary. Restaurant closed D Sun, Mon. Establishment closed Nov. MasterCard, Visa, Diners, Laser. **Directions:** Follow the N72 to Killorglin. Turn left at Beaufort bridge, first stone building on left in village.

Killarney — Bricín

Restaurant   26 High Street Killarney Co. Kerry **Tel: 064 34902** Fax: 064 39030

Upstairs, over a craft shop (which you will find especially interesting if you like Irish pottery, of which there is a very wide range), Paddy & Johnny McGuire's country-style first-floor restaurant has been famous for restoring weary shoppers since 1990 and, although they are no longer open during the day, an early dinner can still round off an afternoon in the town. It's a large area, but broken up into "rooms", which creates a surprisingly intimate atmosphere - and the country mood suits head chef Maighread Forde's wholsesome cooking, in menus offering starters like mussels in white wine sauce or brie tempura with redcurrants and main courses including chargrilled fillet beef and the house speciality, Boxty, which comes with a variety of fillings and a mixed salad. Vegetarian dishes are always available - nutroast, perhaps, served with home-made tomato sauce, potato wedges & salad - and a good range of desserts includes well-balanced choices with plenty of fresh fruit, such as home-made vanilla ie cream with hot raspberrries. A descriptive wine list offers about two dozen bottles in the €16.50-32 band. **Seats 80**. No smoking area; air conditioning. Children welcome. D Mon-Sat, 5.30-9.30. Set D €40, early D (6-7 only), €18; also à la carte. House wine €14. Closed Sun and Dec-Mar. Amex, Diners, MasterCard, Visa, Laser. **Directions:** On the High Street, Killarney.

Killarney | Coolclogher House

Ⓝ Country House   Mill Road Killarney Co. Kerry **Tel: 064 35996** Fax: 064 30933
Email: info@coolclogherhouse.com Web: www.coolclogherhouse.com

Mary and Maurice Harnett's beautiful early Victorian house is just on the edge of Killarney town and yet, tucked away on its 68 acre walled estate, it is an oasis of peace and tranquillity. The house has been extensively restored over the last few years and has many interesting features, including an original conservatory built around a 170 year-old specimen camellia (when camellias were first introduced to Europe, they were mistakenly thought to be tender plants.) Spacious reception rooms are stylishly furnished and comfortable for guests, with newspapers, books, fresh flowers - and open fires in inclement weather - while the four large bedrooms have scenic views over gardens, parkland and mountains. Mary and Maurice enjoy sharing their local knowledge with guests to help them get the most of their stay at what they quite reasonably call 'perhaps the most exclusive accommodation available in Killarney'. Children over 5 welcome. Garden, walking. **Rooms 4** (1 shower only, all no smoking). B&B €85, ss €50. MasterCard, Visa. **Directions:** Leaving Killarney town, take 3rd turning left off the N71 (Muckross Road); gates 1 mile along Mill Road, on right.

Killarney | The Cooperage

Restaurant   Old Market Lane Killarney Co. Kerry **Tel: 064 37716** Fax: 064 37716
Email: chezmart@iol.ie

In an excellent location, in a pedestrianised laneway just off the Glebe public carpark, Martin McCormack and Mo Stafford's striking contemporary restaurant has been pleasing discerning diners consistently since it opened in 1998. A lot of thought went into the decor, which is more than just eye-catching and (unlike many contemporary restaurants) the dining space is comfortable as well as visually impressive - even more so since the fairly recent addition of a lounge area where you can have a relaxing aperitif or after dinner drink. Moody background jazz, played just loud enough for appreciation without interfering with conversation helps make this a restaurant with lots of atmosphere, which is unusual in the modern genre and even more at lunch time as well as evening settings. Better still, the food and service live up to the surroundings: a friendly welcome sets the tone from the outset, followed through by contemporary menus which suggest an element of simplicity and recognition of seasonality and provenance of ingredients as well as eye appeal. Lunch menu are shortish, plus blackboard specials, with more choice in the evening, including game in season (typically a starter of warm game baked loaf with plum chutney and tossed salad leaves) and there's always a list of specials, including several fish dishes. Desserts range from wholesome (apple & mixed berry crumble) to indulgent (rich dark chocolate cake). Apart from a lively atmosphere, what you get here is imaginative good food, well prepared and at reasonable prices (average evening main course about €16). Shortish fairly priced wine list. *The Cooperage was the Guide's Atmospheric Restaurant of the Year in 2001. **Seats 80.** No-smoking area; air conditioning. Children welcome (under parental control). L Mon-Sat 12.30-2.30, D 6-10 daily. A la Carte. House wine €16.45. Closed L Sun, all Mon off-season (Nov-Apr); 25 Dec. MasterCard, Visa, Laser. **Directions:** Located in the heart of Killarney, just off Main St.

Killarney | Dromhall Hotel

Hotel   Muckross Road Killarney Co. Kerry **Tel: 064 39300** Fax: 064 39301
Email: info@dromhall.com Web: www.dromhall.com

A sister hotel to Randles Hotel next door, this completely re-built establishment opened in summer 2000 and includes a leisure centre situated between the two hotels, for their common use. An impressive marbled reception area establishes a positive tone which is confirmed by well-appointed public areas - including Kayne's bar and restaurant where good contemporary food is served - and unusually spacious bedrooms which are furnished to a high standard, with well-designed bathrooms. Conference/banqueting (350/300); business centre; secretarial services; video-conferencing available by arrangement. Leisure centre (17 m indoor pool, gym, sauna, steamroom, therapy suites). Ample parking. **Rooms 72** (23 no smoking, 3 for disabled). Lift. B&B €70 pps, ss €30. Kaynes Bistro: **Seats 76.** D daily, 6-10. Bar meals 12.30-6 daily. Closed Christmas. Amex, Diners, MasterCard, Visa. **Directions:** On right going out of Killarney on the Muckross road, beside Randles Hotel.

Killarney | Earls Court House

Guesthouse   Woodlawn Junction Muckross Road Killarney Co. Kerry **Tel: 064 34009**
Fax: 064 34366 Email: info@killarney-earlscourt.ie Web: www.killarney-earlscourt.ie

Roy and Emer Moynihan's purpose-built guesthouse is quite near the town centre and provides owner-run hotel-type accommodation at a fairly moderate price. The scale is generous: there is plenty of comfortable seating in the large foyer and a sitting room just off it, both furnsihed with antiques. Accommodation has recently been increased to include four suites with canopy beds and spacious bathrooms but all the bedrooms are well-planned and generously-sized, with double and single beds, good bathrooms, phone and satellite TV; tea/coffee-making facilities are available on request. Breakfast is served in a pleasant dining and limited room service is also available. Childre welcome (under 2s free, cot available without charge). Garden. Pets permitted. **Rooms 19** (all no smoking). B&B €68 pps, ss €40. Closed 30 Nov-1 Feb. MasterCard, Visa. **Directions:** Take the firs left at the traffic lights on Muckross road, then 3rd premises.

Killarney — Fuchsia House

Guesthouse   Muckross Road Killarney Co. Kerry **Tel: 064 33743** Fax: 064 36588
Email: fuchsiahouse@eircom.ie Web: www.fuchsiahouse.com

A short walk from the town centre, Toma and Mary Treacy's well-maintained purpose-built guesthouse is set well back from the road, with ample car parking in the front. It offers hotel standard accommodation at fairly moderate prices: spacious bedrooms, which are furnished to a high standard with top quality beds and bedding, have remote-control satellite TV, direct-dial telephone and tea/coffee-making facilities and professional hairdryer - and the well-equipped bathrooms have power showers. The house is surrounded by a lovely garden, which gives protection from the road at the front while also providing a view from a large conservatory (for guests' use) at the back. Children welcome (under 8s free in parents room; cots available without charge; childrens' playroom and playground.) No Pets. **Rooms 9** (all en-suite & no smoking, 1 for disabled). B&B €58pps, ss €20. Open all year. Diners, MasterCard, Visa. **Directions:** N71 south from Killarney 3rd house on the right after traffic lights.

Killarney — Gaby's Seafood Restaurant

Restaurant   27 High St. Killarney Co. Kerry **Tel: 064 32519** Fax: 064 32747

One of Ireland's longest established seafood restaurants, Gaby's has a cosy little bar beside an open fire just inside the door, then several steps lead up to the main dining area, which is cleverly broken up into several sections and has a pleasantly informal atmosphere. Chef-proprietor Gert Maes offers well structured seasonal à la carte menus in classic French style – and in three languages. Absolute freshness is clearly the priority – a note on the menu reminds that availability depends on daily landings – but there's always plenty else to choose from, with steaks and local lamb as back-up. Specialities include wild Atlantic salmon, with chive & lemon cream and red onion marmalade, Atlantic prawns on a bed of tagliatelle in a light garlic sauce and lobster "Gaby": fresh lobster, cognac, wine, cream and spices - cooked to a secret recipe! Lovely desserts include "my mother's recipe" - an old-fashioned apple & raspberry crumble with warm wild honey scented berries, sauce anglaise and caramel ice cream - or you can finish with an Irish cheese selection and freshly brewed coffee. Toilets wheelchair accessible. **Seats 75.** D only, Mon-Sat 6-10pm; à la carte; house wine about €22; sc discretionary. Closed Sun, Christmas/New Year & mid Feb-mid Mar. Amex, Diners, MasterCard, Visa. **Directions:** On the Main Street. ◇

Killarney — Great Southern Hotel Killarney

féile bia Hotel   Killarney Co. Kerry **Tel: 064 31262** Fax: 064 31642
Email: res@killarney.gsh.com Web: www.gshotels.com

This classic railway hotel was established in 1854 and its pillared entrance and ivy-clad facade still convey a sense of occasion - and, now that a major refurbishment programme has been completed with due respect for its age and history, the sparkle has also been restored to the interior of this fine building. A welcoming open fire just inside the door draws guests through to the spacious pillared foyer (where afternoon tea is served) and the adjacent areas - including a homely residents' drawing room and a fine bar, which has also been redeveloped- are also elegant, high-ceilinged rooms with some sense of grandeur, but also a soothing atmosphere which makes a refreshing contrast to the bustle of Killarney town. Accommodation has been dramatically improved, with the introduction of a new range of suites and executive rooms designed to regain the original sense of grandeur in generously-proportioned rooms (with floorspace of up to 500 square feet), elegantly furnished to individual designs with all the necessary modern facilities (modem, email, fax, mini-bar etc). But the pièce de résistance in restoration terms is the great gilt-domed restaurant which has been meticulously refurbished and is now once again a prime example of Victorian opulence. Conference and recreational facilities have also been upgraded - the leisure centre (now known as the Innisfallen Spa) has an extensive range of facilities including an 18 metre pool, jacuzzi, steam room, plunge pool and gym - but perhaps the greatest leisure asset is outside as, belying its central position, the hotel is set in 20 acres of landscaped gardens, providing peace and relaxation on the premises. Conference/banqueting

(800/700); business centre; secretarial services; video conferencing. Leisure centre, swimming pool. Garden. Tennis. Children welcome (under 2s free in parents room; cots available, crèche, playground; children's tea 5.30-6). No pets. **Rooms 172** (2 suites, 34 junior suites, 69 superior rooms, 4 disabled). B&B €140 pps, ss €30 (room-only rate also available: €250, max 3 guests); no SC. Open all year (off-season breaks available). *The moderately priced Torc Great Southern Hotel, is a sister hotel; it makes a good base for a family holiday and for Killarney's championship golf courses - special breaks available. Tel: 064 31611 Fax: 064 31824 Email: res@torc.gsh.ie.

Peppers: While the newly restored Garden Room Restaurant is very grand, Peppers is the hotels' newer bistro-style restaurant. Situated quietly in a corner position behind the bar and overlooking the gardens, it is dashingly decorated in the modern idiom, with high-back chairs, an elegant black, brown and beige/gold colour scheme and (in common with other areas of the hotel) fine paintings. The ambience, professional service and head chef José Caro's imaginative menus and sound cooking made it an immediate success and - unusually for an hotel restaurant - it is now established as one of Killarney's leading eating places. **Seats 60.** D only, Mon-Sat 6.30-9.30. Amex, Diners, MasterCard, Visa, Laser. **Directions:** In the heart of Killarney town beside Railway Station.

Killarney Area — Hotel Dunloe Castle

 Hotel

Beaufort Killarney Co. Kerry **Tel: 064 44111** Fax: 064 44583
Email: sales@kih.liebherr.com Web: www.iol.ie/khl

Sister hotel to the Hotel Europe (Fossa) and Ard-na-Sidhe (Caragh Lake), Dunloe Castle has many features in common with the larger Europe: the style of the building is similar, the same priorities apply – generous space is allowed for all areas throughout, the quality of furnishing is exceptionally high and both maintenance and housekeeping are superb. The original castle is still part of the development, but the hotel is mainly modern and, like the Europe, the atmosphere is distinctly continental. Everything is on a large scale, with wide corridors leading to spacious bedrooms, some with dining areas and all with magnificent views, satellite TV & in-house video, airconditioning and ironing facilities. Major improvements have been made recently, including a re-styling of the exterior to include a new entrance and foyer, a lobby bar, terrrace and a new café. The park around the hotel is internationally renowned for its unique botanical collection, which includes many rare plants. As well as an equestrian centre, the hotel also has its own fishing rights on the River Laune (fishing free of charge to residents; ghillie available on request). Conference/banqueting (150/180). Leisure centre, swimming pool. Snooker, pool table. Garden, fishing, walking, tennis, equestrian. Children welcome (under 2s free in parents' room, cot available without charge; playroom, playground). No pets. **Rooms 110** (1 suite, 40 no smoking). Lift. B&B from €228 (room rate with breakfast, max 2 guests). Closed 1 Oct-mid April. Amex, Diners, MasterCard, Visa. **Directions:** Off main Ring of Kerry road. ◇

Killarney Area — Hotel Europe

Hotel

Fossa Killarney Co. Kerry **Tel: 064 31900** Fax: 064 32118
Email: sales@kih.liebherr.com Web: www.iol.ie/khl

Although now around thirty five years old, the Europe was exceptionally well built and has been so well maintained through the years that it still outshines many a new top level hotel. A facelift to the front façade and improvements to the approach, with landscaping that included the planting of a large number of trees, are the most obvious recent changes but maintenance has always been excellent. Public areas are very large and impressive, furnished to the highest standards and make full use of the hotel's wonderful location. Bedrooms follow a similar pattern, with lots of space, quality furnishings, beautiful views and balconies all along the lake side of the hotel. Leisure facilities include a 25-metre swimming pool, fitness suite and sauna; the hotel adjoins the three Killarney golf clubs - Killeen, Mahony's Point and Lackabane - and the two nine hole courses, Dunloe and Ross, are nearby. The hotel's continental connections show clearly in the style throughout but especially, perhaps, when it comes to food - breakfast, for example, is an impressive hot and cold buffet. Excellent conference and meeting facilities include a 450-seat auditorium with built-in microphones and translation system. Given the high standards and facilities offered, rates are reasonable, and it is also worth inquiring about special breaks. Leisure centre, swimming pool, beauty and hair salons. Equestrian, fishing, (indoor) tennis, snooker. Children welcome (under 12s free in parents room, cot available without charge; playroom, playground). No pets. Lift. **Rooms 204** (8 suites, 60 no smoking, 154 twin rooms). Room Rate from about €228 (max 2 guests), SC incl.

Panorama Restaurant: Aptly-named, this beautifully situated and elegantly appointed restaurant has views over the Lakes of Killarney with the mountains beyond providing a haunting backdrop - a fine setting for classic European cooking which makes full use of local produce like Kerry lamb and salmon through wide-ranging international menus. Table d'hôte and à la carte menus are accurately descriptive (which is unusual at the moment) and offer something to please everyone, including vegetarians. Lovely breads are made in-house - and there's a very extensive range offered at breakfast. Starters might include a well-flavoured seasonal soup and Westphalian ham (presumably from the excellent German butchers shop across the road, which is well worth a visit) appropriately served with a freshly-made coleslaw. This might be followed by a sorbet, or maybe marinated local salmon with rösti & horseradish cream then main courses such as suckling pig in caraway jus, or duck breast in Madeira sauce, served with well-matched vegetables. Delicious desserts - chocolate marquise with redcurrants, maybe, or cherry clafoutis with Black Forest ice cream - then a slow coffee as you watch the light fading behind the mountains... Service is pleasant and very efficient. [*A separate informal restaurant, The Brasserie, offers popular all day food, 11am-11pm daily.] **Seats 450**. D daily, 7-9.30. Set 4-course D about €54. House wine about €25. Hotel closed mid Nov-mid Mar. Amex, Diners, MasterCard, Visa. **Directions:** On main Ring of Kerry road. ◇

Killarney — Kathleen's Country House

Guesthouse Tralee Road Killarney Co. Kerry **Tel: 064 32810** Fax: 064 32340
Email: info@kathleens.net Web: www.kathleens.net

Long before the new wave of purpose-built guesthouses, Kathleen O'Regan Sheppard was offering hotel standard accommodation at guesthouse prices, and this family-run business continues to offer good value, hospitality and comfort in a quiet location – in gardens just a mile from the town centre. All of the individually decorated rooms are non-smoking and furnished to a high standard, with orthopaedic beds, phone, TV, tea/coffee-making facilities and bathrooms with both bath and shower. There is plenty of room to relax in this immaculately maintained house and excellent breakfasts are served in a spacious dining room overlooking the garden. Golf, fishing, pony-trekking, horse riding, walking, cycling and tennis are all nearby, also some of the country's most beautiful scenic drives. Everything served at breakfast is based on the finest produce, local where possible, and beautifully presented - a speciality fresh fruit plate, for example, is as pretty as a picture and, like many other things around the house, reflects Kathleen's love of art. Special rates are offered off-season. Not suitable for very young children (over 5s welcome). **Rooms 17** (all no smoking, 1 for disabled). B&B about €58 pps, ss about €45. Closed early Nov-mid Mar. Amex, MasterCard, Visa. **Directions:** 1 mile north of Killarney Town off N22 (Tralee road).

Killarney — Killarney Lodge

Guesthouse Countess Road Killarney Co. Kerry **Tel: 064 36499** Fax: 064 31070
Email: klylodge@iol.ie Web: www.killarneylodge.net

Catherine Treacy's fine purpose-built guesthouse is set in private walled gardens just a couple of minutes walk from the town centre. It has large en-suite air-conditioned bedrooms with all the amenities expected of an hotel room, including direct dial phone and TV, and large public rooms to relax in. Children welcome (under 10s free in parents room; cots available without charge). Wheelchair accessible. No pets. Garden. Own parking. **Rooms 16** (2 junior suites, 14 superior, 1 shower only, 1 for disabled, all no smoking). B&B €60 pps, ss€40; no sc. Closed 15 Nov-15 Feb. Amex, Diners, MasterCard, Visa, Laser. **Directions:** 2 minutes walk from town centre off Muckross Road.

Killarney — Killarney Park Hotel

🏛 Hotel Kenmare Place Killarney Co. Kerry

Tel: 064 35555 Fax: 064 35266
Email: info@killarneyparkhotel.ie Web: killarneyparkhotel.ie

Situated in its own grounds, a short stroll from the town centre, the Treacy family's luxurious, well run hotel is deceptively modern - despite its classical good looks, it only celebrated its first decade in March 2002. However it has already undergone a transformation, with the refurbishment of all public areas and the leisure centre, the addition of two penthouse suites, several new junior suites and a state-of-the-art conference room. Indeed, constant improvement is so much a theme here that it is hard to keep up with developments as they occur. There is an exceptionally welcoming atmosphere as you pass through Reception into a series of seating areas, with fires and invitingly grouped sofas and armchairs; the same sense of comfort characterises the Garden Bar (which has a sheltered terrace for fine days) and also the quiet Library, which provides a relaxing haven. Public areas generally have an elegant Victorian feel, enhanced by the sweeping staircase that leads to bedrooms that are

furnished in contemporary country house style, with great attention to detail. Housekeeping is immaculate and luxurious suites and deluxe rooms are spacious, with air conditioning, a private entrance hall and a sitting area with fireplace creating a real home from home feeling - and all rooms have been thoughtfully and individually designed, with well-planned bathrooms, judiciously selected antiques and the many small details that make a hotel room really comfortable - a decent hair dryer, iron as well as trouser press, bathrobes & slippers, multi music system as well as satellite TV, and the security of an in-room safe. Most importantly, of course, the staff at this family-run hotel are committed to looking after guests with warmth and discretion, making it an ideal choice for both business and pleasure - and a worthy winner of our Hotel of the Year Award in 2002. (The much older Ross Hotel, nearby, is a smaller sister hotel and equally delightful in its way). Conference/banqueting (150); business centre; secretarial services, video conferencing (on request). Leisure centre, swimming pool, sauna, plunge pool, jacuzzi pool; treatment rooms. Library; billiard room. Garden, walking, cycling. Children welcome (under 2s free in parents room; cots available without charge, playroom). No Pets. **Rooms 70** (3 suites, 25 junior suites, 30 no-smoking, 1 for disabled). Lift. 24 hour room service. B&B €180 pps, ss €180; no sc. Closed 9 -27 Dec.
The Park Restaurant: It is hard to credit that this large and opulent room with its ornate ceiling, heavy drapes and grand paintings is little over ten years old - and due for refurbishment in 2003. Unashamedly designed in the style of the grand hotel dining rooms of yesteryear, the restaurant underlines this hotel's respect for the best of traditional hospitality and it is appropriate that head chef Odran Lucey (who joined the hotel in 1999) should have come here from The Merrion Hotel, Dublin,where the same values are upheld. A lengthy à la carte menu is available in high season, otherwise a table d'hôte with several choices is offered. A house speciality that indicates the style is escalope of foie gras served with Clonakilty black pudding, apple compôte and deep-fried celeriac - a nicely-judged combination of old and new traditions. Similarly a main course of roast duckling (a popular choice in the south-west of Ireland where there are some excellent producers), might be accompanied by champ mash and an elderberry and whiskey jus. A mood of gentle formality pervades, enhanced by courteous service and the presence of a pianist who plays throughout dinner. The wide-ranging wine list includes many of the classics and, not only a fair choice of half bottles, but also a sommelier's choice of the week, offering half a dozen good wines by the glass. An interesting feature of the restaurant is an open wine cellar which guests are free to browse Restaurant seats 150 (private room,40). No smoking area; air conditioning. D daily 7-9.30; L Sun only,12-2. Set D €50. House wines from €24. SC discretionary. Amex, Diners, MasterCard, Visa, Laser.
Directions: Located in Killarney town - all access routes lead to town centre.

Killarney — Killarney Royal

Hotel   College Street Killarney Co. Kerry **Tel: 064 31853** Fax: 064 34001
Email: royalhot@iol.ie Web: www.killarneyroyal.ie

This charming older sister to the luxurious Hayfield Manor Hotel in Cork city (see entry) has recently completed a major refurbishment programme and the results, in an elegant period style that is totally appropriate to the age and design of the building, are very impressive. No expense has been spared to ensure the highest quality of materials and workmanship, air conditioning has been installed throughout the hotel and rooms have been individually designed, all with marble bathrooms and sitting areas. Conference/banqueting (50/110); business centre, video-conferencing. Wheelchair accessible. Children welcome (under 7s free in parents room; cots available). Pets permitted by arrangement. No on-site parking (arrangement with nearby car park.) **Rooms 29** (5 junior suites, 6 no-smoking). 24 hour room service. B&B about €115 pps, ss about €60. Restaurant open L (12.30-2.30) &D (6.30-9.30) daily; bar meals 12-9 daily. Closed 23-27 Dec. Amex, Diners, MasterCard, Visa, Laser. **Directions:** Located in Killarney Town Centre on College Street off the N22.

Killarney — Killeen House Hotel

Hotel   Aghadoe Killarney Co. Kerry **Tel: 064 31711** Fax: 064 31811
Email: charming@indigo.ie Web: www.killeenhousehotel.com

Just 10 minutes drive from Killarney town centre and 5 minutes from Killeen and Mahoney's Point golf courses, this early nineteenth century rectory has become Michael and Geraldine Rosney's "charming little hotel". You don't have to be a golfer to stay here but it must help, specially in the pubby little bar, which is run as an "honour" bar with guest's golf balls accepted as tender. Most visitors clearly relish the bonhomie, which includes addressing guests by first names. Rooms vary in size but all have full bathrooms (one with jacuzzi) and are freshly-decorated, with phone and satellite TV. There's a comfortable traditional drawing room with an open fire for guests, furnished with a mixture of antiques and newer furniture. The hotel is popular with business gests as well as golfers; secretarial services are available, also all day room service. The dining room is open to non-residents. Children welcome (under 12s free in parents' room; cots available without charge). Pets permitted by arrangement. Garden. **Rooms 23** (all en-suite). B&B €67.50 pps, ss €42.50; sc10%. D daily, 7-10; Set D €40, house wine €19.05, restaurant sc discretionary. Closed 1 Nov - 1 Easter. Amex, Diners, MasterCard, Visa. **Directions:** 4 miles from Killarney - just off Dingle Road.

Killarney — Lake Hotel

Hotel   Muckross Road Killarney Co. Kerry **Tel: 064 31035** Fax: 064 31902
Email: lakehotel@eircom.net Web: www.lakehotel.com

Coming into town from Kenmare on the N71, the Huggard family's exceptionally beautifully located hotel is set well back from the road right on the lake shore, with the ruins of McCarthy Mor Castle within the grounds. The hotel was built in 1820 and visited by Queen Victoria when she came to Ireland in 1861 - the hotel still has the original horse-drawn carriage in which she travelled and the spacious high-ceilinged lounges with open log fires also date back to the nineteenth century and give the central area of the hotel real period character. Much-needed refurbishment of the accommodation has recently taken place although in some areas the style of development may seem at odds with the history and old-world character of the original hotel - changes include the addition of 24 new junior suites, with jacuzzis and private balconies overlooking the lakes and, somewhat bizarrely, three wacky Roman and Medieval themed "fantasy suites", which have baths in the bedrooms. Other bedrooms are comfortably furnished in a more conventional style and have the usual modern amenities, although the decor in some rooms may seem a little dated. Exceptionally friendly and helpful staff make every effort to please guests. Conference/banqueting 55/120. Fitness centre with gym, steam room, sauna and hot tub was due to open shortly after the guide went to press. Own fishing, tennis, garden, walking. Children welcome (under 3s free in parents room; cots available without charge). No Pets. Lift. **Rooms 70** (3 theme suites, 35 junior suites). B&B from about €80 pps, ss from €20. Closed mid Dec-Feb. Amex, Diners, MasterCard, Visa, Laser. **Directions:** 18.5 miles from Killarney Town on Muckross Rd.

Killarney — The Old Presbytery Restaurant

Ⓝ Restaurant   Cathedral Place Killarney Co. Kerry **Tel: 064 30555** Fax: 064 30557
Email: oldpresbytery@eircom.net Web: www.oldpresbytery.com

Gerry Browne and Mary Rose Hickey opened their new restaurant in this impressive, beautifully restored 3-storey building in 2001 and it has now taken its place as one of Killarney's leading fine dining establishments. It's very pleasing at several levels: friendly, efficient reception, a comfortable, spacious bar area for aperitifs and elegant, well-appointed dining areas on two floors - the ground floor space is broken up into several small areas, while the first floor provides a large dining room which can be used for private parties. And all this before considering Simon Regan's well-balanced modern menus, which offer nine or ten dishes on each course, including at least one attractive vegetarian main course (and several suitable starters). Simon Regan's previous experience at Dromoland Castle and The Merrion Hotel, Dublin, indicate what to expect - high quality ingredients, sophisticated, attractively-presented dishes and able cooking; all these qualities were noted in dishes recently enjoyed, including a tasty mille feuille of goat cheese & beef tomato, with spinach & red pepper coulis, perfectly cooked seabass with angel hair pasta and a lovely dessert of sautéed strawberries in port, with hazelnut ice cream. Details include good home-baked breads and the generally high standard of food and cooking here are greatly enhanced by excellent staff, who are very professional and cheerful - and a pianist, who plays every night, adds to the atmosphere. Children welcome. Private car park. **Seats 110** (private room, 50). No smoking area; air conditioning. Toilets wheelchair accessible. D Wed-Mon, 6.30-10. A la carte; house wines (15), €21. SC discretionary. Amex, Diners, MasterCard, Visa, Laser. **Directions:** Opposite St Marys Cathedral.

Killarney — Panis Angelicus

Café   15 New Street Killarney Co. Kerry **Tel: 064 39648**

New Street is just the place for this stylish contemporary café and breadshop - the tempting display of freshly baked breads, scones and gateaux will draw you in and then you'll be hooked by the aroma of freshly brewed Italian coffee - which is served with homemade biscuits or Belgian chocolates. No matter what time you drop in there will be plenty to tempt, even if it's just homemade soup with a gourmet sandwich (homebaked Limerick ham with wholegrain Irish mustard, perhaps) or a hot Irish potato cake with garlic butter, green salad and crusty bread. Outside of meal times you can just have that cup of tea or coffee - and maybe take some goodies home for later. Dinner menus are more ambitious and offer a wide choice while retaining a fresh, youthful approach. Unusually, Panis Angelicus not only offers interesting vegetarian food but also specialises in gluten free breads, soups, sauces and desserts. **Seats 35.** No smoking area. Children welcome. Open daily from 10am (to 9.30 pm in summer, 5.30 in winter); L 12-4, D Thu-Mon 6.30-9.30. House wine from €15. Closed D Tue-Wed in Summer; closed at night from Oct. MasterCard, Visa, Laser. **Directions:** Opposite Credit Union.

Killarney — Randles Court Hotel

Hotel   Muckross Road Killarney Co. Kerry **Tel: 064 35333** Fax: 064 35206
Email: info@randlescourt.com Web: www.randlescourt.com

Within easy walking distance of the town centre, but also convenient to attractions such as Muckross House and Killarney National Park, this family-owned and managed hotel has been developed around an attractive house originally built in 1906 as a family residence and extensively refurbished before opening as an hotel in 1992. Although it has grown a little since then it still has some of the domesticity and warmth of the family home - period features, including fireplaces and stained glass windows, have been retained and comfortably furnished public rooms include a small bar, a large drawing room with log fire, tapestries and antiques and an elegant restaurant, Checkers, which opens onto a sheltered patio. Spacious bedrooms are furnished to a high standard, with direct dial telephones, satellite television, radio, hair dryers and well-appointed bathrooms - less "country house" than the public areas. perhaps, but very comfortable. Leisure facilities shared with the neighbouring sister hotel, Dromhall (and accessible from both hotels), include a 17 metre pool, sauna, steamroom, gym and treatment rooms. Conference/banqueting (80/30), secretarial services, video-conferencing (on request). Children welcome (under 5s free in parents' room, cot available without charge). Own parking. Pets permitted by arrangement. *There is a sister hotel in Clonakilty, Co Cork (see entry). **Rooms 52** (3 junior suites, 12 executive, 2 shower only, some no smoking). Lift. 24 hour room service. B&B €85 pps, ss €35, SC inc. Checkers Restaurant: D daily, 7-9.30. Closed Christmas. Amex, Diners, MasterCard, Visa, Laser. **Directions:** On way out of Killarney by Muckross Road, on left just before Dromhall Hotel.

Killorglin — Nick's Seafood Restaurant & Piano Bar

Restaurant   Lr Bridge Street Killorglin Co. Kerry **Tel: 066 976 1219** Fax: 066 976 1233

This is one of the famous old restaurants of Ireland and Nick Foley's cooking – classic French with an Irish accent– has earned a particular reputation for his way with local seafood, although there are always other choices, notably prime Kerry beef and lamb. Moules marinière or provençale, lobster thermidor, shellfish mornay and peppered steak in brandy cream sauce are all typical of his classic style. Vegetarians aren't forgotten either – there's a choice of three dishes on the regular menu. Dessert choices are changed daily and there's a good cheeseboard. Aside from providing excellent food, Nick's is also renowned for its music and great atmosphere. Children welcome. **Seats 80** (private room,30). No-smoking area; air conditioning. D Wed-Sun 6.30-10 in winter, daily in summer. Set D about €40 Extensive wine list; house wine about €20; sc discretionary. Closed all Nov, Mon-Tue in Dec-Mar & Christmas. Amex, Diners, MasterCard, Visa. **Directions:** On the Ring Road of Kerry, 20 km from Killarney. ◇

Listowel — Listowel Arms Hotel

féile bia Hotel   Listowel Co. Kerry **Tel: 068 21500** Fax: 068 22524
Email: listowelarms@ireland.com

This much-loved old hotel is rich in history and especially famous as the main venue for the annual Listowel Writers Week. Since 1996 the hotel has been blessed with the energetic and discerning ownership of Kevin O'Callaghan, who has overseen a major extension and overhaul of the whole premises during the last few years. The extension has provided a new restaurant, kitchen, banqueting area and new bedrooms, all overlooking the River Feale; improvements have all been done with great sensitivity, so greater comfort has been gained throughout the hotel without loss of character. Non-residents find this a handy place to drop into for a bite in the bar where they serve lovely traditional dishes like braised beef & stout casserole (L12-3, D5.30-9.30) and you can have tea or coffee in the lounge at other times. Conference/banqueting (500/400); video-conferencing, ISDN lines. Wheelchair accessible. Lift. Children welcome (under 5s free in parents' room, cots available without charge). Pets permitted by arrangement. **Rooms 37** (all en-suite). B&B from €55 pps, ss €20. (Higher rates apply to Festival weeks, incl Irish Open & Listowel Race Week.) Closed 24-26 Dec. **Directions:** In the corner of the historic old square in Listowel town centre.

Portmagee — The Moorings

Restaurant/Pub/Guesthouse   Portmagee Co. Kerry **Tel: 066 947 7108** Fax: 066 947 7220
Email: moorings@iol.ie Web: www.moorings.ie

Gerard & Patricia Kennedy's fine guesthouse overlooks the harbour and many bedrooms - which are comfortably furnished with phone, TV, tea/coffee making facilities and full bathrooms - have a sea view. Children welcome (under 3s free in parents' room, cot available without charge). No pets. **Rooms** 14 (all en-suite) B&B €40 pps, ss €12.50. Reliably good food is available in the Bridge Bar (12-8 daily) and the restaurant (D Tue-Sun 6-10), all à la carte. Seafood stars and the style is fairly traditional - chowder, seafood selection, deep-fried brie for starters; main courses of seafood platter, poached salmon, steaks - and lobster, which is quite moderately priced. House wine €17.50. Restaurant closed Mon. Establishment closed 1 Nov-1 Mar. MasterCard, Visa, Laser. **Directions:** Turn right for Portmagee 3 miles outside Caherciveen on the Waterville Road.

Sneem — Parknasilla Great Southern Hotel

féile bia Hotel

Sneem Co. Kerry **Tel:** 064 45122 Fax: 064 45323
Email: res@parknasilla-gsh.com Web: www.gshotels.com

Set in 300 acres of sub-tropical parkland, overlooking Kenmare Bay, this classic Victorian hotel is blessed with one of the most beautiful locations in Ireland. The spacious foyer with its antiques and fresh flowers sets a tone of quiet luxury, enhanced by the hotel's impressive collection of original art (currently being catalogued). Whether activity or relaxation is required there are excellent amenities at hand – including an outdoor swimming pool and Canadian hot tub - and an abundance of comfortable places (including a no-smoking drawing room) for a quiet read or afternoon tea. Public rooms include an impressive restaurant and a library (added in 1995 for the hotel's centenary and available for the use of all guests, although also ideal for meetings and small conferences). Bedrooms vary in size and outlook but most have been upgraded recently and all have en-suite bathrooms with bath and shower, tea/coffee making facilities, direct-dial telephone, radio, TV with in-house movie channel, trouser press and hair dryer. Afternoon tea at Parknasilla is a relaxing affair, served in the spacious interconnecting lounges along the front of the hotel. An impressive range of outdoor activities available on-site includes walking (routes marked, map available), golf (9 hole), horseriding, inshore and deep sea fishing and cruises on the hotel's own boat, Parknasilla Princess – this is a place to slow down and take time for yourself. Children welcome (under 2s free in parents' room; cots available without charge; children's tea 5.30-6) Leisure centre, swimming pool. Golf, tennis, snooker, fishing, equestrian, walking. No Pets. **Rooms** 84 (1 suite, 8 junior suites, 13 superior rooms, 1 for disabled). Lift. 24 hour room service. B&B €140, ss €30. No SC. Open all year. Amex, Diners, MasterCard, Visa, Laser. **Directions:** 30 miles outside Killarney, past Kenmare in Sneem Village.

Tahilla — Tahilla Cove Country House

Country House/Guesthouse

Tahilla Cove Sneem Co. Kerry **Tel:** 064 45204 Fax: 064 45104
Email: tahillacove@eircom.net Web: www.tahillacove.com

This family-run guesthouse feels more like a small hotel – it has a proper bar, for example, with its own entrance (which is used by locals as well as residents). This is a low-key place, with an old country house in there somewhere (which has been much added to) and there is a blocky annexe in the garden. It has two very special features, however: the location, which is genuinely waterside, is really lovely and away-from-it-all; and the owners, James and Deirdre Waterhouse. Tahilla Cove has been in the family since 1948, and run since 1987 by James and Deirdre – who have the wisdom to understand why their many regulars love it just the way it is and, apart from regular maintenance (and some recent major refurbishment) little is allowed to change. Comfort and relaxation are the priorities. All the public rooms have sea views, including the dining room and a large sitting room, with plenty of armchairs and sofas, which opens onto a terrace (where there are patio tables and chairs overlooking the garden and the cove with its little stone jetty). Accommodation is divided between the main house and another close by; rooms vary considerably but all except two have sea views, many have private balconies and all are en-suite, with bathrooms of varying sizes and appointments (only one single is shower-only). All rooms have phone, TV, hair-dryer and individually controlled heating. Food is prepared personally by the proprietors and, although the dining room is mainly intended for residents, others are welcome when there is room – James and Deirdre cook for guests and their simple 4-course country house style menus change daily – and light bar food is available from noon to 10 pm. (It's a lovely place to drop into for a cup of tea overlooking the little harbour). Garden; walking; fishing. Wheelchair accessible. Children welcome. Pets permitted in some areas. **Rooms** 9 (1 shower only, 5 no smoking). B&B €60 pps, ss €20. Closed mid Oct-Easter. Amex, Diners, MasterCard, Visa. **Directions:** 11 miles west of Kenmare and 5 miles east of Sneem (N70).

Tralee — Abbey Gate Hotel

féile bia Hotel

Maine Street Tralee Co. Kerry **Tel:** 066 712 9888 Fax: 066 712 9821
Email: info@abbeygate-hotel.com Web: www.abbeygate-hotel.com

Situated in a relatively quiet corner in the centre of Tralee, this big modern hotel makes a good base for a family break as it's moderately priced and children are welcome; although there isn't an on-site leisure centre, there's an outdoor playground and informal eating arrangements (with children's menu) - and Tralee's famous Aquadome is nearby. On arrival it's quite impressive, with a large marble-floored foyer and lounge area (that makes a good meeting place); recently refurbished bedrooms are a good size, comfortably furnished in a modern style with usual amenities including phone, satellite TV, tea/coffee-making facilities and well-finished en-suite bathrooms (all with bath and shower). *Toscana Ristorante, accessible from the hotel foyer or from the street, is an attractive contemporary restaurant with a wide-ranging Italian menu: authentic Italian cooking at very fair prices. Off-season & special breaks available. Children under 4 free in parents room; cots available without charge. Own parking (and multi-storey carpark nearby). No pets. **Rooms 100** (8 for disabled). B&B €76.95 pps, ss €40. 'Bistro Marché' restaurant: L12.30-2.30 &D6.30-9.45 daily; 'Old Market Place' pub: bar meals 12-9.45 daily; Toscana Ristorante Italiano: D Tue-Sat, 6-10. Closed 25 Dec. Amex, Diners, MasterCard, Visa, Switch. **Directions:** Town centre.

Tralee   Ballygarry House Hotel

féile bia Hotel   Killarney Road Tralee Co. Kerry **Tel: 066 712 3322** Fax: 066 712 3322
Email: ballygarry@eircom.net Web: ballygarry.com

Recently renovated and upgraded to a high standard, this pleasant roadside hotel presents a neat face to arriving guests and also has extensive landscaped gardens. The furnishing style is traditional with occasional contemporary twists; warm colours, notably in oriental rugs used on wooden floors, create a welcoming atmosphere in public areas and darkwood furniture in bedrooms is used to effect against contrasting furnishings and pale walls. This is an appealing hotel and moderately priced. Conference/banqueting 150/450. Children welcome (free in parents' room under 6, cot available without charge).garden. No pets. **Rooms 46** (1 for disabled). Lift. B&B about €85pps, ss about €50, sc 12.5%. Special breaks available. Closed 16-28 Dec. Amex, MasterCard, Visa. **Directions:** 1 mile outside Tralee town on the Killarney road. ◇

Tralee   Barrow Guest House

🏛 Guesthouse   West Barrow Ardfert Tralee Co. Kerry
Tel: 066 713 6437 Fax: 066 713 6402
Email: info@barrowhouse.com Web: www.barrowhouse.com

In a stunning shoreside position on Barrow Harbour, this recently renovated guesthouse dates back to 1723 and was once home to the Knight of Kerry. Despite occasional reminders of the modern world from a nearby road, the house has largely retained its unique tranquil setting - and the front bedrooms and public rooms, which include a period drawing room and a breakfast room, where both buffet and hot breakfasts are served, all have wonderful views across water to the Slieve Mish Mountains and Dingle peninsula. Bedrooms are spacious and extremely comfortable, with orthopaedic beds, phone/ISDN lines, satellite TV, bathrobes, tea/coffee facilities and lovely bathrooms, some with jacuzzi baths; everything has has been completed to a very high standard, albeit with a hint of the hotel about some of the furnishings. Angling and golf are major attractions - the Arnold Palmer designed Tralee Golf Club is next door and Killarney, Ballybunion and Waterville are within range - and a helicopter service makes travelling to neighbouring golf courses easier. Children welcome (under 2s free in parents' room; cot available). No dinner, but good restaurants nearby (see entries under Fenit and Tralee). Some rooms are in an adjacent courtyard. garden, fishing, walking. **Rooms 16** (1 suite, 3 superior rooms, 1 for disabled, all no-smoking). B&B €50 pps, ss €20. MasterCard, Visa, Amex, Laser. **Directions:** Follow the R558 after Oyster Tavern follow signs to Churchill and straight on for 4 kms.

Tralee   The Brandon Hotel

Hotel   Princes Street Tralee Co. Kerry
Tel: 066 712 3333 Fax: 066 712 5019

Overlooking a park and the famous Siamsa Tire folk theatre, and close to the Aquadome, Tralee's largest hotel is at the heart of activities throughout the area. Spacious public areas are quite impressive, and while some bedrooms are on the small side, all have been recently refurbished and have direct-dial phone, radio and TV (no tea/coffee-making facilities) and tiled bathrooms. There's a well-equipped leisure centre and good banqueting/conference facilities. B&B from about €45 pps. Closed 22-29 Dec. Amex, Diners, MasterCard, Visa. **Directions:** Town centre. ◇

Tralee — Brook Manor Lodge

Guesthouse — Fenit Road Tralee Co. Kerry **Tel: 066 7120406**
Fax: 066 7127552 Email: brookmanor@eircom.net

Set back from the road, in 3.5 acres of grounds, Vincent and Margaret O'Sullivan's large purpose-built guesthouse offers immaculate accommodation and warm hospitality. Public rooms and bedrooms are spacious and very comfortably furnished - bedrooms have generous beds and all the usual modern facilities - TV, phone, trouser press, tea/coffee making, hair dryer and radio/alarm - everything, in short, that the traveller (and, specifically, the golfing traveller) could need. Breakfast is a special point of pride, cooked to order from an extensive menu. Not very suitable for children, but concessions are given (under 8s free in parents' room, cot available free of charge). No pets. **Rooms 8** (1 suite, 1 junior suite, 2 superior rooms, 2 shower only, 1 for disabled, all no smoking.) B&B €55, ss €10; no SC. Open all year. Amex, MasterCard, Visa. **Directions:** 2 km from town centre on Fenit road.

Tralee — Castlemorris House

Accommodation — Ballymullen Tralee Co. Kerry **Tel: 066 718 0060**
Fax: 066 712 8007 Email: castlemorris@eircom.net

Mary and Paddy Barry's attractive creeper-clad Victorian house makes a lovely place to stay, with good home baking (complimentary afternoon tea in front of the drawing room fire on arrival) and the friendly atmosphere of a family home. Bedrooms are spacious and well-furnished for comfort with style. Breakfast is a speciality and dinner is available by arrangement. Garden. Children welcome (cot available). Pets allowed in some areas. **Rooms 6** (4 shower only). B&B €52 pps, no ss. Closed 24-29 Dec. Amex, MasterCard, Visa. **Directions:** on Killorglin road (Ring of Kerry) leaving Tralee.

Tralee — Meadowlands Hotel

féile bia Hotel — Oakpark Tralee Co. Kerry **Tel: 066 718 0444** Fax: 066 718 0964
Email: medlands@iol.ie Web: www.meadowlands-hotel.com

This hotel in a peaceful part of the town is set in 3 acres of grounds and landscaped gardens, within walking distance of the town centre. Open since 1998, the high quality of materials and workmanship is now paying off as the building mellows and takes on its own personality - and this, together with caring service from well-trained staff, is ensuring its position as one of Tralee's leading hotels. The interior layout and design are impressive; notably the whole hotel is wheelchair friendly and furniture, commissioned from Irish craft manufacturers, is interesting, well-made and practical. Stylish, well-designed bedrooms are spacious and comfortable, with striking decor and the suites have jacuzzis. The main restaurant, An Pota Stóir, is open in the evening only (except Sunday lunch) and booking is advised as it is popular with locals as well as residents. Informal meals (notably seafood, from the proprietor's fishing boats) are available in the bar, Johnny Franks, every day (12.30-9, Sat to 8). New conference and leisure centres due to open as the guide goes to press: conference/banqueting (200/140). Leisure centre: 17m swimming pool, gym, steam room, sauna, jacuzzi, therapies. Garden. Children welcome (cots available, free of charge). Wheelchair accessible. No pets. **Rooms 58** (3 suites, 9 superior rooms, 17 no smoking, 1 for disabled). Lift. 24 hour room service. B&B €100 pps, ss €20. Off-season value breaks available. Closed 24-26 Dec. MasterCard, Visa, Amex, Diners, Laser. **Directions:** 1km from Tralee town centre on the N69.

Tralee — Oyster Tavern

Pub/Restaurant — The Spa Tralee Co. Kerry **Tel: 066 7136102** Fax: 066 7136047

This well-maintained roadside bar and restaurant has achieved high standards of food and service over a long period of time, earning a loyal local following. Wide-ranging menus specialising in seafood are moderately priced and, although the style is largely traditional, there are some unusual dishes - a starter terrine of crayfish & crab with seaweed, for example - and some unfamiliar varieties, such as Black Scabbard and Red Emperor. A shorter choice of non-seafood dishes offers prime meat and poultry and a couple of vegetarian dishes. Sunday lunch is especially good value and very popular. Bar open usual hours (no food served in the bar). Restaurant **Seats 140**. D daily, 5-10.15 (Sun from 6), L Sun only 12.30-2.30. Set Sun L €16, D à la carte, House wine from €15. Closed 25 Dec, Good Fri. Diners, MasterCard, Visa, Laser. **Directions:** 4 miles outside Tralee, on the Fenit road.

Tralee — Restaurant David Norris

☆ Restaurant

Ivy House Ivy Terrace Tralee Co. Kerry
Tel: 066 7185654 Fax: 066 7126600

Restaurant David Norris opened to some acclaim in December 2000 and is now established as Tralee's leading fine dining restaurant. Although located on the first floor of an unprepossessing modern building, it has a nice little reception area with a sofa and stools at a small bar and simple, tasteful decor with lots of plates on the walls and lightwood furniture in the Charles Rennie Macintosh style. Well-spaced tables are dressed with quality linen, plain glasses and white china, relieved by fresh flowers. A Euro-Toques chef, David Norris's sourcing is immaculate: ingredients are organic wherever possible and everything served is handmade on the premises (breads, pasta, ice creams). The emphasis is on taste, and presentation that is beautiful but not over-elaborate - and the aim is to offer the best of food at reasonable prices. This he seems to be achieving very successfully: there's a sense of excitement and energy in seasonal menus which are quite simply written and, while very promising, are not over-ambitious in extent. About five choices are offered on each course of the set dinner menu, although a wide-ranging selection of specials effectively doubles that choice and provides an à la carte option. Seafood is well-represented, as would be expected in this area, but the range of foods offered is wide - Kerry beef may top the bill, for example (with black pepper mash, caramelised onions & lemon thyme, perhaps), also lamb (roast loin, with sautéed new potatoes and onions, red wine & rosemary juices is typical of a summer menu) - and vegetarian dishes like roasted vegetables with white bean purée in puff pastry with poached egg & asparagus tips would tempt the hardiest carnivore. Classic desserts, which include speciality handmade ice creams, round off the meal in style, or there are Irish farmhouse cheeses, served with fresh fruit, home-made preserves and biscuits. Thoughtful detail is evident throughout, from the complimentary amuse-bouche that arrives with your aperitif to the home-made fudge served with your tea or coffee. Excellent cooking, professional service, an informative but sensibly limited wine list and good value for money are all winning this fine restaurant many friends. **Seats 40**. No smoking area. D Tue-Sat, 6.30-10. Set D €32-38; à la carte also available. House wine €17.95; sc discretionary, except 10% (charged on food only) on parties of 10+. Closed Sun, Mon, 1 week Nov, 2 weeks Jan/Feb. Amex, MasterCard, Visa, Laser. **Directions:** Facing Siamsa Tire.

Tralee — Restaurant Uno

Restaurant

14 Princes Street Tralee Co. Kerry **Tel: 066 718 1950**
Fax: 066 718 1951 Email: unos1@eircom.net

Patrick Fitzgibbon and Maeve Duff have built up a great following since taking over these premises just across the road from the town park in 1999. The restaurant is in several areas: a cosy front room doubles as reception and opens into a second high-ceilinged room which is brightly lit and more modern in style, with extra seating also in a balcony area above it. Menus favour the contemporary side of the restaurant's psyche, with a leaning toward Cal-Ital and global influences plus a seasoning of more traditional dishes - thus starters like crispy duck spring roll with sweet chilli dip and spring with smoked chicken, spicy tomato & roast red pepper sauce alongside soup of the day and that enduring favourite, deep fried breaded mushrooms with seasonal leaves and garlic mayonnaise. Similarly, main courses range from Thai red chicken or vegetable curry with coconut rice & poppadums to honey roast duckling and steaks, almost all under €20, and there will always be about five daily specials on. Desserts are quite traditional - home-made tiramisu, crème brûlée, hot apple pie with cream - and the wine list is short (on choice and information) but well-balanced and includes half a dozen house wines. All round this buzzy place is offering a fair deal. Not suitable for children after 8 pm. **Seats 65** (private room 25). No smoking area. L Tue-Fri, 12.30-2.15; D Tue-Sun 5.30-9.30 (Sun from 4); à la carte. House wine from €15.50. Closed L Sat & Sun, all Mon, 25-27 Dec, 1 Jan, 2 weeks in Jan. Amex, Diners, MasterCard, Visa, Laser. **Directions:** Beside Brandon Hotel.

Tralee — Val O'Shea's Bar & Bistro

 Pub/Restaurant

Bridge Street Tralee Co. Kerry
Tel: 066 712 1559 Fax: 066 712 5495

This is the happening place for informal dining and music. Very stylish, designer-driven, it's all of a piece with tinted windows, very dark woods and very dark leather on seats and bar stools - and traditional music most week nights (phone for details). Differing floor heights are cleverly exploited, and there's a mammoth feature area at the bottom of the stairs up to the bistro, which looks like an enormous three-sided sofa seating about 10 people. Although gloomy if you come in out of bright sunlight, the lighting is subtle but effective once your eyes adjust. Consistent standards, of both bar and the upstairs bistro food, have been maintained even when there have been changes of personnel, so the policy of providing quality and good value is likely to continue. Bistro **Seats 50**. Air conditioning. L Mon-Sat,12.30-2.30; D daily 6-10. Closed Sun L, 3 days Christmas, Good Fri. MasterCard, Visa. **Directions:** Town centre, beside Abbey carpark. ◇

Waterville — Butler Arms Hotel

Hotel   Waterville Co. Kerry **Tel: 066 947 4144** Fax: 066 947 4520
Email: reservations@butlerarms.com Web: www.butlerarms.com

One of Ireland's best-known hotels – it is one of several to have strong links with Charlie Chaplin – Peter and Mary Huggards' Butler Arms Hotel dominates the seafront at Waterville. Like many hotels which have been owner-run for several generations, it has established a special reputation for its homely atmosphere and good service. Improvements are constantly being made and public areas, including two sitting rooms, a sun lounge and a cocktail bar, are spacious and comfortably furnished, while the beamed Fisherman's Bar (which also has a separate entrance from the street) has a livelier atmosphere and can be a useful place for a break on the Ring of Kerry route. Bedrooms vary from distinctly non-standard rooms in the old part of the hotel (which many regular guests request) to smartly decorated, spacious rooms with neat en-suite bathrooms and uninterrupted sea views in a wing constructed in the early '90s and 12 new junior suites which opened in 2002. Off season value breaks; shooting (woodcock, snipe) Nov-Jan. Garden; fishing; tennis. Snooker. Wheelchair accessible. Own parking. Children welcome. Lift. **Rooms 40** (12 junior suites, 9 no-smoking rooms, 1 disabled). Lift. B&B €96 pps, ss €45. No SC. Fisherman's Restaurant: D daily, 7-9.30. Fisherman's Bar: bar food available daily 12-3 & 6-8.30. Closed Oct-Apr. Amex, MasterCard, Visa, Laser.

Waterville — The Smuggler's Inn

Pub/Restaurant/Accommodation   Cliff Road Waterville Co. Kerry
Tel: 066 947 4330 Fax: 066 947 4422
Email: thesmugglersinn@eircom.net Web: www.welcome.to/the smugglersinn.com

Harry and Lucille Hunt's famous clifftop inn enjoys a remarkable location right beside the world famous championship Waterville Golf Course - and it's a real inn, providing food, drink and shelter. It can look a little windswept (exterior maintenance was not easy in th wet summer of 2002) but it's a good place to take a break from the Ring of Kerry – garden tables for fine sunny weather overlook a mile of sandy beach to the sea and mountains beyond, or you can eat in the comfortable bar or restaurant on chillier days. Local ingredients provide the base for both modern and traditional cooking by Harry and son Henry, who is also a chef - with seafood (including lobster from their own tank) being the speciality. Non seafood-lovers have plenty of other choices, including Kerry lamb and beef, of course, and there's a separate vegetarian menu available. Restaurant/Bar **Seats 100**. No smoking area; air conditioning. Food served 8.30am-9.30pm daily; L11.30-3, D 6-9.30 (snack menu only 3-6 pm). Set L €20.50, Set D €27-39.50, à la carte also available. House wine €17.50 **Accommodation** is also offered, in modest but pleasantly decorated rooms which vary in size, outlook and facilities (one has a balcony) and price, but all are comfortably furnished if a little dated. There's a first-floor residents' sitting room with sofas and armchairs, books, television – and magnificent sea views. Children welcome (under 6s free in parents' room, cots available without charge). Pets by arrangement. **Rooms 17** (11 shower only). B&B €38, ss €25. Closed 1 Nov-1 Mar. Amex, Diners, MasterCard, Visa, Laser. **Directions:** Before Village of Waterville on coast Road next to Golf Club.

COUNTY KILDARE

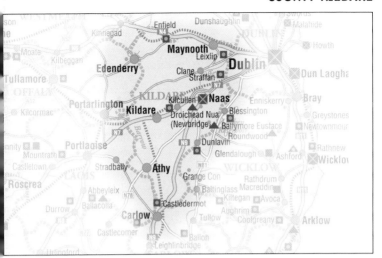

As you'd expect from a place which includes the famed racecourses of The Curragh, Punchestown and Naas among its many amenities, Kildare is the horse county par excellence. The horse is so central and natural a part of Irish life that you'll find significant stud farms in a surprisingly large number of counties. But it is in Kildare that they reach their greatest concentration in the ultimate equine county. Thus it's ironic that, a mere 400 million years ago, Kildare was just a salty ocean where the only creatures remotely equine were the extremely primitive ancestors of sea horses.

However, things have been looking up for the horse in County Kildare ever since, and today the lush pastures of the gently sloping Liffey and Barrow valleys provide ideal country for nurturing and training champions. Apart from many famous private farms, the Irish National Stud in Kildare town just beyond the legendary gallops of The Curragh is open for visitors, and it also includes a remarkable Japanese garden, reckoned the best Japanese rock garden in Europe, as well as the Museum of the Horse.

Once you get away from the busy main roads, Kildare is full of surprises. In fact, getting off the main roads is what enjoyment of life in Kildare is all about. The county's proximity to Dublin means that in the most recent population survey of 1996-2002, Kildare was second only to neighbouring Meath in its increase, the numbers growing by 21.5% to 164,000. Yet it is surprisingly easy to get away from the traffic, and you'll quickly find areas of rural enchantment and unexpected swathes of nature in the raw.

In the northwest of the county is the awe-inspiring Bog of Allen, the largest in Ireland, across whose wide open spaces the early engineers struggled to progress the Grand Canal on its route from the east coast towards the Shannon. Such needs of national transport are intertwined through the county's history. But between the arterial routes, railroads and canals, there is an easier pace of life, and gentle country with it.

Local Attractions and Information

Athy Heritage Centre	0507 33075
Carbury Ballindoolin House & Garden	0405 31430
Celbridge Castletown House	01 6288252
Curragh The Curragh Racecourse	045 441205
Edenderry Grange Castle & Gardens	0405 33316
Kilcock Larchill Arcadian Gardens (follies)	01 6287354
Kildare (Tully) Irish National Stud	045 21617
Kildare (Tully) Japanese Gardens	045 21251
Kildare Tourism Information	045 522696
Kill Goff's Bloodstock Sales (frequent)	045 886600
Naas Kildare Failte	045 898888
Naas Naas Racecourse	045 897391
Newbridge Riverbank Arts Centre	045 433480
Punchestown Punchestown Racecourse	045 897704
Straffan Lodge Park Walled Garden	01 6288412
Straffan Steam Museum	01 6273155

Athy — Coursetown Country House

Country House

Stradbally Road Athy Co Kildare
Tel: 0507 31101 Fax: 0507 32740

Although situated just off the Stradbally road, Jim and Iris Fox's fine 200 year old house is attached to a large arable farm. The house is large, welcoming, immaculately maintained and very comfortable, with some unusual attributes, including Jim's natural history library (where guests are welcome to browse) and extensive, well-tended gardens stocked with many interesting plants, including a number of rare fruit trees. Bedrooms vary according to their position in the house, but all are thoughtfully furnished in a pleasantly homely country house style and have direct dial phones, tea/coffee facilities and hair dryers. Iris takes pride in ensuring that her guests have the comfort of the very best beds and bedding - and the standard of details in the pristine shower rooms is equally high, with lots of lovely towels and quality toiletries. (A bathroom is also available for anyone who prefers to have a good soak in a tub.) Another special feature is a ground floor room near the front door which has been specially designed for wheelchair users, with everything completed to the same high standard as the rest of the house. Then there is breakfast - again, nothing is too much trouble and the emphasis is on delicious healthy eating. The wide selection offered includes fresh juices and fruit salad, poached seasonal fruit (eg plums from the garden) pancakes, French toast with banana & maple syrup, Irish farmhouse cheeses, home-made bread and preserves - and the traditional cooked breakfast includes lovely rashers specially vacuum-packed for Iris by Shiel's butchers, in Abbeyleix. Small weddings catered for (20). Not suitable for children under 8. **Rooms 5** (all with en-suite shower, all no smoking, 1 for disabled). B&B €50, ss €10. MasterCard, Visa. **Directions:** Just outside Athy, on Stradbally Road. Well signposted.

Athy — Tonlegee House

Country House/Restaurant

Athy Co. Kildare **Tel: 0507 31473** Fax: 0507 31473
Email: marjorie@tonlegeehouse.com Web: www.tonlegeehouse.com

Marjorie Molloy's elegant country house just outside Athy was built in 1790 and now combines modern comfort with a pleasing element of old-fashioned style. The individually decorated en-suite bedrooms include one single room and all are comfortably furnished to a high standard with phones, TV and complimentary mineral water and well-finished bathrooms. Children welcome. Pets permitted by arrangement. **Rooms 12** (5 superior, 2 shower only). B&B €62.50pps, ss €22.50; sc incl.
Restaurant: Hugh Johnston has been head chef since 1998 and his seasonal menus are in a modern European style, based on home-grown and local produce. Over an aperitif in the drawing room, imaginative menus make good reading and offer a balanced choice, including house specialities such as a starter of quail in pastry with wild mushroom sauce. Local Kildare lamb is an especially strong option, also beef (typically, fillet with basil mash, red onion marmalade and brandy & grain mustard sauce) also vegetarian dishes like Mediterranean vegetable basket with Roquefort. Tempting desserts might include a thin apple tart with cinnamon cream (cooked to order) or home made ice creams - or make the most of a good Irish farmhouse cheeseboard. **Seats 40.** D only 7-9.30pm (closed Sun & Mon). A la carte. house wine €17; sc discretionary. House closed 24 Dec-10 Jan. Amex, MasterCard, Visa, Laser. **Directions:** From Dublin, take M7, then onto M9 to N78, through Athy, across 2 bridges, passing by the canal take 1st left after Tegral factory.

Ballymore Eustace — Ballymore Inn

féile bia 🍴 Pub/Restaurant Ballymore Eustace Co. Kildare **Tel: 045 864 585** Fax: 045 864 747
Email: theballymoreinn@hotmail.com

It's the food that draws people to the O'Sullivan family's pub and it's wise to book well ahead to get a taste of the wonderful things this country kitchen has to offer, especially at weekends. The outside of the Ballymore Inn gives little away, although the blackboard menu at the door is a hint of what's to come. Inside, the clues begin to add up: unusual craft furniture, imaginative use of colour and striking fresh flowers and plants all add up to the kind of place where details count so the menu, when it arrives, fits into the pattern. Top quality ingredients have always been at the heart of the food operation here: fresh produce is sourced from a local organic grower, while beef, bacon and eggs come from recognised Quality Assurance Schemes and chicken and lamb from pproved Irish farms. Careful sourcing, careful cooking and a relaxed ambience have proved a winning ormula - so much so, in fact, that the bar has been refitted to allow more eating space and food service as been extended to Sundays to meet demand. Menus have plenty to choose from: delicious soups, aesar salad with crispy bacon, excellent meats - Kildare sandwich with baked ham, farmhouse cheese & pricot chutney, for example, or minute sirloin steak with herb butter or grilled Ardrahan cheese, served vith sauté potatoes or champ - and delicious, homely desserts. Creative crisp-based modern pizzas that marry artisan Irish food products with traditional methods are a house speciality, baked in a special pizza ven; their Grilled Fennel, Roasted Peppers, Basil and Ardrahan Cheese Pizza one was a previous winner of our Vegetarian Dish of the Year. You can also construct your own pizza, starting with a choice of five ases (tomato plus a range of cheeses) and select from ten toppings. Evening menus are more structured und offer a much wider choice of dishes: vegetables and salads have always been especially interesting ere and it's no surprise to find that starters major on flavourful garden combinations - chargrilled ubergine & tomato salad with mature Ardrahan, for example, and roast red pepper mousse with black olive dressing - and home-cured salmon is a speciality too, with pickled cucumber & dill dressing. Main courses offer a wider range of more substantial dishes - including roast rack of lamb (with creamed spinach und garlic jus) and fillet of beef (with Doneraile mushrooms) - and will always include an imaginative vegetarian option (grilled vegetable couscous with halloumi cheese, perhaps) and fish of the day. Side dishes are a far cry from the usual tired offering - organic vegetable sauté, for example, and broad bean salad with Irish bacon. Children welcome. **Seats 50**. No smoking area; air conditioning. Food served daily, 12.30-8 (Sun 12.30-7); L12.30-3, D 6-8 (restaurant menu to 9). House wine about €13; sc discretionary. No food 3-6pm Mon-Thu. Closed bank hols, 25 Dec & Good Fri. Amex, MasterCard, Visa, Laser. **Directions:** Turn right @ 2.5 miles after Blessington on Baltinglass Road.

Castledermot — Kilkea Castle Hotel

Hotel/Restaurant   Castledermot Co Kildare. **Tel: 0503 45156** Fax: 0503 45187
Email: kilkea@iol.ie Web: www.kilkeacastle.ie

The oldest inhabited castle in Ireland, Kilkea dates back to the twelfth century and has been sensitively renovated and converted into a hotel without loss of elegance and grandeur. Rooms, many with lovely views over the formal gardens and surrounding countryside, are splendidly furnished to incorporate modern comforts. Public areas include a hall complete with knights in armour and two pleasant ground floor bars - a cosy back one and a larger one that opens onto a terrace overlooking gardens and a golf course. Some of the bedrooms in the main castle are very romantic - as indeed is the whole setting - making it understandably popular for weddings. The adjoining (architecturally discreet) leisure centre, offers state-of-the-art facilities: indoor swimming pool, saunas, jacuzzi, steam room, well-equipped exercise room and sunbed. Outdoor sports include clay pigeon shooting, archery, tennis and fishing. An 18-hole championship golf course, which has views of the castle from every fairway, uses the River Greese flowing through the grounds as a natural hazard and a couple of extra lakes were added to increase the challenge still further; informal meals are served in the golf club. Special weekend breaks at the castle are good value. Conferences/banqueting (300/200). Leisure Centre, swimming pool. Garden. Tennis, Golf (18). Children welcome. No pets. **Rooms 35** (1 suite, 3 junior suites, 8 executive, 2 shower only). 24 hour room service. B&B €110 pps, ss €38.09. SC 12.5%. Closed 22-27 Dec.
Restaurant: Named after Hugh de Lacy, who built Kilkea Castle in 1180, this beautiful first-floor restaurant has a real 'castle' atmosphere and magnificent views over the countryside. It also overlooks the delightful formal kitchen garden (source of much that appears on the table in summer) and has a bright, airy atmosphere. Guests may take coffee on the terrace in summer and wander around to see the old fruit trees, vegetables and herbs. Cooking, service and surroundings make this a very special venue. Restaurant **Seats 60** (private room 40). L daily 12.30-2.00, D 7-9.30. Set L €25.50. Set D €44.50. House wine €20.50; sc 12.5%. Toilets wheelchair accessible. Closed 23-27 Dec. Amex, Diners, MasterCard, Visa, Laser. **Directions:** 3 miles from Castledermot (off M9); signed from village.

The Curragh — Martinstown House

Country House   Curragh Co. Kildare **Tel: 045 441 269** Fax: 045 441 208
Email: info@martinstown.com Web: www.martinstown.com

Just on the edge of the Curragh, near Punchestown, Naas and The Curragh race courses, this delightful 200 year old 'Strawberry Hill' gothic style house is on a farm, set in 170 acres of beautifully wooded land, with free range hens, sheep, cattle and horses and a well-maintained walled kitchen garden that provides vegetables, fruit and flowers for the house in season. Meryl Long welcomes guests to this idyllic setting, aiming to offer them 'a way of life which I knew as a child (but with better bathrooms!), a warm welcome, real fires and good food'. It is a lovely family house, with very nicely proportioned rooms - gracious but not too grand - open fires downstairs, and bedrooms that are all different, very comfortably furnished with fresh flowers and each with its own special character. A stay here is sure to be enjoyable, with the help of a truly hospitable hostess who believes that holidays should be fun, full of interest and with an easy-going atmosphere. Golf and equestrian activities nearby. Not suitable for children under 12. No pets. **Rooms 4** (2 en-suite, 2 with private bathrooms, all no smoking) B&B €95pps, ss €20. Residents D €40 (by arrangment). house wine €22.50. Closed 16 Dec -10 Jan. Amex, MasterCard, Visa. **Directions:** Kilcullen exit off M9 then N78 towards Athy. Sign at 1st crossroads.

Leixlip   Leixlip House Hotel

Hotel/Restaurant   Captains Hill Leixlip Co. Kildare **Tel:** 01 624 2268   Fax: 01 624 4177
Email: info@leixliphouse.com   Web: www.leixliphouse.com

Up on a hill overlooking Leixlip village, this lovely Georgian house is just eight miles from Dublin city centre. It opened as an hotel in 1996 after extensive renovations and is furnished and decorated to a high standard in period style. Gleaming antique furniture and gilt-framed mirrors enhance thick carpeted public rooms in soft country colours, all creating an atmosphere of discreet opulence. Bedrooms include two suites furnished with traditional mahogany furniture; the strong, simple deco particularly pleases the many business guests who stay here. Hotel guests have complimentary use of a nearby gym. Conference/banqueting (70/140). Secretarial services. Children welcome (under 12s in parents' room charged only for breakfast, cots available without charge). No pets. **Rooms 19** (5 executive, 14 shower only). B&B from €70 pps, ss €45.

The Bradaun Restaurant: The commitment to quality evident in the hotel as a whole is continued in the restaurant, a bright, high-ceilinged, formally appointed dining room. Sean Hicks, who has been head chef since the hotel opened, offers consistently good modern Irish cooking; his imaginative, wide-ranging menus are based on fresh seasonal produce and well executed with admirable attention to detail. Set menus offer particularly good value for money. An extensive, informative and carefully chosen wine list includes an interesting and well-balanced Recommended Wines of the Month selection within an accessible price range and a fair selection of half bottles. Not suitable for children after 7.30pm. **Seats 45.** L 12.30-3 (Sun to 4.30) & D 7-10 (Sun to 8.30). Set L €25 (incl Sun). Set D €30; à la carte also available. House wine from €18; sc discretionary. Restaurant closed Mon. Hotel closed 25 Dec. Amex, Diners, MasterCard, Visa, Laser. **Directions:** Leixlip exit off M4 motorway. Take right in Leixlip village at traffic lights.

Maynooth   Glenroyal Hotel & Leisure Club

Hotel   Straffan Road Maynooth Co. Kildare **Tel:** 01 629 0909   Fax: 01 629 0918
Email: info@glenroyal.ie   Web: www.glenroyal.ie

Situated on the outskirts of the university town of Maynooth, and only 20 minutes from Dublin city centre, this large hotel meets local demand for essential facilities covering a wide range of events - conferences, corporate events and weddings - and provides extensive leisure facilities, including a dramatically designed 20 metre pool (with underwater loungers, whirlpool and children's splashpool), a gymnasium and much else besides. Conference and business facilities are the best in a wide area; a new conference centre with five syndicate suites was added in 2002. *A branch of Lemongrass, a small chain of authentic Asian restaurants based in Naas, opened in the hotel in 2002 and is proving a great success. Conferences/Banqueting (550/350); business centre; secretarial services; video conferencing. Leisure centre (now with 2 pools; a new one with hydro-spa is for adult use only). Children welcome (under 4s free in parents room; cots available). No Pets. **Rooms 112** (66 executive, 7 shower only, 2 for disabled). Lift. Wheelchair accessible. B&B €80 pps, ss about €20. Closed 25 Dec. Amex, Diners, MasterCard, Visa, Laser. **Directions:** Off M4, sliproad for Maynooth.

Maynooth   Moyglare Manor

   Country House/Restaurant   Maynooth Co. Kildare **Tel:** 01 628 6351   Fax: 01 628 5405
Email: info@moyglaremanor.ie   Web: www.moyglaremanor.ie

Country hedges and workaday farmland give way to neatly manicured hedging, rolling parkland then beautifully tended gardens as one approaches this imposing classical Georgian manor - and it comes as no surprise to find that the owner, Norah Devlin, lavishes her love of beautiful things on the place, with a passion for antiques that has become legendary. Gilt-framed mirrors and portraits are everywhere, shown to advantage against deep-shaded damask walls. The remarkable abundance of chairs and sofas of every pedigree ensures comfortable seating, even when the restaurant is fully booked with large parties milling around before and after dining. First-time visitors sometimes describe it as 'like being in an antique shop' but, after recovering from the stunning effect of its contents, guests invariably reflect on the immaculate maintenance and comfort of the place under the careful stewardship of long-time manager Shay Curran. Spacious bedrooms are also lavishly furnished in period style, some with four-posters or half testers, and include a ground-floor suite; all have well-appointed bathrooms with quality appointments and good attention to detail. All rooms have recently been upgraded to a very high standard and, despite a long-standing aim for peacefulness, the modern world seem to have caught up with Moyglare and televisions have been installed in bedrooms. Golf nearby (four courses within 10 miles), also tennis and horseriding nearby. Small conferences/banqueting (40); secretarial services. Not suitable for children under 12. No Pets. Garden; walking. **Rooms 16** (1 suite, 4 executive, 2 rooms for disabled). B&B €115 pps, ss €25.

Restaurant: Hotel manager Shay Curran personally supervises the formally-appointed restaurant, which is in several interconnecting rooms; the middle ones nice and cosy for winter, those overlooking the garden and countryside pleasant in fine weather. Grand and romantic, it's just the place for a special occasion and there's a pianist playing background music in the evening. Lunch and dinner menus offer a nicely balanced combination of traditional favourites and sophisticated fare, attractively presented, with a vegetarian option always available. There is an emphasis on seafood and game in season - roast pheasant, perhaps, hung long enough to give it a gamey flavour, perfectly cooked and served off the bone accompanied by a nice little serving of green-flecked champ as well as game chips and Cumberland sauce. Lunch menus offer less choice than dinner, but are nevertheless quite formal and convey a sense of occasion. Fine meals are complemented by an exceptional wine list of special interest to the connoisseur (Moyglare Manor was the winner of our 1999 Wine List of the Year Award). Not suitable for children under 12. Restaurant seats 40 (private room, 25). No smoking area. L Sun-Fri 12.30-2; D daily 7-9. Set L €31.95, Set Sun L €31.95. D à la carte. House wine from €22; sc 12.5%. Restaurant closed L Sat. House closed 24-26 Dec. Amex, Diners, MasterCard, Visa, Laser. **Directions:** From Dublin, N4 west; exit for Maynooth, keep right at church; after 2.5 miles, turn left at Moyglare crossroads, then next right.

Naas — Killashee House Hotel

Hotel — Naas Co Kildare **Tel: 045 879277** Fax: 045 879266
Email: admin@killashee.com Web: www.killasheehouse.com

Set in 80 acres of gardens and woodland just outside Naas town, this recently opened hotel is approached along a driveway just long enough to give a sense of scale and setting (although spoilt a little by the car parking arrangements in front of the building). The entrance and lobby areas are impressive - the latter overlooks a fine inner courtyard planted with Virginia creeper, which will be very attractive when mature. A rather grand staircase leads to a large traditionally furnished lounge area on the first floor, with views of the grounds and courtyard; furnished with attractively grouped seating areas, this is a pleasant place for afternoon tea and informal socialising - there is a pianist at certain times. Conference and business events are well catered for, with conference rooms of various sizes available. Bedrooms, which have been designed with both luxury and practical requirements in mind, include a number of suites and some with four-poster beds; all rooms have multi-line phones, data ports, voicemail, fax (on request), and safe as well as the more usual amenities. Formal dining is offered at the elegant main restaurant, Turners (where a harpist plays at weekends), and informal food is available in other areas. A popular venue for weddings, the hotel is also well located for many of the county's sporting activities including horseracing (four courses nearby), golf (five clubs nearby), car racing (Mondello Park) and attractions such as the Wicklow Mountains, The Japanese Gardens and The National Irish Stud. On site facilities include archery, cycling and woodland walks; a leisure centre and spa opened just before we went to press. Conference/banqueting 1600/800. Business centre; secretarial services; video conferencing. Children welcome (under 2s free in parents' room, cot available without charge), but not in restaurant after 8pm. Garden, walking, cycling. **Rooms 84** (6 suites, 8 junior suites, 4 superior, 5 shower only, 24 no smoking, 6 for disabled). Lift. B&B € about 105 pps, ss about €45. Food available 12-10 daily. MasterCard, Visa, Laser. **Directions:** 30 minutes from Dublin on N7 to Naas, then 1 mile on R448, Kilcullen road.

Naas — Les Olives

Restaurant — 10 South Main Street Naas Co Kildare
Tel: 045 894788 Email: lesolive@indigo.ie

Olivier Pauloin-Valory's successful little restaurant is on the first floor over Kavanagh's pub, in the centre of Naas, and regulars are drawn from a wide area around the town. Seafood is a particular attraction and, in addition to choices on the main menu - which usually includes some unusual items, such as fresh water crayfish cassolette - daily fish specials (prawn kebab, lobster salad) are shown on a blackboard, where you may also find some less likely soulmates, such as ostrich (which is farmed nearby) and, of course, local meats like Kildare beef and lamb. M. Pauloin-Valory's good cooking and friendly efficient service go a long way towards an enjoyable night out - helped along by a wine list, which offers an extensive range of wines, including champagnes, rare vintages and a full page of magnums. Not suitable for children under 10. **Seats 45**. D only 7-10 Tue-Sun; Set D €45, also à la carte. House wine €16.50; sc discretionary. Closed Sun, Mon; Christmas, Good Fri. MasterCard, Visa, Laser. **Directions:** Town Centre.

Naas — Thomas Fletcher

Pub

Commercial House Main Street Naas Co. Kildare
Tel: 045 897 328 Fax: 045 897 328

This great old pub goes back well into the 1800s and has been in the Fletcher family since Tom Fletcher's father ran it in the 1930s. It's the kind of place that puts Irish theme pubs to shame, with its simple wooden floor and long, plain mahogany bar broken up in the traditional way with mahogany dividers and stained glass panels. They did up the back lounge recently, but there's no need to worry - it shouldn't need more work for another couple of hundred years. Open 2.30-11.30. Closed 25 Dec, Good Fri & Bank Hols. **Directions:** Main street Naas beside Superquinn.

Narraghmore — The Pond House

Country House

Narraghmore Co. Kildare
Tel: 045 485 456 Fax: 045 485 456

No need to explain the name of Nuala Clarke's unusual guesthouse, which will become obvious as soon as you reach it. Although it's in a different county, The Pond House is handy enough to Rathsallagh (see entry, Dunlavin, Co Wicklow) to be a regular recipient of overflow custom, a system which pleases all concerned - word has got around and some very interesting people stay here. The house is quietly located and spacious with a large patio area at the back, the atmosphere is distinctly laid back and, unusually for a guesthouse, it even has a proper bar where race-goers and wedding guests can enjoy a small one or two before heading upstairs. Bedrooms are pleasant in a country pine way, but by no means luxurious (no phone or TV and they're all shower only.) Nuala is a natural hostess and clearly enjoys making people feel at home. Chilkdren welcome (under 4s free in parents' room, cots available without charge). Garden, fishing, walking. Pets allowed by arrangement. **Rooms 5** (all shower only). B&B about €40pps, ss about €13. Open all year. MasterCard, Visa. **Directions:** 1 mile off main Dublin Carlow road to Narraghmore, next right-sign posted. ◇

Newbridge — Keadeen Hotel

Hotel

Newbridge Co. Kildare **Tel: 045 431 666** Fax: 045 434 402
Email: keadeen@iol.ie Web: keadeenhotel.kildare.ie

Centrally located and easily accessible off the M7 motorway, this family-owned hotel is set in nine acres of fine landscaped gardens just south of the town (and quite near the Curragh racecourse). The hotel has recently been refurbished and generously spacious accommodation is furnished to a high standard. A fine romanesque Health & Fitness Club has an 18-metre swimming pool and aromatherapy room among its attractions, plus a staffed gymnasium. Extensive conference and banqueting facilities (800/600); secretarial services. Video conferencing can be arranged. Leisure centre, swimming pool. Garden. Parking. No Pets. Children welcome (under 3s free in parents rooms; cots available). Weekend specials available. **Rooms 55** (1 suite, 3 junior suites, 20 executive, 1 for disabled) B&B about €140. Closed 24-27 Dec. Amex, Diners, MasterCard, Visa. **Directions:** From Dublin take N7 off M50, take sliproad sign posted Curragh race course & follow signs for Newbridge. ◇

Newbridge — The Red House

Hotel/Restaurant

Newbridge Co. Kildare **Tel: 045 431 516**
Fax: 045 431 934 Email: info@redhouse.ie

Proprietor-manager Brian Fallon runs a tidy ship at this cosy inn just off the motorway. It has a very relaxed atmosphere, especially in the characterful bar and the restful conservatory and garden at the back, and bedrooms all have good amenities. Conference/Banqueting (400/300); secretarial services. Garden. Children under 5 free in parents' room; cots available. **Rooms 12** (1 suite, 1 junior suite, 2 no-smoking rooms, 1 for disabled). B&B about €65 pps, ss €5. No sc.
Restaurant: Chef Rose Brannock cooks for the excellent Red House café-brasserie, Café Tomat. In a lovely comfortably furnished room with warm contemporary decor at the back of the inn, overlooking

well-maintained gardens, it specialises in deliciously flavourful modern food at reasonable prices (with some rather more traditional dishes on the more extensive evening menu); service is friendly, professional and very efficient. Children welcome. **Seats 45**. L&D daily 12.30-3, D 6.30-10; à la carte. Toilets wheelchair accessible. Closed 25-26 Dec, 1 week early Jan & Good Fri. Amex, Diners, MasterCard, Visa. **Directions:** On the N7 between Naas and Newbridge. ◇

Straffan — Barberstown Castle

 Restaurant/Country House   Straffan Co. Kildare **Tel: 01 628 8157** Fax: 01 627 7027
Email: castleir@iol.ie Web: www.barberstowncastle.com

Barberstown Castle is fascinating; steeped in history through three very different historical periods, it's one of the few houses in the area to have been occupied continuously for over 400 years. The oldest part is very much a real castle - the original keep in the middle section of the building, which includes the atmospheric cellar restaurant, was built by Nicholas Barby in the early 13th century. A more domestic Elizabethan house was added in the second half of the 16th century and Hugh Barton (also associated with nearby Straffan House, now the Kildare Hotel & Country Club, with whom it shares golf and leisure facilities) then built the 'new' Victorian wing in the 1830s. Most recently, in the current ownership of Kenneth Healy, the property has been thoroughly renovated and appropriately refurbished, in keeping with its age and style, to offer a high standard of modern comfort. Very comfortable accommodation is provided in well-appointed, individually decorated en-suite rooms - some are in the oldest section, the Castle Keep, others are more recent, but most are stylish and spacious. Public areas, including two drawing rooms and an elegant bar, have been renovated with the same care, and there are big log fires everywhere. Conferences/Banqueting (45/150); Children welcome (under 6s free in parents' room; cot available without charge). Garden, walking. No pets. **Rooms 22** (1 suite, 1 shower only, 1 for disabled). B&B €110 pps, ss €27.50; sc inc.
The Castle Restaurant: The restaurant is in a series of whitewashed rooms in the semi-basement of the old Castle Keep, which gives it great atmosphere, heightened by fires and candles in alcoves. Head chef Bertrand Malabat, who joined the castle in 1998, presents a six-course Tasting Menu (served to complete parties only) and a seasonal à la carte with about seven choices on each course. The style is classic French with the occasional nod to international fashions; local beef or lamb usually feature, also game in season, and there will be several prime fish dishes. Imaginative vegetarian dishes are offered on the main menu - a creamy Parmesan risotto with vegetables provençale & red pepper coulis, for example. Finish with a classic sweet like dark chocolate bavarois with brandy cream) or a selection of Irish farmhouse cheeses and home-baked breads. **Seats 75** (private rooms 22/32)). No-smoking restaurant. L Mon-Fri, 12.30-3, D Mon-Sat, 7.30-9.30; Sun, all day menu,12.30-8. Set L €29.50, Set D €39.50, Tasting Menu €49.50; à la carte also available. House wine €22.50; sc discretionary. Closed 24-27 Dec & 2nd week Jan. Amex, Diners, MasterCard, Visa. **Directions:** West N4 - turn for Straffan exit/ South N7 - Kill Exit.

Straffan — Kildare Hotel & Golf Club

féile bia  Hotel/Restaurant   Straffan Co. Kildare **Tel: 01 601 7200** Fax: 01 601 7299
Email: hotel@kclub.ie Web: www.kclub.ie

The origins of Straffan House go back a long way - the history is known as far back as 550 AD - but it was the arrival of the Barton wine family in 1831 that established the tone of today's magnificent building, by giving it a distinctively French elegance. It was bought by the Smurfit Group in 1988 and, after extensive renovations, opened as an hotel in 1991. Set in lush countryside, and overlooking its own golf course, the hotel boasts unrivalled opulence. The interior is magnificent, with superb furnishings and a wonderful collection of original paintings by well-known artists, including William Orpen, Louis le Brocqy, Sir John Lavery and Jack B. Yeats, who has a room devoted to his work. (Catalogue available from Reception). All bedrooms and bathrooms are individually designed in the grand style, with superb amenities and great attention to detail. Under the guidance of Ray Carroll, who has been with the hotel from the outset and is Chief Executive of the Resort, it is run with apparently effortless perfection. The hotel and golf course are in the midst of major developments in preparation for the Ryder Cup, which the K Club will host in 2006; these include a new bedroom extension and an extension to the Byerley Turk Restaurant, which both opened in 2001, and a second 18-hole golf course in 2003. However the hotel is never too busy for training and, with the support of the state training agency CERT, the K Club pioneered a 4-year in-hotel Food and Beverage Course in 1998 to attract the high calibre staff required for top hotels. In recognition, a special Skills Development Award was awarded to Ray Carroll and his team at the K Club by the Guide in 2001. Although most famous for its golf, the hotel also offers river fishing for salmon and trout and coarse fishing with a choice of five stocked lakes (equipment bait and tackle provided; tuition available). For guests interested in horticulture there is a mapped garden walk, with planting details. Conferences/ Banqueting (120/180); secretarial services. Leisure centre, swimming pool; specialist therapies; beauty salon. Golf (18), tennis, garden walking, fishing, cycling, equestrian. Snooker, pool table. Children welcome (cots available, €60) Lift. 24 hour concierge, 24 hour room service, twice daily housekeeping. **Rooms 69** (4 suites, 9 junior suites, 34 executive rooms,10 no smoking, 10 for disabled). Room rate from €270. No SC.

★ **The Byerley Turk:** Dramatically draped tall windows, marble columns, paintings of racehorses tables laden with crested china, monogrammed white linen, gleaming modern crystal and silver these all create an impressive background for the hotel's fine food. While the style has not changed noticeably since the restaurant was extended in 2001, the room is now a more interesting shape (enabling one end to be closed off for private parties without affecting normal dining arrangements) and as the old trompe l'oeil cocktail bar has been seamlessly absorbed into the entrance to the new accommodation. A larger bar has been created, with dark green walls creating a pleasingly clubby atmosphere and - the stroke of genius that is the making of this extension - it opens onto an elegant terrace with a distinctly French tone, thus reflecting the changes made in the Barton years. Here, on fine summer evenings, guests consider menus over an aperitif and admire the new golf course taking shape across the river (due for completion during 2003). Executive chef Michel Flamme, who has been with the hotel since it opened, bases his cooking on classical French cuisine, using the best of local and estate-grown produce; his Menu du Jour (€70) is concise, with just three choices on each course but all the little touches - a complimentary amuse-bouche, home-made petits fours with the coffee - that make a special dining experience memorable will be in place. A seasonal à la carte is also offered, and a surprise "Tasting Menu" (on request), for complete parties. All menus are luxurious and notable for a growing number of specialities, which include crispy wontons of Dublin Bay prawns, with basil, pine kernels and olive oil, and some dishes with a definite Irish flavour such as braised loin of organic bacon with Savoy cabbage, onion & parsley cream, also a range of hot soufflés. Service, under the direction of restaurant manager Martin Meade is friendly and professional. Given the intertwined history of Straffan House and the Barton family, it is appropriate that the Bordeaux Reserve from Barton and Guestier should be the label chosen for the hotel's house wine. Children welcome. **Seats 115** (private room 14). No smoking area; air conditioning. Piano at certain times. D 7.30-10 daily. Set D €70; also à la carte. House Wine from €25; sc discretionary. *A less formal dining option is available at The Legends Restaurant at the golf club (12.30-9.45 daily). Amex, Diners, MasterCard, Visa, Laser. **Directions:** 30 mins south west of Dublin airport and city (M50 - N4).

COUNTY KILKENNY

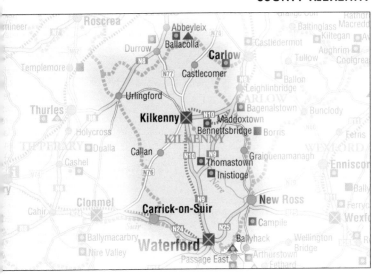

Kilkenny is a land of achingly beautiful valleys where elegant rivers weave their way through a rich countryside spiced by handsome hills. So naturally it's a place whose people care passionately about their county, and the miniature city at its heart. For Kilkenny - the Marble City - is one of Ireland's oldest cities, and proud of it. Its selection of ancient buildings is unrivalled. But, by today's standards of population, this gem of a place is scarcely a city at all. Yet it's a city in every other way, with great and justified pride in its corporate status.

Civic pride is at the heart of it, and in 2003 the city is poised for a sympathetic refurbishment of its ancient quays along the River Nore. Enjoying its reputation as a major centre for civilisation and culture for well over 1500 years, Kilkenny thrives on a diverse mixture of public debates about conservation, arts festivals, and a comedy festival of international standing.

Rivers are the key to the county. Almost the entire eastern border is marked by the Barrow, which becomes ever more spectacularly lovely as it rolls gently through beautiful Graiguenamanagh, then thrusts towards the sea at the tiny river port of St Mullins. The southern border is marked by the broad tidal sweep of the Suir, and this fine county is divided diagonally by the meandering of the most beautiful river of all, the Nore.

Invaders inevitably progressed up its tree-lined course past what is now the lovely river village of Inistioge, towards the ancient site of Kilkenny city itself. They quickly became Kilkenny folk in the process, for this is a land to call home. And a county that is passionate about its sport. Kilkenny became the current All-Ireland Hurling Champions in a convincing display against Clare in the fabulous new Croke Park Stadium in Dublin on September 8th 2002. The celebrations will be continuing well into 2003.

Local Attractions and Information

Callan Edmund Rice House	056 25993
Gowran Gowran Park Racecourse	056 26225
Inistioge Woodstock Gardens	056 52699
Kilkenny Kilkenny Castle	056 21450
Kilkenny Cat Laughs Comedy Festival (May)	056 63416
Kilkenny Rothe House (16c house, exhibitions)	056 22893
Kilkenny City Tourist Information	056 515000
Thomastown Jerpoint Abbey	056 24623
Thomastown Kilfane Glen & Waterfall	056 24558
Thomastown Mount Juliet Gardens	056 73000
Tullaroan Kilkenny GAA Museum	056 69202

Bennettsbridge — Calabash Bistro

féile bia Restaurant

Chapel Street Bennettsbridge Co Kilkenny
Tel: 056 27850 Email: calabash@eircom.net

Brian Kelly (front of house) and Jack Moylan (the chef) have been running this appealing restaurant in the centre of Bennettsbridge village since 1999 and it is a good place to build into visits on the "Kilkenny Craft Trail" as many of the workshops are in and around the village. A comfortable reception area sets the tone for a restaurant that is full of interest (pictures, unusual objects, a rather mysterious staircase and balcony) and doors opening onto a pretty garden patio area at the back give the room a light and spacious feeling. Menus are refreshingly straightforward, with no wordy descriptions and hardly an exotic reference to be found. What you get here is real food and everything is based on fresh ingredients - locally produced beef, fish from Castletownbere - and cooked to order. Shortish à la carte menus include good soups (with home-baked bread) and starters like deep-fried brie with real Cumberland sauce, tandoori chicken vol-au-vent or warm savoury tart with smoked salmon & leek (a choice of five, all very reasonably priced), while main courses range from the perennially popular steak - fillet, with garlic & herb butter & parsnip chips- which is one of the most expensive dishes at €29.50, to vegetarian dish of the day (a pasta bake, perhaps). Ingredients are meticulously sourced - beef is produced and slaughtered by the local Bennettsbridge butcher, Neil Tynan - and everything has that real home-made flavour. A shortish wine list is generally informative (although, oddly, most vintages are not given) and includes four half bottles, a page of Selected Wines includes some interesting bottles. Private parties and buffets for large groups can be arranged. **Seats 26** (private room 14). No smoking area. Children welcome early evening, but not suitable after 8 pm. D Thu-Mon, 6-9.30. A la carte. House wines €15-17. Closed Tue, Wed; 1st fortnight Nov, Christmas & 15 Feb-13 Mar. (Open all bank hols except Christmas.) Amex, MasterCard, Visa. **Directions:** In Bennettsbridge village, just over bridge on Gowran Rd.

Bennettsbridge — Nicholas Mosse Irish Country Shop

Café

The Mill Bennettsbridge Co. Kilkenny **Tel: 056 27505** Fax: 056 27491
Email: reception @nicholas mosse.com Web: www.nicholasmosse.com

One of the best reasons to venture out from Kilkenny city to nearby Bennettsbridge is to visit the Nicholas Mosse Pottery in their old riverside mill. Major renovations have been ongoing for several years and several storeys have now been converted to make spacious premises that allow visitors to watch potters at work and see the full range of products - including handblown glass and table linens, blankets, quilts and knitwear, Clive Nunn furniture and even jewellery from leading craftspeople - as well as acres of the famous spongeware. Their informal little tea shop is on the first floor, overlooking the river, and offers reasonably priced wholesome snacks - including, of course, delicious home-baked scones made with the local Mosse's flour. **Seats 28.** Children welcome. No smoking area. Open Mon-Sat 9-6, Sun 1.30-5. Closed 25-26 Dec & 1 Jan. Amex, Diners, MasterCard, Visa, Laser **Directions:** 4 miles south of Kilkenny, just before bridge turn off.

Graiguenamanagh — Waterside

Restaurant/Guesthouse

Graiguenamanagh Co. Kilkenny **Tel: 0503 24246** Fax: 0503 24733
Email: info@waterside.iol.ie Web: www.watersideguesthouse.com

Brian and Brigid Roberts operate a characterful restaurant with accommodation at this attractive old stone warehouse on the quayside, which was converted some years ago. The restaurant is well-appointed and offers modern European food on varied and enticing menus - in very pleasant waterside surroundings. A la carte dinner menus offer about half a dozen dishes on each course, using fresh local produce wherever possible, including a speciality starter of Graiguenamanagh smoked eel with side salad & horseradish sauce - the eel fishery at Graiguenamanagh dates back to the Cistercian monks who built the town and weirs on the river, and is now active again. Aside from a range of mainstream choices (salmon, pork steak, striploin beef steaks) game might be offered in season and interesting vegetarian choices, such as aubergine & feta cheese in fillo pastry with tomato fondue & mixed herb pesto, are always included. Finish with a nice homely dessert such as apple, sultana & cinnamon tart with home-made vanilla ice cream, or an Irish cheese plate (choice of half a dozen ports to accompany, if you wish). Sunday lunch menus are more restricted, but similar in style. The wine list is fairly priced and makes up in interest anything it may lack in length. **Seats 35.** No smoking restaurant. D 6.45-9.30 daily; L Sun only 12.30-2.30. Set L €18, Set D €30, also à la carte. **Guesthouse:** The accommodation is quite simple but comfortable, with direct dial phones, tea/coffee making facilities and TV in all rooms. Some rooms at the top of the building are especially spacious and all overlook the river. Hillwalking holidays for small groups are offered (guide, maps, acked lunch, transport etc all arranged). Children welcome (under 3s free in parents' room, cot available without charge). (No lift.) **Rooms 10** (all shower only) B&B €50pps, ss €15. Closed Christmas week. Amex, MasterCard, Visa, Laser, Switch. **Directions:** 17 miles south east of Kilkenny city on banks of the River Barrow.

Inistioge — The Motte Restaurant

Restaurant

Plas Newydd Lodge Inistioge Co. Kilkenny
Tel: 056 58655 Email: atmotte@gofree.indigo.ie

On the edge of the picturesque village of Inistioge, with views of extensive parklands and the River Nore, The Motte is situated in the classically proportioned Plas Newydd Lodge, named in honour of the ladies of Llangollen, who eloped from Inistioge in the late 18th century. Although small in size, this unique country restaurant is big on personality - of the host, the irrepressible Tom Reade-Duncan, who makes every guest feel as welcome as the flowers in spring and greatly adds to the enjoyment of the occasion with his offbeat humour and helpful way with local knowledge, and of the chef, Alan Walton, as conveyed through his imaginative menus and distinctive style of cooking. The pair of them combine a special blend of classical style and (sometimes wacky) artistic inspiration. Menus are sensibly limited to five or six choices on each course - starters might include Mediterranean mezze with hummus, aubergine & pitta bread and quail terrine with dressed leaves, while main courses range from variations local meats - classic sirloin steak with grain mustard sauce, perhaps, or pork tenderloin with black pudding and Hoi Sin sauce, to a sound fish dish such as lemon & garlic cod with tomato & basil. Vegetarians are always catered for (penne with spinach and blue cheese sauce is typical), side vegetables invariably imaginative and perfectly cooked and desserts - a delicious baked white chocolate cheesecake is a speciality. A private dining room has recently been added and small weddings or parties can be catered for. Toilets wheelchair accessible. No smoking until after 10.30pm; (from 1 Jan 2003 this becomes a no smoking restaurant). Tom Reade-Duncan was our Host of the Year in 2002. **Seats 40** (Private room, 16). D only, Wed-Sat 7-9.30 (also Sun of bank hol weekends only, 7-9). Set D €31.50. House wine €15.50.; sc discretionary (except 10% on groups of 6+). Closed Mon & Tue, also Sun (except bank hol weekends), 1 week Christmas, 1 week autumn. MasterCard, Visa. **Directions:** Opposite Village "name sign" on Kilkenny side of Village.

Kilkenny — Butler House

Accommodation

16 Patrick Street Kilkenny Co Kilkenny **Tel: 056 65707** Fax: 056 65626
Email: res@butler.ie Web: www.butler.ie

Located close to Kilkenny Castle, this elegant Georgian townhouse was restored by the Irish State Design Agency in the 1970s - and the resulting combination of what was at the time contemporary design and period architecture leads to some interesting discussions. However bedrooms are unusually spacious - some have bow windows overlooking the gardens and Kilkenny Castle - and the accommodation is very adequate, with all the amenities now expected of good 3-star guesthouse accommodation (although bathrooms are curiously utilitarian and only have showers, even though there is plenty of space for more comfort). Three magnificent bow-windowed reception rooms are available for receptions and dinners (10-250). An excellent breakfast is served at the Kilkenny Design Centre, which is just across the gardens in the refurbished castle stables. Three magnificent bow-windowed reception rooms are available for receptions and dinners (10-250). Conferences(120). Children welcome (under 4s free in parents' room; cot available without charge). Parking. Walking, garden. No pets. **Rooms 14** (1 suite, 3 superior,12 shower only) B&B €80, ss €20, sc discretionary. Closed 23-29 Dec. Amex, Diners, MasterCard, Visa, Laser. **Directions:** City centre close Kilkenny Castle.

Kilkenny — Hotel Kilkenny

 Hotel

College Road Kilkenny Co Kilkenny **Tel: 056 62000** Fax: 056 65984
Email: kilkenny@griffingroup.ie Web: www.griffingroup.ie

This well run hotel is a sister property to the Ferrycarrig Hotel near Wexford (see entry); it is set in landscaped gardens on the edge of the city, and has recently been redeveloped and refurbished to a high standard. The style throughout is a light, bright and imaginative contemporary - public areas have more character than is usual in hotels while bedrooms have been done in an unusual modern classic style, using specially commissioned Irish-made furniture, and the result is comfortable, interesting and and very pleasing to the eye. A stylish and highly successful modern restaurant, Brooms Garden Room Bistro, was ahead of the current fashion when it opened several years ago and has now been completely redesigned to reflect the atmosphere of the lovely gardens around the hotel. Informal meals are also available in the Rosehill bar every day (12.30-8.30). An impressive 5-

star health & fitness club has a 20 metre swimming pool and a wide range of facilities includin
special beauty, relaxation and massage treatments and even a hairdressing salon. But it is the sta
who make the real difference to guests and Hotel Kilkenny's clear commitment to customer servic
has recently been recognised with the achievement of a CERT Best Service Awar
Conference/banqueting 400/380. Children welcome (under 2s free in parents' room; cots availabl
without charge). No pets. **Rooms 103** (24 executive rooms, 5 no smoking, 2 disabled). B&B €100
Open all year. Amex, Diners, MasterCard, Visa. **Directions:** On ring road at Clonmel roundabout exit

Kilkenny — Kilkenny Design Centre

féile bia Restaurant   Castle Yard Kilkenny Co Kilkenny **Tel: 056 22118** Fax: 056 6590
Email: info@kilkennydesign.com Web: Kilkennydesign.cor

Situated in what was once the stables and dairy of Kilkenny Castle - and overlooking the cra
courtyard - this first floor self-service restaurant (above the temptations of a different sort o
display in the famous craft shop below) is deservedly popular. Wholesome, healthy and absolutel
delicious fare is consistently provided at very reasonable prices here, and the room is well-designe
to allow attractive and accessible display of their wonderful food. Everything is freshly prepare
every day, home baking is a strong point and salads are always colourful and full of life: roaste
fennel and red pepper, chickpeas with fresh fruit, black onion seed & chilli and pickled asparagus
mangetout, carrot & celery with fresh coriander are just three possible combinations. Vegetaria
dishes like fig, prosciutto & gruyere tart or tagliatelle with preserved lemon, fresh pecorino & wil
rocket can be seriously tempting and contemporary cooking generally is well-represented - but it i
also good to see local ingredients used in well cooked traditional Irish dishes like beef in Kilkenn
beer, local Lavistown sausages with caramelised onion & mustard mash and classic Irish stew. Toile
wheelchair accessible. Lift. **Seats 180** (private room 65-70). No smoking area. Meals Mon-Sat 9-5
Self service. Open all year. Amex, Visa, Laser, Switch. **Directions:** Opposite Kilkenny Castle.

Kilkenny — Kilkenny Hibernian Hotel

Hotel/Pub   1 Ormonde Street Kilkenny Co Kilkenny **Tel: 056 71888** Fax: 056 7187
Email: info@hibernian.iol.ie Web: www.kilkennyhibernianhotel.com

Formerly the Hibernian Bank, this Georgian building has been restored to its former glory to become
The Kilkenny Hibernian Hotel. The nine older rooms at the front are particularly spacious and
furnished to a very high standard in keeping with the character of the building, but the new
accommodation which has been built to blend in achieves this quite well. New rooms are also
generous and impressively furnished in an upbeat cross between traditional and contemporary styles
they have good amenities, well-planned bathrooms - and the advantage of a quieter situation away
from the street. Of the public areas, the old banking hall makes an impressive traditional style bar
the Hibernian Bar, set up with comfortable chairs and tables for informal eating; there is also a
restaurant, Jacob's Cottage, which has been built and decorated to avoid feeling like a hotel dining
room and has its own entrance from the street. Similarly, in contrast to the Hibernian Bar, Morrisons
Bar is the cool place to hang out at night. Conference suites (max 40). **Rooms 46** (3 suites, 3 junio
suites, 1 disabled). Lift. B&B €95 pps, ss €95. Bar meals available 12.30-8 daily. Closed 24-25 Dec.
Amex, Diners, MasterCard, Visa, Laser. **Directions:** City Centre Location.

Kilkenny — Kilkenny Ormonde Hotel

Hotel/Restaurant   Ormonde Street Kilkenny Co Kilkenny **Tel: 056 23900** Fax: 056 23977
Email: info@kilkennyormonde.com

Sister establishment to the famous Aghadoe Heights Hotel, Killarney (see entry), this new hotel enjoys
an outstandingly convenient central location for both business and leisure guests, beside (but not
adjacent to) a multi-storey carpark and within walking distance of the whole city. Spacious public areas
include an impressive foyer, the informal Earls Bistro - where sassy international cooking is available
at lunch and dinner daily - and an elegant restaurant, Fredricks (see below). Generously large bedrooms
are furnished to a high standard in a pleasing contemporary style, with ISDN lines and safes in addition
to the more usual amenities, and both business/conference and on-site leisure facilities are excellent.
Friendly, well-motivated and efficient staff ensure a pleasant stay or well-run business event - the
hotel's excellent conference centre and 10 fully equipped meeting rooms offer the region's premier
conference and business venue and well-trained staff to match. Conference/banqueting (500/400).
Business centre, video conferencing. Leisure centre, 21m swimming pool, crèche. **Rooms 118** (6 suites,
6 executive rooms, 70 no smoking, 4 disabled). Lift. B&B €125pps, ss €35. Children welcome
(under12s free in parents' room, cots available without charge). Earls Bistro: L Mon-Fri 12.30-2, D Thu-
Sat 6.30-9.30; bar meals also available: Sun 1-2.30. Wed-Sat 3-9pm. Closed 24-26 Dec.

Fredricks Fine Dining Restaurant: The restaurant bears the same name as the Killarney restaurant that has earned such a high reputation for Aghadoe Heights over the years. Head chef Will Fitzgerald (previously at the Morrison Hotel, Dublin) has been with the hotel since opening and is also responsible for the food at Earls Bistro (see above); he presents lively international menus based mainly on carefully sourced local produce, cooking is accurate and service, as in other areas of the hotel, a strong point. The restaurant is also used for breakfast. **Seats 68**. No smoking area; air conditioning. Toilets wheelchair accessible. Open D daily 7-10 & L Sun only1-2.30. Set D from €30. House wine €24.50. sc discretionary. Closed L except Sun. Amex, Diners, MasterCard, Visa, Laser. **Directions:** Kilkenny city centre off the Parade opposite castle.

Kilkenny — Kilkenny River Court Hotel

féile bia Hotel

The Bridge John Street Kilkenny Co Kilkenny
Tel: 056 23388 Fax: 056 23389
Email: reservations@kilrivercourt.com Web: www.kilrivercourt.com

Beautifully situated in a courtyard just off the narrow, bustling streets of the city centre, with only the River Nore separating it from Kilkenny Castle, this hotel has the city's premier location. Although equally attractive for business or leisure - bedrooms and public areas are all finished to a high standard and the Health & Leisure Club provides excellent facilities for health, fitness and beauty treatments - the hotel has already established a special reputation for conferences and incentive programmes, with state-of-the-art facilities for groups of varying numbers and plenty to do when off duty in the city, as well as outdoor pursuits - golf, fishing, equestrian - nearby. Conference/Banqueting (210/160). Leisure centre, indoor swimming pool. Wheelchair access. Children under 3 free in parents' room. Limited private parking (access can be a little difficult). **Rooms 90** (2 suites, 41 executive, 19 no smoking, 4 for disabled). B&B from about €80pps, ss about €40. Closed 25-26 Dec. Amex, MasterCard, Visa. **Directions:** Follow city centre signs,directly opposite Kilkenny Castle. Two archways on the Dublin side Bridge - use the castle as a landmark. ◇

Kilkenny — Lacken House

féile bia Restaurant/Accommodation

Dublin Road Kilkenny Co Kilkenny
Tel: 056 61085 Fax: 056 62435
Email: info@lackenhouse.ie Web: www.lackenhouse.ie

This period house on the edge of Kilkenny city has been home to the leading restaurant in the area for over 15 years. It was taken over by Jackie and Trevor Toner in 2001 and they have achieved their intention to run it in the same way and to maintain the high standards of food and hospitality for which it was well- known. The existing staff were retained, including chef Nicola O'Brien, who has now been head chef since 1995 and continues her practice of using the best local produce and mainly organic vegetables and fruit. The style is a combination of traditional and modern cooking - and there is a willingness to meet any special requests wherever possible, whether for dietary reasons or simply preference. Menus are well-balanced, with more seafood than might be expected in a midlands restaurant, but local meats are exceptional: a speciality fillet beef dish, with Clonakilty mash, toasted black pudding and crispy bacon and wholegrain mustard sauce is not to be missed - and the rack of Kilkenny lamb, cooked with a crunchy herb crust and served with rosemary jus - is just as good. Irresistible desserts include some unusual home-made ice creams - and a farmhouse cheese selection comes with scrumptious home-baked biscuits. Private parties and functions are also catered for. **Seats 40.** (Private room, 12-18). D Tue-Sat, 7-10.30; Set D €38; house wine €18. Closed Sun (except bank hol weekends), Mon; 24-27 Dec.
Accommodation: Nine en-suite guest bedrooms are offered; they vary in size and outlook but all have phone TV, tea/coffee-making trays. Excellent breakfasts are served in the restaurant. B&B €55pps, ss €15. Amex, MasterCard, Visa, Laser. **Directions:** On the Dublin/Carlow road into Kilkenny.

Kilkenny — Lautrec's Restaurant

Restaurant

9 St. Kieran Street Kilkenny Co Kilkenny **Tel: 056 62720** Fax: 056 58799
Web: www.restaurantskilkenny.com

This cheerful, informal city centre restaurant is run by manager/chef Denis Rudd (who has also recently taken over Café Nore in Bennettsbridge: light meals, cakes & pastries: Tel: 056 27833.) First appearances are deceptive, as it seems to be very small on first entering, via doors that open out onto the pavement, with some tables semi-alfresco, which is an attractive feature on hot summer evenings. However, most of the restaurant is hidden from view and it is actually quite large. Menus match the informality of the decor, with quite a few pastas and pizzas as well as more substantial bistro fare, like steaks - typically with sun-dried tomato & anchovy butter - and fish dishes such as seared fillet of salmon with tapenade. This is a place to have fun; service can be slow at times, but prices are not over the top, especially if you stick to pizza and pasta. *Proprietor Felix Santor also runs a sister restaurant Silks, at Thomastown (see entry). **Seats 70.** D Sun-Thu 6-10, Fri & Sa 6-11. A la carte (pizzas &main courses€8.35-24.95; house wine about € 17.50. MasterCard, Visa **Directions:** Lane beside Tourist Information Office.

Kilkenny   Marble City Bar

Pub
66 High Street Kilkenny Co Kilkenny
Tel: 056 61143 Email: langtons @oceanfree.ne

This historic bar belongs the well-known local Langton Group of publicans, who normally have a fairly traditional approach to renovations and refurbishments - so the citizens of Kilkenny go quite a shock when the cutting edge international designer David Collins was brought in to cast his highly original eye over the premises with a view to a total re-vamp. The results are fascinating - and of course, controversial (especially the ultra-modern stained glass window which now graces the otherwise traditional frontage and looks strange from the street but much better from the inside looking out), but it is a wonderful space to be in and attracts a varied clientèle, ranging from the merely curious to fans of all ages and many walks of life who are there to enjoy the vibrant atmosphere - and make the most of their excellent contemporary European bar food. The food side of the operation is taken commendably seriously and, although it might not be immediately obvious from the menu, head chef Mike Roberts' ingredients are well-sourced and many local ingredients used - that confit of pork sausages with creamy potatoes and caramelised onion gravy is probably based on the superb lean sausages hand-made nearby by Olivia Goodwillie (who also makes the wonderful Lavistown cheese) and the fresh cod'n'chips in a crispy beer batter will be just in from Dunmore East. Good wines available by the glass. Food service begins with breakfast, from 10am daily; main menus from 12 noon-8.30 pm. Closed 25 Dec & Good Fri. Diners, MasterCard, Visa. **Directions:** Main Street, City Centre.

Kilkenny   Newpark Hotel

féile bía Hotel
Castlecomer Road Kilkenny Co Kilkenny **Tel: 056 60500** Fax: 056 60555
Email: info@newparkhotel.com Web: www.newparkhotel.com

Very much at the heart of local activities, this 1960s hotel on the N77 recently completed a huge extension and renovation programme and the makeover - symbolised by an impressive circular foyer which is really striking from the road and even more so on entering - is a revelation. The whole job has been done with great flair and attention to detail but the older bedrooms are too small for comfort by today's standards and, in many cases, have only a small shower room en-suite, so some challenges regarding the constrictions of the original building still remain to be met. Longterm plans provide for re-building but the project to date is very praiseworthy and the foyer and atrium features, conference and meeting rooms have been particularly imaginatively handled. The Scott Dove Bar & Bistro and banqueting suites have entrances from the hotel and carpark and there's an elegant formal restaurant in clean-lined contemporary style, in a quiet position at the back of the hotel overlooking the gardens. Conference/banqueting (550/400). Children welcome (under 4s free in parents' room; cot available without charge). No pets. **Rooms 111** (50 executive, 16 shower only, 10 no-smoking, 3 for disabled). Lift. B&B €95, ss €49. Open all year. Amex, Diners, MasterCard, Visa, Laser. **Directions:** N7 from Dublin, approx 1.5 hours drive.

Kilkenny   Rinuccini Restaurant

Restaurant/Accommodation
1 The Parade Kilkenny Co Kilkenny
Tel: 056 61575 Fax: 056 51288
Email: info@rinuccini.com Web: www.rinuccini.com

Antonio and Marion Cavaliere's well-established Italian restaurant is in a semi-basement in the impressive terrace opposite Kilkenny Castle and the closely packed tables are an indication of its popularity. When empty it looks a little bleak, but the room quickly fills up with a healthy mixture of locals (who clearly have their preferred tables) and tourists. The cooking style is mainly classic Italian, with quite an extensive à la carte evening menu plus a shorter one available as an option at lunchtime. Service is prompt, from the time fresh bread and butter is delivered speedily with the menu. Food is characterised by freshness of ingredients and a high standard of cooking: excellent minestrone (a classic test), delicious seafood and memorable pasta. The simple things are right, which is always a good sign - but that doesn't necessarily preclude luxury: spaghetti with fresh lobster is one of the house specialities. **Seats 56**. L&D daily: L 12-2.30, D 6-10.30 (Sun D 6-9.30); à la carte. House wine €19.95

Accommodation: Seven bedrooms are available, all are large and en-suite (1 junior suite, all shower-only, 4 no-smoking) with air conditioning, TV, tea/coffee facilities and trouser press with iron. A breakfast tray is supplied, for you to make up your own continental breakfast in the room. Room rate: €100 (max 4 guests). Amex, Diners, MasterCard, Visa. **Directions:** Opposite Kilkenny Castle.

Kilkenny   Zuni

Hotel/Restaurant   26 Patrick St Kilkenny Co Kilkenny **Tel: 056 23999** Fax: 056 56400
Email: info@zuni.ie Web: www.zuni.ie

A centrally located contemporary hotel, Zuni offers a lighter, brighter more youthful style of accommodation than other comparable establishments - some guests may find the minimalist approach rather stark, others will love it. Everything is pristine and there are phones (& ISDN lines) and TV, although no tea/coffee-making facilities. Breakfast is served in the restaurant (see below). Booking advised. Children welcome (under 3s free in parents' room; cot available, €25.) No pets. **Rooms 13** (1 suite, 8 shower only, 5 no smoking, 1 for disabled). Lift. B&B €70ps, no ss. Hotel closed 23-28 Dec.

Restaurant: In a large airy room overlooking a courtyard at the back of the hotel and with a separate entrance on the side of the building, the restaurant is an oasis of contemporary chic in this bustling city and is now well established as an important address for discerning diners. Head chef Maria Raftery, who joined the hotel in spring 2001, offers eclectic menus at lunch and dinner and cooks colourful, attractively presented food that clearly pleases locals as much as visitors. Restaurant **Seats 60**. (Breakfast); L Tue-Sun 12.30-2.30 (Sun from 1), D 6.30-10 (Sun 6-9). A la carte. House wine €17.95. Restaurant closed Mon. Amex, MasterCard, Visa, Laser, Switch. **Directions:** 200 yards from Kilkenny castle.

Maddoxtown   Blanchville House

Country House   Dunbell Maddoxtown Co. Kilkenny **Tel: 056 27197** Fax: 056 27636
Email: info@blanchville.ie Web: www.blanchville.ie

Tim and Monica Phelan's elegant Georgian house is just 5 miles out of Kilkenny city, surrounded by its own farmland and gardens. It's easy to spot - there's a folly in its grounds. It's a very friendly, welcoming place and the house has an airy atmosphere, with matching well-proportioned dining and drawing rooms on either side of the hall and the pleasant, comfortably furnished bedrooms in period style all overlook attractive countryside. Dinner is available to residents (bookings required before noon) and, like the next morning's excellent breakfast, is taken at the communal mahogany dining table. Small parties/celebrations can also be catered for (max 20 guests). No wine licence but guests are welcome to bring their own. Not suitable for children under 10. Well-behaved dogs are permitted by arrangement. The Coach House has been renovated to make four self-catering apartments. Walking, garden, tennis; snooker, pool table; playroom. **Rooms 6** (5 en-suite, 1 with private bathroom, 2 shower only, all non-smoking) B&B €55pps, ss €15. Closed 1 Nov-1 Mar. Amex, MasterCard, Visa, Laser, Switch. **Directions:** From Kilkenny take N10, 1st right 1/2 mile after 'The Pike'. Continue 2 miles to crossroads (Connolly's pub). Take left, large stone entrance 1 mile on left.

Thomastown   Ballyduff House

Ⓝ Country House/B&B   Thomastown Co Kilkenny
Tel: 056 58488 Email: ballyd@gofree.indigo.ie

Set in fine rolling countryside in its own farmland and grounds, Breda Thomas's lovely 18th century house overlooking the River Nore is blessed with an utterly restful location. Breda is a relaxed and welcoming host and offers exceptionally spacious and comfortable accommodation in large period bedrooms with generous bathrooms and beautiful restful views over the river or gardens. Guests also have the use of spacious well-proportioned day rooms furnished with family antiques - and many return often, finding this rural retreat a warm and welcoming home from home. Beautiful walks on the estate. Fishing (salmon, trout). Riding, hunting and other country pursuits can be arranged. Children welcome **Rooms 3**. B&B about €40, ss about €10. **No Credit Cards. Directions:** From Kilkenny: N9 Waterford road, leave Salmon Pool to right; sign to St Mullins to left: 3 miles exactly (big white gate).

Thomastown — Mount Juliet Conrad

Hotel/Restaurant   Thomastown Co. Kilkenny **Tel: 056 73000** Fax: 056 73019
Email: mountjulietinfo@conradhotels.com Web: www.mountjulietconrad.com

Built over 200 years ago by the Earl of Carrick, and named in honour of his wife, Mount Juliet House is one of Ireland's finest Georgian houses and retains an aura of eighteenth century grandeur. Lying amidst 1500 acres of unspoilt woodland, pasture and formal gardens beside the River Nore, it is one of Europe's greatest country estates, with world class sporting amenities and conference facilities. The elegance of the old house has been painstakingly preserved, so that the hand-carved Adam fireplaces, walls and ceilings decorated with intricate stucco work and many other original features can still be enjoyed today - and, since forming an alliance with the Conrad group of hotels in 2002, refurbishment and maintenance programmes have been scaled up. Bedrooms have period decor with all the comfort of modern facilities and, as well as the main house, additional rooms on the estate are in The Club, and the Rose Garden two-bedroom lodgeses. The Jack Nicklaus-designed golf course on the estate went straight into the list of top-ranking courses when it opened in 1991; it hosted the Irish Open for three years consecutively (from 1993 to 1995) and, most recently, the WGC American Express World Golf Championships in September 2002. Conference/banqueting (75/70). Children welcome (under 12 free sharing with two adults; cot available, €25). Equestrian; angling. Clay pigeon shooting, archery, tennis, croquet, cycling, walking trails. Spa & Health Club (15m swimming pool). No pets. **Rooms 59** (2 suites, 2 for disabled). No lift. Room rate €290. Open all year.

Lady Helen Dining Room: Although grand, this graceful high-ceilinged room, softly decorated in pastel shades and with sweeping views over the grounds, is not forbidding and has a pleasant atmosphere. To match these beautiful surroundings, classic daily dinner menus based on local ingredients are served, including wild salmon from the River Nore, vegetables and herbs from the Mount Juliet garden and regional Irish farmhouse cheese. Service is efficient and friendly. **Seats 55** (private room, 25). No smoking restaurant. Toilets wheelchair accessible. D daily 6-10l L Sun only 12-3. A la carte. House wine €23. It can be difficult to get a reservation at the Lady Helen Dining Room, especially for non-residents, so booking well ahead is advised, otherwise opt for one of the other dining choices on the estate. A newer contemporary restaurant, Kendals, is open for breakfast & dinner daily, 7.30am-10pm. *Informal dining is available in The Club, Presidents Bar (8am-9pm). Amex, Diners, MasterCard, Visa. **Directions:** M7 from Dublin, then M9 towards Waterford, arriving at Thomastown on the N9 via Carlow and Gowran.

Thomastown — Silks

Restaurant   Marshes Street Thomastown Co. Kilkenny **Tel: 056 54400** Fax: 056 54400
Email: info @restaurantskilkenny.com Web: www.restaurantskilkenny.com

This rather dashing contemporary restaurant in a converted schoolhouse on the edge of the town brought Mediterranean cuisine to Thomastown with a vengeance when it opened in 1999 and it is well-established as the place to be seen. There are two rooms - the back one, which overlooks garden and pond, would be pleasant on a summer evening or for Sunday lunch, and there's also an outdoor eating area in a walled garden, where there are tables set up with parasols. There is a small bar, but it is more likely that you will be shown straight to your table to have a drink and consider the menu - a choice of menus is offered and the style, which is broadly Mediterranean/global, now includes more oriental dishes including a speciality Thai curry casserole. Some local specialities remain however, also quite classic dishes like honey glazed duck breast with fondant potato with roasted nectarine & mead scented jus - and timeless desserts such as passion fruit crème brulee. The set dinner menu offers good value. Service has improved since Aine Walsh took over as restaurant manager in 2002. Toilets wheelchair accessible. Public car park adjacent. **Seats 70** (private room, 40). L 12-3; D 6.30-9.30; Set D from €22.95, also à la carte. House wine €19. Closed Mon, L Sat & Christmas week. Amex, MasterCard, Visa, Laser. **Directions:** In Thomastown take Mount Juliet Road, past SuperValu.

COUNTY LAOIS

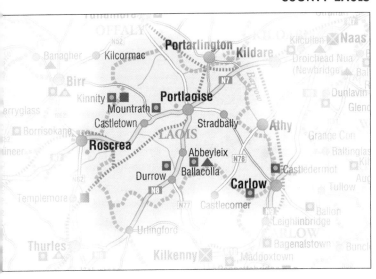

From September 24th to 26th 2002, Ballacolla in County Laois was a remarkable agricultural focal point with the staging of the National Ploughing Championship, Europe's largest farming festival, which was attended by more than 160,000 people in three days of perfect Autumn weather. Overall winner was northerner David Wright from Magherafelt in County Derry. Plans are already well advanced for the next championship, scheduled for Autumn 2003 at Kinnegad on the Meath/Westmeath border, with the administration continuing through Athy and Anna May McHugh, MD of the National Ploughing Association.

With its territory traversed by the rail and road links from Dublin to Cork and Limerick, Laois is often glimpsed only fleetingly by inter-city travellers. But as with any Irish county, it is a wonderfully rewarding place to visit as soon as you move off the main roads. And a salutary place to visit as well. For, in the eastern part, between Stradbally and Portlaois, there's the Rock of Dunamase, that fabulous natural fortress which many occupiers inevitably assumed to be impregnable. Dunamase's remarkably long history of fortifications and defences and sieges and eventual captures has a relevance and a resonance for all times and all peoples and all places.

But there's much more to Laois than mournful musings on the ultimate vanity of human ambitions. With its border shared with Carlow along the River Barrow, eastern Laois comfortably reflects Carlow's quiet beauty. To the northwest, we find that Offaly bids strongly to have the Slieve Bloom Mountains thought of as an Offaly hill range, but in fact there's more of the Slieve Blooms in Laois than Offaly, and lovely hills they are too. And though the River Nore may be thought of as quintessential Kilkenny, long before it gets anywhere near Kilkenny it is quietly building as it meanders across much of Laois, gathering strength from the weirdly-named Delour, Tonet, Gully, Erskina and Goul rivers on the way.

Along the upper reaches of the Nore in west Laois, there has been celebration recently in the neat little village of Castletown. Always a tidy place, Castletown has for the past sixteen years climbed steadily up the rankings in the annual Tidy Towns contest. Having been the tidiest village in all Ireland in 2001, Castletown repeated the performance and then some in 2002. On September 9th 2002, at the annual awards ceremony in Dublin Castle, it was announced that Castletown was both the tidiest village, and the national overall winner in all categories.

Local Attractions and Information

Abbeyleix Abbeyleix Heritage House	0502 31653
Abbeyleix Sensory Gardens	0502 31325
Ballacolla National Ploughing Championship(Sept/Oct)	0507 25125
Ballinakill Heywood (Lutyens gardens)	0502 33563
Donaghmore Castletown House Open Farm	0505 46415

Donaghmore Donaghmore Workhouse Museum	0505 46212
Emo Emo Court (Gandon house & gardens)	0502 26573
Portlaois Dunamase Theatre & Arts Centre	0502 63356
Portlaois Tourist Information	0502 21178
Slieve Bloom Slieve Bloom Rural Development Assoc.	0509 37299
Stradbally National Steam Traction Rally (August)	0502 25444

Abbeyleix — Morrissey's

Pub   Main Street Abbeyleix Co. Laois **Tel: 0502 31281**

One of Ireland's finest and best-loved pubs, Morrissey's is a handsome building on the wide main street of this attractive little town. It's a great place to lift the spirits while taking a break between Dublin and Cork – food is not its strength but a quick cup of coffee and enjoyment of the atmosphere is sometimes all that's needed. Until very recently Morrissey's remained in the same family since it first opened as a grocery in 1775, when it started life as a thatched one-storey house. In 1880 it was rebuilt as the lofty two-storey premises we see today, with high shelf-lined walls and a pot belly stove to gather round on cold days. They have a list of people who have served their time at Morrissey's since 1850 – and, true to the old tradition, television, cards and singing are not allowed. No children after 7 pm. Closed 25 Dec & Good Fri. **Directions:** In the village, on the right heading south. ◇

Abbeyleix — Preston House

féile bia Restaurant/Guesthouse   Main Street Abbeyleix Co. Laois
Tel: 0502 31432 Fax: 0502 31432

A sign on the pavement outside Michael and Allison Dowling's attractive creeper-clad house welcomes people to their friendly and informal country-style restaurant. Allison's good home cooking starts off with delicious scones, served with tea or coffee and home-made preserves before lunch, at which time the choice widens to a short but tempting à la carte – typically including starters like cream of mushroom & thyme soup with freshly-baked brown bread or chicken liver paté with toast and salad followed, perhaps, by fish of the day or a speciality such as stirfry beef with roast vegetables. Vegetarians do very well here too, so if you're in a meat-free mood you can look forward to dishes like tagliatelle with tomato, mushroom, peppers & courgettes. Delicious desserts include sophisticated classics like crème brûlée but there are always simple, wholesome options too, like apple crumble or fresh fruits with low fat yogurt. Dinner menus are also à la carte and, although more formal and offering a wider choice, the same philosophy applies: this is deliciously healthy, well-balanced food with the emphasis on freshness and making best use of local produce - and thanks to the long opening hours and reasonable prices, it is exceptionally accessible. A first-floor ballroom runs across the whole width of the building and, with a library area up a few stairs at one end providing comfortable seating for non-participants and a minstrels' gallery at the other, it makes a superb venue for local events. Not suitable for children under 4 after 6 pm. **Seats 45.** No smoking restaurant. 10am-9pm: L Tue-Sun,12.30-2.45 (Sun 1-3); D Thu-Sat 6-9. A la carte available. House wine €15.50; sc discretionary (10% on parties of 6+). Closed D Sun-Wed, all Mon, Christmas period. **Accommodation:** The four large, high-ceilinged bedrooms are interestingly furnished with antiques and unusual en-suite facilities have been cleverly incorporated without spoiling the proportions of these fine rooms – by hiding them in what appears to be a long wardrobe but which opens up to reveal a row of individual facilities – shower, WC etc. Children welcome (under 4 free in parents' room). Pets permitted by arrangement. **Rooms 4** (all shower only & no-smoking). B&B from €38, ss €7. MasterCard, Visa, Laser. **Directions:** In the village, a few doors down from Morrissey's.

Ballacolla — Foxrock Inn

Pub/B&B   Clough Ballacolla Co. Laois **Tel: 0502 38637** Fax: 0502 38637
Email: foxrockinn@eircom.net Web: www.foxrockinn.com

Sean and Marian Hyland run a very friendly, relaxed little place here for lovers of the country life. Hill walking, fishing (coarse and game), golf and pitch & putt are all in the neighbourhood (golf and fishing packages are a speciality) and they'll make packed lunches to see you through the day. Evening meals, an open fire and traditional music (Tuesdays, May-September) make the pub a welcoming place to come back to and there is accommodation just up the stairs, in six modest but comfortable rooms (5 en-suite, all no smoking). B&B about €32 pps, ss about €6.70. Closed 25 Dec & Good Fri. Visa. **Directions:** On the R434, which links Durrow (N4) and Borris-in-Ossory (N7). ◇

Durrow | Castle Durrow

 Hotel   Durrow Co Laois **Tel: 0502 36555** Fax: 0502 36559
Email: info@castledurrow.com Web: www.castledurrow.com

The restoration of this substantial 18th century country house and grounds has clearly been a labour of love for proprietors Peter and Shelly Stokes - and its position roughly halfway between Dublin and Cork makes it easily accessible for short breaks from either city, or a good place to break the journey. It is an impressive building with some magnificent features and very spacious, luxurious accommodation in high-ceilinged, individually decorated rooms and suites with views over the surrounding parkland and countryside. Public rooms include a large drawing room/bar, which is furnished in a rather wacky style but quite comfortable, and a lovely dining room with a gently pastoral outlook at the back of the house, where dinner is available to guests and also non-residents by reservation (Peter Stokes previously owned Coopers restaurants in Dublin). A lot of restoration work has also been done in the grounds, including the old walled garden at the back which has already been cleared in preparation for a new lease of life at the time of the Guide's visit. Much work clearly remains to be done (including staff training) but this is a brave venture and an interesting place to visit. **Rooms 24.** B&B about €110pps. Open all year. Amex, Diners, MasterCard, Visa. **Directions:** On main Dublin-Cork road, N8. ◇

Mountrath | Roundwood House

Country House   Mountrath Co. Laois **Tel: 0502 32120** Fax: 0502 32711
Email: roundwood@eircom.net Web: www.hidden-ireland.com/roundwood

Ah, Roundwood - how could anybody fail to love this unspoilt early Georgian house, which lies secluded in mature woods of lime, beech and chestnut, at the foot of the Slieve Bloom mountains. A sense of history and an appreciation of genuine hospitality are all that is needed to make the most of a stay here – forget about co-ordinated decor and immaculate maintenance, just relax and share the immense pleasure and satisfaction that Frank and Rosemarie Kennan derive from the years of renovation work they have put into this wonderful property. Although unconventional in some ways, the house is extremely comfortable and well-heated (with central heating as well as log fires) and all the bathrooms have been recently renovated (all have full bath). The Kennans also have several beautifully converted rooms at the back and further outbuildings, Coach House and Forge Cottage, available for self-catering. Restoration is an ongoing process and an extraordinary (and historically unique) barn is possibly the next stage; this enterprise defies description, but don't leave Roundwood without seeing it. Children, who always love the unusual animals and their young in the back yard, are very welcome and Rosemarie does a separate tea for them. Residents dinner (8 pm) is based on the best local and seasonal ingredients (notably locally reared beef and lamb); Rosemarie's food suits the house perfectly – good home cooking without unnecessary frills – and Frank is an excellent host. Children welcome (under 2s free in parents' room, cot available without charge; playroom). Garden, croquet, boule, walking. Stabling available at the house; horse riding nearby. Golf nearby. No pets. Rooms 10 (all en-suite & 4 no-smoking). B&€70 pps, ss €25. No sc. D €45 (non-residents welcome if there is room); please book by noon. Closed Sun & Mon except for guests, 25 Dec & all Jan. Amex, Diners, MasterCard, Visa, Laser. **Directions:** On the left, 3 miles from Mountrath, on R440.

Portlaoise | Ivyleigh House

Guesthouse   Bank Place Church Street Portlaoise Co. Laois
Tel: 0502 22081 Fax: 0502 63343
Email: info@ivyleigh.com Web: www.ivyleigh.com

This lovely early Georgian house is set back from the road only by a tiny neatly box-hedged formal garden, but has a coachyard (with parking), outhouses and a substantial lawned garden at the back. It is a listed building and has clearly fallen into good hands as the present owners, Dinah and Jerry Campion, have restored it immaculately and furnished it beautifully in a style that successfully blends period elements with bold contemporary strokes, which gives it great life. Two lovely sitting rooms (one with television) are always available to guests and there's a fine dining room with a large communal table and a smaller one at the window. Bedrooms are the essence of comfort, spacious, elegant, with working sash windows and everything absolutely top of the range including pocket-sprung mattresses and even real linen sheets and pillowcases. Large shower rooms have many excellent details and terrific power showers (and, unusually, the space to make the most of them) although those who would give anything for a bath to soak in will be disappointed. But it is perhaps at breakfast that this superb guesthouse is at its best. An extensive menu shows a commitment to using quality local produce that turns out to be even better than anticipated: imaginative, perfectly cooked and beautifully presented. Fruits and yogurts include natural yogurt with geranium jelly and (on a late summer visit) poached plums; 'perfect porridge' comes with cream - or you can have cereals, including home-made muesli - and hot dishes include wonderfully creamy baked free range eggs with cream & cheese, and Cashel Blue cheesecakes - light and delicious, like fritters - come with mushrooms and tomatoes. There is also, of course, the option of a Full Irish Breakfast and - very unusually - there's a vegetarian variation on the great traditional fry. The details that count - freshly-baked brown bread, leaf tea or freshly brewed coffee, smooth, friendly service and meticulous timing of hot dishes - all add up to an exceptional experience. And through it all Dinah Campion (who must rise at dawn to bake the bread) is charming, efficient and hospitable. This is one of the best guest houses in Ireland and is well placed for touring the midlands, to break a journey, or for a short break from Dublin. No evening meals, but the Campions direct guests to good restaurants nearby. Not suitable for children under 8. **Rooms 6** (all shower only & no smoking); phone, tea/coffee facilities; television on request. B&B €52.50, ss €17.50. Closed 22 Dec-4 Jan. MasterCard, Visa. **Directions:** Centre of town follow signs for multi storey car park,30 metres from carpark.

Portlaoise | Kingfisher Restaurant

 Restaurant   Old AIB Bank Portlaoise Co Laois **Tel: 0502 62500** Fax: 0502 62700
Email: kingfisherrestaurant.com Web: www.kingfisherrestaurant.com

Situated in the centre of Portlaoise in the old AIB bank, this atmospheric and highly regarded Indian restaurant specialises in Punjabi cuisine. You enter into a very large, high-ceilinged room (the former banking hall), with a reception area off it where you are greeted by immaculately attired and genuinely friendly staff. The decor is unusual, using pale washes to portray the crumbling sandstone walls of an ancient Indian temple, including disintegrating murals with some entertainingly mischievous details. The relaxed ambience and people of all ages enjoying themselves makes for a very atmospheric room. Simple table presentation and enormously long menus may send out warning signals, but there are poppadums with dipping sauces to see you through the decision-making phases and, once food appears, it is clearly accomplished cooking, without recourse to elaborate presentation but well-flavoured with the fresh flavours of individual ingredients and authentic spicing creating satisfying combinations - in dishes that vary from creamy styles with almonds, to very spicy dishes with 'angry' green peppers. Tandoori, balti, biryani, 'exquisite' dishes and 'old favourite' dishes like korma, rogan josh, do piaza are all there, but they are well executed, served with professionalism and charm, and very reasonably priced (main courses about €11.50-17.95). **Seats 63.** L Wed-Fri 12.30-2, à la carte; D daily, 5.30-11; early D €15 (5.30-7); otherwise set D menus from €23.50 per person, also à la carte. House wine €14.75. Closed 25 Dec, Good Fri. Amex, Diners, MasterCard, Visa, Laser. **Directions:** Town Centre.

Portlaoise | The Kitchen & Foodhall

féile bia Restaurant   Hynds Square Portlaoise Co. Laois
Tel: 0502 62061 Fax: 0502 62075

Jim Tynan's smashing restaurant and food shop is definitely worth a little detour. Delicious home-made food, an open fire, relaxed atmosphere - a perfect place to break a journey or for a special visit. The foodhall stocks a wide range of Irish speciality food products (and many excellent imported ones as well) and also sells products made on the premises: home-made terrines and breads for example (including gluten-free breads - which are also available in the restaurant) lovely home-bakes like Victoria sponges, crumbles and bread & butter pudding. You can buy home-made ready meals too and any of the wines from the shop can be bought for the restaurant without a corkage charge. The restaurant offers a great choice of wholesome fare, including at least three vegetarian dishes each day - old favourites like nut roast, perhaps and others like roasted vegetable & cream cheese flan and spinach roulade with cream cheese & pepper. Hereford premium beef is typical of the Irish produce in which such pride is taken - and lunches are served with a wholesome selection of vegetables or salads. **Seats 200** (daytime). Open all day Mon-Sat, 9-5.30; L12.30-2.30. Set L from about €8.25. D à la carte. House Wine from €39.99 Wheelchair access. Closed 24 Dec-3 Jan. MasterCard, Visa. **Directions:** In the centre of Portlaoise, beside the Courthouse.

COUNTY LEITRIM

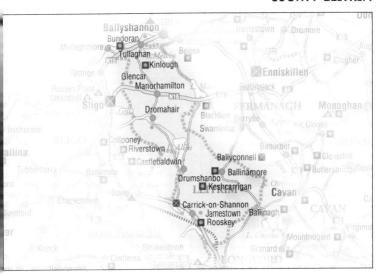

Leitrim is the happening place in 2003. The county town of Carrick-on-Shannon - arguably the most important leisure port on the entire Shannon waterway - has becoming a byword for growing prosperity. Its resurgence is symbolised by the 7.4 million euro which is being allocated to transform the old Courthouse into a major arts centre. When we realise that, less than ten years ago, it was thought that demolition was the only option for this handsome but derelict 19th Century building, we begin to get a sense of Leitrim's new vitality.

Yet despite the new energy, Leitrim is rightly seen as a pleasantly away-from-it-all sort of place which has many attractions for the determined connoisseur. So with some of Ireland's better known holiday areas suffering if anything from an excess of popularity, the true trail-blazers may well find the remoteness they seek in Leitrim.

But is it so remote? Popular perceptions may be at variance with reality. For instance, Leitrim shares the shores of Lough Gill with Sligo, so much so that Yeat's Lake Isle of Innisfree is within an ace of being in Leitrim rather than Sligo of Yeatsian fame. To the northward, we find that more than half of lovely Glencar, popularly perceived as being one of Sligo's finest jewels, is in fact in Leitrim. As for the notion of Leitrim being the ultimate inland and rural county - not so. Leitrim has an Atlantic coastline, albeit of only four kilometres, around Tullaghan.

It's said this administrative quirk is a throwback to the time when the all-powerful bishops of the early church aspired to have ways of travelling to Rome without having to cross the territory of neighbouring clerics. Whatever the reason, it's one of Leitrim's many surprises, which are such that it often happens that when you're touring in the area and find yourself in a beautiful bit of country, a reference to the map produces the unexpected information that you're in Leitrim.

Local Attractions and Information

Ballinamore Shannon-Erne Waterway	078 44855
Ballinamore Slieve an Arain Riverbus Cruises	078 44079
Carrick-on-Shannon Moonriver Cruises	078-21777
Carrick-on-Shannon Tourism Information	078 20170
Carrick-on-Shannon Waterways Ireland	078 50898
Dromahair Parke's Castle (restored 17c fortified hse)	071 64149
Drumshanbo Sliabh an Iarainn Visitor Centre	078 41522
Manorhamilton Glens Arts Centre	072 55833
Mohill Lough Rynn House and Gardens	078 31427
Rossinver Eden Plants & The Organic Centre	072 54122

Carrick-on-Shannon — Bush Hotel

féile bia Hotel

Carrick-on-Shannon Co Leitrim **Tel: 078 20014** Fax: 078 21180
Email: info@bushhotel.com Web: www.bushhotel.com

One of Ireland's oldest hotels, the Bush has undergone considerable refurbishment in recent years and, while rooms will vary in size and comfort, all are en-suite (most with full bath) and have TV, tea/coffee making facilities and trouser press phones - and this is an hotel that makes up in personality anything it may lack in contemporary style and finish. Public areas, including a very pleasant restaurant (refurbished in 2001 and open for lunch and dinner as well as serving a good breakfast) and two bars, have character and a pleasing sense of history. Staff are exceptionally pleasant and helpful and there's direct access to the carpark at the back of the hotel off the N4 bypass. Informal meals are available all day at the self-service coffee shop/carvery (8am-6pm) and there's bar food too (6-9 daily). Conference/banqueting (4350/300). Children welcome (under 5s free in parents' room, cot available without charge); pets allowed in some areas. The hotel has a gift shop, tourist information point and bureau de change and can arrange car, bicycle and boat hire and supply fishing tackle and golf clubs. Golf nearby. Tennis; garden. **Rooms 26** (1 suite, 8 shower only). B&B € about 60pps, ss about €6. Closed 24-31 Dec. Amex, MasterCard, Visa, Laser. **Directions:** Town Centre.

Carrick-on-Shannon — Hollywell Country House

Country House

Liberty Hill Cortober Carrick-on-Shannon Co. Leitrim
Tel: 078 21124 Fax: 078 21124 Email: hollywell@esatbiz.com

After many years as hoteliers in the town (and a family tradition of inn-keeping that goes back 200 years), Tom and Rosaleen Maher moved some years ago to this delightful period house on a rise over the bridge, with beautiful views over the Shannon and its own river frontage. It's a lovely, graciously proportioned house, with a relaxed family atmosphere. Tom and Rosaleen have an easy hospitality (not surprisingly, perhaps, as their name derives from the Gaelic "Meachar" meaning hospitable), making guests feel at home very quickly and this, as much as the comfort of the house and its tranquil surroundings, is what makes Hollywell special. Bedrooms are all individually furnished in period style and have tea & coffee making facilities. Delicious breakfasts are worth getting up in good time for: fresh juice, fruits and choice of teas, coffees and herbal teas, freshly-baked bread, home-made preserves, lovely choice of hot dishes - anything from the "full Irish" to Irish pancakes with maple syrup or grilled cheese & tomato with black olive pesto on toast. No evening meals, but Tom and Rosaleen advise guests on the best local choices and there's a comfortable guests' sitting room with an open fire to gather around on your return. Lovely garden reaching down to the river; fishing (coarse) on site. Lots to do in the area - and advice a-plenty from Tom and Rosaleen on the best places to visit. Not suitable for children. Pets allowed by arrangement. **Rooms 4** (all en-suite). B&B €53pps, ss €10. Closed Christmas-New Year. Amex, MasterCard, Visa. **Directions:** From Dublin, cross bridge on N4, keep left at Gings pub. Hollywell entrance is on left up the hill.

Carrick-on-Shannon — The Landmark Hotel

Hotel

Dublin Road Carrick-on-Shannon Co. Leitrim **Tel: 078 22222** Fax: 078 22233
Email: landmarkhotel@eircom.net Web: thelandmarkhotel.com

This aptly named almost-riverside hotel has brought much-needed business facilities to the area. A dramatic lobby with a large marble and granite fountain feature and imposing cast iron staircase creates a certain expectation and bedrooms, many of which have views over the Shannon, are spacious and comfortable, with individual temperature control as well as the more usual amenities (direct dial phone, TV, tea/coffee facilities, trouser press) and well-finished bathrooms. Informal contemporary dining is offered nightly at Ferrari's restaurant (the reason for the name is obvious when you get there) and is unlike anything else offered nearby; the set-up - on a balcony over a large bar - is a little strange, but it pleases a youthful market and provides a lively contrast for boating visitors ashore after a quiet few days on the river. Conference/banqueting (400/350); secretarial services; business centre. Golf nearby (9). Off-season breaks. Children welcome (under 4s free in parents' room; cots available without charge). No pets. **Rooms 60** (4 suites, 4 for disabled). Lift. B&B about €122 pps. Ferrari's D daily, 6-10. House wine about €13. SC discretionary. Hotel closed 24-25 Dec. Amex, Diners, MasterCard, Visa. **Directions:** On N4, 2 hours from Dublin. ◇

Carrick-on-Shannon — Lynch's Bar/The Sheermore

Pub

Kilclare Carrick-on-Shannon Co Leitrim
Tel: 078 41029

Known from the road as "The Sheermore", Padraig Lynch's friendly bar, grocery and hardware shop presents its much more attractive side to the water and you can sit outside at the back in fine weather, or choose between a conservatory overlooking the bridge or a move right into the bar if the weather dictates. Food isn't elaborate here, but Christine Lynch makes home-made soup every day and cuts sandwiches freshly to order - just the right thing, in the right place. Children welcome. Pets allowed in certain areas. Bar Food served daily, 12.30-9.30. Wheelchair accessible. Closed 25 Dec, Good Fri. MasterCard, Visa, Laser. **Directions:** 6 miles from Carrick-on-Shannon towards Ballinamore, on the Shannon-Erne Waterway.

Carrick-on-Shannon — The Oarsman Bar & Café

⚑ Pub

Bridge Street Carrick-on-Shannon Co Leitrim **Tel: 078 21733** Fax: 078 21124
Email: hospitality@theoarsman.com Web: www.theoarsman.com

This attractive and characterful pub moved into a new era when Conor and Ronan Maher took it over in 2002. The brothers are sons of Tom and Rosaleen Maher (see entry for Holywell) and clearly have what's known as "the hotelier's gene": several visits by the guide at different times of day and days of the week have found everything spick-and-span, very welcoming and efficiently run, even at very busy times. The bar, - which is very pleasantly set up in a solidly traditional style with a fire, comfortable seating arrangements for eating the excellent bar meals, and the occasional gesture towards contemporary tastes in the decor - leads off towards a sheltered patio at the back, which makes a pleasant spot for a sunny day and gives the bar an open atmosphere; just the place for one of their delicious Illy coffes with a complimentary Illy chcocolate.. Upstairs, meanwhile, is what promises to be a seriously interesting restaurant, Upstairs @ The Oarsman; due to open shortly after we go to press, with Sheila Sharpe - previously senior chef at the renowned Cromleach Lodge restaurant near Castlebaldwin - in the kitchen, this is to be a new dining concept and, given the talent and professionalism involved, should help make The Oarsman a destination dining venue. Restaurant **Seats 40** (private room 6); opening times to be confirmed (evenings). Bar meals: Mon-Sat 12-3.30 (will be extended). Not suitable for children after 7pm. Closed 25 Dec. MasterCard, Visa, Laser. **Directions:** Near the bridge in Carrick-on-Shannon, towards the centre of the town.

Carrick-on-Shannon — Shamrat

Ⓝ Restaurant

Bridge Street Carrick-on-Shannon Co Leitrim **Tel: 078 50934**

Although the entrance is small from the street, this new Indian restaurant has a spacious L-shaped first floor dining area and room for a comfortable reception area at the top of the stairs. Uncluttered contemporary decor and well-spaced tables with comfortable high-back chairs add to the sense of thoughtful design that prevails - all of which, together with attentive service from friendly and helpful staff, add to the enjoyment of interesting, authentic and well-cooked food. L&D daily; Mon-Sat L 12.30-2.30, D 6-11.30; Sun, special family lunch 1-4, à la carte 4-11. MasterCard, Visa, Laser **Directions:** Near the bridge, on right-hand side walking into town. ◇

Cootehall — Cootehall Bridge Restaurant & Coffee House

Restaurant/Café

Cootehall Co. Leitrim **Tel: 079 67173**

Cootehall is one of those places which can't decide which county it is in, but, whether it is in Roscommon or Leitrim, Manfred Kan's seasonal restaurant provides a very complete service once it gets going. A substantial à la carte dinner menu is offered, (typically including French onion soup, steaks, Wiener Schnitzel and a separate vegetarian menu) and Manfred's good cooking and great value for money send many a customer happy into the night. There's also a children's menu, varied desserts and waffles and a range of novelty ice cream dishes. Open from St Patrick's Day, Tue-Sun,12.30-10 pm.(Lunch to 3.30, then teas, ices etc; Dinner 6-10pm). Dinner reservations recommended. A phone call to check opening times is recommended. MasterCard, Visa. **Directions:** Right of the bridge as you approach the village. ◇

Cootehall · M J Henry's

Pub · Cootehall Co. Leitrim **Tel: 079 67030**

The more theme pubs and superpubs there are, the better everyone likes James Henry's bar, which hasn't changed in at least 30 years. A visit to Cootehall would be unthinkable without checking on this little gem They don't make them like this any more, alas, but this delightful old pub - complete with formica from the most recent renovation - is a gem. Get in beside the fire with a hot whiskey and the world will do you no harm. Closed 25 Dec & Good Fri. **Directions:** 2 miles off Sligo-Dublin road.

Jamestown · Al Mezza

ⓝ Restaurant · Jamestown Co Leitrim **Tel: 078 25050**

This colourful little Lebanese/Mediterranean restaurant on the edge of the pretty village of Jamestown opened early in 2002. Proprietor-chef Milad Serhan (previously at The Pyramids in Carrick-on-Shannon) offers quite extensive authentic middle eastern menus - mixed dishes are probably the best choice on a first visit. It's an unusual little place for a country area, with friendly service as well as good food. For those arriving in Jamestown by boat, it's about half a mile from the quay, but it's a pleasant walk through the village - pavement all the way and past two particularly enticing pubs for a visit in each direction, perhaps. Open Mon, Wed & Thu 5.30-11, Fri & Sat 5.30-11.30/12; Sun 5.30-10.30. Closed Tue. Open all year. MasterCard, Visa, Laser. **Directions:** On right just before entering Jamestown village. ◇

Keshcarrigan · Canal View House & Restaurant

Restaurant/Accommodation · Keshcarrigen Co. Leitrim **Tel: 078 42404**

A fireside cup of tea and home-baked scones or biscuits in the comfortable residents' lounge (with views of the cruisers passing) welcomes guests on arrival at Jeanette Conefry's immaculate guesthouse and restaurant overlooking the Shannon-Erne Waterway. Bedrooms – some with water views, all with a pleasant outlook – are individually furnished to a high standard, with direct-dial telephones and neat en-suite shower rooms. Peace and quiet are an attraction here, but television is available in bedrooms on request. Families are welcome and well looked after. Pets permitted by arrangement. **Rooms 6.** B&B about €35 pps, ss about €7. Closed Christmas week.
Restaurant: At this well-established waterside restaurant, chef Michael Flaherty offers traditional cooking in a mainly classical style with some international influences. Many house specialities feature on menus that could include homemade pâté with Cumberland sauce, steaks various ways, poached salmon with mushroom & dill sauce and a good choice of vegetarian dishes cheese & spinach vol-au-vent, perhaps, or a spicy vegetable stir-fry. There might be game in season - venison & mushroom pie is a speciality There are private mooring facilities so that restaurant guests on boats can stay there overnight. Children welcome. **Seats 40.** D daily, 6-10; L Sun only 1-3; Set Sun L €18.50, D à la carte. House wine €15.50; sc discretionary. Wheelchair accessible. Open all year except Christmas. Amex, MasterCard, Visa. **Directions:** On Shannon-Erne Waterway, 10 miles from Carrick-on-Shannon.

Kinlough · Courthouse Restaurant

Restaurant/B&B · Main Street Kinlough Co. Leitrim **Tel: 072 42391** Fax: 072 42824
Email: thecourthouserest@eircom.net

In the old courthouse of the attractive village of Kinlough, Piero and Sandra Melis's stylish little restaurant is a particularly welcoming place and offers good contemporary cooking in the Mediterranean style with some more down to earth local influences, especially at lunchtime. A wide ranging menu includes specialities like turbot with squid ink risotto and free range duck with spinach and wild mushrooms and there are always daily specials; ostrich has become popular and the house specialities include ostrich fillet with chargrilled vegetables in a reduced balsamic vinegar sauce - and there' free-range quail, too, wrapped in sage & smoked bacon, with basil champ and wild mushroom sauce. More traditional dishes include starters like Caprese salad (buffalo mozzarella with sliced tomato, fresh basil & home-made pesto), seafood risotto and pasta dishes such as the tasty vegetarian penne four cheeses (tube pasta cooked in a creamy gorgonzola, cheddar, parmesan and smoked cheese sauce, served with a side salad. Traditional desserts include an irresistible panna cotta with home-made chocolate sauce and boozy fruits. Everything is freshly made on the premises - and good food, good value and the helpful attitude of the staff all encourage return visits. Not suitable for children after 8 pm.* A newer sister restaurant "Tamarindo Blu" is at Astoria Wharf, on the seafront in Bundoran; home-made pizzas and pasta specialities. **Seats 35** (private room 15). D

Wed-Mon, 6.30-9.30, L Sun only 12.30-2.30. D à la carte; Set Sun L €18. House wines €15-18; sc discretionary except 10% on parties of 6+. No-smoking area. Closed Tue, 3 days Christmas,2 weeks Nov & 2 weeks Feb.
Accommodation: Neat, freshly decorated bedrooms offer comfortable accommodation at a very reasonable price. **Rooms 4** (all shower only). B&B about €32 pps, ss about €7. MasterCard, Visa, Laser. **Directions:** Off main Donegal-Sligo road (N15), 5 km towards Sligo from Bundoran. Take turning directly opposite Tullaghan House.

Leitrim Village — The Barge Steakhouse

Restaurant/Pub

Leitrim Village Carrick-on-Shannon Co Leitrim
Tel: 078 20807 Fax: 078 22957

This attractive stone building on the main street has been extensively renovated and gradually developed under the current ownership of John and Rose Pierce, so that it now offers a restaurant and conservatory, as well as the characterful bar which was opened in 2001. The whole place is kept scrupulously clean and tidy, including a new beer garden at the back, which is very popular for barbecues when weather permits. Head chef Margaret Melia provides a daytime bar menu as well as an à la carte for the restaurant; while not exactly home cooking, the style is quite traditional - typical starters include deepfried mushrooms, prawn cocktail and egg mayonnaise and, as the name implies, steaks various ways are the speciality of the house. Other regulars include crispy duck and there's always at least one vegetarian dish; there may sometimes be really traditional dishes like beef & Guinness casserole or bacon & cabbage too. There's a little children's menu too, and a short list of popular wines. Open 12.30-9.30 daily, L 12-6, D 6-9. A la carte. **Seats 90** (32 in conservatory; private room 21). Non smoking restaurant. Toilets wheelchair accessible. Closed 25 Dec & Good Fri. Amex, Diners, MasterCard, Visa, Laser, Switch. **Directions:** In Leitrim village: take Drumshambo road out of Carrick-on-Shannon.

Rooskey — Shannon Key West Hotel

Hotel

Rooskey Co. Leitrim **Tel: 078 38800** Fax: 078 38811

This well-run riverside hotel on the Leitrim/Roscommon border has brought valuable facilities to the area and is open all year (except Christmas), making it a particularly good venue for off-season short breaks, meetings and conferences. Comfortably furnished bedrooms have all the usual amenities - direct dial phones, TV with video channel, tea & coffee-making facilities and trouser press; 2 rooms also have fax machines and there is a safe available on request. On-site amenities include a gym, jacuzzi, solarium and steam room (but no swimming pool) and there is plenty to do and see in the area. Reliable bar food also makes this a useful place to bear in mind for breaking a journey. Conference/banqueting (300/220); video conferencing and back-up secretarial services available. Leisure centre. Children welcome (under 4s free in parents' room, cots available without charge). **Rooms 39** (7 no smoking, 1 for disabled). B&B about €60 pps, ss €19. Closed 24-28 Dec. Amex, MasterCard, Visa, Laser, Switch. **Directions:** On N4, main Dublin - Sligo route.

Tullaghan — Tullaghan House

Country House/B&B

Tullaghan Co. Leitrim **Tel: 072 41515** / 42055 Fax: 072 41515
Email: emmccanney@hotmail.com

This delightfully unspoilt Georgian residence is set back from the road in its own garden and is run by the (equally delightful) McCanney sisters: Elizabeth, Cathleen, Suzanne and Rosa, who took over the house in the spring of 1998 and are gradually making improvements, in a gentle way so as not to lose the charming family home atmosphere that is one of its main attributes. The bedrooms are all individually furnished, with very different characters, and public rooms are spacious and comfortable, with old family furniture. No evening meals but the Courthouse Restaurant at Kinlough (see entry) is nearby. Children welcome (under 6s free in parents' room). Pets permitted in some areas. **Rooms 6** (all en-suite). B&B about €35, ss about €15. Closed Christmas-New Year period. MasterCard, Visa. **Directions:** On main Dublin-Sligo road (N15), 1 mile towards Sligo from Bundoran, on right hand side. ◇

COUNTY LIMERICK

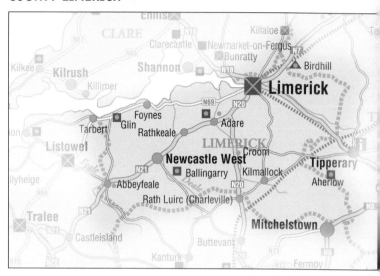

The story of Limerick city and county is in many ways the story of the Shannon Estuary, for in times past it was the convenient access provided by Ireland's largest estuary - it is 60 miles long - which encouraged the development of life along its southern shore and into the River Shannon. Today, the area's focal point for national and global transport is of course Shannon International Airport, which is actually located in south County Clare, but is very much a part of the shores of the Shannon Estuary, the region's dominant geographical feature.

2003 sees Limerick city's renewed focus on its waterfront being further emphasised with spectacular modern riverside buildings. In recent years, the opening of improved waterway links through the heart of town has seen the welcome regeneration of the old city continuing in tandem with the attractive new developments. But significant and all as this is, there's more to Limerick county than waterways.

Inland from the river, the very richness of the countryside soon begins to develop its own dynamic. Eastern Limerick verges into Tipperary's Golden Vale, and the eastern county's Slieve Felim hills, rising to Cullaun at 462 m, reflect the nearby style of Tipperary's Silvermine Mountains.

Southwest of Limerick city, the splendid hunting country and utterly rural atmosphere of the area around the beautiful village of Adare makes it a real effort of imagination to visualise the muddy salt waters of the Shannon Estuary just a few miles away down the meandering River Maigue, yet the Estuary is there nevertheless. Equally, although the former flying boat port of Foynes and the nearby jetty at Aughinish may be expanding to accommodate the most modern large ships, just a few miles inland we find ourselves in areas totally remote from the sea in countryside which lent itself so well to mixed farming that the price of pigs in Dromcolliher (a.k.a. Drumcolligher) on the edge of the Mullaghareirk Mountains reputedly used to set the price of pigs throughout Ireland.

The growth of the computer industry in concert with the rapid expansion of the remarkably vibrant University has given Limerick a completely new place in Irish life, and the city's energy and urban renewal makes it an entertaining place to visit, while the eclectic collection on stunning display in the unique Hunt Museum in its handsome waterside setting has a style which other areas of Limerick life are keen to match.

With newfound confidence, Limerick has been paying greater attention to its remarkable heritage of Georgian architecture, with Limerick Civic Trust restoring the Georgian house and garden at 2 Pery Square. It acts as the focal point for an area of classic urban architecture which deserves to be better known.

That said, Limerick still keeps its feet firmly on the ground, and connoisseurs are firmly of the opinion that the best pint of Guinness in all Ireland is to be had in this no-nonsense city, where they insist on being able to choose the temperature of their drink, and refuse to have any truck with modern fads which would attempt to chill the rich multi-flavoured black pint into a state of near-freezing tastelessness aimed at immature palates.

Local Attractions and Information

Adare Heritage Centre	061 396666
Adare May Fair	061 396894
Ballysteen Ballynacourty Gardens	061 396409
Bruree Heritage Centre and de Valera Museum	063 91300
Croom Waterwheel and Heritage Centre	061 397130
Foynes Flying Boat Museum	069 65416
Glin Glin Castle Pleasure Grounds & Walled Garden	068 34364
Limerick Belltable Arts Centre, 69 O'Connell St	061 319866
Limerick Georgian House & Garden, 2 Pery Square	061 314130
Limerick Hunt Museum, Customs House, Rutland St	061 312833
Limerick King John's Castle	061 360788
Limerick Limerick City Art Gallery, Pery Square	061 310633
Limerick Limerick Museum, John's Square	061 417826
Limerick Tourism Information	061 317522
Limerick University of Limerick	061 333644
Lough Gur Interpretive centre, 3000BC to present	061 360788
Patrickswell Limerick Racecourse (Greenmount Park)	061 355055

Limerick — Aubars Bar & Restaurant

Pub/Restaurant

49-50 Thomas Street Limerick Co. Limerick
Tel: 061 317799 Fax: 061 317572

Padraic Frawley's new look city centre bar and restaurant typifies the renewal of Limerick itself - a university city with a youthful population and city, it is said, with more cafés, pubs and restaurants than any other in Ireland. Padraic, a hotel management graduate who trained at the highly respected catering college nearby in Shannon, returned to his home city at the grand old age of 27 bursting with ideas collected during experience abroad and proceeded to transform an old pub into a dashing new bar and restaurant (and nightclub) that has achieved national recognition. The layout is on several levels with no hard divisions and a mixture of seating in various areas, which can lead to confusion between customers coming in to eat rather than have a drink, although watchful staff soon have new arrivals sorted. While the style is uncompromisingly modern, down to the designer crockery, the solid traditional values of good training and supervsion prevail - and the emphasis is on providing consistently excellent contemporary cooking, professional service and value for money. Well-balanced menus (inspired by the Gary Rhodes style: 'dishes that are simple to make, tasty and look great') change monthly - and offer clean-lined modern cooking in a range of hot dishes, several salds, low-fat options: seafood crêpes, Caesar salad with char-grilled chicken (presented in a filo basket), roast fillet of salmon on potato & celeriac purée and home-made pork & herb sausages with champ & onion gravy are all typical - and nice old-fashioned desserts that even include apple pie made by Padraic's octogenarian grandmother. A short well-selected wine list includes weekly specials by the glass. Food available 8 am-9pm daily. Amex, Diners, MasterCard, Visa, Laser. ◇

Limerick — Brulées Restaurant

féile bia Restaurant

Corner of Henry St & Mallow St Limerick Co. Limerick
Tel: 061 319 931

Just a stroll across from Jurys Limerick Inn, Donal and Teresa Cooper's well-appointed corner restaurant is deservedly recognised as the leading fine dining restaurant in Limerick and is a first choice destination for discerning diners visiting the city. Dining areas on several levels break groups up nicely and are elegantly furnished in a simple classic style that makes the most of limited space. A soothing ambience and welcoming details - olives and freshly baked breads to nibble - get guests off to a good start while reading Teresa's appealing menus. She takes pride in using the finest of ingredients, both local and imported, in imaginative, colourful modern Irish cooking, which is as good as it sounds - mixed green salad leaves with bacon, toasted pine nuts, semi-dried tomatoes & basil dressing make a tasty starter, or a vegetarian dish like vegetable spring rolls on bed of noodles, with chilli dip can be a tempting option. Main courses also offer a balanced combination of international influences and dishes with their hearts closer to home such as a speciality dishes of Irish beef fillet serves on black pudding mash, or grilled liver and bacon with champ and grain mustard & mushroom cream. Each dish sounds more tempting than the one before - vegetarian dishes are invariably imaginative, also fish and seafood which will always include daily specials. Cooking is accurate, presentation attractive without being fussy and, with main courses averaging around €20, this is good value for the quality. Simple, attractively prepared and carefully cooked side vegetables are another plus point, also a good cheese selection, supplied by Sheridans cheesemongers - and gorgeous puddings include (what else) a classic crème brûlée, served with crunchy shortbread and warm berry compôte. Interesting, fairly priced wine list. Seats 30. No smoking area. L Tue-Fri, 12.30-2.30; D Tue-Sat, 6.30-10. A La carte. House wine €17; SC discretionary. Closed Sun, Mon; 24-25 Dec, 31 Dec, 1 Jan. Amex, Diners, MasterCard, Visa, Laser. **Directions:** On the corner of Henry St.and Lower Mallow Street, near Jury's Inn roundabout.

Limerick — Castletroy Park Hotel

 Hotel   Dublin Road Limerick Co. Limerick **Tel: 061 335 566** Fax: 061 331 117
Email: sales@castletroy-park.ie Web: www.castletroy-park.ie

This blocky redbrick hotel has mellowed a little with time and has a warm and welcoming atmosphere in the large foyer and all the public areas. While not individually decorated, spacious rooms (regularly refurbished, the latest phase completed in 2002) are thoughtfully furnished with special attention to the needs of the business traveller (good desk space, second phone, fax and computer points). The hotel is much sought after as a conference venue and, after work, excellent leisure facilities and The Merry Pedlar pub offer a change of scene. Conferences / Banqueting (450-250); secretarial services. Business centre. Leisure/fitness centre, swimming pool. Children welcome (under 12s free in parents room, cot available without charge). Garden. **Rooms 107** (2 suites, 5 junior suites, 25 executive, 50 no-smoking, 1 for disabled). Lift. 24 hour room service. B&B €115 pps, ss €90. SC incl. Hotel closed 24-25 Dec.
Mc Laughlin's: The hotel's fine dining restaurant provides a comfortable formal setting for head chef Tom Flavin's international cuisine. In addition to the table d'hôte menus, a wide-range à la carte ensures that guests staying in the hotel for several days have plenty of choice. Wide-ranging starters include several soups and specialities like Castletroy Park Atlantic Salmon platter (with wasabi, pickled ginger & Kikkoman soy sauce), while main courses are almost equally balanced between meat/poultry, seafood and vegetarian dishes. Some are quite unusual-oven-roasted ostrich fillet with salad & Mediterranean vegetables, for example, but there are plenty of familiar choices too. Desserts range from the pretty (selection of ice creams in a cassis tuile) to the homely (warm rhubarb crumble). An informative wine list includes quite a strong selection of half bottles. Seats 75. No smoking area; air conditioning. L & D Daily, 12.30-2 &5.30-10 (Sun 6-9.30) Set L €25, Set D €38; D also à la carte. House wine, €17.85. SC discretionary except 12.5% on groups of 8+. Amex, Diners, MasterCard, Visa, Laser. **Directions:** On main Dublin-Limerick road (N7); 3 miles from Limerick city, 25 minutes from Shannon airport.

Limerick — Clarion Hotel

🏨 Ⓝ Hotel   Steamboat Quay Limerick Co Limerick **Tel: 061 444100** Fax: 061 444101
Email: info@clarionhotellimerick.com Web: www.clarionhotellimerick.com

 This exciting new cigar-shaped 17-storey hotel right on the River Shannon waterfront in the centre of Limerick city enjoys panoramic views over the city and the Shannon region - although, strangely, bedroom windows are quite high in the walls so the full benefit of the location is missed while sitting. Like the Clarion IFSC in Dublin (see entry), clean-lined contemporary elegance is the theme throughout and there are many similarities between the two hotels, including the semi-open plan arrangement of foyer, bars and dining spaces (which take full advantage of the location). As at IFSC, business facilities are excellent and bedrooms - which vary more than usual in hotels due to the unusual shape of the building - are offered in several pleasingly simple, modern colour schemes. All, however, have striking maple furniture, the best of beds and bedding, air conditioning, ISDN lines, cable TV - everything, in short, that makes an hotel room the perfect retreat. Leisure facilities are also good - a health and fitness club up on the nth floor (it's easy to lose count) has a gym, sauna, jacuzzi and even a 12 metre swimming pool, with personal fitness consultant and nutritionist on hand to advise. Several decked balconies and terraces at different levels allow guests to take full advantage of fine weather - and the top two floors have suites and penthouses available for long lets. Conference/banqueting 93/70. Business centre. Video-conferencing. leisure centre; swimming pool. **Rooms 123.** (30 suites, 21 executive, 62 no smoking, 5 disabled). Lift. 24 hour room service. Children welcome (under 4s free in parents' room; cot available without charge). B&B 69pps, ss €69. (Room-only rate €110: opening offer

vailable to 31.12.02). Sinergie Restaurant open for breakfast, lunch & dinner daily. Kudos Bar serves ood Mon-Sat, 12-8.30. Closed 24-25 Dec. Amex, Diners, MasterCard, Visa, Laser. **Directions:** 3rd exit ff Newbridge roundabout, 1st right off Dock road.

Limerick | DuCartes at the Hunt Museum

Restaurant

Hunt Museum Old Custom House Rutland Street Limerick Co. Limerick
Tel: 061 312662 Fax: 061 417929

This delightful modern café/restaurant is at the back of the museum, overlooking the river, with ables outside on the terrace in fine weather. As well as providing an appropriately elegant space to estore visitors to the museum, it is a popular lunchtime venue for locals. All ingredients are sourced ocally and prepared daily: attractively presented and healthy home-cooked food in the modern idiom hould not disappoint, although it may be a little short on personality. [D, for groups only by rrangement] Seats 70. No smoking area; air conditioning. Meals daily 5-5 (Sun 2-5), L 12-3. Set L about €17. House wine about €16. Closed Sun morning, 25 Dec. MasterCard, Visa. ◇

Limerick | Eastern Tandoori

Restaurant

2-3 Steamboat Quay Limerick Co. Limerick
Tel: 061 311575 Fax: 061 311578

This lavishly furnished richly-coloured glass-fronted waterside restaurant looks especially enticing rom the outside at night - a good impression that is confirmed when the white-coated proprietor greets arriving guests personally. Well-appointed tables reflect the rich decorative themes and are enhanced by lovely lighting, altogether creating an exceptionally pleasant ambience. Menus in the amiliar Indian style are arranged by category and descriptive, with clear pride taken in regional specialities. Cooking is excellent and service is very professional and formal: waiters in regional costume present dishes in the traditional Indian way, with serving dishes on hotplates and accompaniments served separately. There's a good range of beers to complement the food. Prices are very reasonable and, together with reliably enjoyable food and good service, this is a restaurant that deserves more recognition. Children welcome, but not after 7pm. Seats 80. No smoking area; air conditioning. Toilets wheelchair accessible. L daily,12-2.30; D daily 6-11. Set menus from €25.95; also à la carte. House wine €15. No SC. Eastern Tandoori Amex, Diners, MasterCard, Visa, Laser. **Directions:** Waterfront, near new Clarion Hotel.

Limerick | Finn's Bar & The Milestone

Pub

62 William Street Limerick Co. Limerick **Tel: 061 313495** Fax: 061 313496
Email: info@finnsbar.ie Web: www.finnsbar.ie

The Flannerys, father and sons, have reason to be proud of this fine city centre pub - Michael Flannery, who has been in charge since 1960, handed over the reins to Seamus and Liam in 1999 and, while it still has a traditional pub front, the new generation decided that the building, which is over 200 years old, needed a complete makeover - and it's now uncompromisingly 21st century. Changes were made with great care, however, and the new design is both striking and warm: 'modern but comfortable' was the brief. A dramatic sculptural chandelier makes an unusual focal point in the high-ceilinged front bar, which also has a gallery around it, creating interesting spatial relationships which can be studied from above as well as below. Clean lines are emphasised by another feature which is unusual, possibly unique, in Irish pubs: a total absence of advertising; the only branding allowed is their own and their swirling black and gold logo appears on everything. Providing a comfortable place where quality food and drink is served by friendly staff is the aim, and it is achieved with commendable consistency at The Milestone. After breakfast (fresh orange juice, toasted bagel & cream cheese etc), then a lunch menu offering a tasty selection of soups, sandwiches and salads; hot dishes are cooked to order and attractively presented; seafood is quite prominent and everything is home-made, including a speciality chowder, scones and desserts of the day. (Average main course about €7.50, seafood a little more). Service is pleasant and informal - and speciality coffees come with complimentary chocolates. DJ music on weekend evenings; the more traditional Milestone bar downstairs is quieter. Seats 60. Food available Mon-Sat, 9.30am-7.30pm: B 9.30-11.30, L 11.30-3.30; D 3.30-7.30. (No food on Sun). House wine about €17). Closed 25 Dec & Good Fri. Amex, MasterCard, Visa, Laser. **Directions:** 100 metres off Wiliam Street/O'Connell Street Junction.

Limerick | Jurys Inn Limerick

 Hotel

Lower Mallow Street Limerick Co. Limerick **Tel: 061 207000**
Fax: 061 400966 Email: jurys_inn@jurysdoyle.com

Like other Jurys Inns, this budget hotel enjoys a prime city centre location and has carparking available in an adjacent multi-storey carpark. Rooms are large, comfortable and furnished to a high standard, especially considering the moderate cost, although maintenance may not always be up to the high standard required of relatively spartan budget accommodation. Bathrooms are fairly basic but have everything required including a proper (if budget-sized) bath as well as overbath shower. Don't expect high levels of service - that's what keeps the costs down - but there is a restaurant and pub-like bar as part of the development. Traffic noise can be disturbing in front rooms, as the trucks head to and from the west all night. Room rate from €75 (max 3 guests). Closed 24-26 Dec. Amex, Diners, MasterCard, Visa. **Directions:** City centre. ◇

Limerick   The Locke Bar & Restaurant

féile bia Pub/Restaurant   3 Georges Quay Limerick Co. Limerick **Tel: 061 413733**
Fax: 061 412796 Email: lock@eircom.net Web: www.lockebar.com

Well-located right beside the pontoons on George's Quay, this atmospheric 18th century pub has open fires in winter and a riverside beer garden in summer. There's a carvery lunch in the bar every day (and traditional Irish music on Sunday, Monday & Tuesday evenings) and the first floor restaurant provides a more formal setting for à la carte dining by candle light - and a balcony for fine weather, overlooking the Abbey River. Fresh local produce is used in traditional dishes with modern touches, such as Limerick bacon & cabbage with colcannon & mustard sauce; seafood is a speciality, including oysters and lobster from their own fish tank, and vegetarian dishes are always available. The early evening dinner menu is particularly good value. (Meetings/banqueting, Bridge Bar: 80). Restaurant Seats 75 (private room, 35) Food available daily, 12-5; L12-3, D 5-10.30 (Sun to 9). Set L €16.20 (Set Sun L €17.20); Early D € 19 (5-7pm), Set D from €16, also à la carte. House wine €17.50. SC discretionary. Closed 25 Dec, Good Fri. Amex, Diners, MasterCard, Visa, Laser. **Directions:** City Centre beside St Mary's Cathederal.

Limerick   Manna

Restaurant   Unit C2 Cornmarket Square Robert Street Limerick Co. Limerick
Tel: 061 318317 Fax: 061 318233

Pale walls decorated with striking modern pictures, light wood floor and tables, good lighting, lovely flowers and stylish, comfortable high-back chairs all create a good impression at this pleasing contemporary restaurant. On the whole it's a calm and relaxing place to be, although tightly-packed tables and loud music may make communication difficult. Lively modern international menus are quite extensive and cooking can be impressive in specialities as diverse as salt baked Mediterranean seabass, flambéed king prawns, New York striploin (14 oz) and Moroccan style ostrich. Unusual side orders include lemon spinach with sour cream and mint scented couscous - and tempting desserts include luscious pannacotta with fresh fruits - all at reasonable prices. New menus recently introduced include a shorter, more casual family-friendly à la carte Sunday menu and a good value early dinner menu available on weekdays. No private parking. Seats 60. No smoking area. Toilets wheelchair accessible. D daily 5-10.30 (Sat 6-11). Early D €22 (Mon-Fri 5-7pm); otherwise à la carte. Closed 24-25 Dec, Good Fri, bank hols. Amex, MasterCard, Visa, Laser. **Directions:** Off O'Connell St, between Denmark St & the Cornmarket.

Limerick   South Court Business & Leisure Centre

Hotel   Adare Road Limerick Co. Limerick **Tel: 061 487 487** Fax: 061 487 499
Email: cro@lynchotels,com Web: www.lynchotels.com

Ideally located for Shannon Airport and the Raheen Industrial Estate, the South Court Hotel presents a somewhat daunting exterior, but once inside visitors soon discover that it caters especially well for business guests, both on and off-duty - hence the Guide's Business Hotel Award to Lynch Hotels in 2000; since then, these facilities have seen further major improvement with the opening of a 1,250 seater International Convention Centre. In addition to excellent conference and meeting facilities, comfortable bedrooms are impressively spacious and well equipped, with generous desk areas and the latest technology, including fax/modem/ISDN points, in every room. Executive bedrooms have a separate work area providing a 'mini-office' with a leather desk chair and private fax machine - and 67 new Paul Costelloe designed 'lifestyle suites' have an in-room gym. Leisure facilities include a 'Polo Lifestyle Club', designed with international rugby player (and local hero) Keith Wood. A new Paul Costelloe designed café bar, The CreamRoom,opened in 2002. Conference/banqueting (1250/1000); business centre; video conferencing. Gym, sauna, solarium (swimming pool due early 2003). Hairdressing. Children welcome (cot available without charge). No Pets. **Rooms 127** (1 suite, 15 junior suites, 55 executive, 14 no-smoking). Lift, 24 hour room service. B&B €75 pps, ss €26; room-only rate also available, €135 (max 3 guests). Amex, Diners, MasterCard, Visa, Laser. **Directions:** Located onthe main N20 Cork/Killarney road, 20 minutes from Shannon Airport.

Limerick — The Radisson SAS Hotel

  Hotel

Ennis Road Limerick Co Limerick **Tel: 061 326666** Fax: 061 327418
Email: elaineryan@radissonsas.com Web: www.radissonsas.com

This low rise hotel is set well back from the road in its own grounds and, although just a short drive from the city centre, enjoys an almost rural setting and views of the Clare Mountains. The original building dates back to the 1970s but, having been taken over by Radisson SAS, it opened in a completely new and elegant guise in July 2002. The size and layout of the building suits the Radisson style well - public areas, notably the large open-plan foyer/lounge, have a great sense of space and style, with seating groups arranged around glass-topped tables on marbled floors softened by beautiful specially commissioned rugs and a few dramatic pieces of art. A sense of generosity characterises the whole hotel and accommodation is also notable for its spaciousness: all rooms are styled deluxe, with the comfort and amenities that implies (air conditioning, TV with video, ISDN line, personal safe, bathroom with full bath and shower) but, for people who like a bit of room around them, the sense of space is the main attraction of this hotel over its city centre rivals. Fine conference and business facilities have ample parking. Conference/banqueting (375); secretarial services. Leisure centre (indoor swimming pool, steam room, sauna, fitness room, treatments). Tennis courts. Children's adventure playground. Gardens. Parking. Helipad. **Rooms 154**. Lift. 24 hour room service. B&B €105pps, ss€60. Room-only rate available: €180 (max 2 guests). Amex, Diners, MasterCard, Visa. **Directions:** On N18, 5 minutes from city centre.

Limerick — Tiger Lilies Bistro

Restaurant

9B Ellen Street Limerick Co. Limerick
Tel: 061 317484 Fax: 061 317868

The black beams, exposed stone walls and wooden floors and beams of an old bonded warehouse in a redevelopment area provide a characterful setting for this terrific informal restaurant. Pleasant lighting, fresh flowers, light background jazz and art displays by local artists create a pleasing ambience. Modern menus (colourfully presented) with fashionable global influences offer some more down to earth dishes too, like venison sausage with champ potato (albeit with chilli jam). Strong fish options include less usual choices like chargrilled swordfish (with mango salsa, guacamole & crème fraîche) alongside more familiar dishes - and vegetarian dishes are imaginative too. Prices may seem high for the casual ambience (evening main courses rise to as much as €26.95) but this is above average bistro food, based on fresh local produce, accurately cooked and complemented by well-trained service. Well selected, interesting wine list. Tables outside for al fresco dining. Seats 95. No smoking area. Toilets wheelchair accessible. L Mon-Sat 12-3.20, D Tue-Sat 6-10 (Fri/Sat to 11). A la carte. House wine about €18. Closed all Sun, D Mon, 24-28 Dec, bank hols *Also now at 18 Abbey Street, Ennis, Co Clare. Tel: 065 6829264 (Ennis branch open Sun, Closed Mon.) Amex, MasterCard, Visa, Laser. **Directions:** Between Cruises Street and the Gateway.

Abbeyfeale — Whytes Restaurant & Bar

féile bia **Restaurant**

The Square Abbeyfeale Co Limerick
Tel: 068 32917 Fax: 068 32916

Style and panache - that pretty well sums up Armel Whyte's new venture in Abbeyfeale; it's a sassy place from top to bottom, with creamy floor tiles, colourful contemporary furniture and (a lot of) good modern paintings making a strong design statement. Better still, however, you'll get a genuinely warm welcome and efficient service from caring staff - and food to match. Predictably enough, the food is in tune with the decor but here it's good enough to revive interest in the by now overworked modern/fusion cooking style: top quality ingredients are used in generous, accurately cooked dishes like Vietnamese sesame noodles with roasted crispy duck with a star anise, chilli, soya & ginger glaze (two whole legs, really well crisped but still succulent) and seafood dishes - usually from a separate listing of half a dozen - such as faultless pan-seared scallops (a dish that is so easy to get wrong, but deliciously done here with julienne of bacon served on a potato & parsnip purée). Finish with a delicious pud (a big bowl of home-made ices, perhaps, or scrumptious bread and butter pudding). A shortish international wine list includes a 'Private Cellar' page of special bottles (€52-€165), but there's also French house wine wine on tap at the bar, sold by the glass or carafe; it's a new system and proving very popular. Stylish surroundings, excellent food, efficient service and value for money too - no wonder this place is hopping. Seats 75 (private room 35). Air conditioning. Toilets wheelchair accessible. D Wed-Sat, 5-10; Sun Jazz Brunch 12.30-6.30. A la carte. SC discretionary. Closed D Sun, all Mon & Tue. MasterCard, Visa, Laser. **Directions:** In the square across from Bank of Ireland.

Adare — Adare Manor Hotel & Golf Club

féile bia   🏨   Hotel   Adare Co. Limerick **Tel: 061 396566** Fax: 061 396124
Email: reservations@adaremanor.com Web: www.adaremanor.com

The former home of the Earls of Dunraven, this magnificent neo-Gothic mansion is set in 900 acres on the banks of the River Maigue. Its splendid chandeliered drawing room and the glazed cloister of the dining room look over formal box-hedged gardens towards the Robert Trent Jones golf course. Other grand public areas include the gallery, named after the Palace of Versailles, with its unique 15th century choir stalls and fine stained glass windows. Luxurious bedrooms have individual hand carved fireplaces, fine locally-made mahogany furniture, cut-glass table lamps and impressive marble bathrooms with strong showers over huge bathtubs. recent additions include a new clubhouse in the grounds (complete with full conference facilities) and a state of the art Spa, which offers a wide variety of massage and beauty treatments. A new "golf village" of two and four bedroom townhouses provides a comfortable accommodation option for longer stays, large groups and families. Conference/banqueting (160). Leisure centre, swimming pool. Golf (18), Equestrian; fishing; walking. Garden. **Rooms 135** (1 stateroom, 5 suites). Wheelchair access. Lift. Children welcome (cot available, without charge). Room rate from €375. Open all year.
Oak Room Restaurant: The beautifully appointed Oak Room Restaurant provides a fine setting for cooking based on local produce, including vegetables from the estate's own gardens. Head chef Thomas Andrews' seasonal menus change every two days and, although based on classical French cuisine, the style includes some modern Irish food, as in honey roasted suckling pick with sage & apple stuffing, sautéed Savoy cabbage and smoked bacon, for example. A separate vegetarian menu is offered. Not suitable for children after 7pm. Seats 76 L&D daily; no SC. *Meals also available from the Clubhouse Bar & Restaurant, 10am-10 pm daily. Open all year. Amex, Diners, MasterCard, Visa, Laser. **Directions:** On N21 in Limerick.

Adare — Carrabawn Guest House

Guesthouse   Killarney Road Adare Co. Limerick **Tel: 061 396 067**
Email: Bridgetcarrabawnhouseadare.com Web: www.carrabawnhouseadare.com

In an area known for high standards, with prices to match, this immaculate owner-run establishment set in large mature gardens provides a good alternative to the local luxury accommodation. Bernard and Bridget Lohan have been welcoming guests here since 1984 - and many of them return on an annual basis because of the high level of comfort and friendly service provided. Bedrooms are very well maintained with all the amenities required and a good Irish breakfast is served in a conservatory dining room overlooking lovely gardens. Children welcome (cot available without charge). Pets permitted in some areas. **Rooms 8** (all shower only & no smoking). B&B €45 pps, ss€20. Open all year except Christmas. MasterCard, Visa, Laser. **Directions:** On N21 in Adare.

Adare — Dunraven Arms Hotel

féile bia   🏨   Hotel/Restaurant   Adare Co. Limerick **Tel: 061 396 633** Fax: 061 396 541
Email: murphy@dunravenhotel.com Web: www.dunravenhotel.com

Established in 1792, and set in one of Ireland's most picturesque villages, the Dunraven Arms has seen many changes over the last few years and is now a large hotel. Yet, under the personal management of Bryan and Louis Murphy, it somehow manages to retain the comfortable ambience of a country inn. A very luxurious inn nevertheless: the furnishing standard is superb throughout, with antiques, private dressing rooms and luxurious bathrooms, plus excellent amenities for private and business guests, all complemented by an outstanding standard of housekeeping. It's a great base for sporting activities - equestrian holidays are a speciality and both golf and fishing are available nearby - and also extremely popular for both conferences and private functions, including weddings, which are held beside the main hotel (with separate catering facilities). Leisure centre, indoor swimming pool, beauty salon. Snooker. Walking. Garden. Pets permitted by arrangement. **Rooms 74** (6 suites, 14 junior suites, 54 executive rooms). Lift. 24 hour room service. B&B €129.50pps, ss €49.50. Room-only rate €195. SC 12.5%. Hotel closed 25 Dec.

Maigue Restaurant: Named after the River Maigue, which flows through the village of Adare, the restaurant is delightfully old fashioned - more akin to eating in a large country house than in an hotel. Sandra Earl, who has been head chef since 1998, takes pride in using the best of local produce in meals that combine the traditions of the area with influences from around the world on menus that offered a balanced selection of about half a dozen dishes on each course. Although particularly renowned for their roast rib of beef (carved at your table from a magnificent trolley), other specialities like River Maigue salmon and local game in season, especially pheasant, are very popular. Seats 80. D daily 7.30-9.30, Set D €40; L Sun only 12.30-2.30, Set L €26.50. House wines €16.50-20, SC 12.5%. [*The Inn Between, across the road in one of the traditional thatched cottages, is an informal restaurant in common ownership with the Dunraven Arms; D daily, 6-10. * Light bar food (soup and sandwiches) available daily, 12.30-6.] Amex, Diners, MasterCard, Visa, Laser. **No Credit Cards. Directions:** First building on RHS as enter the village coming from Limerick (approx. 11 miles).

Adare — Fitzgeralds Woodlands House Hotel

 Hotel

Knockanes Adare Co. Limerick **Tel: 061 605 100** Fax: 061 396 073
Email: reception@woodland-hotel.ie Web: www.woodland-hotel.ie

Just outside Adare, this low, grey-tiled building is set in well-kept gardens and presents a neat and welcoming appearance from the road. It has grown dramatically since the Fitzgerald family opened it in 1983 and is now in an energetic second generation ownership, who have systematically upgraded and developed the whole hotel over the years It has always been a popular venue for weddings and is particularly well suited to large gatherings, with spacious public areas throughout, including two bars, and a restaurant and banqueting suite overlooking gardens and countryside. New and recently upgraded bedrooms offer spacious and very comfortable accommodation and there's an excellent leisure centre, with 20 metre pool, jacuzzi, sauna, steamroom and gym; numerous therapies and treatments are offered and balneotherapy seaweed baths are a speciality. For summer gatherings, Timmy Mac's bar has a barbecue garden area with thatched cottage feature. Conferences/Banqueting (350/330); secretarial services. Leisure centre, swimming pool; hairdresser; beauty salon; massage; therapies/treatments. Children welcome (under 4s free in parents' room; cots available without charge, playroom. Kids Club for 4+ age group, weekends off season, daily in summer). Garden. **Rooms 94** (3 junior suites). B&B €75 pps, ss €20. Closed 24-25 Dec. Amex, Diners, MasterCard, Visa, Laser. **Directions:** Take N21 from Limerick, turn left at roundabout before Adare.

Adare — The Wild Geese Restaurant

féile bia Restaurant

Rose Cottage Adare Co. Limerick **Tel: 061 396451** Fax: 061 396451
Email: wildgeese@indigo.ie

David Foley and Julie Randles' restaurant is in one of the prettiest cottages in the prettiest village in Ireland - and a charming atmosphere, caring service and good cooking all add up to an irresistible package. David Foley is a fine chef who sources ingredients with care - and his dinner menus are considerately priced by course, so you're not tied into the full meal, and offer about half a dozen choices for starters and main courses. Typical starters might include a terrine of smoked bacon, guinea fowl and Clonakilty black pudding with a plum chutney and seasonal salad and steamed mussels with a lemon butter sauce, while well-balanced main courses might include a speciality fish dish of chargrilled escalope of yellowfin tuna on a cassoulet of chickpeas, garlic & chorizo and a local poultry dish of roast Drumcollogher duckbreast with a spring roll of leg confit with a red wine jus. Finish off with an interesting dessert - apple & raisin tartlet topped with Italian meringue for example - or a selection of Irish cheeses, served with treacle bread and water biscuits. There's a separate vegetarian menu, offering a choice of three tempting dishes on each course, and a very different lunch menu of gourmet sandwiches, light lunch plates (like starters with a little extra garnish) and platters (hot main courses like chargrilled sirloin steak). Friendly, caring service from long-serving staff adds greatly to the dining experience. Not suitable for children after 7 pm. Seats 42 (private room 30). No-smoking area. L Tue-Sat 12.30-2.30, D Tue-Sat 6.30-10; L à la carte, Set D from €32. House wine €20.50. Closed Sun, Mon, Christmas & all Jan. Amex, Diners, MasterCard, Visa, Laser. **Directions:** From Limerick, at top of Adare village, opposite Dunraven Arms Hotel.

Ballingarry — The Mustard Seed at Echo Lodge

🏛 Country House/Restaurant

Ballingarry Co. Limerick **Tel: 069 68508** Fax: 069 68511
Email: mustard@indigo.ie Web: www.mustardseed.ie

One of the country's prettiest and most characterful restaurants, Dan Mullane's famous Mustard Seed started life in Adare in 1985. Having celebrated its first decade it began the next one by moving just ten minutes drive away to Echo Lodge, a spacious Victorian country residence set on seven acres of lovely gardens, with mature trees, shrubberies, kitchen garden and orchard - and very luxurious accommodation. Elegance, comfort and generosity are the key features - seen through decor and furnishings which bear the mark of a seasoned traveller whose eye has found much to delight in while wandering the world. The main house and garden having been put in order, Dan's next project was the conversion of an old schoolhouse in the garden, to provide three new superior suites, a new residents' lounge and a small leisure centre with sauna and massage room. This stylish development offers something quite different from the older accomodation and is in great demand from regulars who make Echo Lodge their base for golf and fishing holidays. Small conferences (20); banqueting (65). Garden. **Rooms 17** (3 suites, 1 superior, 5 shower only, 1 for disabled). Not suitable for children but cots available for small babies (under 1 year). B&B €86 pps, ss €39. Special winter breaks offered, depending on availability. Closed Christmas week.

☆ **The Mustard Seed Restaurant:** Food and hospitality are at the heart of Echo Lodge and it is in ensuring an enjoyable dining experience, most of all, that Dan Mullane's great qualities as a host emerge (he was the Guide's Host of the Year in 2001). The evening gets off to an auspicious start when aperitifs, served in the Library, come with a tasty amuse-bouche, and it is evident that attention to detail is the hallmark here - an impression confirmed when you go in to the beautiful dining room to find fresh flowers on each table, carefully selected to suit the decor. Head chef Tony Schwartz cooks in what he accurately describes as an "interesting Irish" style. The kitchen gardens supply much of the produce for the restaurant, other ingredients are carefully sourced from organic farms and artisan food producers. Menus are wide-ranging and very seasonal - the components of a delicious tossed salad (with chorizo sausage, garlic croûtons & parmesan shavings, with soya & balsamic dressing, perhaps) will be dictated by the leaves and herbs in season and the soup course - typically of roast vegetable - may also be influenced by garden produce. Main courses are based on the best local meats (typically, Irish beef (sirloin of fillet) with oven-dried tomato polenta, ratatouille & pesto crust and red wine jus, seafood just up from the south-western fishing ports and game, in season - and, with so such an abundance of garden produce, vegetarians need no fear of being overlooked. Using the best Irish farmhouse cheeses at their peak of perfection is another point of honour - or you can finish with gorgeous puddings, which are also likely to be inspired by garden produce. Finally, irresistible home-made petits fours are served with tea or coffee, at the table or in the Library. All absolutely delicious - and the hospitality element is truly exceptional. Seats 50. Not suitable for children. No smoking restaurant. D 7-9.30pm, Set D €48. House wines from €23. Closed Sun & Mon in low season; house closed Christmas week. Amex, MasterCard, Visa, Laser. **Directions:** From top of Adare village take first turn to left, follow signs to Ballingarry - 8 miles.

Castleconnell — Castle Oaks House Hotel

Hotel/Restaurant

Castleconnell Co Limerick **Tel: 061 377666** Fax: 061 377717
Email: info@castle-aks.com Web: www.castle-oaks.com

Set quietly in 26 acres of wooded countryside on the banks of the Shannon, this attractive hotel is in an idyllic waterside location on the edge of the picturesque village of Castleconnell, just a few miles on the Dublin side of Limerick. The old part of the hotel is a Georgian mansion, with the gracious proportions and elegance that implies, although a new wing provides extra accommodation which makes up in comfort and convenience anything it might lack in character. Suites have luxurious bathrooms with jacuzzi baths and one bedroom is designed for asthmatics, with hard surfaces and specially chosen fabrics. Private fishing is a particular attraction, and the hotel also offers an unusual venue for conferences and weddings in a converted chapel. Nice, helpful staff and a family-friendly attitude make this a pleasant hotel. Conference/banqueting (200/250); business centre; secretarial services. Leisure centre (15-metre pool). Fishing, tennis, cycling, walking. Garden. Children welcome (under 4s free in parents room; cots available without charge). No Pets. **Rooms**

0 (2 suites, 2 executive, 2 shower only, 1 no-smoking room). B&B about €65 pps, ss about €13. **\corn Restaurant:** A gracious room with river views, the restaurant is pleasantly furnished with hintz, velvet and flowers giving it a nice country house feeling. Well-appointed tables look romising, with crisp linen and polished glasses and, (although it may not be obvious from reading nenus which fail to do justice to the food), quality local produce is the foundation on which quite mpersonal-sounding dishes are based. After an amuse-bouche presented with the compliments of xecutive chef Brian Dunne, simple, freshly-cooked dishes will impress through their attention to he essentials of accurate cooking and good flavour. Staff are keen to please and service, under the irection of restaurant manager Niall Dooley, is friendly and efficient. Amex, Diners, MasterCard, Visa, aser. **Directions:** N7 from Limerick left for Castleconnell, on left as you enter village. ◇

Croom Mills

:room

féile bia Restaurant/Café   Croom Co Limerick **Tel: 061 397130** Fax: 061 397199
Email: croommills@eircom.net Web: www.croommills.com

)ne of the most imaginatively handled restorations of its type, a visit to Croom Mills has much to nterest young and old alike - and entry is free. Exhibits illustrate milling operations and crafts - the)lacksmith, for instance, in his 19th century forge - and several primary power sources are to be seen n action, including the giant 16 foot cast iron waterwheel, built in Cork in 1852. The tour takes about n hour as visitors are encouraged to become involved by working with interactive exhibits, but there re other attractions here too, notably one of the country's best craft and gift shops. All-day food is vailable from the Waterfront Bistro (9-6 daily), although there now seems to be less emphasis on he wholesome country fare and good home baking for which they are well-known and more on carvery tyle fare. Just before the guide went to press a new fully-licensed fine dining evening restaurant, he Mill-Race Restaurant, opened. Bistro Seats 60 (9am-6pm daily); Mill Race Restaurant Seats 46 private room 12). No-smoking restaurant. D Wed-Sun, 6-9.30, L Sun only, from 12.30. Set D €29; à a carte also available. House wine €17. Restaurant closed Mon & Tue evening. Mill closed 25 Dec. MasterCard, Visa, Laser. **Directions:** On N20 to Cork/Limerick road, at Croom.

Glin Castle

Glin

Country House   Glin Castle Glin Co. Limerick **Tel: 068 34173** Fax: 068 34364
Email: knight@iol.ie Web: www.glincastle.com

The Fitzgeralds, hereditary Knights of Glin, have lived in Glin Castle for 700 years and it is now the home of the 29th Knight and his wife Madame FitzGerald. The interior is stunning, with beautiful interiors enhanced by decorative plasterwork and collections of Irish furniture and paintings. Guests are magnificently looked after by manager Bob Duff. Accommodation was originally all in suites - huge and luxurious, but not at all intimidating because of the lived-in atmosphere that characterises the whole castle - but additional rooms ("smaller, friendly, with a family atmosphere") have more recently been opened. Furnished and decorated in traditional country house style (there was no need for this family to haunt the auctions in order to furnish the new rooms), everything has been done just right and every room feels as if it has always been that way; attention to detail is seen in all sorts of small thoughtfulnesses - the guests' information pack, for example, is exceptionally well-presented, with possible outings and itineraries listed under different interests (gardens, historical or whatever) and the amount of time required. When the Knight is at home he will take visitors on a tour of the house and show them all his pictures and old furniture. Not to be missed while in Glin is O'Shaughnessy's pub, just outside the castle walls; one of the finest pubs in Ireland, it is now in its sixth generation of family ownership and precious little has changed in the last hundred years. The garden and house are open to the public at certain times. Small conferences/private parties (20). Garden. Walking. Tennis. Children over 10 welcome. Pets permitted by arrangement. **Rooms 15** (3 suites, all no-smoking). B&B €140pps. Dinner is available by reservation; an attractive menu with about four choices on each course is offered. Dining Room Seats 30. Non-smoking. D 7-9.30, Set D €47. House wine from about €15; sc discretionary. Closed 1 Nov-15 Mar. Amex, Diners, MasterCard, Visa, Laser. **Directions:** 32 miles west of Limerick on N69, 4 miles east of Tarbert Car Ferry.

COUNTY LONGFORD

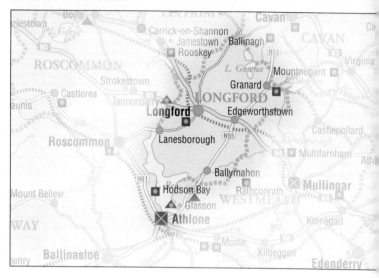

Longford is mostly either gently undulating farming country, or bogland. The higher ground in the north of the county up towards the intricate Lough Gowna rises to no more than 276m in an eminence which romantics might call Carn Clonhugh, but usually it's more prosaically known as Corn Hill. The entertainingly named Molly Hill to the east which provides the best views of the lake in an area which arouses passionate patriotism. A few miles to the north is Ballinamuck, scene of the last battle in the Rising of 1798, in a part of Longford renowned for its rebellions against foreign rule.

To the southeast, there is even less pulling of the punches in the name of the little market town in its midst, for Granard - which sounds rather elegant - may be translated as "Ugly Height". Yet this suggests a pleasure in words for their own sake, which is appropriate, for Longford produced the novelist Maria Edgeworth from Edgeworthstown, a.k.a Mostrim, while along towards that fine place Ballymahon and the south of its territory on the Westmeath border, Longford takes in part of the Goldsmith country.

Goldsmith himself would be charmed to know that, six kilometres south of the road between Longford and Edgeworthstown, there's the tiny village of Ardagh, a place of just 75 citizens which is so immaculately maintained that it has been the winner of the Tidiest Village in the Tidy Towns awards three times during the past ten years.

Another award-winner is Newtowncashel in the southwest of the county, atop a hill immediately eastward of Elfeet Bay on northern Lough Ree, where the scenery becomes more varied as County Longford has a lengthy shoreline along the Shannon's middle lake.

There is also has pretty Richmond Harbour west of Longford town at Clondra, where the Royal Canal - gradually being restored along its meandering track from Dublin - finally gets to the Shannon. And as for Longford town itself, they're working on it, and some day the rest of Ireland will wake up to find that there's life a-plenty going on there, if you just know where to look for it. A good start is at O'Connor's Florist at 6 Ballymahon Street. On September 9th 2002, they were adjudicated the best shopfront in all Ireland in the Tidy Town awards.

Local Attractions and Information

Ardagh Heritage Centre	043 75277
Ballinamuck 1798 Memorial & Visitor Centre	043 24848
Ballymahon Bog Lane Theatre	0902 32252
Kenagh Corlea Trackway (Bog Road) Visitor Centre	043 22386
Longford Backstage Theatre & Arts Centre	043 47885
Longford Carrigglas Manor (Gandon stableyard, lace museum)	043 41026
Longford Tourism Information	043 46566
Newtowncashel Heritage Centre	043 25021

Granard — Toberphelim House

armhouse

Granard Co. Longford **Tel: 043 86568** / 087 996 3249
Email: tober2@eircom.net Web: www.toberphelimhouse.com

Ian and Mary Smyth's Georgian farmhouse is about half a mile off the road, on a rise that provides lovely view of the surrounding countryside. Very much a working farm – cows, beef cattle and sheep lus an assortment of domestic animals and hens – it is a hospitable, easy-going place. Guests are welcome to wander around and walk the fields. ("Rubber boots are a must"). There's a guests' sitting oom with television and three bedrooms: two en-suite (shower) with a single and double bed in ach and one twin room with a separate private bathroom. All are comfortably furnished and well-maintained, but don't expect amenities like phones and TV in the rooms. Families are welcome – and ight meals and snacks can usually be arranged. Children welcome (under 6s free in parents' room); hildren's playground & playroom. Garden, fishing, walking. **Rooms 3** (2 en-suite shower only, 1 rivate bathroom). B&B €40pps, ss €10. Minimum stay 2 nights; prior booking advisable. Closed 1 Sep-1 May. MasterCard, Visa. **Directions:** Take the N55 at the Cavan end of Granard, turn off at he Statoil station taking a right at the next junction. The house is situated about half a mile owards Abbeylara, to the left.

Longford — Aubergine Gallery Café

Restaurant

Ballymahon Street Longford Co. Longford
Tel: 043 48633 Web: www.themarketbar.com

Stephen and Linda Devlin have run this restaurant overlooking the market square since 1998 and it draws customers from a wide area. It's up a steep staircase from the Market Bar, in an L-shaped room with chunky wooden furniture, an unusual display of local art (an interesting distraction between ourses) and a long service bar along one side. Large candles all around the room make for an atmospheric space after dark - in daylight, by contrast, the eye is drawn to a window table that pens onto a plant-filled balcony over the square. Stephen's menus are Irish/Mediterranean - a house peciality is (of course) char-grilled aubergine, feta cheese, basil & tomato bruschetta - and it summarises the style quite well. There's more emphasis on vegetables than in most restaurants and vegetarians do very well here - several first courses and at least one main course will be vegetarian and quite a few of the other dishes are potentially adaptable. Which is not to say that the wider icture is ignored: a good steak is de rigeur in these parts, for example - here it may be a 10 oz aged sirloin steak with whiskey and pepper cream - and there will be poultry (crispy duck leg confit perhaps). The sea is never far away in Ireland and Stephen's seafood nage - monkfish, salmon, haddock & mussels in tarragon, tomato & leek beurre blanc sauce - is an elegant and well-flavoured dish. Desserts include a welcome amount of fruit, in a delicious deep apple pie with custard sauce pehaps, or pearoffi tart with chocolate sauce. Service, under the direction of Linda Devlin, is friendly and helpful. **Seats 35**. No smoking area. Children welcome. L Tue-Sun, 12-2.30; D Wed-Sat, 6.30-9.30. Closed D Sun, all Mon, D Tue, 4 weeks annual holidays each year. MasterCard, Visa, Laser. **Directions:** Right side of market square over Market Bar. ◇

Longford — Longford Arms Hotel

Hotel

Main Street Longford Co. Longford **Tel: 043 46296**
Fax: 043 46244 Email: longfordarms@eircom.net

Located right in the heart of the midlands, this comfortable family-run hotel has recently been renovated to a high standard. The hotel always presents a neat face to the street and public areas give a good impression on arrival. Bedrooms are comfortably furnished and particularly convenient for business guests as they have adequate desk space and the amenities required for this type of travel (including trouser presses and irons); all have good bathrooms (with both bath and shower). The coffee shop provides wholesome casual daytime food and they do all their baking in-house – a good place to take a break. (Bar/coffee shop food is open all day, 12 -8). Conference/banqueting (500/550); video-conferencing; business centre; secretarial services. Children welcome (under 3s free in parents' room; cots available). Wheelchair accessible. Pets permitted by arrangement. **Rooms 60**. (20 no-smoking; ISDN lines available). B&B about €85pps. Own parking. Closed 24-26 Dec. Amex, Diners, MasterCard, Visa. **Directions:** Centre of Longford town. ◇

COUNTY LOUTH

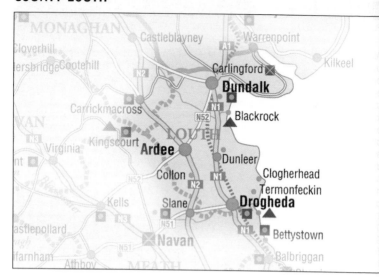

Louth is in the business of being by-passed in 2003, and is all the better for it. Plumb in the middle of the main East Coast corridor between Dublin and Belfast, Louth is leaping at the opportunities provided by the extension of the M1, which crosses the River Boyne by the largest cable-stayed bridge of its type in Ireland. With traffic pressure removed from its other roads, Louth begins to find itself. And though it may be Ireland's smallest county at only 317 square miles, it still manages to be two or even three counties in one.

Much of Louth is fine farmland, at its best in the area west of the extensive wildfowl paradise of Dundalk Bay, on whose shores we find the attractive village of Blackrock, one of Ireland's better kept secrets. But as well there are the distinctive uplands in the southwest, whose name of Oriel recalls an ancient princedom. And in the north of the county, the Cooley Mountains sweep upwards in a style which well matches their better-known neighbours, the Mountains of Mourne, on the other side of the handsome inlet of Carlingford Lough.

Its name might suggest that this is a genuine fjord, but it isn't. However, its beauty is such that there's more than enough to be going along with, and on its Louth shore the ancient little port of Carlingford town used to be a best-kept secret. It was a quiet little place imbued with history, but today it is happily prospering both as a recreational harbour for the Dundalk and Newry area, and as a bustling visitor attraction in its own right.

The county's three main townships of Ardee, Dundalk and Drogheda each have their own distinctive style, and all three have been coming vibrantly to life in recent years. The historic borough of Drogheda is the main commercial port while Dundalk is the county town, and home to the Louth Museum, where the most recent acquisition is the riding jacket worn by William of Orange at the Battle of the Boyne in 1690.

Local Attractions and Information

Ardee (Tallanstown) Knockabbey Castle & Gardens	042 9374690
Carlingford Heritage Trust, Tourism Information	042 9373888
Carlingford Carlingford Adventure Centre	042 9373100
Carlingford Carlingford Sea School	042 9373879
Drogheda Beaulieu House and garden	041 9838557
Drogheda Droichead Arts Centre	041 9833946
Drogheda Millmount Museum	041 9833097
Drogheda (Tullyallen) Old Mellifont Abbey	041 9826459
Drogheda Tourism Information	041 9837070
Dundalk Louth County Museum	042 9327056
Dundalk Tourism Information	042 9335484
Termonfeckin Irish Countrywomens Assoc. College	041 9822119

Blackrock — The Brake

Pub/Restaurant

Main Street Blackrock Co. Louth
Tel: 042 932 1393 Fax: 042 932 2568

Although it may not look especially inviting from the outside, first-time visitors are always amazed by the warmth and country charm of The Brake once they get inside the door – all old pine and rural bric-à-brac, it has open fires and friendly staff. It's a great place to stop just for a cup of tea, but even better if you're hungry – it has a well-deserved reputation for good bar meals, and not just the usual pub staples, but a very wide choice including home-made chicken kiev, for example and all kinds of seafood including prawn or crab cocktail,wild smoked salmon, smoked mussels and prawns or crab claws in garlic butter - and that's just for starters. Main course seafood includes a seafood platter (hot or cold). poached wild salmon in season, jumbo prawns and maybe even lobster. There are lots of meat dishes, too, especially steaks (beef and gammon) with a range of sauces and creamy dishes that come with rice, such as prawns provençal, beef stroganoff and pork à la crème. Salads and accompaniments are particularly good, all arranged buffet style. Prices are fairly moderate - hot main courses range from €14.50 (chicken curry or pork in cream & herb sauce) to €19.95 for jumbo prawns and €22.95 fillet steak, but many of the lighter dishes and salads are much less. Beware of the unusual opening hours though – this is a late afternoon into evening place. No children under 12. **Seats 130**. No smoking area; air conditioning. Bar open 5-11.30. D daily 6.30-10.30 (Sun 6-9.30). A la carte; house wine €14; sc discretionary. *The Clermont Arms, a few doors along the front, is in the same family ownership. Closed 25 Dec, Good Fri. MasterCard, Visa, Laser. **Directions:** Turn off the main Dublin-Belfast road 3 miles south of Dundalk.

Carlingford — Beaufort House

Guesthouse

Ghan Road Carlingford Co. Louth **Tel: 042 937 3879** Fax: 042 937 3878
Email: michaelcaine@beauforthouse.net Web: www.beauforthouse.net

Michael and Glynnis Caine's immaculate property is well-placed to maximise on the attractions of a quiet and beautiful waterside position with wonderful sea and mountain views, while also being just a few minutes walk from Carlingford village. All areas are spacious and furnished to high specifications: hotel standard bedrooms have phone, TV with video channel and tea/coffee making facilities. The Caines were previously restaurateurs and dinner is available by arrangement for parties of eight or more. (Set D about €32). Associated activities include a sailing school and yacht charter - corporate sailing events (team building and corporate hospitality), including match racing in Carlingford Lough, are a speciality. Golf nearby. Helipad; ample car parking. Small conference/banqueting (20). Children welcome (under 2s free in parents' room). Fishing, cycling, hill walking, bird watching walking, garden. No pets. **Rooms 5** (2 shower only). B&B €39 pps, ss €26. Open all year. MasterCard, Visa. **Directions:** Approaching from Dundalk, turn right just before the village and harbour; house on shore.

Carlingford — Georgina's Tearooms

Café

Castle Hill Carlingford Co. Louth
Tel: 042 9373346 Email: tedf@eircom.net

Although not the handiest place to find, Georgina Finegan's little daytime restaurant high up in the web of small roads above King John's Castle is well worth seeking out. It is a (relatively) recent addition to a 20-year old small bakery specialising in meringues and desserts and, since opening in 1997, has built up a loyal customer base including "people who return on a daily, weekly or even annual basis for the good food and friendly tea room setting." They come from Belfast, Dublin and "places in between", they're local, and they're visitors from all over the world - the fact is that there is something for everyone at this unpretentious café. Although a recently added conservatory has brought some extra space, the original café is really quite small, but it's cosy and seems just right for simple fare like soup of the day with a traditional sandwich like egg, tomato & parsley, or open sandwiches like ham & apple salad or ploughman's cheese platter, made with home-made wholemeal or white soda bread. Savoury summer specials might include tomato & mozzarella salad or feta, leek & cherry tomato tart (very reasonable too, like everything else at this little place, at €4 & 5.50 respectively) and there are contemporary snacks like tortilla wraps (smoked salmon & cream cheese, for example) and pastrami & gouda on toast, with sweet beetroot. But many people just drop in for a wedge of lemon meringue pie or Austrian apple pie, or maybe a slice of carrot cake and a cup of tea - after all, that's where it all started. **Seats 35**. Children welcome. Open daily, 10.30-6. Closed 1 week Sep, Christmas, 1 week Jan. **No Credit Cards. Directions:** Opposite King Johns Castle.

Carlingford | Ghan House

Country House/Restaurant

Carlingford Co. Lout
Tel: 042 937 3682 Fax: 042 937 377:
Email: ghanhouse@eircom.net Web: www.ghanhouse.cor

This 18th century house is attractively located in its own walled grounds on the edge of Carlingfor: village and it is of interest for both accommodation and food - and there's more to that than th: delicious meals you will enjoy for dinner or breakfast, as the Carroll family run a cookery school o: the premises. The accommodation is in four very different country rooms of character in the mai: house, each with sea or mountain views, and eight new bedrooms, which have been finished to : high standard in a separate building. In addition to the cookery school (contact Paul Carroll for th: 2003 programme), Ghan House is also an increasingly popular venue for small conferences anc meetings, including team development and corporate hospitality; details of services and rate: available on request. Conference/banqueting (50/80). Garden; walking. Children welcome (under 5: free in parents' room; cots available without charge). Pets permitted by arrangement. **Rooms 12** (al en-suite, 1 shower only, all no-smoking) B&B €75pps, ss €20.

Restaurant: Dinner is, of course, a high priority at Ghan House – the style is contemporary, basec mainly on quality local produce, notably seafood; oysters are synonymous with Carlingford (in corr and parmesan crusted oysters with smoked chilli butter, perhaps) smoked salmon and crab (the latte: typically served in a salad with fennel) come from nearby Annagassan. A set dinner menu with abou: five choice on each course is also priced by course, allowing considerable flexibility without havinç a separate à la carte. Typical dishes on a summer menu might include crispy duck confit with Asiar potato salad, roast hake with prawn orzo & basil cream and red goosberry cheesecake with blackcurrant cream Interesting, fairly priced wine list. Non-residents welcome (bookings advised). **Seats 54**. No smoking restaurant. D only, Fri & Sat 7-9.30 (other times by arrangement); Set C €47.50; 8-course gourmet menu €68 (available six times a year); house wine €19; sc discretionary. Children welcome. Closed Sun-Thu, except for groups by arrangement. House closed 23 Dec-10 Jan. MasterCard, Visa, Amex, Laser. **Directions:** 15 minutes from main Dublin - Belfast Road N1.10 metres after 30 mph on left hand side after entering Carlingford from Dundalk direction.

Carlingford | Kingfisher Bistro

Restaurant

Darcy MaGee Court Dundalk Road Carlingford Co. Louth
Tel: 042 937 3716

Mark and Claire Woods took over this little restaurant at the heritage centre in 1998 and it's already built up a great following. Although tiny, it packs quite a punch; it's amazing how much variety Mark manages to create a kitchen with very limited space and how well Claire manages the service. Modern menus begin with a "something soup" and a selection of eight starters (risotto of ham and pea with basil oil & fresh parmesan and smoked fish cakes with olive tapenade & crème fraîche are typical), while a similar number of main courses offers dressed up old favourites like sirloin steak (with potato rösti, garlic & parsley butter and onion sauce) alongside ideas from further afield like Thai spiced pork with sticky rice, curry oil, sweet soy & Asian salad. There are quite a few vegetarian dishes (including a house special). Desserts are not a particular priority (choice of four, possibly including apple strudel) but the wine list is another surprise for such a tiny place - not long by some standards, but interesting and fairly priced. Pricing generally is very reasonable and the minimum charge given on the menu is fair; if there is a criticism it would be that the menu would be more attractive to regular customers if changes could be introduced more often. Not suitable for children. **Seats 26**. D Tue-Sun 6.30-9.30 (Sun 5.30-8.30). A la carte (minimum charge about €16 per person). House wine about €21. MasterCard, Visa. **Directions:** Dundalk Road, Carlingford. ◇

Carlingford | O'Hares

Pub

Carlingford Co. Louth **Tel: 042 73106**

Thankfully, this renowned pub seems to be resistant to change. It's one of those lovely places with a grocery at the front and an unspoilt hard-floored pub with an open fire at the back - loos (always clean) are in the yard and the food is simple but good. You can have soup and sandwiches if you like, but the speciality is Carlingford oysters - with a pint of stout of course. Live music: traditional on Thursday nights, jazz on Sunday afternoons. Closed 25 Dec & Good Fri. **Directions:** In centre of village. ◇

Carlingford   The Oystercatcher Lodge & Bistro

 Restaurant/B&B

Market Square Carlingford Co. Louth **Tel: 042 937 3922** / 3987
Email: info@theoystercatcher.com Web: www.theoystercatcher.com

Brian and Denise McKevitt's popular little restaurant with rooms has been doing great business on the square in Carlingford village since 1998. Seafood is the main offering – Carlingford oysters, of course (several ways), crab puffs and scampi with home-made tartare sauce are all typical first courses. There are half a dozen seafood main courses to match (baked fillet of hake with sauté leks & red peppers suace or Denise's fish pot, for example) but carnivores do well too. Typically, you'll get local lamb (braised shank on garlic mash), steaks (various ways), duck (with plum & ginger sauce) and pork (with apple & orange sauce). There are also some vegetarian choices and excellent range of salads and vegetables which are laid out for self-service with the main course. Not suitable for children 7 pm. **Seats 40** (private room, 24) No smoking area. D 6-9.30 daily (Sun 5-8.30). Set D €40, also à la carte. House wine €16; sc discretionary. Phone to check opening times off season. Closed Mon, 22-28 Dec.
Accommodation: Guest rooms are bright, spacious and very clean, with polished floors. **Rooms 8** (all shower only) B&B €65 pps. Children welcome (cot available, €4). MasterCard, Visa, Laser.
Directions: In the centre of Carlingford village.

Clogherhead   Little Strand Restaurant

Restaurant

Strand Street Clogherhead Co. Louth
Tel: 041 988 1061 Fax: 041 988 1062

This neat modern building, on the righthand side as you go through the village of Clogherhead to the beach, is set back a little from the road, with steps up to the front door. The fairly large ground floor restaurant is surprisingly formally appointed for the location and, upstairs, there's an impressive lounge area, used for aperitifs and coffee at busy times. You don't have to be a fish-lover to enjoy a meal here - menus offer a range of meat and vegetarian dishes including, intriguingly, Skipper's Choice (a 12 oz sirloin steak topped with Clogherhead prawns) but local seafood, brought in to the nearby fishing harbour of Port Oriel, is of course the speciality and very good it is too. House specialities include crab claws in garlic/lemon butter, lobster thermidor and sole on the bone with lemon, lime and dill butter; an exceptional dish is Clogherhead scampi, cooked and served the traditional way with sauce tartare - and very good value at about €16. The restaurant is still fairly new, but the proprietor, Catherine Whelahan, continues to work hard to get the details right. **Seats 60** (Private room 12-16). No-smoking area; air conditioning. D Wed-Sun, 7-"late" (Sun from 5); à la carte; also autumn & spring special menus, about €19; house wine about €15, sc discretionary. Closed Mon, Tue, bank hols. MasterCard, Visa. **Directions:** 7 miles from Drogheda, 3 miles from Termonfeccin village. ◇

Collon   Forge Gallery Restaurant

Restaurant/Guesthouse

Church Street Collon Co. Louth **Tel: 041 982 6272**
Fax: 041 982 6584 Email: forgegallery@eircom.net

For the best part of twenty years this charming two-storey restaurant has been providing good food, hospitality and service, earning a great reputation as the best eating place for miles around and a loyal following. It's a most attractive place – the building itself is unusual and has been furnished and decorated with flair, providing a fine setting for food that combines country French and New Irish styles, with a few other influences along the way. Seasonal produce stars, much of it local – seafood, game in season, vegetables, fruit – and typical main course selections include a special vegetarian dish such as pillows of filo with leeks and roquefort as well as local meat, such as rack of tender Cooley lamb, and seafood like the 'Forge Rendezvous' of prawns and scallops in chablis & cream. *Accommodation is now also available - contact the restaurant for details. **Seats 60**. No smoking area; air conditioning. D Tue-Sat, 7-10. Set D from about €40; à la carte also available. House wine from about €20; sc discretionary). Closed Sun & Mon; Christmas & 2 weeks Jan. Amex, Diners, MasterCard, Laser. **Directions:** On N2, 35 miles from Dublin due north, midway between Slane and Ardee, in centre of village. ◇

Drogheda   Boyne Valley Hotel & Country Club

Hotel

Drogheda Co. Louth **Tel: 041 983 7737**
Email: reservations@boynevalleyhotel.ie Web: www.boynevalleyhotel.ie

At the heart of this substantial hotel, set in large gardens just on the Dublin side of Drogheda town, lies an 18th century mansion. It is not as obvious as it used to be since developments created a completely new entrance, but it is still there and provides some unspoilt, graciously proportioned rooms that contrast well with the later additions. Owner-run by Michael and Rosemary McNamara since 1992, it has the personal touch unique to hands-on personal management and is popular with locals, for business and pleasure, as well as a base for visitors touring the historic sites of the area. While rooms in the old building have more character, the new ones are finished to a high standard. A new conference room and excellent leisure centre add greatly to the hotel's facilities. Conference/banqueting (400/300); secretarial services. Leisure centre, indoor swimming pool. All weather tennis; pitch & putt; garden. Pets allowed in some areas. **Rooms 37** (10 shower only, 9 no-smoking). B&B from about €76.50 pps, ss about €30.47. Open all year. Amex, Diners, MasterCard, Visa, Laser. **Directions:** On southern edge of Drogheda town, on N1. ◇

Dundalk   Ballymascanlon House Hotel

Hotel   Dundalk Co. Louth **Tel: 042 935 8200**   Fax: 042 937 1598
                              Email: info@ballymascanlon.com   Web: www.ballymascanlon.com

Set in 130 acres of parkland, this hotel just north of Dundalk has developed around a large Victorian house. It has been in the Quinn family ownership since 1948 and major improvements made over the last few of years have been done with great style, lifting the hotel into a different class; bright and spacious public areas are furnished and decorated in a warm, comfortably contemporary style with plenty of table lamps, good pictures and a variety of seating - comfy sofas and armchairs, Lloyd loom chairs - all of which combines to create a stylishly homely atmosphere. Spacious and very attractive new bedrooms share the same qualities, with specially commissioned furniture adding interest - and, in many cases, views over lovely gardens, the golf course or the attractive old stable yard, which is in the process of restoration. Corporate facilities include three versatile meeting rooms, with back-up business services available. Impressive new leisure facilities include a 20 metre deck level pool and tennis courts. With so much to do on the premises and easy access to areas of great natural beauty and historical interest, this hotel makes a good base for a break (special interest and off-season deals available). Conference/banqueting (250/250); secretarial services. Leisure centre, tennis, golf (18), garden, walking. Children welcome (under 2s free in parents' room; cots available without charge). **Rooms 96** (4 suites, 2 junior suites, 90 executive rooms, 13 no smoking, 6 for disabled). Lift. All day room service B&B about €70pps. Open all year. Amex, Diners, MasterCard, Visa, Laser. **Directions:** N1 from Dublin, 3 miles north of Dundalk.

Dundalk   Café Metz

🅝 Restaurant/Café   Williamsons Mall Dundalk Co. Louth **Tel: 042 933 9106**

Smart modern two-storey all-day restaurant conveniently located in the town centre. Good contemporary food - and great Illy coffees... **Directions:** Town centre. ◇

Dundalk   Fitzpatrick's Bar & Restaurant

Restaurant/Pub   Jenkinstown Rockmarshal Dundalk Co. Louth
                                                   Tel: 042 937 6193 Fax: 042 937 6193

Flowers and a neat frontage with fresh paintwork always draw attention to this attractive and well-run establishment. It has plenty of parking and is well organised for the informal but comfortable consumption of food in a series of bar/dining rooms, all with character and much of local interest in pictures and artefacts. Prompt reception, friendly service and unpretentious home-cooked food at resonable prices all add up to an appealing package and its obvious popularity with locals is well deserved. **Seats 70** (private room 40). Smoking unrestricted; air conditioning. Open Tue-Sun 12 noon -10pm, L from 12.30, D 6-10. A la carte menus. Closed Mon, Good Fri, 25 Dec. MasterCard, Visa. **Directions:** Just north of Dundalk town, take Carlingford road off main Dublin-Belfast road. ◇

Dundalk   McKeown's

🅝 Pub   16 Clanbrassil Street Dundalk Co. Louth **Tel: 042 933 7931**

This well-run pub of character has a great atmosphere and friendly staff - just the place for a pint before or after a meal across the road at Quaglino's. Closed 25 Dec, Good Fri. **Directions:** Town centre - across the road from Quaglino's Restaurant. ◇

Dundalk   No 32

🅝 Restaurant   32 Chapel Street Dundalk Co. Louth
                              Tel: 042 933 1113 Email: no.32@ireland.com Web: www.no32.ie

Attractively situated in a leafy corner of town near the museum, Susan Heraghty's great little place is the neighbourhood restaurant par excellence and a great asset to Dundalk. It occupies a corner site, with windows all along one side giving it a sense of space, a feeling emphasised by the smart simplicity of the decor and table settings. Menus are written in an admirably down-to-earth style - and the same can be said of the prices, notably an exceptional early evening menu (the 'Express') which allows you two courses (from a generous selection of about half a dozen starters and main courses, plus several daily fish and vegetarian specials) and includes coffee with a mini-dessert. For this you might get such delicious starter combinations as tossed salad with black pudding & caramelised apples or a beautifully light crisp-pastried baked wild mushroom cream tartlette, or a warm grilled chicken salad with balsamic dressing - and main courses like poached smoked haddock, garlic mash, spinach, roast vegetables, tomatoes & shaved parmesan or a hot fillet of beef sandwich on wholemeal bread with garlic mayonnaise, caramelised onions & chips. There's a terrific generosity of spirit here - not in overladen plates, but in quality of food and service; the later menu is like the Express only more so - more choice, slightly more sophisticated dishes - but prices are still very reasonable. Everything is just as delicious as it sounds (or even more so), service is good-humoured and efficient. Would that every town in Ireland had a place like this. **Seats 35**. No smoking area. Children welcome. D Mon-Sat, 5.30-10. Early D €15 (Mon-Fri 5.30-7); Set D €22. House wine €16.95. No SC. Closed Sun, bank hols. Amex, MasterCard, Visa, Laser. **Directions:** Town centre, near the museum.

Dundalk   Quaglino's

féile bia Restaurant   88 Clanbrassil Street Dundalk Co. Louth **Tel: 042 933 8567**
                               Fax: 042 932 8598 Email: quaglinosrestaurant@eircom.net

At this long-established and highly regarded restaurant in Dundalk, owner-chef Pat Kerley takes great pride in the active promotion of Irish cuisine and uses as much local produce as possible. The restaurant is run on traditional lines, with good service a priority. As in most Louth restaurants, generosity is the keynote. Children welcome. **Seats 80**. No smoking area; air conditioning. D daily, 6-10.30 (Sun 6-9), L Sun only, 12.45-3. Set D about €24-32, also à la carte; sc discretionary. Amex, Diners, MasterCard, Visa, Laser, Switch. **Directions:** Town centre, upstairs restaurant.

Dunleer   Carlito's

Ⓝ Restaurant   Main Street Dunleer Co. Louth **Tel: 041 686 1366**

People come from miles around to eat at this unassuming Italian restaurant, so it is wise to book well ahead, especially at weekends. Although quite unremarkable from the street, the interior is welcoming, in warm shades of deep red and orange and a comfortable seating area just inside the door where groups can assemble over an aperitif before heading for their table. Tables are simply set (nightlight, cutlery and a paper napkin) but the welcome is very friendly and you'll very quickly be settled into a menu that is well-constructed to please everyone, regardless of age or the occasion. Expect lovely home-baked bread, real minestrone soup with heaps of flavour, mixed leaf salads with creamy home-made dressing, deliciously crisp thin-based pizzas, a range of pastas and daily specials - such as herb-crusted cod, perfectly cooked and served with local vegetables (choice of boiled or chipped potatoes). Desserts are equally god: real tiramisu, crème brulée with fresh strawberries perhaps, and freshly brewed coffee to finish. Great value, great place. D Tue-Sat, 6pm-"late", Sun 5-9pm. *No-smoking area is at back of restaurant en route to toilet doors - tables at front in smoking area are preferable. MasterCard, Visa. **Directions:** On main street. ◇

Termonfeckin   Triple House Restaurant

Restaurant   Termonfeckin Co. Louth
                                          Tel: 041 982 2616 Fax: 041 982 2616

The pretty village of Termonfeckin provides a fine setting for Pat Fox's popular restaurant, which is in a 200-year-old converted farmhouse in landscaped gardens surrounded by mature trees. In winter you can settle in front of a log fire in the reception area on cold evenings when pondering the menu over a glass of wine (there's also a conservatory, used for aperitifs in summer). Committed to using the best of local produce, Pat offers wide-ranging menus and daily blackboard seafood extras from nearby Clogherhead – fresh Clogherhead prawns, Annagassan crab, and a dish he entitles, intriguingly, Port Oriel Pot-Pourri. But locally-reared meats feature too, in roast Drogheda smoked loin of pork with a nectarine & Calvados sauce, for example. Specialities include lovely spinach-filled crêpes(baked wuith cream sauce, tomato sauce and Parmesan) and, for dessert, a chewy meringue dacquoise that varies with the season's fruits. Plated farmhouse cheeses typically include Cashel Blue, Cooleeney and Wexford Cheddar. The wine list reflects Pat's particular interests and special evenings are sometimes held for enthusiasts off-season. Children welcome. **Seats 40**. No smoking area. D Tue-Sat 6.30-9.30, L Sun only 1-3; Set D €30, à la carte available; early D €22, 6.30-7.30 only; Set Sun L €22. House wines €17-20; sc discretionary. Toilets wheelchair accessible. Closed Mon, 26-28 Dec. MasterCard, Visa. **Directions:** 5 miles north east of Drogheda.

COUNTY MAYO

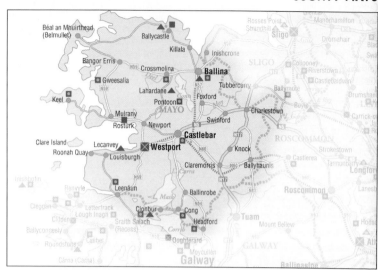

Mayo - far Mayo - might have been a byword for remoteness and declining population in times past, but in 2003 it is thriving. The six year Census to July 2002 showed a population increase of 5.3% (to 118,000), and they are people who enjoy the present as much as savouring the past.

Five kilometres east of the bustling county town of Castlebar, the Museum of Country Life at Turlough Park House, the first fully-fledged department of the National Museum to be located anywhere outside Dublin, celebrates Irish country life as it was lived between 1850 and 1960 with a remarkable display of artefacts which were in regular everyday use, yet now seem almost exotic.

As often does Mayo itself, for Mayo is magnificent. All Ireland's counties have their devotees, but enthusiasts for Mayo have a devotion which is pure passion. In their heart of hearts, they feel that this austerely majestic Atlantic-battered territory is somehow more truly Irish than anywhere else. And who could argue with them after experiencing the glories of scenery, sea and sky which this western rampart of Ireland puts on ever-changing display?

Yet among Mayo's many splendid mountain ranges we find substantial pockets of fertile land, through which there tumble fish-filled streams and rivers. And in the west of the county, the rolling hills of the drumlin country, which run in a virtually continuous band right across Ireland from Strangford Lough, meet the sea again in the island studded wonder of Clew Bay. At its head, the delightful town of Westport is a cosmopolitan jewel of civilisation set in dramatic country with the holy mountain of Croagh Patrick (762 m) soaring above the bay.

Along Mayo's rugged north coast, turf cutting at Ceide Fields near Ballycastle has revealed the oldest intact field and farm system in existence, preserved through being covered in blanket bog 5,000 years ago. An award-winning interpretive centre has been created at the site, and even the most jaded visitor will find fascination and inspiration in the clear view which it provides into Ireland's distant past. A few miles eastward, the charming village of Ballycastle is home to the internationally-respected Ballinglen Arts Foundation, creative home-from-home for artists worldwide.

Nearby, the lively town of Ballina is where the salmon-rich River Moy meets the sea in the broad sweep of Killala Bay. It takes a leap of the imagination to appreciate that the sheltered Moy Valley is in the same county as the spectacularly rugged cliffs of Achill Island. But leaps of the imagination is what Mayo inspires.

Local Attractions and Information

Ballina Street Festival/Arts Week (July)	096 70905
Ballina Tourism Information	096 70848
Ballycastle Ballinglen Arts Foundation	096 43184 / 43366
Castlebar Linenhall Arts Centre	094 23733

Castlebar Tourism Information	094 21207
Castlebar Turlough House (see entry under Turlough)	094 31589
Ceide Fields Interpretive Centre	0996 43325
Clare Island Ferries	098 27685
Foxford Woollen Mills Visitor Centre	094 56756
Inishkea Island Tours Belmullet	097 85741
Inishturk Island Ferries	098 45520 / 45541
Killasser (Swinford) Traditional Farm Heritage Centre	094 52505
Kiltimagh Glore Mill Follain Arts Centre	094 82184
Knock International Airport	094 67222
Moy Valley Holidays	096 70905
Turlough Turlough Park House. Museum of Country Life.	
Open Tuesday to Saturday 10am to 5pm,	
Sundays 2pm to 5pm, closed Mondays	094 31589
Westport Westport House & Children's Zoo	098 25430 / 27766
Westport Tourism Information	098 25711

Achill Island — The Beehive

Café/Restaurant
Keel Achill Island Co. Mayo
Tel: 098 43134 / 43018 Fax: 098 43018

At their informal restaurant and attractive craft shop in Keel, husband and wife team Patricia and Michael Joyce take pride in the careful preparation and presentation of the best of Achill produce, especially local seafood such as fresh and smoked salmon, mussels, oysters and crab. Since opening, in 1991, they have extended both the menu and the premises and now offer all-day self-service food, which you can have indoors or take out to a patio overlooking Keel beach in fine weather Everything is homemade, and they make great soups such as cheddar & onion, courgette & onion, leek & mussel, seafood chowder and traditional nettle soup (brotchán neantóg) all served with homemade brown scones. As baking is a speciality, there's always a tempting selection of cakes, bracks, teabreads, fruit tarts, baked desserts and scones with home-made preserves or you can simply have a toasted sandwich, or an Irish farmhouse cheese plate (with a glass of wine perhaps). *The family also has accommodation on the island; details from the restaurant. **Seats 100** (private rooms, 20/40). Toilet wheelchair accessible. No smoking area. Meals 10-6 daily, Easter-early Nov. A la carte; wine licence: house wines €15-19 (plus large selection of quater bottles, around €3.75). Amex, MasterCard, Visa, Laser. **Directions:** Situated inthe centre of Keel overlooking beach and Minuan cliffs.

Achill Island — The Boley House Restaurant

Restaurant
Keel Achill Island Co. Mayo **Tel: 098 43147** Fax: 098 43427

Noreen McNamara Cooney has run this picturesque, immaculately maintained cottage restaurant for 30 years and there is no sign of its popularity diminishing. Local seafood is of course the star - and this, together with the unique atmosphere, is what keeps bringing people back. Children welcome. **Seats 60.** No smoking restaurant. D only, 6.30-9.15 daily; Set D about €30; à la carte also available; house wine about €18 sc discretionary. Toilets wheelchair accessible. Open all year. MasterCard, Visa. **Directions:** 10 miles from Achill Sound. ◇

Achill Island — Gray's Guest House

Accommodation/Guesthouse
Dugort Achill Island Co. Mayo **Tel: 098 43244** / 43315

Vi McDowell has been running this legendary guesthouse in the attractive village of Dugort since 1979, and nobody understands better the qualities of peace, quiet and gentle hospitality that have been bringing guests here for the last hundred years. It is an unusual establishment, occupying a series of houses, and each area has a slightly different appeal. There's a large, traditionally furnished sitting room with an open fire and several conservatories for quiet reading. Bedrooms and bathrooms vary considerably due to the age and nature of the premises, but the emphasis is on old-fashioned comfort; they all have tea & coffee-making trays, phones for incoming calls have just been introduced and there are extra shared bathrooms in addition to en-suite facilities. Children are welcome and have an indoor playroom and safe outdoor play area, plus pool and table tennis for older children. It's a nice place to drop into for coffee, light lunch or afternoon tea (which is served in the garden in fine weather) and the dining room is open to non-residents for evening meals by arrangement. (Lovely old-fashioned menus like hot spiced grapefruit, poached Keem Bay salmon with hollandaise sauce, apple tart with cream). Packed lunches supplied. Pets permitted by arrangement.

Children welcome before 8pm; (under 3s free in parents' room). Garden, fishing, walking. **Rooms 1**
(all en-suite). B&B €40pps, ss €6. D 7pm. Set D €26 (non residents €32), house wine €15. Close
25 Dec. Personal cheques accepted. **No Credit Cards. Directions:** Castlebar, Westport, Newport
Achill Sound - Dugort!

Ballina   Gaughans

👿 Pub   O'Rahilly Street Ballina Co. Mayo **Tel: 096 7009**
                                    Email: edmg@eircom.net Web: http://gaughans.hypermart.net

This is one of the great old pubs of Ireland and has a gentle way of drawing you in, with the menu
up in the window and a display of local pottery to arouse the curiosity. It's a fine old-fashioned bar
with everything gleaming and a great sense of the pride taken in its care. Michael Gaughan opened
the pub in November1936 and his son, Edward, took over in 1972. Edward's wife Mary is a great cook
and, once they started doing food in 1983 they never looked back; everybody loves the way they
run the place and Mary still does all the cooking. Her specialities (all good home cooking) include
home-made quiche Lorraine with salad, fresh crab salad and good old-fashioned roasts - roast stuffed
chicken with vegetables and potatoes, perhaps, or baked gammon. There's always a daily special
(€7) and old favourites like lemon meringue pie and pineapple upside down pudding for dessert.
There are lighter options on the menu too, like open smoked salmon or crab sandwich, smoked
salmon salad, ploughman's lunch. Great wholesome fare. And, charmingly listed along with the
Bewley's tea and coffee, the wine and Irish coffee "Glass of spring water: Free." Now that's style.
Pets permitted. Children welcome. No smoking area. Bar food served Mon-Sat,. Closed 25 Dec & Good
Fri. MasterCard, Visa, Laser. **Directions:** Up to post office on left.

Ballycastle   Mary's Bakery & Tea Rooms

Restaurant   Main Street Ballycastle Co. Mayo. **Tel: 096 43361**

Mary Munnelly's homely little restaurant is the perfect place to stop for some good home cooking.
Baking is the speciality but she does "real meals" as well - home-made soups like mushroom or
smoked bacon & potato, wild salmon various ways and free range chicken dishes. And, if you strike
a chilly day, it's very pleasant to get tucked in beside a real fire too. There's also a garden with sea
views for fine weather - and home-made chutneys and jams on sale to take home. **Seats 30.** No
smoking area. Toilets wheelchair accessible. Open 10am-7pm in summer (shorter hours off season);
Closed Sun Oct-Easter & first 3 weeks Jan. **No Credit Cards. Directions:** From Ballina - Killala - main
road to Ballycastle, on way to Ceide Fields. ◇

Ballycastle   Polke's

Pub   Main Street Ballycastle Co. Mayo **Tel: 096 43016**

This lovely old-established general merchants and traditional pub is just across the road from Mary's
Bakery and well worth a visit. It was established in 1820 and has remained in the family since then.
Not much has changed it seems: the long, narrow bar behind the shop is completely unspoilt,
friendly and a joy to find yourself in. The whole place is immaculate too (including the outside loo
in a whitewashed yard at the back), giving the lie to the widely-held view that "character" pubs are,
by definition, scruffy. Closed 25 Dec & Good Fri. **Directions:** On main street.

Ballycastle   Stella Maris Hotel

Ⓝ Hotel   Ballycastle Co. Mayo **Tel: 096 43322** Fax: 096 43965
                            Email: info@stellamarisireland.com Web: www.stellamarisireland.com

Built in 1853 as a coast guard regional headquarters, this fine property was later acquired by the
Sisters of Mercy who named it Stella Maris and, most recently, opened as an hotel under the current
management in 2002. Extensive renovations have restored the building to its original impressive
condition and then some - proprietor Frances Kelly has acquired a remarkable collection of antiques
and interesting pieces for the hotel and mixed them with contemporary furniture, creating a warm
and interesting interior with a welcome emphasis on comfort. But the location is this hotel's major
asset and a conservatory built all along the front takes full advantage of it, allowing guests to relax
in comfort and warmth while drinking in the majestic views of the surrounding coastline and sea.
Accommodation is very comfortable - uncluttered rooms furnished with antiques enjoy the best of
both worlds, with modern bathrooms and power showers. Dinner- cooked by head chef Thomas
O'Leary, who has previous experience in several respected kitchens - is a very enjoyable experience:
menus are well-balanced and imaginative without being over-influenced by fashion: sautéed lambs
kidneys, tomato & gin soup with chive cream, rack of Mayo lamb with a herb crust, herbed cous cous

and rosemary-flavoured jus are all typical and there is usually choice of two fish dishes (vegetarian option on request). Classic desserts include refreshing seasonal fruits - stewed rhubarb with crème anglaise, perhaps - or there's an Irish farmhouse cheese plate - then it's back to the conservatory for a digestif... This is indeed a wonderful retreat. Local staff are young and make up in friendliness anything they might yet lack in professionalism. Helipad. **Rooms 12** (1 suite, all no smoking, 1 disabled). B&B €90 pps, ss €50. Children welcome (under 4s free in parents' room, cot available without charge). Restaurant **Seats 24**. D Tue-Sun, 7-9, L Sun only 1-3; D à la carte, Set Sun L €25; house wine €16.95. Restaurant closed Mon; hotel closed Jan-Feb. MasterCard, Visa, Laser. **Directions:** West of Ballina on R314.

Bangor Erris — Teach Iorrais Hotel

Hotel — Geesala Bangor Erris Ballina Co. Mayo **Tel: 097 86888** Fax: 097 86855
Email: teachior@iol.ie Web: www.teachiorrais.com

Facilities in this remote and fascinating Gaeltacht area were pretty thin on the ground before this new hotel opened in 1998 and it has proved a great success. It's a great place to drop into during the day for a bite to eat or just a cup of tea - there's always a welcoming fire in the bar (which has character, although the hotel is modern) and staff are very friendly. Bedrooms are comfortably furnished, with neat en-suite bathrooms, direct dial phone, tea/coffee facilities and television with video channel. Off-season breaks offer especially good value and there are many activities nearby, including golf, horse riding, walking, boating and fishing (there's a drying room for tackle and bait). Teach Iorrais is a popular place for weddings and would also be an interesting choice for conferences and corporate events - or for a very different Christmas or New Year break. Conference/banqueting (400/325); secretarial services. Pets permitted by arrangement. Children welcome (under 5s free in parents' room; cots available without charge). Garden, fishing, walking. **Rooms 31** (all en-suite,1 suite, 10 no-smoking, 1 for disabled). B&B €55 pps, ss €10. Light bar food 1-5pm daily.L & D offered daily, 12.30-3 (Sun to 4), 7-9.30. Open all year. MasterCard, Amex, Visa, Laser. **Directions:** 40 minutes drive from Ballina.

Castlebar — Breaffy House Business & Leisure Hotel

 Hotel — Breaffy Road Castlebar Co. Mayo **Tel: 094 22033** Fax: 094 22276
Email: cro@lynchhotels.com Web: www.lynchhotels.com

This handsome hotel set in its own grounds just outside Castlebar town dates back to 1890 and retains some of its original country house atmosphere. It has undergone major renovation and refurbishments over the last few years and, since a change of ownership in 2000, the restaurant and some of the bedrooms have already been refurbished and sixty five new deluxe bedrooms (including two presidential suites and 20 interconnecting family rooms) and a leisure complex (with pools, treatment rooms and gym) are all due to open in time for the 2003 season. In addition, twenty new 3-bedroom holiday suites are planned for 2003. Conference/banqueting (500); business centre; video conferencing on request. Preferential local golf rates. Garden. Off season value breaks. Children welcome (cots available without charge). No pets. Garden, walking. **Rooms 60** (8 no smoking, 2 disabled). Lift. B&B €75pps, ss €26. (Room only rate also available: €135, max 3 guests). SC discretionary. Closed 24-26 Dec. Amex, Diners, MasterCard, Visa, Laser. **Directions:** 4 km outside Castlebar on Claremorris Road (N60).

Cong — Ashford Castle

Hotel
☆Restaurant

Cong Co. Mayo **Tel: 092 46003** Fax: 092 46260
Email: ashford@ashford.ie Web: www.ashford.ie

Ireland's grandest castle hotel, with a history going back to the early 13th century, Ashford is set in 350 acres of beautiful parkland. Grandeur, formality and tranquillity are the essential characteristics, first seen in the approach through well manicured lawns, in the entrance and formal gardens and, once inside, in a succession of impressive public rooms that illustrate a long and proud history – panelled walls, oil paintings, balustrades, suits of armour and magnificent fireplaces. Accommodation at the castle varies considerably due to the size and age of the building, and each room in some way reflects the special qualities of this unique hotel. The best bedrooms and the luxurious suites at the top of the castle - many with magnificent views of Lough Corrib, the River Cong and wooded parkland - are elegantly furnished with period furniture, some with enormous and beautifully appointed bathrooms, others with remarkable architectural features, such as a panelled wooden ceiling recently discovered behind plasterwork in one of the suites (and now fully restored). A bijou fitness centre has computerised exercise equipment; steam room; sauna and whirlpool, all strikingly designed in neo-classical style. A specialist team backs up impressive conference facilities and the hotel's exceptional amenities and sports facilities are detailed in a very handy little pocket book; in it you'll find everything you need to know about the equestrian centre, falconry, hunting, clay target shooting, archery, cycling, pony & trap tours, golf (resident instructor & equipment hire), tennis, lake & river fishing, lake cruising, jogging, guided walking & cycling tours on the estate - and a guide to scenic routes and attractions in Mayo and Galway - this little book is a gem. Conference/banqueting (110/75); business centre; secretarial services; video conferencing on request. Fitness centre. Equestrian centre, falconry, tennis, golf (9), fishing, cycling, walking, snooker. Children welcome (cot available without charge) No pets. **Rooms 83** (4 suites, 2 junior suites, 5 executive). Lift. 24 hour room service. Room rate: €414 (max 2 guests); SC 15%.

The Connaught Room: This small room is the jewel in Ashford Castle's culinary crown and one of Ireland's most impressive restaurants. Denis Lenihan, who has been Executive Chef at the castle since 1975, oversees the cooking for both this and the George V Dining Room. The style is classical French using the best of local ingredients – Atlantic prawns, Galway Bay sole, Cleggan lobster, Connemara lamb – in sophisticated dishes that will please the most discerning diner. Irish farmhouse cheeses and warm soufflés are among the tempting endings for luxurious meals, which are greatly enhanced by meticulous attention to detail. Service is discreet and extremely professional. An extensive wine list includes a special selection of Wines of the Month, of varying styles and from several regions, at friendly prices. **Seats 25** D only, 7-9.15 (usually residents only). No smoking restaurant.

George V Dining Room: Lunch and dinner are served in this much larger but almost equally opulent dining room, and an all-day snack menu is also available. A five-course dinner menu is offered and although the standard of cooking and service equals that of The Connaught Room, there is a more down to earth tone about the menus, which are in English, with a choice of about five on the first and middle courses. Local smoked salmon carved at your table and tails of Cleggan lobster in a rich Newburg sauce with spaghetti of vegetables are typical of menus that major in seafood but have plenty of other options to choose from. A separate vegetarian menu has less choice but is more modern and includes some tempting suggestions. If at least two people (preferably a whole party) are agreed, a 7-course Menu Surprise tasting menu is available - and after dinner you will be presented with a souvenir copy of the Menu Surprise: a wonderful way to commemorate a special occasion. Lunch offers a shortened and somewhat simplified version of the dinner menu, but the same high standards apply. **Seats 150**. No smoking restaurant. L 1-2.15, D 7-9.15. Set L €38, Set D €57. A la carte D also available; house wine €28. SC.15%. Amex, Diners MasterCard, Visa, Laser. **Directions:** 1/2 hour drive from Galway City (on R345).

Crossmolina   Enniscoe House

Country House   Castlehill Ballina Co. Mayo **Tel: 096 31112** Fax: 096 31773
                                        Email: mail@enniscoe.com Web: enniscoe.com

In parkland and mature woods on the shores of Lough Conn, Enniscoe is stern and gaunt, as Georgian mansions in the north-west of Ireland tend to be, but any intimidating impressions of "the last great house of North Mayo" are quickly dispelled once inside this fascinating old place. Built by ancestors of the present owner, Susan Kellett, (they settled here in the 1660s), Enniscoe attracts anglers and visitors with a natural empathy for the untamed wildness of this little known area - the house has great charm and makes a lovely place to come back to after a day in the rugged countryside. Family portraits, antique furniture and crackling log fires all complement Susan's warm hospitality and deliciously simple, wholesome dinners (Irish country house cooking), which non-residents are welcome to share by reservation. It is the activities at the back of the house that have attracted special interest lately however: in the old farm buildings, the local Historical Society operates a genealogy centre, The Mayo North Family History Research Centre (096 31809) that researches names and families of Mayo origin. Alongside there's a small but growing agricultural museum where old farm machinery is displayed, and there's a small conference centre in the courtyard along with three delightful self-catering units. Perhaps the most exciting developments are in the gardens and woodlands, however; a network of paths has made much of the beautiful woodland area around the house more accessible to guests and major renovations have recently taken place in the walled gardens, which are now open to the public and have tearooms - and, most recently, a shop stocking a good range of quality "non-tourist" items and some garden plants.

Another garden produces organically grown vegetables, herbs and fruit for the house. There is brown trout fishing on Lough Conn and other trout and salmon fishing nearby; boats, ghillies, tuition and hire of equipment can be arranged. Children are welcome (under 2s free in parents' room, cot available without charge) and dogs are also allowed by arrangement. Small conferences (30). **Rooms 6** (all en-suite, 2 with power showers; 2 no smoking) B&B €80 pps, ss €15. **Restaurant: Seats 16.** D daily, 8pm - non residents welcome by reservation; house wines €12-17. No smoking restaurant Closed 14 Oct-end Mar. Amex, MasterCard, Visa. **Directions:** 2 miles south of Crossmolina on R315.

Foxford — Healy's Hotel

féile bia Hotel — Pontoon Foxford Co. Mayo **Tel: 094 56443** Fax: 094 56572
Email: info@healyspontoon.com Web: www.healyspontoon.com

This famous old hotel, loved by fisherfolk, landscape artists and many others who seek peace and tranquillity, changed hands in 1998, and there has since been considerable renovation and refurbishment, without spoiling the old-fashioned qualities that have earned this hotel its special reputation: just a good bit of painting and decorating, some overdue refurbishment in the bar and a general tidy up around the front. At the back, overgrowth has been cleared to re-establish old gardens (500 new roses have been planted), and also to develop a beer garden. Accommodation is modest but comfortable - and also very moderately priced. There's a great feeling of people happy in what they're doing around here (notably the fisherfolk); it's all very relaxed and the hotel has lots of information on things to do in the area - including golf at around a dozen courses within an hour's drive. Aside from fishing, other country pursuits available nearby include shooting, horse racing, mountain climbing and golf (links and parkland courses nearby). Small banqueting facilities (60); garden, fishing. Packed lunches available. Children welcome (under 3s free in parents' room; cots available). Pets permitted by arrangement. The restaurant is open for dinner every evening and lunch on Sunday. **Rooms 14** (all shower only). B&B €49pps, ss €10. *Bar food available 12-9 daily. Closed 25 Dec. Amex, Diners, MasterCard, Visa, Laser. **Directions:** From Dublin take the N4 to Longford, switching to the N5. 3 miles from Foxord.

Lahardane — Leonard's

Pub — Lahardane Ballina Co. Mayo **Tel: 096 51003**

This unspoilt roadside traditional pub & grocery shop was established in 1897 and the original owners would be proud of it today. If you get hungry, there's the makings of a picnic on the shelves. Closed 25 Dec & Good Fri. **Directions:** Crossmolina-Pontoon road (R315). ◇

Lecanvey — T. Staunton

Pub — Lecanvey Westport Co. Mayo **Tel: 098 64850** / 64891

Thérèse Staunton runs this great little pub near the beginning of the ascent to Croagh Patrick - genuinely traditional, with an open fire it has the feeling of a real 'local'. Not really a food place, but home-made soup and sandwiches or plated salads are available every day until 9pm. Occasional traditioal music sessions - and frequent impromptu sing-songs. Closed 25 Dec & Good Fri. **No Credit Cards. Directions:** 8 miles from Westport on Louisburgh Road.

Mulrany — Rosturk Woods

Accommodation — Mulrany Westport Co. Mayo **Tel: 098 36264** Fax: 098 36264
Email: stoney@iol.ie Web: www.rosturk-woods.com

Beautifully located in secluded mature woodland, with direct access to the sandy seashore of Clew Bay, Louisa and Alan Stoney's delightful family home is between Westport and Achill Island, with fishing, swimming, sailing, walking, riding and golf all nearby. It is a lovely, informal house; the three guest bedrooms are all en-suite and very comfortably furnished. Louisa Stoney enjoys cooking for guests, but please book dinner 24 hours in advance. There is also self-catering accommodation available. Garden. Pets allowed by arrangement. **Rooms 3** (all en-suite & no-smoking). B&B about €45pps, ss about €16. Residents' D about €32, 7-8pm (24 hours notice). Closed Christmas. **No Credit Cards. Directions:** 7 miles from Newport on Achill Road. ◇

Newport — Newport House

🏛 Country House/Restaurant

Newport Co. Mayo **Tel: 098 41222** Fax: 098 41613
Email: info@newporthouse.ie Web: www.newporthouse.ie

To its many visitors, a stay at Newport House symbolises all that is best about the Irish country house, and it was the Guide's Country House of the Year in 1999. Currently in the caring hands of Kieran and Thelma Thompson, Newport has been especially close to the hearts of fishing people for many years, but the comfort and warm hospitality of this wonderful house is accessible to all its guests – not least in shared enjoyment of the club-fender cosiness of the little back bar. The house has a beautiful central hall, sweeping staircase and gracious drawing room, while bedrooms, like the rest of the house, are furnished in style with antiques and fine paintings. The day's catch is weighed and displayed in the hall and the fisherman's bar provides the perfect venue for a reconstruction of the day's sport. Fishing, garden, walking, snooker. **Rooms 18** (16 en-suite, 2 with private (unconnecting) bathroom, 2 shower only) Children welcome (under 2s free in parents' room; cots available). Wheelchair accessible. Pets allowed in some areas. **Rooms 18** (2 shower only, 2 private, 16 en-suite) B&B about €110, ss about €23, no s.c.
Restaurant: John Gavin, who has been head chef since 1983, presents interesting five course menus in the country house style. Not surprisingly, perhaps, fresh fish is a speciality – not only freshwater fish caught on local lakes and rivers, but also a wide variety of sea fish from nearby Achill island - and, of course, the freshest of produce from their own walled garden in soups, salads, delicious desserts and preserves as well as main courses. Home-smoked salmon is also a particular speciality (prepared to a secret recipe...) An outstanding wine list includes a great collection of classic French wines – 170 clarets from 1961-1990 vintages, a great collection of white and red burgundies, excellent Rhones – and a good New World collection too. Restaurant **Seats 38**. No smoking restaurant; air conditioning. D daily 7-9.30; Set D about €46; house wine about €17. Toilets wheelchair accessible. Non-residents welcome by reservation. **Directions:** In village of Newport. ◇

Westport — Ardmore House Hotel & Restaurant

Ⓝ 🏛 Restaurant/Country House

The Quay Westport Co. Mayo
Tel: 098 25994 Fax: 098 27795
Email: ardmore@anu.ie Web: www.ardmorecountryhouse.com

Pat and Noreen Hoban's small family-run hotel is well-located near Westport harbour with lovely views over Clew Bay and, since recent major refurbishment, offers a tempting combination of warm hospitality, very comfortable accommodation and good food. Open fires in the foyer and bar set a welcoming tone and there is usually a family member at hand to greet arriving guests. Although expensive, guest rooms are spacious, individually decorated and furnished to a high standard - the style is quite luxurious, they have the full range of facilities expected of better hotel rooms (including an iron and ironing board) and most have separate bath and shower. Not suitable for children. No pets. Garden. **Rooms 13** (all superior, all no smoking). Limited room service. B&B €125, ss €30.
Restaurant: Owner-chef Pat Hoban presents pleasingly classic menus with a strong emphasis on seafood, which make good reading over an aperitif in the comfortable bar. An unusually wide selection of first and middle courses is offered - cold and warm starters, soups and sorbets - including an hors d'oeuvre plate - while main courses offer a good range of meat and poultry as well as the dominant seafood dishes, which includes shellfish such as scallops and lobster when available. The restaurant is well-appointed, bright and airy with tables well separated by plants, and staff work well to ensure that an enjoyable evening is had by all. **Seats 50**. No smoking area. D only (daily in summer, Mon-Sat low season), 7-9.30. Set D €40, also à la carte. House wine €17.50. Closed Sun in low season, 24-26 Dec, Jan & Feb. Amex, MasterCard, Visa, Laser. **Directions:** 1.5 kms from Westport town centre.

Westport   Atlantic Coast Hotel

Hotel   The Quay Westport Co. Mayo **Tel: 098 29000** Fax: 098 29111
Email: info@atlanticcoasthotel.com Web: www.atlanticcoasthotel.com

Behind the traditional stone façade of an old mill on Westport harbour, this bright and interesting modern hotel has many pleasant surprises in store. Spacious public areas are designed and furnished in a pleasing combination of traditional and contemporary themes and materials and the tone is continued through to bedrooms, which are spacious, with stylish Italian bathrooms; direct dial phone, hairdryers, satellite TV, tea/coffee tray and trouser press are standard in all rooms; fax/modem ports available on request. Although it may seem like an impersonal city hotel in some ways, staff (including those in the excellent leisure centre) are exceptionally friendly and efficient. The same is true of The Blue Wave Restaurant, which is situated right up at the top of the building (a good idea, although the view is somewhat restricted by sloping roof windows and the room can become very hot in summer). Here Eamon O'Reilly, who has been head chef since 2000, presents interesting and well-balanced menus offering plenty of local produce, especially seafood - and delivers with panache. (Breakfast, however, may be disappointing in comparison.) Conferences/banqueting (160/140). Children welcome (under 4s free in parents' room, cots available without charge). Leisure centre, swimming pool; fishing; discount at local golf club. Prices have risen steeply during the last year making it worthwhile to shop around, but better value off-season/special interest breaks are often available. **Rooms 85** (3 suites, 10 superior, 25 no smoking, 3 for disabled). Lift. 24 hour room service. B&B €135pps, ss €20; No SC%. Closed 24-27 Dec. Amex, MasterCard, Visa, Laser. **Directions:** Located at Westport harbour, 1 mile from town centre on main Louisburgh and coast road.

Westport   The Creel

Restaurant   The Harbour Westport Co. Mayo **Tel: 098 26174**
Email: bennett@gofree.indigo.ie

Frank and Julie Bennett run this attractive daytime restaurant on the harbour front - it's a pleasant, cottagey place with pine furniture and warm tones in the terracotta tiled floor, nautical bric-a-brac and traditional baskets used for display. There's some comfortable seating too, and magazines lying around - the idea is to make it a homely place where people can lounge about and relax awhile. An imaginative blackboard menu offers a range of hot dishes and snacks, all under €15 - typically hot meals like beef & mushroom pie with red wine (served with potatoes and vegetables) and chef's chicken & coconut korma (served with basmati rice), lighter dishes such as smoked salmon tart with salad and light bites like toasted paninis (with goats cheese & tomato relish for example). Home-made desserts are temptingly displayed at the counter (where you'll also find well-priced wines alongside the juices and mineral waters). Tasty, lively food well-cooked, pleasant service and surroundings - and good value - make this the perfect place for a daytime bite. **Seats 50.** Open daily, 11-6 (Sat to 7, Sun to 5). Closed Mon & Tue off-season (Sep-Mar) and 2 weeks in winter. MasterCard, Visa. **Directions:** On front at Westport Harbour. ◇

Westport   Hotel Westport

Hotel   Newport Rd Westport Co. Mayo **Tel: 098 25122** Fax: 098 26739
Email: sales@hotelwestport.ie Web: www.hotelwestport.ie

Just a short stroll from Westport town centre this large modern hotel is set in its own grounds and offers excellent facilities for both leisure and business guests. It makes a good base for a holiday in this lovely area and numerous short breaks are offered, including family breaks at times when special children's entertainment is available (June-August). The conference and business centre provide a fine venue for corporate events of all kinds, including incentive breaks, and the hotel and surrounding area provide all the activities and amenities necessary for off-duty delegates. Bedrooms, which include some with four-poster beds, are well-appointed, with phone/ISDN lines, TV/video, tea/coffee facilities and trouser press; constant refurbishment and upgrading is an ongoing feature of this well-managed hotel: bedrooms corridors, public and banqueting areas have recently received special attention and this current improvement programme will continue into 2003. The whole hotel is unusually wheelchair-friendly, without steps or obstacles, and staff are invariably helpful and friendly. Conference/banqueting (500/350); video conferencing; business centre. Leisure centre, swimming pool. Garden. Children welcome (under 3s free in parents' room; cots available without charge.) **Rooms 129** (6 suites, 7 for disabled) Wheelchair accessible. Lift. B&B €115 pps, ss €20, sc discretionary. Open all year. Amex, Diners, MasterCard, Visa, Laser. **Directions:** On Castlebar road, turn right onto north mall, then turn onto Newport Road, 1st left and at the end of the road.

Westport — Knockranny House Hotel

féile bia Hotel — Westport Co. Mayo **Tel:** 098 28600 Fax: 098 28611
Email: info@khh.ie Web: www.khh.ie

Set in landscaped grounds on an elevated site overlooking the town, this Victorian-style hotel opened in 1997. The spacious foyer, friendly staff and the sight of a welcoming fire create an agreeably warm atmosphere: the foyer sets the tone for a hotel which has been built on a generous scale and is full of contrasts, with spacious public areas balanced by smaller ones - notably the library and drawing room - where guests can relax in more homely surroundings. Bedrooms are also large - the suites have four poster beds and sunken seating areas with views and all rooms are very comfortable with high quality furnishings, television, tea/coffee-making facilities and trouser press, some have jacuzzi baths and phones with ISDN. Contemporary Irish cooking is offered in the hotel dining room, La Fougère Restaurant ("the fern"), which is at the front of the hotel, with views across the town to Clew Bay and Croagh Patrick. Guests currently have use of a nearby leisure centre, but on-site facilities are expected to be completed by mid-2003. **Rooms 54** (3 suites, 9 deluxe, 3 shower only, 4 no smoking, 2 for disabled.) B&B €115, ss €55. Closed 22-27 Dec. Amex, MasterCard, Visa, Laser. **Directions:** Take N5/N60 from Castlebar. Hotel is on the left just before entering Westport.

Westport — The Lemon Peel

Restaurant — The Octagon Westport Co. Mayo **Tel:** 098 26929 Fax: 098 26965
Email: robbie@lemonpeel.ie Web: www.lemonpeel.ie

Proprietor-chef Robbie McMenamin's simply-furnished little town centre restaurant just off The Octagon has been a favourite with locals and visitors alike ever since it opened in 1998 - and despite the arrival of more restaurants in the area, it remains the most popular restaurant in town. The atmosphere is buzzy and friendly and the food interesting. Robbie sources ingredients with care and his cooking is creative and accurate. Menus are considerately sprinkled with symbols to help your selection meet the mood: red pepper for hot and spicy, yellow for medium and v for vegetarian - thus starters like crostini mozzarella (vegetarian) and crab duglère (a house special topped with light cheddar), typically followed by cajun crusted salmon with fruit salsa, lemon & basil cream (medium hot) or a more traditional dish of lamb fillet roasted with rosemary & garlic and served with wholegrain mustard sauce - these and lots more like them keep tempting people back for more. Specials change on a weekly basis and everything comes with a choice of mashed potatoes - plain, basil, champ, garlic, or olive olive - in addition to the vegetables of the day. Lovely homely puddings like rhubarb & apple crumble and gorgeous chocolate mousse and freshly brewed coffee to finish. Good food, good service - good place. Not suitable for children under 12. **Seats 32.** No smoking area; air conditioning. D only 6-10 (Sun 6-9). Early menu €21.50 (6-7 daily), Also à la carte. House wines €15.95-18.95; SC discretionary. Closed Mon, 24-26 Dec & all Feb. (Telephone off season to check opening times.) MasterCard, Visa, Laser. **Directions:** Westport Town Centre.

Westport — Matt Molloy's Bar

Pub — Bridge Street Westport Co. Mayo **Tel: 098 26655**

If you had to pick one pub in this pretty town, this soothingly dark atmospheric one would do very nicely – not least because it is owned by Matt Molloy of The Chieftains, a man who clearly has respect for the real pub: no TV (and no children after 9 pm). Musical memorabilia add to the interest, but there's also the real thing as traditional music is a major feature in the back room or out at the back in fine weather. Matt is often away on tour, but he's a real local when he's back and takes great pride in this smashing town. It's worth noting that normal pub hours don't apply – this is an afternoon into evening place, not somewhere for morning coffee. Closed 25 Dec & Good Fri. **No Credit Cards.**

Westport — The Olde Railway Hotel

Hotel — The Mall Westport Co. Mayo **Tel:** 098 25166 Fax: 098 25090
Email: railway@anu.ie Web: www.anu.ie/railwayhotel

Once described by William Thackeray as 'one of the prettiest, comfortablist hotels in Ireland', The Olde Railway Hotel was built in 1780 as a coaching inn for guests of Lord Sligo. Attractively situated along the tree-lined Carrowbeg River, on the Mall in the centre of Westport, it remains a hotel of character, well known for its antique furniture and a slightly eccentric atmosphere. Warm, friendly reception and a complimentary cup of tea on arrival (and at any other time during your stay) immediately makes guests feel welcome - and certain concessions have been made to the demands of modern travellers, including en-suite bathrooms, satellite television and private car parking. There's a conservatory dining room quietly situated at the back of the hotel and several very spacious ground floor rooms with smart en-suite shower rooms were recently added. The large bar, which is the public face of an otherwise quite private hotel, serves very acceptable bar food - a private garden now supplies organic herbs and vegetables for the hotel. Own parking. Garden, fishing, cycling (bicycles provided without charge). Children welcome (cots available). No pets. **Rooms 26** (12 superior rooms, some shower only, all no-smoking). 24 hour room service. B&B €65 pps, ss €20. Food served 12.30-2.30 & 6.30-9.30 daily. Open all year. Amex, MasterCard, Visa, Laser. **Directions:** Entering Westport from N5 (Dublin-Westport) road, turn right just before bridge. Hotel is on the mall overlooking the river.

Westport — Quay Cottage

Restaurant   The Harbour Westport Co. Mayo **Tel: 098 26412** Fax: 098 28120
Email: kirsten@oceanfree.net Web: www.quaycottage.com

Kirstin and Peter MacDonagh have been running this charming stone quayside restaurant just outside Westport since 1984, and it never fails to delight. It's cosy and informal, with scrubbed pine tables and an appropriate maritime decor, which is also reflected in the menu (although there is also much else of interest, including steaks and imaginative vegetarian options. But seafood really stars, typically in starters of chowder or garlic grilled oysters and main courses like baked medallions of monkfish with fennel & orange marmalade & creamy lemon sauce - or whole seabass, pan-fried and served with a warm baby potato salad & wholegrain mustard sauce. Daily specials are often especially interesting (duckling, turbot, scallops, lobster for example) and there are nice homely desserts – or a plated farmhouse cheese selection such as Cashel Blue, smoked Gubbeen and an Irish brie. Freshly-brewed coffee by the cup to finish. Service, supervised by Kirstin, is friendly and efficient. Children welcome. **Seats 90** (private rooms, 45/15). No smoking area; air conditioning. Toilets wheelchair accessible. D 6-"late" daily. Set D from €35; also à la carte; house wine €15.50; SC discretionary. Closed 24-26 Dec, 2 weeks Jan. Amex, MasterCard, Visa, Laser. **Directions:** On the harbour front, at gates to Westport House.

COUNTY MEATH

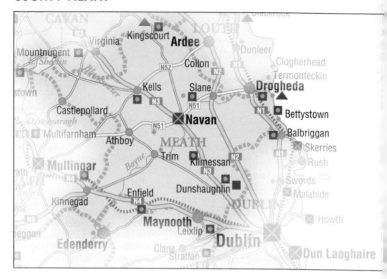

Royal Meath. Meath of the pastures. Meath of the people. Meath of many people.......The six year Census completed in the summer of 2002 confirmed what had been suspected. The population of Ireland may have increased by 8%, but Meath was the fastest-growing place of all, its increase clocking in at 22.1% to bring the county total to 134,000.

Not a huge number in today's overcrowded world, perhaps, but nevertheless Meath in 2003 is a county which finds itself living in interesting times. The proximity of Dublin, with the inevitable pressures of prosperity and population, poses problems. There is talk - and it is more than just talk - of the county town of Navan entering a development phase which, by 2015, will find it has become a riverside city of some 80,000 citizens.

Nevertheless such changes - and the need to find ways through the county for new major roads - are projects which you feel Meath can absorb. For this is a county which is comfortable and confident with itself, and rightly so. The evidence of an affluent history is everywhere in Meath. But it's a history which sits gently on a county which is enjoying its own contemporary prosperity at a pace which belies the bustle of Dublin just down the road.

That said, anyone with an interest in the past will find paradise in Meath, for along the Boyne Valley the neolithic tumuli at Knowth, Newgrange and Dowth are awe-inspiring, Newgrange in particular having its remarkable central chamber which is reached by the rays of sun at dawn at the winter solstice.

Just 16 kilometres to the southwest is another place of fascination, the Hill of Tara. Royal Tara was for centuries the cultural and religious capital of pre-Christian Ireland. Its fortunes began to wane with the coming of Christianity, which gradually moved the religious focal point to Armagh, though Tara was a place of national significance until it was finally abandoned in 1022 AD.

Little now remains of the ancient structures, but it is a magical place, for the approach by the road on its eastern flank gives little indication of the wonderful view of the central plain which the hill suddenly provides. It is truly inspiring, and many Irish people reckon the year is inccomplete without a visit to Tara, where the view is to eternity and infinity, and the imagination takes flight.

Local Attractions and Information

Donore Bru na Boinne Visitor Centre	041 988 0300
Dunboyne Hamwood House & Gardens	01 825 5210
Kells Grove Gardens & Tropical Bird Sanctuary	046 34276
Kinnegad National Ploughing Championships 2003	0507 25125
Laytown Sonairte (National Ecology Centre)	041 982 7572
Navan Tourism Information	046 73442

Navan Navan Racecourse	046 21350
Newgrange (inc Dowth & Knowth)	041 988 0300 / 982 4488
Oldcastle Loughcrew Historic Gardens	049 854 1922
Oldcastle Loughcrew Passage Tombs (3000BC)	049 854 2009
Ratoath Fairyhouse Racecourse	01 825 6167
Summerhill Larchill Arcadian Gardens	01 628 7354
Tara Interpretive Centre	046 25903
Trim Butterstream Garden	046 36017
Trim Tourism Information	046 37111
Trim Trim Castle (restored Norman stronghold)	046 38619

Bettystown — Bacchus At The Coastgaurd

 Restaurant

Bayview Bettystown Co. Meath
Tel: 041 982 8257 Fax: 041 982 8236

Right beside the beach, with views over Bettystown Bay - where, even at night, it is interesting to see the lights of the ships waiting in the bay to go up the river to the port at Drogheda - Kieran Greenway and Anne Hardy have been running the area's leading restaurant since 1996. The entrance is from the road side (actually the back of the building, as the sea is at the front) and opens into a pleasant bar overlooking the sea, where aperitifs are served. The menu majors in seafood, supplied by local fishermen and from the west coast – in starters like deep fried prawns in filo with mango salsa and citrus sauce, perhaps, and main courses such as roast fillet of salmon with vegetable julienne and & chive beurre blanc. But the choice is far from being restricted to seafood; vegetarian dishes are usually offered - just ask if there doesn't happen to be one on the day - and there's a good selection of poultry and red meats. This is an excellent restaurant with creative, accurately-cooked food, a cosy ambience and friendly, efficient service. Not suitable for children after 7.30pm. **Seats 70** (private room, 30). No smoking area. D Tue-Sat, 6-10 (Mon-Sat in summer); Sun L, 12.30-2.30. D €45 & à la carte; early D €26 (6-7.30 only); Set Sun L €25. House wine €17; SC discretionary. Closed D Sun, also Mon Sep-June; 2 weeks Feb, 2 weeks Sep. Amex, MasterCard, Visa, Laser. **Directions:** N1 to Julianstown, then coast road to Bettystown.

Bettystown — Neptune Beach Hotel

Hotel

Bettystown Co. Meath **Tel: 041 982 7107** Fax: 041 982 7412
Email: info@neptunebeach.ie Web: www.neptunebeach.ie

In a great location overlooking the famous long sandy beach at Bettystown and adjacent to a golf links, this striking modern hotel also has excellent in-house leisure facilties, notably a leisure club with 20m swimming pool. Spacious public areas include a large bar with sea views and a characterful traditonal lounge bar on the road side of the building plus a large lounge area designed around a well feature and a second bar overlooking the beach. Bedrooms are generous and have all the usual modern amenities (best ones at the front have the view). Restaurant meals are well above the standard expected of an hotel - both for Sunday lunch (a jazz buffet, served in a funtion room overlooking the beach) and dinner, in Le Pressage restaurant. **Rooms 38.** B&B from about €127 pps; midweek specials offered. Restaurant D daily, L Sun only. Open all year. Amex, MasterCard, Visa. **Directions:** N1 to Julianstown follow coast road through Laytown to Bettystown. ◇

Castletown — Mountainstown House

Country House

Castletown Kilpatrick Navan Co. Meath **Tel: 046 54154**
Fax: 046 54154 Email: pollock@oceanfree.net

If you want to experience something out of the ordinary in a really rural setting, this is the place for you: on a 750-acre farm amidst unspoilt rolling countryside, John and Diana Pollocks' home is a huge house of great character. It was bought by the Pollock family in 1796, from Samuel Gibbons who ran it as a sporting estate. The front door is approached up seriously impressive steps, which give some inkling of what is to come - not only does this magnificent place have the grandly proportioned reception rooms and large countryhouse bedrooms that might be expected, but there's a wonderful 18th century courtyard at the back, complete with a spring well and original carriagewash. Peacocks and all kinds of poultry stroll around this amazing place with measured insouciance... It's a marvellously romantic venue for a wedding reception (max 80). Garden, snooker/billiards, children's playground & playroom. **Rooms 6** (1 suite, 3 en-suite, 2 with private bathrooms, all no smoking). B&B €72pps, ss €12. Residents' D at 8 pm, about €32 (24 hrs notice required). Children welcome (under 3s free in parents' room, cots available). Pets by arrangement. Own parking. Closed 22 Dec-2 Jan. Amex, MasterCard, Visa. **Directions:** From Dublin - N3 Navan. Turn right 3rd set of traffic lights for Kingscourt - Wilkinstown.

Clonard   The Monastery Inn

 Pub   Clonard Co. Meath **Tel: 044 75121** Fax: 044 75707
Email: monastery@eircom.net   Web: www.themonasteryinn.ie

This well-maintained roadhouse makes a very good place to break a journey across the country, or as a destination in its own right. Set back a little from the main road, with its own car park (and an enclosed garden at the back, not visible from the road), its neat but otherwise unexceptional appearance does little to prepare the first time visitor for the energy and professionalism that is obvious inside. The name refers to a nearby 6th century monastic site, a theme which continues in the interior; work is far from finished at the time of going to press but refurbishment already completed is to a high standard. The monastic theme also makes its way onto the menu (stir friars, Reverent cold meat salad...) but there are no gimmicks in the kitchen: quality ingredients, local produce and suppliers are highlighted on the menu and everything is home-made including good brown bread used for open sandwiches - and hand-cut chips. Presentation which is attractively modern (large white plates - round for hot food, square for salads and sandwiches) fits comfortably with the traditional ambience - and historic references are highlighted and explained throughout (visitors are even presented with a little book on local history in addition to notes on the menu), which adds greatly to the interest of a visit. All this, plus friendly, efficient staff, add up to a recipe for success. Food served daily, 12-8.30 (Sun to 7.30). Closed 25 Dec, Good Fri. MasterCard, Visa, Laser. **Directions:** On N4, near Enfield.

Dunboyne   Caldwell's Restaurant

 Restaurant   Summerhill Road Dunboyne Co. Meath **Tel: 01 8013866**
Email: d.caldwell2002@yahoo.com

In a neat modern building in the centre of Dunboyne, this smart new two-storey restaurant is simple and modern in style - clean lines, unfussy table settings (heavy cutlery, quality paper napkins, no extras), comfortable high-back chairs; the high-ceilinged ground floor area overlooks a large patio, which gives it a light, bright atmosphere, while tables on the balcony area above have a cosier ambience. Guests are shown straight to their tables to look over the menus (a moderately priced dinner menu on week nights and an à la carte) and order aperitifs; home-made breads are offered (probably more than once before food is served). Promising menus are refreshingly simply worded and sources highlighted - suppliers named, vegetables from the family garden - along with membership of Feile Bia, which is all confidence-inspiring. Set menus offer a choice of three on each course - spring rolls of Boilie soft cow's cheese with roasted pinenuts & onion marmalade, followed by roasted leg of lamb with champ mash & gravy, perhaps - while the à la carte is wider ranging and dishes sound more luxurious: starters may include Dublin Bay prawn 'cocktail', for example and the roast lamb is upgraded to become roasted rack, with red wine reduction with mushroom & onion. Well-balanced menus include several seafood specialities, but the leaning is towards red meats - and, like the vegetables, very tasty they are too. Except for an ill-judged deep-fried vanilla ice cream, desserts tend to be enjoyable classics, possibly including a refreshing citrus themed selection (lemon pannacotta, grapefruit marmalade, lime tuile, lemon sorbet). Caldwell's is a welcome newcomer to the area and offers good food and a pleasant ambience at fair prices; on the down side, service can be inexplicably slow. A compact wine list is to be expanded for 2003 with specially imported wines offered at reasonable prices. Longer opening hours are also under consideration at the time of going to press. **Seats 55** (private balcony area 20). No smoking area. Children welcome (Sun L only). D Wed-Sat, 6-10; L Sun only 1.30-5.30. Set D & Sun L €21.50, D also a la carte. House wine €16.50. Closed D Sun, all Mon & Tue, bank hols. MasterCard, Visa, Laser. **Directions:** Dunboyne village, through lights, 2nd building on left.

Dunshaughlin

Guesthouse

The Old Workhouse

Dunshaughlin Co. Meath **Tel: 01 8259251**
Fax: 01 825951 Email: comfort@a-vip.com

IRISH BREAKFAST AWARD - LEINSTER

It's hard to imagine that this striking cut-stone listed building was once a workhouse – having been restored by Niamh and Dermod Colgan it makes a beautiful old house of great character and charm, with highly individual bedrooms, one of which has a kingsize four-poster bed. Each has been furnished and decorated with great attention to detail, using carefully sourced antiques and an ever-growing collection of old plates. Of the five rooms, three are officially shower-only but the Colgans have got around the problem of space with ingenuity by installing half-baths instead of shower trays. More power to them for their thoughtfulness (others please take note). There are thoughtful touches everywhere and Niamh, who is an enthusiastic cook, lavishes attention on breakfast: freshly squeezed orange juice, fresh fruit salad, dried fruit compôte poached in tea, bananas in orange juice with lime zest, homegrown rhubarb with star anisé, fresh strawberries, fresh citrus segments, home-made granola and other cereals, smoked salmon ham cooked in cider, farmhouse cheeses (including Silke Cropp's Corleggy and Drumlin cheese, from Cavan) and an array of home-baked breads, scones and croissants with home-made preserves. And, of course, there's a wonderful traditional Irish hot breakfast cooked to order as well. Just wonderful. Wheelchair accessible. Not suitable for children. **Rooms 5** (1 junior suite, 1 with four-poster, 1 for disabled, all no-smoking). B&B from €70pps, ss €25.39. Closed 1 Dec-1 Feb. MasterCard, Visa. **Directions:** On N3 1 mile south of Dunshaughlin Village.

Enfield

Hotel/Restaurant

Johnstown House Hotel

Enfield Co. Meath **Tel: 0405 40000** Fax: 0405 40001
Email: info@johnstownhouse.com Web: www.johnstownhouse.com

This new hotel opened in August 2001 and has still a considerable amount of development to complete at the time of going to press, including the Spa and leisure centre which is to be a central theme. It's well-located in 80 acres of woods and parkland only about half an hour's drive from Dublin's western suburbs (traffic permitting), and has at its heart a mid 18th century house which has been carefully restored. Although the original house is only a small part of the hotel it is the focal point and the main entrance; the original wings are replaced by a large banqueting area on one side and the spa and leisure centre (now due to open in 2004) on the other. An unusually fine feature of the old house is a drawing room with a plasterwork ceiling designed by the renowned Francini brothers, who were responsible for some of Ireland's finest plasterwork in great houses of the time; as the house was not of comparable importance with others they worked on, there is a theory that they did it in return for a favour, such as free use of a hunting lodge on the estate. Bedrooms are elegantly and very comfortably furnished. The hotel has become extremely popular as a wedding venue. Conference/banqueting 800; business centre; video conferencing. Children welcome (cots available without charge). **Rooms 80** (4 for disabled). Lift. 24 hr room service. Room rate from €115.
Pavilion Restaurant: All accommodation is in new areas, but a fine dining restaurant, The Pavilion, and a private dining room are among the rooms in the old building. Executive head chef Eric Faussurier, well known from the Portmarnock Hotel & Country Club, in Co. Dublin, presents à la carte menus based on classical French cuisine, with a contemporary tone. Luxurious, perfectly executed signature dishes include a starter of ravioli of langoustine tail and scallops with a sweet ginger and saffron nage and a main course of aiguillette of beef fillet on a bed of wild mushrooms and pommes maxim, served with a foie gras and truffle sauce. M. Faussurier is also responsible for the Atrium Brasserie, where less formal dining is available, and his lively popular menus there offer good value. For further relaxation, there's a Coach House Bar, a traditional bar with a mezzanine Whiskey and Cigar lounge. Amex, MasterCard, Visa, Laser. **Directions:** Take N4 from Dublin - first village after motorway.

Kells — The Ground Floor Restaurant

 Restaurant

Bective Square Kells Co. Meath
Tel: 046 49688 Fax: 046 28347

A bright and attractive contemporary restaurant in the centre of Kells, The Ground Floor is a younger sister of The Loft in Navan and has much in common with it: wacky pictures and a youthful buzzy atmosphere, plus interesting, colourful food at accessible prices - the most expensive dish on the regular menu is a fillet steak at about €20, but most main courses are much less. Popular dishes from around the world abound in starters like kofta kebabs, spicy buffalo wings and crostini and main courses ranging from Greek and caesar salads, through home-made burgers to steaks, pastas and pizzas. Interesting daily blackboard specials are often a good bet - and there are new wight-watching options on the menu. Exceptionally pleasant and helpful staff add greatly to the relaxed ambience. Children welcome up to 8pm (baby changing facility available). Wheelchair access. **Seats 60.** Air conditioning, no smoking area. D daily, 5.30-10.30 (Satto 11.30, Sun 5-10). A la carte. House wine €16.50. 10% SC on parties of 4+. MasterCard, Visa, Laser. **Directions:** Centre of Kells on the Athboy/Mullingar Road.

Kells — Vanilla Pod Restaurant

féile bia Ⓝ Restaurant Headfort Arms Hotel Kells Co. Meath **Tel: 046 40084** Fax: 046 40587
Email: headfortarms@eircom.net Web: www.headfortarms.ie

Although reached through an entrance just inside the foyer of the Headfort Arms Hotel and in common ownership, The Vanilla Pod is run as an independent entity. In contrast to the rest of the hotel, it is very modern since its recent makeover, with lots of pale wood, recessed lighting and sleek informal table settings. Efficient staff show you straight to your table to choose from a well-structured contemporary menu - grilled goats cheese salad wih Mediterranean salsa & basil pesto, char-gtrilled cajun spiced chicken with Creole sauce, coriander & lime yogurt & saffon rice are typical examples - which is very professionally presented, and perhaps raises expectations that may be hard to meet consistently. However, this new operation makes a welcome alternative to hotel dining and there is clearly a serious desire to please. The wine list is a strong point and 'Pod Wine Club' gourmet wine evenings, hosted by wine producers, are held bi-monthly - an interesting development for the area and a good feature to build on. **Seats 65.** No smoking area; air conditioning. Vegetarian dishes offered. D Tue-Sun, 5.30-10 (Fri & Sat to 11, Sun to 9.30), L Sun only, 12-3. Set L from €20.25. Early D (5.30-7.30) €15.50, also à la carte. SC10%on parties of 4+. Closed Mon, 25 Dec, Good Fri. Amex, MasterCard, Visa, Laser. **Directions:** On main Dublin road, black &white building on right.

Kells — White Gables

B&B

Headfort Place Kells Co. Meath **Tel: 046 40322**
Fax: 046 49672 Email: kelltic@eircom.net

Just across the road from the Heritage Centre, Joe and Penny Magowan's delightful old house is on a slip road with trees and a little park between it and the main road, although light sleepers may find the traffic noise disturbing. It has a restful garden at the back - overlooked by the residents' sitting room and dining room - for guests' use and the comfortable, cottagey bedrooms have all been recently refurbished. Penny is a Cordon Bleu cook and previously ran a restaurant in the town: breakfasts are extensive and evening meals are available by arrangment for groups of eight or more. "Kelltic Walking Holidays" operates from White Gables, so a range of information on the locality is available for guests. **Rooms 4** (3 en-suite, 1 with private bathroom & all no smoking). B&B €30 pps, ss €10. Children welcome, cots available. Open all year. **No Credit Cards. Directions:** On the outskirts of Kells, within walking distance of all amenities.

Kilmessan — The Station House Hotel

Hotel/Restaurant

Kilmessan Co. Meath **Tel: 046 25239** Fax: 046 25588
Email: info@thehousehotel.com Web: www.thestationhousehotel.com

Chris and Thelma Slattery's unique establishment is at an old railway junction, which has been closed since 1963, and all the various buildings have been converted to a new use. Major renovations have recently been completed, with the addition of new rooms, an upgraded reception area and a larger bar, which overlooks a large patio (platform) and gardens which are a particularly attractive aspect of the hotel and supply all the fresh flowers. The old engine and goods building is now a conference and banqueting suite which, with its original stone walls and natural light giving it character, is now understandably popular for both business and leisure gatherings, notably weddings (and the old ignal box is now a 2-room honeymoon suite). Conference/banqueting (400/170) **Rooms 20** (1 suite, 10 no-smoking, 2 disabled). B&B €63.50, ss €25.

he Signal Restaurant: The bar is a pleasant spot to have an aperitif and look at the menu before joing in to the restaurant, which is a comfortable, homely place furnished with antiques and spread over two rooms. Daily set dinner menus and an à la carte that take both traditional tastes and urrent food trends into account are offered, and there is always an imaginative vegetarian choice. ome less usual ingredients have crept in of late - ostrich (which is reared nearby), kangaroo and rocodile (which are not) - but more typical dishes include home-made duck liver paté with Cumberland sauce or a red fruit compôte and fingers of toast, rack of Kilmessan lamb (with rosemary & redcurrant jus perhaps) and farmhouse cheeses or desserts such as chocolate and orange parfait or warm lemon tart. Live music (mandolin/piano) give a sense of occasion to dinner on Saturday night. Sunday lunch is extremely popular and justifies two sittings - staff somehow remain calm and cheerful throughout. Food is also served in the bar 11-5.30 daily. **Seats 90**. Children welcome. No smoking area. L 12.30-3 (Sun to 5.30), D7-10 (Sun to 9.30) Set L €19.95. Set Sun L €19.95; Set D from €19.95 (Sat €39.95), also à la carte; house wine from €15.10; no SC. Food is also served n the bar, 11-5.30 daily. Amex, Diners, MasterCard, Visa, Laser. **Directions:** From Dublin N3 to Dunshaughlin and follow signposts.

Navan   Adam & Eve's

Ⓝ Restaurant   18 Ludlow Street Navan Co. Meath **Tel: 046 71444** Fax: 044 64378
Email: adamandeves@eircom.net Web: meathtourism.ie

This small restaurant is just across the road from one of the area's finest old pubs, P Bermingham (unspoilt and friendly - well worth dropping into for an aperitif or digestif). Decor is light and airy n smart neutral tones, with stylish high-back chairs, white linen and primrose napkins - and service s confident and friendly. Colourful international menus of mainly Mediterranean influence are well executed and attractively presented: fried halloumi cheese with fresh lemon and olive oil arrives atop a pretty mixed salad, while risotto - pumpkin, perhaps - is made with good stock and is redolent of the flavours of vegetables used, such as spinach and red pepper; grilled salmon fillet, cooked to your liking, may be served on a delicious salad of cannelloni beans with diced tomatoes, red onion a generous drizzle of salsa verde. Good coffee, good value for money. Children welcome. **Seats 50.** D Tue-Sat, 6-10.30 (later on Sat), L Sun, from 12.30. Early D €16, otherwise à la carte. House wines from €14. Closed Mon, 25 Dec, bank hols. MasterCard, Visa, Laser. **Directions:** Town centre, opposite Bermingham's pub.

Navan   Ardboyne Hotel

Hotel   Dublin Road Navan Co. Meath **Tel: 046 23119** Fax: 046 22355
Email: ardboyne@quinn-hotels.com Web: quinn-hotels.com

Standing in its own grounds on the outskirts of town, this modern hotel has a thriving conference and function trade. The entrance and all public areas give a good first impression, although bedrooms are on the small side and could be more comfortable with a little more attention to detail. Restaurant: As has been the case for a number of years, the restaurant is above average for a country hotel. The atmosphere may leave a lot to be desired but friendly, helpful staff and an interesting, well-balanced menu are plus points and the cooking is sound and generous. Conference/banqueting (600/400). Parking. Children under 2 free in parents' room; cots available. Wheelchair accessible. **Rooms 29** (all en-suite). B&B about €60ps, ss about €20. Children welcome. Restaurant seats 80. No smoking area; air conditioning. L 12.30-3 & D 6-10 daily. Set L about €16; Set Sun L about €17, Set D about €27, also à la carte, house wine about €16, sc discretionary. Toilets wheelchair accessible. Closed 24-26 Dec. Amex, Diners, MasterCard, Visa. **Directions:** From Dublin, N3 to Navan, hotel on left approaching town. ◇

Navan   Fada

Ⓝ Café   Callan & Harte 31 Railway Street Navan Co. Meath **Tel: 046 74285**

A light, airy atrium room at the back of an arty giftshop, this daytime coffee shop has flagstones and plants that give it a soothing greenhouse feeling - and make it the perfect place to drop into for a break when shopping. Simple menus ofer a choice of soup, sandwiches, toasties and paninis - and a 'lite bites' menu with a Weightwatchers-ointed option and low fat cappucino and café bainne. Imaginative sandwiches might include open smoked salmon with walnuts on Spicers country white bread and a typical panini could be spicy sausage in tomato fondue & caramelised onions. Savoury and sweet crêpes too - hot pear with chocolate sauce, perhaps. Immaculately clean too, with friendly, helpful staff. Open all day. MasterCard, Visa. **Directions:** Town centre, near Tourist Office. ◇

Navan — Hudson's Bistro

Restaurant   30 Railway Street Navan Co. Meath **Tel: 046 29231** Fax: 046 7338.

Since Richard and Tricia Hudson's stylish, informal bistro opened in 1991 it has built up a stron
following and is long-established as a leading restaurant in the area. Richard's menus include a
exciting à la carte based on wide-ranging influences – Cal-Ital, Mexican, Thai, French and moder
Italian. Appealing vegetarian and healthy options are a feature – and, traditionalists will be please
to hear, the ever-popular sirloin steak has not been overlooked; on the whole, menus taste as we
as they read, although some dishes are blanded down. There are Irish cheeses and/or some ver
tempting puddings to finish. The wine list echoes the global cooking and is informative and keenl
priced. Service is a weak point, with new arrivals often left at the door waiting for directions an
the pace uneven throughout a meal. Children welcome. **Seats 54.** No smoking area. D Tue-Sun 6
9.30/10. Early D menu €16.20 (6-7 pm only); also à la carte. House wine €15.50; SC 10%. Closec
Mon, 24-26 Dec. Amex, MasterCard, Visa, Laser. **Directions:** Follow directions to town centre, tak
right off roundabout, 5th house down on left.

Navan — Killyon House

Guesthouse   Dublin Road Navan Co. Meath **Tel: 046 71224** Fax: 046 7276(
Email: killyonguesthouse.com Web: www.info@killyonguesthouse.con

Just across the road from the Ardboyne Hotel, Michael and Sheila Fogarty's modern guesthous
immediately attracts attention, with its striking array of colourful flowers and hanging baskets. The
house is furnished with interesting antiques, and made comfortable by modern double-glazing which
reduces traffic noise. The back of the house, which leads down to the banks of the Boyne, i
unexpectedly tranquil, however, and the dining room overlooks the river, giving guests the addec
interest of spotting wildlife, sometimes including otters and stoats, along the bank from the window
The Fogartys are extremely hospitable hosts and nothing (even preparing a very early breakfast) i
too much trouble. The house is very well run and rooms are all en-suite and comfortable. There's alsc
a separate guests' sitting room and, although they are too close to the restaurants of Navan to make
evening meals a viable option, they do a particularly good breakfast. Own parking. Children welcome,
cots available without charge. garden; fishing. **Rooms 6** (all en-suite, 4 shower only). B&B €40pps
ss €10. Closed 3 days at Christmas. MasterCard, Laser. **Directions:** On N3, opposite Ardboyne Hote
on River Boyne.

Navan — The Loft Restaurant

féile bia Restaurant   26 Trimgate Street Navan Co. Meath **Tel: 046 71755**
Fax: 046 28347 Email: theloft@tgavigan.con

Older sister to The Ground Floor in Kells (and the much newer Side Door in Cavan), this thriving two-
storey restaurant has much in common with it, notably strong modern decor (including some
interesting original paintings by the Northern Ireland artist Terry Bradley), exceptionally pleasant,
helpful staff and a lively global menu at reasonable prices that lays the emphasis on accessibility: this
is a place for all ages and every (or no particular) occasion. The menu is similar to The Ground Floor
(see entry), also with daily blackboard specials - typically a main course of poached supreme of Boyne
salmon with a light yogurt & prawn sauce and desserts like bread & butter pudding, served fashionably
stacked, surrounded by strawberry coulis. Children welcome.*A sister restaurant, The Side Door, has
opened in Cavan town. **Seats 70.** Air conditioning, no smoking area. D daily: Mon-Thu 5.30-10.30, Fri
& Sat 6-11.30, Sun 5-10. Early D about €16 (Mon-Fri 5.30-7.30 only), otherwise à la carte. House wine
€16.50. 10% sc added to tables of 4+. Closed 25 Dec, 1 Jan. MasterCard, Visa, Laser. **Directions:** Centre
of Navan, corner of Main Street and Railway Street.

Navan — Ryan's Bar

Pub   22 Trimgate Street Navan Co. Meath **Tel: 046 21154** Fax: 046 78333

This very pleasantly refurbished pub makes a good meeting place for a drink or lunch, when
contemporary light meals are offered - soups, hot panini bread (stuffed with smoked salmon, cream
cheese & tomato perhaps, or chicken with a satay sauce), wraps (including a vegetarian one filled
with grated cheese, apple, carrot and a chive mayonnaise) and toasties (honey baked ham, pehaps,
with a salad garnish). Apple pie and cream may be predictable but it's enjoyable nonetheless - and
there's always a dessert among the daily specials. It's good value, the airy bar makes for a comfortable
atmosphere and staff are friendly and efficient. Disc parking. Open from 11.30 am; L Mon-Fri. 12.30-
2.30. Closed 25 Dec & Good Fri. MasterCard, Visa, Laser. **Directions:** Main Street Navan. ◇

Navan — Shahi Tandoori

Restaurant 19 Watergate Street Navan Co. Meath **Tel: 046 28762**

Mahammad Kahlid's attractive, well-maintained and conveniently restaurant is situated beside a carpark in the main street. Once inside, the traditional Indian decor is welcoming - and hospitable staff promptly offer the menu and wine list. An extensive menu includes a couple of set dinners and an à la carte that offers many dishes not usually encountered in Irish/Indian restaurant - and also some simple western dishes - steak and chips, roast chicken - providing an alternative if someone in a group wants the choice. It is clear that they know and love Indian food: after a complimentary starter of poppadoms and various dips, appetising main dishes are served Indian style, with silver dishes on table heaters, with dips and excellent breads to accompany. This well-run establishment offers good food and service at very fair prices). An otherwise fairly standard wine list includes several especially suited to spicy food. Open from 5.30pm daily. MasterCard, Visa. **Directions:** Main Street, Navan town centre. ◇

Navan — The Willows Restaurant

Restaurant Old Bridge Inn Navan Co. Meath **Tel: 046 22682**

A warm welcome, good cooking and a sprinkling of less usual dishes are all part of the appeal of this attractive Chinese restaurant on the edge of Navan town. A long menu offers a mixture of Cantonese and Szechuan dishes, with a few western ones as well. A starter platter of house specials immediately indicates a confident cook at work and service details, such as the hot towels provided with finger foods and a big pottery bowl with a lid to keep the rice warm, are authentic and pleasing. The standard set meals are available but the more unusual dishes may be a better bet. Carpark (entrance via a side road). D daily, Sun all day (12.30-9.30 pm). Set menus & à la carte. MasterCard, Visa. **Directions:** On Dublin-Navan road, on left after the bridge as you approach the town. ◇

Oldcastle — The Fincourt

Pub/Guesthouse Oliver Plunkett Street Oldcastle Co. Meath
Tel: 049 854 1153 Fax: 049 854 2242

Garry and Jackie O'Neill are running a fine inn in this small country town near the Loughcrew Hill passage graves and historic gardens. The pub has plenty of character and an open fire, bar food is served all day (9am-8pm) Monday-Saturday and 12-9 on Sundays; at certain times, including Sunday lunch, meals are available in the little restaurant, which also has an open fire in winter and can be reached through the bar or its own street entrance. (Phone for details.) Accommodation is to a high standard - the rooms are more like hotel bedrooms than B&B, with phone, multi-channel TV, hair dryer and tea/coffee facilities. Fax, photocopy and email also available on request. Self catering accommodation also offered. **Rooms 5** (all en-suite). B&B €35, ss €10. Closed 25 Dec. Amex, MasterCard, Visa, Laser. **Directions:** Dublin - Navan - Kells - Oldcastle: in the centre, near the Diamond.

Slane — Boyles Licensed Tea Rooms

Pub/Café Main St. Slane Co. Meath
Tel: 041 982 4195 Email: info@meathtourism

Boyle's has been run for over a decade by Josephine Lenehan (née Boyle), the third generation of the family to do so. The tea rooms lie behind a superb traditional black shopfront with gold lettering, with an interior that has barely changed since the 1940s. Visitors from all over the world come here, often after visiting nearby Newgrange – hence the unlikely facility of menus in 12 languages! Traditional afternoon tea (Devon style, with scones, jam and cream) is perhaps the main event, although soup and sandwiches are available for those with more savoury tastes. But the food – which includes home-made oups, scones, desserts, cakes, pancakes and preserves – is not really the point here, as people come for the character. Theoretically, at least, there's food service all day 11-11 (Sun from 12.30), but this is a place where they decide for themselves when to close the door - if you're going specially, a phone call might be wise. Closed Tuesdays, 25 Dec & Good Fri. Diners, MasterCard, Visa. **Directions:** From Dublin direction, turn left at square in Slane village; 2nd business house.

Slane   Conyngham Arms Hotel

féile bia Hotel   Slane Co. Meath **Tel: 041 988 4444** Fax: 041 982 420.
                                          Email: enquiry@conynghamarms.com Web: www.conynghamarms.cor

This attractive stone hotel creates a good impression with its lovely signage and twin bay trees a
the main entrance. Chintzy fabrics and wood panelling make for a cosy country feeling in th
restaurant and bar areas; the self-service counter in the bar serves traditional home-made food a
day (12 noon - 8 pm) – roast chicken with stuffing, bacon and cabbage, apple tart – and offer
country fare at fair prices. All the bedrooms have recently been refurbished and are very comfortabl
furnished in appropriate traditional style; some have four poster beds, all have direct line phone
and tea/coffee-making facilities and iron & ironing boards are available on request. The hotel i
understandably popular for weddings, but it is also well placed as a base to visit the great histori
sites of Newgrange, Knowth and Dowth, the site of the Battle of the Boyne, and the Hill of Tara. Gol
nearby. Conference/banqueting (350/22) **Rooms 15** (1 suite, all en-suite). B&B about €50 pps
Children welcome (cots available without charge). Closed 23-27 Dec. Diners, MasterCard, Visa, Laser
Directions: Centre of Slane in Navan direction.

Tara Area   O'Connell's

Pub   Skryne Nr Tara Co. Meath **Tel: 046 25122**

Three generations of O'Connells have been caretakers of this wonderfully unspoilt country pub. The
present owner, Mary O'Connell, has been delighting customers old and new for over ten years now
It's all beautifully simple – two little bars with no fancy bits, lots of items of local interest, and a
welcoming fire in the grate. What more could anyone want? As for directions: – just head for the
tower beside the pub, which is visible for miles around. Closed 25 Dec & Good Fri. **No Credit Cards**

Trim   Franzini O'Briens

  Restaurant   French's Lane Trim Co. Meath
                                                           Tel: 046 31002 Fax: 046 31118

Modern, spacious and with an exceptional location looking out onto Trim Castle, this smart
restaurant is set to become the benchmark for a wide area. Well-trained staff greet and seat arriving
guest with commendable professionalism, immediately presenting menus, taking drink orders and
ensuring that guests settle in comfortably from the start and setting a tone of relaxed efficiency
that prevails throughout. Space is attractively broken up around a central carpeted square with
leather sofas to provide a variety of seating areas (the more intimate ones, with banquette seating,
towards the back) and simple, uncluttered table settings are modern and elegantly functional - tall
water carafes, finger bowls for nachos and paper napkins (replaced with each course). Light-hearted
menus offer an excellent range of choices in the international style and, together with an informal,
buzzy atmosphere, indicate that this is a place for a good night out. And attractively served food
does not disappoint - typically, a tomato-based seafood chowder is served with delicious dark treacle
bread, and skilfully prepared fajitas come with a generous amount of tasty nachos and well-made
accompaniments - service is excellent (nobody appears to be kept waiting, even at very busy times).
Interesting wine list (supplied by Jim Nicholson), but no wine offered by the glass (quarter bottles
only). [Benninis daytime restaurant next door is under the same ownership but run separately.]
Seats 100. No smoking area. Air conditioning. D Mon-Sat, 6.30-10 (Sun 5-9). Closed 25-26 Dec,
Good Fri, also Mon of-season (Nov-Apr). Amex, Diners, MasterCard, Visa, Laser, Switch. **Directions:**
Beside Trim Castle, adjacent to car park.

COUNTY MONAGHAN

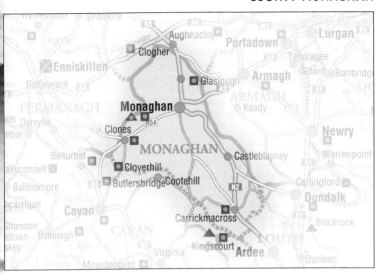

Of all Ireland's counties, it is Monaghan which is most centrally placed in the drumlin belt, that strip of rounded glacial hills which runs right across the country from Strangford Lough in County Down to Clew Bay in Mayo. Monaghan, in fact, is all hills. But as very few of them are over 300 metres above sea level, the county takes its name from Muineachain - "Little Hills". Inevitably, the actively farmed undulating country of the little hills encloses many lakes, and Monaghan in its quiet way is a coarse angler's paradise.

Much of the old Ulster Canal is in Monaghan, while the rest is in Armagh and Tyrone. Once upon a time, it connected Lough Erne to Lough Neagh. It has been derelict for a very long time, but with the success of the restored Shannon-Erne Waterway along the line of the old Ballinamore-Ballyconnell Canal bringing new life to Leitrim, Cavan and Fermanagh, the even more ambitious vision of restoring the Ulster Canal is being given serious consideration.

Vision of a different sort is the theme at Annaghmakerrig House near the Quaker-named village of Newbliss in west Monaghan. The former home of theatrical producer Tyrone Guthrie, it is now a busy centre for writers and artists who can stay there to complete 'work in progress'. In the east of the county at Castleblayney, there's a particularly attractive lake district with forest park and adventure centre around Lough Mucko. Southwards of Castleblayney, we come to the bustling town of Carrickmacross, still famous for its lace, and a Tidy Towns trophy winner.

In northeast Monaghan at Clontibret, there's gold in them thar little hills. Whether or not it's in sufficient quantities to merit mining is a continuing matter of commercial debate, but the fact that it's there at all is another of Monaghan's more intriguing secrets. Another is the county's uncrowded character. The Census completed in 2002 revealed that Monaghan's population has risen by only 2.8% since 1996, the smallest increase of any county, bringing Monaghan's total population to a modest 52,772. In an overcrowded world, this is surely good news.

Local Attractions and Information

Carrickmacross Carrickmacross Lace Gallery	042 9662506
Carrickmacross (Kingscourt Rd) Dun a Ri Forest Park	042 9667320
Castleblayney Lough Muckno Leisure Park	042 9746356
Clones Clones Lace Exhibits	047 51051
Glaslough Castle Leslie Gardens	047 88109
Inniskeen Patrick Kavanagh Centre	042 9378560
Monaghan town Tourism Information	047 81122
Monaghan town Monaghan County Museum	047 82928
Monaghan town (Newbliss Rd.) Rossmore Forest Park	047 81968
Newbliss Annaghmakerrig (Tyrone Guthrie Centre)	047 54003

Carrickmacross — Nuremore Hotel & Country Club

féile bia Hotel/Restaurant   Carrickmacross Co. Monaghan **Tel: 042 966 1438** Fax: 042 966 1853
Email: nuremore@eircom.net Web: www.nuremore-hotel.ie

Set in a parkland estate just south of Carrickmacross with its own 18-hole golf course, this fine well-managed country hotel has its own 18-hole golf course and serves the sporting, leisure and business requirements of a wide area very well. As you go over the little bridge ("Beware - ducks crossing") and the immaculately maintained hotel and golf club open up before you, worldly cares seem to recede - this is a place you can get fond of. The hotel gives a very good impression on arrival and this sense of care and maintenance is continued throughout all the spacious, comfortably arranged areas and generous, attractively furnished bedrooms which are regularly refurbished. It would make an excellent base to explore this little known area - and there is plenty to do on site. The superb country club has a full leisure centre with swimming pool and a good range of related facilities (including a recently added gymnasium and beauty treatment rooms) and there's a conference centre with state-of-the-art audio-visual equipment. Conference/banqueting (500/350); business centre, secretarial services on request. Leisure centre, swimming pool, beauty salon; golf (18), fishing, walking, tennis, garden; snooker. Children welcome (cots available, €13; playroom). No pets. **Rooms 72** (7 junior suites, 11 executive, 1 for disabled, 18 no smoking). B&B €120 pps, ss €50. Amex, Diners, MasterCard, Visa, Laser. **Directions:** Just south of Carrickmacross, 55 miles from Dublin on N2.

The Restaurant at Nuremore: The restaurant is well-appointed in a fairly formal country house style, with generous white-clothed tables and a couple of steps dividing the window area and inner tables, allowing everybody to enjoy the view over golf course and woodland. Good food has always been a high priority at the Nuremore, which is well established as the leading restaurant in the area, and this aspect of the hotel has been further emphasised since Raymond McArdle, previously head chef at Deane's Brasserie in Belfast, took over as head chef in 2000. His ambitious plans for the restaurant have had the full backing of proprietress Julie Gilhooly and their spacious, state-of-the art kitchen is now the envy of chefs throughout the country. Raymond sources ingredients meticulously, using local produce as much as possible in top rank daily set lunch and dinner menus, a vegetarian menu and an evening à la carte. A recent visit by the Guide confirmed the excellence of the cooking, seen in perfectly executed and well-flavoured starters like rillette of duck & Parma ham with carrot & orange purée & port reduction and an exquisitely luxurious roast tranche of foie-gras with spiced brioche and caramelised peaches (which was also outstanding value, offered on the dinner menu with no supplement). From a choice of five main courses on the dinner menu, dishes like steamed turbot with monkfish ravioli, baby spinach & basil froth and roast Lincolnshire duck with potato confit, roast salsify & sauce à l'orange are similarly impressive - and, given Raymond McArdle's previous experience with Michael Deane, it is no surprise to find dishes like a deliciously light and refreshing Granny Smith apple bavarois with apple crisp and apple jus on a tempting dessert menu. Wonderful petits fours are served with cappuccino or espresso which - like the side orders of vegetables - are charged on top of the dinner menu price. This is exceptional cooking and it needs to be backed up by a similar standard throughout the restaurant team. The dining room, while well-appointed in a traditional style, is at odds with the cutting edge cuisine as there is no dress or behaviour code, resulting in an uncomfortable mixture of guests dressed for an evening out and family groups in from the leisure centre in track suits and a casual attitude which undermines the hard work in the kitchen (the official policy is that the restaurant is not suitable for children after 7.30, but this does not seem to be enforced). Floor staff, while smartly uniformed and pleasant, seem not to have been trained to the high level the kitchen deserves; a serious error on the Guide's visit, for example, was to offer only the dinner menu with no mention of the à la carte, or vegetarian menus (although the vegetarian menu is mentioned in passing, on the second page of the dinner menu where it is easy to overlook). This is a good country hotel restaurant with exceptional talent in the kitchen, but decisions are needed regarding its future policy if its full potential is to met. **Seats 100** (private room, 50). No smoking area; air conditioning. L daily, 12.30-2.30; D daily 6.30-9.30 (Sun to 9). Set L €23 (Set Sun L €25); Set D €40, also à la carte. House wine €19; sc discretionary. Open all year. Examples from an early autumn lunch menu offering a choice of four on each course indicate the style: to start, terrine of duck, braised ham & foie gras pressé, with pickled girolles, quail eggs and balsamic jus, followed by fillet of Irish Angus beef (a speciality), with parsnip gratin, ceps and truffle butter, then classic desserts like pear & almont tart with fresh cream. Evening menus are in a similar style, but are more luxurious and offer a wider choice, including fresh foie gras and lobster.

Clones — Hilton Park

Country House

Clones Co. Monaghan **Tel: 047 56007** Fax: 047 56033
Email: jm@hiltonpark.ie Web: www.hiltonpark.ie

Once described as a "capsule of social history" because of their collection of family portraits and memorabilia going back 250 years or more, Johnny and Lucy Madden's wonderful 18th century mansion is set in beautiful countryside, amidst 200 acres of woodland and farmland (home to Johnny's sheep). With lakes, Pleasure Grounds and a Lovers' Walk to set the right tone, the house is magnificent in every sense, and the experience of visiting it a rare treat. Johnny and Lucy are natural hosts and, as the house and its contents go back for so many generations, there is a strong feeling of being a privileged family guest as you wander through grandly-proportioned, beautifully furnished rooms. Four-posters and all the unselfconscious comforts that make for a very special country house stay are part of the charm, but as visitors from all over the world have found, it's the warmth of Johnny and Lucy's welcome that lends that extra magic. The gardens are also of particular interest - formal gardens have recently been restored to their former glory and Lucy, an enthusiastic organic gardener and excellent cook, supplies freshly harvested produce for meals in the house and other ingredients are carefully sourced from trusted suppliers of organic and free-range products. Residents' dinners are served in a beautiful dining overlooking the gardens and lake - and memorable breakfasts are taken downstairs in the Green Room next morning. This is exceptional hospitality, with an Irish flavour – and, in recognition, Hilton Park was presented with the Guide's International Hospitality Award in 1999. The Maddens offer special weekend breaks and discounts for 2-night stays; they also have a picturesque gate lodge available for self-catering (sleeps 4). Not suitable for children under 8 (except babies, free in parents' room, cot available), playroom for older children. Pets allowed in some areas. Small conferences. Gardens, fishing (own lake), walking, cycling. **Rooms 6** (all en-suite & no smoking). B&B €110 pps, ss €30. Residents D €45 at 8 pm; (Wed-Sat only; please give 24 hours notice). House wine €18 &21. No SC. Closed Oct-Mar, except groups. MasterCard, Visa. **Directions:** 3 miles south of Clones on Scotshouse Road.

Glaslough — Castle Leslie

féile bia Country House/Restaurant

Glaslough Co. Monaghan **Tel: 047 88109** Fax: 047 88256
Email: ultan@castleleslie.ie Web: www.castleleslie.com

During the three centuries that this extraordinary place has been in the Leslie family it has changed remarkably little - and its fascinating history intrigues guests as much as the eccentricity of Castle Leslie as they find it today. Once inside the massive front door (guarded by family dogs who snooze in beds flanking the stone steps) there is no reception desk, just a welcoming oak-panelled hall (and afternoon tea in the drawing room), and there are no phones, television sets or clocks in the rooms, although concessions to the 20th century have been made in the form of generous heating and plentiful hot water. The fourteen bedrooms are all different, furnished and decorated around a particular era, with en-suite bathrooms a feature in their own right with huge baths, wacky showers and outrageous toilets, all done in a tongue-in-cheek style, reflecting the family's eccentric history and the wonders of Victorian plumbing. In a charming reverse of circumstances, the family lives in the servants' wing, so guests can enjoy the magnificence of the castle to the full - it has all the original furniture and family portraits. The estate has wonderful walks, and pike fishing, boating and picnic lunches on the estate are available by arrangement. Due to the nature of the castle (and the fact that the Leslies see it as a wonderful refuge from the outside world for adults) this is not a suitable place to bring children. Despite the extreme eccentricity suggested by details asuch as the answering machine ("please leave your message after the (scream)", which makes callers think they are just nuts, this is actually a professionally run business and a little more 'hotel-like' than the publicity suggests. Conferences/banqueting (100/90) **Rooms 14** (3 suites, 13 en-suite, 5 shower only, 1 with private bathroom, all no smoking). B&B €88, ss €25. MasterCard, Visa. **Directions:** 10 mins from Monaghan Town.

Restaurant: Food is an important element of a visit to Castle Leslie and non-residents are welcome to come for dinner, by reservation. It is all done in fine old style with pre-dinner drinks in the drawing room (or the Fountain Garden in summer) and dinner, which is served in rooms including the original dining room, unchanged for over a century, by waitresses wearing Victorian uniforms.

However, despite the obvious oddities of faded grandeur - tables with a slight list, chairs and sofas which have long since lost their stuffing - it is essentially a restaurant dining experience rather than a country house dinner. Many entertaining wine and food events are held during the year - contact the Castle for details - and the Castle Leslie range of preserves and speciality foods is available from the castle and Brown Thomas, in Dublin. **Seats 75**. No smoking area. D daily 7-9.30; Set D €43 (Gourmet Menu with wine €76). House wine about €20. Directions: Monaghan town-Armagh road-Glaslough. ◇

Monaghan | Andy's Bar and Restaurant

 Restaurant/Pub

12 Market Street Monaghan Co. Monaghan
Tel: 047 82277 Fax: 047 84195

Right in the centre of Monaghan, opposite the old market house, the Redmond family's bar is furnished and decorated in traditional Victorian style, with a lot of fine mahogany, stained glass and mirrors. It has a strong local following, and it is easy to see why: everything is gleaming clean and arranged well for comfort, with high-backed bar seats and plenty of alcoves set up with tables for the comfortable consumption of their good bar food. Substantial bar meals include a range of mid-day specials on a blackboard as well as a concise written menu. The evening restaurant upstairs, which has recently been refurbished but retains its pleasingly old-fashioned ambience, offers a much more extensive range of popular dishes, including a good choice of prime fish and steaks various ways - specialities include garlic Monaghan mushrooms and crispy half roast duckling (with orange & brandy sauce); while not adventurous, this is good cooking based on quality ingredients and the results are extremely tasty, satisfying - and good value. Traditional desserts like pavlova, lemon cheesecake, fresh fruit salad and home-made ices are served from a trolley, and there might be something comforting like a hot treacle sponge pudding in cold weather. Members of the Redmond family are everywhere, keeping an eye on things, and service is charming and efficient. Bar meals daily, 12-3. Restaurant D Tue-Sat, 6-10.15 (Sun to 9.30). Set D €28; house wine €14.60. Closed Sun L, Mon D, 25 Dec, Good Fri, bank hols & 1-14 July. Amex, MasterCard, Visa, Laser. **Directions:** Town centre, opposite the Market House.

Monaghan | Hillgrove Hotel

Hotel

Old Armagh Rd Monaghan Co. Monaghan **Tel: 047 81288** Fax: 047 84951
Email: hillgrove@quinnhotels.com Web: quinnhotels.com

Overlooking the town from a fine hillside location, the appropriately named Hillgrove is the leading hotel in the area. Like its sister properties in the Quinn Group, an impressive foyer sets the tone and it is generally well-run although, judging by a recent visit, bedrooms and bathrooms could benefit from an update. Good conference and banqueting facilities (1000/600). Garden. Children welcome (free in parents' room to 3, cots available). No pets. **Rooms 44** (2 suites, 2 junior suites, 2 for disabled). B&B about €65 pps, ss about €20. Closed 24-25 Dec. Amex, Diners, MasterCard, Visa. **Directions:** Take N2 from Dublin to Monaghan town. ◇

COUNTY OFFALY

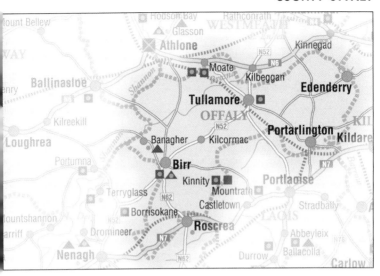

At the heart of the old Ely O'Carroll territory, Offaly is Ireland's most sky-minded county. At Birr Castle, there's the Parsons family's famous restored 1845-vintage 1.83 m astronomical telescope, through which the 3rd Earl of Rosse observed his discovery of the spiral nebulae. And in Tullamore, there's a thriving amateur Astronomical Society whose members point out that the wide clear skies of Offaly have encouraged the regular observation of heavenly bodies since at least 1057 AD, when astronomy was the province of moon-minded monks.

Back in Birr meanwhile, the restored gardens of Birr Castle are an added attraction, but still the sky calls, and the annual Irish Hot Air Balloon Meeting has been run with increasing success since 1970. It attracts serious international balloonists who welcome the opportunity for participation in a relaxed fun event where everyone wins a prize, and is equally suitable for beginners, as Offaly's bogs provide a soft landing - "there's a bit of give in a bog".

Offaly is also historic hunting country. It is home to the Ormonde, which may not be Ireland's largest or richest hunt, "but it's the oldest and undoubtedly the best." Once upon a time, they invited the neighbouring County Galway Hunt for a shared meet, and afterwards the carousing in Dooley's Hotel in Birr reached such a hectic pitch that the hotel was joyously torched by the visitors. Dooley's was rebuilt to fulfill its central role in Birr, and the hunt from across the Shannon has been known as the Galway Blazers ever since.

The Grand Canal finally reaches the great river at Shannon Harbour in Offaly, after crossing Ireland from Dublin, and on the river itself, waterborne travellers find that Offaly affords the opportunity of visiting Clonmacnoise, where the remains of an ancient monastic university city give pause for thought. In the south of the county, the Slieve Bloom Mountains rise attractively above Offaly's farmland and bogs. These are modest heights, as they attain just 526 m on the peak of Arderin. However, it is their understated charms which particularly appeal, and in the Slieve Blooms we find Ireland's first organised system of gites, the French concept whereby unused farmhouses have been restored to a comfortable standard for self-catering visitor accommodation.

Nestling in a valley of the Slieve Blooms is the unspoilt village of Kinnitty, where Offaly's quality of life is most in evidence. And in the far east of the county, where Offaly marches with Kildare, we find Clonbulloge, top title holder in Offaly in the current Tidy Towns awards, a pretty place on the banks of the stream known as the Figile River.

Local Attractions and Information

Banagher Cloghan Castle (15C Tower House)	0509 51650
Birr Castle Demesne & Historic Science Centre	0509 20336 / 22154
Birr Tourism Information	0509 20110
Clonmacnoise Visitor & Interpretive Centre	0905 74195
Edenderry Canal Festival (June)	0405 32071
Shannonbridge Clonmacnoise & West Offaly Railway	0905 74114
Slieve Bloom Rural Development Society	0509 37299
Tullamore Offaly Historical Society	0506 21421
Tullamore Offaly Tourist Council	0506 52566
Tullamore Tullamore Dew Whiskey Heritage Centre	0506 25015
Tullamore Tourism Information	0506 52617

Banagher   J.J.Hough

Pub — Main Street Banagher Co. Offaly **Tel: 0509 51893**

Hidden behind a thriving vine, which threatens to take over in summer, this charming 250-year old pub is soothingly dark inside – making a fine contrast to the cheerful eccentricity of the current owner, Michael Hough. Very much a local, it's also popular with people from the river cruisers, who come up from the harbour for the pints and the craic. There's traditional Irish music every night from St Patrick's Day to the end of October, then Friday, Saturday & Sunday in winter. Children and pets welcome. Closed 25 Dec & Good Fri. **Directions:** Lower Main Street.

Banagher   The Shannon Hotel

Hotel — West End Banagher Co. Offaly **Tel: 0509 51306** Fax: 0509 51941

A charming place dating back the to the 17th century, this hotel was once the home of Anthony Trollope and is now in the energetic ownership of Joseph and Patricia Moran who provide welcoming fires, a real sense of hospitality and live music (traditional and contemporary) at weekends. The bar is a very pleasant place to be at any time of day, whether for a quiet cup of coffee in the morning or something more substantial, like traditional lamb stew, later on. Simple en-suite bedrooms have all been recently refurbished with phone, multi-channel TV, hairdryers & tea/coffee facilities. Bar food available 8am-10pm daily. Own parking. **Rooms 12** (all en-suite) B&B about €40, ss about €7. Closed 25 Dec. MasterCard, Visa, Laser. **Directions:** At the bottom of the main street, near the harbour. ◇

Banagher   The Vine House

Pub/Restaurant — Banagher Co. Offaly **Tel: 0509 51463** Fax: 0509 51463

This atmospheric bar and restaurant is the perfect haven for boating people - head chef Adam Ashton has been sending guests happy into the night for 10 years now. Music nightly May-August (bands at weekends, weekdays ballads & traditional); Saturday nights only off-season. Food served: 12 noon - 3.30 pm and 7-9.30 pm daily from Easter-late September/early October; off-season: evenings only, closed Mondays. MasterCard, Visa. **Directions:** At the bottom of the village, very close to the harbour. ◇

Birr   Dooly's Hotel

Hotel — Emmet Square Birr Co. Offaly **Tel: 0509 20032** Fax: 0509 21332
Email: doolyhotel@esatclear.ie Web: www.dooleyshotel.com

Birr is a lovely old town steeped in history and it makes a good holiday centre, with plenty to do locally – Birr Castle and its magnificnetly restored gardens are very near, also golfing, fishing, riding and river excursions. This attractive, old-fashioned hotel is one of Ireland's oldest coaching inns, dating back to 1747 and is right on Emmet Square, the centre of Georgian Birr. Public rooms, including two characterful bars, are traditional in furnishing style but have all been refurbished recently. Bedrooms have been upgraded and now include a junior suite and an executive room; all are en-suite with full bathrooms (bath and shower). It's popular for weddings but when there's a function on, the hotel tries to allocate quiet rooms if possible. Conference/banqueting 300/250. Children welcome (under 5s free in parents' room, cots available without charge). **Rooms 18.** B&B €47.50pps, no ss. Weekend breaks available. Coffee shop/bistro open 8.30am-9.30pm daily; bar meals available; brasserie (light food) 11am-7pm. 12.30-9.15 pm daily. Closed 25-26 Dec. Amex, Diners, MasterCard, Visa, Laser. **Directions:** Town centre, on main square.

Birr — Spinners Town House & Bistro

Restaurant/Guesthouse
Castle Street Birr Co. Offaly **Tel: 0509 21673** Fax: 0509 21672
Email: spinners@indigo.ie Web: www.spinners-townhouse.com

This unusual establishment in the centre of Birr runs through five Georgian townhouses and, after a change of ownership in 2000, was restored and refurbished throughout in a simple contemporary style. Four spacious new rooms (similar in style but "with a hint of the baronial gothic") were added, and then the bistro refurbished making the central courtyard garden and its surrounding arches a major feature. Stylish, thoughtfully designed bedrooms include family rooms, doubles and twins, all with en-suite or private bathrooms. In addition to their own sitting room and a breakfast room, where a traditional hot Irish breakfast based on organic bacon and sausages is served, guests have the use of the enclosed courtyard garden. Children welcome (cots available). No pets. **Rooms 13** (10 en-suite, 3 with private bathrooms, all shower only and no smoking). B&B €32.50pps, ss €12.50. Closed 5-31 Jan.
Spinners Bistro: Everything is based on fresh ingredients, local and organic wherever possible, with fish and seafood the main speciality, accounting for about four starters (try their house special of wild salmon, potato & herb cakes, served with chive mayonnaise) and a similar number of main courses. But there is plenty else to choose from too, including interesting vegetarian alternatives (a starter tomato & goat's cheese tart and main course yoghurt & lentil chicken curry are typical). Meats are organic - a 12 oz sirloin steak, perhaps, with a choice of sauces or Somerset pork, where the fillet is panfried and dressed with fresh apple & cider creame. Desserts tend to be old favourites, like warm pear and almond flan and home-made lemon meringue pie. Open to non-residents; full bar licence. **Seats 46.** D Tue-Sat, 5-10 (Sun 4-9); à la carte. House wine from €12.50 sc discretionary; licensed. Closed Mon, 5-31 Jan. Amex, Diners, MasterCard, Visa, Laser. **Directions:** Beside Birr Castle.

Birr — The Stables Restaurant & Townhouse

Restaurant/Accommodation
Oxmantown Mall Birr Co. Offaly
Tel: 0509 20263 Fax: 0509 21677
Email: cboyd@indigo.ie Web: www.thestablesrestaurant.com

The Boyd family's characterful establishment is in a lovely old Georgian house overlooking the tree-lined mall and it has a strong local following. The restaurant is in the converted stables and coach house and has lots of atmosphere, with attractive exposed bricks and stonework, arches and an open fire in the period drawing room (which is used as a bar and reception area). The cooking style is quite traditional – a blend of Cordon Bleu and traditional Irish, but with some unexpectedly adventurous options like pan-fried ostrich and more seafood than might be expected in the midlands – and hearty country portions are the norm. Children welcome. Banqueting (90). **Seats 65.** D Tue-Sat, 5.30-9.30 (also Sun 6.30 -8.30 Jun-Sep) L Sun only, 12.30-3. Set D about €33, à la carte also available; Set Sun L about €19; house wine about €16; sc discretionary. No smoking area; air conditioning. Closed all Mon, also D Sun Oct-May, Ash Wednesday, Good Fri.
Accommodation: Old world en-suite bedrooms overlooking the mall or the courtyard include two large newer rooms added in 2000. **Rooms 8.** B&B about €32pps, ss about €6.35. Amex, Diners, MasterCard, Visa, Laser, Switch. **Directions:** Town centre, opposite original gates of Birr castle. ◇

Birr — The Thatch Bar & Restaurant

 Pub/Restaurant
Crinkle Birr Co. Offaly **Tel: 0509 20682** Fax: 0509 21847
Email: thethatchcrinkill@eircom.net

This characterful little thatched pub and restaurant just outside Birr shows just how good a genuine, well-run country pub with imaginative, freshly cooked food can be. Since 1991 the energetic owner, Des Connole, has worked tirelessly to improve standards with the help of head chef Brian Maher. Five-course dinner menus change weekly and include a mixture of traditional dishes such as sirloin steaks with mushrooms in garlic and more unusual things – a lot of seafood, exotics like ostrich (which is farmed in Ireland) and kangaroo; local produce is there as well, of course, in Rudd's black pudding & mushroom gateau with apple & spring onion dressing, for example, and there's a good choice for vegetarians. Good food and warm hospitality make this one of the best eating places in the area. Children welcome. Parking. **Seats 50** (private room, 15-20). D 6.30-9.30 daily, à la carte; L Sun-12.30 & 2.30; Set Sun L €20; early evening bar menu Mon-Sat 5.30-7.30, à la carte; house wine €17; sc discretionary. Bar meals 12.30-2.30 & 5-7.30 Mon-Sat. No smoking restaurant; air conditioning. Toilets wheelchair accessible. Restaurant closed D Sun, establishment closed 25 Dec, Good Fri. Diners, MasterCard, Visa, Laser. **Directions:** 1 mile from Birr (Roscrea side).

Edenderry — Tyrrells Restaurant

 N Restaurant

Ballindoolin House & Gardens Edenderry Co. Offaly
Tel: 0405 32400 Fax: 0405 32377
Email: tyrrells@ballindoolin.com Web: www.ballindoolin.com

Fairly well signed, off the Edenderry-Kinnegad road (R401), David and Nikki Molony's unusual country restaurant is in converted outbuildings at the back of a large house of historical interest (currently undergoing renovations) and adjacent to a lovely recently restored kitchen garden (which supplies produce to the restaurant) and charming woodland walks. The restaurant has more character than first impressions suggest, with a welcoming open fire, flagstone flooring, attractive simply laid wooden tables and large windows overlooking a yard inhabited by rare breed farm stock and the occasional strutting peacock, all of which is both interesting and entertaining. A prompt warm welcome with menu and wine list delivered to your table is swiftly followed by a plate of bread - a dark, close-textured loaf with a hint of spice - and your choice from a wine list weighted heavily in favour of the New World. Well-constructed menus offer starters like a soup of the day (split pea with curry, perhaps) or seared rare beef salad with oriental beansprout salald & wasabi dressing and main courses such as char-grilled rib eye steak with caramelised shalots and black & green peppercorn sauce or fish of the day. Finish off with a classic dessert - vanilla panna cotta, perhaps, with poached rhubarb, or may be a liqueur coffee. Quality ingredients, a sure hand in the kitchen, characterful surroundings, caring service by well-trained staff and good value add up to an operation that merits its success. It certainly makes a most enjoyable outing for all age groups. **Seats 50.** No smoking restaurant, wheelchair accessible. L Wed-Sun, 12-2.30 (Sun to 3.30), D Wed-Sat, 6.30-10. House wines from €17.15. Visa, Laser. **Directions:** Follow the signs to Ballindoolin House & Gardens.

Kinnity — Ardmore House

Country House

The Walk Kinnitty Co. Offaly **Tel: 0509 37009**
Email: ardmorehouse@eircom.net Web: www.kinnity.net

Set back from the road in its own garden, Christina Byrne's stone-built Victorian house offers old-fashioned comforts: brass beds, turf fires and home-made bread and preserves for breakfast. Bedrooms are deliberately left without amenities, in order to make a visit to Ardmore a real country house experience and encourage guests to spend less time in their rooms and mix with each other - tea is available downstairs at any time. Two new rooms were added in 2001 - one with jacuzzi bath and the other a wheelchair friendly ground floor room. There's a traditional Irish night every Friday, at nearby Kinnitty Castle. Children welcome (under 3s free in parents' room); pets allowed in certain areas. **Rooms 5** (4 en-suite, 3 shower only, 1 with private bathroom, all no smoking). B&B €32pps, ss €11. Closed 25 Dec. **No Credit Cards. Directions:** In village of Kinnity, 9 miles from Birr.

Kinnity — The Glendine Bistro

Restaurant/B&B

Kinnitty Co. Offaly
Tel: 0509 37973 Fax: 0509 37975

Situated in a charming village at the foot of the Slieve Bloom mountains, the clean-lined simplicity of Percy and Phil Clendennan's attractive contemporary restaurant provides a welcome contrast to other, more traditional, dining options nearby, giving visitors to this unspoilt area a choice of styles. Head chef Jamie Owens offers wide-ranging menus that suit the surroundings: this is steak country and prime Hereford beef features in steaks various ways, but there are also many more international dishes like barbecued tiger prawns & king scallops with chargrilled peppers or Irish ostrich on a bed of pesto courgettes, with balsamic dressing - and sound cooking is backed up by friendly service. Vegetarian options, typically stir frys and fresh pasta dishes, are always available. **Seats 60** (private room 30). No smoking area; air conditioning. D Wed- Sun, 6.30-9.30. L Sun only, 12.30-4. Set Dine L €18; Set D from €26.50, also à la carte. House wine €15.24. Closed all Mon &Tue, all Jan & Feb. **Accommodation:** Five bright, comfortably furnished en-suite bedrooms are offered, all with direct dial phones, TV and tea/coffee-making facilities. Children under 6 free in parents' room; cot available. **Rooms 5** (all shower-only & no smoking). Accommodation open all year. **Rooms 5** (all en-suite, shower only and no smoking). B&B €32, SS €87. MasterCard, Visa, Laser. **Directions:** 7 miles from Birr, in centre of Kinnitty Village.

Kinnity | Kinnitty Castle

Hotel

Kinnitty Co. Offaly **Tel: 0509 37318** Fax: 0509 37284
Email: kinnittycastle@eircom.net Web: www.kinnittycastle.com

Furnished in keeping with its dramatic history and theatrical character, this luxurious Gothic Revival castle in the foothills of the Slieve Bloom Mountains is at the centre of a very large estate (accessible for horse-riding and walking) with 650 acres of parkland and formal gardens. Public areas – a library bar, Georgian style dining room, Louis XV drawing room and an atmospheric Dungeon Bar where there is traditional music on Friday nights all year – are mainly furnished in the style expected of a castle hotel. The accommodation, however, is slightly different: bedrooms are all interesting and comfortable but vary considerably according to their position in the castle: the best are big and romantic, with stunning views over the estate (and sumptuous, dramatically styled bathrooms). There are medieval-style banqueting/conference facilities for up to 180/200 in a courtyard at the back of the castle, which are new but atmospheric (and understandably popular for weddings), aalso a small leisure centre (no swimming pool as yet). Tennis, fishing, equestrian, garden. Children welcome (Under 12s free in parents' room; cots available without charge). No pets. **Rooms 37** (10 suites, 11 junior suites, 16 executive rooms). No lift (long corridors and a lot of stairs). B&B €100pps, ss €45 (room only rate also available, €230); s.c.12.5%. Open all year. Amex, Diners, MasterCard, Visa, Laser, Switch. **Directions:** On the R422- EMO to Birr Road,off main N7 Limerick Road.

Shannonbridge | The Village Tavern

Pub

Main Street Shannonbridge Co. Offaly **Tel: 0905 74112**

At J.J. Killeen's wonderful pub weary travellers can be restored, particularly by the house special of hot rum and chocolate, perfect after a damp day on the river. Meanwhile you can also top up on groceries, fishing bait and gas. Music nightly May-September; weekends only off-season. **Directions:** On the main street of Shannonbridge, between Ballinasloe and Cloghan. ◇

Tullamore | Annaharvey Farm

Farmhouse/B&B

Tullamore Co. Offaly **Tel: 0506 43544** Fax: 0506 43766
Email: info@annaharveyfarm.ie Web: www.annaharveyfarm.ie

Henry and Lynda Deverell's restored grain barn, with pitch pine floors and beams, open fires and comfortable accommodation, provides a good base for a holiday offering all the pleasures of the outdoor life. Equestrian activities are the main attraction (including tuition in indoor and outdoor arenas), but walking, cycling and golfing also lay their claims - and, for the rest days, major sights including Clonmacnoise and Birr Castle are nearby. Small conference/banqueting (40/50). Equestrian, walking, garden, children's playroom. D 7-9.30; set residents' dinner about €25; house wine about €15; toilets wheelchair accessible. Children welcome (under 4s free in parents' room; cots available without charge). Pets allowed in some areas. **Rooms 7** (all en-suite & no-smoking). B&B €32pps, ss €10. Residents' D €28, light lunch €6.50. Closed Dec & Jan. MasterCard, Visa, Laser. **Directions:** R420 Tullamore - Portarlington.

Tullamore | Tullamore Court Hotel Conference & Leisure Centre

féile bia Hotel

Tullamore Co. Offaly **Tel: 0506 46666** Fax: 0506 46677
Email: info@tullamorecourt.hotel.ie Web: www.tullamorecourthotel.ie

An attractive building, set back from the road a little and softened by trees, this large modern hotel has an extensive foyer and public areas are bright and cheerful. It serves the local community well, with fine conference and banqueting facilities (750/550) and an excellent leisure centre and it's an ideal base for business or pleasure. Bedrooms are very pleasantly decorated in an easy modern style, using warm colours and unfussy fabrics and the staff are exceptionally friendly and helpful. There are interesting things to do in the area - Clonmacnoise and Birr Castle are both quite near, golf and horseriding are available nearby and walkers will love the unspoilt Slieve Bloom Mountains. The hotel has been building up a reputation for good food and could make a refreshing place to break a journey, as there's an interesting bar menu available all day and the restaurant is open for both lunch and dinner. Leisure centre, swimming pool, crechè, garden. Children welcome (Under 4s free in parents' room; cots available). Pets permitted by arrangement. **Rooms 72** (3 junior suites, 9 executive rooms, 10 no smoking, 4 for disabled). Lift. B&B €145 pps, ss €20. Closed 3pm Christmas Eve until 3pm 26 Dec. Amex, Diners, MasterCard, Visa, Laser. **Directions:** South end of town.

COUNTY ROSCOMMON

It could be said that in times past, Roscommon was a county much put upon by the counties about it. Or, put another way, to the casual visitor it seemed that just as Roscommon was on the verge of becoming significant, it became somewhere else. In one notable example - the hotel complex at Hodson's Bay on the western shores of Lough Ree - the location is actually in Roscommon, yet the exigencies of the postal service have given it to Athlone and thereby Westmeath.

But Roscommon is a giving sort of county, for it gave Ireland her first President, Gaelic scholar Douglas Hyde (1860-1949), it was also the birthplace of Oscar Wilde's father, and as well the inimitable songwriter Percy French was a Roscommon man. Like everywhere else in the western half of Ireland, Roscommon suffered grieviously from the Great Famine of the late 1840s, and at Strokestown, the handsome market town serving the eastern part of the county, Strokestown Park House has been sympathetically restored to include a Famine Museum. A visit to it will certainly add a thoughtful element to your meal in the restaurant.

Roscommon town itself has a population of barely 1,500, but the presence of extensive castle ruins and a former gaol tell of a more important past. The gaol was once noted for having a female hangman, today it has shops and a restaurant. Northwestward at Castlerea - headquarters for the County Council - we find Clonalis House, ancestral home of the O'Conor Don, and final resting place of O'Carolan's Harp.

In the north of the county, the town of Boyle near lovely Lough Key with its outstanding Forest Park is a substantial centre, with a population nearing the 2,000 mark. Boyle is thriving, and symbolic of this is the restored King House, a masterpiece from 1730. Reckoned to have been the most important provincial town house in Ireland, it is today filled with exhibits which eloquently evoke the past. Nearby, the impressive riverbank remains of Boyle Abbey, the largest Cistercian foundation in Ireland, date from 1148.

Lough Key is of course on one of the upper reaches of the inland waterways system, and a beautiful part it is too. In fact, all of Roscommon's eastern boundary is defined by the Shannon and its lakes, but as the towns along it tend to identify themselves with the counties across the river, Roscommon is left looking very thin on facilities. But it has much to intrigue the enquiring visitor. For instance, along the Roscommon shore of Lough Ree near the tiny village of Lecarrow, the remains of a miniature city going back to mediaeval times and beyond can be dimly discerned among the trees down towards Rindown Point.

These hints of of an active past serve to emphasise the fact that today, Roscommon moves at a gentler pace than the rest of Ireland - something which is reflected in its pubs to people ratio. It is second only to Leitrim on this scale, as Leitrim has just 153 people for every pub licence, while Roscommon has 170. Slainte!

Local Attractions and Information

Boyle Boyle Abbey (12th C Monastery)	079 62604
Boyle Frybrook House (18thC town hse)	079 62513
Boyle King House (500 years of Irish life)	079 63242
Boyle Lough Key Forest Park	079 62363
Boyle Tourism Information	079 62145
Castlerea Clonalis House	0907 20014
Elphin Restored windmill	078 35181
Frenchpark Dr Douglas Hyde Interpretive Centre	0907 70016
Roscommon town Arts Centre	0903 25824
Roscommon town County Museum	0903 25613
Roscommon Town Race Course	0903 26231
Roscommon town Tourism Information	0903 26342
Roscrea Clonalis, Ancestral Home of the O'Conors	0907 20014
Strokestown Park House, Garden & Famine Museum	078 33013
Strokestown Roscommon County Heritage Centre	078 33380

Carrick-on-Shannon — Glencarne Country House

Country House/Farmhouse

Ardcarne Carrick-on-Shannon Co. Roscommon
Tel: 079 67013 Fax: 079 67013

On the border between Leitrim and Roscommon - Glencarne House is physically in Leitrim, but the postal address is Roscommon - the Harrington family's large Georgian house is set well back from the road, with a large garden in front and farmland behind, so it is easy to find, yet without interference from traffic. Spacious and elegantly furnished with antiques, this is very much a family home and Agnes Harrington has won lots of awards for hospitality and home-cooked food based on their own farm produce. Garden. Children welcome; pets permitted by arrangement. **Rooms 4** (all en-suite & no smoking). B&B €35pps, ss €5. Set D €25.50, 7.30pm (book by 6pm); wine licence. Closed Oct-Mar. **No Credit Cards. Directions:** On the N4,halfway between Carrick-on-Shannon and Boyle.

Castlerea — Clonalis House

Country House

Castlerea Co. Roscommon **Tel: 0907 20014**
Fax: 0907 20014 Email: clonalis@iol.ie

Standing on the land that has been the home of the O'Conors of Connacht for 1,500 years, this 45-roomed Victorian Italianate mansion may seem a little daunting on arrival but it's magic and the hospitable owners, Pyers and Marguerite O'Conor-Nash, enjoy sharing their rich and varied history with guests, who are welcome to browse through their fascinating archive. Amazing heirlooms include a copy of the last Brehon Law judgment (handed down about 1580) and also Carolan's Harp. Everything is on a huge scale: reception rooms are all very spacious, with lovely old furnishings and many interesting historic details, bedrooms have massive four poster and half tester beds and bathrooms to match and the dining room is particularly impressive, with a richly decorated table to enhance Marguerite's home cooking. A reduction is offered for stays of three or more nights. Horse riding, fishing, shooting and golf (9) are all nearby. Unsuitable for children. No pets. B&B €78pps, ss €15. Set Residents D €35; wines €12-19. (24 hours notice necessary; not available Sun or Mon.) Closed 1 Oct-mid Apr. Amex, MasterCard, Visa. **Directions:** N60 west of Castlerea.

Rooskey — Shannon Key West Hotel

Hotel

Rooskey Co. Roscommon **Tel: 078 38800**
Fax: 078 38811 Web: keywest.firebird.net

This large riverside hotel on the Leitrim/Roscommon border has brought valuable facilities to the area and is open all year (except Christmas), making it a particularly good venue for off-season short breaks, meetings and conferences. On-site amenities include a gym, jacuzzi, solarium and steam room (but no swimming pool) and there is plenty to do and see in the area. Reliable bar food also makes this a useful place to bear in mind for breaking a journey. Conference/banqueting (250/220); business centre; video conferencing and back-up secretarial services. Leisure centre. Children welcome (under 4s free in parents' room, cots available). **Rooms 39**, all en-suite. B&B about €60 pps, ss about €8. Closed 24-26 Dec. Amex, MasterCard, Visa, Laser. **Directions:** On N4, main Dublin-Sligo route, midway between Longford and Carrick-on-Shannon. ◊

Roscommon — Abbey Hotel & Leisure Centre

 Hotel

Galway Road Roscommon Co. Roscommon **Tel: 0903 26240**
Fax: 0903 26021 Email: cmv@indigo.ie

The heart of this pleasant town centre hotel is an old manor house and, although there are more recent extensions - and plans for a leisure centre and new rooms - the atmosphere of the original building prevails. There's a romantic honeymoon suite with a four-poster in the old house and major improvements that have been taking place recently, include the addition of spacious new bedrooms (well-appointed andwith good views), a new restaurant and bar serving food all day. This, together with excellent leisure facilities and good value offered, will add greatly to the hotel's appeal for short breaks. Conference/banqueting (250); business centre. Leisure centre; swimming pool. Children welcome (under 12s free in parents' room; cots available). Garden. No pets. **Rooms 50** (all en-suite, 13 no smoking, 2 disabled). Lift. B&B €85 pps, ss €15. Restaurant L 12.45-2.45, D 7-9.30. Set L €20, Set Sun L €25; Set D €35, also à la carte. House wines from €15, SC discretionary.

Restaurant: A fairly recent addition, the restaurant is designed on two levels in a semi-brasserie style and makes a popular meeting place, where friendly, helpful staff serve unpretentious wholesome fare. **Seats 70** (private room, 50). L 12.45-2.30 daily. D 7-9.30 daily. Set L about €19; Set Sun L about €21.50; à la carte available. House wine about €14. No smoking area. Toilets wheelchair accessible. Hotel closed 24-25 Dec. Amex, Diners, MasterCard, Visa, Laser. **Directions:** Galway Road, Roscommon Town.

Strokestown — Strokestown Park Restaurant

Restaurant

Strokestown Park House Strokestown Co. Roscommon
Tel: 078 33013 Fax: 078 33712
Email: info@strokestownpark.ie Web: www.strokestownpark.ie

Strokestown House, the famine museum, gardens and parkland have much of interest to offer the visitor and it would be easy to spend a whole day there - fortunately, wholesome fare is available from the restaurant at the house, which is open all day. There's a carvery lunch and you can also expect simple, tasty dishes like baked potatoes with ham and cheese, good salads and vegetarian dishes like roasted vegetables on a toasted bap with herby cheese sauce - local strawberries or rhubarb crumble for pudding or scones and other home bakes with tea and coffee. Pets allowed (on a lead) in gardens and parklands. Own parking. Wheelchair access. Open 9am-5.30, L 12-4.30. Closed 1 Nov-31 Mar. Amex, MasterCard, Visa. **Directions:** At side of Strokestown House.

Tarmonbarry — Keenans Bar Restaurant

 Pub/Restaurant

Tarmonbarry (via Clondra) Co. Roscommon
Tel: 043 26052 / 26098 Fax: 043 26198
Email: info@keenans.ie Web: www.keenans.ie

Just beside the bridge over the Shannon in Tarmonbarry, this well-run bar and restaurant is a favourite watering hole for river folk and makes a great place to break a journey between Dublin and the north-west. The bar is comfortably set up for food and informal meals - mostly quite traditional but with more international influences in the more expensive evening dishes - are served all day; open sandwiches on home-made wholemeal or soda bread, toasted sandwiches, salads and scones with jam & cream are typical, plus half a dozen daily specials (including specialities such as fish casserole and bacon & cabbage at lunch, perhaps, and more elaborate dishes like roast half duckling on a peach stuffing with a red onion, ginger and orange marmalade in the evening). A la carte menus are similar in tone but more extensive - wholesome, hearty fare that pleases all age groups; the steak sandwich (served with onions, chips, garlic butter & home-made horseradish sauce) is not to be missed - while the set dinner menu is a little more formal. Good unpretentious food and cheerful, efficient service keep happy customers coming back. Restaurant **Seats 30**. No smoking restaurant. Food served daily 12.30-8.30; L 12.30-2.30, D 6.30-8.30. Set D €32, Set Sun L €19.50. House wine €11.90. Restaurant closed D Sun. Establishment closed 25 Dec, Good Fri. Amex, MasterCard, Visa, Laser. **Directions:** On N5, west of Longford town.

COUNTY SLIGO

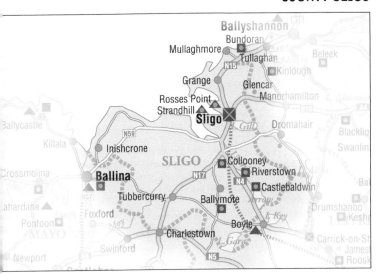

There's a stylish confidence to Sligo which belies its small area as one of Ireland's smallest counties. Perhaps it's because they know that their place and their way of life have been immortalised through association with two of the outstanding creative talents of modern Ireland, W.B.Yeats and his painter brother Jack. The former's fame seems beyond question, while the latter's star was never higher than it is today.

But whatever the reason for Sligo's special quality, there's certainly something about it that encourages repeat visits. The town of Sligo itself is big enough to be reassuring, yet small enough to be comfortable. It is seeing a welcome revival of civic spirit, the impressively restored Courthouse (originally built 1780, extended 1878) receiving the Royal Institute of Ireland's annual Regional Award on July 30th 2002.

Mankind has been living here with enthusiasm for a very long time indeed, for in recent years it has been demonstrated that some of County Sligo's ancient monuments are amongst the oldest in northwest Europe. Lakes abound, the mountains are magnificent, and there are tumbling rivers a-plenty. Yet if you wish to get away from the bustle of the regular tourist haunts, Sligo can look after your needs in this as well, for the western part of the county down through the Ox Mountains towards Mayo is an uncrowded region of wide vistas and clear roads.

Local Attractions and Information

Carrowmore Largest Megalithic Cemetry in Ireland	071 61534
Drumcliff Drumcliffe Church & Visitor Centre (Yeats)	071 44956
Drumcliff Lissadell House	071 63150
Inniscrone Seaweed Bath House	096 36238
Lough Gill Waterbus Cruises	071 64266
Sligo Discover Sligo Tours	071 47488
Sligo Model Arts & Niland Gallery	071 41405
Sligo Sligo Abbey (13thC Dominican Friary)	071 46406
Sligo Sligo Airport, Strandhill	071 68280
Sligo Sligo Art Gallery	071 45847
Sligo Tourism Information	071 61201
Sligo Yeats Memorial Building, Hyde Bridge	071 42693
Strandhill Seaweed Baths, Maritime House	071 68686

Ballymote   Temple House

Country House   Ballymote Co. Sligo **Tel: 071 83329** Fax: 071 83808
Email: guests@templehouse.ie   Web: www.templehouse.ie

One of Ireland's most unspoilt old houses, this is a unique place – a Georgian Mansion situated in 1,000 acres of farm and woodland, overlooking the original lakeside castle which was built by the Knights Templar in 1200 A.D. The Percevals have lived here since 1665 and the house was redesigned and refurbished in 1864 – some of the furnishings date back to that major revamp. The whole of the house has retained its old atmosphere, and in addition to central heating, has log fires to cheer the enormous rooms. Spacious bedrooms are all furnished with old family furniture and guests have the use of an elegant sitting room with open fires. Deb Perceval's evening meals are served in the very beautiful dining room and are a treat to look forward to – she is a Euro-Toques chef and takes pride in preparing fine meals based on produce from the estate and other local suppliers. A typically delicious menu might include: crabcakes with a citrus sauce on salad leaves, seared pork medallions with bell peppers & sherry sauce, French lemon tart and and Irish cheeseboard. NB: Sandy Perceval is seriously allergic to scented products, so guests are asked to avoid all perfumes, aftershave and aerosols. Children welcome (under 2s free in parents' room; cots available). No pets in house. **Rooms 6** (5 en-suite, 2 shower only, 1 with private bathroom). B&B €65pps, ss €15. Residents D €30, 7.30pm (book by 1pm); house wine €12. Children's tea 6.30pm; sc discretionary. Closed 30 Nov-1Apr. Amex, MasterCard, Visa, Laser. **Directions:** Signposted on N17 south of Ballinacarrow Village.

Castlebaldwin   Cromleach Lodge

Hotel/Restaurant   Castlebaldwin via Boyle Co. Sligo **Tel: 071 65155** Fax: 071 65455
Email: info@cromleach.com   Web: cromleach.com

Set in the hills just above Lough Arrow, Cromleach Lodge enjoys one of the finest views in Ireland. The building, which is uncompromisingly modern in style and occupies a prominent position, has been the source of some controversy – however, proprietors Moira and Christy Tighe wanted to maximise the view from both restaurant and rooms and find that their design has served them very well. But it is not architecture that brings people to Cromleach, rather the drive and dedication of Christy and Moira, which translates into high standards of both food and accommodation. Most importantly, they have the magic ingredient of genuine hospitality, doing everything possible to ensure comfort and relaxation for their guests. Spacious bedrooms are thoughtfully furnished with king-size and single beds, excellent bathrooms and every comfort to please the most fastidious of guests: this is a supremely comfortable place and everything is of the highest quality. Hospitality, housekeeping and attention to detail are all outstanding (for example, this is one of the very few places to provide not only a mini-bar but, more importantly, a jug of fresh milk in the fridge for your tea and coffee). Other extras include a complimentary basket of fruit and miniature of Baileys in your room. Small conferences (14). Children welcome. Pets permitted by arrangement. **Rooms 10** (5 junior suites, 2 executive, 5 no-smoking) B&B about €135 pps, ss about €40.

★ **Restaurant:** The restaurant (which is totally non-smoking) is arranged as a series of rooms, creating a number of individual dining areas for varying numbers of people – a system which works better for groups than couples dining alone. Immaculate maintenance and lovely simple table settings – crisp linen, modern silver and crystal, fine, understated china and fresh seasonal flowers – provide a fit setting for dinner, the high point of every guest's visit to Cromleach. Moira Tighe and her personally trained kitchen team work superbly well together, producing some memorable cooking. A growing number of specialities are in constant demand so menus have to include these as a base, with new dishes added as appropriate. The cooking style is modern (without being slavishly fashionable) but it's Moira's scrupulously careful sourcing of ingredients, pride in local produce and consistently excellent cooking that makes this restaurant so special. Menus offered include an 8-course Gourmet Tasting Menu (for residents only, included in the dinner bed & breakfast rate) and a 5-course table d'hôte (about €55). Specialities include simple starters like warm smoked salmon on creamed organic spinach and a sophisticated tasting selection of award-winning desserts. The wine list leads with 26 accessible house wines from around the world, in the €23-38 bracket, and the dessert menu comes with helpful suggestions of dessert wines and ports. Moira is an exceptional chef and the Guide was proud to present her with the Chef of the Year Award in 2000. Well-trained, friendly staff provide xcellent service to complement the high standards pf the kitchen. The consistent achievement of xcellence in all areas at Cromleach - food, hospitality, accommodation - is truly exceptional. **Seats** •0 (private rooms, 4-24). D only, 6.30-9 daily (Sun to 8) Set D about €55, also à la carte; house ⁄ines from about €23; sc discretionary. No smoking restaurant. Toilets wheelchair accessible. Closed ⁄ov-Jan. Amex, MasterCard, Visa. **Directions:** Signposted from Castlebaldwin on the N4. ◇

Cliffoney — La Vecchia Posta

Restaurant   Cliffoney Co. Sligo **Tel: 071 76777** Fax: Fax 071 76788

After thirty years in Italy the Dunlevy family returned to their native Sligo to open an Italian estaurant in this neat stone-faced house, with views towards Classiebawn Castle and Mullaghmore headland in the distance. Guests are greeted with the offer of an aperitif, in a spacious seating area, where old furniture lends atmosphere, or at your table in a big high-ceilinged room with large uncurtained windows and high light fittings. Promptly presented menus are in Italian, with English translations and especially strong on antipasti (some of which are suitable as light main courses); Italian-speaking staff are happy to explain dishes: authentic Italian cooking is the strength of the restaurant, as seen in good pasta dishes - tortelli toscani (parcels with a potato & onion stuffing and mushrooms sauce), for example, or delicious ravioloni (filled with ricotta and spinach in a rosemary sauce). Fish, delivered from Killybegs, is a speciality - sole, salmon and crab are all in regular dishes, and there may be some not mentioned on the menu, so it's worth asking. Attractive meat dishes include grilled sirloin steak strips drizzled with extra virgin olive oil and sprinkled with rosemary and more unusual choices like rabbit, cooked in a tomato sauce with onions and herbs. Desserts - a choice of five including fresh fruit salad - are a weak point (it would be nice to see some really good Italian ice creams) but Italian coffees are predictably good. Children welcome. **Seats 60.** No smoking area; air conditioning. Jazz dinners on Fridays. D Tue-Sun, 6-10, L Sun only, from 12.30. Set D about €26, also à la carte; Set Sun L about €18. House wine about €18; s.c. discretionary. Closed Mon (inc bank hols), all Feb. (Times and prices not confirmed at time of going to press, please phone for details.) MasterCard, Visa, Laser. **Directions:** On side of main Sligo/Bundoran/Donegal road in the village of Cliffoney. ◇

Collooney — Glebe House

Country House   Collooney Co. Sligo **Tel: 071 67787** Fax: 071 30438
Email: glebehouse@esatbiz.com Web: glebehousesligo.com

Brid and Marc Torrades' renowned establishment just outside Collooney village (which they have been running as a restaurant with rooms since 1990) is now operated as a country house with meals for residents only. Brid, who is an enthusiastic Euro-Toques chef, was the winner of the Guide's Natural Food Award in 2001 and is a great example to the many chefs and restaurateurs who source their ingredients impeccably but may fail to pass this information on to their guests. Not only does Brid take great pride in sourcing the best of local ingredients for her cooking - which is imaginative without being fussy - but she also presents guests with a detailed list of the items used on each night's menu and their provenance. Thus, for example, salads, herbs, garden vegetables and soft fruits are grown in their own walled garden and are grown without chemicals and using organic seed. Listed cheeses may be from Corleggy Farm, Co Cavan, Cliffoney Farm, Co. Sligo, West Cork natural Cheese Co, Knockalara Cheese, Co Wexford, Cashel Blue Cheese, Co Tipperary and Cooleeney Cheese, Co Tipperary. Sea fish are landed at Killybegs; beef and lamb come from local co Sligo farms, ducks from Thornhill Poultry, Co Cavan. Brid's delicious dinner menus are changed daily and always include strong vegetarian choices. Garden & fishing available to guests. Children welcome. **Rooms 4** (all en-suite). B&B €45 pps, ss €15. Residents' D Tue-Sun 6.30-9,30; Set D about €35; house wine about €16; no sc. No smoking area. Closed Nov-Mar. Amex, Diners, MasterCard, Visa, Laser, Switch. **Directions:** Leave the N4 at the Collooney, exit at Collooney roundabout, take the first right 400 yards, turn left 400 yards to top of lane.

Collooney — Markree Castle

Hotel/Restaurant   Collooney Co. Sligo **Tel: 071 67800** Fax: 071 67840
Email: markree@iol.ie Web: markreecastle.ie

Sligo's oldest inhabited house has been home to the Cooper family for 350 years. Set in magnificent park and farmland, this is a proper castle, with a huge portico leading to a covered stone stairway that sweeps up to an impressive hall, where an enormous log fire always burns. Everything is on a very large scale, and it is greatly to the credit of the present owners, Charles and Mary Cooper, that they have achieved the present level of renovation and comfort since they took it on in a sad state of disrepair in 1989 - and they have always been generous with the heating. Ground floor reception areas include a very comfortably furnished double drawing room with two fireplaces (where light food – including their famous afternoon tea – is served). There is a lift and also disabled toilets but the layout of the castle makes it difficult for elderly people or wheelchair users to get around a phone call ahead to ensure the (very willing) staff are available to help would be wise. Conferences/banqueting (50/150). Children welcome (under 4s free in parents' room; cot available). Pets permitted. **Rooms 30** (all en-suite, 5 executive rooms, 1 for disabled). Lift. B&E from about €92 pps, ss about €10. Closed 24-27 Dec.

Restaurant: There is a beautiful dining room, where head chef Tom Joyce has been serving very good food since 1993. Standards of food and service here have generally remained high - and the surroundings alone make dining here a memorable occasion. Non-residents are welcome (Reservations recommended). **Seats 80** (private room, 40) D 7.30-9.30 daily; L 1-2.30 Sun only. Se D about €30, Set Sun L about €18; house wine about €14; no sc. No smoking restaurant. Hote closed 24-27 Dec. Amex, Diners, MasterCard, Visa. **Directions:** Just off the N4, take the Dromohai exit at Collooney roundabout. ◇

Mullaghmore — Eithna's Seafood Restaurant

Restaurant
The Harbour Mullaghmore Co. Sligo **Tel:** 071 66407
Email: eithnasrestaurant@eircom.net **Web:** www.eithnaseafood.com

Situated right on the harbour at Mullaghmore, Philippe and Eithna Huel's atmospheric seafood restaurant specialises in fish and shellfish caught by local fishermen in Donegal Bay. Since opening in 1990 they have gradually built up a reputation that now extends far beyond the local population - those in the know now travel specially for Eithna's cooking, particularly lobster (served various ways) and the seafood platter which, at €29, is much better value than the various lobster dishes served separately. For this you get a cold half lobster, prawns, crab, crab claws, razor fish, mussels and clams; all served in the shell - the exact ingredients may vary a little according to availability but it will balance out. The platter is attractively served and comes with tossed organic salad greens, mayonnaise, fresh lemon, a bread basket and a dish of potatoes (quite probably from Normandy). There are some options other than seafood offered, including starters like roasted quail, also vegetarian dishes - and tempting desserts might include iced chocolate mousses, home-made ice cream with meringue & fruit sauce, and possibly a refreshing choice like rhubarb with strawberries. **Seats 50**. No smoking area. Children welcome. D daily in high season, 6.30-9.30, also L Sat & Sun, 12.30-3 in Jul-Aug. (Opening variable Sep-Easter; phone for information). Set D from about €32, also Set L in high season. House wine €15. MasterCard, Visa, Laser. **Directions:** 16 miles from Sligo on N15 (Donegal) turn at Cliffoney.

Riverstown — Coopershill House

Country House
Riverstown Co. Sligo **Tel:** 071 65108 **Fax:** 071 65466
Email: ohara@coopershill.com **Web:** www.coopershill.com

Undoubtedly one of the most delightful and superbly comfortable Georgian houses in Ireland, this sturdy granite mansion was built to withstand the rigours of a Sligo winter – but its numerous chimneys suggest there is warmth to be found within its stern grey walls. Peacocks wander elegantly on the croquet lawns (and roost in the splendid trees around the house at night) making this lovely place, home of the O'Hara family since it was built in 1774, a particularly perfect country house. Nothing escapes Brian O'Hara's disciplined eye: in immaculate order from top to bottom, the house not only has the original 18th century furniture but also some fascinating features – notably an unusual Victorian free-standing rolltop bath complete with fully integrated cast-iron shower 'cubicle' and original brass rail and fittings, all in full working order. Luxurious rooms are wonderfully comfortable and have phones and tea/coffee making facilities. Lindy runs the house and kitchen with the seamless hospitality born of long experience, and creates deliciously wholesome, unpretentious food which is served in their lovely dining room (where the family silver is used with magnificent insouciance – even at breakfast). Tennis, boating, fishing, garden, croquet; snooker room. Children welcome (under 2s free in parents' room; cots available, about €6.50. No pets. **Rooms 8** (7 en-suite, 1 shower only, 1 private). B&B about €90 pps, ss about €20. Dining Room **Seats 16-20**. Residents' D 8.30 daily; Set D about €40-€45, house wines from about €15; sc discretionary. No smoking restaurant. Closed 11 Nov-31 Mar (off season house parties of 12-16 people welcome.) Amex, Diners, MasterCard, Visa, Switch. **Directions:** Signposted from N4 at Drumfin crossroads. ◇

Rosses Point | Austie's

 Pub/Restaurant

Rosses Point Co. Sligo
Tel: 071 77111 / 087 263 4216

This 200 year-old pub overlooking Sligo Bay has always been associated with a seafaring family and is full of fascinating nautical memorabilia. It has a very nice ship-shape feeling about it and friendly people behind the bar. The sea stars on the simple bar menu too, with local seafood in dishes like garlic mussels, seafood chowder and in open sandwiches or salads made with crab, prawns and salmon - although there are other choices, including ever-popular steaks and home-made burgers. Not a daytime pub (except in high summer the usual opening time is 4 pm). If you're going out to Rosses Point specially, it's wise to ring ahead and check opening times off-season. **Seats 70**. No smoking area. Children welcome. Bar food served daily 4-9.30 in summer (12.30-9.30 at weekends), evenings only off-season (Sept-Mar). A la carte menu; house wine from about €14; sc discretionary. Restaurant D daily in summer 6-9.30. No food available Mon & Tue off season. Closed 25 Dec & Good Fri. MasterCard, Visa, Laser. **Directions:** On the seafront.

Sligo | Coach Lane Restaurant @ Donaghy's Bar

 Pub/Restaurant

1-2 Lord Edward Street Sligo Co. Sligo
Tel: 071 62417 Fax: 071 71935

The restaurant over Orla and Andy Donaghy's pub is approached by an attractive side alley, with a menu board dislayed on the street. It's a long narrow room, furnished in a comfortable mixture of traditional and contemporary styles, with well-appointed white-clothed tables, soft lighting and neatly uniformed waitresses in black polo shirts and trousers with white aprons all creating a good impression. On the down side background music can be intrusively loud and service slow to get started, but Andy's menus are lively and attractive - and the cooking is confident. Specialities using local produce include a porterhouse steak (marinated in herbs and chargrilled), fresh whole lobster and Sligo Bay salmon. There's also a wide choice of salads, pasta dishes and chicken - and the cooking style ranges from traditional (steak with home-made fries, crispy onion rings & HP sauce) to spicy (cajun chicken with a fresh fruit salsa). **Seats 65** (plus 40 on a new outside terrace, weather permitting). Air conditioning. Toilets wheelchair accessible. D daily 6.30-10, Set D about €32, also à la carte; L Sun 12-4. House wine about €15; service discretionary except 10% on parties of 8+. Closed 25 Dec & Good Fri. Amex, MasterCard, Visa, Laser. **Directions:** N4 to Sligo,Left at Adelaide St. make a right into Lord Edward St. ◇

Sligo | Garavogue & Café Bar Deli

Pub/Restaurant

Rear 15/16 Stephens Street Sligo Co. Sligo
Tel: 071 40100 Fax: 071 40104 Email: garavogue@hotmail.com

Named after the Garavogue river which flows past the wide paved area outside the front door, this dashing restaurant has been popular since opening in 1999 with locals who know their food and relish the sheer style of the place. It's in a particularly attractive building that maximises the natural advantages of the site - town centre yet with space, light and water around it - and also has a cleverly designed interior, with height and loads of drama giving visual impact. A central bar takes pride of place on the ground floor and is the initial focal point, before the eye is drawn up towards the first floor restaurant area. Snazzy bar food - nachos with salsa, sour cream, melted cheddar & guacamole; crispy chicken strips with creamy curry dip - is served here, while the upstairs restaurant has now been re-launched as a branch of Café Bar Deli, a concept already highly successful in Dublin and Cork (see entries). Outside seating. No children after 8 pm. Smoking unrestricted; air conditioning. Lift. **Seats 150** (private room 12). Open daily 12-9 (L12-3, evening menu 3-9; Sun brunch 12-3). House wine from about €16. sc discretionary. Open all year except 25 Dec & Good Fri. MasterCard, Laser. **Directions:** Located on bank of Garavogue River access through rear of Bank of Ireland carpark. ◇

Sligo | Hargadon Bros.

Pub

O'Connell Street Sligo Co. Sligo **Tel: 071 70993**

Unquestionably one of Ireland's greatest old pubs, the best time to see Hargadon's properly is early in the day when it's quiet – they'll give you good coffee (and probably a newspaper to go with it) and you can relax and take in the detail of this remarkable old place. It still has the shelves which used to hold the groceries when it was a traditional grocer-bar, the snugs and the old pot belly stove – and it's still owner-run and unspoilt. Later in the day it gets very busy, especially at weekends –

but by then it's time for a bit of craic anyway. **Seats 100.** Light food available in the morning; meals served Mon-Sat, 12-4. No smoking area; air conditioning. Toilets wheelchair accessible. Closed 25 Dec & Good Fri. Amex. **Directions:** In town centre on the main street. ◇

Sligo   Montmartre

féile bia Restaurant   Market Yard Sligo Co. Sligo **Tel: 071 69901**
                                    Fax: 071 40065 Email: montmartre@eircom.net

French run and staffed, this restaurant has been thriving since opening in December 1999 and bookings are strongly advised, especially at weekends. Although not big, it has a light and airy feel and a restful atmosphere enhanced by strategically placed potted palms and a lack of clutter. A small bar area doubles as reception, staff are smartly uniformed and the restaurant is well-appointed in the French style, with comfortable chairs and white crockery. Proprietor-chef Stephane Magaud presents varied menus offering imaginative French cuisine in a light, colourful style, matched by sound cooking and attractive presentation. Local produce feaures in some dishes, especially seafood - Lissadell oysters and mussels, for example, also lobster and wild salmon; there may also be game in season. From a wide selection of dishes on several menus (including the early dinner, which is exceptional value), typical examples arecheese parcel with smoked onion & tomato coulis and a speciality main course dish of braised quail à l'échalote with basil mash. Finish with classic desserts - white & dark chocolate bavarois, tarte à l'orange et aux amandes - or a cheese plate. The wine list is mostly French, with a token gesture to the New World, and includes ten wines available by the glass. **Seats 50.** No smoking area; air conditioning. Toilets wheelchair accessible. D Tues-Sun, 5-11. A la carte. Early D €18 (5-7pm). House wines €16-22. Closed Mon, 24-27 Dec, 5-21 Jan. Amex, Diners, MasterCard, Visa, Laser, Switch. **Directions:** 150 yards from theatre & tourist office.

Sligo   Tower Hotel Sligo

Hotel   Quay Street Sligo Co. Sligo **Tel: 071 44000** Fax: 071 46888
                             Email: reservations@ths.ie Web: www.hotelsligo.com

This neat redbrick hotel is very centrally located and makes a comfortable base for business or leisure. First impressions in the spacious, colourful lobby area are good and the standard of interior design throughout the hotel is quite high. Conference/banqueting (190/170). Children welcome (under 3s free in parents' room; cots available). No pets. **Rooms 55** (3 suites). Lift. B&B €67.50 pps, ss €17.50. Closed 24-29 Dec. Amex, Diners, MasterCard, Visa, Laser. **Directions:** Located next door to city hall in the centre of Sligo.

Strandhill   Strand House Bar

Pub   Strandhill Co. Sligo
                                                Tel: 071 68140 Fax: 071 68593

Just ten minutes drive from Sligo, close to the airport and one of Europe's most magnificent surfing beaches, this well-known bar has a big welcoming turf fire, cosy snugs and friendly staff. No children after 9pm. Bar meals served all day (12-3pm). [An oriental restaurant beside the bar is leased] Toilets wheelchair accessible. Air conditioning. Closed 25 Dec & Good Fri. **No Credit Cards. Directions:** Follow signs to Sligo airport (Strandhill). Strand House is situated at the end near the beach. ◇

COUNTY TIPERARY

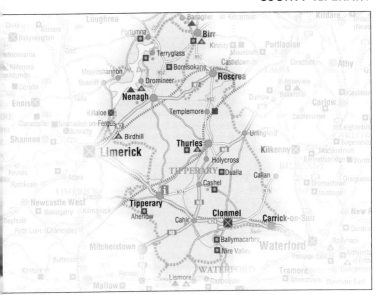

The cup of life is overflowing in Tipperary. In this wondrously fertile region, there's an air of fulfilment, a happy awareness of the world in harmony. And the placenames reinforce this sense of natural bounty. Across the middle of the county, there's the evocatively-named Golden Vale, with prosperous lands along the wide valley of the River Suir and its many tributaries, and westwards towards County Limerick across a watershed around Donohill.

The county's largest town, down in the far south under the Comeragh Mountains, is the handsome borough of Clonmel - its name translates as "Honey Meadow". Yet although there are many meadows of all kinds in Tipperary, there's much more to this largest inland county in Ireland than farmland, for it is graced with some of the most elegant mountains in the country.

North of the Golden Vale, the Silvermine Mountains rise to 694 m on Keeper Hill, and beyond them the farming countryside rolls on in glorious profusion to Nenagh - a town much improved by by-passes on either side - and Tipperary's own "sea coast", the beautiful eastern shore of Lough Derg. Inevitably, history and historic monuments abound in such country, with the fabulous Rock of Cashel and its dramatic remains of ancient ecclesiastical buildings setting a very high standard for evoking the past. But Tipperary lends itself every bit as well to enjoyment of the here and now. Tipperary is all about living life to the full, and they do it with style in a place of abundance.

Local Attractions and Information

Aherlow, Glen of Glenbrook Trout Farm	062 56214
Birdhill Tipperary Crystal Visitor Centre	061 379066
Cahir Cahir Castle	052 41011
Carrick-on-Suir Ormond Castle	051 640787
Carrick-on-Suir Tipperary Crystal Visitor Centre	051 641188
Cashel Bru Boru Culture Centre	062 61122
Cashel Rock of Cashel	062 61437
Cashel Tourism Information	062 61333
Clonmel Clonmel Racecourse	052 23422
Clonmel Tourism Information	052 22960
Nenagh Heritage Centre	067 32633
Nenagh Tourism Information	067 31610
Roscrea Roscrea Heritage - Castle & Damer House	0505 21850
Thurles Race Course	0504 21040
Tipperary Race Course (Limerick Junction)	062 51357
Tipperary town Tourism Information	062 51457

Ballinderry — Brocka-on-the-Water Restaurant

Restaurant   Kilgarvan Quay Ballinderry Nenagh Co. Tipperary **Tel: 067 22038**

Anthony and Anne Gernon's almost-waterside restaurant has attracted a following disproportionate to its size over the years and, although it has recently been extended to include a new high-ceilinged conservatory style room at the back, which opens onto a garden patio, it is still basically carved out of the lower half of a family home that is by no means huge. The atmosphere is very much a "proper restaurant" - yet with all the warmth of welcome that the family situation implies. There's a reception room with an open fire, comfy chairs, interesting things to read and look at (Anthony's a dab hand at wood carving) - and aperitifs served in generous wine glasses, while you read a menu that promises good things to come in the adjoining dining room and conservatory. Guests arriving in daylight will notice hens clucking around a garden well-stocked with fruit and vegetables - promising the best of all possible beginnings for your dinner. Seasonal menus depend on availability of course, but there are always some specialities retained by popular demand, including deep-fried Cooleeney cheese with home-made chutney and Gaelic steak with home-grown vegetables (Cooleeney is one of Ireland's finest cheeses, made by Breda Maher on the family farm near Thurles). Seats 50 (private room, 30). Air conditioning. Toilets wheelchair accessible. Booking essential. D 7-9.30 Mon-Sat in summer (call to check opening times off season). Set D about €40, also à la carte. Sc discretionary. House wine about €22. Closed Sun. **No Credit Cards. Directions:** Lough Derg drive, half way between Nenagh and Portumna. ◇

Birdhill — Matt The Thresher

Pub   Birdhill Co. Tipperary **Tel: 061 379227** Fax: 061 379219

Ted and Kay Moynihan's large roadside pub makes a useful stopping place for a quick bite. Children welcome. Bar Food daily. Wheelchair accessible. Closed 25 Dec & Good Fri. Amex, Diners, MasterCard, Visa. **Directions:** N7, halfway between Nenagh-Limerick. ◇

Borrisokane — Ballycormac House

Country House   Aglish Borrisokane Roscrea Co. Tipperary
Tel: 067 21129 Fax: 067 21200
Email: ballyc@indigo.ie Web: www.ballyc.com

John and Cherylynn Lang's farmhouse is a charming, cottagey place, delightfully furnished and very comfortable in a laid-back way – and one of the five bedrooms is a romantic suite with its own fireplace. Country pursuits are the big attraction here, esepcially equestrian activities - the Langs have up to 30 horses and ponies on site so there's something to suit everyone, from the novice to the experienced rider. They are approved by A.I.R.E. (Irish Association of Riding Establishments) and offer trail riding and cross country riding in spring and summer, also fox hunting breaks in winter. Golf, fishing, watersports and rough shooting can also be arranged. Cherylynn cooks a country house style dinner for guests, based on fresh local ingredients (including produce from their own garden). Non-residents are welcome for dinner by reservation, if there is room, also Sunday lunch. Mention any special dietary requests (including vegetarian meals) when booking. Children and well-behaved pets welcome (children under 2 free in parents' room; cot available). **Rooms 5** (1 suite, 1 with private bathroom, all no smoking). B&B €32, no ss). Dining Room Seats 12 (no smoking). Set D €28; Set L €15.24. House wine €15.24. 8pm (book by 12). [Times & prices not confirmed at time of going to press; please phone for details.] Open all year. MasterCard, Visa. **Directions:** Take N54 towards Portumna. Turn right once through Bossisokane, signposted all the way in. ◇

Borrisokane — Dancer Cottage

Accommodation   Curraghmore Borrisokane Co. Tipperary **Tel: 067 27414** Fax: 067 27414
Email: dcr@eircom.net Web: dancercottage.cjb.net

A neat well planned garden and plenty of parking make a good impression at Carmen and Wolfgang Roedder's modern tudor style house nera Borrisokane. An extensive array of tourist literature in the big hall guarantees that no guest here will ever be short of things to do in the area and there's a comfortable L shaped sitting/dining room to relax in when you get back, with a wood-burning stove and lots of books. Bedrooms include two recently purpose-built ones with wheelchair access and a family room with an extra bed; all are comfortably furnished with some lovely pieces of antique German furniture, immaculate bathrooms and tea/coffee facilities. Extensive breakfast menus include several home-baked breads, speciality porridge, stuffed pancakes and French toast as well as the traditional Irish fry - and, like the evening meals, breakfast is served at a communal table overlooking the lovely back garden, which has furniture for guests' use. Children welcome (under 2s free in parents' room, cot available without charge, small children's playground). Pets allowed by arrangement. Garden, cycling. **Rooms 4** (all with shower & no smoking, 2 for disabled). Residents D €23 (when boooked in advance). B&B from €28, ss €7. Closed 15 Dec-1 Feb. Amex, MasterCard, Visa. **Directions:** N52 from Nenagh or Birr to Borrisokane; road signs in town.

Cahir — Clifford's at The Bell

féile bia ☆ Restaurant

2 Pearce Street Cahir Co. Tipperary
Tel: 052 43232

On two floors over a pleasant pub in the centre of Cahir, Michael and Deirdre Clifford's renowned restaurant has lots of character, with the Cliffords' collection of original art (lining the stone walls alongside many well-earned accolades), well-planned lighting, crisp linen and - a trademark dating back to the original Cliffords in Cork city - a single flower floating in a huge glass of water. Michael, who is a classical French chef with Irish influences, sources his ingredients with immense care: meats come from two butchers - Kennedy's of Cahir and O'Dwyers of Cashel - the weekly Cahir country market is a source of local vegetables and flowers and Deirdre's father also supplies home-grown garden produce. Over a tasty amuse-bouche, the early dinner menu tempts with exceptional value and the carte offers a great choice: starters will include Michael's famous gateau of Clonakilty Black Pudding and main courses will almost certainly offer Tipperary lamb - roast rack, perhaps, with roasted pear & thyme sauce (the saucing is invariably excellent) and daily specials like roast monkfish with chilli & tomato - accompanied by exceptionally imaginative vegetables. Finish, perhaps, with tarte au citron with a gin & tonic sorbet, or the cheeseboard - typically Ardrahan, St Tola, Milleens, Carrigbyrne and Cashel Blue, all in perfect condition, with crackers and grapes, then aromatic dark-roasted coffee and a plate of scrumptious petits fours. There are no gimmicks here, just delightful, thoughtfully organised surroundings; warm hospitality and professsional service; superb ingredients and a truly great chef with the maturity to "faites simple".[There may ba a change of premises in spring 2003; phone for details.] Children welcome. Seats 50. No smoking area; air conditioning. D Tue-Sun 6.30-10.30. D à la carte (early D, 6.30-8, €23). House wines about €20. Visa, Amex. **Directions:** Main Street Cahir, 1st turn left.

Cashel — Carron House

Farmhouse

Carron Cashel Co. Tipperary **Tel: 052 62142**
Fax: 052 62168 Email: hallyfamily@eircom.net

Mary Hally's farmhouse is on an award-winning dairy farm, in a peaceful location in the heart of the Golden Vale, yet only minutes from Cashel and just an hour from Kilkenny. Approached up a long, well-maintained drive, first impressions are very encouraging, as there's a lovely front garden in front of the large, modern house - and separate entrances for the house and farm. Good-sized individually decorated bedrooms include one on the ground floor with wheelchair access and all are very comfortably furnished, with generous beds, television, tea/coffee facilities, hair dryers and neat en-suite shower rooms. Housekeeping throughout is immaculate and there's a guest sitting room with antique furniture and interesting books, and a large sun room/dining room overlooking the garden which are both always available to guests. Mary, who is a friendly, attentive and informative hostess, gives guests a good send-off in the morning, with a generous, well-cooked and nicely presented breakfast. **Rooms 4** (all with en-suite shower & all no smoking). B&B €32pps, ss €15. Closed 1 Nov-1 Apr. MasterCard, Visa. **Directions:** Take N8 south bound from Cashel for 2.5 miles. Sign posted at left of crossroads.

Cashel — Cashel Palace Hotel

Hotel

Main Street Cashel Co. Tipperary **Tel: 062 62707** Fax: 062 61521
Email: reception@cashel-palace.ie Web: www.cashel-palace.ie

One of Ireland's most famous hotels, and originally a bishop's residence, Cashel Palace is a large, graciously proportioned Queen Anne style house (dating from 1730) set well back from the road in the centre of Cashel town. The beautiful reception rooms and some of the spacious, elegantly furnished bedrooms overlook the gardens and the Rock of Cashel at the rear. The present owners, Patrick and Susan Murphy, took over the hotel in 1998 and, although much remains to be done, they are gradually renovating and refurbishing both public areas and bedrooms. The restaurant overlooks beautiful gardens at the back and informal meals are available downstairs, in the old stone-flagged bar. Closed 24-26 Dec. Amex, Diners, MasterCard, Visa, Laser. **Directions:** On N8 which runs through main street - Cashel. Situated just off main road. ◇

Cashel — Chez Hans

Restaurant   Moor Lane Cashel Co. Tipperary **Tel: 062 6117**

Although many others have since followed suit, the idea of opening a restaurant in a church wa highly original when Hans-Peter Matthia did it in 1968. The atmosphere and scale – indeed the whol style of the place – is superb and provides an excellent setting for the fine food which Hans-Pete and his son Jason prepare for appreciative diners (some of whom travel great distances for th treat). The wide range of starters include choices like cream of mushroom soup with tarragon, speciality pâté of chicken liver and foie gras with spiced tomato chutney & hot toast, or smoke Irish salmon with new potato & marinated red onion salad, boiled eggs & capers. Main courses offe an equally wide choice: half a crispy roast duckling with caramel & orange sauce, perhaps o speciality seafood dishes like the cassoulette (half a dozen varieties of fish and shellfish with a delicate chive velouté sauce) or lobster with lemongrass & coriander. This very popular restaurant i always busy and this can sometimes affect the standard of service. Booking ahead is essential.* A the time of going to press a new café was due to open. Seats 80 D Tue-Sat, 6-10. Set D €40, als à la carte; early D €27 (6-7.30 only). House wine from €21. Closed Sun, Mon, 1st 2 weeks Jan, 1s week Sep. MasterCard, Visa, Laser.

Cashel — Dualla House

Country House   Dualla Cashel Co. Tipperary **Tel: 062 61487** Fax: 062 6148. Email: duallahse@eircom.net Web: www.tipp.ie/dualla-house.htm

Set in 300 acres of of rolling Tipperary farmland in the "Golden Vale", Martin and Mairead Power': fine Georgian manor house faces south towards the Slievenamon, Comeragh, Knockmealdown anc Galtee Mountains. Just 3 miles from the Rock of Cashel, this is a convenient base for exploring the area but its special appeal is peace and tranquillity which, together with comfortable accommodation in large airy bedrooms (with tea/coffee trays), great hospitality and Mairead's home cooking, keep guests coming back time and again. An extensive breakfast menu includes local apple juice as well as other fresh fruits and juices, farmhouse cheeses, porridge with local honey, also free-range eggs and sausages from the local butcher in the traditional cooked breakfast - and home-made bread and preserves. Children welcome (under 3s free in parents' room, cot available without charge). **Rooms 4** (3 en-suite, 1 with private bathroom, all no smoking). B&B €40 pps, ss €10. Closed Dec-Feb. MasterCard, Visa. **Directions:** 3 miles from Cashel on R691. Coming from Dublir signed from N8, 5 miles after Horse & Jockey. Sign on left. 2.5 miles to house.

Cashel — Legends Townhouse & Restaurant

féile bia Guesthouse/Restaurant   The Kiln Cashel Co. Tipperary **Tel: 062 61292** Fax: 062 62876 Email: info@legendsguesthouse.com Web: www.legendsguesthouse.con

Tucked just under the Rock of Cashel (and with direct access from the Bru Boru carpark at the back), Rosemary and Michael O'Neill's neat purpose-built guesthouse offers comfortable accommodation and makes an hospitable base for visiting the area's many sites. Although the building is fairly new, open fires and old furniture give the house a pleasingly old-world feeling and, as Michael is an experienced chef, food is an important part of the visit. He offers shortish but well-balanced menus based on carefully sourced ingredients and including familiar dishes: starters like warm black pudding and apple salad or Cashel Blue in filo pastry with a walnut salad, are typical and main courses are likely to include Tipperary lamb, typically a roast rack in a herb crust. Cheerful, efficient serving staff under Rosemary's supervision. D Tue-Sat and Sun L, open to non-residents. **Rooms 7** (3 shower only), B&B about €32 pps. ss about €13. [Times and prices not confirmed at time of going to press; please phone for details.] Amex, MasterCard, Visa. **Directions:** Adjacent to Rock of Cashel carpark. ◇

Cashel — Spearmans Bakery & Tea Room

Café   97 Main Street Cashel Co. Tipperary **Tel: 062 61143**

After a long spell running their well-known restaurant here, David and Louise Spearman took a change of direction and re-opened in the autumn of 2001 as a home-bakery and tea rooms. Using the best ingredients - including butter in all their pastries - they make a wide range of breads, cakes and pastries: sponges of every kind, swiss rolls, flans and cheesecakes, real sherry trifle, apple slices, meringues and strawberry shortcake. Freshly-made sandwiches, home-made soup and brown bread are also available daily, and chutneys & relishes like home-made basil pesto and honey & mustard dressing. "Greenbean" coffee is freshly ground for every cup - and you can choose between sitting in or taking out. A good place to break a journey with a wholesome little bite. **Seats 25**. Open Mon-Sat, 9-6. Closed Sun. Amex, Diners, MasterCard, Visa, Laser. **Directions:** Opposite turn for Clonmel on the main street.

Angela's Restaurant

Clonmel
féile bia Restaurant

14 Abbey Street Clonmel Co. Tipperary
Tel: 052 26899

A great little daytime restaurant in the centre of town, Angela's is renowned for delicious, wholesome food - and wholefoods. Baking is a speciality and seasonal and organic produce goes into an imaginative range of dishes with both traditional and contemporary influences. There will always be savoury flans - roast aubergine, semi-dried tomatoes and basil, perhaps and special sandwiches include bruschetta (with peppers & tomato, topped with Cooleeny cheese - vegetarians do well here) and warm wraps like chicken with Thai stir-fry vegetable & sweet chilli sauce. Hot specials might include roast chicken supreme with sweet potato chips, thyme & garlic and desserts tend to towards the comforting - bread & butter pudding, plum & almond tart. They're open all day for tea, coffee and sandwiches - La Scala coffee is served ("skinny" and decaff available) - and cuppa with one of their special oaten Anzac biscuits is just ace. Takeaway and outside catering service also available. Seats: 60. No smoking area. Children welcome. L 12.30-3 Mon-Sat. All à la carte. Closed Sun, Christmas-New Year, Good Fri, bank holidays. **Directions:** Near Friary Church on River Suir.

Clonmel Arms Hotel

Clonmel
Hotel

Sarsfield Street Clonmel Co. Tipperary **Tel: 052 21233** Fax: 052 21526
Email: theclonmelarms@eircom.net Web: clonmelarms.htm

This pleasant old town centre hotel has plenty of atmosphere, a welcoming open fire, a characterful bar and comfortable, reasonably priced accommodation. Recently refurbished rooms have all the usual amenities - phone, TV, tea/coffee making - and full bathrooms. A useful base for business visitors: secretarial service are available and there's a carpark nearby. Conferences/banqueting (300); secretarial services available. Lift. 24 hr room service. Children welcome (under 10s free in parents' room, cot available without charge). Pets permitted by arrangement. **Rooms 30** (2 executive). B&B €57 pps, ss €20 (Room-only rate also available, €50). Bar food available 10-9.30 daily; L&D served daily in the Old Bank restaurant. Closed 25 Dec. Amex, Diners, MasterCard, Visa, Laser. **Directions:** Town Centre.

Hotel Minella

Clonmel
féile bia Hotel

Coleville Road Clonmel Co. Tipperary **Tel: 052 22388** Fax: 052 24381
Email: hotelminella@eircom.net Web: www.hotelminella.ie

Just on the edge of Clonmel, in its own grounds overlooking the River Suir, the original house was built in 1863 as a private residence andwas purchased in 1962 by the current owners, Jack and Babs Nallen. The Nallen family are great racing enthusiasts and have stables nearby, where their Minella horses are trained and the racing theme is carried throughout the hotel. They've expanded the hotel over the years, to provide extensive banqueting and conference facilities and, most recently, self-catering apartments beside the leisure centre. Public areas in the old house, including a cocktail bar, restaurant and lounge areas, have a lovely view over well-kept lawns and the river. Accommodation includes suiteswith four-posters and steam rooms, and junior suites with jacuzzis; all are furnished to a high standard with well-finished bathrooms and housekeeping is exemplary. Excellent facilities and the romantic situation make the hotel especially popular for weddings. Leisure centre with 20 metre swimming pool and outdoor Canadian hot tub, jacuzzi, steam room and gym. **Rooms 70** (3 suites, 5 junior suites, 10 no smoking, 1 disabled). B&B €80pps, ss€20. Closed 23-29 Dec. Amex, Diners, MasterCard, Visa, Laser, Switch.

Kilmaneen Farmhouse

Clonmel Area
Farmhouse

Ardfinnan Newcastle Clonmel Co. Tipperary
Tel: 052 36231 Fax: 052 36231
Email: kilmaneen@eircom.net Web: www.kilmaneen.com

As neat as a new pin, Kevin & Ber O'Donnell's delightfully situated farmhouse is on a working dairy farm, surrounded by three mountain ranges - the Comeraghs, the Knockmealdowns and the Galtees - and close to the river Suir and the Tar, making it an ideal base for walking and fishing holidays. Kevin is trained in mountain skills and leads walking groups and trout fishing in the Suir and Tar on the farm is free (hut provided for tyoing flies, storing equipment and drying waders). It's an old house but well restored to combine old furniture with modern comforts. Bedrooms are not especially big, but they are very thoughtfully furnished (including tea/coffeee facilties and iron/trouser press) and, like the rest of the house, immaculate. There's a big garden, where guests can relax and enjoy the peaceful setting and Ber's dinners are based on fresh farm produce. Fishing, walking. **Rooms 3**

(2 shower only, all en-suite & no smoking). B&B €32.50 pps, ss €6.50. Children welcome (under 2 free in parents' room, cots available). Dining room seats 12; no-smoking. D from 7pm (book i advance) Set D €22.50. No sc. Closed Nov-Mar. MasterCard, Visa. **Directions:** In Ardfinnan, follo signs at the Hill Bar.

Clonmel   Mr. Bumbles

Restaurant/B&B
Kickham St. Clonmel Co. Tipperar
Tel: 052 29188 Fax: 052 2938

With a stylish seating area at reception, attractively laid tables and plenty of plants, the atmospher of Declan Gavigan's large bistro-style restaurant in the centre of town is relaxed and informa Catering for a changing clientèle throughout the day and evening, seven days a week the menus a light morning and afternoon menu, a fairly short à la carte lunch menu and a choice of à la cart or set dinner in the evening – offer straightforward, popular dishes with an international tone a well as the hearty steaks (char-grilled with green peppercorn sauce or garlic & parsley butter) an Tipperary lamb (cutlets with a basil crust, garlic mash potatioes & its own jus) for which the area is renowned. Lunchtime main courses may include home-made burgers, pasta dishes and a roast o the day with hot vegetables, while evening menus are more extensive and offer more ambitiou dishes. Consistently high standards, friendly service, fair pricing - and long opening hours - mak this cheerful restaurant a great asset to the area. Seats 65. No smoking area. L 12.30-2.30 daily (Sur to 3); D 6-10 daily (Sun to 9.30). Set Sun L €22, Set D €35, also à la carte; house wine €16; s discretionary (10% on parties of 6+). Closed 25-26 Dec. MasterCard, Visa, Laser. **Directions:** Situated beside Superquinn car park, opposite the Omniplex Cinema.

Clonmel   Sean Tierney

Pub/Restaurant
13 O'Connell Street Clonmel Co. Tipperar
Tel: 052 24467

This tall, narrow pub is warm, welcoming and spotlessly clean in spite of the huge amount of memorabilia and bric a brac filling every conceivable space. No "characterful" dust here; every bit of brass o copper, every glass and bottle glints and gleams to an almost unbelievable degree. The front bar, especially, is seriously packed with "artefacts of bygone days – in short a mini-museum". A giant screen is discreetly hidden around the corner, for watching matches. Upstairs (and there are a lot of them – this is a four storey building) there's a relaxed traditional family-style restaurant. Food starts with breakfast at 10.30 and there are all sorts of menus for different times and occasions. Expect popular, good value food like potato wedges, mushrooms with garlic, steaks and grills rather than gourmet fare, although the evening restaurant menus are more ambitious. Toilets are at the very top, but grand when you get there. Children welcome before 8 pm. Food served daily: Mon-Sat,10.30-9.30 (Sun to 8.30); L 12-3.30 (Sun from 12.30), D 7-9.30 (Sun to 8.30). No smoking area; air conditioning. Closed 25 Dec, Good Fri. Visa. **Directions:** Situated 1/2 way down O'Connell St. on the left opposite Dunnes Stores.

Dromineer   The Whiskey Still

Pub
Dromineer Nenagh Co. Tipperary **Tel: 067 24129**

Dromineer is one of the Shannon's most-visited places, popular with cruisers, anglers, sailing folk (and even walkers) alike. Declan Collison and Fiona Neilan took over The Whiskey Still in 1999 and have made great improvements to the building - and established a well-deserved reputation for good food. It's a characterful old place just up from the harbour, with a stove in the bar for cold days and table service to wherever you're sitting. The cooking style is lovely - the kind of thing a good home cook would make when not too pressured for time but with a some professional flair in the presentation. Baked garlic mussels, poached chicken breast in a lovely spring onion cream and a generous smoked haddock bake are all typical, followed by a well-made lemon meringue pie, perhaps, or apple cobbler with fresh cream. Just the job for boating folk. Food served all year: Mon-Sat 12.30-9.30 pm, Sundays & bank holidays 12.30-9pm.[Times not confirmed at time of going to press; please phone for details.] Closed 25 Dec & Good Fri. ◇

Fethard — Mobarnane House

Ⓝ Country House

Fethard Co Tipperary **Tel: 052 31962** Fax: 052 31962
Email: info@mobarnanehouse.com Web: www.mobarnanehouse.com

Approached up a stylish gravel drive with well-maintained grass verges, Richard and Sandra Craik-White's lovely 18th century home has recently been restored to its former glory and makes a wonderfully spacious house for guests. A large, beautifully furnished drawing room is the only room where smoking is allowed. All rooms have lovely views and comfortable seating (two have separate sitting rooms), quality bedding and everything needed for a relaxing stay, including tea/coffee making facilities, phones and television. Bathrooms vary somewhat (bedrooms without sitting rooms have bigger bathrooms), but all have quality towels and toiletries. An excellent breakfast gets the day off to a good start - and, as well as being well-placed to explore a large and interesting area blessed with beautiful scenery, an interesting history, local crafts and sports, there's plenty to do on-site (extensive walks in the grounds, tennis, bowls). Pets by arrangement. **Rooms 4** (2 suites, all no smoking). Not suitable for children under 5 except babies (cot available). B&B €75 pps, ss 25. Residents D 8pm, €40. House wine €15. SC discretionary. Closed Nov-Feb. MasterCard, Visa. **Directions:** From Fethard, take Cashel road for 3.5 miles, Turn left, signed Ballinure and Thurles; 1.5 miles on left.

Glen of Aherlow — Aherlow House Hotel

Hotel

Glen of Aherlow Co. Tipperary **Tel: 062 56153** Fax: 062 56212
Email: aherlow@iol.ie Web: www.aherlowhouse.ie

Romantically located in a forest on the slopes of a famous glen this hotel - which was originally a hunting lodge - enjoys stunning views of the surrounding mountains and countryside. The old house is lovely, with well-proportioned rooms furnished in an appealing country house style; the drawing room, bar and dining room are all well-placed to take advantage of the view, and there is a large terrace for fine weather. The bedrooms in the original house also reflect the gracious style, while newer ones have less character, but are comfortably furnished and have all the modern conveniences. Fourteen recently added self-catering houses unfortunately dominate the site but are quite appealing in a "mountain lodge" style. Most recently, a private dining room has been added. Outdoor pursuits like horse riding, fishing, walking and mountain climbing are all on site or nearby; special breaks available. Conference/banqueting (400/300); secretarial services. Children welcome (under 6s free in parents' room). No Pets. **Rooms 29** (all en-suite). B&B €82pps, ss €15.50. Open all year. Amex, Diners, MasterCard, Visa, Laser. **Directions:** From Tipperary town take the R664 road. Signposted to the right after 4 miles.

Nenagh — Country Choice Delicatessen & Coffee Bar

Café/Restaurant

25 Kenyon Street Nenagh Co. Tipperary
Tel: 067 32596 Fax: 067 32736
Email: peter@countrychoices.com Web: www.countrychoice.ie

Food-lovers from all over the country make sure of building in a visit to Peter and Mary Ward's unique shop when planning a journey anywhere near Nenagh. Old hands head for the little café at the back first, fortifying themselves with the superb, simple home-cooked food that reflects a policy of seasonality - if the range is small at a particular time of year, so be it. Meats, milk, cream, eggs, butter and flour: "The economy of Tipperary is agricultural and we intend to demonstrate this with a finished product of tantalising smells and tastes." Specialities developed over the years include Cashel Blue and broccoli soup - served with their magnificent home-baked breads (made with local flours) - savoury and sweet pastry dishes (quiches, fruit tarts) and tender, gently-cooked meat dishes like lamb ragout and beef and Guinness casserole. The shop carries a very wide range of the finest Irish artisan produce, plus a smaller selection of specialist products from further afield, such as olive oil and an unusual range of quality glacé fruits that are in great demand for Christmas baking (they probably make Ireland's best Christmas puddings for sale in the shop too). Several specialities deserve special mention: there's a great terrine, made from the family's saddleback pigs; the preserves - jam (Mary Ward makes 12000 pots a year!) and home-made marmalade, based on oranges left to caramelise in the Aga overnight, producing a runny but richly flavoured preserve; then there is Peter's passion for cheese. He is one of the country's best suppliers of Irish farmhouse cheeses, which he minds like babies as they ripen and, unlike most shops, only puts on display when they are mature: do not leave without buying cheese. As well as all this, they run regular art exhibtions in the shop, wine courses and poetry readings. Definitely worth a detour. Seats 40. No smoking area. Picnic service available. Open all day (9-5.30); L 12-3.30 daily, à la carte; house wine from €15. Children welcome. Closed Mon, bank hols & Good Fri. **No Credit Cards. Directions:** Centre of town,on left half way down Kenyon Street.

Roscrea Area — Fiacri Country House Restaurant

 N Restaurant

Boulerea Knock Roscrea Co. Tipperary
Tel: 0505 43017 Fax: 0505 43017

Not the easiest place to find (it is sensible to get directions when booking) but, once discovered, what a welcome sight Enda & Ailish Hennessy's neat pink-painted farmhouse presents. After showing guests through to a comfortable leather sofa in the bar, Enda quickly offers menus and an aperitif and leaves you to enjoy the open fire and relax with Ailish's five-course menu : six or seven dishes on each course - crab salad with tomato and cognac dressing, deep-fried Cooleeney cheese with spring salad & chutney are typical starters, soup (an unusual cream of peach and tomato perhaps) and fairly traditional main courses like rack of lamb with parsnip purée, rosemary jus & mint sauce, pan-fried medallions of pork with caramelised apple, calvados & wholegrain mustard cream sauce or the more contemporary escalope of salmon with pesto & mozzarella cheese and a basil cream sauce. In the restaurant, warm traditional shades of deep green and red, an open fire and tables elegantly set up with white linen and mahogany chairs all create a relaxed atmosphere in which to enjoy flavoursome, generous country house cooking, enhanced by professional well-paced service and a real sense of hospitality. To finish, try the excellent Assorted Dessert Plate - miniature servings of the day's desserts such as hazelnut meringue roulade, rhubarb ginger & strawberry crumble, strawberry shortcake - or farmhouse cheese. A compact, informative and fairly priced wine list spans the old and new worlds. Cookery classes also available. Seats 80. Not suitable for children under 12. D Tue-Sat, 7-9.15. Set D €38. House wine €16. Full bar licence. Closed Sun, Mon. Amex, MasterCard, Visa, Laser. **Directions:** Roscrea 6 miles,Erril 4.5, Templemore 8.

Templemore — Saratoga Lodge

N Country House

Barnane Templemore Co. Tipperary
Tel: 0504 31886 Fax: 0504 31491

In a particularly unspoilt and peaceful part of the country, just below the famous Devil's Bit in the Silvermine mountain range, Valerie Beamish's lovely classically proportioned house on a working stud farm is well-situated on an open, sunny site looking out over the hills. Good equestrian paintings enhance the large, traditionally furnished reception rooms opening off a spacious hall and there is also a little TV room for children (under 3s free in parents' room, cots available free of charge). Bedrooms are very comfortably furnished, although the bathroom arrangements are a little complicated: two share a well-appointed intercommunicating bathroom and the third shares with the hostess (who uses a downstairs bathroom if guests want it to themselves.) However, guests seem to cope with this unusual arrangement quite happily - no doubt the breakfasts that Valerie takes great pride in are more important, also the fact that she's willing to cook 4-course dinners on request (using home-produced vegetables, herbs and honey), and make picnics - and be extremely hospitable all round. **Rooms 3** (2 en-suite but shared, 1 shower only, all no smoking). B&B €40 pps, no ss. Residents D €20-30 (depending on the number of courses), on request. House wine, €15. Closed 23 Dec-3 Jan. **No Credit Cards. Directions:** N7 from Dublin/Limerick, N62 Templemore, R510 from Templemore/Borrisoleigh 2 miles. First turn right, first turn left.

Terryglass — The Derg Inn

 Restaurant/Pub

Terryglass Co. Tipperary **Tel: 067 22037**
Fax: 067 22297 Email: derginn@eircom.net

Tables set up outside the Derg Inn please the summer crowd and a crackling fire is a welcome sight on a cold day - like many country pubs, this is a place perhaps seen at its best off season. This is one of the area's best pubs for food and the sight of tables set up for the comfortable enjoyment of a good meal quickly gets hungry guests into a relaxed mood (especially boating visitors, after the walk up from the harbour). Head chef Rob Oosterbaan, who is from Holland, sources everything with great care, using the best of local produce including organic food when possible - and endangered fish species, such as cod, have been removed from the menu. Traditional Irish dishes like bacon & cabbage and beef & Guinness pie are always a treat here and evening menus are quite wide-ranging with a choice that usually includes delicious house specialities like home-made paté with Derg Inn mango chutney & garlic bread and salmon in filo pastry with lemon & caper sauce - and maybe fillet steak with wholegrain mustard sauce (Lakeshore mustard is made nearby, at Ballinderry) along with more-ish desserts like praline parfait with cinnamon syrup. Sunday lunch is also quite a speciality, but you don't have to eat at the Derg - there's an interesting little wine list to enjoy with or without food and a very pleasant bar. Music in summer - sometimes Friday nights and usually Saturday, various styles; Sunday night is the one for traditional music enthusiasts. Seats 150 (private function room, 70+). No smoking area. Toilets wheelchair accessible. Open daily: food available 10-10. Breakfast from 10am, L 12-5, D 6-10. A la carte. House wine €15. Sc discretionary. Closed Good Fri, 25 Dec. Amex, MasterCard, Visa, Laser. **Directions:** In the heart of Terrryglass Village.

Terryglass — Kylenoe

Country House — Balinderry Terryglass Nenagh Co. Tipperary
Tel: 067 22015 Fax: 067 22275

Virginia Moeran's lovely old stone house on 150 acres of farm and woodland offers homely comfort and real country pleasures close to Lough Derg. The farm is home to an international stud and the woodlands provide a haven for an abundance of wildlife, including deer, red squirrel, badgers, rabbits and foxes. With beautiful walks, riding (with or without tuition), golf and water sports available on the premises or close by, this is a real rural retreat. Spacious, airy bedrooms are furnished in gentle country house style, with antiques and family belongings, and overlook beautiful rolling countryside. Downstairs there's a delightful guests' sitting room and plenty of interesting reading. Virginia enjoys cooking – her breakfasts are a speciality – and dinner is available to residents by arrangement. Importantly for people who like to travel with their dogs, this is a place where man's best friend is also made welcome – and Kylenoe was the recipient of the Guide's Pet Friendly Establishment Award in 1999. Children welcome (under 2s free in parents' room; cot available) **Rooms 4** (2 en-suite, all no-smoking) B&B €45pps, ss €6.35. Residents D 8pm, €34 (book by noon). Closed 21-30 Dec. MasterCard, Visa. **Directions:** Nenagh - Borrisokane - through Terryglass, 1.5 miles out on left hand side.

Thurles — Dwan Brew Pub & Restaurant

Pub — The Mall Thurles Co. Tipperary
Tel: 0504 26007 Fax: 0504 26060

This trendy bar and microbrewery opened in the centre of Thurles in 1998 - it's an old building which has been given the contemporary design treatment and this, together with the entertainment value of the in-house brews, means it is understandably popular with a young crowd who like their music very loud. The staff are friendly and helpful, the food style is world cuisine - panfried tiger prawns, cajun chicken are typical, also the ubiquitous steak - and adequately executed. Ground floor wheelchair accessible. Children welcome before 9 pm, Barfood served 10.30am-9.30pm (Mon-Sat). [Times not confirmed at time of going to press; please phone for details.] Parking nearby. Closed 25 Dec & Good Fri. MasterCard, Visa. **Directions:** Off Liberty Square. ◇

Thurles — Inch House Country House & Restaurant

féile bia Restaurant/Country House — Bouladuff Thurles Co. Tipperary
Tel: 0504 51348 Fax: 0504 51754
Email: inchhse@iol.ie Web: http:www.tipp.ie/inch-house.htm

Built in 1720 by John Ryan, one of the few landed Catholic gentlemen in Tipperary, this magnificent Georgian house managed to survive some of the most turbulent periods in Irish history and to remain in the Ryan family for almost 300 years. John and Norah Egan, who farm the surrounding 250 acres, took it over in a state of dereliction in 1985 and began the major restoration work which has resulted in the handsome, comfortably furnished period house which guests enjoy today. Reception rooms on either side of a welcoming hallway include an unusual William Morris-style drawing room with a tall stained glass window, a magnificent plasterwork ceiling (and adjoining library bar) and a fine dining room which is used for residents' breakfasts and is transformed into a restaurant at night. Both rooms have period fireplaces with big log fires. The five bedrooms are quite individual and are furnished with antiques. Children welcome (under 3s free in parents' room; cot available). No Pets. **Rooms 5** (all en-suite, 1 shower only). B&B €52.50 pps, ss €7.50.
Restaurant: Polished wood floors, classic country house decor and tables laid with crisp white linen and fresh flowers provide a pleasing setting for dinner, especially when the atmosphere is softened by firelight and candles. French country cooking and Irish influences combine in dishes like local Cooleeney cheese fritters with pear coulis and entrecôte steak with brandy & mushroom cream sauce. Banqueting (45). No children after 7 pm. **Seats 50.** No smoking restaurant. D Tue-Sat 7-9.30; Set D from €36; house wine about €17; sc discretionary. Closed Sun & Mon, Christmas week. MasterCard, Visa, Laser. **Directions:** Four miles from Thurles on Nenagh Road.

COUNTY WATERFORD

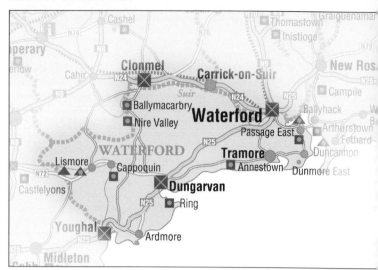

On the quays of Waterford city, we are witness to a trading and seafaring tradition which goes back at least 1,150 years. But this sense of history also looks to the future, as Waterford - the city of crystal and quality glassware - has been selected as the assembly port for the Tall Ships of all nations at the beginning of their European sail training programme in July 2005. Today's larger commercial ships may be berthed downstream on the other side of the river at Belview, but the old cityside quays on the south bank retain a nautical flavour which is accentuated by very useful marina berthing facilities in the heart of town.

This fine port was founded in 853 AD when the Vikings - Danes for the most part - established the trading settlement of Vadrefjord. Its strategic location in a sheltered spot at the head of the estuary near the confluence of the Suir and Barrow rivers guaranteed its continuing success under different administrators, particularly the Normans, so much so that it tended to overshadow the county of Waterford, almost all of which is actually to the west of the port.

But for many years now, the county town has been Dungarvan, which is two-thirds of the way westward along Waterford's extensive south coast, which includes the attractive Copper Coast - between Fenor and Stradbally - in its midst. This spreading of the administrative centres of gravity has to some extent balanced the life of the Waterford region. But even so, the extreme west of the county is still one of Ireland's best kept secrets, a place of remarkable beauty between the Knockmealdown, Comeragh and Monavullagh mountains, where fish-filled rivers such as the Bride, the Blackwater, and the Nire make their way seawards at different speeds through valleys of remarkable variety and beauty, past pretty towns and villages such as lovely Lismore which, on September 9th 2002, was awarded the top award for small towns in the national Tidy Towns competition, while September 22nd 2002 saw the people of Old Parish near Clashmore win the ESB Conservation Volunteers national award for their successful conservation project with the rare pearl mussels of the River Lickey.

West Waterford is a place of surprises. For instance, around the delightful coastal village of Ardmore, ancient monuments suggest that the local holy man, St Declan, introduced Christianity to the area quite a few years before St Patrick went to work in the rest of Ireland. And across the bay from Ardmore, the Ring neighbourhood is a Gaeltacht (Irish-speaking) area with its own bustling fishing port at Helvick.

Dungarvan itself is in the midst of an attractive revival. It has relinquished its role as a commercial port, but is enthusiastically taking to recreational boating and harbourside regeneration instead. Along the bluff south coast, secret coves gave smugglers and others access to charming villages like Stradbally and Bunmahon. Further east, the increased tempo of the presence of Waterford city is felt both at the traditional resort of Tramore, and around the fishing/sailing harbour of Dunmore East, which devotees would claim as the Number One Enjoyment Centre in all Ireland.

Local Attractions and Information

Ballymacarbry Nire Valley & Comeraghs on Horseback	052 36147
Cappoquin Mount Melleray Activity Centre	058 54322
Cappoquin Tourism Information	058 53333
Dungarvan Tourism Information	058 41741
Kilmeaden Old School House Craft Centre	051 853567
Lismore Lismore Castle & Gardens	058 54424
Passage East Car Ferry (to Ballyhack, Co Wexford)	051 382480
Tramore Tramore House Gardens	051 386303
Waterford Airport	051 875589
Waterford Christ Church Cathedral (18c Neoclassical)	051 858958
Waterford Waterford Crystal Glass Centre	051 332500
Waterford Heritage Museum	051 871227
Waterford Int. Festival of Light Opera (Sept)	051 375437
Waterford Reginald's Tower 13th C Circular Tower	051 304220
Waterford Theatre Royal	051 874402
Waterford Tourism Information	051 875823
Waterford Waterford Treasures at the Granary	051 304500

Annestown — Annestown House

B&B

Annestown Co. Waterford **Tel: 051 396160** Fax: 051 396474
Email: relax@annestown.com Web: www.annestown.com

John and Pippa Galloway's comfortable home overlooks a small bay, with a private path leading to the beach below. In front of the house are manicured lawns – one for croquet, one for tennis – while inside there are several lounges with log-burning fires and a billiard room with full-size table. Everywhere you look there are books – a catholic collection ranging from classics to thrillers. For the evening meal there will be dishes such as mushroom soup, roast duck and rhubarb crumble and, next morning, a hearty Irish breakfast (with excellent breads) will set you up for the day ahead. All the centrally-heated bedrooms are en suite with direct-dial telephone and tea-making facilities (and hot water bottles are thoughtfully provided for those who still feel cold). **Rooms 5** (all en-suite & no-smoking), B&B €60 pps, ss €15. Residents' D Mon-Sat €33, at 7.45pm; house wine €23 (book by noon). No D on Sun. Closed 1 Nov-1 Mar. Amex, MasterCard, Visa. **Directions:** Midway between Tramore and Bunmahon on coast road R675.

Ardmore — White Horses Restaurant

féile bia Restaurant

Ardmore Co. Waterford
Tel: 024 94040 Fax: 024 94040

Christine Power and Geraldine Flavin's delightfully bright and breezy café-restaurant on the main street of this famous little seaside town is one of those places that changes its character through the day but always has style. They're open for all the little lifts that visitors need through the day - morning coffee, afternoon tea - as well as imaginative lunches (plus their traditional Sunday lunch, which runs all afternoon) and a more ambitious a la carte evening menu. Vegetarian dishes feature on both menus - a noodle stir-fry during the day perhaps, and Ardsallagh goat's cheese with sesame seed salad in the evening - and there's a good balance between traditional favourites like steaks and more adventurous fare: the daytime fish could be deep-fried plaice with tartare sauce, for example, while its evening counterpart might be Helvick salmon with a crust of cousous, served with a sauce verte. Attractive and pleasant to be in - the use of local Ardmore pottery is a big plus on the presentation side - this is a friendly, well-run place and equally good for a cuppa and a gateau or pastry from the luscious home-made selection on display, or a full meal. **Seats 60.** No smoking area; air conditioning. In summer (May-Sep) open: Tue-Sun 11am-"late" (around 11pm); L 11-4, D 6-11; (also open Mon in Aug). In winter (Oct-Apr) open weekends only: Fri from 6 pm, Sat 11 am-late & Sun 12-4. A la carte except Sun Set L, about €18. Licensed; sc discretionary. Closed Mon all year, except Aug. [Times not confirmed at time of going to press; please phone for details.] MasterCard, Visa. **Directions:** Centre of village. ◇

Ballymacarbry — Melody's Nire View Bar

Pub

Ballymacarbry Co. Waterford
Tel: 052 36147

This well-known pony-trekking and horse riding centre in the upper reaches of the Nire Valley has been in the family for over a hundred years - and it's a great place to take a break if you're walking or simply touring the area. When something simple but good is needed, Melody's is just the spot for a bowl of Carmel's home-made soup served with freshly baked brown bread, or a freshly-cut sandwich and a bit of crisp-crusted apple tart. The soup might be mulligatawny, mixed vegetable, simple mushroom or carrot & tomato, but it will certainly be made from fresh ingredients that morning and the sandwiches - typically turkey, ham, cheese or salad - are freshly made up to order. Recent renovations and extensions have made the pub brighter and more comfortable without losing its atmosphere and its most important features - genuine hospitality, real open fires and simple good food - remain unchanged. There's live music on Tuesdays, Wednesdays & (usually) Sundays in summer too. Maps are available for a number of walks taking from 1.5-4 hours. Light meals. Closed 25 Dec & Good Fri. **No Credit Cards. Directions:** On Nire Valley scenic route, R671, between Clonmel and main Dungarvan-Lismore road (N72).

Ballymacarbry — Glasha Farmhouse Accommodation

Farmhouse

Glasha Ballymacarbry Co. Waterford
Tel: 052 36108 Fax: 052 36108
Email: glasha@eircom.net Web: www.glashafarmhouse.com

Paddy and Olive O'Gorman's spacious farmhouse is set in its own gardens high up in the hills and provides a very comfortable base for a relaxed rural break. Fishing is a major attraction (the Nire runs beside the farmhouse and permits are available locally), also walking (Glasha links the Comeragh and Knockmealdown sections of the famous Munster Way), pony trekking (see Melody's Nire View Bar, above), golf (available locally) and painting this beautiful area. Olive thinks of everything that will help guests feel at home and bedrooms have lots of little extras including TV/radio, hair dryers, electric blankets, tea/coffee-making, spring water and magazines; all rooms are en-suite and the newer ones have lovely bathrooms with jacuzzi baths. There's plenty of comfortable lounging room for guests' use, including a conservatory - and the nearest pub is just 3 minutes' walk from the house. Children welcome, cots available. **Rooms 9** (4 with jacuzzi, 5 shower only, all no-smoking). B&B from €45 pps, ss €8. Closed Christmas. MasterCard, Visa. **Directions:** Off 671 road between Clonmel and Dungarvan; signed on 671.

Ballymacarbry — Hanora's Cottage

🏛 Restaurant/Guesthouse

Nire Valley Ballymacarby Co. Waterford
Tel: 052 36134 Fax: 052 36540
Email: hanorascottage@eircom.net Web: www.hanorascottage.com

Although the latest phase of seemingly endless improvements at the Wall family's gloriously remote country guesthouse has created a very substantial building, Hanora's still nurtures the spirit of the ancestral home around which it is built. The Walls are caring and hospitable hosts and this, plus the luxurious accommodation and good food they provide, makes Hanora's a very special place - and especially wonderful for foot-weary walkers. Spacious, thoughtfully furnished rooms are now all new or recently refurbished, all have jacuzzi baths and there is am especially romantic ones for honeymooners or special occasions. There's also a new conservatory with a spa tub, overlooking the garden with views of the mountains. Overnight guests have the privilege of starting the day with Hanora's legendary breakfast buffet, which was the Munster and National Winner the Denny Irish Breakfast Awards in 2002; it takes some time to get the measure of this feast, so make sure you get up in time to make the most of it. Local produce and an amazing variety of exotics (some of which you may not previously have encountered) jostle for space on the beautifully arranged buffet: the menu begins in orderly fashion with freshly squeezed orange and grapefruit juice and luscious Crinnaghtaun Apple Juice from Lismore, moves on to Seamus Wall's homemade muesli and Mary's Nire Valley Porridge then launches into an amazing list of more fresh fruits before reaching the bread section... Seamus is the baker, beginning at 6am every day so that, when guests come down for breakfast, he'll have an incredible dozen or more types of bread, scones, muffins and buns ready, including organic and gluten free varieties. Alongside the breads you'll find local farmhouse cheeses, smoked salmon and home made jams - and, while that rounds off the buffet, the cooked breakfast options are yet to come: for your hot dish you can have Syl Murray's home-made sausages, Clonakilty black & white puddings, Biddy Cooney's free-range eggs (various ways) and much else besides. This is truly a gargantuan feast, designed to see you many miles along the hills before stop for a little packed lunch (based on Seamus's delicious freshly-baked breads) and ultimately return for dinner... Small weddings (40). **Rooms 11** (1 suite, 3 junior suites, all no smoking). Not suitable for children. No pets. B&B from €75 pps. Closed 22-27 Dec.

Hanoras Cottage: A completely new restaurant and kitchen emerged from the extension of Hanora's Cottage, to the delight of chefs Eoin and Judith Wall. Dinner visitors travel from far and wide to mingle with residents at the fireside in the spacious, warmly furnished seating areas which now extend into the old dining room. Here you can have an aperitif and ponder on Eoin and Judith's imaginative, well-balanced menus, before moving through to the restaurant, which overlooks a new garden and the riverside woodland. Enthusiastic supporters of small suppliers, Eoin and Judith use local produce whenever possible and credit them on the menu - fresh fish from Dunmore East, free range chickens from Stradbally and local cheeses, for example. There's a separate vegetarian dinner menu on request as well as an à la carte which offers a choice of six or seven dishes on each course, usually including some vegetarian options. A typical menu might include starters of sautéed lambs kidneys with wholegrain mustard mash and mushroom paté on crostini with mixed salad and, as lamb is abundant locally, roast rack of lamb makes an excellent main course choice (served, perhaps, with a delicious mint hollandaise), while fish from doesn't have far to travel either and is beautifully fresh and accurately cooked. Classical dessets include home-made ice creams, and are often fruit based. Not suitable for children under 12. **Seats 30/40** D Mon-Sat, 7-9, Set D €40, also à la carte. House wine €14.50. Closed Sun, bank hols.MasterCard, Visa, Laser. **Directions:** Take Clonmel/Dungarvan Road to Ballymacarby.

Cappoquin   **Richmond House**

féile bia Country House/Restaurant

Cappoquin Co. Waterford
Tel: 058 54278   Fax: 058 54988
Email: info@richmondhouse.net   Web: www.richmondhouse.net

Genuine hospitality, high standards of comfort, thoughtful service and excellent food are all to be found in the Deevy family's fine 18th century country house and restaurant just outside Cappoquin - no wonder this is a place so many people like to keep as a closley guarded secret. A good impression is made from the outset, as you approach through well-tended grounds, a feeling confirmed by the climbing plants beside the door, the welcoming hall with its wood-burning stove and the well-proportioned, elegantly furnished reception rooms opening off it. Nine individually decorated en-suite bedrooms vary in size and appointments, as is the way with old houses, but all are comfortably furnished in country house style with full bathrooms. As well as creating wonderful dinners in the restaurant (see below) Paul ensures that guests also have a memorable breakfast a winning combination of genuine hospitality, high standards of comfort, thoughtful service and excellent food Children welcome; cots available without charge. **Rooms 9** (all en-suite & no smoking). B&B €80pps, ss €13. Closed 23 Dec-20 Jan.

Restaurant: The restaurant is the most important single element at Richmond House, and non-residents regularly make up a high proportion of the guests. Warm and friendly service begins at the front door, then menus are presented over aperitifs, in front of the drawing room fire or in a conservatory overlooking the garden. Herbs, fruit and vegetables are grown on the premises for use in the kitchen and Paul is an ardent supporter of local produce, buying seafood from Dunmore East and Dungarvan, beef, lamb, bacon and sausages from his trusted local butcher, and extra organic produce grown nearby. Paul constantly seeks ways to improve the range and style offered and there is a sureness of touch in his kitchen, seen in stimulating menus that always include imaginative vegetarian choices and offer a balance between traditional country house cooking and more adventurous dishes inspired by the current trend towards global cuisine. Dinner menus offering about five choices on each course are changed daily (although based on a core of speciality dishes, such as roast rack of West Waterford lamb on braised puy lentils with a feta croquette, home-made mint jelly and rosemary jus); a slightly shorter separate vegetarian menu is also offered - and one or two local specialities such as Crinnaghtaun apple juice will always feature. Under Claire's direction, service is excellent and admirably discreet care continues throughout. A carefully selected and fairly priced wine list includes interesting house wines and a dozen half bottles. Children welcome (under 3s free in parents' room). Restaurant **Seats 40.** No smoking area. D 7-9 daily (Sun & Mon residents only); Set D €46 (Vegetarian Menu €43); house wine €18; sc discretionary. Amex, Diners, MasterCard, Visa, Laser. **Directions:** Half a mile outside Cappoquin on N72.

Cheekpoint | McAlpin's Suir Inn

féile bia Restaurant | Cheekpoint Co. Waterford **Tel: 051 382 220**
Email: frances@mcalpin.com Web: www.mcalpins.com

This immaculately maintained black-and-white painted inn is 300 years old and has been run by the McAlpin family since 1972. During that time they have earned an enviable reputation for hospitality and good food served at a moderate price, notably local seafood. It's a characterful, country style place with rustic furniture, cottagey plates and old prints decorating the walls. Seasonal menus offer a choice of about six starters (nearly all seafood and under €6.50) and ten main courses, including three cold dishes and two vegetarian ones, again all moderately priced - specialities include a generous seafood platter and home-made seafood pie. All meals come with brown soda bread, butter and a side salad – and there's a nice little wine list including a special selection of eight good New World wines, "The €14 Cellar". Own parking. No children after 8 pm. **Seats 36.** No smoking area; air conditioning. D 6-9.45 Mon-Sat; à la carte; sc discretionary. Closed Sun, Christmas-mid Jan. MasterCard, Visa, Laser. **Directions:** 7 miles east of Waterford.

Dungarvan | Gortnadiha House

Farmhouse/B&B | Ring Dungarvan Co. Waterford
Tel: 058 46142 Email: ringcheese@tinet.ie

Eileen and Thomas Harty's home is on a working dairy farm in a lovely setting, with woodland gardens and sea views. Accommodation in the family home is comfortable, hospitality is warm and breakfasts offer a very wide selection of local and home produce, including fresh fish in season. Children welcome. Pets by arrangement. **Rooms 3** (2 shower only). B&B about €35 pps, ss about €7. Closed Nov-Mar. **Directions:** N25 Rosslare to Cork, 3 km from Dungarvan; follow the sea. ◇

Dungarvan | The Park Hotel

Hotel | Dungarvan Co. Waterford **Tel: 058 42899** Fax: 058 42969
Email: photel@indigo.ie Web: www.flynnhotels.com

This attractive hotel on the outskirts of Dungarvan is owner-run by the Flynn family, who have many years of experience in the hotel business It has views over the Colligan River estuary and fits comfortably into its surroundings, with mature trees softening the approach. Public areas include a cosy traditional bar with panelled walls and a spacious, elegantly appointed dining room. Bedrooms are furnished and decorated to a high standard, with well-finished bathrooms, phone, multi-channel TV, tea/coffee-making facilities and trouser press - and generous desk space as well as easy chairs. In addition to the many outdoor activities in the area – including tennis, fishing, windsurfing, walking, horse-riding, pony-trekking as well as shooting and hunting in season – there's an aqua and fitness centre with 20-metre pool, separate children's pool and many other features. Exceptionally friendly and helpful staff ensure an enjoyable stay at this relaxing hotel. Conference/banqueting (300/300). Own parking. Leisure centre. Children welcome (under 4s free in parents' room; cots available without charge, baby sitting by arrangement). Pets allowed in some areas. Garden. **Rooms 45** (3 shower only). B&B €62.25pps, ss €19.05. Closed Christmas. Amex, Diners, Visa, MasterCard, Laser. **Directions:** Outskirts of Dungarvan just off N25.

Dungarvan | Powersfield House

féile bia Couunrty House | Ballinamuck Dungarvan Co. Waterford **Tel: 058 45594** Fax: 058 45550
Email: powersfieldhouse@cablesurf.com Web: www.powersfield.com

Edmund and Eunice Power's fine guesthouse has proved a very welcome addition to the limited amount of quality accommodation in this lovely area. Although new, it has been furnished in traditional country house style with antiques and interesting fabrics creating a soothing and relaxing atmosphere. Each bedroom has been individually decorated and finished to a high standard, with all the necessary comforts including phones (with ISDN & fax facilities), TV and tea/coffee trays. Children are welcome (under 4s free in parents' room; cot availabe without charge; children's playground). Eunice also runs a small restaurant at the house several nights a week, offering a set menu based on local produce such as Helvic seafood, local organic vegetables and Knocklara cheese. The raw new look that was inevitable around the house in its first season has now mellowed. **Rooms 6** (all en-suite and no smoking, 1 for dsiabled). B&B €45 pps, ss €12. Restaurant not suitable for children under 12. **Seats 18.** D Thu-Sat, 7-9.30. Set D €36; à la carte will also be offered in 2003; SC 10% on parties of 8+. House wine €18.75; sc discretionary. Closed Sun-Wed, 24-28 Dec. MasterCard, Visa, Laser, Switch. **Directions:** Take the main Killarney road R672 from Dungarvan, second turn left first house on right.

Dungarvan
☆ Restaurant

The Tannery Restaurant

10 Quay Street Dungarvan Co. Waterford
Tel: 058 45420 Fax: 058 45118
Email: tanneryecablesurf.com Web: www.tannery.ie

Paul and Maire Flynn's stylish contemporary restaurant is in an old leather warehouse which was imaginatively converted a few years ago and is now home to one of the country's foremost eating places. Paul and his team can be seen at work in the open kitchen as guests go upstairs to the first-floor dining area and the tannery theme is echoed throughout the light, clean-lined interior, creating a sense of history that, along with dramatic paintings and fresh flowers, adds greatly to the atmosphere. Colourful, modish dishes are equally contemporary and wide-ranging menus inspired by global trends are based mainly on local ingredients, which Paul supports avidly and souces with care: local seafood features in a successful modern rendition of grilled hake niçoise, for example, or baked seafood stew with garlic bread. Pork and bacon supplied by local butcher JD Power are rightly a source of pride (tournedos of pork with puy lentils & colcannon perhaps) and meatless magic is also there for the tasting in, for example, a seemingly simple soup of potato, spring onion and wild garlic: simply heaven. Dashing desserts are invariably (very) tempting - pannacotta is a speciality - with mango and passionfruit perhaps - and other deliciously fruity combinations, like hazelnut parfait with red fruit compôte, are equally hard to resist. But don't miss the cheese, which won the Guide's Farmhouse Cheese Award in 2000: a carefully balanced selection is presented in perfect conditionwith oatcakes and chutney. The à la carte is fairly priced for food of this quality, but interesting and frequently changed lunch and early evening menus are especially good value. Toilets wheelchair accessible. Children welcome before 8.30pm. **Seats 52** (private room up to 30, wheelchair accessible). No smoking area. L Tue-Sun, 12.30-2.30; D Tue-Sat (also Sun in Jul & Aug), 6.30-9.30. Early D €22.50 (Tue-Fri, 6.30-7.30 only); Set Sun L €23; house wine €18; sc discretionary (10% on paties of 6+). Closed late Jan-early Feb. Amex, Diners, MasterCard, Visa, Laser.
Directions: End of lower main street beside Old Market House.

Dunmore East
Restaurant

The Ship

Dunmore East Co. Waterford
Tel: 051 383 141 Fax: 051 383 144

The Prendivilles' well-known bar and restaurant is in a Victorian corner house, with a patio on the harbour side which is used mainly for casual lunches in summer. Inside, an atmospheric bar and informal restaurant are designed around a nautical theme - and, although concessions are made to non-seafood eaters, seafood is emphatically the star. Starters might feature an imaginative creation such as cured fillets of monkfish with chervil and dill, served with a sorbet "bloody mary style". and soups will usually include a good bisque. Main courses range from simple pan-fried fish of the day to luxurious dishes such as poached fillets of dover sole and prawns with a lobster and brandy sauce; simpler dishes tend to win the day, however, and specialities like fresh crab claws tossed in garlic & herb butter, or pan-fried black sole are enduring favourites. Tempting desserts tend to be variations on classic themes and there's always an Irish farmhouse cheeseboard. Set Sunday lunch menus, offered in spring and autumn only, are shorter and simpler, but also major on seafood. Children welcome before 8.30 pm. **Seats 85.** No smoking area; air conditioning. D 7-10 daily in summer, closed D Sun & Mon Nov-Mar. L daily Jun-Aug, 12.30-2; otherwise L Sun only in Apr-May & Sep-Oct. D 7-10 daily in summer, closed D Sun & Mon Nov-Mar. Set Sun L €18.41; D à la carte; house wine €17.14; sc discretionary. Closed 25-26 Dec. Amex, Diners, MasterCard, Visa, Laser. **Directions:** 12 miles from Waterford on the Dunmore Road.

Faithlegg
Hotel/Restaurant

Faithlegg House Hotel

Faithlegg Co. Waterford **Tel: 051 382000** Fax: 051 382010
Email: rerservations@fhh.ie Web: wwwfaithlegg.com

This lovely 18th century house is set in wooded landscape with magnificent views over its own golf course and the Suir estuary. The house has been sensitively developed as a luxury hotel - the tone is set in the reception area, with its original stone floor, classic fireplace and Waterford Crystal chandelier, and a similar sensitivity to the essentials of conversion is evident throughout. Public areas are spacious and elegant and bedrooms, in both the old house and a discreetly positioned new wing, are furnished to a high standard; large, graciously proportioned rooms and suites in the old house are really lovely, while those in the new wing are more practical. Somewhere along the line an architectural sense of humour has been at work too, as visitors to the snooker room will discover Self-catering accommodation is also offered in the grounds. Conference/banqueting (180/140) secretarial services. Ample parking. Golf (18), fishing, tennis, gardens, walking; leisure centre swimming pool; treatments; snooker. Children welcome (under 3s free in parents' room; cot available without charge). No pets. **Rooms 82** (14 suites, 14 executive, 10 no-smoking, 6 for disabled). Lift. B&B about €120pps, ss about €25. Closed Christmas & 3 Jan-8 Feb.

Roseville Rooms: The bar is comfortably furnished in a clubby style - a good place to have an aperitif and look at the menu; orders may be taken here and you will be called through when your table is ready. Chef de Cuisine Eric Thèze's well balances classic French menus change daily. The restaurant is shared between two lovely classical, formally appointed dining rooms; cooking is reliable rather than inspired and presentation rather plain (which is preferably to the overdressed look), both perfectly acceptable considering the reasonable price of a 5-course dinner in this beautiful dining room. Service can be a little uneven, notably on busy nights. **Seats 80** (private room 40). No smoking restaurant. Not suitable for children after 7pm. D daily, 6.30-9.30; L 12.30-2.30. Set menu €42, House wines from €18. Amex, Diners, MasterCard, Visa, Laser. **Directions:** Off Dunmore East Road 6 miles out side of Waterford city.

Lismore — Ballyrafter Country House Hotel

Hotel/Restaurant — Lismore Co. Waterford **Tel: 058 54002** Fax: 058 53050
Email: info@waterfordhotel.com Web: ballyrafter@waterfordhotel.com

Fishing is a big draw to Joe & Noreen Willoughby's welcoming country house hotel, but a relaxing atmosphere, log fires and good home cooking appeal to a growing number of people who simply enjoy the area and have come to see the unpretentious comforts of Ballyrafter as a home from home. The bar, where informal meals are served, is lined with photographs of happy fisherfolk - if you are dining in the restaurant, you can have an aperitif here while looking at the menu, or beside the fire in the drawing room next door. Bedrooms in the main house are simple and comfortable and one side of the the courtyard area at the back of the hotel has been thoughtfully developed to provide five new executive bedrooms, all very carefully designed to replicate the older ones. (New PVC windows were installed for practical reasons, but even these were sourced to match existing sash windows); there is also large new first floor room which could be used as a boardroom or for small functions and, on the ground floor, the existing function area overlooking the yard has been completely rebuilt as a conservatory, which allows light through to the bar and transforms that section of the hotel. **Rooms 14** (5 shower only). B&B about €51 pps, ss about €20. Closed Dec-Feb.

Restaurant: An open fire, family antiques and flowers from the garden create a caring atmosphere in the restaurant and the Duke of Devonshire's fairytale castle looks magical from window tables when floodlit at night. Appetising home-cooked meals are based on local ingredients including, of course, fresh and smoked Blackwater salmon, along with home-produced honey and local cheeses like Knockanore and Ring, and service is friendly and helpful. **Seats 30.** No Smoking Restaurant. D 7.30-9.30 daily (Mon residents only); Set D about €31; L Sun only 1-3 pm, Set L about €16. House Wine: about €13; 10% sc. Bar Meals 12-6.30 daily, L 1-2.30. Closed Dec-Mar. Amex, Diners, MasterCard, Visa. **Directions:** On the edge of Lismore town, From Cappoquin direction. ◇

Lismore — Buggys Glencairn Inn

  Restaurant/Pub/B&B — Glencairn Lismore Co. Waterford
Tel: 058 56232 Fax: 058 56232
Email: buggysglencairninn.net Web: www.lismore.com

Ken and Cathleen Buggy's dream of a country pub just oozes character throughout - everything from the little fire-lit bar to the beckoning old-world bedrooms is full of charm. Ken is a talented artist - his delightfully quirky drawings have become symbolic of the West Waterford hospitality scene - but his artlessly rustic food (he describes it as "non-gourmet") is the main attraction here. Everything in this miniscule pub is based on top quality fresh ingredients and "made on the day" so be prepared for limited choice, especially towards the end of service. There's no particular statement about local produce but you'll notice sources mentioned in the decriptions of many of the dishes; about four to six are offered on each course, and food is served in the bar as well as two little dining rooms charmingly set up with a stylish country informality. Paté de campagne is a favourite starter, full of texture and rich flavours, or there's a daily soup such as purée of tomato & gin (with home-made brown soda bread); this may be followed by fish (from Helvick) as available on the day - cooked simply in butter, olive oil and lemon juice - or pot-roasted fillet of pork and apricots (stuffed with spicy black pudding, apricots and apples), all served with crisp little chips, vegetable of the day and a side salad. Finish up with something like fresh lime and lemon flan (with home-made ice cream), or farmhouse cheeses (Durrus, Milleens, Carrigaline, Cashel & Dubliner), then cafetière coffee or an Irish coffee in the bar. An unusual wine list is assembled on individual inserts in a business card index book, a flexible system that allows for weekly changes: brilliant. Cathleen supervises the restaurant and service is both charming and efficient. Upstairs there are five delightful en-suite rooms, all no smoking (€55 pps). Not suitable for children. **Seats 20.** No smoking area. D daily in summer, 7.15-9 (Sun 7-8.30), Wed-Sun in winter; all à la carte, SC 10%; house wine €16.95; sc 10%. Closed Mon & Tue off season, Christmas period & occasionally throughout the year. (Times of opening are somewhat flexible - a phone call ahead is wise, especially off season; dinner reservations strongly advised). Visa. **Directions:** Between Tallow & Lismore on B road between Ballydubh and Lismore, south side of Blackwater.

Millstreet — The Castle Country House

Farmhouse   Millstreet Dungarvan Co. Waterford **Tel: 058 68049** Fax: 058 68099
Email: castlefm@iol.ie Web: www.castlecountryhouse.com

Set in recently landscaped gardens overlooking the River Finisk, the Nugent family's unusual farmhouse is in the 18th century wing of a 16th century castle. Although most of the house seems quite normal inside, it blends into the original building in places - so, for example, the dining room has walls five feet deep and an original castle archway. Spacious, comfortably appointed rooms have king size beds, television, tea/coffee facilities and neat shower rooms; (there is also a full bathroom available for any guest who prefers a bath). Meticulous housekeeping, a very pleasant guests' sitting room and fresh flowers everywhere all add up to a very appealing farmhouse indeed, and Joan uses their own produce - fruit, vegetables, meats and herbs - in her cooking. Excellent breakfasts. Children welcome. Pets by arrangement. **Rooms 5** (all en-suite). B&B €40pps, ss €15. Dining Room **Seats 20**; Residents D €25. Closed 1 Nov-1 Mar. Visa, MasterCard. **Directions:** Off N72 on R671.

Tallowbridge — The Brideview Bar & Restaurant

Restaurant/Pub   Tallowbridge Co. Waterford **Tel: 058 56522**
Fax: 058 56729 Email: annemariecostello@hotmail.com

This attractive bar and restaurant is beautifully located just outside Tallow, beside an old stone bridge over the River Bride and with parking space in a yard beside the pub. Extensions and renovations have kept some character in the older bar - which is along the road side of the building and has an open fire - while creating a fine informal dining space with large windows maximising on views over the river and a large garden which is well away from the road, with picnic tables set up for sunny days. Menus are not over-ambitious and change weekly (plus daily blackboard specials); the emphasis is on providing home-cooked food and good value. Panfried lambs kidneys flamed in brandy and finished in a grainy mustard cream sauce, salmon with a sweet chilli & basil cream sauce are both typical of the evening Bistro menu, while Sunday lunch balances traditional and less predictable dishes rather well. Home-cooked bar food is available all day, making this a useful place to know if you are touring or walking in the area. Children welcome. Restaurant **Seats 45.** L from 12.30 (Sun 12.30-2.30), D 6-9.30 (Sun 5.30-8.30). Set Sun L €19.95, otherwise à la carte. House wine €16.95. Bar food 12.30-9.30 (Sun to 8.30). Closed 25-26 Dec & Good Fri. Amex, MasterCard, Visa, Laser. **Directions:** Near Tallow on N72 12 miles Fermoy - 3 Lismore.

Tramore — Rockett's "The Metal Man"

Pub   Westown Tramore Co. Waterford **Tel: 051 381496**

Open fires and a friendly, welcoming atmosphere will always draw you into this unusual pub but it's the speciality of the house, Crubeens (pig's trotters) which has earned it fame throughout the land. Crubeens (cruibins) were once the staple bar food in pubs everywhere but, as they've been supplanted by crisps, peanuts and lasagne & chips, Rockett's is one of the few places to keep up the old tradition. Two bars are set up with tables for the comfortable consumption of these porcine treats - and you can forget about finger bowls here: the back room even has a sink in the corner for rinsing sticky fingers! Food served Wed-Sat 7-9 pm & Sun 1-6 (weekends only in winter). Phone ahead to check times. Closed 25 Dec & Good Fri. **Directions:** 25 Dec, Good Fri. ◇

Waterford — Chez K's Steak & Seafood Restaurant

Restaurant

26-31 Johns Street Waterford Co. Waterford
Tel: 051 844180 Fax: 051 856925 Email: muldoons@iol.ie

First impressions of this restaurant may be off-putting, as it's self-service, with non-existent decor, poor lighting and very basic table settings. But, once you get past the block, you'll find that lots of young local people have discovered what good food and value for money are offered here - and a cheerful young crowd enjoying themselves creates atmosphere, so eating here might be more enjoyable than anticipated. A wide choice of food is displayed in chilled cabinets around the cooking area and the quality is there for all to see; cutting costs on the frills clearly pays off, as they are able to offer, for example, black (Dover) sole at a mere €20.32. (Black sole has become the benchmark for pricing in east coast restaurants recently and there are some who would cheerfully charge twice that and get away with it.) It comes perfectly cooked, served simply with a lemon beurre blanc - and a full complement of vegetables, including boiled new potatoes (in season). On the steak side, a carpaccio of beef, for example, comes with rocket, roasted beetroot and Parmesan shavings: surprising - and simply delicious. D daily 6-10pm. Diners, MasterCard, Visa, Laser. **Directions:** Head for the junction at Parnell Street; restaurant is on the left. ◇

Waterford — Dwyers Restaurant

Restaurant

8 Mary Street Waterford Co. Waterford Tel: 051 877478 Fax: 051 877480
Email: info@dwyersrestaurant.com Web: www.dwyersrestaurant.com

Quietly located in an elegantly converted old barracks, chef-proprietor Martin Dwyer and his wife Sile have been running this highly regarded restaurant since 1989, and Clive Nunn designed refurbishments have more recently introduced a classy contemporary tone to the decor. Without show or fuss, they consistently provide excellence: low-key presentation of some of the country's finest food is accompanied by discreet, thoughtful service. Martin carefully sources the best seasonal local produce which he prepares in a style that is basically classic French, with some country French and modern Irish influences. He sums up his philosophy with admirable simplicity: "We feel that the basis of good food is taste rather than presentation or fashion". Menus change monthly and main courses lean towards seafood – seared turbot on a bed of fennel, with fennel cream sauce and roast fillet of hake with prawn vinaigrette would both be typical – but there are strong choices for carnivores and vegetarians too. Classic desserts are well worth leaving room for, and there's always an Irish cheese plate. Espresso and herbal teas are offered as well as regular cafetière coffee and tea. Like the cooking, the wine list favours France, although Spain, Italy, Germany and the New World are also represented. The early evening menu is particularly good value. Children welcome before 8 pm. **Seats 32** (private room, 8). No smoking area. D 6-8 Mon-Sat, Set D, early evening menu, 6-7 pm only; à la carte also available; house wine about €14; sc discretionary. No private parking. Toilets wheelchair accessible Closed Sun, Christmas week & bank hols. Amex, Diners, MasterCard, Visa, Laser. **Directions:** 25 yards south of Bridge, turn right into Mary Street.

Waterford — Foxmount Farm & Country House

Country House/Farmhouse

Passage East Road Waterford Co. Waterford
Tel: 051 874 308 Fax: 051 854 906
Email: foxmount@iol.ie Web: www.iol.ie/tipp/foxmount.htm

Foxmount Farm, the Kent family's 17th century country house and working dairy farm, is just 15 minutes drive from the centre of Waterford city. The house is lovely, with classically proportioned reception rooms, and it is a haven of peace and tranquillity. Margaret Kent's home-cooked food is one of the main reasons guests keep returning to Foxmount - dinner, prepared by her personally and based on the farm's own produce, is available for residents by arrangement; vegetarian or other special dietary requirements can be built into menus if mentioned on booking. Margaret is a great baker, as guests quickly discover when she serves afternoon tea in the drawing room (or in the morning, when freshly-baked breads are presented at breakfast). Five very different rooms are all thoughtfully furnished, but bear in mind that peace and relaxation are the aim at Foxmount, so don't expect phones or TVs in bedrooms or a very early breakfast. There is a hard tennis court on the premises (plus table tennis). Children welcome, pets by arrangement. **Rooms 5** (all en-suite & no-smoking). B&B €45pps, ss 15. Residents' D €30, at 7pm (book by noon). BYO wine. Closed1 Nov-10 Mar. **No credit cards. Directions:** From Waterford city, take Dunmore Road - after 4 km, take Passage East road for 1 mile.

Waterford — Gatchell's

 Restaurant

Waterford Crystal Visitor Centre Kilbarry Waterford Co. Waterford
Tel: 051 332575 Fax: 051 332561

If you intend visiting the Waterford Crystal Visitor Centre it might be useful to know that a tasty bite to eat can be part of the plan. Well-known Waterford restaurateurs, Paula and Peter Prendiville, run this stylish all-day restaurant at the centre - and don't be put off by the fact that it's self-service, as Paula cooks interesting, wholesome fare based on local produce, albeit with some international themes. Irish potato & coriander soup, prawn pasta & pineapple salad and fresh salmon salad are all typical - and visitors who despair of ever finding traditional Irish food in the current tidal wave of global cooking will be pleased to see dishes with a respect for tradition here, such as Muphys Irish beef. **Seats 160.** No smoking restaurant. Children welcome. Open daily 8.30am-5.30 (in winter 9-5). A la carte (average main course about €8.85). House wine €12. Closed 21 Dec-2 Jan. MasterCard, Visa, Laser. **Directions:** Waterford Crystal Visitor Centre.

Waterford — The Gingerman Bar

 Pub

6/7 Arundel Lane Waterford Co. Waterford
Tel: 051 879522 Fax: 051 879522

Michael Tierney's renovated pub is in the old Norman area of the city, in a pedestrianised lane just off Broad Street. It's a very pleasant place, with welcoming open fires in several bars, and is now consolidating its quickly earned reputation for good food. Carefully sourced ingredients come from trusted local suppliers and the emphasis is on fresh, home-made and healthy. (They don't serve chips and don't even have a deep fryer in the kitchen). The style is mainly modern, with an all day menu offering snacks like hot sandwiches, paninis and filled baked potatoes (the latter popular as an alternative to sandwiches for people on a gluten-free diet) and there are four hot specials, changed daily, including some traditional choices, like beef & Guinness stew, served with home-made soda bread and bacon ribs with colcannon & parsley sauce. Good cooking is complemented by efficient service, provided by keen, friendly young staff. Open 10am-11.30pm. Food served Mon-Sat, 12-6. A la carte (average snack €7.50; hot specials about €8.85). No food on Sun. Amex, Diners, MasterCard, Visa, Laser, Switch. **Directions:** Off John Roberts Square.

Waterford — Goose's Barbecue Restaurant & Wine House

Restaurant

19 Henerietta Street Waterford Co. Waterford
Tel: 051 858426 Fax: 051 858426

Waterford people seem to have taken to self-service in a big way recently - this one is a little different from the others listed, but the same principles of high quality and good value apply. Here, in an historic site (the details of which are given on the menu), they have a self-service salad buffet and all the main meals are freshly prepared when you order them and cooked in view of customers. There are little starters like cajun chicken wings and saucy sausages and main dishes like boozy beef steaks and medallions of lamb barbecued with rosemary & herbs, served with jacket potato. Vegetarians can have mixed veg & tofu skewers and there's a blackboard giving the fish of the night and desserts. Not suitable for children after 7pm. **Seats 40.** D Tue-Sat, 5-10.30. Early d €20 (5-7.30 only), otherwise à la carte (average main course €16-18). House wine €18. Closed Sun, Mon, 1 week in winter, 1 week in summer. **Directions:** Across from Plaza on the quay.

Waterford — Granville Hotel

 Hotel

The Quay Waterford Co. Waterford **Tel: 051 305 555** Fax: 051 305 566
Email: stay@granville-hotel.ie Web: www.granville.hotel.ie

One of the country's oldest hotels, this much-loved quayside establishment in the centre of Waterford has many historical connections – with Bianconi, for example, who established Ireland's earliest transport system, and also Charles Stuart Parnell, who made many a rousing speech here. Since 1979, it's been owner-run by the Cusack family, who have overseen significant restoration and major refurbishment. It's a large hotel – bigger than it looks perhaps – with fine public areas and well-appointed bedrooms (all with well-designed bathrooms with both bath and shower). This is a good choice for business guests and would also make a comfortable base for touring the area or participating in the many activities available locally, including boating, fishing, golf, walking and horse riding. Off season value breaks available. Conference/banqueting (200/200), secretarial services. Parking nearby. Children welcome (under 3s free in parents' room; cots available without charge). No pets. **Rooms 98** (4 suites, 94 executive rooms, 20 no-smoking). Lift. B&B €90 pps, ss €20. Closed 25-26 Dec. Amex, Diners, MasterCard, Visa, Laser. **Directions:** In city centre, on the quays opposite Clock Tower.

Waterford   Henry Downes

Pub   8-10 Thomas St. Waterford Waterford City **Tel: 051 874 118**
Established in 1759, and in the same (eccentric) family for six generations, John de Bromhead's unusual pub is one of the few remaining houses to bottle its own whiskey. Although not the easiest of places to find, once visited it certainly will not be forgotten. Large, dark and cavernous – with a squash court on the premises as well as the more predictable billiards and snooker – it consists of a series of bars of differing character, each with its own particular following. It achieves with natural grace what so-called Irish theme pubs would dearly love to capture (and can't). Friendly, humorous bar staff enjoy filling customers in on the pub's proud history – and will gladly sell you a bottle of Henry Downes No.9 to take away. Wine about €9 (to drink in pub). Open from 4.30pm to normal closing time. Closed 25 Dec & Good Fri. **No credit cards. Directions:** Second right after Bridge Hotel, halfway up Thomas Street on right. ◇

Waterford   O'Grady's

Restaurant/Guesthouse   Cork Road Waterford Co. Waterford
                                                    Tel: 051 378 851 Fax: 051 374 062
                                            Email: info@gradyshotel.com Web: wwwogradys.ie
Off-road parking and a warm reception from the proprietors get guests off to a good start at Sue and Cornelius O'Grady's restaurant in a restored Gothic lodge on the main Cork road. The dining area is well-situated at the rear of the building, away from the road and, while this has always been a reliable restaurant, recent visits have been impressive. Menus change weekly and include 2/3 course lunch menus and an interesting, well-balanced à la carte; they always offer tempting vegetarian dishes mozzarella & courgette stack, with sesame seed & balsamic dressing for example and dishes which sound quite plain on the menu - a starter of smoked salmon risotto, perhaps, or a main course like pork fillet with apples & calvados - turn out to be delicious. The best of local seafood features in starters like rock oysters gratinée with shallots & white wine, straightforward oysters or a well-made chowder - while main courses offer a well-balanced selection including ever-popular choices like steaks. Finish with a classic dessert like bread 7 butter pudding with rum-soaked raisins & crème anglaise, or farmhouse cheeses, perhaps, which are served plated. Children welcome. **Seats 60** (private room, 14). No smoking area. L 12.30-2.15 & D 6.30-9.30 daily. Set L €23, Set D €35, à la carte also available; house wine €18.75; sc 10%. [There are also 9 en-suite bedrooms, €50 pps.] Closed Christmas/New Year. Amex, Diners, MasterCard, Visa, Laser, Switch. **Directions:** On main Cork road, 5 minutes from city centre.

Waterford   Tower Hotel Waterford

Hotel   The Mall Waterford Co. Waterford **Tel: 051 875801** Fax: 051 870 129
                                    Email: reservations@the.ie Web: www.towerhotelwaterford.com
A central location, within easy walking distance of everything in the city, ample private parking, large conference/banqueting capacity and excellent on-site leisure facilities are major attractions at this big hotel. Considerable investment over the last few years has seen an improvement in standards throughout the hotel: an impressive new bistro, a carvery restaurant and a new state of the art conference centre are all quite recent additions and the lobby and reception area have been renovated. However, refurbishment is still ongoing at the time of going to press and some bedrooms may not yet have been completed - it is worth checking on this when making a reservation as there is a big difference between old and new rooms. Conference/banqueting facilities (450/4350), Leisure Centre, indoor swimming pool. Children welcome (cots available free of charge). Own parking. **Rooms 140** (3 suites, 3 executive, 3 for disabled). Lift. B&B €75 pps, ss €40. Closed 24-27 Dec. Amex, Diners, MasterCard, Visa, Laser, Switch. **Directions:** Waterford city centre overlooking the marina.

Waterford   Waterford Castle Hotel & Golf Club

Hotel   The Island Ballinakill Waterford Co. Waterford
                                                    Tel: 051 878 203 Fax: 051 879 316
                                    Email: info@waterfordcastle.com Web: www.waterfordcastle.com
This beautiful hotel dates back to the 15th century. It is uniquely situated on its own 310 acre wooded island (complete with 18-hole golf course) and is reached by a private ferry. The hotel combines the elegance of earlier times with modern comfort, service and convenience - and the

ocation is uniquely serene. Its quietness (and the golf facility for off-duty relaxation) makes the astle a good venue for small conferences and business meetings, but it is also a highly romantic ocation and perfect for small weddings. All guestrooms have recently been refurbished and, although they inevitably vary in size and outlook, all are very comfortably furnished in a luxurious ountry house style. Dinner is served daily in the Munster Dining Room: expect a classical style with modern influence. Conference/banqueting (30/70). Golf, fishing, tennis, walking. Children welcome under 4s free in parents' room; cots available). No Pets. **Rooms 19** (5 suites, 14 en-suite) Lift. 'oom rate from about €150 (2 guests). Open all year. Amex, Diners, MasterCard, Visa, Laser. **Directions:** Outskirts of Waterford City just off Dunmore East road. ◇

Waterford — The Wine Vault

 Restaurant High Street Waterford Co. Waterford **Tel: 051 853 444** Fax: 051 853 444
Email: info@waterfordwinevault.com Web: www.waterfordwinevault.com

ituated in the medieval part of the city, in an 18th century bonded warehouse with the remains of a 15th century tower house, David Dennison's informal little wine bar and restaurant includes a vaulted wine merchant's premises and has great atmosphere. Informal, bistro-style menus are international in tone and strong on vegetarian choices and local produce, notably seafood - as seen in specialities like Wine Vault gravadlax, seared scallops with puff pastry shell with wilted spinach and a chive beurre blanc and hot seafood platter. Other carefully sourced ingredients include local beef, pork, eggs and poultry; organic vegetables and farmhouse cheeses. A special gourmet tasting menu has wines specifically chosen by wine-man David to complement each course. Lunchtime specials and early evening menu (5.30-7) are especially good value. Exceptional wine list. Toilets wheelchair accessible. Children welcome **Seats 50** (private room 50). No smoking area; air conditioning. L& D Mon-Sat, 12.30-2.30 & 5.30-10.30. A la carte; early D €22 (5.30-7.30 only); house wine €18.50-€22. sc discretionary. Closed Sun (excep bank hol weekends), 25 Dec, Good Fri. Amex, MasterCard, Visa, Laser. **Directions:** Take right turn off quay - City Square car park. Take next left to High Street.

COUNTY WESTMEATH

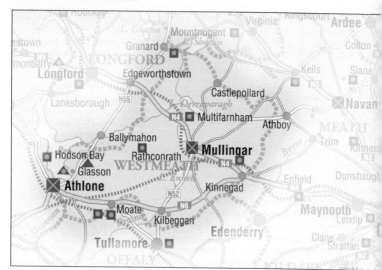

As its name suggests, in the distant past Westmeath tended to be ruled by whoever held Meath. But today, Westmeath is a county so cheerfully and successfully developing its own identity that perhaps they should find a completely new name for the place. For this is somewhere that makes the very best of what it has to hand.

Its highest "peak" is only the modest Mullaghmeen of 258 m, 10 kilometres north of Castlepollard. But this is in an area where hills of ordinary height have impressive shapes which make them appear like miniature mountains around the spectacularly beautiful Lough Derravaragh, famed for its association with the legend of the Children of Lir, who were turned into swans by their wicked step-mother Aoife, and remained as swans for 900 years until saved by the coming of Christianity.

Westmeath abounds in lakes to complement Derravaragh, such as the handsome expanses of Lough Owel and Lough Ennell on either side of the fine county town of Mullingar, where they've been making life even more watery in recent years with schemes to speed the restoration of the Royal Canal on its way through town from Dublin to the north Shannon.

Meanwhile, Athlone to the west has - like Mullingar - greatly benefited from having a by-pass built to remove through traffic bound for the west coast. Thus Athlone is confidently developing as one of Ireland's main inland river towns, its Shannonside prosperity growing on a useful mixture of electronics, pharmaceuticals and the healthcare industry.

Despite such modern trends, this remains a very rural place - immediately south of the town, you can hear the haunting call of the corncrake coming across the callows (water meadows). But Athlone itself has a real buzz, particularly in the compact area around the old castle by the west bank quayside. And north of it, there's Lough Ree in all its glory, wonderful for boating in an area where, near the delightful village of Glasson, the Goldsmith country verges towards County Longford, and they have a monument to mark what some enthusiasts reckon to be the true geographical centre of all Ireland. You really can't get more utterly rural than that.

Local Attractions and Information

Athlone	All Ireland Amateur Drama Festival (May)	0902 73358
Athlone	Athlone Castle Visitor Centre	0902 92912
Athlone	River Festivals	0902 94981
Athlone	Tourism Information	0902 94630
Ballykeeran	MV Goldsmith Lake & River Cruises	0902 85163
Castlepollard	Tullynally Castle & Gardens	044 49060
Clonmellon	Ballinlough Castle Gardens	046 33135
Glasson	Glasson Rose Festival (August)	0902 85677
Kilbegggan	Locke's Distillery Museum	0506 32134

Kilbeggan Race Course 0506 32176
Kinnegad National Ploughing Championship 2003 0507 25125
Moate Dun na Si Folk Park 0902 81183
Mullingar Belvedere House, Gardens & Park 044 49060
Mullingar Tourism Information 044 48761
Mullingar Westmeath Tourism Council 044 48571

Athlone — Hodson Bay Hotel

féile bia Hotel   Hodson Bay Athlone Co. Westmeath **Tel: 0902 80500** Fax: 0902 80520
Email: info@hodsonbayhotel.com Web: www.hodsonbayhotel.com

This waterside hotel adjoins Athlone Golf Club on the shores of Lough Ree, just four miles outside Athlone town. With lovely lake and island views and a wide range of leisure activities on site – including boating and fishing and a fine leisure centre – it's in great demand as a venue for both business and social occasions. It is the only establishment providing such facilities in the locality and, until this year, has also been the only hotel offering quality accommodation in the area. To meet the demand it has grown considerably since opening in 1992 - the Waterfront Bar & Buttery were recently extended and refurbished, new bedrooms added, and also a children's playroom and the Garden Restaurant breakfast room. Bedrooms are bright and comfortable, with contemporary decor, well-finished en-suite bathrooms and double and single beds in most rooms; many also have lough views. If there is a downside, it is that the hotel is almost always so busy that it is difficult for maintenance and routine refurbishment to keep pace with ongoing wear and tear, especially in public areas - and, similarly, keeping food standards up to the high quality to which the hotel clearly aspires is a challenge which is difficult to meet. Excellent banqueting/conference facilities (700/500); secretarial services, business centre; video conferencing available. Helipad. Leisure centre, swimming pool; beauty salon. Golf (18), fishing, equestrian, tennis, walking, garden. Children welcome (under 2s free in parents' room; cots available without charge. playroom, children's playground). No pets. **Rooms 133** (2 suites, 6 junior suites, 36 executive rooms, 1 for disabled).2 Lifts. Limited room service. B&B €110pps, ss €25. Open all year.
L'Escale Restaurant: The restaurant is on the lake side of the hotel, well-appointed in traditional style. Head chef Tony Hanevy has been at the hotel since 1992 and food is generally above the usual expectation for hotels. In addition to the basic à la carte, daily set menus ensure variety for residents. While not adventurous, the quality of ingredients, cooking, presentation and service all ensure an acceptable meal. Expect popular dishes: steaks may be predictable but this is great beef country and they are well-cooked, with a choice of sauces. The seafood selection sometimes includes lobster, along with several fish. There is a short vegetarian menu and farmhouse cheese is always available in addition to traditional desserts. **Seats 150.** No smoking area; air conditioning. L 12.30-2.30 & D 7-9.30 daily. Set L €17, (Sun L €20), Set D €32, à la carte available, house wines from €17; sc discretionary. [Bar food available 10-9 daily]. Open all year. Amex, Diners, MasterCard, Visa, Laser. **Directions:** Located off the Roscommon road, just 5 minutes from Athlone town.

Athlone — The Left Bank Bistro

Restaurant   Fry Place Athlone Co. Westmeath **Tel: 0902 94446** Fax: 0902 94509
Email: mail@leftbankbistro.com Web: www.leftbankbistro.com

Athlone has alway been a great place to break the journey if you're travelling across the country, but it has recently become much more than a handy stopover: now recognised as the culinary capital of the inland waterways, it has become a destination town for discerning travellers, whether by car or by boat. Annie McNamara and Mary McCullough's wacky little Left Bank Bistro was one of the cornerstones of that reputation - and their philosophy lives on in their elegant and spacious newer premises near the river. Here architectural salvage materials and interesting, subtle colours combine well with contemporary wooden furniture and a gently minimalist style to create a space which is both impressive and relaxing. Bare tables and paper napkins convey an informal atmosphere that suits their lively food: short, keenly-priced lunch menus - plus several extra lunch-time savoury dishes chalked up on a blackboard - offer a wide range of delicious-sounding dishes with the multi-cultural stamp which, together with carefully sourced ingredients and good cooking, make this the number one choice for an informal meal in Athlone. Wraps, bruschetta, focaccia feature a lot, especially on the lunch menu (try the marinaded steak sandwich on focaccia with sauté onions, sautépotatoes & mixed leaves), and accompanying salads and vegetables are always oustanding - colourful and full of zing. Fresh fish dishes have their owen menu, and vegetarians can choose between blackboard specials and regular dishes from the menu, including Greek salad, Left Bank

Salad (with a wedge of foccacia) and Vegetable Spring Rolls (or samosas). Dinner menus are mor extensive and tend to be based on more expensive ingredients, but the style is similar and, her again, vegetarian dishes are especially attractive. After a choice of delicious desserts or farmhous cheeses, dip into a nice little drinks menu that offers a range of coffees, teas and hot chocolate **Seats 70**. No smoking area; air conditioning. Wheelchair access. Open 10.30-9.30. L 12-5 & D 6 9.30 Tue-Sat; all à la carte; main courses from about €7.50 (L), €16 (D); house wine €17. Close Sun, Mon, bank hols & Christmas. Amex, MasterCard, Visa, Laser. **Directions:** Behind Athlone Castle west side of the Shannon.

Athlone   Manifesto

Restaurant   Custume Place Athlone Co. Westmeath
                                              Tel: 0902 73241 Fax: 0902 7324

Up a flight of wide, carpeted stairs reminiscent of 1950s cinemas, this stylish restaurant just eas of the bridge offers contemporary food in chic minimalist surroundings inspired by cocktail bars o the '60s - and the focal point on arrival is a Manhattan Cocktail Bar, complete with an abundance of cream leather seating. Quality materials - marble, leather, fine woods - and bare tables graced b white linen napkins and a single long-stemmed rose set the tone. French-influenced seasonal menu are backed up by professional service. **Seats 75**. Open daily: Fri-Sun from 12.30-"late", Mon-Thu from 4pm. Closed 25 Dec, 1 Jan, Good Fri. MasterCard, Visa. **Directions:** Heading west through town, on the right just before the bridge. ◇

Athlone   The Olive Grove

Restaurant   Bridge St. Custume Place Athlone Co. Westmeath
                                              Tel: 0902 76946 Fax: 0902 71248

Garry Hughes and Gael Bradbury opened their charming little restaurant in the autumn of 1997 and it has quickly built up a following for its pleasant, informal atmosphere (seasoned with a good dash of style), excellent home-cooked food from noon until late (light food in the afternoon), good value and a great willingness to do anything which will ensure a good time being had by all. The style is Mediterranean-influenced and youthful - as seen in starters such as bruschetta and vegetarian specials like Greek salad - but this is beef country and the speciality of the house is chargrilled steaks. Children welcome. Parking nearby. **Seats 50**. No smoking area. L &D Tue-Sun,12-4 & 5.30- 10); à la carte (average main course about €10 (L); €18 (D); house wines €15.50, sc discretionary. Closed Mon, 24-28 Dec. Amex, MasterCard, Visa, Laser. **Directions:** Travelling from Dublin, take the left before the bridge in Athlone town centre.

Athlone   Restaurant Le Chateau

Restaurant   St. Peter's Port The Docks Athlone Co. Westmeath
                                              Tel: 0902 94517 Fax: 0902 93040
                                    Email: lechateau@eircom.net Web: www.rlc.net

Steven and Martina Linehan's atmospheric quayside restaurant is in a converted Presbyterian Church just west of the bridge. The church, which was closed in the early 1970s, has been magnificently transformed into a two-storey restaurant of great character which complements the couple's well-earned reputation for excellent food and hospitality. Designed around the joint themes of church and river, the upstairs section has raised floors at each end, like the deck of a galleon, while the church theme is reflected in the windows - notably an original "Star of David" at the back of the restaurant - and the general ambience, which is extremely atmospheric. Candles are used generously to create a relaxed, romantic atmosphere, notably during their renowned Candlelight Dinners. (Le Chateau was the Guide's Atmospheric Restaurant of the Year in 1999.) Steven Linehan is a talented chef and, backed up by a well-trained front of house staff, is providing a superb dining experience at formal meal times and a valuable service to locals and visitors alike by remaining open for lighter fare during the day. He seems to have looked after every dining requirement with menus that include an express lunch (2/3 course and very good value), an à la carte lunch for those with time to linger, accessible Sunday lunch and early evening menus that allow families to eat out well together without breaking the bank - and a fine dining experience later in the evening. Local produce is very much in evidence - notably Angus beef and rack of lamb - the cooking style is modern, with some international influences but a sense that the chef is in control rather than the fashion; presentation is attractive, with a nod to current styles - but it is for real flavour, attention to detail and professional service that a meal at Le Chateau will be remembered Children welcome. **Seats 100** (private room, 20) No smoking area; air conditioning. Open 12.30-10 daily: L 12.30-3 (Sun to 5.30), D 5.30-10; Set L €12, Set Sun L €23, Early D €23 (5.30-6.45 pm only); also à la carte; house wines from €18.75; SC10%. Full bar. Closed 24-16 Dec. Amex, MasterCard, Visa, Laser. **Directions:** Heading west through Athlone,over Shannon and left at castle, left again and onto bank of Shannon.

Athlone — Sean's Bar

Pub   13 Main Street Athlone Co. Westmeath **Tel: 0902 92358**

West of the river, in the interesting old town near the Norman castle (which has a particularly good visitors' centre for history and information on the area, including flora and fauna of the Shannon), Sean Fitzsimons' seriously historic bar lays claim to being the pub with the longest continuous use in Ireland – all owners since 900 AD are on record. (It has actually been certified by the National Museum as the oldest pub in Britain and Ireland - and the all-Europe title is currently under investigation.) Dimly-lit, with a fine mahogany bar, mirrored shelving, open fire and an enormous settle bed, the bar has become popular with the local student population and is very handy for visitors cruising the Shannon (who have direct access to the river through the back bar and beer garden). The sloping floor is a particularly interesting feature, cleverly constructed to ensure that flood water drained back down to the river as the waters subsided (it still works). A glass case containing a section of old wattle wall original to the building highlights the age of the bar, but it's far from being a museum piece. Food is restricted to sandwiches (Mon-Sat), but the proper priorities are observed and they serve a good pint. Closed 25 Dec & Good Fri. **Directions:** On the west quayside, just in front of the castle. ◇

Glasson — Glasson Golf Hotel and Country Club

Ⓝ Hotel   Killinure House Glasson Athlone Co. Westmeath
                                           Tel: 0902 85120 Fax: 0902 85444
                                     Email: info@glassongolf.ie Web: www.glassongolf.ie

Beautifully situated in an elevated position overlooking Lough Ree, the Reid family's impressive new hotel has been developed around their fine old family home (now the clubhouse) and, it will delight all discerning visitors - not just golfers to this lovely area. The golfing dimension pre-dated the hotel (Christy O'Connor Junior course) and has earned an international reputation as one of Ireland's premier inland courses, but the hotel is equally geared to business guests and those looking for peace and relaxation in beautiful surroundings. It is bright and contemporary, with a welcoming atmosphere; guest rooms are spacious, thoughtfully furnished with the needs of business travellers in mind and decorated in an attractive modern style which is not over-designed and allows views over the lough and golf course to take centre stage. The bar and restaurant are in the clubhouse section of the hotel, and both have been refurbished in a more traditional style appropriate to the older building. There's also a private jetty between the 15th and 17th greens, where visiting cruisers coming to the hotel may berth, or residents can arrange a private cruise. The hotel is a great addition to the limited accommodation choice around Athlone and will be a real asset to the area. **Rooms 29** (1 junior suite, 12 executive, 1 disabled). Lift. B&B from €85pps, ss€50. Special breaks offered. Children welcome (under 3s free in parents' room, cots available without charge). Conference/banqueting 100/120. Food available to non-residents all day (7.30am-10pm). Closed 25 Dec. Amex, Diners, MasterCard, Visa, Laser. **Directions:** 6 miles north of Athlone on the N55 Cavan-Longford road.

Glasson — Glasson Village Restaurant

Restaurant   Glasson Co. Westmeath **Tel: 0902 85001**

In an attractive stone building which formerly served as an RIC barracks, chef-proprietor Michael Brooks opened the Village Restaurant in 1986, making his mark as a culinary pioneer in the area. On the edge of the village, there's a real country atmosphere about the place, enhanced by old pine furniture and a conservatory which is particularly pleasant for Sunday lunch. As has been the case since they opened, fresh fish features strongly on the menu – Michael takes pride in having introduced fresh seafood at a time when it wasn't popular locally, and aims to maintain the special reputation earned for fresh fish (including shellfish in season and freshwater fish like Lough Ree eel). His cooking has long set the standard for the area which, together with caring service under the supervision of Marie Brook, who is restaurant manager, has earned the restaurant enduring popularity with a loyal following. The style is imaginative and fairly traditional – country French meets modern Irish perhaps; à la carte menus change with the seasons, set menus weekly and there are always a couple of vegetarian dishes. Consistent standards and good value will ensure enduring popularity. Parking. Children welcome. **Seats 50**. No smoking area. D Tue -Sat 6-9.30; L Sun only 12.30-2.30. Set D €31.50, also à la carte; early D €21,50 (6-7pm only). Set Sun L €18.50. House wines €16-20.50; sc discretionary. Closed D Sun, all Mon, 3 weeks from mid Oct, 24-26 Dec. Amex, Diners, MasterCard, Visa, Laser. **Directions:** 5 miles from Athlone on Longford/Cavan road (N55).

Glasson — Grogan's Pub

Pub   Glasson Co. Westmeath **Tel: 0902 8515**

It's hard to cross the Midlands without being drawn into at least a short visit to this magic pub in Goldsmith's "village of the roses". It's one of those proudly-run, traditional places with two little bars at the front (one with a welcome open fire in winter) and everything gleaming; it was established in 1750 and feels as if the fundamentals haven't changed too much since then. There's traditional music on Wednesday nights, when three generations of the same family play and visiting musicians are also welcome. At the back, in a very pleasant informal bar/restaurant known as "Nannie Murph's", Anne Casey offers light (and some more substantial) meals in a colourful contemporary style. Nannie Murph's open: Mon-Sat, 12 noon-4 pm & 5.30-9pm, Sun 4-8 pm; closed 24-26 Dec, 31 Dec, 1 Jan. & Good Fri. Pub closed 25 Dec, Good Fri . [Times not confirmed at time of going to press, please phone for details.] Visa, MasterCard, Laser. **Directions:** Centre of village. ◇

Glasson — The Three Jolly Pigeons

Pub   Glasson Co. Westmeath **Tel: 0902 85162**

McCormack's "Three Jolly Pigeons" is an unspoilt country pub, with an open fire and a friendly welcome - but its special claim to fame is that Oliver Goldsmith (1728-1774) was reared nearby at Lissoy parsonage - and the area inspired some of his most famous work, including the poem "The Deserted Village" - and The Three Jolly Pigeons is actually named in the play "She Stoops to Conquer" (1773). Closed 25 Dec & Good Fri. **Directions:** Outside Glasson on the N55, halfway between Glasson & Ballymahon. ◇

Glasson — Wineport Lodge

 Restaurant/Accommodation   Glasson Co. Westmeath
Tel: 0902 85466 Fax: 0902 85471
Email: lodge@wineport.ie Web: www.wineport.ie

HIDEAWAY OF THE YEAR

Since the opening of their stunning new accommodation in 2002, Ray Byrne and Jane English's lovely lakeside lodge now styles itself as Ireland's first wine hotel - and it has certainly brought something sensationally different to the Midlands. A covered boardwalk in front of the restaurant brings you to the front door: enter your guest key card and step into a different world. A lofty residents lounge with a stove and its own bar simply oozes style and comfort, a hint of the high pamper quota waiting above in the ten spacious new bedrooms, all with private balconies overlooking the lake. Superbly comfortable beds with goose down duvets and extra large pillows face the view - a clear invitation to relax and take it all in. There's flat screen TV too, if the view is not enough - in fact, why not have a little drink courtesy of your hosts - Ray and Jane decided to build on the history of the townland of Wineport by naming each room after a wine or a region famous for its wine and including related artefacts in the decor - and a little taste of that particular wine to enjoy with your hosts' compliments! The careful planning, inspired design and attention to detail throughout is exceptional: seriously luxurious bathrooms have separate double-ended bath and walk-in shower, de-mist mirrors, underfloor heating and many little extras; complimentary drinks trays include individual cafetières - and fresh milk in the fridge; business guests will be delighted by the amount of state-of-the-art technology that is hidden discreetly away yet instantly accessible (not a network of ugly wires to be seen anywhere). Nothing has been overlooked - even the decor, which is designed around a palette of warm neutrals and natural materials, complements the view rather than distracting from it and has universal appeal. Skilful use of a wide range of woods is perhaps the strongest design theme throughout and, not only is it a perfect complement to the natural backdrop, but Jane's brother, the cabinetmaker and designer Robert English, did all the woodwork for them. Wineport is now a place with a huge amount to offer and certain to become a hot choice for business and corporate events - every technological requirement has been thought of and one look at the first floor board room, which is also dramatically planned to take full advantage of the beautiful location, would sway anyone arranging a meeting. Luxurious, romantic, beautiful, businesslike, this boutique hotel is a place of many moods: Wineport has everything. **Rooms 10** (all no smoking; 1 for disabled, shower only). All day room service. Conference/banqueting (40/100). Garden, fishing, walking. Children welcome (cots available €50). B&B €137.50pps, ss €137.50; (single rate €175 available Sun-Thu); sc discretionary.

Wineport Lodge: This lovely lakeside restaurant is almost a second home to many regulars guests. Its stunning location and exceptional hospitality draw guests back time and again – guests who return with additions to the now famous Wineport collections (nauticalia, cats) and find the combination of the view, the company and a good meal irresistible. Head chef Feargal O'Donnell is a member of Euro-Toques and presents strongly seasonal menus based on local ingredients including game in season, eels, home-grown herbs, free range eggs and wild mushrooms. However, the style is diverse - international, with an occasional nod to traditional Irish themes - so you could start a meal with duck dim sum & sesame dipping sauce or tomato, mozzarella & pesto salad and follow with dishes as ranging from Dublin Bay prawns sautéed with crab claws, chilli, coriander & coconut cream to a traditional dish like carved whole rack of Midlands lamb for two, with sweet mustard crust & sauce paloise. There's always at least one dish based on certified Irish Angus beef, (rib-eye or fillet with a choice of sauces) and interesting vegetarian dishes too. Finish with pretty seasonal desserts - updated desserts like pink grapefruit cheesecake with a sesame tuile - or, for cheese lovers, a choice of cheese plates: the Irish selction (Boilie, smoked Gubbeen and Cooleeney camembert and Cashel Blue) or 'Blue For You' (Cashel Blue, Stilton & Roquefort), both served with a glass of Fonseca Bin 27 port. Ray and Jane were the Guide's Hosts of the Year in 1999. **Seats 100** (private room, 50). No smoking restaurant; air conditioning. Children welcome. D daily 6-10 (Sun to 9); L Mon-Fri, 12.30-2.30; D daily, 6-10 (Sun 4-9); Set D €50; à la carte L&D available; house wine €19; sc discretionary. Closed 24-26 Dec. Amex, Diners, MasterCard, Visa, Laser. **Directions:** Midway between Dublin and Galway; take the Longford/Cavan exit off the Athlone relief road; fork left after 2.5 miles at the Dog & Duck; 1 mile, on the left.

Kinnegad | The Cottage

Restaurant | Kinnegad Co. Westmeath **Tel: 044 75284**

In the village of Kinnegad, just at the point where the Galway road forks to the left, this delightful homely cottage restaurant is one of Ireland's best-loved stopping places, with comfy traditional armchairs and real home-made food – anything from proper meals with a glass of wine at given times to snacks at any time and a really great afternoon tea. Baking is a speciality, with scones and home-made preserves, a wide variety of cakes and irresistible cookies always available. Home-made soups, hot dishes like poached salmon, quiches and omelettes served with a salad are all typical, along with desserts such as apple pie or gateaux. The only sad thing is that they're closed at weekends, when so many people are travelling between Dublin and the west coast - and for several months in the winter. Children welcome. **Seats 40.** No smoking restaurant. Open Mon-Fri, 8am-6pm; à la carte. Closed Sat, Sun, bank hol Mons & Dec-Mar. **No Credit Cards. Directions:** On the N4, 37 miles from Dublin - Galway/Sligo road.

Moate | P. Egan

Pub | Main Street Moate Co. Westmeath
Tel: 0902 82014 Email: peganspub@eircom.net

Easy to recognise with its bright red and black paintwork and the bikes outside, this cheerful traditional pub in the centre of Moate has a turf range in the back bar and it's a friendly place to drop in for a drink and some low-down on the area. Traditional Irish music is a speciality. Own parking. Children welcome up to 6pm. Pets allowed by arrangement. Visa. **Directions:** Directly beside Bank of Ireland on Main Street. Visa. **Directions:** Beside the Bank of Ireland on the Main Street.

Moate | Temple Country House & Spa

Country House | Horseleap Moate Co. Westmeath
Tel: 0506 35118 Fax: 0506 35008 Web: www.spiders.ie/templespa

Relaxation is the essence of Declan and Bernadette Fagan's philosophy at Temple, their charming and immaculately maintained 200 year-old farmhouse in the unspoilt Westmeath countryside. On its own farmland - where guests are welcome to walk - close to peat bogs, lakes and historical sites, outdoor activities such as walking, cycling and riding are all at hand. There are three lovely country style en-suite rooms in the house and a further five newer ones in the courtyard. Relaxation programmes and healthy eating have always been available at Temple, but when they introduced Spa this side of the operation moved into a new phase, offering yoga, hydrotherapy, massage, reflexology and specialist treatments such as Yon-Ka spa facial and seaweed body contour wraps. Temple is a member of the Health Farms of Ireland Association, which means that Bernadette gives special attention to healthy eating guidelines (and caters for vegetarian, vegan and other special diets). She uses the best of local produce - lamb from the farm, their own garden vegetables, best midland beef, cheese and yogurts - in good home cooking. And, although the Spa is a major attraction, you do not have to be a Spa guest to enjoy a stay at Temple. Garden, cycling, sauna, steam room, children's playground. **Rooms 8** (all en-suite, 5 no-smoking) B&B about €65 pps, ss about €25 (min 2-night stay at weekends). Spa weekends from about €275 pps (ss about €40). Residents' D Tue-Sat, about €26 (book by 10 am; no D Sun, Mon). Wine licence. Closed Christmas-New Year.[Prices not confirmed at time of going to press; please phone for details.] Amex, MasterCard, Visa. **Directions:** Just off N6, 1 mile west of Horseleap. ◇

Mullingar — The Belfry Restaurant

Restaurant — Ballynegall Mullingar Co. Westmeath **Tel: 044 4248** Fax: 044 40094 Email: belfryrestaurant@eircom.net

The tall spire will lead you to tthe Murphy family's restaurant in a magnificently converted church near Mullingar. The design is brilliant, with (excellent) toilets near the entrance, perfect for a quick freshen up before heading up thickly carpeted stairs to a mezzanine lounge which is luxuriously furnished with big lounge-around leather sofas, striking lamps and fresh flowers. Everything has been done to the very highest specifications, colours schemes are subtle and elegant - and the whole setup is highly atmsopheric. Head chef Thérèse Gilsenan, who has already made her mark on several places around Westmeath, has a very down to earth approach to cooking, sourcing ingredients well and working in a style that is refreshingly unselfconscious - professionally presented but never over the top, with more elements of good home cooking than cheffy tricks. Menus are carefully constructed to offer a good balance of ingredients and styles, to suit big country appetites and also more urban tastes. Sunday lunch menus, for example, include traditional dishes (braised lamb shanks with pearl barley & root vegetables, served with champ) alongside modern dishes like chargrilled chicken paillard & crispy pancetta, sautéd new potatoes & mustard butter and a vegetarian pasta dish of penne with broccoli, goats cheese & sundried tomatoes. Younger guests also get special choices like fresh mini pizza with tomato bacon & fresh mozzarella - a good way to introduce children to quality dining. Evening menus are similar, but offer slightly more ambitious dishes. A second staircase descends to the dining area, which is very striking and extremely atmospheric, especially when seen in candlight with a room full of people enjoying themselves, with background music from the grand piano where the altar used to be. Well-made breads and soups, cooking everything freshly to order - the details are right, down to the choice of coffees. Charming, helpful and well-timed service adds greatly to the enjoyment of the visit - and there's a always pianist on Thursday nights. 'Wines from the Crypt' are listed - and you are invited to browse. *Cookery classes given, evening and day courses; call the restaurant for details. **Seats 68** (private room 22). No smoking restaurant; air conditioning. Children welcome. D Wed-Sat, 5.45-9.30; L 1-3.30 (Sun 1-4). Early D €27 (5.45 -6.45), otherwise D à la carte. Set Sun L €25.50; house wine €18.95. Closed Mon,Tue, & last 3 weeks Jan. MasterCard, Visa, Laser. **Directions:** Castlepollard road off the Mullingar bypass.

Mullingar — Canton Casey & Fat Cats Brasserie

Pub/Restaurant — Market Square Mullingar Co. Westmeath **Tel: 044 49969**

Canton Casey's pub is a lovely old-fashioned place, a real traditional pub with friendly staff and a welcoming fire in winter - a pleasant place to read the paper over a pint at quiet times, although it has become fashionable with a youthful crowd and can be very busy in the evenings. Over the pub, there's an informal brasserie serving contemporary food in a high-ceilinged room on the first floor. It has a slightly French atmosphere, with its tall softly draped windows and oil-clothed tables and - predictably enough - the decor is distinctly feline. Irish Angus beef is a speciality. L Tue-Fri,12.30-2.30; D Tue-Sun, 6-9.45 (Sun 4.30-8.30). Closed L Sat-Sun, all Mon. MasterCard, Visa, Laser. **Directions:** Centered intown centre abover Canton Casey's Pub.

Mullingar — Gallery 29 Café

Café — 16 Oliver Plunkett St. Mullingar Co. Westmeath **Tel: 044 49449** Fax: 044 49449 Email: corbetstown@eircom.net

Ann & Emily Gray finally opened in their smart black-painted traditionally-fronted premises just across the street, from their original restaurant in the summer of 2002. They're great bakers and their food reflects that interest - freshly baked breads, scones, muffins, baked puddings, tarts and gateaux are all on display - but there's much else beside, including good soups, salads (warm bacon salad with avocado, croutons & toasted pine nuts, perhaps), savoury tart of the day tailor-made sandwiches, fashionable focaccia with every imaginable filling and hot main courses, like oven-baked salmon with sweet chilli sauce, champ & salad and steak sanwich on ciabatta, with spicy salsa & mixed salad. Everything is home-made and it's a good place for any time of day, including breakfast (with freshly squeezed juice) and afternoon tea. Outside catering, picnics and freshly made dishes or home freezing are also offered. **Seats 50.** No smoking area. Open Mon-Sat, 9.30-5.30 (late opening with a bistro menu Thu-Fri evenings). All a la carte. Wine licence. Closed Sun, 24 Dec-7 Jan. **No Credit Cards. Directions:** From Dublin throughtraffic Lightsat Market Square in town centre. About 60 - 70 m on right hand side. ◇

Mullingar — Ilia A Coffee Experience

Ⓝ Restaurant

28 Oliver Plunkett Street Mullingar Co. Westmeath **Tel: 044 40300**
Fax: 044 40050 Email: juliekenny@eircom.net

Julie Kenny's delightful 2-storey coffee house and informal restaurant in the centre of Mullingar opened in the summer of 2002 and was an immediate hit. It's attractively set up - the first floor area is particularly pleasing, with a seating area of sofas, low tables and plants at the top of the stairs setting a relaxed tone and making a good place to wait for a friend or to sip a cup of coffee while reading the paper at quiet times; the rest is more conventionally furnished in café style - and a more comfortable height for eating a real meal. Menus cater for all the changing moods though the day, beginning with an extensive breakfast (everything from porridge with brown sugar and cream to traditional breakfast, to toasted bagels with cream cheese), then there are the mid-day bites like home-made, soup paninis, steak baguettes, bruschetta, Ilia salad and much more (plenty for vegetarians) - and lots of pastries and desserts including a range of crêpes, both savoury and sweet. More predictably, there's a nice little drinks menu offering everything from big glasses of freshly squeezed orange juice through iced teas, smoothies, teas - and, of course, coffees (Java Republic), any way you like, including flavoured coffees. Everything is deliciously fresh and wholesome, staff are charming and efficient, prices reasonable - you'd be hard pushed to find anything over €7.50. Takeaway also available. Unlicensed. **Seats 50.** No smoking area; air conditioning. Open Mon-Fri 8am-5pm, Sat 9 am-5pm. Closed Sun. **No Credit Cards. Directions:** Centre of Town.

Mullingar — Oscars Restaurant

Ⓝ Restaurant

21 Oliver Plunkett Street Mullingar Co. Westmeath
Tel: 044 44909 Web: www.oscars-restaurant.com

An attractive centrally located restaurant: a long room has an old stone wall and beams adding character, skylight windows and a large open kitchen at the end. It's extremely popular locally, pleasing people of all ages for its lively atmosphere and mix of traditional and contemporary favourites at reasonable prices. This is beef country, so a section of the menu given over to steaks should come as no surprise, but there's much else besides, ranging from 80s classics like deep-fried mushrooms with garlic & cucmber dip, through spicy chicken wings to simple smoked salmon with lemon, capers & home-made bread. Main courses cover a similar range, also specialities which, apart from steaks various ways, offer everything from chicken Italienne to honey glazed lamb shanks on a bed of chunky garlic & spring onion mash. This is popular food, well executed at fair prices - the dearest main course is about €22.50 (large fillet steak) but the average is about €15 - and with cheerfully efficient service to match. An affordable outing with something for everyone and wines starting at €10. D Tue-Sat, L Sun. A la carte. Closed 2nd week Jan. MasterCard, Visa, Laser. **Directions:** Centre of town opposite town mall.

Mullingar — Woodville House

féile bia Restaurant/Accommodation

Gaybrook Mullingar Co. Westmeath
Tel: 044 43694 Fax: 044 42941

About five miles outside Mullingar, the Cooney family's early 19th century two-storey over-basement house makes a fine setting for a restaurant of character. On the ground floor there's a welcoming fire in the drawing room/reception area and a proper little bar; down in the semi-basement, arched ceilings and open stone walls create a great atmosphere in several dining areas - but there are also windows, so it isn't gloomy or oppressive. Eunan Gallagher has been head chef since 1996 - his menus change weekly, but house specialities include a starter of Gorbetstown goats cheese, served with a hazelnut crust on a compôte of pears and local beef - in roast sirloin for Sunday lunch, perhaps, with a cognac & pink peppercorn cream sauce. Well-appointed tables, friendly service and generous country portions make an appealing packag, earning this restaurant a local following. Banqueting - weddings & special occasions (30). Restaurant seats 80. (private room, 10). No smoking area. Children welcome. D 6.30-10 Tues-Sat, L Sun only 12.30-3, Set Sun L €238. Set D from €20 (2-course)-€32; early D €23,(6.30-7.30); Closed D Sun, all Mon, 3 days Christmas, Good Fri.
Accommodation: There are six en-suite rooms in a converted coachhouse behind the restaurant. B&B about €45 pps. MasterCard, Visa, Laser. **Directions:** 5 miles south of Mullingar.

Multyfarnham   Mornington House

Country House   Mornington Multyfarnham Co. Westmeath
                                         Tel: 044 72191 Fax: 044 72338
                            Email: info@mornington.ie Web: www.mornington.ie

Warwick and Anne O'Hara's gracious Victorian house is surrounded by mature trees and is just a meadow's walk away from Lough Derravarragh where the mythical Children of Lir spent 300 years of their 900 year exile. The Lough is now occupied by a pleasing population of brown trout, pike, eels and other coarse fish. It has been the O'Hara family home since 1858 and is still furnished with much of the original furniture and family portraits and, although centrally heated, log fires remain an essential feature. Bedrooms are typical of this kind of country house - spacious and well-appointed, with old furniture (three have brass beds) - but with comfortable modern mattresses. Anne cooks proper country breakfasts and country house dinners for residents and Warwick does the honours front-of-house. Pets allowed by arrangement. Garden; fishing. **Rooms 5** (3 en-suite, 2 with private bathrooms, all no smoking). B&B €60 pps, ss €20. Set residents D €37.50, at 8pm (book by 2pm) Closed Nov-Mar. Amex, MasterCard, Visa. **Directions:** Exit N4 for Castlepollard.

COUNTY WEXFORD

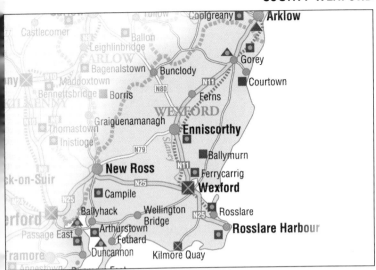

The popular view of Wexford is beaches, sunshine and opera. The longest continuous beach in all Ireland runs along the county's east coast, an astonishing 27 kilometres from Cahore Point south to Raven Point, which marks the northern side of the entrance to Wexford town's shallow harbour. As for sunshine, while areas further north along the east coast may record marginally less rainfall, in the very maritime climate of the "Sunny Southeast" around Wexford, the clouds seem to clear more quickly, so the chances of seeing the elusive orb are much improved.

And opera..? Well, the annual Wexford Opera Festival every October is a byword for entertaining eccentricity - as international enthusiasts put it, "we go to Wexford town in the Autumn to enjoy operas written by people we've never heard of, and we have ourselves a thoroughly good time."

All of which is fine and dandy, but there's much more to this intriguing county than sun, sand and singing. Wexford itself is but one of three substantial towns in it, the other two being the market town of Enniscorthy, and the river port of New Ross. While much of the county is relatively low-lying, to the northwest it rises towards the handsome Blackstairs Mountains. There, the 793m peak of Mount Leinster may be just over the boundary in Carlow, but one of the most attractive little hill towns in all Ireland, Bunclody, is most definitely in Wexford.

In the north of the county, Gorey is a pleasant and prosperous place, while connoisseurs of coastlines will find the entire south coast of Wexford a fascinating area of living history, shellfish-filled shallow estuaries, and an excellent little harbour at the much-thatched village of Kilmore Quay inside the Saltee Islands.

Round the corner beyond the impressive Hook Head, home to Ireland's oldest lighthouse, Wexford County faces west across its own shoreline along the beauties of Waterford estuary. Here, thee's another fine beach, at Duncannon, while nearby other sheltered little ports of west Wexford - Arthurstown and Ballyhack - move at their own sweet and gentle pace.

In New Ross, where the authentic re-creation of a 19th Century emigrant ship - the impressive Dunbrody - is proving to be a very effective focal point for the revival of the picturesque waterfront, a fitting place for the lovely River Barrow to meet ships in from sea in an area historically linked with President John F Kennedy.

Local Attractions and Information

Ballygarrett Shrule Deer Farm	055 27277
Ballyhack Ballyhack Castle	051 389468
Campile Kilmokea Gardens	051 388109
Dunbrody Abbey & Visitor Centre	051 388603
Duncannon Duncannon Fort	051 388603
Enniscorthy National 1798 Visitor Centre	054 37596

Enniscorthy Tourism Information	054 34699
Enniscorthy Wexford County Museum	054 46506
Ferrycarrig National Heritage Park	053 20733
Gorey (Coolgreany) Ram House Gardens	0402 37238
Hook Head Hook Head Lighthouse	051 397055
Johnstown Castle Demesne & Agricultural Museum	053 42888
Kilmore Quay Saltee Island Ferries	053 29684
New Ross Dunbrody - re-creation of 19th C ship	051 425239
New Ross Galley River Cruises	051 421723
New Ross John F Kennedy Arboretum	051 388171
New Ross John F Kennedy Homestead, Dunganstown	051 388264
New Ross Tourism Information	051 421857
Rosslare Ferry Terminal	053 33622
Saltmills (nr Fethard-on-Sea) Tintern Abbey	051 562650
Wexford North Slobs Wildfowl Reserve	053 23129
Wexford Opera Festival (October)	053 22144
Wexford Tourism Information	053 23111

Arthurstown — Dunbrody Country House Hotel & Cookery School

féile bia — Hotel

Arthurstown Co. Wexford **Tel: 051 389 600** Fax: 051 389 601
Email: dunbrody@indigo.ie Web: www.dunbrodyhouse.com

Catherine and Kevin Dundon have created something very special at their elegant Georgian manor. Set in twenty acres of parkland and gardens on the Hook Peninsula, just across the estuary from Waterford city, this was the ancestral home of the Chichester family and the long tradition of hospitality at this tranquil and luxurious retreat is very much alive and well. Catherine and Kevin are thoughtful and caring hosts and there is a feeling of true welcome here - beginning, perhaps, with a gentle greeting from their affectionate dogs (who look out for newcomers from their vantage point on the granite steps at the front door). Well-proportioned public rooms, which include an impressive entrance hall and gracious drawing room, are all beautifully furnished and decorated with stunning flower arrangements and the occasional unexpectedly modern piece that brings life to a fine collection of antiques. Spacious bedrooms, including those in a new wing which blends admirably with the original building, have superb bathrooms and offer all the comforts expected of such a house - and fine views over the gardens. Constant improvement is the ongoing quest at Dunbrody and this year is no exception - first of all they rustled up a couple more luxurious bedrooms at the top of the house then, in a development that is fairly dramatic even by the Dundons' high standards, they converted outbuildings just across from the front door into Ireland's most stylish cookery school. Whatever next? (Course brochure available on request.) An exceptional breakfast offers a magnificent buffet - fresh juices, fruit compôtes, cheeses - as well as hot dishes from a tempting menu. While Dunbrody provides a wonderfully relaxing place for a leisure break, they also cater for business meetings, small conferences, product launches and incentive programmes (full details available on request). Conference/banqueting (60/110). Business centre, secretarial services. Cookery school. Garden, walking. Children welcome (cot available without charge). No pets. Dunbrody was the Guide's Country House of the Year in 2001. **Rooms 22** (7 suites, 7 junior suites, 4 executive, 3 no-smoking, 3 disabled). B&B €117.50 pps; ss €20. Closed 22-27 Dec.

☆**The Harvest Room:** The restaurant looks out onto a pleasure garden and, beyond, to an organic vegetable and fruit garden. A well-proportioned, elegant room with an open fire in winter and stunning flower arrangements all the time, it presents a striking blend of classic and contemporary style - bold choices which bring life to the room include some beautiful modern rugs, specially commissioned from Ceadogan Rugs at Wellington Bridge. Likewise, chef/proprietor Kevin offers tempting à la carte and set menus that succeed unusually well in combining classical and international influences with local produce and Irish themes: specialities of the house include, for example, roast loin of bacon with a clove and Irish Mist, served on a bed of braised cabbage leaves & potato cake, a dish which brilliantly marries traditional and contemporary tastes. (In recognition it was selected for the Guide's Irish Bacon Award in 2000.) Rack of Wexford lamb with a whiskey marmalade crust, leek confit & caramelised kumquat jus perhaps, is another such dish and, while beautifully presented, this is not ostentatious cooking - Kevin's creations are outstanding for flavour before all else. Catherine leads a well-trained and efficient dining room staff with the charm and panache that typifies all aspects of the hospitality at this exceptional country house. An informative wine list which leans towards the classics includes a nice selection of half bottles and wines by the glass. **Seats 70.** No-smoking area. Toilets wheelchair accessible. D Mon-Sat 6.30-9.15. L 1.15-3 (Sun to 2.30). Set L €32. Set D €50. House wines €18.50. SC discretionary. Not suitable for children after 8pm. Closed 22-27 Dec. Amex, Diners, MasterCard, Visa, Laser. **Directions:** N11 from Dublin, R733 from Wexford to Arthurstown.

Bunclody — Chantry Restaurant

Restaurant   Bunclody Co. Wexford **Tel: 054 77482** Fax: 054 76130

Beautifully located on the River Slaney, at the foot of the Blackstairs Mountains, Bunclody is an attractive little town - and The Chantry is especially attractively situated within it. The fine old house, which was originally a Wesleyan chapel, enjoys a position of unexpected serenity above its own lovely waterside gardens, where guests can relax and enjoy the lovely trees and plants, including many rare species. The restaurant - which is lined with fascinating old pictures relating to local history - is in a high room with a little gallery (just the right size for a grand piano) but, with its deep red walls and chandeliers, it doesn't feel too churchy. Menus offered vary considerably depending on the time of day - all day food tends to be casual, with a carvery lunch from 12.30, but evening service is more formal. At dinner, the self-service buffet is removed and an à la carte menu with table service is offered instead. Typical dishes from the carte might include a first course salad of smoked chicken with cherry tomato, scallions & balsamic vinaigrette while main courses include a speciality of traditional honey-glazed baked Chantry ham, with fresh parsley sauce and vegetarian dishes like tofu & vegetable stirfry. Early bird specials are good value - and what all the various menus have in common is good home cooking. **Seats 50** (private room, 14). No smoking area. Children welcome. Toilets wheelchair accessible. Own parking. Pets in certain areas. Open 9am-9pm Mon-Sat, 10-4 Sun. Sun L 12.30-4. House wine about €16. All a la carte menus. SC discretionary. Open all year. MasterCard, Visa. **Directions:** In town centre. ◇

Campile — Kilmokea Country Manor & Gardens

Country House   Great Island Campile Co. Wexford **Tel: 051 388 109** Fax: 051 388 776
Email: kilmokea@indigo.ie Web: www.kilmokea.com

Mark and Emma Hewlett's peaceful and relaxing late Georgian country house is set in 7 acres of Heritage Gardens, including formal walled gardens (open to the public, 9-5; cream teas, for guests and garden visitors, are served in a Georgian conservatory). The house is elegantly and comfortably furnished, with a drawing room overlooking the Italian Loggia, an honesty library bar, and a classic country house dining room. The individually-designed and immaculately maintained bedrooms command lovely views over the gardens and towards the estuary beyond. They have no television to disturb the tranquillity (though there is one in the drawing room). In an adjoining coach house there's a billiards room (where smoking is allowed), newer rooms and self-catering suites; they have a separate entrance and lighter, more contemporary atmosphere than the main house - as they are so different it is wise to discuss your preferences when booking. Emma is a powerhouse of energy and does a great deal herself, but she now has Ballymaloe-trained chef, Aoife McCann, to help in the kitchen - as well as dinner for residents, they provide light refreshments in the conservatory for garden visitors: home-made flapjacks and scones with jam and cream, for example, plus light lunches like quiches and salads. Mark and Emma have also continued their ongoing programme of improvements to the property - the latest additions are a a tennis court and an indoor swimming pool, no less, plus a gym and aromatherapy treatment rooms (Emma is a trained aromatherapist). As if that isn't enough, they're also working on a large organic vegetable garden, planted in the old potager design - it's great to see a revival of this charming fashion. Conferences/banqueting (30/50). Garden, fishing, tennis, walking; games room (billiards, table tennis), swimming pool, gym, aromatherapy. Children welcome (cots available without charge; playground, playroom). Pets allowed by arrangement. **Rooms 6** (5 en-suite, 1 with private bathroom, 2 shower only, 1 for disabled, all no-smoking). No smoking establishment (except Billiards Room). B&B €80 pps; ss €20. Residents D €38; book by noon. Light meals in conservatory 10-5 daily when house and gardens are open. Closed 5 Nov-1 Mar. MasterCard, Visa, Laser, Switch. **Directions:** Off R733 from New Ross to Ballyhack, sign posted for Kilmokea Gardens.

Duncannon — Sqigl Restaurant & Roches Bar

féile bia ⓝ Pub/Restaurant   Quay Road Duncannon New Ross Co. Wexford
Tel: 051 389700 Fax: 051 389346 Email: sqigl@hotmail.com

Bob and Eileen Roche's fine traditional bar in the centre of Duncannon village serves the local community (and discerning visitors) well. There's an old bar at the front, pleasingly free of improvements, and it gradually develops more towards the back which keeps the younger crowd and the oldies in their preferred spaces. Bar food has recently been introduced, offering a selection of hot dishes, salads and sandwiches, plus some daily specials - a well-balanced mixture of traditional (breaded cod with french fries tartare sauce & side salad) and contemporary (grilled goats cheese with red onion salad & pesto dressing). While it is not an especially long menu, there is something for everyone - and, in a rather nice piece of role reversal, adult portions of the children's menu are also offered. Bar Food served 12.30-5 daily. Pub closed 25 Dec, Good Fri.

Sqigl Restaurant: Sqigl (pronounced Squiggle) is located in a converted barn behind the pub and is run by Bob and Eileen's daughter Cindy Roche, supported by Wayne Neville, a young Irish chef newly returned from cooking in the West of England (who is also responsible for the bar food.). Squigl opened in August 2001 and has made a promising start; it aims to make the most of local produce and does it well with a sensibly limited menu, particularly the white fish landed at the harbour round the corner, wild locally caught salmon and Wexford beef and lamb. Décor is light, bright and modern and the cooking style is modern too, except that portions are aimed at generous Wexford appetites: sweet potato cake, Clonakilty pudding with peppered quails eggs and paprika hollandaise, for example, makes a fine substantial starter. Of recent main courses, baked turbot with cèpe risotto and butter sauce, pork fillet, spring onion and green chilli paste with ginger and garlic noodles and roast duck breast with ribbon vegetables and five spice are all typical, successful dishes - and there's always an interesting vegetarian option such as celeriac, asparagus, roasted pepper & wild mushroom croustade. Desserts tend to be quite rich - home-made baklava with pistachio ice cream, or double chocolate & Baileys mousse cake for example - so it would be wise to arrive with a well-primed appetite. The wine list is brief but interesting: Domaine de Subremont rouge 1999/2000 is a thoughtful selection for a house red at only €14.50 and there are some other interesting choices - good value, too. **Seats 32.** No smoking area. D Tue-Sat, 7-10.30 (Sun, Jul-Aug only, to 9.30); L Sun only, 1 pm. Closed D Sun (except Jul-Aug), D Mon, 24-26 Dec, 2 weeks Jan, Good Fri. MasterCard, Visa, Laser. **Directions:** Centre of Dunncannon Village (15 miles from Rosslare).

Enniscorthy — Ballinkeele House

Country House
Ballinkeele House Enniscorthy Co. Wexford
Tel: 053 38105 Fax: 053 38468
Email: info@ballinkeele.com Web: www.ballinkeele.com

Set in 350 acres of parkland, game-filled woods and farmland, this historic house is a listed building; designed by Daniel Robertson, it has been the Maher family home since it was built in 1840 and remains at the centre of their working farm. It is a grand house, with a lovely old cut stone stable yard at the back and some wonderful features, including a lofty columned hall with a big open fire in the colder months, beautifully proportioned reception rooms with fine ceilings and furnishings which have changed very little since the house was built. Nevertheless, it is essentially a family house and has a refreshingly hospitable and down-to-earth atmosphere. Large bedrooms are furnished with antiques and have wonderful countryside views; central heating has recently been installed - the coming year's project is clean out the lake and re-stock it with fish. Margaret is a keen cook and enjoys preparing 4-course dinners for guests (nice little wine list to accompany); she's also an enthusiastic amateur painter and runs small art workshops at Ballinkeele with Patricia Jorgensen, who is well-known for her botanical paintings. Croquet and bicycles are available for guests' use and horse riding, fishing and golf can be organised nearby. Garden. Children are welcome, but there are no concessions; cot available, €15.) Smoking is allowed only in the large drawing room. No pets. **Rooms 5** (2 superior, 3 shower only, all no-smoking). B&B €70 pps; ss 20. Residents Set D €35 at 7:30 (book by noon; no D on Mon); house wine about €14. Private parties up to 14. Closed 12 Nov-28 Feb. MasterCard, Visa, Laser. **Directions:** From Wexford N11 north to Oilgate Village, turn right at signpost.

Enniscorthy — Monfin House

Country House
St Johns Enniscorthy Co. Wexford **Tel: 054 38582** Fax: 054 38583
Email: info@monfinhouse.com Web: www.monfinhouse.com

This classic Georgian house just outside Enniscorthy was built in 1823 and has all the simplicity and elegance of that period. Having carried out major refurbishment, Chris and Avril Stewart opened their house to guests in 2001, with the aim of providing a quiet and relaxing haven, with the emphasis on comfort, personal service and, particularly, the joys of food and wine. This they do very well: guests are free to stroll around the grounds and see the walled garden (which is destined for restoration to its original design and purpose) and your bedroom will provide a tranquil sanctuary - spacious and very comfortably furnished with a whirlpool or antique bath, although kept without the worldly intrusion of amenities like television (phone and modem connection are available on request however). Avril sources food carefully, using local and organic produce wherever possible in her country house style cooking. A candlelit dining room with an open fire provides a soothing setting for a 5-course no choice dinner, and there is an interesting wine list with refreshingly low mark-up prices. (Chris has a "day job" in the wine business.) A typical dinner might start with a salad of fresh crab with red pepper chutney, then a seasonal soup such as pea & coriander; there might be roast rack of Wexford lamb for the main course, then a classic dessert like orange soufflé. This is not the end, however, as there is still a cheese plate to come - and chocolates with your coffee, which is served in front of another fire, in the drawing room. Breakfast is to the same high standards - and you may well need a walk afterwards. Not suitable for children under 12. **Rooms 4** (all en-suite & no smoking). B&B about €65 pps, ss €20. Residents' D €35; wine from €18. MasterCard, Visa. **Directions:** From Enniscorthy take New Ross road - turn left after Grain Mill. 0.5 mile upon right hand side.

Enniscorthy — Riverside Park Hotel

 Hotel   The Promenade Enniscorthy Co. Wexford **Tel:** 054 37800   Fax: 054 37900
Email: info@riversideparkhotel.com   Web: www.riversideparkhotel.com

While this riverside hotel may be visually at odds with the pleasing traditional style of the area, it has brought welcome amenities to the town. Public areas are quite impressive of their type, rooms are comfortably furnished in a moderate contemporary style and there are good facilities for conferences and functions. Off-season and special interest breaks are offered and there is plenty to do in this beautiful area, including fishing, golf and horse riding. There is a pleasant riverside path in a linear park beside the hotel and this can be a useful place to break a journey to stretch the legs and have a bite to eat; head chef David Anderson has been with the hotel since it opened and, in the guide's experience, does a good job. Conference/banqueting facilities (800/600), secretarial services. Own parking. No pets. Children welcome (cots available without charge). **Rooms 60** (1 suite, 4 for disabled). Lift. B&B €105pps. Bar food available 12.30-7.30 daily; Moorings Restaurant D daily & L Sun; Alma (Tex-Mex) D daily. Hotel closed 25-26 Dec.
Moorings Restaurant: In the Guide's experience, food and ambience are both above the standard expected of a country hotel. David Anderson, who has been head chef since the hotel opened. His seasonal à la carte and daily set menus successfully marry the demands for both traditional and contemporary dishes and the cooking is sound. There is also an informal Tex-Mex restaurant in the hotel and bar food is available 12.30-7.30 daily. L 12.30-2.30, D 7-9. Set Sun €18.50, Set D from €29; à la carte also available L&D. Amex, Diners, MasterCard, Visa, Laser. **Directions:** 0.5 km from the new bridge centre Enniscorthy Town. Just off N11 Dublin - Rosslare road.

Enniscorthy — Salville House

Country House   Salville Enniscorthy Co. Wexford **Tel:** 054 35252   Fax: 054 35252
Email: info@salvillehouse.com   Web: www.salvillehouse.com

Set high on a hillside outside Enniscorthy, Gordon and Jane Parker's large mid-nineteenth century house has sweeping views over the Slaney River Valley but the main point of interest is indoors, in the dining room where Gordon Parker's confident modern cooking is offered to guests around a communal table in the evening - and splendid breakfasts are served next morning. Seasonal four course dinners are served at a communal table, with an emphasis on local seafood and organic produce from the garden - but there isn't formal menu with choices, so it's wise to mention any allergies or dislikes when booking. After dinner, guests can relax in front of the drawing room fire, or play a game of backgammon before heading up to one of the three large rooms in the main house, which have views over the Slaney and are comfortably furnished with some style, or one of the two in a self-contained apartment at the back. (All have tea/coffee making facilities, but no TV.) A really good breakfast sends everyone on their way in good heart - freshly squeezed juice, lovely fruit compôte, freshly-baked bread warm from the oven and hot dishes cooked to order, like undyed smoked haddock with rösti and poached eggs, or local smoked salmon with scrambled egg. Laid back hospitality, great food and good value make this comfortable house a fine base for exploring the area, or somewhere to break a journey. **Rooms 5** (2 en-suite, 3 with private bathrooms, all no-smoking). Children welcome (under 8s free in parents' room). Garden; tennis. B&B €38, ss €10. Residents' 4-course D €30, at 8pm (book a day ahead; no D on Sun). BYO wine. **No Credit Cards.** **Directions:** 2 miles from Enniscorthy on Wexford side (not signed until off main road).

Ferrycarrig Bridge — Ferrycarrig Hotel

 Hotel/Restaurant   Ferrycarrig Bridge Co. Wexford **Tel:** 053 20999   Fax: 053 20982
Email: ferrycarrig@griffingroup.ie   Web: www.griffingroup.ie

Although very close to the main Rosslare road - steeply sloping gardens have steps from the main entrance up to the car park which is almost adjacent to the road - this modern hotel is in a lovely location overlooking the Slaney estuary and has excellent amenities, including a superb health and fitness club with 20 metre swimming pool and state-of-the-art facilities for conferences and business meetings. Neatly uniformed staff are exceptionally welcoming and friendly (although not every guest will relish being on first name terms as soon as the receptionist has checked it on the computer); service generally is caring without being intrusive. All bedrooms, including original ones recently upgraded as well as 13 new bedroom and suites, have splendid views across the water and some have balconies with wooden loungers; in-room facilities are good, including a safe (which uses the room key card) and an iron/trouser press unit as well as the usual phone, television, tea/coffee tray, although some power points and cables are inconveniently positioned. Housekeeping is of a high standard and generous bathrooms have a phone extension and large baths with good showers. Special interest and off-season value breaks are offered. Conference/banqueting (400/350). Leisure centre. Garden. Children welcome (cots available, €6.50; playroom). No pets. **Rooms 103** (4 suites, 5 junior suites, 35 no smoking, 2 for disabled). Lift. B&B €115 pps; ss €35. Open all year.

Restaurant: The smaller of the hotel's two restaurants, Tides, offers discerning guests modern cooking in the atmosphere of an independent restaurant rather than an hotel dining room. It has its own reception/bar area and is formally appointed with linen cloths and napkins, quality tableware, fresh flowers and chilled water in stoppered bottles. Tony Carty, who has been head chef since 1999, presents imaginative and well-balanced à la carte menus offering a selection of about eight on each course, always including interesting vegetarian options; expect updated classics like organic chicken Cordon Bleu: supreme of chicken filled with smoked Gubbeen cheese and honey roast ham with wholegrain mustard sauce and a sprinkling of more international dishes. Tables are set up to maximise on the waterside position and most have a lovely view in which to enjoy specialities based on local produce, such as a well-judged Kilmore crabmeat spring roll with Asian greens & hoi sin sauce, and fillet or sirloin of prime Hereford beef, which is outstanding for its excellent flavour and served various ways; menus are quite informative about the provenance of their ingredients, and side vegetables are organic. Imaginative desserts include an intriguing home-made banana pizza with rum ice cream & caramel sauce and home-made chocolates come with coffee (including cappuccino/espresso) or tea (herbal teas available). Food presentation is fashionable but not over the top and service is pleasant and professional. **Seats 45.** No-smoking area. Air conditioning. D Tue-Sat 7-9:15 (limited opening in winter). A la carte. House wines from €17. sc discretionary. Not suitable for children after 7.30. *The popular 150-seater Boathouse Bistro, serves modern Irish/international cooking L & D daily; three seasonal evening menus are used in rotation, ensuring variety for guests staying several nights; the calorie content of dishes is given alongside the price... *Bar food is also available daily: Mon-Thu, 12.30-8.30; Fri-Sun 12.30-6. Amex, Diners, MasterCard, Visa, Laser. **Directions:** Located on N11.3 miles north of Wexford Town.

Gorey   Marlfield House

🏛️🏛️ Country House/Restaurant

Courtown Rd Gorey Co. Wexford
Tel: 055 21124 Fax: 055 21572
Email: info@marlfieldhouse.ie Web: www.marlfieldhouse.com

INTERNATIONAL HOSPITALITY AWARD

Often quoted as 'the luxury country house hotel par excellence', Marlfield House was once the residence of the Earls of Courtown and, thanks to the dedication and professionalism of Ray and Mary Bowe, has now been a leading light in the quest for excellence in Irish hospitality for 25 years. During that time they have lavished care and attention on this lovely house, creating an elegant oasis of unashamed luxury, where guests are cosseted and pampered in sumptuous surroundings - and matching these exceptional standards with a reputation for outstanding hospitality and service. Imposing gates, a wooded drive, a fine kitchen garden all set the scene - and the interior features marble fireplaces, antiques, notable paintings, glittering chandeliers and fine fabrics: all the creation of Mary Bowe, who has also ensured that housekeeping is immaculate throughout, service from committed staff thoughtful and unobtrusive. These are all qualities that have made Marlfield an important destination for the most discerning of international guests, people who value the exceptional level of comfort and care provided for them - and return home to pass on the good word about high standards and warm hospitality in Ireland. By aiming for the stars and having the determination and dedication to reach them, Mary and Ray Bowe - now joined by their daughter Margaret Bowe, who is continuing the family tradition as manager of Marlfield - are contributing a great service to Ireland's hospitality industry. Conference/banqueting (20/40). Tennis. Dogs and children are welcome by prior arrangement. (Children under 2 free in parents' room, cots available without charge). **Rooms 20** (6 state rooms, 14 superior). B&B €130pps. Closed mid Dec-1 Feb.

Restaurant: The graceful dining-room and Turner style conservatory merge into one, allowing views out across the gardens. The conservatory, with its hanging baskets, plants and fresh flowers (not to mention the odd stone statue), is one of the most romantic spots in the whole of Ireland, further enhanced at night by candlelight - a wonderful setting in which to enjoy chef Henry Stone's accomplished cooking. Henry sources ingredients with care and a lot of the fruit, vegetables and herbs are grown in their own gardens, ensuring a strongly seasonal dimension to menus which are always interesting and attractive without being slavishly fashionable. The main emphasis is on flavour and this fine chef has a down to earth quality which is most refreshing in a fine dining restaurant. Typical examples that indicate the style include chicken liver parfait with beetroot, balsamic reduction and toasted brioche; tempura of lemon sole with stir fried vegetables, sweet chilli sauce; carrot & lemongrass soup and (a somewhat unlikely speciality but a superb dish that has captured the hearts of regular diners for its flavoursome succulence) roast belly of pork served, perhaps, with champ potato, buttered green cabbage, apple and pear chutney. Vegetarian choices are always offered - gratin of char-grilled aubergine, goats cheese and plum tomato served with piperade and roast cherry tomatoes, perhaps - and an Irish cheeseboard, which is temptingly displayed on a side table. Elegant desserts might include a dashing high-rise banana gratin with Malibu sabayon topped with a ball of superb dark chocolate sorbet, then it's off to the drawing room for coffee and petits fours to round off the feast. As in every other area of the house, service is exemplary. An extensive wine list, long on burgundies and clarets, is informative. **Seats 65** (private room, 20). No-smoking restaurant. Air conditioning. Not suitable for children at D. D daily, 7-9 (Fri & Sat to 9.30, Sun to 8 ; L Sun only 12.30-1.45. Set D €58 & à la carte; Set Sun L €37. House wine €26. SC discretionary. Light à la carte lunches are served daily in Library, 12.30-5.30. Amex, Diners, MasterCard, Visa, Laser. **Directions:** 1 mile outside Gorey on Courtown Road (R 742).

Gorey — Pooles Porterhouse

Restaurant/Pub

78 Main Street Gorey Co. Wexford **Tel: 055 21271**
Fax: 055 80856 Web: www.pooles.ie

With its traditional darkwood decor and open fires, this substantial town-centre premises looks and feels as if it has always been a pub - and it has in fact been in the family for three generations and was run as a restaurant for some years by the parents of the three Poole brothers, Eric, Colin and Brian. Its renewed success is down to these three energetic and far-sighted young men, who did up the building, obtained a licence and re-opened it as a pub and restaurant. Eric, a chef with wide-ranging experience beginning nearby at Marlfield House where the foundation stone of his "no short cuts" philosophy was laid, and culminating as head chef at a demanding Dublin pub, started the food side of the Porterhouse himself while Colin and Brian looked after other aspects of the business. Their reputation for good food spread fast so Eric soon had two other chefs working with him - and everyone shares responsibility for menus which are very impressive. Daytime fare tends to be light and snacky (but classy too - try the quenelles of duck liver paté with fruit coulis and home-made brown bread, for example), augmented by daily main course specials on the blackboard: everything is cooked to order. Evening menus are more formal, offering a choice of about eight starters and a dozen or so main courses ranging from updated versions of the traditional meat and poultry dishes popular in rural areas to some sophisticated seafood (typically a skewered selection of seafood & scallops, marinated in soy sauce and served with mandarin and peach coulis, one of the most expensive main courses at €20.75) and game in season; there's always a vegetarian special and - an indication of the massive changes that have taken place in Irish eating habits if ever there was one - kangaroo and wild boar take their place alongside the produce Wexford is famous for, like lamb and seafood, notably mussels. Home-made desserts are also a speciality - this is the place to break a journey if you can. **Seats 65.** No smoking area; air conditioning. Children welcome (but not after 6 pm). Food available daily, 12.30-9: L 12-2.30; Bar menu 2.30-9 (Sat & Sun to 8); D 7-9. Set Sun L €15.50, otherwise à la carte. House wines €15.15. Closed 25 Dec, Good Fri. Amex, Diners, MasterCard, Visa, Laser. **Directions:** Centre of Main Street.

Kimore Quay — Kehoe's Pub & Maritime Heritage Centre

 Pub

Kilmore Quay Co. Wexford **Tel: 087 2395363** Fax: 053 29820
Email: info@kehoe.iol.ie Web: kehoes.com

Harbour developments with a marina brought an extra surge of activity to this thriving fishing village – and well-informed visitors all head straight for Kehoe's. It has been family-owned for generations - James and Eleanor Kehoe have been running it since 1987 - and, among the changes made over the years, the most challenging was in 1994 when they decided to do a really good refurbishment job, to enhance the pub's traditional ambience – everything was done correctly, from the roof slates to the old pitch pine flooring (and ceiling in the Parlour). At the same time, the interior was used to display a huge range of maritime artefacts, some of them recovered from local wrecks by James and his diving colleagues. They have created what amounts to a maritime museum; even the beer garden at the back of the pub is constructed from a mast and boom discarded by local trawlers - it now also has patio heaters to encourage people to eat outdoors on summer evenings. The other major change has been to the food side of the business, which has crept up on Kehoe's gradually: a few years ago they did little more than soup and sandwiches but now the pub has an established reputation for the quality and range of its bar meals – seafood, such as Ocean Pie (a selection of locally caught fish, topped with sauce and baked) - as well as vegetarian dishes and other main courses such as lasagne and stuffed chicken breasts wrapped in bacon. There's a short but very adequate wine list in addition to normal bar drinks. Kehoe's was the Guide's Pub of the Year Award for 2001. Children welcome. Wheelchair access. Open daily for food 12.30-8 (times not confirmed at time of going to press, please phone for details). Closed 25 Dec, Good Fri. Visa. ◇

Kilmore Quay — Quay House Guesthouse

Guesthouse/Restaurant — Kilmore Quay Co. Wexford **Tel: 053 29988** Fax: 053 29808 Web: www.quayhouseguesthouse.com

Siobhan and Pat McDonnell's pristine guesthouse is centrally located in the village (not on the quay as might be expected) and is especially famous for its support of sea angling and diving – they have an annexe especially geared for anglers with drying/storage room, fridges and freezers, live bait and tackle sales. Packed lunches an be provided and non-residents are welcome for breakfast as well as evening meals. The whole place is ship shape, with attractive, slightly nautical bedrooms ("a place for everything and everything in its place"), practical pine floors and neat en-suite rooms (most shower only). The breakfast room and restaurant, Quay Plaice, has been extended into an existing patio - overlooking the village's pretty thatched cottages, the sea and beach - which has now been covered to provide extra seating as the restaurant side of the business has expanded: a full à la carte menu is offered, in a contemporary style, majoring in seafood. Children welcome (infants free in parents' room, cots available without charge). Pets by arrangement. Garden. **Rooms 7** (all en-suite, most shower-only, 4 no smoking). B&B about €36 pps; ss about €20. Restaurant: D daily in summer, 6-9.30 pm Set D about €45, also à la carte; house wine about €15. Accommodation open all year; restaurant closed Mon & Tue in winter. MasterCard, Visa, Laser. **Directions:** Wexford 14 miles, Rosslare Ferry route. ◇

Kilmore Quay — The Silver Fox

Restaurant — Kilmore Quay Co. Wexford **Tel: 053 29888**

Absolute freshness is the key to chef Nicky Cullen's reputation at this busy seafood restaurant close to the harbour, where popular dishes and more ambitious seafood creations appear unselfconsciously side by side. Menus at The Silver Fox are wide-ranging and offer some poultry and meat dishes (also vegetarian dishes, by arrangement) as well as the wide choice of seafood for which they have become famous; in the Guide's experience, simplest choices have always been wisest. Harbour developments at Kilmore Quay, including a marina, have been done with an admirable regard for the size and character of the village, but the growing number of visitors means booking is strongly advised, especially in summer. Children welcome. **Seats 130** (private room, 35). No-smoking area. Air conditioning. Toilets wheelchair accessible. Open Mon-Sat, L 12:30-6, D 6-9:30. Sun L 12:30-2:30, Sun D 6-9. Set Sun L about €13. L&D à la carte available. House wines about €13; sc discretionary. Closed 24-26 Dec, Jan 10 days. [Times and prices not confirmed at time of going to press. please phone for details.] MasterCard, Visa. **Directions:** 20 min. drive from Rosslare ferry, Wexford Town and Ballyhack ferry. ◇

Rosslare Area — Churchtown House

Country House — Tagoat Rosslare Co. Wexford **Tel: 053 32555** Fax: 053 32577 Email: info@churchtownhouse.com Web: wwwchurchtownhouse.com

Patricia and Austin Cody's Georgian house is set in about eight and a half acres of wooded gardens and dates back to 1703. It has been completely renovated and elegantly furnished to make a comfortable country house retreat for discerning guests and is extremely handy for the Rosslare ferryport, about four miles away. The Codys are renowned for their hospitality and, if you're lucky enough to arrive at this well-run house at around teatime, you'll be served delicious home-made cake and tea in the drawing room. Good food is an important feature here and a fine Irish breakfast is served in the bright dining room, where dinner is also available for residents by arrangement. Spacious en-suite bedrooms decorated in country house style have phones and TV. Garden. Not suitable for hildren under 10. Pets by arrangement. **Rooms 12** (2 junior suites, 4 shower only, 1 for disabled, all no-smoking). B&B €80 pps; ss €20. Residents' D, 8pm; Set D €39, book by noon. House wines €25. Closed 30 Nov-1 Mar. MasterCard, Visa, Laser. **Directions:** On R736 half mile from N25, at Tagoat.

Rosslare — Kelly's Resort Hotel

féile bia Hotel/Restaurant

Rosslare Co. Wexford **Tel: 053 32114** Fax: 053 32222
Email: kellyhot@iol.ie Web: www.kellys.ie

The history of this renowned family-run hotel spans three centuries - yet constant renovating, refurbishing and building work each winter keep raising standards ever higher. Quite simply, the hotel has everything, for both individuals and families, many of whom return year after year (the number of children is limited at any one time, so as not to create an imbalance). The many public rooms range from a quiet reading room and the snooker room to a supervised crèche and gallery lounge: pictures (mostly modern) throughout the hotel form an outstanding art collection. Many of the bedrooms have sea views, some with balconies; housekeeping throughout is immaculate. Leisure facilities include a therapeutic spa, two indoor swimming pools, indoor tennis, and, a bit of fun for francophiles, boules. Outside the summer holiday season (end June-early Sept), ask about special breaks (including special interest breaks - everything from wine appreciation to golf clinics), when rates are reduced. Conferences (30). Leisure centre, swimming pools. Tennis. Fishing (sea). Snooker. Hair dressing. Health & beauty centre (to be reconstructed for 2003). Playroom & children's playground. Garden. Parking. No pets. **Rooms 99** (all superior, 1 for disabled). Lift. B&B about €100 pps, ss €10; sc10%.
Main Dining Room: This L shaped room, which is exceptionally well run under the eagle eye of Pat Doyle, features wonderful examples from the hotel's renowned art collection and is cleverly designed to have an intimate atmosphere. The Chef de cuisine Jim Aherne and his team provide excellent value for money and continue to satisfy literally hundreds of guests daily. Menus reflect the value placed on fresh local produce: Rosslare mackerel, Slaney salmon and locally sourced vegetables, for example, are used in daily-changing menus offering fairly traditional cooking in starters like chicken liver pate maison with Cumberland sauce and leek, bacon & Cheddar quiche with tossed greens; followed by char-grilled lamb burgers with sautéed onions & mushrooms and pan grilled lemon sole fillets with sauce tartare. Finish with desserts like bread & butter pudding & cream or banoffi pie with vanilla custard. The hotel's renowned wine list is meticulously sourced and excellent value. **Seats 250** (private room 40); no smoking area, air conditioning. L 1-2.15 D 7.30-9; Set Sun L €25; Set D €40. House wine €18; s.c. discretionary.

☆ **La Marine:** This cool contemporary restaurant adjacent to the hotel complements the main restaurant perfectly and has its own separate entrance. A stunning zinc bar imported from France is the focal point of a lovely area where you can have an aperitif in comfort (although the turnover is brisk and you will be encouraged to go directly to your table if it is ready). Offering the perfect informal dining option, La Marine is the place to see and be seen - and it can be hard to get a table, especially for dinner at weekends. The atmosphere can be electric, although comfort is not a top priority; fashionably sparse tables have fresh flowers, good quality cutlery and paper napkins, but space is at a premium so be prepared for a bit of a squeeze. Head chef Eugene Callaghan was instrumental in the development of the restaurant from the outset and recent visits have confirmed a consistently high standard seen in well-judged menus, excellently executed. Ingredients are carefully sourced, using local seasonal produce as much as possible and a finely judged balancing act between traditional and fusion fare is achieved, thus starters like creamy seafood & saffron chowder find themselves alongside a melt-in-the mouth salt & pepper squid with sesame & soy dip and down to earth main courses like grilled rib-eye steak with gratin dauphinois & Café de Paris butter rub shoulders with crispy duck confit with Caesar dressed green beans. Desserts are deliciously classic - panna cotta with summer fruits, perhaps, or there's a selection of Irish cheese. Wines reflecting the style of food, are fairly priced (selection off main list). Service is swift and friendly. Sunday lunch is more traditional and may feature upbeat versions of traditional roasts. A light snack menu is also available every afternoon, 3-6pm. **Seats 60.** L daily, 12.30-3; D 6.30-9.30. Amex, Diners, MasterCard, Visa, Laser. **Directions:** Take the signs for Wexford/Rosslare/Southeast. Outside Wexford Town alongside Rosslare Strand beach.

Rosslare Harbour — Great Southern Hotel

féile bia Hotel

Rosslare Harbour Co. Wexford **Tel: 053 33233** Fax: 053 3354
Email: res@rosslare-gsh.ie Web: www.gshotels.com

A popular family venue, this 1960s' hotel is perched on a clifftop overlooking the harbour – very handy for the port and a useful place to get a fortifying breakfast if you're coming off an overnight ferry, or if there are delays. It has good facilities and recent refurbishment has included the exterior, all public areas, most of the bedrooms, the restaurant, function rooms and the Maritime Bar (which has an extensive collection of memorabilia covering the history of shipping in the area) Conference/banqueting (200/150). Bedrooms are well-equipped, with phone, TV with video channel tea/coffee making facilities and trouser press. Bar food is available every day and there's an evening restaurant. Leisure centre, indoor swimming pool. Tennis. Snooker. Parking. Children welcome (under 2s free in parents' room, cots available without charge; children's playground, playroom, crèche). No pets. **Rooms 100** (8 no-smoking, 1 for disabled). Lift. B&B €90 pps; ss €30. Closed Jan-mid Feb. Amex, Diners, MasterCard, Visa, Laser. **Directions:** Overlooking Rosslare Harbour and ferry terminal.

Wexford — Forde's Restaurant

féile bia Restaurant

Crescent Quay Wexford Co. Wexford
Tel: 053 23832 / 22816 Fax: 053 23832

In a renovated building near the Ballast Office, proprietor-chef Liam Forde's bistro-style first-floor restaurant overlooking the harbour has great atmosphere - created by many happy customers and excellent use of lighting, with mirrors reflecting lots of candles. Tables are quite well-spaced and comfortable and the varied seasonal à la carte menus offer a wide choice, with vegetarian (and vegan) options prominently listed and a leaning towards seafood. From a dozen or so starters, try button mushrooms filled with brie & garlic then deep-fried in an almond coating (a nice little twist on the old favourite) or a delicious salad of marinated seared scallops, with mini crab spring rolls and a lemon dressing. Main courses might include a fish special trio of salmon, scallops & turbot in a light cream sauce (a well-judged dish, perfectly cooked) and rack of local lamb with rosemary and raspberry jus and accompanying vegetables (small buttered steamed potatoes in their jackets, a mixture of julienne courgette, finely sliced onion & broccoli florets, stir fried briefly in butter and spring rolls filled with mashed potato). Everything is made on the premises - stocks, pastas, ice creams - the cooking is spot on and details excellent. Interesting, informative wine list. The early evening menus is particularly good value. **Seats 100**. No smoking area, air conditioning. Children welcome. D Mon-Sat,6-9.30. Early D, €20 (5-6pm only). Set D €34, also à la carte. House wine €18.50; s.c.discretionary. Closed Sun (except during Opera Festival), 24-26 Dec. Diners, MasterCard, Visa, Laser. **Directions:** The Quay Front.

Wexford — La Dolce Vita

Restaurant

Westgate Wexford Co. Wexford
Tel: 053 23935 Fax: 053 935

Chef-proprietor Roberto Pons greets guests personally to his popular restaurant, which has earned a strong local following since he moved here in 1998. The exterior of the building is promising and perhaps leads first-time guests to expect more character - and, unusually for an Italian restaurant, the ambience tends to be rather quiet. A committed Euro-Toques chef, Roberto cooks in traditional Italian style - risotto, osso bucco, rombo in salsa verde - and, except for necessary Italian imports, everything is based on the freshest and best of local Irish produce. In line with this style of restaurant, presentation is rather plain (no bad thing perhaps), but the cooking is reliably good in dishes like meltingly tender lambs liver with butter & sage,which comes with excellent side vegetables, and a perfect pannacotta. **Seats 60**. No-smoking area. Wheelchair access. D daily 6-10; à la carte. House wines about €14.60. Children welcome. Closed 2 weeks Feb. [Times & prices not confirmed at time of going to press, please phone for details.] MasterCard, Laser. **Directions:** Opposite County Hall, 200m on left. ◊

Wexford — La Riva

féile bia Restaurant

2 Henrietta Street Wexford Co. Wexford
Tel: 053 24330

Just off the quays, Warren Gillan took over this first floor restaurant in May 2001 and, since then, has earned the respect of discerning diners from Wexford and beyond. The restaurant is bright and pleasant, with views through to the kitchen, where Warren takes pride in using as much local and organic produce as possible. Opening times are quite flexible - at "busy seasons" (high summer, Wexford Opera Festival period and the festive time around Christmas) they're open every night so, even on Sunday, it's always worth a call. **Seats 42**. No-smoking area. Air conditioning. D Mon-Sat, 6-"late". A la carte. House wine €15.20; sc discretionary. Children welcome. Closed Sun. Mastercard, Visa.

Wexford — Mange 2

Restaurant
100 South Main St. Wexford Co. Wexford
Tel: 053 44033 Web: www.trailblazer.ie

Although the setting is simple - farmhouse-style pine tables, terracotta walls - and may not give away any clues about the standard of the food, it does have views through to the kitchen, where Richard Trappe and his team work hard to retain their reputation as one of Wexford's most exciting restaurants. The menu is also very understated - a single A4 page plainly laid out in a double column, but it is in fact an ambitious menu and there is something about its directness that suggests that the priorities lie elsewhere: what you get is genuinely creative cooking which is also good value for money, a rare enough combination these days. And it is a warm and welcoming place; tables are cleared very promptly and everything possible is done to ensure guests enjoy the food. Vegetarians are well looked after (there are blackboard specials daily in addition to à la carte menus) and vegetables are used creatively within each dish. Expect colourful starters like buffalo mozzarella & beetroot stack with tomato & basil dressing and garlic utilise and main dishes roast tenderloin of pork with champ potato braise, savoy cabbage and toasted pinenut & almond butter. There is something here to please everyone, speedy service - and good value; this team lives up to their policy "that customers will never leave disappointed." Admirable. **Seats 40**. Wheelchair access. Air conditioning. D 6-10.30 daily. A la carte. House wines about €12.50 SC discretionary 10% on parties of 8+). Children welcome. Open all year. Amex, MasterCard, Visa, Laser. **Directions:** Wexford town centre, near Talbot Hotel.

Wexford — McMenamin's Townhouse

B&B
3 Auburn Terrace Redmond Road Wexford Co. Wexford
Tel: 053 46442 Fax: 053 46442
Email: mcmem@indigo.ie Web: www.wexford-bedandbreakfast.com

Seamus and Kay McMenamin's redbrick end-of-terrace Victorian house is within walking distance of the town centre and has been one of the most highly-regarded places to stay in this area for some years. It is useful for first or last night overnight stops for travellers on the Rosslare ferry, as a base for the Wexford Opera or for a short break in this undervalued corner of Ireland. Bedrooms have neat shower rooms and they take pride in providing top quality beds and everything that could be required including TV and tea/coffee-making facilities. The McMenamins' extensive local knowledge is generously passed on to guests and this, together with a good breakfast - quite extensive menus include home-made yogurt old-fashioned treats like kippers and lambs' kidneys in sherry sauce, served with freshly baked breads and home-made preserves - gets you off to a good start and helps to make the most of every day. Children welcome (under 2s free in parents' room, cots available without charge). No pets. **Rooms 5** (all shower only & no-smoking). B&B €40 pps; ss €10. Closed 20-30 Dec. Visa, MasterCard. **Directions:** Central near bus/rail station opposite cineplex.

Wexford — The Sky & The Ground

féile bia Restaurant/Pub
112 South Main Street Wexford Co. Wexford
Tel: 053 21273 Fax: 053 21832

Candle light, framed old advertisements, basic tables and chairs and a worn wooden floor create the atmospheric drinking space at the Sky & the Ground, a genuine old-style pub that frequently features traditional Irish music sessions. A varying bar menu is offered throughout the day - quite brief at lunchtime and early evening, rather more extensive for dinner. Expect dishes like lemon sole with half shell green mussels or farmhouse style chicken with roast shallots & thyme jus, served with potatoes and vegetables - then maybe desserts like freshly-made apple & almond flan, served with a drizzle of lemon syrup. There's a patio garden around at the back where they serve food, weather permitting. There is also no segregation of drinkers from customers who are eating, which can sometimes make the service a bit erratic. "Heavens Above" restaurant upstairs also has lots of character - and the appropriately named "Next Door" off-licence is also under the same management; it stocks over 300 wines from all over the world and an unusually wide range of bottled beers from different countries (all available to customers in the bar or restaurant). However, there are big changes afoot, with plans to build a brasserie bar beside the existing premises and a 10 bedroom hotel section beside the present pub. Pub seats 50. Food served Mon-Sat: L 12-3 Limited snack menu 3-6. Restaurant: Mon-Sat, D 6-10; closed Sun. MasterCard, Visa, Laser. **Directions:** On the south end of Wexford's Main Street.

Wexford   Talbot Hotel

féile bia Hotel   Trinity St. Wexford Co. Wexford **Tel: 053 22566** Fax: 053 23377
Email: talbotwx@eircom.net Web: talbothotel.ie

Sister hotel to the Stillorgan Park Hotel in Dublin, this 1960s hotel actually dates back to 1905. It is well-located on the harbour-front location and also convenient to the town centre - indeed, so many activities revolve around it that many would say the Talbot is the town centre. A warm welcome from friendly staff, plus the contented crowd that always seems to be milling around the foyer, immediately sets arriving guests at ease - and one is immediately struck by the range and quality of original paintings, which is a feature of great interest throughout the hotel. Bedrooms are inevitably somewhat limited by their age and the style of the building, but quite pleasant and comfortable, with phone, TV and tea/coffee trays as standard. The basement leisure centre is an unexpectedly characterful area, confirming the feeling that the Talbot will always spring a few surprises - one of which is that 'The Slaney Gourmet Club' meet at the hotel on the last Tuesday of each month for 'a taste of the exotic'; there's also live jazz in the Trinity every Thursday night in summer and weekend entertainment all year. Conference/banqueting facilities (300/350). Leisure centre, indoor swimming pool. Children welcome (under 14s free in parents' room). Wheelchair access. Lift. Own parking. No pets. **Rooms 99** (all en-suite, 2 for disabled) B&B about €70 pps, ss about €20. Open all year. Amex, Diners, MasterCard, Visa. **Directions:** On harbour front. ◇

Wexford   White's Hotel

Hotel   Georges Street Wexford Co. Wexford **Tel: 053 22311** Fax: 053 45000
Email: info@whiteshotel.iol.ie Web: www.wexfordirl.com

From the outside this famous hotel looks relatively modern, certainly when approached from the car park, but the reality is that there was a hostelry on this site in the late 18th century, which is more apparent when viewed from George Street. Older bedrooms have been modernised and there's a health and fitness club (but no swimming pool) in the basement. Major improvements are due shortly. Conference/banqueting (600/450). Secretarial services. Parking. Children welcome (under 3s free in parents' room, cots available). Pets by arrangement. Lift. **Rooms 82** (all en-suite). B&B about €60 pps; ss about €20. Open all year. Amex, Diners, MasterCard, Visa. **Directions:** Follow signs when leaving N25 or N11.

COUNTY WICKLOW

Wicklow is a miracle. Although the booming presence of Dublin is right next door, this spectacularly lovely county is very much its own place, an away-from-it-all world of moorland and mountain, farmland and garden, forest and lake, seashore and river. It's all right there, just over the nearest hill, yet it all seems so gloriously different.

In times past, much of Wicklow was recorded (by those who kept the official histories) as a mountain stronghold where rebels and hermits alike could keep their distance from the capital. But modern Wicklow has no need to be in a state of rebellion, for it is an invigorating and inspiring place which captivates everyone who lives there, so much so that while many of its citizens inevitably work in Dublin, they're Wicklow people first, and associate Dubs - if at all - an extremely long way down the line.

Their attitude is easily understood, for even with today's traffic, it is still only a very short drive to transform your world from the crowded city streets right into the heart of some of the most beautiful scenery in all Ireland. Such scenery generates its own strong loyalties and sense of identity, and Wicklow folk are rightly and proudly a race apart. Drawing strength from their wonderful environment, they have a vigorous local life which keeps metropolitan blandness well at bay.

While being in a place so beautiful is almost sufficient reason for existence in itself, they're busy people too, with sheep farming and forestry and all sorts of light industries, while down in the workaday harbour of Arklow in the south of the county - a port with a long and splendid maritime history - they've been so successful in organising their own seagoing fleet of freighters that there are now more ships registered in Arklow than any other Irish port.

Local Attractions and Information

Arklow Tourism Information	0402 32484
Ashford Mount Usher Gardens	0404 40116
Avoca Tourism Information	0402 35788
Blessington Russborough House & Gardens	045 865239
Bray Kilruddery House & Gardens	01 2863405
Bray National Sealife Centre	01 2866939
Derrynamuck Dwyer McAllister Traditional Cottage	0404 45325
Enniskerry Powerscourt House & Gardens	01 2046000
Glendalough Tourism Information	0404 45688
Glendalough Visitor Centre	0404 45325
Kilmacanogue Avoca Handweavers Garden	01 2867466
Kilquade National Garden Exhibition Centre	01 2819890
Rathdrum Avondale House	0404 46111
Rathdrum Kilmacurragh Arboretum	01 6473000

Wicklow County Gardens Festival (May-July)	0404 20100
Wicklow Mountains National Park	0404 45425
Wicklow Town Wicklow Historic Gaol	0404 61599
Wicklow Town Tourism Information	0404 69117

Arklow   Christy's

Pub   38 Lr Main Street Arklow Co. Wicklow **Tel: 0402 32145**

New arrivals at Michael Murray's attractively renovated town centre bar are immediately set at ease by friendly staff who show you to your table, immediately offer a drink and present menus - just the kind of treatment that gets hungry guests off to a good start. An interesting menu offers a nicely balanced selection of the traditional and the contemporary - and the sight of appetising food at neighbouring tables is encouraging too. Choose between fashionably international fare like crostinis, fajitas, paninis and wraps and more down to earth meals like bacon chops with Irish whiskey sauce & rustic potatoes or a 12 oz steak with hand cut chips; Christy's House Salad (mixed leaves with croûtons, cherry tomatoes, cucumber, red onions & peppers plus feta or bacon and house dressing) makes a healthy main course which can be vegetarian or not depending on your choice of cheese or bacon. Cooking and presentation both live up to the promise of the menu, making this a place people will return to. The wine selection is restricted to a small selection of quarter bottles, which is a pity as the food deserves more choice. Live music at weekends. Children welcome up to 7pm. Own parking at rear. Food served 12-7pm daily (evening menu 5-7). Closed Good Fri, 25 Dec. MasterCard, Visa, Laser. **Directions:** Directly on Main Street opposite AIB. Parking at rear.

Arklow   Kitty's of Arklow

 Restaurant/Pub   56 Main Street Arklow Co. Wicklow
                                                            Tel: 0402 31669 Fax: 0402 31553

A big blue double-fronted building in the centre of town, Kitty's is something of an institution in Arklow. Large and airy ground floor bar areas are decorated in retro 50s style (with big comfortable chairs and old-fashioned radiators) and there's a lofty first floor restaurant with a slightly olde-world feel (open fireplaces and lots of wood), which is divided into a non-smoking section along the front of the building and an area for smokers at the back. It's very popular with locals ranging from young commuters to large family groups, who like the informal atmosphere and modern food at affordable prices - the early evening menu is especially good value. There's no reception area downstairs, but greeting and seating (at uncovered wooden tables with good, simple appointments) is efficiently handled on arrival at the top and menus, offering about nine choices on each course, are promptly produced. Menus include a wide range of seafood and descriptions aren't too fussy: typical starters include a goats cheese & spinach tartlet with tomato relish (more vegetarian - and coeliac - options available on request), while main courses might include several fish dishes, such as sugar spiced salmon with tossed Asian greens, dress in basil & coriander yogurt and an intriguing 'tempura of tilapia & John Dory' with strawberries and bok choi in a peppered syrup. Traditionalists will be relieved to find more familiar dishes too, like prime Angus medallions of beef and rack of lamb. Good quality ingredients are used and it's a place you could find yourself going back to, not least because notably friendly, efficient and professional staff make sure everyone's happy. Children welcome. **Seats 110** (private room 24). No smoking area; air conditioning. D daily 6-10. Early D from €25 (6-7pm). Set D €34, also à la carte. House wine €17. Bar food daily, 12-5 (Sun from 12.30). Closed 25 Dec & Good Fri. Amex, Diners, MasterCard, Visa, Laser. **Directions:** Off N11, centre of main street Arklow.

Arklow   The New Riverwalk Restaurant

Restaurant   Riverwalk Lane, Arklow, Co Wicklow **Tel: 0402 31657**

An unpretentious, good value restaurant specialising in seafood and steaks would be a welcome addition to most Irish towns, but particularly so in a coastal town popular with anglers - and a growing number of visitors to the marina. So The New Riverwalk Restaurant - in a neat building just a few yards from Main Street - has got off to an auspicious start and, although we will watch with interest in the coming year, it appears to be delivering the goods. The restaurant is divided between a ground floor room (rather tightly packed) and one on the first floor (with four better-spaced tables), each with a couple of window tables. A sensibly short printed menu is offered, supplemented by five or six fish specials (depending on the catch of the day). A choice of soups (one fish) might be offered among half a dozen starters, maybe also an extra seafood starter like mussels, while main courses may include several meat dishes - steaks, Wicklow lamb, pork fillet and one or two vegetarian dishes as well as the fish dishes: pan-fried red snapper, perhaps, with a well-made white wine sauce with onion and cheese, also locally-caught fish like whole plaice, simply pan-fried whole on the bone, served with garlic potatoes and a generous platter of vegetables. Popular desserts - pears in red wine, profiteroles with cream, ice cream - and good coffee to finish. Sound fish cooking, pleasantly efficient service and reasonable prices should be a recipe for success here - and French anglers visiting the town seem to have taken it to their hearts already. D only, 5.30-10.30. Mastercard, Visa. **Directions:** off the river walk, near Main Street.

Arklow   Plattenstown House

Country House
Coolgreaney Road Arklow Co. Wicklow
Tel: 0402 37822 Fax: 0402 37822
Email: mcdpr@indigo.ie Web: www.wicklow.ie/farm/f-plattn.htm

About halfway between Dublin and Rosslare (each about an hour's drive away) and overlooking parkland, this quiet, peaceful place is set in 50 acres of land amidst its own lovely gardens close to the sea - and Margaret McDowell describes her period farmhouse well as having "the soft charm typical of the mid 19th century houses built in scenic Wicklow". There is plenty to do in the area, with golf, riding stables and forest walks all nearby, as well as the sea. There's a traditional drawing room furnished with family antiques overlooking the front garden, a TV lounge (where smoking is allowed) available for guests' use and a lovely dining room where breakfast is served - and evening meals are also offered by arrangement. Bedrooms vary in size and outlook according to their position in the house and have interestingly different characters, but all are comfortably furnished. beautiful, well-maintained gardens. Children welcome (under 3s free in parents' room). No pets. **Rooms 4** (3 en-suite with shower only, 1 with private bathroom, all no-smoking). B&B €39pps, ss €9. Closed at Christmas. MasterCard, Visa. **Directions:** Top of Arklow town, small roundabout, straight on to Coolgreaney Road. 5 km on left.

Arklow   Woodenbridge Hotel

féile bia Hotel
Vale of Avoca Arklow Co. Wicklow **Tel: 0402 35146** Fax: 0402 35573
Email: wbhotel@iol.ie Web: www.woodenbridgehotel.com

This pleasant country hotel lays claim to the title of Ireland's oldest hotel, with a history going back to 1608, when it was first licensed as a coaching inn on the old Dublin-Wexford highway - and later came to great prominence when gold and copper were mined in the locality. Michael Collins stayed at the hotel during secret meetings with senior British Army officers in February 1922 (the room he stayed in can be booked, subject to availability) and Eamon and Sinead De Valera spent their honeymoon here. Today it is still very popular for weddings and makes a friendly and relaxing base for a visit to this beautiful part of County Wicklow. The many other historical associations in the area include the home of Charles Stewart Parnell, nearby at Avondale. Bedrooms - many of them overlooking Woodenbridge golf course - are comfortably furnished, with phone, TV and tea/coffee trays. As well as a more formal restaurant, food is available in the lively bar (traditional Irish music in summer). Children welcome (under 4s free in parents' room; cots available without charge). Popular for weddings; golf nearby. **Rooms 23.** B&B €70pps, ss €12. Food available 12.30-9. No pets. Closed 25 Dec. Amex, MasterCard, Visa. **Directions:** N11 to Arklow turn off 7 km.

Ashford   Ashford House

Pub
Ashford Co. Wicklow **Tel: 0404 40481** Fax: 0404 40990
Email: tom@ashfordhouse.ie Web: www.ashfordhouse.ie

This well-maintained large pub in the centre of Ashford village presents a neat face to the world and has cheering open fires, plenty of natural materials and friendly staff to create a warm and welcoming tone. A variety of carefully planned areas with completely different styles and atmospheres seem to provide something for every taste and time of day - the main bar, for example, while far from olde worlde, is traditional enough to please those who enjoy a classic Irish pub and, behind it, there's an informal, high-ceilinged bistro (also with an open fire); daytime food can be served in either area. There's also a separate restaurant , Ashford Oriental, run by chef-manager Burt Tsang. Bar menu all day, 12.30-closing. Ashford House Bistro: L&D daily (12.30-3, 6-9.30); Oriental Restaurant open D daily (5-11) & L Sun (3-5). House wine from €15.25. Children welcome up to 8pm. Toilets wheelchair accessible. Amex, Diners, MasterCard, Visa, Laser. **Directions:** Dublin-Wexford road (N11); off roundabout on Main St.

Ashford — Ballyknocken House

Farmhouse/Guesthouse   Gleanealy Ashford Co. Wicklow **Tel: 0404 44627**   Fax: 0404 4469█
Email: cfulvio@ballyknocken.com   Web: www.ballyknocken.com

Perfectly placed for walking holidays in the Wicklow Hills, playing golf, or simply for touring the area, Catherine Fulvio's charming Victorian farmhouse provides comfort, cosiness, good food and hospitality. After a period working at nearby Tinakilly House, Catherine took over this family busines█ in 1999 - the farm has been in the Byrne family for three generations and they have welcomed guest█ for over thirty years - and she has since refurbished it throughout in old country style. A gentl█ Victorian theme prevails throughout (not too fussy): bedrooms have been charmingly done up, with antique furniture and very good beds - and pretty bathrooms, five of which have Victorian baths. The dining room, parlour and sitting room have also had the makeover and her energetic quest fo█ perfection also extends to the garden, where new fruit tree, roses and herbs are now settling in Comfort and style aside, Catherine cooks splendid dinners based on local produce, including vegetables and herbs from the Ballyknocken farm (with wine list including some specially imported wines); the cooking style is modern and (influenced by her Italian husband Claudio) there's a█ Mediterranean flavour. All this plus extensive breakfasts and a relaxing atmosphere ensure guests keep coming back for more. **Rooms 7** (1 shower only, all no smoking) B&B €50pps, ss €30. Residents D Tue-Sat, Set D €28, houses wines 16.90. No D on Sun. Non-resident group (8+) lunche█ catered for, by arrangement. Open all year. MasterCard, Visa. **Directions:** From Dublin turn right after Texaco Petrol Station in Ashford. Continue for 3 miles. House on right.

Aughrim — Clone House

Ⓝ Country House   Aughrim Co Wicklow **Tel 0402 36029** Email:stay@clonehouse.com

The oldest part of Jeff and Carla Watson's rambling country house in the lovely unspoilt south Wicklow countryside goes back to the 1600s, although it was largely rebuilt in 1805 after burning in the 1798 Rebellion. Today this elegantly furnished and hospitable house is full of comfort, providing a quiet and relaxing haven, away from the stresses of modern life. Open fires in every room are a particularly attractive feature - and thoughtful little touches abound, including fresh fruit in chocolates in each bedroom (some with four posters), as well as tea and coffee making facilities - and no television to intrude into this tranquil retreat. Carla cooks a 5-course dinner by arrangement - and non-resident parties of four or more can be accommodated if there is room. Not suitable for children except babies (cot available). No pets. Gym, weight room, sauna; table tennis; garden. **Rooms 4** (all en-suite, 3 shower only, all no smoking.) Dinner at 8-8.30pm by arrangement, €45. Wine about €15 (BYO, corkage €5). SC discretionary (10% on parties of 4+). Open all year. Amex, Mastercard, Visa. **Directions:** Follow the brown signs from Aughrim or Woodenbridge.

Aughrim — Lawless Hotel

Restaurant/Hotel   Aughrim Co. Wicklow **Tel: 0402 36146**   Fax: 0402 36384
Email: lawhotel@iol.ie   Web: www.lawlesshotel.com

Picturesquely situated beside the river in the lovely village of Aughrim, the O'Toole family's historic hotel dates back to 1787; it was a popular meeting place during the 1798 uprising and, with the arrival of the railway in the 1800s, began a new lease of life as the Railway Hotel. Recent renovations and extensions have, on the whole, been undertaken with respect for the character of the original building although, unfortunately, the adjacent development of holiday homes now dominates the village. Recently refurbished bedrooms are in character with a country inn, although on the small side which has limited bathroom design. The most recent investment has been completely rebuilding the "Thirsty Trout" bar and the "Snug" lounge area, which is now much larger, with a carvery (12.30-2.30 & 5.30-8.30 daily). There's a lovely dining room overlooking the river beside the bridge and a paved riverside area at the back is used for informal summer food - and makes a romantic spot for wedding photographs. A man-made angling park beside the hotel offers all year angling, with special disabled facilities. Conference/banqueting (250/250). Secretarial services. Fishing. Garden. Parking. Children welcome (under 2s free in parents' room). No pets. **Rooms 14** (5 no-smoking). B&B €77.50 pps, ss €25.50. Wheelchair access (ground floor only). Closed 24-26 Dec. MasterCard, Visa, Laser. **Directions:** From Arklow Town take R753 via Woodenbridge to Aughrim.

Avoca Village — Avoca Handweavers

 Café

Avoca Village Co. Wicklow **Tel: 0402 35105** Fax: 0402 35446
Email: info@avoca.ie Web: www.avoca.ie

FÉILE BIA AWARD - *(see page 20)*

Avoca handweavers, established in 1723, is Ireland's oldest business. It's a family owned craft design company which now has half a dozen branches throughout Ireland (most of which feature in this Guide) and the business originated here, at Avoca village, where you can watch the hand weavers who produce the lovely woven woollen rugs and fabrics which became the hallmark of the company. Today the appeal of Avoca shops is threefold: the high standard of crafts sold, their beautiful locations, and restaurants that have built up a well-deserved reputation for imaginative, wholesome home-cooked food. Garden. Parking. Children welcome. Pets allowed in some areas. **Seats 75**. Open all day (10-5) Mon-Sun. House wine about €12.50. No-smoking area. No service charge. Wheelchair access. Closed 25-26 Dec. Amex, Diners, MasterCard, Visa, Laser. **Directions:** Leave N11 at Rathnew and follow signs for Avoca.

Blessington — Downshire House Hotel

 Hotel

Blessington Co. Wicklow **Tel: 045 865 199** Fax: 045 865 335
Email: info@downshirehouse.com Web: www.downshirehouse.com

Situated just 18 miles from Dublin on the N81, in the tree-lined main street of Blessington, this friendly village hotel offers unpretentious comfort which is very winning. Blessington is an attractive village in an area of great natural beauty and archaeological interest – and it's also very close to Ireland's great Palladian mansion, Russborough House, home of the world-famous Beit art collection. The present owner, Rhoda Byrne, has run the hotel since 1959 and instigated many improvements, including conference facilities for up to 200 and refurbishment of public areas. Simply furnished bedrooms, which include two single rooms, all have en-suite bathrooms with full bath and shower. This is a place that people feel comfortable with, because it exudes that indefinable sense of being well-run and genuinely hospitable that goes with caring family management. You will also eat well here - not the competitive cutting-edge food of young chefs in the city, but wholesome, satisfying country fare served by friendly and professional staff with a real desire to please: a soothing and restorative place to take a break. Conference/banqueting (200/250). Garden, walking. Children welcome; cots available (€8). **Rooms 25** (all with full en-suite bathrooms). B&B €76pps; ss€8. Closed 22 Dec-6 Jan. MasterCard, Visa, Laser, Switch. **Directions:** 18 miles from Dublin on the N81.

Bray — The Tree of Idleness Restaurant

Restaurant

Seafront Bray Co. Wicklow
Tel: 01 286 3498 Fax: 01 282 8183

This much-loved seafront restaurant opened in 1979 when the owners, Akis and Susan Courtellas, arrived from Cyprus bringing with them the name of their previous restaurant (now in Turkish-held north Cyprus). A collection of photographs of old Cyprus in the reception area establishes the traditional Mediterranean atmosphere of the restaurant – and the menu cover bears a drawing of the original Tree of Idleness. Since Akis' death some years ago, Susan has run the restaurant herself with the help of Tom Monaghan, restaurant manager since 1980 and, since 2001, Derek Cooling (who was previously second chef) has assumed the mantle of head chef, so it is he who now offers modern Greek Cypriot/Mediterranean menus based on the style which has made this restaurant famous - and the most remarkable feature of the Tree of Idleness is its consistency, in maintaining both high standards and the unique house style. Alongside the classics – tzatziki, humus, taramasalata, Greek salad, dolmades, moussaka (including a vegetarian variation), souvlaki – there are some specialities which have had the world beating a path to the door for over 20 years. First, there is the roast suckling pig: boned and filled with apple and apricot stuffing, it is served crisp-skinned and tender, with a wonderful wine and wild mushroom sauce; following hard on its heels is Arni Kapnisto, roast smoked loin of lamb with redcurrant sauce on potato rosti - a dish with contemporary elements but unlike anything likely to be encountered elsewhere. Then there is the dessert trolley, which is nothing less than temptation on wheels: it always carries a range of fresh and exotic fruits, baklava, home-made ice creams, several chocolate desserts, Greek yogurt mousse and much else besides. Service is invariably excellent and the wine list includes a wide selection of house wines (some Greek) and some rare vintages, including wines from the Russian Massandra Collection, which go back to 1923. No children under 10 after 8 pm. **Seats 50**. No-smoking area. D Tue-Sun, 7.30-10.30 (Sun to 10). Set D €40, à la carte also available. House wines from €20.10% SC. Closed Mon, Christmas & 2 weeks Aug. Amex, MasterCard, Visa, Laser. **Directions:** On seafront towards Bray Head.

Delgany — Glenview Hotel

Hotel   Glen O' The Downs Co. Wicklow **Tel: 01 2873399** Fax: 01 2877511
Email: sales@glenview.com Web: www.glenviewhotel.com

Famous for its views over the luxuriantly green and leafy Glen O' The Downs, this well-located hotel has all the advantages of a beautiful rural location, yet is just a half hour's drive from Dublin. Major renovations and additions to the hotel have brought about a dramatic improvement of all facilities and, equally importantly, landscaping and upgrading of the hotel exterior and a new reception area gives a much more favourable impression of the hotel on arrival. State-of-the-art facilities are offered in the conference centre, there's an excellent Health and Leisure Club (now including beauty treatment and therapy rooms), the newer bedrooms include a penthouse suite - and all bedrooms, which are attractively furnished in warm colours and a gently modern style, have good facilities including safe, phone with computer terminal, trouser press, tea/coffee making facilities. Public areas include a very pleasant, comfortably furnished conservatory bar, which is a good place for an informal meal (Conservatory Bistro menu, international cooking, 12.30-9). All this, together with special breaks (golf, health and fitness, riding) offering good value, make the hotel a valuable asset to the area. Conference/banqueting (250/180). Secretarial services, ISDN lines, video conferencing. Leisure centre (indoor swimming pool). Snooker room (adults only). Garden, woodland walks. Children welcome (under 2s free in parents' room, cots available without charge, play room). Pets by arrangement. **Rooms 70** (1 suite, 12 executive rooms, 14 no-smoking rooms). Lift. B&B €115, ss € 38. Hotel closed 25 Dec.

Woodlands Restaurant: The restaurant has a great natural asset in forest views over the Glen-O'-the-Downs although it can otherwise be somewhat short on atmosphere. The presence of head chef Derek Dunne, a well-known successful competitor in the Irish Culinary Team, puts the food on a more ambitious level than most hotel dining rooms. He presents interesting table d'hôte and à la carte menus based on local ingredients - quite a lot of seafood, Wicklow lamb, venison - and mainly classical French in style. Cooking is competent but may not always live up to the promise of the menu. Restaurant not suitable for children after 7.30pm. **Seats 80**. No-smoking area; air conditioning. Pianist some evenings. D daily, 6.30-9.30; L Sun only, 12.30-2.30. Set D €45, à la carte also available; Set Sun L €25. House wines from €19. SC discretionary. Closed 25 Dec, bank hols. Amex, Diners, MasterCard, Visa, Laser. **Directions:** On N11, turn left 2 miles southbound of Kilmacanogue.

Dunlavin — Rathsallagh House, Golf & Country Club

féile bia 🏨 Country House   Dunlavin Co. Wicklow **Tel: 045 403 112** Fax: 045 403 343
Email: info@rathsallagh.com Web: www.rathsallagh.com

This large, rambling country house is just an hour from Dublin, but it could be in a different world. Although it's very professionally operated, the O'Flynn family insist it is not an hotel and - despite the relatively recent addition of an 18-hole golf course with clubhouse in the grounds - the gentle rhythms of life around the country house and gardens ensure that the atmosphere is kept decidedly low-key. Day rooms are elegantly furnished in country house style, with lots of comfortable seating areas and open fires. Accommodation includes beautiful big rooms with luxurious bathrooms in a new block, built discreetly behind the main courtyard in materials which will age gracefully to match the older buildings while, as in all old houses, the original rooms do vary; some are very spacious with lovely country views while other smaller, simpler rooms in the stable yard have a special cottagey charm. Rathsallagh is renowned for its magnificent Edwardian breakfast buffet, which was recognised in 2001 through selection as National winner of the Guide's Irish Breakfast Awards. Breakfast at Rathsallagh offers every conceivable good thing: not only fresh juices, fresh and stewed fruits, dried fruit compôtes, home-made muesli, Irish farmhouse cheeses, smoked salmon and kedgeree but also a whole ham on the bone and silver chafing dishes full of reminders of yesteryear - liver, lambs kidneys wrapped in bacon, kidneys and juicy field mushrooms as well as the more usual rashers, sausages, black and white pudding tomatoes - the list goes on and on - and there's more to come from the kitchen too, as eggs to accompany this feast are cooked to order and, of course, there's a selection of home-made breads, croissants and toast, local honey and home-made jams and chutney. It's a sight to gladden the heart of any guest and a few rounds of golf or a good walk in the hills (or at least around the lovely walled garden) will definitely be needed afterwards. Good food, warm hospitality and surroundings that are quiet or romantic to suit the mood of the day make Rathsallagh an ideal venue for conferences and small weddings. Conference/banqueting 150. Golf (18), gardens, tennis, cycling, walking. Pool table. Beauty salon. Pets allowed by arrangement. **Rooms 29** (2 suites, 2 for disabled, all no smoking). B&B €145, ss30. Closed 6-30 Jan.

Restaurant: Head chef John Luke creates interesting menus based on local produce, much of it from Rathsallagh's own farm and walled garden. A drink in the old kitchen bar is recommended while reading the 4-course menu - country house with world influences - then guests can settle down in the graciously furnished dining room overlooking the gardens and the golf course. Menus are not over-complicated but offer a well-balanced selection of about five dishes on each course, changed daily; roast local beef is a speciality, as is Wicklow lamb. John Luke sources his ingredients with care and there is a welcome directness and simplicity of style on the menu that is carried through in confident cooking of dishes that are well-conceived and visually tempting but especially memorable for flavour. Leave room for some Irish farmhouse cheese served from a traditional trolley, or delicious desserts which are often based on fruit from the garden. **Seats 120** (private room, 48) D Daily, 7.30-8.45. Set D €50; house wine €18; SC discretionary. *Not suitable for children under 12. Lunch is available only for residents, but food is served at Rathsallagh Golf Club, 11-8.45 daily. (Closed Jan).Amex, Diners, MasterCard, Visa, Laser. **Directions:** 15 miles south of Naas off Carlow Road, take Kilcullen Bypass (M9), turn left 2 miles south of Priory Inn, follow signposts.

Enniskerry — Powerscourt Terrace Café

féile bia Restaurant/Café

Powerscourt House Enniskerry Co. Wicklow **Tel: 01 204 6070**
Fax: 01 204 6072 Email: simon@avoca.ie Web: www.avoca.ie

FÉILE BIA AWARD - (see page 20)

Situated in a stunning location overlooking the famous gardens and fountains of Powerscourt House, the Pratt family of Avoca Handweavers opened this self-service restaurant in the summer of 1997. It is a delightfully relaxed space, with a large outdoor eating area as well as the 160-seater café, and the style and standard of food is similar to the original Avoca restaurant at Kilmacanogue. So head chef Eimer Rainsford ensures that everything is freshly made, using as many local ingredients as possible – including organic herbs and vegetables – with lots of healthy food. Avoca cafés are renowned for interesting salads, home-bakes and good pastries, and also excellent vegetarian dishes many of which, such as oven-roasted vegetable and goat's cheese tart, have become specialities. A new room in the East Wing was opened in 2001, providing a private room for groups of 20-90 people. Parking (some distance from the house). Children welcome. **Seats 160** (indoors; additional 140 outside terrace; private rooms 20-90). No-smoking area. Toilets wheelchair accessible. Open daily 10-5 (Sun to 5.30). House wine about €13. Closed 25-26 Dec. Amex, Diners, MasterCard, Visa, Laser.

Enniskerry Village — Wingfields Bistro

Restaurant

Church Hill Enniskerry Co. Wicklow **Tel: 01 204 2854**

This attractive restaurant has recently expanded into the adjoining building, which has created a more spacious setting for its well-appointed linen-clad tables and lots of original modern paintings. Proprietor/manager Toni Sinnott and head chef Martin Cuddihy opened here in autumn 2000 and they seem to be doing a consistently good job. Martin's menus are not over-long, offering a well-balanced choice of about half a dozen starters and slightly more on the main course selection; local seafood features strongly and, of course, the lamb which is virtually synonymous with the county - specialities include Dublin Bay prawns with a roast garlic & cherry tomato dressing and rack of Wicklow lamb served on a bed of pea purée with a rosemary jus. Cooking is accurate and food attractively presented in an admirably simple house style (no towering culinary architecture here), with the emphasis on sound combinations and flavour. Details, like home-baked bread and freshly cooked vegetables are good and service is professional, unobtrusive and relaxed. A shortish, carefully chosen wine list includes a range of house wines (about €15-20) and a few half bottles. **Seats 60**. No smoking area; air conditioning. D Mon-Sat, 7-9, L Sun 1-7.30. D à la carte, Set Sun L about €25. House wine about €16. Closed D Sun. MasterCard, Visa, Laser, Switch. **Directions:** Into village from monument,head uphill towards Powerscourt Demense. 50 yards up on the right. ◇

Glendalough — Derrymore House

B&B

Lake Road Glendalough Co. Wicklow **Tel: 0404 45493** Fax: 0404 45517
Email: patkelleher@eircom.net Web: http://homepage.eircom.net/~derrymore/

Very close to Glendalough, on a six-acre site of natural mountain woodland, Pat and Penny Kelleher's friendly B&B is in an unique position in the valley of Glendalough, overlooking the Lower Lake. It makes a quiet base for the outdoor pursuits which can be so enjoyable in the area - notably walking, fishing and horse riding - and seems like an oasis of calm when there are too many visitors around fo comfort. Bedrooms are appropriately furnished in a fresh country style with antique furniture, TV/VCR and neat en-suite shower rooms. A guests' sitting room has multi-channel TV/VCR and a library o videos and, in fine weather, it is very pleasant to have a private garden to sit in. Home-baked brea for breakfast. Not suitable for children under 8. No pets. **Rooms 5** (all no-smoking). B&B €30 pps; s €10. Closed Nov-Feb. Visa. **Directions:** Follow signs tor Glendalough - on the right as you approach.

Grangecon   Grangecon Foodstore & Café

Ⓝ Café   Grangecon Co. Wicklow
Tel: 045 403 982 Fax: 045 403 982

Wholesome aromas at Jenny and Richard Street's smashing little place in the charming village o Grangecon bode well for the hungry traveller, also the sight of contented locals relaxing, books in hand, over a post-prandial coffee. It really is little, with just two simple wooden communal tables, a display area for their lovely cold meats, salads, home-bakes and farmhouse cheeses, a larder freeze stocked with home-cooked ready meals to take home and a few shelves displaying speciality products not usually found in country villages, many of them organic - pasta, rice, orzo, olive oils, mustards teas, coffees, home-made preserves. The stated aim of Grangecon Foodstore & Café is "to provide you with a really good food stop": this they do in spades. Rustic the table setting may be, but how encouraging to find good butter in a little dish, a pepper mill and Maldon salt. The menu is understandably brief but the quiche is a little classic and comes with a scrumptious salad; similarly moist, freshly-baked brown bread arrives with cooked ham (Rudd's), cheese (Sheridans) and chutney (home-made), also garnished with salad: simple and excellent - why aren't there more places like this? No wine but you can opt for delicious chilled Crinnaughton apple juice, which comes from Cappoquin, instead and B-Y-O is fine (the pub across the road can supply wine if required). Luscious Illy coffee to finish and maybe a slice of wholesome dried apricot cake - just don't leave without a packet of their absolutely delectably light and crispy home-baked crackers for cheese. **Seats 12**. No smoking. Open all day Tue-Sat, 10-5.30. Closed Sun, Mon. **No Credit Cards. Directions:** A short detour off the main Dublin-Carlow road (N9), south of Dunlavin, between Crookstown and Baltinglass.

Greystones   The Hungry Monk

🍃 *féile bia* Restaurant   Church Road Greystones Co. Wicklow **Tel: 01 287 5759**
Fax: 01 287 7183 Email: hungrymonk@eircom.net

Well-known wine buff Pat Keown has run this hospitable first floor restaurant on the main street since 1988. Pat is a great and enthusiastic host; his love of wine is infectious and the place is spick and span – and the monk-related decor is a bit of fun. It all adds up to a great winding-down exercise. A combination of hospitality and interesting good quality food at affordable prices are at the heart of this restaurant's success – sheer generosity of spirit ensures value for money as well as a good meal. Seasonal menus offered include a well-priced all-day Sunday lunch and an evening à la carte menu. Menus are well-balanced to include traditional dishes – rack of Wicklow lamb with minted gravy and redcurrant jelly, steak with garlic & chive butter – as well as more unusual ones such as chicken El Greco (breast stuffed with feta cheese & roast courgette, served with a cep cream sauce) and several vegetarian dishes with an international flavour. Blackboard specials include the day's seafood dishes and also any special wine offers; the outstanding wine list includes a wide range of half bottles and wines by the glass. *Downstairs, The Hungry Monk Wine Bar offers a short well-chosen menu of about eight varied dishes and a carefully selected short wine list. Children welcome. Restaurant **Seats 50**. No-smoking area; air conditioning. D Tue -Sat 7-11; L Sun only, 12.30-8. D à la carte; Set Sun L €22. House wines from €17, SC 10%. *Wine Bar open Tue-Sat, 5-12, Sun 4-10 Closed Mon, 24-26 Dec. Amex, MasterCard, Visa, Laser. **Directions:** Centre of Greystones village beside DART.

Greystones   Vino Pasta

Restaurant   Church Road Greystones Co. Wicklow
Tel: 01 287 4807 Fax: 01 287 4827

Attractive awnings and clear signage make a good impression at Bill and Avril Tyrrell's popular neighbourhood restaurant and, once past the tiny bar/reception area, terracotta walls, ethnic bric-à-brac and a crowd of happy diners create a warm atmosphere. Tables settings are bistro-style - paper cloths & napkins - and Avril's menu is moderately priced, majoring in pastas and pizzas, with daily fish specials on a blackboard menu. Prompt, friendly service, sound cooking and generous portions add up to a good deal, making this the kind of place that locals pop into frequently. Limited wine list. **Seats 50**. No smoking area. Air conditioning. Children welcome up to 7pm. D Tue-Sun 5-11 daily

Sun 3-9). A la carte. House wine €16. 10% sc on parties of 6+. Closed Mon, 25 Dec, 2 wks July. mex, MasterCard, Visa, Laser. **Directions:** Beside Greystones DART Station.

Kilmacanogue — Avoca Café

féile bia Café

Kilmacanogue Co. Wicklow **Tel: 01 286 7466**
Fax: 01 286 2367 Web: www.avoca.ie

ÉILE BIA AWARD

Avoca Handweavers is one of the country's most famous craft shops but it is also well worth allowing time for a meal when you visit. Head chef Leylie Hayes has been supervising the production of the famously wholesome home-cooked food at Avoca Handweavers since 1990 and people home in to the cafés in county Wicklow and Dublin city, to tuck into fare which is as healthy as it is delicious. The importance of using only the very best ingredients has always been recognised at Avoca. Their food is based on the best available produce, as much of it as possible local and artisan and, when the Féile Bia programme was initiated, Leylie Hayes was one of the first to recognise its benefits and sign up to the Féile Bia Charter - which is a commitment to using products from recognised Quality Assurance Schemes, identifying the origin of these quality products on their menus and developing dishes and menus to profile local foods. "Quality in, quality out" is the motto at the heart of the Avoca philosophy: they have always strived to source the highest quality, least processed, best raw materials to make good, honest food which is produced with passion and attention to detail. More than ever, says Leylie Hayes, they have a sense of the critical importance of fresh, top quality seasonal ingredients: organic is great but if it has travelled half way around the world to reach us in a suspended state of refrigeration there is no point in that. So an emphasis on quality and sourcing the best ingredients locally has become a cornerstone of the Avoca ethic. *Also at Avoca, Powerscourt and Suffolk Street Dublin (see entries). Children welcome. **Seats 200.** No-smoking area; air conditioning. Open daily, 10-5. House wine about €12.50. No s.c. Closed 25-26 Dec. Amex, Diners, MasterCard, Visa, Laser. **Directions:** On N11 sign posted before Kilmacanogue Village.

Kiltegan — Barraderry Country House

Country House

Barraderry Kiltegan Co. Wicklow **Tel: 0508 73209** Fax: 0508 73209
Email: jo.hobson@oceanfree.net Web: www.barraderrycountryhouse.com

Olive and John Hobson's delightful Georgian house is in a quiet rural area close to the Wicklow Mountains and, now that their family has grown up, the whole house has undergone extensive refurbishment and alteration for the comfort of guests. Big bedrooms with country views are beautifully furnished with old family furniture and have well-finished bathrooms, and there's a spacious sitting room for guests' use too. Barraderry would make a good base for touring the lovely counties of Wicklow, Kildare, Carlow and Wexford and there's plenty to do nearby, with six golf courses within a half hour drive, several hunts and equestrian centres within easy reach and also Punchestown, Curragh and Naas racecourses - and, of course, walking in the lovely Wicklow Mountains. Garden. Children welcome (under 3s free in parents room). Pets allowed in some areas. **Rooms 4** (all en-suite, all no-smoking). B&B €40 pps; ss €5. Closed 15 Dec-15 Jan. MasterCard, Visa. **Directions:** 7 km from Baltinglass on R747, 1 km Kiltegan.

Kiltegan — Humewood Castle

Country House

Kiltegan Co. Wicklow **Tel: 0508 73215** Fax: 0508 73382
Email: humewood@iol.ie Web: www.humewood.com

Humewood was the Guide's Romantic Hideaway of the Year in 1999 and it's easy to see why. You arrive on a perfectly ordinary Irish country road, stop at a large (but not especially impressive) gate and press the intercom button, as instructed. Slowly the gate creaks open - and you are transported into a world of make-believe. It's impossible to imagine anywhere more romantic to stay than Humewood Castle. A fairytale 19th-century Gothic Revival castle in private ownership set in beautiful parkland in the Wicklow Hills, it has been extensively renovated and stunningly decorated. While th castle is very large by any standards, many of the rooms are of surprisingly human proportions. Thu for example, while the main dining room provides a fine setting for some two dozen guests, the are more intimate rooms suitable for smaller numbers. Similarly, the luxuriously appointed bedroom and bathrooms, while indisputably grand, are also very comfortable. Country pursuits are a important part of life at Humewood too - horseriding, fishing, shooting, deer stalking, hunting ar falconry can all be arranged - but even if you do nothing more energetic than just relaxing besid the fire, this is a really special place for a break. It's also a wonderful location for a wedding ar confeences, product launches and corporate entertaining packages can be tailored to meet specif requirement. Conference/banqueting (150/100). Business centre, secretarial services. Snooke Garden, tennis, walking, cycling. Parking. Children welcome. Pets by arrangement. **Rooms 13** (suites, all no-smoking). Room rate with breakfast, from €350 high season. Residents' D €65; hous wine about €22; s.c.15%. Amex, Diners, MasterCard, Visa. **Directions:** Dublin - N81- Baltinglass R747 Hacketstown Road.

Macreddin Village   The BrookLodge Hotel

Hotel   Macreddin Village Co. Wicklow **Tel: 0402 36444** Fax: 0402 3658
                               Email: brooklodge@macreddin.ie Web: www.brooklodge.co

NATURAL FOOD AWARD

Built on the site of a deserted village in a Wicklow valley, th extraordinary food, drink and leisure complex exists thanks to th vision of three brothers, Evan, Eoin and Bernard Doyle. The drivin force is Evan, a pioneer of the new organic movement when he ra The Strawberry Tree in Killarney, a fine restaurant which wa outstanding for its commitment to using wild, free-range an organic produce long before these became buzz words among wider public. Now their new "village" has taken root and is thriving with an hotel and restaurant already receiving national recognitio for their strong position on organic food, and a little "street" wit an olde-worlde pub (Actons), a micro-brewery and gift shops sellin home-made produce and related quality products. Organic foo markets, held on the first Sunday of the month (first and third i summer) have proved a great success and attracting a lot of regular (both stall-holders and customers), many of whom stay on to enjo an organic lunch in the hotel cooked by Frederic Souty, who ha

been head chef since 2001. The hotel is spacious and welcoming, with elegant country house furnishings, open fires and plenty of places to sit quietly or meet for a sociable drink. (There's choice of two bars in the hotel, in addition to Actons pub). A large, bright conference room overlooks the garden and bedrooms are furnished and decorated to a high standard in an old-worl style with lots of country furniture. Midweek, weekend and low season special offers are good value Conference/banqueting (150). Secretarial services, video conferencing. Equestrian centre. Garden walking. Snooker. Children welcome (cots available). Pets allowed in some areas by arrangement **Rooms 40** (1 suite). Lift. B&B from €105 pps; ss €40. Open all year.

The Strawberry Tree: The Strawberry Tree restaurant, which is descended from Evan Doyle's famous restaurant of the same name in Killarney, is in an unusual room, with a mirrored ceiling - quite unlike the rest of the hotel - a little strange in the daytime, but very romantic when candleli at night. The original philosophy prevails here and the most interesting aspect of the menu is the page headed 'Organic, Free Range and Wild Food' which both lists the suppliers and sets out the BrookLodge philosophy, of sourcing from producers using slow organic methods and harvesting in their correct season: "A menu is only as good as its ingredients and the main ingredient at The Strawberry Tree is our suppliers". Thus, for example, farmhouse cheeses are from Sheridans Cheesemongers, meat from Hugh Robson's organic farm in Co Clare and organic vegetables from Denis Healy - plus, of course, their own produce grown just outside the kitchen, when available. Menus are not too long, or too fussy: dishes have strong, simple names followed by letters indicating that the ingredients are Organic, Wild, Free-range or Vegetarian (or a combination of any of these). Frederick Souty's background is classical French - as good base as there is when it comes to sourcing the best and cooking with finesse - and, given the quality of ingredients used and the standard of cooking, meals at Macreddin represent very good value. Evan Doyle has created a climate here where like-minded people can work and prosper - and their success inspires and encourages others: BrookLodge is an eminently worthy recipient of the Euro-Toques Natural Food Award 2003. **Seats 80** (private room, 30). No-smoking area; air conditioning. Toilets wheelchair accessible. D Mon-Sat 7-10, L Sun only 1-7. Set D €48, Set Sun L €30. House wines

€21. SC discretionary. Closed D Sun. *William Actons Pub - Bar food daily, 12.30-9. Amex, Diners, MasterCard, Visa, Laser. **Directions:** Signed from Aughrim.

Newtownmountkennedy   Druids Glen Marriott Hotel

   Hotel

Newtownmountkennedy Co. Wicklow
Tel: 01 2870800 Fax: 01 2870801
Email: vari.mcgreevy@marriotthotels.com Web: www.marriott.com

BUSINESS HOTEL OF THE YEAR

The first (of several planned) Marriott International Hotel to open in Ireland, its chosen location makes this an especially welcome newcomer as Co. Wicklow is limited in quality accommodation and services. Just 20 miles south of Dublin, in a stunning location between the sea and the mountains and adjacent to the famous Druids Glen Golf Club, the hotel has general appeal but is particularly attractive for the business guest and for conferences and corporate events; Marriott Hotels have long experience in this field and the hotel is extremely well-equipped to meet it. Convenient to the capital and easy to reach, there's a feeling of space throughout which is increasingly difficult to achieve in the city - and an away-from-it-all atmosphere that can be conducive to productive meetings. Public areas are impressive - the tone is set in the large marbled foyer with its dramatic feature fireplace and seating areas, bars and dining areas lead off it in a seem open plan arrangement.

There are eight conference rooms and seven meeting rooms (with natural light, overlooking the golf course and hotel grounds), with all the necessary back-up facilities and well-trained, exceptionally helpful staff. Bedrooms, many of them "double/doubles" (with two queen sized beds), are all very spacious and have individual 'climate control' (heating and air conditioning), phone with message light, data port, voice mail, in-room safe (big enough for a laptop), mini-bar, iron/ironing board etc. - and all bathrooms have separate bath and walk-in shower. Generous desk space is well-organised, with conveniently located power points and terminals, in-room dining is comfortably provided for and, of course, entertainment - satellite TV, movie channel etc. By the same token, the wide range of recreational activities provided on site is creates the perfect environment for the business guest - as well as golf (a second 18-hole championship golf course, Druids Heath, is due to open for the 2003 season), the hotel's spa and health club has an 18m swimming pool, gymnasium, steam room, sauna, whirlpool and aroma steam room, plus solarium, hydrotherapy and treatment rooms. Other activities nearby include horse riding, archery, quad biking, orienteering and team building - and, of course, gentler attractions like the Wicklow Mountains National Park and Powerscourt Gardens are on the doorstep. A place to relax and unwind as well as do business. Conference/banqueting 250/220; business centre, secretarial services. Golf (18); leisure centre, swimming pool, beauty/treatment rooms, walking, garden. **Rooms 148** (11 suites, 120 no smoking, 6 disabled). Lift. Children welcome (under 12s free in parents' room, cots available without charge; playroom). 24 hr room service, laundry/valet service. B&B €280, ss €40. Room-only rate 280 (max 4 guests).

Flynns Steakhouse: Despite the name - which Irish guests may interpret as being the more informal of the two restaurants, Flynns Steakhouse is the premier dining room. Quite small and intimate, with an open log fire and candlight, it has more atmosphere than the bigger daytime Druids Restaurant (where breakfast, carvery lunch and dinner are served). American style steaks and grills are the speciality but, demonstrating a welcome commitment to using Irish produce, a note on the menu points out that, although 90% of Ireland's best beef is exported, a supply of Certified Irish Angus has been contracted for the hotel; just remember that American-style means big - 24oz porterhouse and ribeye, for example... Rack of Wicklow lamb is another speciality and there's a sprinkling of other dishes with an Irish flavour which might not be expected in an international hotel, like Dingle crab cakes, Guinness braised mussels - and an Irish cheese platter. **Seats 55** (private room 15). No smoking restaurant. Not suitable for children under 12. D Thu-Sat, 7-10. Set D from €40, also à la carte. House wine, from €22; SC discretionary. Closed Sun-Wed. *The larger Druid's Restaurant serves breakfast, lunch & dinner daily; L carvery, Set D from €40, Druids Irish Menu à la carte. Bar meals also available in 'The Thirteenth' bar or, in fine weather, on a sheltered deck outside the two restaurants. Amex, Diners, MasterCard, Visa, Laser. **Directions:** South of Dublin on N11.

Rathdrum — Avonbrae Guesthouse

Guesthouse   Rathdrum Co. Wicklow **Tel: 0404 46198** Fax: 0404 4619
Email: info@avonbrae.com Web: www.avonbrae.co

Lovers of the outdoor life will find that Paddy Geoghegan's hospitable guesthouse makes
comfortable and relaxed base - walking, cycling, riding, pony-trekking, golf and fishing are maje
attractions to this beautiful area, but it's also ideal just for a quiet break. (Paddy offers weekly ar
weekend rates and off-season breaks which are very reasonable.) Simply furnished bedrooms vary i
size and outlook but all have tea and coffee trays and en-suite facilities (only the smallest room ha
a bath). There are open fires as well as central heating and a comfortable guest sitting room. Fc
fine weather, there's a tennis court in the well-kept garden, and although this perhaps sound
grander than it is, there is even a nice little indoor swimming pool. Children welcome (under 2s fre
in parent's room, cot available). Pets permitted by arrangement. **Rooms 7** (6 shower only, 1 wit
private bathroom). B&B €33 pps; ss €8. Evening meals €20 at 6.30pm; packed lunches availabl
by arrangement (€4.50). Closed 1 Dec-1 Mar. Amex, MasterCard, Visa, Laser. **Directions:** About 50
yrds outside Rathdrum on Glendalough Road.

Rathnew — Hunter's Hotel

Hotel   Newrath Bridge Rathnew Co. Wicklow **Tel: 0404 40106** Fax: 0404 4033
Email: reception@hunters.ie Web: www.indigo.ie/~hunter

A rambling old coaching inn set in lovely gardens alongside the River Vartry, this much-loved hote
has a long and fascinating history – it's one of Ireland's oldest coaching inns, with records indicatin
that it was built around 1720. In the same family now for five generations, the colourful Mrs Mauree
Gelletlie takes pride in running the place on traditional lines with her son Richard, who is the
manager. This means old-fashioned comfort and food based on local and home-grown produce – wit
the emphasis very much on 'old fashioned' – which is where its charm and character lie. There's i
proper little bar, with chintzy loose-covered furniture and an open fire, a traditional dining room witl
fresh flowers – from the riverside garden where their famous afternoon tea is served in summer – an
comfortable country bedrooms. Conference (30). Garden. Parking. Children welcome. No pets. **Rooms
16** (1 junior suite, 1 shower only, 1 disabled). Wheelchair access. B&B from €89 pps, ss about €20
Restaurant: In tune with the spirit of the hotel, the style is traditional country house cooking
simple food with a real home-made feeling about it - no mean achievement in a restaurant and much
to be applauded. Seasonal lunch and dinner menus change daily, but you can expect classics such
as chicken liver pâté with melba toast, soups based on fish or garden produce, traditional roasts –
rib beef, with Yorkshire pudding or old-fashioned roast stuffed chicken with bacon – and probably
several fish dishes, possibly including poached salmon with hollandaise and chive sauce. Desserts
are often based on what the garden has to offer, and baking is good, so fresh raspberries and cream
or baked apple and rhubarb tart could be wise choices. **Seats 50.** Non-smoking restaurant. Toilets
wheelchair accessible. L daily, 1-2.30 (Sun 2 sittings: 12.45 & 2.30). D daily 7.30-9. Set D about
€35. Set L about €24. No s.c. House wine about €16. Closed 3 days at Christmas. Amex, Diners,
MasterCard, Visa. **Directions:** Off N11 at Ashford or Rathnew. ◇

Rathnew — Tinakilly Country House & Restaurant

🏛 Hotel/Restaurant   Rathnew Co. Wicklow **Tel: 0404 69274** Fax: 0404 67806
Email: reservations@tinakilly.ie Web: www.tinakilly.ie

Josephine and Raymond Power have been running this fine hotel
since January 2000 and they have retained those things which
Raymond's parents, William and Bee Power achieved to earn its
reputation, while also bringing a youthful enthusiasm and energy
which has contributed a new liveliness of atmosphere. It first
opened for guests in 1983, after completion of a sensitive
restoration programme and the first of many extensions, all carefully
designed to harmonise with the original building. Since then, caring
owner-management and steadily improving amenities have
combined to make it a favourite destination for both business and
leisure. It's a place of great local significance, having been built in
the 1870s for Captain Robert Halpin, a local man who became
Commander of The Great Eastern, which laid the first telegraph cable
linking Europe and America. Now, there's always a welcoming fire
burning in the lofty entrance hall, where a fascinating collection of

Halpin memorabilia is of special interest and an original chandelier takes pride of place among many fine antiques. Tinakilly is one of the country's top business and corporate venues, but there is also a romantic side to its nature as bedrooms all have views across a bird sanctuary to the sea, and there are also period rooms, some with four-posters. To all this, add personal supervision by caring owners, friendly, well-trained staff, lovely grounds and a very fine kitchen and the recipe for success is complete. Tinakilly House was the Guide's Hotel of the Year in 2001. Conference/banqueting (65). Secretarial services. Fitness suite. Garden, walking, tennis. Children welcome (under 2s free in parents' room, cots available without charge). No pets. **Rooms 51** (6 suites, 33 junior suites, 12 executive, 1 suitable for disabled). Lift. B&B €125 pps; ss €61.

Brunel Dining Room: This panelled split level restaurant is in the west wing of the house, which catches the evening sunlight, and it has a relaxed, intimate atmosphere. Head chef Jason Wall presents a range of menus including a daily table d'hôte. Local meats – notably Wicklow lamb and venison – and seafood, provides the basis for his cooking, plus herbs from the kitchen garden. While also putting his personal stamp on the kitchen, Jason Wall is successfully maintaining Tinakilly's house style of sophisticated country house cooking and the main influence remains classic French. Signature dishes include local lobster salad with orange segments and raspberry vinaigrette, loin of Wicklow lamb with fondant potatoes, ratatouille & thyme and caramel roast pineapple with coconut Malibu ice cream. **Seats 80** (private room, 30). No smoking restaurant. Air conditioning. D Mon-Sat 7.30-9, Sun 6.30-8.30. Set D €50. House wine from €21. SC discretionary. Open all year. Amex, Diners, MasterCard, Visa, Laser. **Directions:** From N11/M11 main Dublin - Wexford Road to Rathnew Village, Tinakilly is 500 metres from village on R750 to Wicklow Town.

Roundwood — Roundwood Inn

  Pub/Restaurant

Roundwood Co. Wicklow
Tel: 01 281 8107

Jurgen and Aine Schwalm have owned this 17th century inn in the highest village in the Wicklow Hills since 1980. There's a public bar at one end, with a snug and an open fire, and in the middle of the building the main bar food area, furnished in traditional style with wooden floors and big sturdy tables. The style that the Schwalms and head chef Paul Taube have developed over the years is their own unique blend of Irish and German influences, seen in dishes like. Excellent bar food includes substantial soups like Hugarian golash, or fresh crab bisque, specialities such as Galway oysters, smoked Wicklow trout, smoked salmon and hearty hot meals, notably the excellent house variation on Irish stew. Blackboard specials often include home-made gravad lachs, lobster salad and a speciality dessert, Triple Liqueur Parfait. The food at Roundwood has always had a special character, which together with the place itself and a consistently high standard of hospitality, has earned it an enviable reputation with hillwalkers, Dubliners out for the day and visitors alike. No smoking during food service. Bar meals 12-9.30 daily. Bar closed 25 Dec, Good Fri.

Restaurant: The restaurant is in the same style and only slightly more formal than the main bar, with fires at each end of the room (now converted to gas, alas) and is available by reservation. Restaurant menus offer a different choice, leaning towards more substantial dishes such as rack of Wicklow lamb, roast wild Wicklow venison, venison ragout and other game in season - and they do a wonderful dish of roast suckling pig, which is not to be missed when available. German influences are again evident in long-established specialities such as smoked Westphalian ham and wiener schnitzel and a feather-light Baileys Cream gateau which is also a must. An interesting mainly European wine list favours France and Germany, with many special bottles from Germany unlikely to be found elsewhere. Not suitable for children after 6.30. **Seats 45** (private room, 25). D Fri & Sat, 7.30-9; à la carte. L Sun only, 1-2. (Children welcome for lunch). House wine from about €16; SC discretionary; reservations advised. No smoking restaurant. No SC. Restaurant closed L Mon-Sat, D Sun-Thu. Amex, MasterCard, Visa, Laser. **Directions:** In the centre of Roundwood village.

Wicklow — The Bakery Restaurant

Restaurant

Church Street Wicklow Co. Wicklow **Tel: 0404 66770** Fax: 0404 66717
Email: info@thebakeryrestaurant.net Web: www.thebakeryrestaurant.net

This fine stone building has retained some of its old bakery artefacts, including the original ovens in the café downstairs. It changed hands in 2002 but, except that the ground floor area has been completely refurbished to make a bright and comfortable area for dining, or private functions such as small weddings, it is not startlingly different and the food quality seems to have been maintained. Stone walls and beams give the first floor restaurant character and, although a little dark, it is a room with natural atmosphere and especially attractive in candlelight. Menus, which change monthly, offer a choice of seafood all the way or a more balanced selection including a fair sprinkling of appealing vegetarian dishes - tempura of baby vegetables with chilli jam, for example, or a main course spring roll of marinated vegetables with goats cheese, pine nuts and honey dressing. Otherwise, a good range of meats and poultry is offered (a list topped with beef fillet (Yorkshire pudding, sauce béarnaise) and tailed with sirloin steak); of the prime seafood options, a tasting starter plate has particular appeal (crab spring roll, sushi nori, spicy fish cake & filo prawns, with chilli sweet & sour) and there a matching main course seafood plate for two (€45): half lobster, oysters, mussels, prawns & crab claws); roast whole lobster (€32.95 with saffron aoili & asian greens) is not too badly priced for an east coast restaurant. The early dinner menu and Sunday brunch offer good value. Good coffee and friendly service. The early dinner menu and Sunday brunch offer good value. Children welcome. **Seats 100** (private room, 50). No-smoking area. D daily, 6-10; Early D €22 (Sun-Thu, 6-8), otherwise à la carte. Sun brunch 11.30-3.30; €11.95 & à la carte. House wine €16-17. SC discretionary. Closed Good Fri. MasterCard, Visa, Laser. **Directions:** Centre of Wicklow Town.

Wicklow   The Grand Hotel

Hotel   Abbey Street Wicklow Co. Wicklow **Tel: 0404 67337** Fax: 0404 6960
                                    Email: grandhotel@eircom.net Web: www.grandhotel.i

At the centre of local activities, this friendly moderately priced hotel has large public areas including the Glebe Bar, which is very popular for bar meals (especially the lunchtime carvery). The conference/banqueting facilities for up to 300/250 are in constant use, especially for weddings. Pleasant, comfortably furnished bedrooms are all en-suite and warm, with all the necessary amenities. Wheelchair access. Open all year. No pets. Children welcome (under 5s free in parents' room, cot available free of charge). Walking, fishing nearby ; garden.*50 new rooms are to be built during 2003, due to open Jan 2004. **Rooms 32** (all en-suite, 2 executive). Lift. Food available 12.30-9 daily. MasterCard, Visa, Laser. **Directions:** Travelling from Dublin, first hotel in Wicklow.

Wicklow   Rugantino's River Café

🄝 Restaurant   Schooner House South Quay Wicklow Co. Wicklow
                                                        Tel: 0404 61900

First time visitors may not find this restaurant on the quay easily so, if the traffic is busy in high season, it may be best to park at one of the central parking places (all nearby) and ask directions. The exterior doesn't present itself especially attractively and the restaurant itself (cramped tables, minimal table settings and uncomfortable bentwood chairs) has no immediate appeal except that it has large windows all along the river side of the building. However, it is extremely popular - and the main attraction is the fish and seafood, which are very fresh, top quality - and superbly cooked. Medallions of monkfish with prawns, in garlic butter, is a typical example - firm, succulent, moist and tender - or plaice with a herbed bread stuffing: perfectly cooked and moist, still translucent at the bone. Simply cooked side vegetables accompany and presentation is plain - food that looks exactly like what it is meant to be is a rarity these days, so this confident, pared-down style makes a welcome change. Other aspects of the meal may be unremarkable, but it's worth coming here for the fish alone. Good coffee, too, and friendly, pleasantly efficient service. Children welcome. **Seats 56.** D daily: Sun-Thu 6-11, L Sun only, 1-4. A la carte. Early D €25 (6-7.30 only). House wines from €15. Closed 24-26 Dec, 1 Jan, Good Fri. MasterCard, Visa, Laser. **Directions:** On the river, centre of Wicklow town.

NORTHERN IRELAND

BELFAST

The cities of Ireland tend to be relatively recent developments which started as monastic centres, and then were overrun by the Vikings to become trading settlements that later "had manners put on them" by the Normans. But Belfast is much newer than that. When the Vikings in the 9th century raided what is now known as Belfast Lough, their target was the wealthy monastery at Bangor, and thus their beach-heads were at Ballyholme and Groomsport further east. Then, when the Normans held sway in the 13th Century, their main stronghold was at Carrickfergus on the northern shore of the commodious inlet which was known for several centuries as Carrickfergus Bay.

At the head of that inlet beside the shallow River Lagan, the tiny settlement of beal feirste - the 'mouth of the Farset or the sandspit' - wasn't named on maps at all until the late 15th Century. But Belfast proved to be the perfect greenfield site for rapid development as the Industrial Revolution got under way. Its rocketing growth began with linen manufacture in the 17th Century, and this was accelerated by the arrival of skilled Huguenot refugees in 1685.

There was also scope for ship-building on the shorelines in the valleymouth between the high peaks crowding in on the Antrim side on the northwest, and the Holywood Hills to the southeast, though the first shipyard of any significant size wasn't in being until 1791, when William and Hugh Ritchie opened for business. The Lagan Valley gave convenient access to the rest of Ireland for the increase of trade and commerce to encourage development of the port, while the prosperous farms of Down and Antrim fed a rapidly expanding population.

So, at the head of what was becoming known as Belfast Lough, Belfast took off in a big way, a focus for industrial ingenuity and manufacturing inventiveness, and a magnet for entrepreneurs and innovators from all of the north of Ireland, and the world beyond. Its population in 1600 had been less than 500, yet by 1700 it was 2,000, and by 1800 it was 25,000. The city's growth was prodigious, such that by the end of the 19th Century it could claim with justifiable pride to have the largest shipyard in the world, the largest ropeworks, the largest linen mills, the largest tobacco factory, and the largest heavy engineering works, all served by a greater mileage of quays than anywhere comparable. And it was an essentially Victorian expansion - the population in 1851 was 87,062, but by 1901 it was 349,180 - the largest city in Ireland.

Growth had become so rapid in the latter half of the 19th Century that it tended to obliterate the influence of the gentler intellectual and philosophical legacies inspired by the Huguenots and other earlier developers, a case in point being the gloriously flamboyant and baroque Renaissance-style City Hall, which was completed in 1906. It was the perfect expression of that late-Victorian energy and confidence in which Belfast shared with total enthusiasm. But its site had only become available because the City Fathers authorised the demolition of the quietly elegant White Linen Hall, which had been a symbol of Belfast's less strident period of development in the 18th Century.

However, Belfast Corporation was only fulfilling the spirit of the times. And in such a busy city, there was always a strongly human dimension to everyday life. Thus the City Hall may be on the grand scale, but it was nevertheless right at the heart of town. Equally, while the gantries of the shipyard may have loomed overhead as they still do today, they do so near the houses of the workers in a manner which somehow softens their sheer size. Regrettably, they will soon be a thing of the past, as Belfast's shipbuilding days are now coming to an end. Admittedly this theme of giving great projects a human dimension seems to have been forgotten in the later design and location of the Government Building (completed 1932) at Stormont, east of the city. But back in the vibrant heart of Belfast, there is continuing entertainment and accessible interest in buildings as various as the Grand Opera House, St Anne's Cathedral, the Crown Liquor Saloon, Sinclair Seamen's Church, the Linenhall Library, and Smithfield Market, not to mention some of the impressive Victorian banking halls, while McHugh's pub on Queen's Square, and Tedford's Restaurant just round the corner on Donegall Quay, provide thoughtful reminders of the earlier more restrained style.

Today, modern technologies and advanced engineering have displaced the old smokestack industries in the forefront of the city's work patterns, with the shipyard being only a shadow of its former self in terms of employment numbers. However, the energy of former times has been channeled into impressive urban regeneration along the River Lagan. Here, the flagship building is the Waterfront Hall, a large state-of-the-art concert venue which has won international praise, complemented by the Odyssey Centre on the other side of the river. In the southern part of the city, Queen's University (founded 1845) is a beautifully balanced 1849 Lanyon building at the heart of a pleasant university district which includes the city's noted Lyric Theatre as well as the respected Ulster Museum & Art Gallery, while the university itself is particularly noted for its pioneering work in medicine and engineering.

Thus there's a buzz to Belfast which is reflected in its own cultural and warmly sociable life, which includes the innovative energy of its young chefs. Yet in some ways it is still has marked elements of a country town and port strongly rooted in land and sea. The hills of Antrim can be glimpsed from most streets, and the farmland of Down makes its presence felt. They are quickly reached by a somewhat ruthlessly implemented motorway system, relished by those in a hurry who also find the increasingly busy and very accessible Belfast City Airport a convenient boon. So although Belfast may have a clearly defined character, it is also very much part of the country around it, and is all the better for that. And in the final analysis, Belfast is uniquely itself.

Local Attractions and Information

Arts Council of Northern Ireland	028 90 385200
Belfast Castle & Zoo	028 90 776277
Belfast Crystal	028 90 622051
Belfast Festival at Queens (late Oct-early Nov)	028 90 665577
City Airport	028 90 457745
City Hall	028 90 270456
Citybus Tours	028 90 458484
Fernhill House: The People's Museum	028 90 715599
Grand Opera House	028 90 241919
International Airport	028 94 484848
Kings Hall (exhibitions, concerts, trade shows)	028 90 665225
Lagan Valley Regional Park	028 90 491922
Linenhall Library	028 90 321707
Lyric Theatre	028 90 381081
National Trust Regional Office	028 97 510721
Northern Ireland Railways	028 90 899411
Odyssey (entertainment & sports complex)	028 90 451055
St Anne's Cathedral	028 90 328332
Sir Thomas & Lady Dixon Park (Rose Gardens)	028 90 320202
Tourism Information	028 90 246609
Ulster Historical Foundation (genealogical res.)	028 90 332288
Ulster Museum & Art Gallery	028 90 383000
Waterfront Hall (concert venue)	028 90 334455
West Belfast Festivals	028 90 313440

Belfast   **Aldens Restaurant**

☆ Restaurant

229 Upper Newtownards Road Belfast BT4 3JF
Tel: 028 9065 0079 Fax: 028 9065 0032

A discreet public face belies the warmth and elegance of this contemporary restaurant - and it is greatly to proprietor Jonathan Davis's credit that he had the courage and foresight to introduce this shaft of bright light to an area until then bereft of good eating places. It was one of Belfast's wave of chic, uncluttered modern restaurants (the second wave is currently taking the city by storm) and has always been smartly maintained; at the time of going to press they are in the process of doing a makeover and, given past experience, it will be a great success - and probably a little ahead of its time. A welcoming bar/reception area has comfortable seating and welcome details - fresh flowers, choice of olives, newspapers and food guides to browse over a drink - while tables re smartly set up with quality linen, tapenade, olive oil and butter, along with three types of bread. The attention to detail bodes well for a good meal and head chef Cath Gradwell, who has been here since the restaurant opened in 1998, (bringing a raft of cosmopolitan experience at Roux restaurants and others) will not disappoint. Her lively international menus change daily and make the most of local and seasonal ingredients in a cooking style that is now well established, with strong emphasis on flavour combinations, fish and local produce: dishes that combine classic and contemporary influences and employ a wide range of ingredients are well-conceived and executed with flair. Menus are admirably simple, with no pretentious or over-complicated explanation of dishes and, while not overlong, there is plenty of choice. The simplest of choices - say, charentais melon - takes its place alongside luxurious dishes like carpaccio of beef with seared foie gras & peppered port dressing and affordable classics, perhaps with an update, such as steamed mussels with cider, apple & mustard sauce. Main courses offer a similarly wide range and prime dishes like fillets of Dover sole with lemon parsley & capers sit happily beside humbler everyday foods like pork and leek sausages with champ - an excellent dish, worth seeking out. Vegetarian dishes are always offered and display the same combination of down to earth qualities and creativity - two or three options on each course are usually vegetarian, perhaps including a tempting twice-baked spinach soufflé with wild mushrooms. Lunch specials and the short dinner menu offer particularly good value and side dishes are imaginative. Consistently excellent food and and professional service from smartly-uniformed staff make this one of Northern Ireland's finest restaurants. An interesting, well-priced wine list mixing the old and new world, includes an extensive house wine selection and a fair number of half bottles. **Seats 70**. Children welcome. No smoking area; air conditioning. L Mon-Fri,12-2.30; D Mon-Thu 6-10, Fri & Sat 6-11; Set D £14.95, Lunch special (main course & coffee) £8.95; à la carte also available. House wines £11.95-16.95; sc discretionary. Closed L Sat, all Sun, public hols, 2 weeks July. Amex, Diners, MasterCard, Visa, Switch. **Directions:** On the Upper Newtownards Road towards Stormont.

Belfast — An Old Rectory

Ⓝ B&B

148 Malone Road Belfast BT9 5LH
Tel: 028 9066 7882 Fax: 028 9068 3759
Email: info@anoldrectory.co.uk Web: www.info@anoldrectory.co.uk

Conveniently located to the King's Hall, Public Records Office, Lisburn Road and Queen's University, Mary Callan's lovely late Victorian house is set well back from the road in mature trees, with private parking. A former Church of Ireland rectory, it had the benefit of being in the Malone conservation area and retains many original features, including stained glass windows. Public areas include a lovely drawing room with books, sofas, comfortable armchairs with cosy rugs over the arms - and a very hospitable habit of serving hot whiskey in the drawing room at 9 o'clock each night. Accommodation is on two storeys, every room individually decorated (and named) and each has both a desk and a sofa, magazines to browse, also beverage trays with hot chocolate and soup sachets as well as the usual tea and coffee; better still there's a fridge on each landing with iced water and fresh milk, helpful advice on eating out locally is available (including menus) and, although they don't do evening meals, breakfast is an event. **Rooms 6** (3 en-suite, 3 with private bathrooms - 2 shower only, 1 with bath & shower). Closed 1 week Christmas, 1 week Easter, all July. **Directions:** Very near junction with Balmoral Ave, on city side; on left as you leave the city.

Belfast — Beatrice Kennedy

Ⓝ Restaurant

22 University Road Belfast BT7 1NJ
Tel: 028 9020 2290 Fax: 028 9020 2291
Email: reservations@beatrice.kennedy.co.uk Web: www.beatrice-kennedy.co.uk

Word of mouth has spread the good news about this unusual restaurant, which is named after the lady whose home it once was. The dining area, beginning in what would have been her front room and extending into adjoining areas towards the back, retains something of the authentic lived-in feeling of a private period residence; although now furnished with white-damasked tables, it has a Victorian atmosphere with a small open fireplace and mantelpiece and a few books and leftover personal effects: softly-lit, atmospheric, intimate, it exudes an atmosphere of calm in which to enjoy proprietor-chef Jim McCarthy's accomplished cooking. Ingredients are carefully sourced, smoked dishes smoked on the premises and breads, desserts and ice creams are all home-made. The style is modern, with Thai and Chinese influences seen in dishes like red braised pork (with spiced aubergine salad) and Thai smoked duck, but also flavours closer to home in roast cod with crushed potato and sauce vierge. Presentation is very special, especially the desserts - which are minor works of art; desserts come with a BK signature in cocoa on the rim of each plate, then the motif is repeated on little home-made chocolate medallions served with coffee - a nice touch. **Seats 80** (private room 25). D Sun-Sat, 5-10.30 (Sun to 8.30); L Sun only 12.30-2.30. Early D £10 (5-7), Set Sun L £15. Closed Mon, 24-26 Dec, 11-14 Jul. Amex, MasterCard, Visa, Switch. **Directions:** Adjacent to Queen's University.

Belfast — Benedicts of Belfast

Hotel

7-21 Bradbury Place Belfast BT7 IRQ
Tel: 028 9059 1999 Fax: 028 9059 1998
Email: info@benedictshotel.com Web: www.benedictshotel.com

Very conveniently located - a wide range of attractions including the Botanic Gardens, Queen's University, Queen's Film Theatre and Ulster Museum are within a few minutes walk - this new hotel combines comfort and contemporary style with moderate prices. ISDN lines. Parking arrangement with nearby carpark. Children welcome (cot available without charge) but not in restaurant after 9pm. No private parking. Pets permitted by arrangement. **Rooms 32** (12 executive rooms, 2 shower only, 2 for disabled). Lift. Wheelchair accessible. B&B £37.50 pps, ss £25. Closed 24-25 Dec. Amex, Diners, MasterCard, Visa, Switch. **Directions:** City centre hotel situated in Bradbury Place - just off Shaftsbury Place in the heart of Belfast's "Golden Mile."

Belfast — Café Clementine

Ⓝ Restaurant

245 Lisburn Road Belfast BT9 7EN
Tel: 028 9038 2211 Fax: 028 9038 2547 Email: theclemclem@aol.ie

In a red-painted mid-terrace house with stylish silver lettering signalling a promising interior, this attractive, airy addition to the busy Lisburn Road food scene, is an all-day restaurant on three levels. Food service begins with breakfast in the bright contemporary ground floor area, merging into lunch (including a soup & gourmet sandwich deal - baguette or ciabatta with a range of luscious fillings like chargrilled vegetables or salmon gravadlax) and a more serious evening menu (tapas plate, confit of crispy duck, assiette of seafood, local venison in season) begins at 5 o'clock and may be served upstairs in a smaller room with a little bar. Interesting quality food, great staff - including a dedicated chef committed to sourcing quality ingredients - customer-friendly hours and fair prices make this a great find. Finishing with a frappuchino (iced cappuccino) will send you off with a spring in your step on a hot day. **Seats 100.** (Private rooms 40/16). Smoking unrestricted; air conditioning. Open all day: breakfast 10-11.30, L 11.30-3, D from 5 (except Sun & Mon, closes 4.30pm). House wine from £10.50, also BYO. Closed 12 Jul week, 3 days Christmas. Amex, Diners, MasterCard, Visa, Switch. **Directions:** 1 mile out of City Centre passing City Hospital, bright red building on right hand side.

Belfast — Café Paul Rankin

Ⓝ Café

27-29 Fountain Street Belfast BT1 **Tel: 028 9031 5090**

A little sister of Paul and Jeanne Rankin's acclaimed restaurant, Cayenne, Café Paul Rankin offers informal quality food (notably their speciality baking) throughout the day - be it for a quick cup of coffee or a more leisurely bite with a glass of wine, this is the in place for a shopping break. Smart pavement tables for fine weather too - and food to go. *Also at 12-14 Arthur Street. Open Mon-Sat 7.30am-6pm (Thu to 9pm). **Directions:** Town centre, neat City Hall.

Belfast — Café Zinc

Ⓝ Restaurant

12 Stranmillis Road Belfast BT95AA
Tel: 028 9068 2266 Fax: 028 9066 3189
Email: info@cafezinc.com Web: www.cafezinc.com

Chameleon-like, this smart modern wine bar in the Malone area - cool marble floors, glass and chrome, monochrome paintings, luxurious seating - changes character as the day progresses. Opening with a sassy breakfast menu (bagels, croissants, traditional fry - including vegetarian and delicious Lily coffees), open sandwiches and some temptingly down to earth specialities like Guinness pie, home-made Lincolnshire sausages come on stream at lunch time. The evening brings another change of tempo, with fresh pasta, tapas and a rather more formal arrangement of starters, main courses etc that takes in some of the lunchtime specialities plus a few more heavyweight dishes. Cooking is good and it's the cool place to be - all this and cocktails too. (Cocktails £3,50, shooters £2.50). **Seats 60** (private room 20). Children welcome. Toilets wheelchair accessible, air conditioning. Breakfast daily: Mon-Sat 10-12, Sun to 2. L from 12, D daily 5-9 (Thu-Sat to 10). Closed 25-26 Dec. Amex, Diners, MasterCard, Visa, Switch. **Directions:** Located beside Botanic Gardens.

Belfast — Cargoes Café

Café

613 Lisburn Road Belfast BT9 7GT **Tel: 028 9066 5451**

This is a special little place run by partners Radha Patterson and Mary Maw, who take a lot of trouble sourcing fine produce for the delicatessen side of the business and apply the same philosophy to the food served in the café. Modern European, Thai and Indian influences work well together here; simple preparation and good seasonal ingredients dictate menus - where you might find dishes like smokey bacon & potato soup, Moroccan chicken with couscous, vegetarian dishes such as goats cheese & tarragon tart or wild mushroom risotto. There are classic desserts like lemon tart or apple flan, and a range of stylish sandwiches. Children welcome. **Seats 30**. No smoking restaurant. Open Mon-Sat 9 am-5 pm, L 12-3. A la carte; sc discretionary. Toilets wheelchair accessible. MasterCard, Visa. ◇

Belfast	Cayenne Restaurant

★ Restaurant
7 Ascot House Shaftesbury Square Belfast BT2 7DB
Tel: 028 9033 1532 Fax: 028 9026 1575
Email: reservations@cayennerestaurant.com Web: www.cayennerestaurant.com

Behind the opaque glass façade of Cayenne, Paul and Jeanne Rankin continue to offer exciting quality food without frills at accessible prices. Fine dining this is not: eating is very definitely fun at Cayenne and the anteroom bar is filled with the hungry long before the first sitters have finished their desserts. Given the number of good quality restaurants Belfast offers these days, this says much for the quality of Paul Rankin's quick fire cooking - and it is a credit to the legendary teamwork of this kitchen that the food is equally good when he cannot be here himself. However, although the accent is now on accessibility, it is not at the expense of quality: the decor may be minimalist, but furnishings and table appointments are very good (and we liked the bog oak centrepieces used instead of flowers on some larger tables). Choice is generous, with many dishes having equal appeal, and the menu is constructed to allow flexibility, with soups, salads, rice and noodle dishes offered separately between the appetisers and main courses. The quality of ingredients is excellent, as always, and flavours remain global - mainly oriental with some Mediterranean touches: eel teriyaki with cucumber & radish salad, chicken & prawn wontons with scallions, Chinese leaves & spicy soy dressing goat cheese & potato flan with mixed leaves, tomato, olive and red onion relish, for example. These tantalising tastes and textures from around the world are served with charm and friendliness by smart well-trained young staff - bringing accessible excellence to contemporary diners who enjoy an animated environment and don't mind rubbing shoulders with neighbouring diners in the café atmosphere of this long narrow, warmly decorated dining room. A recent visit confirmed the consistently high standard of this trend-setting restaurant - and it remains terrific value. Fine wine list; an extensive drinks menu also includes cocktails, shooters, mocktails (non-alcoholic) and an after dinner range. *A new sister restaurant is expected to open in the university area during 2003. **Seats 90**. No smoking area; air conditioning, L Mon-Fri 12-2.30, D Mon-Sat 6-11. A la carte. House wine from £11.50. sc discretionary (except 10% on parties of 6+). Closed Sun, Easter Mon, 12-13 July, 25-26 Dec. Amex, Diners, MasterCard, Visa, Switch. **Directions:** 5 mins from Europa Hotel.

Belfast	Conor Café Bar

Ⓝ Café
11A Stranmillis Road Belfast BT9
Tel: 028 9066 3266 Fax: 028 9020 0233

Just across the road from the Ulster Museum, Manus McConn's unusual high-ceilinged room is bright with natural light from a lantern roof and was originally the William Conor studio (1944-1959). The art theme is carried through to having original work always on show - there's a permanent exhibition of Neill Shawcross's bold and colourful work. Open for breakfast and brunch, through coffee, lunch, afternoon tea and eventually dinner, this is a casual place with a distinctive style - light wood booths along the walls and a long refectory-style table down the centre. Good coffee, home-baked scones, informal food such as warm chicken salad, hot paninis with mozzarella, modern European dishes including lots of pastas, comfort food (like fish & chips with mushy peas) and classic dishes such as moules mariniere and steak & Guinness pie. Popular with locals - this place is a real find for those visiitng the Museum (especially on Sundays). **Seats 45**. Open daily 9.30-11pm. A la carte. Licensed. Own parking. Closed 25 Dec. MasterCard, Visa. **Directions:** Opposite Ulster Museum.

Belfast	The Crescent Townhouse

Hotel/Restaurant
13 Lower Crescent Belfast BT71NR
Tel: 028 9032 3349 Fax: 028 9032 0646
Email: info@crescenttownhouse.com Web: www.crescenttownhouse.com

This is an elegant building on the corner of Botanic Avenue, just a short stroll from the city centre. The ground floor is taken up by the Metro Brasserie and Bar/Twelve, a stylish club-like bar with oak panelling and snugs, particularly lively and popular at night (necessitating 'greeters' for the entrance). The reception lounge is on the first floor. Spacious bedrooms, which have phones with data points, TV and trouser press, are furnished in country house style, with practical furniture, colourful fabrics and good tiled bathrooms. In addition, there are two superior rooms, decorated more elaborately in a period style with canopied beds and luxurious bathrooms with roll-top baths and separate showers. Fax, photocopying and secretarial services are available through reception. Breakfast is taken in the contemporary split-level Metro Brasserie, which is also open for dinner; lunch is available at Bar/Twelve: Mon-Sat 12-3. The wine list includes quite an extensive cocktail menu and a number of wines by the glass. Children welcome before 7pm (under 12s free in parents' room, cots available without charge). No pets.* Weekend breaks offer very good value. **Rooms 11** (2 superior, 3 no smoking) 24 hour room service. B&B £50 pps, ss £30. Metro Brasserie **Seats 70**. D Mon-Sat 6-10; Early D £9.50-£12.50, otherwise à la carte sc discretionary. Closed Sun. Amex, MasterCard, Visa, Switch. **Directions:** Opposite Botanic Railway Station.

Belfast — Crown Liquor Saloon

Pub
46 Great Victoria Street Belfast BT2 7 BA
Tel: 028 9027 9901 Fax: 028 9027 9902

Belfast's most famous pub, The Crown Liquor Saloon, was perhaps the greatest of all the Victorian gin palaces which once flourished in Britain's industrial cities. Remarkably, considering its central location close to the Europa Hotel, it survived The Troubles virtually unscathed. Although now owned by the National Trust (and run by Bass Leisure Retail) the Crown is far from being a museum piece and attracts a wide clientele of locals and visitors. A visit to one of its famous snugs for a pint and half a dozen oysters served on crushed ice, or a bowl of Irish Stew, is a must. The upstairs restaurant section, "Flannigans Eaterie & Bar", is built with original timbers from the SS Britannic, sister ship to the Titanic. Crown: ar food served Mon-Sat 12-3. Flannigans: 11-9. Closed 25-16 Dec. Diners, MasterCard, Visa. **Directions:** City centre, opposite Europa Hotel. ◇

Belfast — Deanes Brasserie

Restaurant
34-40 Howard Street Belfast BT1 6PF
Tel: 028 9056 0000 Fax: 028 9065 0001
Email: deanes@deanesbelfast.com Web: www.deanesbelfast.com

On the ground floor under Restaurant Michael Deane, this much larger restaurant is all buzz and offers an eclectic contemporary menu, with something for everybody. Risotto of seafood with lemongrass & herb cream and grilled beef sausage with mashed potatoes and onion marmalade are both typical, also modish fish & chips - there's a separate vegetarian menu, prices are moderate, service slick and efficient and everything on the wine list is under £20 (except champagne). **Seats 100**. Air conditioning. Children welcome. L Mon-Sat 12-2.30, D Mon-Sat 5.30-10.30 (post theatre menus, last orders 11 pm). A la carte; sc charge discretionary (10% on parties of 6+). Closed Sun, Christmas, New Year, Easter. Amex, MasterCard, Visa, Switch. **Directions:** 200 metres from back of City Hall on left.

Belfast — Dukes Hotel

Hotel
65-67 University Street Belfast BT7 1HL
Tel: 028 9023 6666 Fax: 028 9023 7177
Email: info@dukes-hotel-belfast.co.uk Web: dukeshotelbelfast.com

First opened in 1990, this bright, modern hotel is constructed within an imposing Victorian building and well-located near Queen's University, the Ulster Museum and the Botanic Gardens. Spacious double-glazed bedrooms are comfortably furnished, with quality fabrics and good facilities, including satellite TV and an ironing board and iron hidden in the wardrobe. Conference/banqueting (120/150); secretarial services. Wheelchair accessible. Street parking (ticketed 8am-6pm). Gym; sauna. Children (Under 12s free in parents' room; cots available). **Rooms 20** (1 executive, 11 no smoking, 1 for disabled) B&B about £35-55 pps, ss about £40. Directions: City centre behind Queens University on junction of University St. and Botanic Avenue. Open all year. Amex, Diners, MasterCard, Visa. Directions: City centre behind Queen's University on junction of University St. and Botanic Avenue.

Belfast — Hastings Europa Hotel

Hotel
Great Victoria Street Belfast BT2 7AP
Tel: 028 9032 7000 Fax: 028 9032 7800
Email: res@eur.hastingshotels.com Web: www.hastingshotels.com

This landmark 1970s city centre building is the largest hotel in Northern Ireland and particularly striking when illuminated at night. The location is exceptionally convenient, both to the business and commercial districts and the city's entertainment and shopping areas. It has undergone many changes since first opening in the '70s and has recently been renovated and refurbished to a high standard, including the addition of new executive rooms, with air conditioning, ISDN lines and safe as well as usual facilities expected of a top hotel. The location is exceptionally convenient, both to the business and commercial districts and the city's entertainment and shopping areas. Off the impressive tall-columned entrance foyer, is an all-day brasserie (6am-midnight) and the lobby bar, featuring Saturday afternoon jazz and other live musical entertainment. Upstairs on the first floor you'll find the Gallery lounge (afternoon teas served here to the accompaniment of a pianist) and a cocktail bar with circular marble-topped counter. But perhaps the hotel's greatest assets are the function suites, ranging from the Grand Ballroom to the twelfth floor Edinburgh Suite with its panoramic views of the city. Nearby parking (special rates apply) can be added to your account. Staff are excellent (porters offer valet parking), and standards of housekeeping and maintenance are high. Children welcome (under 14s free in parents' room; cots available without charge). Conference/banqueting (750/600); business centre; secretarial services. Pets by arrangement. **Rooms 240** (1 presidential suite, 4 junior suites, 56 executive rooms, 115 no smoking, 2 for disabled). Lifts. B&B £92 pps, ss £30; Room rate from £160. Closed 24-25 Dec. Amex, Diners, MasterCard, Visa, Switch. **Directions:** Located in the heart of Belfast.

Belfast — Hastings Stormont Hotel

Hotel

Upper Newtownards Road Belfast BT2 7AP
Tel: 028 9065 1066 Fax: 028 9048 0240
Email: res@stor.hastingshotels.com Web: www.hastingshotels.com

Four miles east of the city centre, the hotel is directly opposite the imposing gates leading to Stormont Castle and Parliament Buildings. There's a huge entrance lounge, with stairs up to a more intimate mezzanine area overlooking the castle grounds. The main restaurant and informal modern bistro are pleasantly located. Spacious, practical bedrooms have good worktops and offer the usual facilities; several rooms are designated for female executives. The hotel also has eight self-catering apartments with their own car parking area, featuring a twin bedroom, lounge and kitchen/dinette, available for short stays or long periods. The self-contained Confex Centre, comprising ten trade rooms, complements the function suites in the main building. Weekend rates and short breaks are good value. Conference/banqueting 500/300. Own parking. Wheelchair accessible. No pets. **Rooms 109** (2 suites, 34 executive rooms, 23 no-smoking, 1 for disabled). Lift. B&B about £60 pps, ss about £25. Closed 25 Dec. Amex, Diners, MasterCard, Visa. **Directions:** 4 miles East of Belfast city centre, directly opposite Stormont Parliament Buildings. ◇

Belfast — Hawthorne Coffee Shop

Café/Restaurant

Fultons Fine Furnishings Store Boucher Crescent Belfast BT2 6HU
Tel: 028 9038 4705 Fax: 028 384701

If you're shopping or have business in the area, this stylish contemporary café in a well known furniture store is great place to know about, as they specialise in real home cooking. There's nothing flashy about the food: expect lovely flavoursome dishes like home-made soup with wheaten bread, quiches - asparagus & salmon, vegetable - seafood pie and streak & mushroom hot-pot. There's always a large selection of salads and home-made desserts like banoffee and lemon meringue pie. **Seats 127.** Mon-Sat: morning coffee, lunch, afternoon tea. A la carte. MasterCard, Visa, Switch. **Directions:** Off M1, take Stockmans Lane exit off roundabout, left into Boucher Road, left again into Boucher Crescent (At Fultons Fine Furnishings Store).

Belfast — Hilton Belfast

Hotel

4 Lanyon Place Belfast BT1 3LP
Tel: 028 9027 7000 Fax: 028 9027 7277

Occupying a prominent position on a rise beside the Waterfront Hall, the interior of this landmark hotel is impressive: the scale is grand, the style throughout is of contemporary clean-lined elegance - the best of modern materials have been used and the colour palette selected is delicious - and, best of all, it makes the best possible use of its superb waterside site, with the Sonoma Restaurant and several suites commanding exceptional views. Outstanding conference and business facilities include the state-of-the-art Hilton Meeting service tailored to individual requirements and three executive floors with a Clubroom. All rooms have air-conditioning, satellite TV, in-room movies, no-stop check out in addition to the usual facilities. Recreational facilities are also excellent. The absence of private parking could be a problem, as the multi-storey carpark next door is not owned by the hotel. Conference/banqueting (400/260); secretarial services; business centre; video conferencing; ISDN lines. Leisure centre; indoor swimming pool; beauty salon. Children welcome (cots available). Pets by arrangement. **Rooms 195** (6 suites, 7 junior suites, 38 executive rooms, 68 no-smoking, 10 for disabled). Lifts. Room rate (max 2 guests),from about £165. Open all year. Amex, Diners, MasterCard, Visa, Switch. **Directions:** Belfast city centre, beside Waterfront Hall. ◇

Belfast — Holiday Inn Belfast

Hotel

22 - 26 Ormeau Avenue Belfast BT28HS
Tel: 0870 400 9005 Fax: 028 9062 6546
Email: belfast@bc.com Web: www.belfast.holiday-inn.com

Conveniently located less than half a mile from most of the main city centre attractions, this contemporary hotel offers luxurious modern accommodation, with excellent business and health and leisure facilities. The style is classy and spacious bedrooms are designed particularly with the business guest in mind - the decor is unfussy and warm, with comfort and relaxation to match its use as a workbase; superior rooms all have modem points, fridge, interactive TV with on screen checkout facility and Sky Sports, trouser press, power shower, cotton bathrobe and Neutrogena toiletries, while suites have a hallway as well as a separate sitting/dining room. 'The Academy' offers sate-of-the-art conference and training facilities, and business support. Conference/banqueting (120/100); business centre, secretarial services, video-conferencing. Children welcome (under 16s free in parents' room, cot available without charge). Leisure centre; swimming pool; beauty salon. **Rooms 136** (2 suites, 72 executive, 102 no smoking, 10 for disabled). Lift. 24 hour room service. B&B 77.45pps (Room only £127, max 2 adults & 2 children). Special weekend rates available. Open all year. Amex, Diners, MasterCard, Visa, Switch. **Directions:** Opposite BBC, 2 minutes walk from City Hall via Bedford Street.

Belfast — Jurys Inn Belfast

Hotel

Fisherwick Place Great Victoria St. Belfast BT2 7 AP
Tel: 028 9053 3500 Fax: 028 9053 3511
Email: bookings@jurys.com Web: www.jurysdoyle.com

Located in the heart of the city, close to the Grand Opera House and City Hall and just a couple of minutes walk from the major shopping areas of Donegall Place and the Castlecourt Centre, Jurys Belfast Inn set new standards for the city's budget accommodation when it opened in 1997. The high standards and good value of all Jurys Inns applies here too: all rooms are en-suite (with bath and shower) and spacious enough to accommodate two adults and two children (or three adults) at a fixed price. Rooms are well-designed and furnished to a high standard, with good amenities for a hotel in the budget class. **Rooms 190**. Room rate about £71, (max 3 guests w/o b'fst). Closed 24-26 Dec. Amex, Diners, MasterCard, Visa. **Directions:** City centre, close to Opera House.

Belfast — La Belle Epoque

Restaurant

61 Dublin Road Belfast BT2 7HE
Tel: 028 9032 3244

Since 1984 Alain Rousse's authentic French cooking has been giving Belfast diners a flavour of old Paris. Set menus include "Le Petit Lunch" (Mon-Fri), which is terrific value at just £6.25 for a starter and main course from a short à la carte menu (terrine de campagne aux pruneaux, perhaps, and tarte aux légumes, vinaigrette aux tomatoes sechées) and a similarly keenly priced set dinner, which offers a choice of three options within each course and is augmented by an equally fairly priced à la carte. All the timeless French favourites are here - if only there were more places like it. Not suitable for children. **Seats 84**. No smoking area. L Mon-Fri 12-5, Mon-Sat D 5-11. Set L from £6.25; Set D from £15; also à la carte; no sc, Closed L Sat, all Sun, 10-13 Jul & Christmas. Amex, Diners, MasterCard, Visa, Switch. **Directions:** 5 minutes walk from City Centre. ◇

Belfast — Manor House

Restaurant

43/47 Donegall Pass Belfast BT71DQ
Tel: 028 9023 8755 Fax: 028 9023 8755

Easily found just off Shaftesbury Square, this well-established Cantonese restaurant has been in the Wong family since 1982; it has since expanded to meet demand and there have been recent renovations and refurbishment. In common with many other Chinese restaurants, the menu is long, but Joe Wong's menu - which is given in Chinese as well as English - offers more unusual choices in addition to the many well-known popular dishes. There is, for example, a wide range of soups - and specialities include Cantonese-style crispy chicken and seafood dishes like steamed whole seafish with ginger and scallions. Children welcome. Parking in nearby carpark. **Seats 80** (private room, 40). Air conditioning. L 12.30-2.15 Mon-Fri, D 5.30-11 daily, Set L £5.95, Set D £12.95-£20; also à la carte. House wine £9.95. SC discretionary. Closed 25-26 Dec, 12 Jul. MasterCard, Visa, Switch. **Directions:** Off Shaftesbury Square, within town centre.

Belfast · McCausland Hotel

Hotel

34–38 Victoria Street Belfast BT1 3GH
Tel: 028 9022 0200 Fax: 028 9022 0200
Email: info@mccauslandhotel.com Web: www.mccauslandhotel.com

Well-located close to the Waterfront Hall, this sister establishment to The Hibernian Hotel in Dublin is in a magnificent landmark building designed by William Hastings in the 1850s in Italianate style - its ornate four storey facade has carvings depicting the five continents and looks particularly impressive when floodlit at night. Classic modern design and high quality materials combine to create an exclusive venue for business and leisure guests. Individually appointed bedrooms - decorated in a contemporary country house style, all with some items of antique furniture - include wheelchair-friendly and lady executive rooms (with thoughtful little emergency overnight kits in the bathroom for unplanned visits). Rooms also have fax/modem points and entertainment systems which include TV/CD/radio and VCR. Conference/banqueting (60/64); secretarial services. Children welcome (under 2s free in parents' room; cots available without charge). No pets. **Rooms 60** (9 junior suites, 30 no smoking, 3 for disabled). Lift. 24 hour room service. Parking in nearby carpark (Mon-Sat only). B&B £70 pps. Merchants Brasserie: L Mon-Fri 12.30-2.30; D daily. 7-9.30. Bar meals served in Café Marco Polo, 12-9.30 daily. Closed 24-26 Dec. Ames, Diners, MasterCard, Visa, Laser, Switch. **Directions:** On Victoria Street, centre of Belfast.

Belfast · McHugh's Bar & Restaurant

Restaurant/Pub

29-31 Queen's Square Belfast BT1 3FG
Tel: 028 9050 9999 Fax: 028 9050 9998
Email: info@mchughsbar.com Web: www.mchughsbar.com

This remarkable pub is in one of Belfast's few remaining eighteenth century buildings. It has been extensively and carefully renovated allowing the original bar (which has many interesting maps, photographs and other memorabilia of old Belfast) to retain its character while blending in a new café-bar and two restaurants (one in the basement, the other upstairs). Good modern food includes an interesting lunch menu (braised lamb shank, sweet & sour pork with shredded vege & soba noodles - 'open flame' wok cooking is a speciality), a slightly more formal evening menu and light food through the day. **Seats 100** (private room, 35). Air conditioning. L Sun-Fri,12-3; D daily 5-10.30 (Sun to 9); à la carte. Bar food 12-10.30 daily. House wine from £9.95. Toilets wheelchair accessible. Parking in nearby carpark. Closed 25 Dec, 12 Jul. MasterCard, Visa, Switch. **Directions:** Turn left at Albert Clock.

Belfast · The Morning Star

Pub

17-19 Pottinger's Entry Belfast Co. Antrim BT1 4DT
Tel: 028 9023 5986 Fax: 028 9032 9311

Situated in a laneway in the middle of the city, The Morning Star is a listed building and has been trading as a public house since about 1840 (although it was mentioned even earlier in the Belfast Newsletter of 1810 as a terminal for the Belfast to Dublin mail coach). The Morning Star always had a good name for food and Corinne and Seamus McAlister, who have been running the business since 1989, have built on that and earned a reputation for carefully sourced 'real' food, much of it local, including salmon smoked by Charles Mulholland of Belfast and pork sausages made on the premises - and The Morning Star does not knowingly serve any Genetically Modified Foods. With due respect for the special character of the pub, the McAlisters have made changes that now allow an impressive range of menus through the day, offering a wide range of food, including traditional specialities like Irish stew, champ and sausage, local Strangford mussels, roast Antrim pork and aged Quality Assured Northern Ireland beef (which is a particular source of pride, cooked and served on cast iron sizzle platters, with grilled tomatoes & sautéed onions), as well as many universal pub dishes. Daily chef's specials, blackboard specials, there seems no end to the choices offered each day. There's also a restaurant upstairs where more ambitious meals are served, including themed dinners and special wine evenings. It is worth remembering that this can be a very busy pub, especially at weekends. **Seats 120** (private room 18). No smoking area; air conditioning. Toilets wheelchair accessible. Food served Mon-Sat 12-9. Set D £18.95 otherwise à la carte. Restaurant (upstairs) closed Sun, pub closed 25 Dec, 12 Jul. Amex, MasterCard, Visa, Switch. **Directions:** Beside HI Park.. Between Ann Street and High Street.

Belfast	Nick's Warehouse

Restaurant/Pub

35-39 Hill St. Belfast BT1 2LB
Tel: 028 9043 9690 Fax: 028 9023 0514
Email: nicks@warehouse.net.co.uk Web: www.nickswarehouse.co.uk

Nick's Warehouse is a clever conversion on two floors, with particularly interesting lighting and efficient aluminium duct air-conditioning. It's a lively spot, notable for attentive, friendly service and excellent food, in both the wine bar (where informal light meals and some hot dishes are served) and the restaurant (slightly more formal with structured à la carte menus). A network of trusted suppliers provide the superb ingredients that are the basis for lively contemporary menus offering a wide range of dishes which are consistently interesting and often offer unusual items including game in season. There's always an imaginative selection of vegetarian dishes and menus are considerably marked with symbols indicating dishes containing nuts or oils and also shellfish. The cheese selection is interesting too - you can choose between house cheeses (St Amie, Brie, & Bellingham Blue) or Irish cheeses (Cashel Blue, smoked Gubbeen & Cooleeney). Wide choice of teas of coffees and an informative, well-priced wine list that makes good reading - and includes a small selection of fine wines, a special Spanish listing and about eight keenly priced house wines. Children welcome before 9 pm. Air conditioning. **Seats 135** downstairs (+ 45 upstairs, available as private room at night). L Mon-Fri 12-3, D Tue-Sat 6-10. House wines from £11.50. Closed Sat L, all Sun, D Mon, 25-26 Dec, 15 Jan, Easter Mon/Tue, 12 July. Amex, Diners, MasterCard, Visa, Switch. **Directions:** Near St. Anne's Cathedral, off Waring St.

Belfast	Northern Whig

🔊 Restaurant

2 Bridge Street Belfast BT1 1LU
Tel: 028 9050 9888 Fax: 028 9050 9880
Web: www.thenorthernwhig.com

Located in the former offices of the Northern Whig newspaper and convenient to the city's now fashionable Cathedral Quarter, this is an impressive bar venue of grand proportions. The high ceilings of the old press hall have been retained - and now look down on several gigantic statues that have been salvaged from Eastern Europe and are in keeping with the scale of the building. A long bar has comfortable contemporary seating in coffee and cream, where Belfast's trend-setters meet for drinks or a bite to eat - or you can take a pavement table on a sunny afternoon and watch the world go by, sipping cocktails or sampling something from the reasonably priced menu very popular with the local business fraternity for lunch and for a relaxing drink after work - and many stay on for a bite to eat. Expect upmarket bar food - pasta, risotto, tandoori chicken with wild rice - and good service from black-clad young staff. **Seats 160** (private room 40). No smoking area; air conditioning. Toilets wheelchair accessible. Children welcome. Open 10 am-11 pm; bar food 12-9. MasterCard, Visa, Switch. **Directions:** From front of City Hall: walk to 2nd set of traffic lights, turn right, left at next lights; cross road - Northern Whig is on the corner.

Belfast	The Olive Tree Company

Café

353 Ormeau Road Belfast BT7 5GL **Tel: 028 9064 8898**
Email: oliver@olivetreeco.fsnet.co.uk Web: www.olivetreecompany.com

This unique delicatessen/café specialises in freshly marinated olives, handmade cheeses and salamis - and also sells an exclusive range of French specialities, notably from Provence. The café offers authentic French patisserie and food with a Mediterranean flavour, mainly based on the best of local Irish produce. Think sandwiches with tapenade (olive paté with vine-ripened tomatoes & sping onions, or dolmades (vine leaves) salad with organic natrural yogurt and ciabatta bread and you'll get the flavour. Hot dishes include specialities like 'brodetto' a traditional Italian fish stew, or contemporary dishes such as warm duck salad wth chilli & lime dressing. **Seats 26**. No smoking restaurant. Shop open daily: Mon-Sat 9am-6pm (café to 5), Sun 11-5. (No wine but BYO allowed.) Closed 8-15 July, 24 Dec-2 Jan. MasterCard, Visa, Switch. **Directions:** From Belfast City Centre take the direction for Newcastle/Downpatrick cross the Ormeau Bridge - spot the Ormeau Bakery landmark and The Olive Tree Company is on the Right.

Belfast	Oxford Exchange

🔊 Restaurant

1st Floor St George's Market Oxford Street Belfast BT1 3NQ
Tel: 028 9024 0014 Fax: 028 9023 5675
Email: oxfordexchange@mountcharles.com

Dining in an historically interesting building has a certain cachet at any time, but this stylish venue over the recently renovated glass-roofed St George's Market is particularly fascinating. The market is a redbrick listed Victorian building and Paul Horshcroft's successful conversion has created a pleasing

estaurant with views of either the daytime market scene below or, at night, the attractively lit
Laganside area. There's a small bar area, with comfortable seating, and a large restaurant with many
triking features (including a designer gas fire) where interesting good-value lunches are served
spanning everything from mezze plates or Thai marinated chicken with lime & coriander chutney to
bangers and mash with red onion gravy) and, later, a fine dining dinner menu takes over. Head chef
Sean Jones came here from London's Canteen (and, before that, the Peat Inn in Fife) which explains
ambitious dinner menus that offer chargrills and traditional food with a modern twist: try a witty
Ulster Fry Salad or steamed mussels with smoked bacon, garlic and spring onion to start, then follow
with char-grilled wild boar and garlic sausages or blackened hake; desserts are updated classics:
steamed lemon pudding, perhaps, with raspberry sorbet and exotic fruit coulis. Stylish food,
attractively presented, with professional service and (especially at lunch time) good value - no
wonder this place is popular with a broad range of discerning diners, from visitors to the market to
barristers from the nearby law courts. Quite convenient to Waterfront Hall for pre-theatre meals.
Seats 110. Open Mon-Thu 12-10, Fri 10- 11, Sat 5-11). A la carte. House wine £10.95. SC
discretionary (except 10% on parties of 8+). Closed L Sat, all Sun. 25 Dec, 1 Jan, 11-15 Jul.
MasterCard, Visa, Switch. **Directions:** Opposite Waterfront Hall.

Belfast — Ramada Belfast

Hotel

117 Milltown Road Shawbridge Belfast BT87XP
Tel: 028 9092 3500 Fax: 028 9092 3600
Email: mail@ramadabelfast.com Web: www.ramadabelfast.com

This new hotel near Shaws Bridge in Belfast was the first of the Marriott Hotels in Ireland and its
setting in the Lagan Valley Regional Park, overlooking the River Lagan, is beautiful. Bedrooms are
decorated in a fairly neutral modern style and have all the facilities expected of a new hotel,
including in-room safes, TV with satellite and movie channels, telephone with voicemail and either
a king-size bed or two singles. There are also executive suites available, intended mainly for business
guests. Conference and banqueting facilities include 12 meeting rooms of various sizes, with up-to-
date technology, and there is a ballroom suitable for weddings, conferences and exhibitions. On-site
leisure facilities include sauna, steam room, spa and fitness suite as well as an indoor swimming
pool and there's free parking for 300 cars. Conference/banqueting 900/550. Garden, walking. No
pets. Children welcome, (under 5s free in parents' room, cot available without charge). **Rooms 120**
(4 suites, 116 executive, 83 no smoking, 6 for disabled). Lift. 24 hour room service. B&B £44.50
pps, ss £15; room-only rate £110 (max 2 guests). Open all year.
Belfast Bar and Grill: Well-known Belfast chef Paul Rankin was a consultant here at the time of
opening the Belfast Bar & Grill in 2001 (he devised the menu and supervised the chefs cooking for
the restaurant) but, just before the guide went to press, that connection came to an end. However
his influence in helping the hotel to create a restaurant specialising in traditional Irish cuisine lives
on - cream walls display prints of Belfast by the noted Irish photographer Christopher Hill and this
Belfast theme is carried through to the menu where the food is distinctly Irish traditional with
inspiration from land sea and shore. (Function catering has a separate team of chefs and has no
connection to theBelfast Bar and Grill). **Seats 120**. Open for lunch & dinner daily. Amex, MasterCard,
Visa, Switch. **Directions:** In Lagan Valley Regional Park, near Shaws Bridge.

Belfast — Ravenhill Guest House

Ⓝ Guesthouse

690 Ravenhill Road Belfast BT6 0BZ
Tel: 028 9020 7444 Fax: 028 9028 2590
Email: book @ravenhillguesthouse.com Web: www.ravenhillguesthouse.com

Although it is beside a busy road, the Nicholson family home is a late Victorian redbrick house and
has some sense of seclusion, with mature trees, private parking and a quiet tree-lined street
alongside. A comfortable ground floor lounge has an open fireplace., a comfortable big sofa, lots of
books and a PC for guests who want to use the internet, at a modest charge. Breakfast is served in
bay-windowed dining room with white-damasked tables and the breakfast buffet is displayed on the
sideboard in a collection of Nicholas Mosse serving bowls - a feel for craft objects that is reflected
elsewhere, including the fact that beds and other furniture has been specially commissioned from
an Islandmagee craftsman - bedrooms, which are a mixture of single, twin and double rooms, are
comfortably furnished with style, are all en-suite with tea/coffee making facilities and TV. A printed
breakfast menu reflects a commitment to using local produce of quality and includes a vegetarian
cooked breakfasts; the Nicholson's use the St George's Farmers' Market and support the concept
behind it. They also make what they can on the premises, including marmalade and wheaten bread
for breakfasts. All these good things, plus a particularly helpful attitude to guest, make this an
excellent base for a stay in Belfast. **Rooms 5** (all en-suite, 3 shower only, with with bath).

Belfast — Restaurant Michael Deane

★★Restaurant

36-40 Howard Street Belfast BT1 6P
Tel: 028 9033 1134 Fax: 028 9056 000
Email: deanes@deanesbelfast.com Web: www.deanesbelfast.com

Michael Deane remains unshakeable in his resolve to offer meticulously prepared dishes, served with old world efficiency and charm in an elegant ambience. Without this dedicated chef' uncompromising commitment to offer fine dining, there would be no real choice available to discerning diners in in Belfast - or indeed in the whole of Northern Ireland. Perhaps the contrast i all the more striking as, to reach the oasis of the restaurant, diners walk through the bustling groun floor brasserie, climb the broad staircase and are admitted to the inner sanctum. Here all is comfort the fin de siècle sitting room, the elegant dining room, the smart, attentive and knowledgeable staf and that open kitchen with the ever-present Deane meticulously controlling the pace of events an timing food to perfection. To experience the sheer breadth and refinement of Michael Deane' cooking, the eight course Menu Prestige (£55) is the yardstick against which all serious cooking i Ireland should be judged: 'Amuse Bouche'(a delectable prawn bisque with four fantastic fresh prawns perhaps); 'Thai style squab'; 'roast foie gras'; velouté of monkfish, peas & basil; 'breast of duck creamed & fried parsnip' 'selection of cheese'; dessert du chef; coffee & chocolate. Simple on the page -simply superb on the plate. The main menu offers two courses for £29 and dishes tasted on a recent visit which reflect the richness and deftness of the cooking confirmed the exceptional talen and skill of this great chef and there is a thoughtfully crafted Vegetarian Menu (two courses £21) Interestingly, Michael Deane was one of the first chefs in Ireland to cook fusion food - something in which he succeeded brilliantly although it has failed miserably in so many other hands - yet it is now for his classic skills that he is (rightly) receiving recognition. The wine list is grand but no overawing, and the discreet advice given to match wines with the meal is outstanding. This is fine dining in Ireland at its best and extremely good value for what is offered, so head North - and book early. **Seats 30-35.** Air conditioning D Wed-Sat 7-9.30; L Fri only, 12.15-2. D £21-£55, L £19.50; s discretionary (10% added to bills of 6+). Closed Sun-Tue, Christmas & New Year, Easter,1 week July Amex, MasterCard, Visa, Switch. **Directions:** 200 metres from rear of City Hall on left.

Belfast — Shu

Restaurant

253 Lisburn Road Belfast BT9 7EN
Tel: 028 9038 1655 Fax: 028 9068 1632
Web: www.shu-restaurant.com

The smartly painted Victorian frontage and traditional arched windows provide a vivid contrast to the stainless steel efficiency of the bar and de rigeur 'on view' kitchen of this fashionable restaurant. After a courteous welcome, guests are led into a large L shaped room which is light and airy, with shiny metal muted by terracotta pillars and discreet covers. Opened in October 2000, this is a smoothly run operation, with many regulars of all age groups. Belfast born head chef, Paul Catterson (ex Quaglino's and Zinc in London, and La Stampa in Dublin) runs a slick engine room and his classical and brasserie fare is complemented by restaurant manager Julian Henry's marshalling of a tip top waiting staff. And the food should not disappoint. Paul provides a menu founded on his classical training but with wider world influences: kedgeree of smoked haddock, asparagus, curry & soy oil and baby omelette of smoked bacon, potato, cheddar & chive are typical, well-executed starters and main courses like miso marinated salmon with glass noodles & spiced foam and rump of lamb with braised vegetables & jus are in the same vein, allowing choice equally for the adventurous and more conservative diner. Upbeat classical desserts to finish, or Irish farmhouse cheese. Downstairs in the basement cocktail bar "Simply Shu", a simpler, more casual menu is offered with dishes like salt & chilli squid, Thai green curry with chicken and ribeye steak with peppered sauce, all in the £4-£8 range (also available for private hire with buffet food or canapés from £5 per person.) Not suitable for children under 10 after 7 pm. **Seats 76** (private room 22). L Mon-Sat, 12-2.30, D Mon-Sat 6-10. 2-course menu £12.50; otherwise à la carte (average main course £14). House wines £11.50-13.50; s.c. discretionary (10% on parties of 6+). Closed Sun, 24-26 Dec, 12-14 Jul. Amex, MasterCard, Visa, Laser, Switch. **Directions:** 0.5 mile south on Lisburn Road of City Centre.

Belfast — Sun Kee Restaurant

Restaurant

38 Donegall Pass Belfast BT7 1BS
Tel: 028 9031 2016

Edmund Lau's little place just off Shaftesbury Square has earned widespread recognition as the city's most authentic Chinese restaurant. What you get here is a combination of the classic Chinese dishes which are already familiar - but created in uncompromising Chinse style, without the usual "blanding down" typical of most oriental restaurants. They also offer more unusual dishes, which offer a genuine challenge to the jaded western palate: be prepared to be adventurous. It is unlicensed (but you may bring your own). The main difficulty is getting a reservation, as its popularity is matched only by its tiny size. Children welcome. **Seats 30.** D 5-11 Sat-Thu, all à la carte. Closed mid-Jul – mid-Aug. **No Credit Cards. Directions:** Beside Police Station. ◇

Belfast   Ta Tu

Restaurant/Pub
701 Lisburn Road Belfast BT9 7GU
Tel: 028 9038 0818 Fax: 028 9038 0828
Email: info@ta-tu.com Web: www. ta-tu.com

Publican/restaurateur Bill Wolsey opened Ta Tu in the late spring of 2000. It immediately became one of 'the' places and both bar and restaurant are packed with the young and young and heart at weekends. Local architect Colin Conn (who also designed Altos) was responsible for the design, which incorporates an ultra-modern high-roofed 'warehouse' with a long bar where the bright young things meet and greet and, at the rear, a more intimate restaurant area reminiscent of photographs depicting pre-war airship lounges, with comfortable high-backed armchairs, sofas and discreet, individual table lighting. Menus from a dynamic kitchen team change monthly and the food is, as one might expect, adventurous and beautifully presented; an all day menu offers a wide range of dishes in various practical combinations - Caesar salad, for example, is available as a starter, with grilled chicken, or as a main course with chicken; vegetarian dishes are highlighted with a V and a number of dishes, including a vegetarian starter and main course, are picked out as 'express' for extra-fast service; evening à la carte menus are longer and more relaxed. Excellent waiting staff really know the menus; the wine list offers a wide range of carefully chosen wines at reasonable prices and there's a long list of wines by the glass. No children after 7pm. *The very trendy Bar Bacca in Franklin Street is in the same ownership. Restaurant **Seats 90.** Air conditioning. L 12-6, D 6-9.30 (Sun to 8.30). A la carte. House wines from £9.95. Bar food served 12-9.30 daily. Closed 25 Dec. MasterCard, Visa. **Directions:** From the city centre, take Lisburn Road - about 1 mile on the right.

Belfast   Tedfords Restaurant

Restaurant
5 Donegall Quay Belfast BT1 3EF
Tel: 028 9043 4000 Fax: 028 9024 8889

Sailing folk may remember Tedfords as a ships chandlers - you can almost smell the sisal even now, especially as there are reminders a-plenty of this listed building's venerable maritime past. An informal ground floor restaurant is pleasantly arranged on two levels with a railing around the upper one, which makes the small area seem more spacious and allows staff to move around the tables without disturbing diners too much. There's an appropriate emphasis on things from the sea and good fish cookery is the strength of this restaurant: New England seafood chowder, smoked salmon in various combinations (with crab mayonnaise, wheaten bread & lemon salad perhaps) and Thai steamed mussels are typical light dishes that might appear on lunch or evening menus, while main courses vary more in style: fish & chips at lunchtime, perhaps, turbot with celeriac dauphinoise, wild mushroom jus & straw potatoes for dinner. Should you prefer non-fishy fare, there are plenty of other choices including a vegetarian dish of the day. Service can be a little slow. Informative, fairly priced wine list. **Seats 45.** No smoking area. L Mon-Fri 12-2.30; D Mon-Sat from 5. Pre-theatre D Mon-Sat, 5-6.30, £14.95-£16.95. Otherwise à la carte. House wine from £9.95; sc discretionary. Toilets wheelchair accessible. Children welcome. Parking in multi-storey carpark next door. Closed L Sat, all Sun, bank hols. MasterCard, Visa, Switch. **Directions:** 3 minute walk Waterfront Hall, next to multi storey car park.

Belfast — TENsq

🏨 Hotel
Restaurant

10 Donegall Square South Belfast Co. Antrim BT1 5JD
Tel: 028 9024 1001 Fax: 028 9024 3210
Email: mail@ten-sq.com Web: www.ten-sq.com

NEWCOMER OF THE YEAR AWARD

This delightful boutique hotel opened just before the 2002 Guide went to press and has established a special niche for discerning visitors to Belfast during its first year in business. It is situated in a particularly attractive listed Victorian building and the location - just opposite the City Hall and within walking distance of the whole city centre area - is superb. Renovation throughout the building has been completed to an exceptionally high standard and, although the end result is refreshingly contemporary, it has been achieved with great sensitivity to the original building: a striking feature, for example, is the lovely old stained glass in many of the original windows, which is now subtly echoed in the interior design. Accommodation - in generous high-windowed rooms. theatrically decorated in an uncompromisingly modern style - is both simple and very luxurious; even the most dyed-in-the-wool traditionalist would be won over by the sheer style - and unexpected homeliness - of these rooms and, of course, they have wonderful bathrooms to match. Features include well-planned lighting, state of the art entertainment systems and - going a stage further than the usual mini-bar - a collection of drinks, nibbles and bits and pieces that would be worthy of a small corner shop, all neatly tucked away out of sight.

The restaurant and bar (and also a private members' club which is not yet fully established) attract discerning non-residents and it is a bonus for residential guests to have amenities of this standard on-site. Staff are warm, welcoming and generally efficient, with none of the stuffiness sometimes encountered in exclusive hotels. All round, this stylish and increasingly accomplished hotel is a tremendous asset to Belfast - and a worthy winner of our Newcomer of the Year Award for 2003. Conference/banqueting 70/160. **Rooms 23** (3 deluxe, 20 superior, 2 for disabled). Air conditioning, safe, ISDN, TV/DVD/video channel, tea/coffee-making facilities, iron & trouser press. **Rooms 23**. (3 junior suites, 20 superior, 15 no smoking, 2 for disabled). Lift. B&B room rate £99-200 (max 2 guests). Closed 25 Dec.

☆**Porcelain:** In discreetly oriental surroundings on the first floor, with beautifully set (if rather tightly packed) tables, this elegant restaurant may seem a little impersonal at a quiet lunch time but comes to life at night when the grand piano is played and the restaurant is busy. Head chef John Russell joined the hotel in 2002, bringing with him recent experience at Nico @ Ninety Park Lane - which explains a tone that is now more classical than the strongly oriental flavour that dominated when the hotel first opened: his accomplished and creative cooking is based on the best quality ingredients and skilfully executed. European/Asian fusion remains the official style and monthly à la carte menus are not overlong, offering about half a dozen choices on each course, ranging from miso soup with mushrooms and onions or crispy duck rolls with pickled cucumber and sweet soy to lobster and herb salad with truffle oil dressing and ham hock and foie gras terrine with sauce gribiche. Main courses offer a similar palette of flavours and a slight leaning towards fish (five pepper monkfish with pak choi and wasabi oil is typical) although poultry and red meats are represented (as in rack of lamb with summer vegetables and a nage vinaigrette) and vegetarian dishes are always offered on the main menu; cooking and presentation are consistently excellent, although service can sometimes be friendly and helpful rather than professional and efficient. Stylish desserts might include a classy cappuccino mousse with petits fours, and a cheese selection is offered. A good wine list is augmented by the range of Momokawa Sakes offered on the menu. Service can be friendly and helpful rather than professional. **Seats 165**. L Mon-Sat 12.30-3; D Mon-Sat 6-11. Set L £16; Porcelain Express 2/3 course menu 12-3 & 6-10.30 (Fri & Sat available 6-7.30pm only), £12.95/£14.95. Set D from £17.95. Also à la carte. House wine £12.50. SC discretionary. [Food is also available at the Red Bar, 12-6 daily.] Closed 25 Dec. Amex, MasterCard, Visa, Switch. **Directions:** Corner of Linenhall Street at rear of City Hall.

Belfast — The Water Margin

Restaurant

159-161 Donegall Pass Belfast BT7 1DP
Tel: 028 9032 6888 Fax: 028 9032 7333

A big, brassy 200-seater in a converted church at the bottom of the Ormeau Road is now the biggest Chinese restaurant in Ireland - and this shrine to oriental cooking quickly attracted hundreds of followers. Inside, East meets West - a comfortable reception lounge with red leather sofas leads into the large open dining space with round tables of various sizes, lots of artificial plants and garish stained glass windows, all bright reds and greens and mythical beasts. An open bar runs the length of the inside wall and the dining area is divided between the ground floor and a gallery with purple painted vaulted ceiling and an adjoining opaque glass walled function room. The menu is massive and it pays to either know Chinese food really well or have inside information to find your way about. An extensive Dim Sum menu offers uncompromising authentic Chinese dishes such as steamed ox tripe and steamed fish head (in black bean sauce), a reminder that there is a large Chinese community in Belfast. Finally you arrive at the safe haven of the set banquets, and the familiar territory of Western favourites: aromatic duck, sesame toast, sweet and sours, sizzlings and fried rice are all here - also desserts like chocolate gateau, mango pudding with cream and the fresh orange segments. At this level the food is pretty average (and by no means cheap), but there is plenty of noisy atmosphere and the Water Margin is somewhere to experience on a busy night for that alone. [There is an older sister restaurant in Coleraine, Co Londonderry.] **Seats 200**. Open 7 daily, 12-11.30. Set menus from about £20 per person. House wine about £20. Open all year. MasterCard, Visa, Laser. **Directions:** Bottom of Oremau Road. ◇

Belfast — Wellington Park Hotel

Hotel

2 Malone Road Belfast Co. Antrim BT96RU
Tel: 028 9038 1111 Fax: 028 9066 5410
Email: mooneyhotelgroup@talk21.com Web: www.mooneyhotelgroup.com

Located in the fashionable Malone Road area close to the University, just five minutes from the city centre, this friendly, family-owned and managed hotel is quite a Belfast institution. It is a popular conference venue and has all the most up to date audio-visual equipment and conference facilities, but private guests need not worry about being overrun by conference delegates, since one of the bars is exclusively for their use. The spacious foyer and public areas are comfortably furnished, as are the refurbished bedrooms, featuring the usual facilities, some with modem points and voice-mail. Guests have free use of Queen's University sports centre, a few minutes from the hotel. The Dunadry Hotel & Country Club, a fifteen minute drive from the city, is in the same ownership, also the new Armagh City Hotel (see entries). Conference/banqueting (400/250); secretarial services. Own parking. Wheelchair accessible. Children welcome (under 12s free in parents' room; cots available without charge). No pets. **Rooms 75** (1 for disabled). Lift. 24 hour room service. B&B £65 pps, ss £40 (room-only rate £110). Closed 25 Dec. Amex, Diners, MasterCard, Visa. **Directions:** From Queen's University, head south up Malone Road, hotel is on the right hand side.

Belfast — Zego

Ⓝ Restaurant/Café

32 Botanic Avenue Belfast BT9
Tel: 028 9080 8088 Fax: 028 9080 8089
Web: www.zegorestaurant.co.uk

This smart all-day coffee bar and bistro is well-located in an interesting part of the city (and handy to an attended carpark). Frosted glass to head height obscures a striking modern interior in deep mauve with touches of lime green and brown, alleviated by lightwood flooring; it's a small, long space with a mirror-back bar on the rea wall, coordinating batik wall panels displayed behind perspex squares, mauve seats and a couple of comfy sofas under the stairs (with glossy magazines, to help wile away the time if you're waiting for a table). They start early with a brunch menu (croissants, bagels, traditional breakfast, designer sandwiches) and gradually ease into lunch (warm Italian breads with soup, fresh salmon & leek tart, penne pasta with roast veg) and, eventually dinner (beef & Guinness sausage with mustard mash & onion gravy, tempura fried fish with leafy salad & chilli lime dressing)... Pleasing surroundings, interesting choices, fresh-flavoured cooking and good value make this a useful place to know about - and there's a taxi deal available to bring guests to the restaurant in the evening and deliver them home again afterwards, which is free up to a certain amount. Open: Mon-Sat 8 am-10pm. Closed Sun. **Directions:** Off Shaftesbury Square, nearly opposite Arts Theatre. ◇

COUNTY ANTRIM

The Antrim Coast may be timeless in its beauty, but today its picturesque ports are enjoying the fruits of restoration and development at places as various as Ballycastle, Glenarm and Carrickfergus.

With its boundaries naturally defined by the sea, the River Bann, the extensive lake of Lough Neagh, and the River Lagan, County Antrim has always had a strong sense of its own clearcut geographical identity. This is further emphasised by the extensive uplands of the Antrim Plateau, wonderful for the sense of space with the moorland rising to heights such as Trostan (551m) and the distinctive Slemish (438m), famed for its association with St Patrick.

The plateau eases down to fertile valleys and bustling inland towns such as Ballymena, Antrim and Ballymoney, while the coastal towns ring the changes between the traditional resort of Portrush in the far north, the ferryport of Larne in the east, and Carrickfergus in the south.

In the spectacularly beautiful northeast of the county, the most rugged heights of the Plateau are softened by the nine Glens of Antrim, havens of beauty descending gently from the moorland down through small farms to hospitable villages clustered at the shoreline and connected by the renowned Antrim Coast Road. Between these sheltered bays at the foot of the Glens, the sea cliffs of the headlands soar with remarkable rock formations which, on the North Coast, provide the setting for the Carrick-a-Rede rope bridge and the Giant's Causeway. From the charming town of Ballycastle, Northern Ireland's only inhabited offshore island of Rathlin is within easy reach by ferry, a mecca for ornithologists and perfect for days away from the pressures of mainstream life.

Local Attractions and Information

Antrim town Lough Neagh cruises	028 94 481312
Antrim town Shanes Castle	028 94 428216
Antrim town Tourism Information	028 94 428331
Ballycastle Carrick-a-Rede Rope Bridge	028 20 731582
Ballymena Tourism Information	028 25 660300
Ballymoney (Dervock) Benvarden Garden	028 20 741331
Ballymoney Leslie Hill Open Farm	028 27 666803
Bushmills Antrim Coast and Glens	028 20 731582
Bushmills Irish Whiskey- World's Oldest Distillery	028 20 731521
Carnlough AlwaysIreland Activity Holidays	028 28 885995
Carrickfergus Castle	028 93 351273
Carrickfergus Waterfront	028 93 366455
Carrickfergus Andrew Jackson Centre	028 93 366455
Dunluce Castle Visitor Centre	028 20 731938
Giants Causeway	028 20 731855

Giants Causeway & Bushmills Railway	028 20 741157
Glenariff Forest Park	028 21 758232
Larne Carnfunnock Country Park	028 28 270451
Larne Ferryport	028 28 872100
Larne Tourism Information	028 28 260088
Lisburn Irish Linen Centre & Lisburn Museum	028 92 663377
Lisburn Tourism Information	028 92 660038
Portrush Tourism Information	028 70 823333
Rathlin Island Ferries	028 20 769299
Rathlin Island Visitors Centre	028 20 763951
Templepatrick Patterson's Spade Mill	028 94 433619

Ballycastle — The House of McDonnell

Pub
71 Castle Street Ballycastle Co. Antrim BT40 6AS
Tel: 028 2076 2975 Fax: 028 2076 2586
Email: toms1744@aol.com Web: www.houseofmcdonnell.com

The House of McDonnell has been in the caring hands of Tom and Eileen O'Neill since 1979 and in Tom's mother's family for generations before that – they can even tell you not just the year, but the month the pub first opened (April 1766). Tom and Eileen delight in sharing the history of their long, narrow premises with its tiled floor and mahogany bar: it was once a traditional grocery-bar, and is now a listed building. The only change in the last hundred years or so, says Tom, has been the addition of a toilet block "but outside the premises you understand" and, most recently, some old photographs which have come to light have now been put on display. Music is important too – they have a good traditional music session every Friday and love to see musicians coming along and joining in. They're usually open from 11 am until "late" in summer, but only in the evenings in winter although it's worth checking out at weekends anyway, all year. **Directions:** Near the Diamond.

Ballygally — Hastings Ballygally Castle Hotel

Hotel
Coast Road Ballygally Co. Antrim BT40 2Q2
Tel: 028 9074 5251 Fax: 028 9074 8152
Email: info@hastingshotels.com Web: hastingshotels.com

This coastal hotel really has got a (very) old castle at the heart of it - and they've even got a ghost. (You can visit her room at the top of the castle). The whole thing is quite unlike any of the other Hastings hotels and, although ongoing investment is dramatically improving standards, the hotel still has character and some rooms are quite romantic. The beach is just a stone's throw away, across the road. Conference/banqueting (200/130). Children welcome; under 14s free in parents' room; cots available). Wheelchair accessible. Parking. Children welcome. Pets by arrangement. **Rooms 44** (2 suites, 8 executive rooms, 6 shower only) B&B about £42 pps, ss about £14; no sc. Toilets wheelchair accessible. Open all year except Christmas. Amex, Diners, MasterCard, Visa. **Directions:** Situated on the coast road between Larne and Glenarm. ◇

Ballygally, nr Larne — Lynden Heights

Restaurant
97 Drumnagreagh Rd. Ballygally Co. Antrim BT40 2RR
Tel: 028 2858 3560 Fax: 028 2858 3560

On a clear day, the Doran family's restaurant high up above the coast road has the most amazing views - and the dining room is in a conservatory, to make the most of it. There's a cosy bar, where orders are taken by friendly, neatly uniformed waiting staff. Well-balanced menus offer a wide choice of dishes on every course, with seafood the main strength, and also game in season - although this is less obvious on the set menus where the choice is more limited. On the carte, three of the seven starters and three main courses are seafood dishes, cooked in a fairly classic style and given the occasional contemporary twist: coquille of baked crab, or king prawns in oriental pastry to start, for example, and grilled Dover sole (lemon & dill butte) or baked halibut steak (on braised leeks & olives, with prawn & tomato sauce). Steaks also get a predictably good showing too, and Ballymoney ham, with traditional parsley cream sauce; vegetarian dishes are not much in evidence, but a separate menu is available on request. Good ingredients, sound cooking and efficient service all complement this restaurants natural appeal. Interesting, informative and well-priced wine list supplied by Direct Wine Shipments. **Seats 60.** D Thu-Sat, 6-9, Sun 5-7.30; L Sun only, 12.30-3. Set D £16.50, also à la carte; Set Sun L £15. Children welcome. Toilets wheelchair accessible. Closed Mon-Wed. Amex, MasterCard, Visa, Switch. **Directions:** Situated between Larne and Glenarm - signed off the coast road.

Ballymena — Adair Arms Hotel

Hotel

Ballymoney Road Ballymena Co. Antrim BT43 5BS
Tel: 028 2565 3674 Fax: 028 2564 0436
Email: reservations@adair.com Web: www.adairarms.com

Located in the centre of Ballymena town, this attractive creeper-covered hotel has been owned and managed by the McLarnon family since 1995. Very much the centre of local activities – the bar and lounge make handy meeting places, and there are good conference and banqueting facilities (250/230) – it's also a popular base for visitors touring the Glens of Antrim and the coastal beauty spots. Bedrooms are not especially big, but they are comfortably furnished and well-maintained, with all the usual amenities. Children welcome (under 4s free in parents' room. Pets by arrangement. **Rooms 44** (all en-suite) B&B about £43 pps, ss about £15. Weekend specials available. Closed 25-26 Dec. Amex, MasterCard, Visa. **Directions:** In the town centre. ◇

Ballymena — Galgorm Manor Hotel

🏛 Hotel

136 Fenaghy Road Ballymena Co. Antrim BT42 1EA
Tel: 028 2588 1001 Fax: 028 2588 0080
Email: mail@galgorm.com Web: www.galgorm.com

Set amidst beautiful scenery, with the River Maine running through the grounds, this converted gentleman's residence was completely refurbished before opening under the present management in 1993 and it is now one of Ireland's leading country house hotels. Approaching through well-tended parkland, one passes the separate banqueting and conference facilities to arrive at the front door of the original house, (which is a mere 100 yards from the river). An impressive reception area with antiques and a welcoming log fire sets the tone of the hotel, which is quite grand but also friendly and relaxed. Day rooms include an elegant drawing room and a traditional bar, as well as the more informal Ghillies Bar in a characterful converted buildings at the back of the hotel (where light meals are also served). Accommodation includes three suites; two rooms have four-posters. All rooms are very comfortably furnished with good bathrooms, and most have views over the river. The latest phase of development adds 48 new bedrooms, a new conference suite and a leisure centre with swimming pool, jacuzzi and fitness suite. Conference/banqueting (500/500) golf (9/18), fishing, horse-riding,walking & garden. Wheelchair accessible. **Rooms 24** (3 suites, 3 executive rooms,8 for disabled) B&B about £65 pps, ss about £40. Open all year.
Restaurant: Galgorm Manor has had a good reputation for its food since opening. Table d'hôte menus with an emphasis on local produce are offered at lunch and dinner. Menus are changed monthly and always include vegetarian dishes. The panelled Board Room has an antique dining table seating 12, for private parties. **Seats 73** (private room, 16). L &D daily. Toilets wheelchair accessible Children welcome. Parking. Amex, Diners, MasterCard, Visa. **Directions:** From the Galgorm roundabout, take the third exit for Cullybackey (Feneghy road). About 2 miles, on the left. ◇

Ballymoney — Harmony Hill Country House

Ⓝ Restaurant/Country House

Balnamore Ballymoney Co. Antrim BT537PS
Tel: 028 2766 3459
Email: webmaster@harmonyhill.net Web: www.harmony.net

Trish and Richard Wilson's lovely country house is very peacefully situated in a 5-acre woodland garden, with a mill race bordering and lots of birdlife in the old mill building. The house itself is something of an enigma, with an interesting and rather grand eighteenth century section - including a beautiful light-filled drawing room - on the left as you go in, while accommodation across the hall is in a very different style: generous, rather low-key rooms have steps up to optional sleeping platforms (not necessarily used - hence the possibility of accommodating a family of five in one room) and, at the end of a mysterious plant-filled passage towards the back of the house, there is quite a substantial restaurant which, again, divides into two areas of very different character. One section is divided into booths, providing a homely spot for solitary guests dining in the company of a good book or for times when the restaurant is not busy enough to use all the tables; the other section is more open, with traditional dining tables but the whole set-up is very appealing. The menu, incidentally, is also most unusual: instead of simply naming the dishes, head chef Orla Maxwell presents them as little recipes, hence 'Soused Trout: Gently poach the freshest trout fillets in white wine vinegar & court bouillon peppered with star anise & pickling spice, chill well then serve with a light salad of mixed leaves, radish and quail's eggs'. Ingenious. Open fires play a major part in the life of this house - an open peat fire can be lit in every bedroom (so romantic!), there's a big fire in the drawing room and one in the restaurant too - the logistics of running so many fires must be quite a challenge, but they give the house great atmosphere. Garden. **Rooms 6** (4 en-suite, 2 shower only, 2 with private bathrooms). Limited room service. children welcome (under 2s free in parents' room; cot £5). B&B32.50 pps, ss £6.50. (Restaurant D Wed-Sat, 6.30-9.30; L Sun, 12.30-2. Restaurant closed Mon, Tue, 25-26 Dec.). House open all year. MasterCard, Visa, Switch. **Directions:** Off A26, 1.5 miles outside Ballymoney.

Bushmills — Bushmills Inn

Hotel/Restaurant

9 Dunluce Road Bushmills Co. Antrim BT57 8QG
Tel: 028 2073 2339 Fax: 028 2073 2048
Email: georgi@bushmillsinn.com Web: www.bushmillsinn.com

Only a couple of miles from the Giant's Causeway, Bushmills is home to the world's oldest distillery – a tour of the immaculately maintained distillery is highly recommended. The Bushmills Inn is one of Ireland's best-loved hotels. It has grown since its establishment as a 19th-century coaching inn, but its development under the current ownership – including complete restoration before re-opening in 1987 – has been thoughtful, and a recently added wing was so skilfully designed that it is hard to work out where the old ends and the new begins. Inside, it's the same story: all the features which made the old Inn special have been carried through and blended with new amenities. The tone is set by the turf fire and country seating in the hall and public rooms – bars, the famous circular library, the restaurant, even the Pine Room conference room – carry on the same theme. Bedrooms are individually furnished in a comfortable cottage style and even have "antiqued" bathrooms – but it's all very well done and avoids a theme park feel. It's hard to think of a better base for a holiday playing the famous golf courses of the area (Royal Portrush is just four miles away) - or simply exploring this beautiful coastline and its hinterland; since the Magilligan-Greencastle ferry opened in 2002 day trips can comfortably include a visit to the beautiful Inishowen peninsula in Co Donegal. The inn is also a popular venue for small conferences, held in an oak-beamed loft. Conference/banqueting (50). Wheelchair accessible. Garden. Fishing. Children welcome. Pets permitted by arrangement. **Rooms 32:** 22 in Mill House, 10 in Coaching Inn; (4 superior, 7 shower only, 22 no smoking, 1 for disabled) B&B £49 pps in Coaching Inn, £74 pps in Mill House, ss £10-20.
Restaurant: Seats 120 (private room, 50) D daily 7-9.30 (Sun 6-9), L Sun only, 12-6; all à la carte. House wines from £10; SC discretionary. Day menu served in restaurant, 12-6.45 (Sun: after carvery L to 6pm). Open all year. Amex, MasterCard, Visa, Switch. **Directions:** On the A2 Antrim coast road, in Bushmills village, as it crosses the river.

Bushmills — The Distillers Arms

Ⓝ Restaurant/Pub

140 Main Street Bushmills Co. Antrim BT57 8QE
Tel: 028 2073 1044 Fax: 028 2073 2843
Email: simon@distillers.com Web: www.distillers.com

Housed in an 18th century building which was once the home of the distillery owners, Simon Clarke's stylish modern bar and restaurant underwent major renovations before re-opening late in 2001 and the results are impressive. The bar - which leads into the restaurant at the far end - is clean-lined but not hard-edged: smart modern lightwood bar stools have comfortable curved backs and fresh flowers on the bar, the use of different woods and using table lamps to soften the lighting all help to create a warm atmosphere, emphasised by comfortably domestic seating groups and sofas inside the door. The restaurant is more rustic by comparison, with open stonework and a fireplace giving it an old-world character, but head chef Dylan Starrs - who is earning a reputation in the area for accomplished cooking, especially of fish - has no intention of taking the traditional route with his menus. As much as half of the menu could be seafood, including imports like tiger prawns and sea bass as well as local catches, including lobster and crab from Rathlin Island. Starters include steamed Irish mussels in a creamy garlic sauce, with French bread (and a suggestion to try it as the Belgians do, with Hoegaarden Bière Blanche) and prime salmon fillet cured with Old Bushmills whiskey, thinly sliced and filled with seasonal salad, then served with chive salsa (suggested with Cava, available in 1/4 bottles - but also well worth trying with Bushmills whiskey); a wide selection of other equally interesting dishes ranges from warm duck liver salad to imaginative vegetarian choices like crisp golden choux fritters with Cashel Blue and parmesan on salad. Main courses are in the same vein, with seafood and mainstream vegetarian dishes especially appealing although there is plenty to choose from (steaks, various, pork cutlets with Lakeshore grain mustard & thyme cream, braised lamb shank). A dynamic young team with genuine enthusiasm for the industry is clearly at work here and their achievement so far is impressive. They are tackling the wine list imaginatively, with many wines sourced directly from auction and sold with only a small mark up, so the value offered is excellent. **Seats 76.** L 12.30-2.30, D 5.30-9 (Sat to 9.30). Sun L £7.95-13.95, otherwise à la carte. House wines from £9.95. Winter times not confirmed at time of going to press. Toilets wheelchair accessible. Children welcome. MasterCard, Visa, Switch. **Directions:** 300 yards from Old Bushmills Distillery.

Carnlough — Londonderry Arms Hotel

Hotel

20 Harbour Road Carnlough Co. Antrim BT44 0EU
Tel: 028 2888 5255 Fax: 028 2888 5263
Email: ida@glensofantrim.com Web: glensofantrim.com

Carnlough, with its charming little harbour and genuinely old-fashioned atmosphere (they still sell things like candyfloss in the little shops) is one of the most delightful places in Northern Ireland – and, to many people, the Londonderry Arms Hotel is Carnlough. Built by the Marchioness of Londonderry in 1848 as a coaching inn, it was inherited by her great grandson, Sir Winston Churchill, in 1921. Since 1948 it has been in the caring hands of the O'Neill family. The original building and interior remain intact, giving the hotel great character. They do good home-made bar meals or afternoon tea which you can have in the bar or beside the fire in a comfortably old fashioned lounge. Bedrooms - which are all en-suite and include 14 newer ones added at the back of the hotel - are comfortable and well-furnished in keeping with the character of the building. Many of the older rooms have sea views. The hotel is a good conference venue and makes a very pleasant base for a short break exploring the Glens of Antrim. Conferences/banqueting (100/140). Parking. Wheelchair accessible. Children under 4 free in parents' room; cots available. No pets. Walking, cycling. **Rooms 35** (5 superior, 6 no smoking, 2 for disabled). Lift. B&B £70 pps. Restaurant: D daily, L Sun only. Barfood served daily. Closed 25 Dec. Local ingredients – wild salmon, crab, lobster and mountain lamb – are used in contemporary international cooking, with an emphasis on seafood. Typical starters, for example, are tempura of prawn, panfried crab cake with avocado guacomole, crème fraîche & sweet potato crisps - but it's not all seafood, as you could equally begin with confit of duck and follow with a main course of char-grilled beef fillet on Chinese greens with beetroot, pesto & saute potatoes. Children welcome. D daily, L Sun only. Barfood served daily. Amex, Diners, MasterCard, Visa, Switch. **Directions:** On the A2 Antrim coast road.

Carrickfergus — Quality Hotel Carrickfergus

Hotel

75 Belfast Road Carrickfergus Co. Antrim BT38 8BX
Tel: 028 9364 556 Fax: 028 9335 1620
Email: info@qualityinncarrickco.uk

Conveniently located to Belfast airport (10 miles) and the scenic attractions of the Antrim coast, this modern hotel makes a comfortable base for business and leisure visitors. It has good conference facilities (600), meeting rooms (max 60) and in-room amenities (desk, fax/modem line) for business guests. Bedrooms include three suitable for disabled guests, two suites, two junior suites and 20 non-smoking rooms; all are furnished to a high standard with well-finished en-suite bathrooms (all with bath and shower). The Glennan Suite ("simply the best suite on the island") has jacuzzi bath and separate shower, his & hers washbasins, private dining room, leather furniture and a raised American king size bed overlooking Belfast Lough through balcony doors. B&B about £45 pps, ss about £30. Restaurant open daily 5.30-10; food available in Mac's Pub Mon-Sat 12-3, Mon-Sun 5.30-9.30. Open all year. Amex, Diners, MasterCard, Visa, Switch. **Directions:** Main Coast Road exit Belfast North (8 miles). ◇

Dunadry — Dunadry Hotel & Country Club

Hotel

2 Islandreagh Drive Dunadry Co. Antrim BT41 2HA
Tel: 028 9443 4343 Fax: 028 9443 3389
Email: info@dunadryhotel.co.uk Web: mooneyhotelgroup.com

This attractive riverside hotel is well-located close to Belfast International Airport and only about 15 minutes from the city centre. It was formerly a mill and it succeeds very well in combining the character of the old buildings with the comfort and efficiency of an international hotel. It has excellent facilities and is surrounded by ten acres of grounds, making it a good choice as a business and conference venue - and, equally, as a weekend retreat. Stylish, spacious bedrooms include three suites and eleven executive rooms – all have good amenities, including satellite TV, and executive rooms have computer points and fax machines. The most desirable rooms have French windows opening on to the gardens or the inner courtyard and a new informal restaurant makes the most of its situation overlooking the river. Leisure facilities within the grounds include a professional croquet lawn, fun bowling, trout fishing and cycling, as well as a leisure centre with the most up to date fitness equipment, indoor swimming pool and professional beauty therapist. *Sister hotel to the Wellington Park Hotel in Belfast city and the new Armagh City Hotel (see entries). **Rooms 83** (1 executive, 3 shower only). B&B £77pps, ss £42.50; room-only rate also available, £67.50 (max 2 adults & 2 children). Restaurant: D Tue-Sat, L Sun; Bistro: 7.30am-10pm daily; Bar snacks: 11-11. Closed 24-26 Dec. Amex, Diners, MasterCard, Visa, Switch. **Directions:** Near Belfast airport; look for signs to Antrim/Dunadry.

Portballintrae — Sweeney's Public House & Wine Bar

Pub/Restaurant   Seaport Avenue Portballintrae Co. Antrim BT57 8SB
Tel: 028 2073 2405 Fax: 028 2073 1850 Email: seaport@freeuk.com

This attractive stone building is on the sea side of the road as you drive into Portballintrae and is very handy to both the Royal Portrush Golf Club and the Giant's Causeway. It's a pleasant place, with a welcoming open fire in the bar and a choice of places to drink or have a bite to eat. During the day the conservatory is an attractive option, but on chillier days, the fireside in the main bar wins over the conservatory and its view. Unpretentious food in the modern international café/bar style is prepared by Pauline Gallagher (who has been head chef since 1995); seafood, including lobster, wild salmon and locally caught white fish, is a speciality. Although likely to suit all age groups during the day, it can get very busy during the evening, especially on live music nights (folk & country; there is a late licence to 1 am on Friday and Saturday). A useful place to break a day exploring the area, Sweeney's is reassuringly consistent - the only recent change has been a welcome decision to accept credit cards. Children welcome. **Seats 120** (private room, 32) No smoking area; air conditioning. Food available every day (12-9.30pm), à la carte; house wines from about £7.50; sc discretionary. Toilets wheelchair accessible. Own parking. No reservations. Closed 25 Dec. Amex, Diners, MasterCard, Visa, Switch. **Directions:** Centre of village overlooking bay & harbour.

Portrush — Academy Restaurant

Restaurant   NI Hotel & Catering College Ballywillan Road Portrush Co. Antrim BT56 8JL
Tel: 028 7082 3768 Fax: 028 7082 4733
Email: contact@nihcc.ac.uk Web: www.nihcc.ac.uk

It is not widely known beyond the immediate area that the Portrush's School of Hotel, Leisure & Tourism at the University of Ulster (previously the the renowned NI Hotel & Catering College) is also open to the public as a normal commercially-operated restaurant - and it is one of the best in the province. Lunch in the Academy offers a brasserie style menu with quick, professional service, while dinner offers fine dining and a more formal style of service including plated dishes, silver service and guéridon preparation and flambé work - their catchphrase "tomorrow's chefs cooking today" is only the beginning of it, as guests have the benefit of tomorrow's best restaurant staff as well. The kitchen and restaurant are staffed by students following higher education programmes in hospitality and the culinary arts under the guidance of professional restaurant manager, Martin Caldwell, and head chef, Martin Devaney. Menus and wine lists are bang up to date, the food is excellent and beautifully presented and service is friendly, attentive - and highly efficient. The quality and value offered are both outstanding. They also do theme evenings, wedding receptions/banqueting and conferences - and even have accommodation. A major refurbishment programme is under way as we go to press. **Seats 80** (private room available on request). No smoking restaurant. L Mon-Fri 12.30-1 (also Sun in Jun-Jul); D Wed-Sat, 7-8. Set L £9.50, Set D £15.95; à la carte L&D also available. House wine about £8.50. Closed Sun (except Jun-Jul), Christmas. Visa. **Directions:** M2 from Belfast, A26 to Portrush - Ballywillan Road. ◇

Portrush — Maddybenny Farmhouse

Farmhouse   18 Maddybenny Park Portrush Co. Antrim BT52 2PT
Tel: 028 7082 3394 Email: accommodation@maddybenny22.freeserve.co.uk
Web: www.maddybenny.freeserve.co.uk

Just two miles from Portrush, Rosemary White's Plantation Period farmhouse was built before 1650. Since extended and now modernised, it makes a very comfortable and exceptionally hospitable place to stay, with a family-run equestrian centre nearby (including stabling for guests' own horses). There is also snooker, a games' room and quiet sitting places, as well as a a garden and an area for outdoor children's games. The accommodation is just as thoughtful. The bedrooms are all en-suite and there are all sorts of useful extras – electric blankets, a comfortable armchair, hospitality tray complete with teacosy, a torch and alarm clock beside the bed, trouser press, hair dryer – and, on the landing, an ironing board, fridge and pay phone for guest use. Across the yard there are also six self-catering cottages, open all year (one wheelchair friendly). No evening meals, but Rosemary guides guests to the local eating places that will suit them best - and her breakfasts are legendary, so make sure you allow plenty of time to start the day with a feast the like of which you are unlikely to encounter again. Maddybenny was the Guide's Farmhouse of the Year in 2000. Golf, fishing, tennis and pitch & putt nearby. Children welcome (cot available without charge, children's playground). Garden. **Rooms 3** (all en-suite) B&B £25pps (children £10), ss £5 Parking. Closed Christmas. MasterCard, Visa. **Directions:** Off A29 Portrush/Coleraine signposted.

Portrush — Ramore Wine Bar

Restaurant
The Harbour Portrush Co. Antrim BT56 8BN
Tel: 028 7082 4313 Fax: 028 7082 3194

An upmarket fast food operation is all that remains of the wonderful Ramore Restaurant, which was once the leading light of cosmopolitan fine dining in Northern Ireland. However, the informal style of this large restaurant overlooking the harbour is clearly popular with the holiday market and is a real hit with the young - teenagers, families with young children - who appreciate the fun & friendly atmosphere, the speed and prices which are reasonable for the quality of food. Menus are much the same as the old wine bar - a wide selection of contemporay dishes ranging from tortilla chips with dips, through bang bang chicken with oriental salad, peanut & garlic dips, chilli steak in pitta with salad & garlic mayo or lamb steaks with red pepper & cherry tomato salsa on bruschetta to jumbo prawn salad or vegetarian options like cheese & spinach flan. Prices are very accessible - almost everything is still around £10 - but the downside is noise, discomfort and scanty service.* The nearby Harbour Bar is in the same ownership; the old front retains its original character. **Seats 170.** L&D daily:L12.15-2.15, D 5-10 (Sun,12.15-3 & 5-9). A la carte; house wine about £7.50. sc discretionary. Toilets wheelchair accessible. Closed 25 Dec. MasterCard, Visa, Switch. **Directions:** At the harbour in Portrush. ◇

Portrush — Royal Court Hotel

Hotel
233 Ballybogey Rd Portrush Co. Antrim BT56 8NF
Tel: 028 7082 2236 Fax: 028 7082 3179
Email: royalcourthotel@aol.com Web: www.royalcourthotel.co.uk

Set in a spectacular clifftop location just outside Portrush, and a 10 minute drive from the Giant's Causeway, the Royal Court offers the most desirable hotel accommodation in the area. Public areas are spacious and comfortable – the dining room has the sea view. Bedrooms are all well-furnished with good bathrooms, but vary considerably in size and outlook – the best are on the sea side and have little private balconies. Very handy to a number of golf links including the Royal Portrush and an excellent base for touring this lovely area. Conference/banqueting (300/240). Wheelchair accessible. Children under 4 free in parents' room; cots available. No pets. **Rooms 18** (5 suites, 3 executive rooms) B&B about £45pps, no ss. Closed 26 Dec. Amex, MasterCard, Visa, Switch. **Directions:** From Ballymena head north on M2, at Ballymoney roundabout take 3rd exit to Portrush (B62). Hotel at end on right hand side.

Templepatrick — Hilton Templepatrick

Hotel
Castle Upton Estate Templepatrick Co. Antrim BT39 0DD
Tel: 028 9443 500 Fax: 028 9443 5511
Web: www.templepatrickhilton.com

This purpose-built hotel and resort is very close to Belfast International Airport, yet it is located in 220 acres of parkland in the Castle Upton Estate, on the banks of Six Mile Water. Business and leisure facilities are very good, especially for golf - in the hotel as well as on the course - and bedrooms have views over the golf course and estate, making it an attractive weekend retreat and a good venue for conference / team-building events. An interesting Hilton 'discovering wine' initiative, introduced to make wine less intimidating for guests, merits special mention: instead of an ordinary wine list there's an A4 magazine-style information package, giving background information on wine types and the specific ones offered (with illustrations of the labels) and lots of hints; there's also a wine trolley containing a wide selection of the wines listed, available to sample before ordering. Conference/banqueting (500). Business centre; secretarial services; video conferencing. Health Club, swimming pool. Golf (18), pitch & putt, fishing, equestrian, tennis. Garden, walking. Children under 15 free in parents' room; cots available. Pets permitted by arrangement. **Rooms 130** (1 suite, 56 executive rooms, 65 no-smoking, 7 for disabled). Lift. B&B from about £75 pps, ss about £20; no sc. Open all year. Amex, Diners, MasterCard, Visa, Switch. **Directions:** M2 from Belfast; Templepatrick roundabout, 3rd exit. ◇

Templepatrick   The Moat Inn

Ⓝ Country House

12 Donegore Hill Templepatrick Co. Antrim BT41 2 HW
Tel: 028 9443 3659 Fax: 028 9443 3726
Email: info@themoatinn.com Web: www.themoatinn.com

Robert and Rachel Thompson's pretty blue-painted house dates from about 1740 and was originally part of the estates of the Earls of Donegal. Today - having previously been a farmhouse, coaching inn and public house - it makes a home of character, with unusual guest accommodation. The Thompsons undertook daunting renovation work with equanimity before opening for guests in 2000 and the house - which is packed with antiques, books and musical memorabilia (Robert's special interest) - now feels as if their family has lived here for generations. Bedrooms are individually furnished as if in a private house - the Red Room, the Print Room and the Blue Room (with original Victorian four-poster bed) - with immaculately arranged tea/coffee trays and lots of interesting collectibles on display. Guests assemble for dinner in front of the drawing room fire, where aperitifs are served and wine orders taken - which can be tricky as you may not know what Rachel's no-choice menu has in store - and then move through to the dining room where you dine by candlelight at fine old mahogany dining tables. The Moat Inn is only 10 minutes' drive from Belfast International Airport, and close to the M2. **Rooms 3** (all with en-suite shower or bath and no smoking). B&B £30 pps, no ss. Children welcome (under 5s free in parents' room, cot available without charge). **Restaurant: Seats 16.** Dinner 8pm (residents £22.50; non-residents by arrangement, for parties who select their menu beforehand, £27.50). House wines from £10.50. Closed Christmas. MasterCard, Visa, Switch. **Directions:** Follow Donegore signs from Templepatrick (M2 Junction 5).

COUNTY ARMAGH

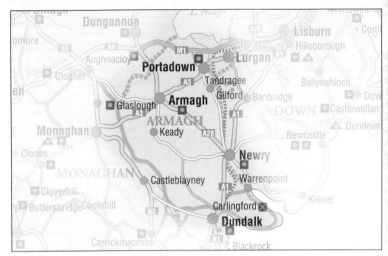

Armagh - the Orchard County - goes into 2003 with new confidence. On September 22nd 2002, before a crowd of 79,500 people in the spectacularly modernised Croke Park in Dublin, Armagh became the All-Ireland Gaelic Football Champions for the first time ever in 120 years of competition. Manager Joe Kernan of Crossmaglen brought his team to a fabulous victory - they bested Kerry by just one point, snatched ten minutes from the end of a nail-biting match. The feel-good factor will suffuse county life for months and years ahead.

Mention Armagh, and most people will think of apples and archbishops. In the more fertile northern part of the county, orchards are traditionally important in the local economy, with the lore of apple growing and their use a part of County Armagh life. And the pleasant cathedral city of Armagh itself is of course the ecclesiastical capital of all Ireland, and many a mitre is seen about it.

But in fact Armagh city's significance long pre-dates Christian times. Emhain Macha - Navan Fort- to the west of the town, was a royal stronghold and centre of civilisation more than 4,000 years ago. Marking the county's northern coastline, the inland freshwater sea of Lough Neagh provides sand for the construction industry, eels for gourmets, and recreational boating of all sorts. In times past, it was part of the route which brought coal to Dublin from the mines in Coalisland in Tyrone, the main link to the seaport of Newry being the canal from Portadown which, when opened in 1742.

That County Armagh was a leader in canal technology is only one of its many surprises. The discerning traveller will find much of interest, whether it be in the undulating farmland and orchards, the pretty villages, or the handsome uplands rising to Carrigatuke above Newtownhamilton, and on towards the fine peak of Slieve Gullion in the south of the county, down to Forkhill and Crossmaglen and the Gaelic football heartlands.

Local Information and Attractions

Annaghmore (nr Portadown) Ardress (NT house)	028 38 851236
Armagh County Museum	028 37 523070
Armagh Planetarium	028 37 523689
Armagh Astronomical Observatory	028 37 522928
Armagh Palace Stables Heritage Centre	028 37 529629
Armagh St Patrick's Trian Visitor Centre	028 37 521801
Bessbrook Derrymore House	028 30 830353
Forkhill (Slieve Gullion) Ti chulainn Cultural Centre	028 30 888828
Loughgall Loughgall Country Park	028 38 892900
Lough Neagh Discovery Centre, Oxford Island	028 38 322205
Markethill Gosford Forest Park	028 37 551277
Moy The Argory (NT Mansion)	028 87 784753
Newry Derrymore House	028 30 830353
Scarva Newry Canal Visitor Centre	028 38 832163
Slieve Gullion Forest Park	028 30 848226

Armagh — Armagh City Hotel

Hotel

2 Friary Road Armagh Co Armagh BT61 7QJ
Tel: 028 3751 8888 Fax: 028 3751 2777
Email: info@armaghcityhotel.com Web: www.mooneyhotelgroup.com

Located at the heart of the "orchard county" of Armagh, this new hotel is a sister establishment to the Dunadry Inn, Co Antrim and Wellington Park Hotel, Belfast (see entries). While its uncompromisingly blocky design and modern materials may disappoint those who had hoped for an hotel that would have empathy with the traditional style of Ireland's historic ecclesiastical capital, it has brought welcome facilities to the area, including the largest hotel conference facility in Northern Ireland. An events entrance with its own parking area separates delegates from other guests and has an impressive foyer, with separate check-in facilities. The main hotel entrance may seem disappointing by comparison - a cafeteria style 'Deli' and informal dining area located in the foyer give a bad impression on arrival - but the bar and more formal restaurant areas are at the back of the hotel, looking out onto pleasant landscaped gardens. Clean-lined contemporary bedrooms are practical - and well-equipped for business guests, with air conditioning, ISDN lines, safe and TV with video as well as the usual phones, tea/coffee making facilities and trouser press. Conference/banqueting (1,200/600); back up business services; leisure centre with swimming pool. Telephone for details, including information on any introductory offers and special breaks. **Rooms 82** (10 executive, 30 no smoking, 4 disabled, 2 shower only). B&B £40 pps, ss £29. Room-only rate about £60 (max 2 adults & 2 children). Amex, Diners, MasterCard, Visa, Switch. **Directions:** From Dublin Take A28 to Armagh City, when the police station is in sight, follow the road round to the left to the hotel. From Belfast take M1 to Junction 11, then M12 on to A3, hotel is situated just before Palace Stables.

Lurgan — The Brindle Beam Tea Rooms

Restaurant

House of Brindle 20 Windsor Avenue Lurgan Co Armagh BT67 9BG
Tel: 028 3832 1721

This in-store self-service restaurant is a real one-off. Nothing is bought in and Alannah Gilpin, who has been head chef for nine years, puts the emphasis firmly on real home cooking. There are two freshly-made soups each day and hot dishes like beef stew, made with well trimmed fat-free chump steak - with no onions. None of the pies or casseroles contain onions as some customers don't like them, but they're still full of flavour. Their salad cart is a special attraction, with anything up to 30 different salads served each day, and several different hot dishes including baked or grilled chicken breasts, salmon and always some vegetarian dishes too. There's also a huge variety of tray bakes and desserts - and only real fresh cream is used. Scrupulously clean, with reasonable prices (not cheap but good value for the quality) and real home cooking, this place is a gem. **Seats 110** (private room 50). No smoking restaurant, Open Mon-Sat, 10-5, L 12-2, Aft Tea 2-4.30 (Sat to 4.45). A la carte self-service except special set menus, eg Christmas. Unlicensed. Closed Sun, 25-26 Dec, Easter, 12-13 Jul. Amex, Diners, MasterCard, Visa, Switch. **Directions:** Town centre. ◇

Portadown — Seagoe Hotel

Hotel

Upper Church Lane Portadown Co Armagh BT63 5JE
Tel: 028 3833 3076 Fax: 028 3835 0210
Email: info@seagoehotel.com Web: www.seagoehotel.com

Attractively situated in its own grounds on the edge of Portadown, this fine hotel has been in the same ownership for many years but underwent a complete makeover a few years ago. The design is innovative and exceptionally easy on the eye and, once inside, the tone of the whole development is set by stylish public areas which are outstanding not only for grace and scale of design, but also the use of extremely high quality materials in construction, furnishing and decor. Easy wheelchair access throughout the building has been thought through in detail (the pay phone in the lobby is wheelchair accessible, for example). Bedrooms have contemporary simplicity teamed with warm, rich fabrics and good work space for business guests; executive rooms also have modem and fax facilities. Business/conference facilities are equally special - but it's not all work, as there's a separate function entrance (popular for weddings as well as conferences), with its own dramatic lobby/reception area - and there are two superb honeymoon suites. Bar and restaurant areas are designed with equal care, looking on to a delightful courtyard garden in the centre of the building. Own parking. Garden. **Rooms 34** (all en-suite, 2 disabled with shower only). Lift. Restaurant open for lunch and dinner daily. 12-2.30 & 5-930 (Sun to 9) and bar meals (paninis, ciabatta, steak etc) are available at the same times. Closed 25 Dec. Amex, Diners, MasterCard, Visa, Switch. **Directions:** Off A27 (Old Lurgan Road).

COUNTY DOWN

County Down rings the changes in elegant style, from its affluent shoreline along Belfast Lough - the "Gold Coast" - through the rolling drumlin country which provides Strangford Lough's many islands, and on then past the uplands around Slieve Croob, with the view southward being increasingly dominated by the purple slopes of the Mountains of Mourne.

The Mournes soar to Northern Ireland's highest peak of Slieve Donard (850m), and provide excellent hill-walking and challenging climbing. But when seen across Down's patchwork of prosperous farmland, they have a gentleness which is in keeping with the county's well-groomed style. In the same vein, Down is home to some of Ireland's finest gardens, notably Mount Stewart on the eastern shore of Strangford Lough, and Rowallane at Saintfield, while the selection of forest and country parks is also exceptional.

Within the contemporary landscape, history is much in evidence. St Patrick's grave is in Downpatrick, while the Ulster Folk and Transport Museum at Cultra near Holywood provides an unrivalled overview of the region's past. The coastline is much-indented, so much so that when measured in detail County Down provides more than half of Northern Ireland's entire shoreline. Within it, the jewel of Strangford Lough is an unmatched attraction for naturalists and boat enthusiasts, while Portaferry has one of Ireland's longest-established saltwater aquariums in Exploris.

Local Attractions and Information

Bangor Events Office	028 91 278051
Bangor Tourism Information	028 91 270069
Bangor North Down Heritage Centre	028 91 271200
Castle Espie Wildfowl and Wetlands Centre	028 91 874146
Cultra Ulster Folk & Transport Museum	028 90 428428
Downpatrick Down Cathedral	028 44 614922
Downpatrick St Patrick Centre	028 44 619000
Dromore Kinallen Craft Centre	028 97 533733
Dundrum Murlough National Nature Reserve	028 43 751467
Greyabbey Mount Stewart House	028 42 788387
Hillsborough Hillsborough Castle Gardens	028 92 681300
Kilkeel Nautilus Centre	028 41 765555
Millisle Ballycopeland Windmill	028 91 861413
Mourne Mountains Guided Wildlife Walks	028 43 751467
Newcastle Tollymore Forest Park	028 43 722428
Newtownards Kingdoms of Down Tourism	028 91 822881
Portaferry Exploris Aquarium	028 42 728062
Rathfriland Bronte Interpretive Centre	028 40 631152
Saintfield Rowallane Gardens	028 97 510131
Strangford Castle Ward	028 44 881204
Strangford Lough Wildlife Centre	028 44 881411

Bangor — Clandeboye Lodge Hotel

Hotel

10 Estate Road Clandeboye Bangor Co. Down BT19 1UR
Tel: 028 9185 2500 Fax: 028 9185 2772
Email: info@clandeboyelodge.com Web: www.clandeboyelodge.com

Set in woodland on the edge of the Clandeboye estate, this comfortable modern hotel fits in well with its rural surroundings. The stylish foyer creates a good impression, with a welcoming fire and plentiful seating areas. Off it is the Lodge Restaurant with gothic-style windows and furnishings (where breakfast is also served). Good-sized bedrooms have neat, well-planned bathrooms (suites have whirlpool baths); standard amenities include phones with voicemail and fax/modem points. A country-style pub, The Poacher's Arms, is in an original Victorian building beside the hotel. Conference/banqueting (300/300) Golf (18/9), walking & garden available. Children under 4 free in parents' room; cots available). Wheelchair accessible. No Pets. Credit card numbers are taken when booking - and the deduction may be made before your arrival. Children welcome. Parking. Weekend specials. **Rooms 43** (2 suites, all en-suite,13 no-smoking, 2 for disabled) Lift B&B about £45 pps, ss about £11. Closed 24-26 Dec. Amex, Diners, MasterCard, Visa. **Directions:** 15 minutes from Belfast, on outskirts of Bangor. ◇

Bangor Area — Islet Hill

Country House/B&B

21 Bangor Road Groomsport Bangor Co. Down BT19 6JF
Tel: 028 9146 4435 Web: www.islethill.com

Just outside the town of Bangor, Islet Hill is a lovely old farmhouse set in fields overlooking the North Channel. It is a comfortable place to stay but it is the hospitality offered by Denis and Anne Mayne that make it really special. Children are particularly welcome and can play safely in the lovely garden. Both bedrooms are suitable for family use – one has a double bed and a single, the other a king-size bed and adjoining bunk room; and, in addition to en-suite showers, there's a shared guest bathroom on the landing. Bedrooms have fresh flowers, electric blankets, hair dryer and tea/coffee-making facilities - and phone, television, video and ironing facilities are available in the house. Short on rules and regulations and long on welcome, there is no set time for breakfast (which is a major event), guests can use the house at any time and there's a fire in the guests' private sitting room in winter. A copy of a 9000 word essay "Fifty-seven Acres and a Rood, A History of Islet Hill Farm" is presented to every guest. Garden, walking. Children under 2 free in parents' room; cots available. Pets permitted by arrangement. **Rooms 2** (both with en-suite shower & no-smoking) B&B £25pps, no ss. Open all year. **No Credit Cards. Directions:** On B511, 1/4 mile west of Groomsport.

Bangor — Marine Court Hotel

Hotel

18-20 Quay Street Bangor Co Down BT20 5ED
Tel: 028 9145 1100 Fax: 028 9145 1200
Email: admin@marinecourttsnet.co.uk

Excellent leisure facilities at the Marine Court's Oceanis Health & Fitness Club are this hotel's greatest asset – these include an 18 metre pool, steam room, whirlpool and sunbeds, plus a well-equipped, professionally-staffed gym. The hotel overlooks the marina (beyond a public carpark) but the first-floor restaurant is the only public room with a real view and only a few bedrooms are on the front - most overlook (tidy) service areas. While the decor is very neutral, furnishings are good quality, with plenty of worktop and tea/coffee tray, hair dryer and trouser press standard in all rooms. Noise from a disco at the back of the hotel may be a problem on some nights. There are three restaurants in the hotel: two informal ones and the first-floor Lord Nelson's Bistro, overlooking the marina. Conference/banqueting (300/260). Leisure centre; swimming pool. Children welcome (cots available without charge). Private parking. No Pets. **Rooms 52** (2 suites, 15 executive rooms, 16 no smoking, 1 for disabled). Lift. 24 hour rooms service. B&B £45pps, ss £55. Closed 25 Dec Amex, Diners, MasterCard, Visa, Switch. **Directions:** 14 miles from Belfast/10 miles Belfast City Airport, A2.

Bangor — Royal Hotel

Hotel

26/28 Quay Street Bangor Co. Down BT20 5ED
Tel: 028 9127 1866 Fax: 028 9146 7810
Email: royalhotelbangor@cs.com Web: www.the-royal-hptel.com

This old hotel near the marina came into new ownership a few years ago but has lost none of its friendliness or old-fashioned charm. There's a warm personal welcome, a clear willingness to help guests in any way possible and the building has some endearing idiosyncrasies - although, alas, the early 20th century lift with folding grille doors and a mind of its own, which amused the Guide on an earlier visit, has been replaced by a sleek new early 21st century one. Rooms vary - the best are the new ones on the front, overlooking the marina. Small conferences (40); Children welcome (under 5s free in parents' room; cots available). No Pets. **Rooms 50** (7 executive rooms, 8 shower only, 1 for disabled). Lift. B&B about £40-45pps, ss £15. Special offers sometimes available. Nearby parking. Closed 25-26 Dec. Amex, Diners, MasterCard, Visa. **Directions:** A2 from Belfast, at bottom of Main Street bear right (keeping in left lane). Hotel is 300 yards on right facing marina. ◇

Bangor — Shanks Restaurant

☆ Restaurant

Blackwood Golf Centre 150 Crawfordsburn Road
Bangor Co Down BT19 1GB **Tel: 028 9185 3313**
Fax: 028 9185 2493 Web: www.shanksrestaurant.com

The setting is unusual for Robbie and Shirley Millar's restaurant, which was designed by Sir Terence Conran's company. On two floors (the first floor is mostly taken up by the bar and reception area, with some tables in use for extra-busy sittings, and a balcony for al fresco eating), the main restaurant is downstairs. The interior is attractive, in soft mauves and greys upstairs with plush new leather and suede furniture, and warm blue and dove grey walls downstairs with deep red leather banquette seating, lightwood chairs and

smart table settings. The windowed kitchen at one end allows you to watch chef-patron Robbie Millar and his team of chefs at work, while Shirley supervises the front-of-house team with quietly attentive efficiency. At its best, Robbie's contemporary cooking brings together the best local ingredients in really creative combinations, often demonstrating Mediterranean influences and some from Asia. The 3-course dinner menu is good value, although some dishes carry a supplement (mostly £3); a price structure avoiding this policy might be more customer-friendly. Menus are wide-ranging but not over-elaborate,offering a choice of six or seven dishes on each course at dinner, about three for lunch, with dinner menus including the luxurious ingredients expected at this level: seared foie gras with crispy duck spring roll, mango, ginger & basil salsa (a good dish experienced on a recent visit although the spring roll may be a little dry), for example or local lobster with truffled macaroni, tomato, asparagus & chives (both of which attract a £3 supplement); starters sometimes read like main courses, making choices more difficult - for example, a first course of crispy duck confit with sauté potatoes, baby leeks, honey & chilli dressing could easily be a main dish. Accomplished fish cooking is a strength, confirmed in a perfectly executed dish of wild Donegal salmon in puff pastry, with pinenuts, ginger & raisins and vermouth sauce. Desserts and petits fours are good but not exceptional - cheese is probably a better choice (although it also attracts a supplement). Shanks remains one of the country's finest restaurants and, in the Guide's experience, cooking seems to be more consistent and the style to have been simplified somewhat (to advantage) during the the last year. Food here is based on the highest quality ingredients, ambience and service are excellent, the wine list is well balanced;also, for the quality, Shanks generally offers good value - although this is compromised somewhat by the number of supplements. Children welcome; vegetarian menu available. **Seats 60** (private room, 36) L & D Tue-Fri, L 12.30-2.30, D 7-10. Set 2/3 course L, £17/21. Set D £38 (vegetarian £33). House wine from £15; SC discretionary. Closed Sun, Mon; Christmas; Easter & July 12th period. Amex, Diners, MasterCard, Visa, Switch. **Directions:** 2km off A2 dual carriageway from Belfast to Bangor.

Comber — The Old Schoolhouse Inn

Restaurant/Accommodation

100 Ballydrain Road Castle Espie Comber Co. Down BT23 6EA
Tel: 028 9754 1182 Fax: 028 9754 2583
Email: info@theoldschoolhouseinn.com Web: www.theoldschoolhouseinn.com

Almost next door to Castle Espie, The Old Schoolhouse is run by Avril (chef) and Terry (the host) Brown. Depending on your viewpoint, the restaurant has old-world charm and character or it's in need of a face-lift, but it has always been a magnet for returning regulars, who enjoy the straightforward and traditional cooking (with a hint of modernism). Local produce is used as much as possible in, for example, a speciality of seared clams with locally smoked bacon & crispy mangetout; oysters come from a local oyster farm and other fresh produce like bacon and fresh vegetables and herbs also come from local suppliers. The separate bedroom block is self-contained with its own breakfast room and honesty bar/lounge. Bedrooms, which are comfortably furnished in hotel style, are named after American Presidents of Ulster descent. Conference/banqueting (60/85). Children welcome (under 2s free in parents' room, cots available without charge). Garden. **Seats 85** (private room, 45). No smoking area. D Mon-Sat, 7-10; L Sun Sun only (except for parties, by arrangement),12-3. Set D from £17.95; Set Sun L £13.95. House wine £11.95. SC discretionary. Closed D Sun. Open all year. **Rooms 10** (all en-suite, 2 for disabled) B&B about £32.50 pps, ss £12.50. Amex, MasterCard, Visa, Switch. **Directions:** A22 from Belfast to Comber 3 miles out of town. 1 mile past Castle Espie on left.

Crawfordsburn · The Old Inn

Hotel

Main Street Crawfordsburn Co. Down BT19 1JH
Tel: 028 9185 3255 Fax: 028 9185 2775
Email: e-mailinfo@theoldinn.com Web: www.theoldinn.com

The pretty village setting of this famous 16th century inn – the oldest in continuous use in all Ireland – belies its convenient location close to Belfast and its City Airport. Oak beams, antiques and gas lighting emphasise the natural character of the building, an attractive venue for business people and private guests alike. Individually decorated bedrooms vary in size and style, most have antiques, some have four-posters and a few have private sitting rooms. The conference and banqueting suite has been recently extended: weddings of up to 125 guests can now be accommodated and there's a delightful little garden that is popular for photographs. The Ulster Folk and Transport Museum and the Royal Belfast Golf Club are also nearby. There are several eating areas in the hotel - food is served in the olde worlde bar during afternoon and early evening and Restaurant 1614 is open for dinner and Sunday lunch; the Churn Bistro serves informal evening meals daily (7-9.30). Conference/banqueting (120/125) Ample parking. Garden, walking. Children welcome. Pets allowed by arrangement. **Rooms 32** (1 suite, 3 mini-suites, 18 executive) B&B about £37.50pps, ss about £32.50. Closed Christmas. Amex, Diners, MasterCard, Visa, Switch. **Directions:** Off A2 Belfast-Bangor Road. 6 miles after Holywood, Crawfordsburn is signed left at lights junction; 1 mile to village; hotel on left. ◇

Donaghadee · Grace Neill's

 Pub/Restaurant

33 High Street Donaghadee Co Down BT21 0AH
Tel: 028 9188 4595 Fax: 028 9188 2553
Email: stephen@graceneills.freserve.co.uk Web: www.graceneills.co.uk

Dating back to 1611, Grace Neill's lays a fair claim to be one of the oldest inns in all Ireland; Grace Neill herself was born when the pub was more than two hundred years old and died in 1916 at the age of 98. Extensions and improvements under the present ownership have been completed with due sensitivity to the age and character of the original front bar, which has been left simple and unspoilt. The back of the building has been imaginatively developed in contemporary style, creating a bright, high-ceilinged restaurant area called Bistro Bistro. Delicious easy-going food is along the lines of risotto of crab with saffron & spring onion, a starter portion salad of rare beef, blue cheese, walnuts & mustard mayonnaise and (a great favourite this) homemade pork & leek sausage with champ & red onion marmalade; quite a few dishes are available as starter or main course portions. Good desserts include an unmissable chocolate & Guinness flavoured brownie cake and there might be Cashel Blue cheese, with grapes & oat biscuits. Consistently good, imaginative food, efficient service and (fairly) reasonable prices make this a place people keep coming back to. Sunday Brunch is a speciality, with live jazz. Children welcome before 7 pm. Own parking. No smoking area. Toilets wheelchair accessible. **Seats 72.** L Tue-Sun,12-2.30 (Sun to 3.30); D Tue-Sat, 6-9.30; Set D £21,50, also à la carte; sc discretionary. Closed D Sun, all Mon; 25-26 Dec, 1 Jan & 12-13 July. (Please phone to check times.) MasterCard, Visa. **Directions:** A2 from Belfast, located at junction in New Street heading back around one way system. Through an arch, off the main High Street.

Donaghadee · Pier 36

Pub/Restaurant

36 The Parade Donaghadee Co Down BT210HE
Tel: 028 9188 4466 Fax: 028 9188 4636
Email: info@pier36.co.uk Web: www.pier36.co.uk

Good food, especially seafood, is attracting the crowds to Denis and Margaret Waterworth's harbourside pub. Denis is the front of house part of the team, while Margaret oversees the kitchen - and the food is excellent for pub cooking, with some traditional dishes and also plenty of choice for palates hungry for flavours from all around the world. Menus change through the day, but fresh home baked breads are a point of pride and simply grilled local lobster is a speciality - but global influences show in dishes like Thai fishcakes with a sweet chilli dressing and orange & cardamom duck breast on a lentil dhansak with poppadom crisps, pear & apple chutney. Aside from a good selection of seafood, there is plenty else to choose from - wild boar comes from Moyallen foods, there's organic free range chicken; menus offered include a dedicated salad menu and an unusually extensive separate vegetarian menu too, with three starters and six main courses to choose from. Desserts, listed on a blackboard, tempt with lots of old favourites, like lemon tart, sticky walnut tart, profiteroles and rice pudding brulée, all served with ice cream, fresh cream or custard - and there's also a nice little coffee menu. Prices are keen, with most evening main courses around £10-12, and you'd better book early at weekends as plenty of people seem to like the idea of a stroll on the pier before supper here. Children welcome. **Seats 130**. No smoking area. Toilets wheelchair accessible. L daily 12-2.30, D Mon-Sat 5-9.30 (Sun 12-8.30). Early D menu available 5-6.30pm. A la carte; house wine £8.25. Bar food served daily, 12-9.30 (Sun to 8.30) Closed 25 Dec. MasterCard, Visa, Switch. **Directions:** At the pier, Donaghdee.

Downpatrick — Denvirs

Pub   14 English Street Downpatrick Co. Down BT30 6AB
Tel: 028 4461 2012

What a gem this ancient place is. It's a wonderful pub with two old bars and an interesting informal restaurant, genuinely olde-worlde with an amazing original fireplace and chimney discovered during renovations. There's also delightful accommodation in sympathetically updated rooms. And there's a first floor room, with some remarkable original features, suitable for meetings or private parties. Go and see it - there can't be another place in Ireland quite like it. Conferences (70). Wheelchair accessible. Parking. Children welcome. Pets permitted. **Rooms 6** (all en-suite) B&B about £30pps, ss £5. Bar/Restaurant: Food served from 12-2.30pm daily & 6-8pm Mon-Fri (6-9pm Sat). [Data not confirmed at time of going to press; please phone to check details.] Closed 25 Dec. Amex, Diners, MasterCard, Visa. **Directions:** On same street as Cathedral and Courthouse in Downpatrick. ◇

Downpatrick — The Mill At Ballydugan

Hotel/Restaurant   Drumcullen Road Ballydugan Downpatrick Co Down BT30 8HZ
Tel: 028 4461 3654 Fax: 028 4483 9754
Email: nkillen@internet.com Web: www.ballyduganmill.com

Hidden away in rolling County Down countryside just outside Downpatrick the site of this 18th century flour mill is very atmospheric: looking out onto ruined stone outbuildings, it is almost like being in a medieval castle courtyard. The Mill would be worth a visit if only to see the magnificent restoration undertaken by the owner, Noel Killen, over more than a decade - but, since opening for business in 2000, there is much more to it than that. The building now houses a bistro/coffee shop on the ground floor, a more formal restaurant on the first floor and, above it, function rooms and accommodation. Bedrooms are appropriately furnished in traditional country style, with exposed beams and brass-and-iron beds, but have also the convenience of phones, TV with video channel, tea/coffee-making facilities and safe. Just a few hundred yards away, Ballydugan Lake is stocked with fish - all round, this is an ideal base for fishing, golfing. Downpatrick races and touring holidays in this lovely area. The restaurant is open to non-residents, and also available for private functions, such as weddings. Conference/banqueting (120/86); secretarial service. Garden. Children welcome, under 5s free in parents' room (cots available free of charge). **Rooms 10** (1 shower only, 6 no smoking, 1 for disabled) Restaurant seats 50. Times and prices not confirmed at time of going to press. MasterCard, Visa, Switch. **Directions:** Downpatrick enroute to Newcastle past race course take first right hand turn and follow road to the Mill.

Downpatrick — Pheasants Hill Country House

Country House   37 Killyleagh Road Downpatrick Co Down BT30 9BL
Tel: 028 4461 7246 / 838707 Fax: 028 4461 7246
Email: info@pheasantshill.com Web: www.pheasantshill.com

In 'St Patrick's country' Pheasants' Hill was a small Ulster farmstead for over 165 years until it was rebuilt in the mid-'90s - and is now a comfortable country house on a seven-acre organic small-holding within sight of the Mourne Mountains, 12 miles away. It is in an area of outstanding natural beauty and abundant wildlife bordering the Quoile Pondage (a wetland wildlife reserve and favoured fishing spot) and the property is right on the Ulster Way walking trail. It is an idyllic spot, as guests soon discover when they are welcomed with tea in front of the fire, or in the orchard on fine summer afternoons. The bedrooms, which are named after flowers and herbs, differ in character and outlook but are all comfortably furnished with generous beds and the advantages of modern facilities, including television, radio alarm clock, tea/coffee making facilities, quality toiletries, hair dryer and books and magazines to read; rooms away from the road at the back are quieter. Breakfast is a major event and worth factoring in as a main meal in your day - the extensive menu even includes a vegetarian cooked breakfast mini-menu within it, although anyone who is not a dedicated vegetarian will find it hard to resist dry-cured bacon and home-made sausages made with their own free range Tamworth pork and many other serious temptations. Perhaps the wisest action is to stay for several nights to allow the opportunity of trying as many variations as possible - it can be difficult to make the best choices on a one-night stay anyway, as you will be asked to make a selection the night before, when you haven't had a chance to get the measure of it. *Farm shop: rare breed free range pork, bacon, lamb, beef & organic poultry sold. Delivery service available. Children welcome (babies under 1 free in parents'; room; cots available, £5). Internet access available (£5 per 10 minutes). Garden, fishing, walking. **Rooms 4** (3 en-suite, 2 shower-only,1 with private bathroom). B&B £29, ss £10. Closed 20 Dec-2 Jan. Amex, Diners, MasterCard, Visa, Switch. **Directions:** On A22, 3 miles north of Downpatrick, 3 miles south of Killyleagh.

Dundrum — The Buck's Head Inn

Restaurant

77 Main Street Dundrum Co. Down BT33 0LU
Tel: 028 4375 1868 Fax: 028 4481 1033
Email: buksheadi@aol.com Web: www.thebucksheadinn.co.uk

Michael and Alison Crothers have developed this attractive, welcoming place from a pub with bar food and a restaurant, to its present position as a restaurant with bar. Alison is in charge of the kitchen and sources local produce, especially seafood, including oysters from Dundrum Bay, which might be baked with a garlic & cheddar crust and Kilkeel cod, with mushy peas and chips. Well-balanced and interesting menus have a pleasing sense of place - aside from the seafood, county Down beef is used for the Sunday roast sirloin and steaks on the dinner menu, lamb is from the Mournes, the famous butchers McCartneys of Moira supply sausages for the traditional bangers & champ; many tempting dishes are offered and, although there has been a move towards more global dishes, the range of styles ensures there is something to please all tastes. desserts are tempting and a short but imaginative vegetarian menu is also offered. At lunch time there's a shortish à la carte and daily blackboard specials - and they are open for high tea as well as dinner. Regular visits here confirm that the cooking is consistently good (and, indeed, always becoming more interesting) and service under the direction of the proprietor Michael Crothers, is friendly and efficient. The atmosphere is always pleasant - and, since the conservatory at the back was replaced with a more contemporary dining room (overlooking a walled garden), it is larger and more comfortable for all-year dining. This is a fine restaurant, providing an admirably comprehensive service: well worth planning a journey around. Interesting wines are supplied by the highly respected wine merchant James Nicholson. Children welcome. *Ask about accommodation - a previous owner, Maureen Griffith, offers B&B nearby. **Seats 80** (private room, 50) No smoking area L 12-2.30, High Tea 5-6.45, D7-9.30 (Sun to 8.30). Set Sun L £14.50; otherwise à la carte. House wine from £11; sc discretionary. Closed Mon off-season (Oct- Mar); 25 Dec. Amex, MasterCard, Visa, Switch. **Directions:** On the main Belfast-Newcastle road, approx 3 miles from Newcastle.

Gilford — Oriel of Gilford

Restaurant

2 Bridge Street Gilford Co Down BT63 6HF
Tel: 028 3883 1543 Fax: 028 3883 1180
Email: orielrestaurant@aol.com Web: www.orielrestauran.com

Tucked away in a corner of County Down, alongside the River Bann, proprietor-chef Barry Smyth's charming country restaurant is in a series of rooms with a cottage-like atmosphere. A cosy, relaxing bar/reception room has a welcoming open fire (and newspapers and magazines to browse over an aperitif or coffee) mixed furniture which combines character with comfort - and the restaurant areas alongside are well-lit with a pleasantly contemporary feeling. The decor in the back room has a slightly 'café' atmosphere despite quality table settings, but all are well set up and the round tables, especially, are both sociable and pleasing on the eye, with beautiful crisp white linen and fine porcelain - and the combination of a warm welcome and caring, professional service gets a visit off to a good start. Barry Smyth's accomplished cooking is seen through menus characterised by lively, colourful dishes that aren't afraid to be bold with flavours: imaginative starters might include a pressed terrine of chicken, rabbit and duck with a frisée salad & truffle dressing or an exotic fresh fruit medley, while a speciality main course that those with a heart appetite should try is prime fillet of Aberdeen Angus beef with caramelised pig's trotter, Pommes Anna & fried quail's egg - or there might be a luxurious alternative from the sea, such as seared supreme of Glenarm salmon with truffle & chive potato, langoustine ravioli & a wholegrain mustard sauce. Delicious desserts range from traditional hot 'club' puddings (irresistible in winter) to refreshing offerings including a range of home-made icecreams and sorbets - and the niceties are observed to the end, when home-made petits fours served with cafetière coffee (or any other from a coffee menu) sends guests off with a smile on their faces. A well-priced wine list includes some unusual bottles and all the menus offered represent good value. **Seats 50** (private room, 16). No smoking restaurant; air conditioning. L Tue-Fri & Sun,12-2.30, D Tue-Sat, 6.30-9.30; 2/3 course Set L £12/15; early D £9.95 (Tue-Fri, 5-7); also à la carte. House wine from £8.95; sc discretionary. Closed D Sun, all Mon, Christmas, 1 week Jan. Amex, Diners, MasterCard, Visa, Laser, Switch. **Directions:** 4 miles from Banbridge on Tandragee Road.

Hillsborough — The Plough Inn

Pub/Restaurant

3 The Square Hillsborough Co. Down BT26 6AG
Tel: 028 9268 2985 Fax: 028 9268 2472
Email: derekpatterson@theploughn.ifreserve.co.uk

Established in 1752, this former coaching inn enjoys a fine position at the top of the hill. Since 1984, it has been owned by the Patterson family who have built up a national reputation for hospitality and good food, especially seafood. Somehow they manage to run three separate food operations each day, so pleasing customers looking for a casual daytime meal and more serious evening diners. The evening restaurant is in the old stables at the back of the pub and booking is required; although renowned for seafood, a sprinkling of meat and poultry dishes will always include fine Angus steaks – a fillet with cracked peppercorn crust and Bushmills whiskey cream perhaps – and there's a vegetarian menu available. A major redevelopment programme completed in 2002 has mercifully left the characterful old bar intact (fairly traditional bar food is still available there) and also the original Plough Restaurant, which has a separate entrance between the back of the pub and the carpark. However the rest of the pub, including the adjacent building on the opposite side of the entrance (left, as you approach through the arch) has been given a seriously stylish contemporary makeover and now rejoices in the name Barretro-Café-Bar-Grill. If that sounds confusing on paper it is much the same on site; the new café, which specialises in pastries, savouries and coffees, is open most of the day and can be accessed directly from the street (look out for the dashing blue canopy), while the grill is above the old bar and offers bistro fare,which can be roughly translated as more substantial dishes from all over the world; bookings are taken there for business lunches but not in the evening. The Guide enjoyed a flavourful, well-cooked bistro lunch here shortly after opening and found the whole thing extremely impressive: lots of cool leather seating, interesting lighting, existing features like the old mahogany bar incorporated into a design which is uncompromisingly modern, yet warm and welcoming; while there is obvious youth appeal, people of all ages feel comfortable here and the staff, who are clearly very proud of it, are friendly and helpful. It is very extensive, so allow yourself time to have a good look around and get your bearings before settling down to eat; if the weather is fine, you might find a seat on the new sun terrace, which is away from the road at the back of the building, off the new bar. Childen welcome in the café, but the Unsuitable for children. Parking. **Seats 150** (private room, 40) No smoking area. Air conditioning. L daily, 12-2.30 (Sun to 3) D 6-9.30 daily. Closed 25 Dec (no food 26 Dec). *The Pheasant Inn at Annahilt is a sister establishment. Amex, Diners, MasterCard, Visa, Switch. **Directions:** Off the main Dublin-Belfast Road, turn off at Hillsborough in village square.

Holywood — Fontana Restaurant

Restaurant

61A High Street Holywood Co. Down BT18 9AE
Tel: 028 9080 9908 Fax: 028 9080 9912
Email: colleen@btopenworld.com Web: www.fontanasrestaurant.com/.co.uk

A first floor restaurant over a classy kitchen shop ("down the alley & up the stairs"), Fontana is fresh and bright, with clear yellow walls which work very well with lightwood chairs and vinyl banquette seating. Proprietor chef Colleen Bennett was one of the first of the new wave of chefs who have taken Northern Ireland by storm in recent years and she offers lovely zesty, loosely structured menus that suit the atmosphere of the room. Starters and main courses overlap to a great extent, with small and large portions of many dishes offered. A dish like Caesar salad with garlicky croutons, black olives and char-grilled chicken might come in two sizes, for example and appear on both the lunch and dinner menus. Seafood features strongly - in an updated chowder with coconut milk & fresh lime, perhaps, or teriyaki salmon on cucumber ribbons, with Asian greens and new potatoes: accomplished cooking, stylishly simple presentation and clear flavours make an appealing combination. Imaginative use of fresh produce (locally sourced where possible) is a striking characteristic of the food at Fontana - and, as well as systematically incorporating a wide range of vegetables and salad ingredients into regular dishes, there's an unusually extensive vegetarian choice offered separately. Outside eating area. Toilets wheelchair accessible. On street parking. Children welcome. **Seats 56**. L Tue-Sat 12.30-2.30 (Sun brunch 11-3), D Tue-Sat 5-9.30. Set L £14.50, Set 2/3 course D £12.50/£14.50, otherwise à la carte (average meal about £25); house wine from about £12; SC discretionary, except 10% added on tables of 6+. Closed Mon, 25-26 Dec & 1 Jan. MasterCard, Visa. **Directions:** Three doors from Maypole flag pole.

Holywood · Hastings Culloden Hotel

Hotel

Bangor Road Holywood Co. Down BT18OEX
Tel: 028 9042 5223 Fax: 028 9042 6777
Email: res@cull.hastingshotels.com Web: www.hastingshotels.com

Hasting Hotels' flagship property, on the main Belfast to Bangor road, is set in 12 acres of beautifully secluded gardens and woodland overlooking Belfast Lough and the County Antrim coastline. The building was originally the official palace for the Bishops of Down, and is a fine example of 19th-century Scottish Baronial architecture – though we do wonder what the bishops would have made of the glass cabinet containing yellow plastic ducks signed by visiting dignitaries. The elegant and luxurious surroundings include fine paintings, antiques, chandeliers, plasterwork ceilings, stained glass windows and an imposing staircase. The spacious bedrooms include a large proportion of suites and the Presidential Suite, with the best views; all are lavishly furnished and decorated and offer the usual facilities, plus additional details such as bathrobes and fine toiletries in the splendidly equipped bathrooms, a welcoming bowl of fruit and nice touches like ground coffee and a cafetière on the hospitality tray.

Business and conference facilities have been further improved recently, making the Culloden an even more attractive venue. The hotel also has a fine health club, the 'Cultra Inn' (an informal bar and restaurant in the grounds), and an association with The Royal Belfast Golf Club, four minutes away by car (book the complimentary hospitality limousine). Conference/banqueting (500); business centre, secretarial services. Leisure centre; swimming pool. Hairdresser. Garden. Children welcome (under 12s free in parents' room; cots available). No pets. **Rooms 79** (16 suites, 21 executive rooms, 29 no-smoking). Lift. B&B £80 pps, ss £48. Room-only rate also available, £140 (2 guests). Open all year. Amex, Diners, MasterCard, Visa, Switch. **Directions:** 6 miles from Belfast city centre on A2 towards Bangor.

Holywood · Rayanne Country House

Country House

60 Demesne Road Holywood Co. Down B18 9EX
Tel: 028 9042 5859 Fax: 028 9042 5859
Web: www.kingdomsofdown.com/rayannecountryhouse

Situated almost next to the Holywood Golf Club and Redburn Country Park, and with views across Belfast Lough, the McClellands' family-run country house is a tranquil spot in which to unwind and a fine alternative to impersonal hotels. Bedrooms, some with views of Belfast Lough, are individually decorated to a high standard with phones and television - and little extras like fresh fruit, spring water, sewing kit, stationery and a hospitality tray with bedtime drinks and home-made shortbread as well as the usual tea & coffee facilities. Numerous other facilities available in the house on request include fax/photocopying, trouser press. It's a relaxing place, with friendly staff and an outstanding breakfast, offering an exceptionally wide range, including unusual dishes such as prune soufflé, French toast topped with black and white pudding & served with a spiced apple compôte, grilled kippers and a 'healthy house grill' (with nothing fried). Friendly staff are helpful and make families with children most welcome (cot available free of charge); beach, shops and restaurants are all just a few minutes' walk away - and evening meals are also offered at Rayanne, in a restaurant which is open to non-residents. Garden, walking, cycling. Parking. Wheelchair accessible. Pets by arrangement. **Rooms 7** (all no smoking) B&B £35pps. Open all year. MasterCard, Visa, Switch. **Directions:** Take A2 out of Belfast towards Holywood (6 miles).

Holywood — Sullivans Restaurant

Restaurant

2 Sullivan Place Holywood Co. Down BT18 9JF
Tel: 028 9042 1000 Fax: 028 9042 6664
Web: www.sullivansrestaurant.co.uk

Chef-proprietor Simon Shaw's bright, friendly and informal bar, restaurant & café celebrates a decade in business in 2003 - and excellent food, varied menus, a lively atmosphere and fair prices are the secret of his success. He offers lively lunch and sandwich menus ranging from a choice of home-made soups served with crusty bread to pork & leek saussages & mash or salmon skewer with stir-fried rice. Quality ingredients have always been the building blocks of his cooking anf he seeks out interesting produce from trusted suppliers like La Rousse Foods and Helens Bay Organics; vegetarians do well here, with interesting choices on the regular menus as well as a separate vegetarian menu offering about half a dozen dishes that can be mixed and matched as starters or main courses. Generosity is a key feature as well as good cooking - seen in portion sizes, and also special offers: the early dinner menu is a steal and there's also a great short dinner menu for two, including a bottle of wine, at £32.50. **Seats 70**. Air conditioning. Open for L&D daily: L daily 12-2.30 (Sun from 11), D Tue-Thu 6-9, Fri & Sat 5-10, Sun 5-9. Early D £10 (5-7pm, 2-course),also à la carte; house wine from £10; sc 10% on parties of 6+. Closed D Mon, 2 days Christmas,1 week Jul. Amex, MasterCard, Visa, Switch. **Directions:** Just off main Belfast-Bangor dual carriageway.

Newcastle — Burrendale Hotel & Country Club

Hotel

51 Castlewellan Road Newcastle Co. Down BT330JY
Tel: 028 4372 2599 Fax: 028 4372 2328
Email: reservation@burrendale.com Web: www.burrendale.com

Just outside the traditional seaside holiday town of Newcastle, and close to the championship links of the Royal County Down golf course, this area on the edge of the Mourne mountains has a remote atmosphere yet it is just an hour's drive from Belfast. Public areas in the hotel are spacious and include the Cottage Bar with an open log fire, welcome on chilly days. Well-appointed accommodation includes family rooms and all rooms are well-equipped with phone, writng desk, TV with video, tea/coffee making facilities and trouser press; new superior rooms are furnished to a higher standard, and have air conditioning. Golf is a major attraction to the area but a varied programme of other special breaks is also offered throughout the year and it is a popular conference venue. Conference/banqueting (250 /200); business centre, secretarial srvices; video conferencing available. Leisure centre, swimming pool; beauty salon. Snooker, pool table. Children welcome (under 4s free in parents' room; cots available without charge; playroom, crèche). Garden, walking, cycling. **Rooms 68** (3 suites, 18 executive rooms, 20 no smoking, 10 for disabled, 4 shower only). Lift. 24 hour room service. B&B £55 pps, ss £20. Bar and restaurant meals avilable L&D daily. Open all year. Amex, Diners, MasterCard, Visa, Switch. **Directions:** On A50 Castlewellan Road.

Belfast — Hastings Slieve Donard Hotel

Hotel

Downs Road Newcastle Co. Down BT33 OAH
Tel: 028 4372 1066 Fax: 028 4372 4830
Email: res@sdh.hastingshotel.com Web: www.hastingshotels.com

This famous hotel stands beneath the Mournes in six acres of public grounds, adjacent to the beach and the Royal County Down Golf Links. The Victorian holiday hotel par excellence, the Slieve Donard first opened in 1897 and has been the leading place to stay in Newcastle ever since. Recent years have seen great improvements in both the public rooms and accommodation. Bedrooms are finished to a high standard and all the bathrooms sport one of the famous yellow Hastings ducks. The nearby Tollymore Forest Park provides excellent walking on clearly marked trails, just one of the many outdoor pursuits that attract guests; should the weather be unsuitable, the Elysium health club has enough facilities to keep the over-energetic occupied for weeks - and is soon to be extended. The hotel also offers a wide range of special breaks. Conference/banqueting (825/400). Business centre; secretarial services. Leisure centre. (18), Leisure centre, swimming pool, beauty salon. Pitch & putt. Own parking. Children welcome (under 14s free in parents' room; cots available without charge). No pets. **Rooms 124** (2 suites, 10 junior suites, 112 executive rooms,1 for disabled). 2 Lifts. B&B £95 pps, ss £25. Open all year. Amex, Diners, MasterCard, Visa, Switch. **Directions:** Situated 32 miles south east of Belfast.

Newcastle — Sea Salt Bistro

Café/Restaurant

51 Central Promenade Newcastle Co Down BT330HH
Tel: 028 4372 5027 Email: seasalt@euphony.net

A good meal will add greatly to your enjoyment of a visit to this traditional holiday town on the sea edge of the Mountains of Mourne, so make a point of seeking out Caroline (front of house) and Andrew (the chef) Fitzpatrick's restaurant in a seafront terrace, wedged between an ice-cream parlour and a chemist's shop. Seasalt opened in 1997 as a delicatessen and café, seating only a dozen or so at lunch time - now, having recently redesigned the interior in a classy contemporary style inspired by the sea, they have re-opened with renewed energy and a commitment to using local produce creatively in global cooking. Daytime snack menus feature gourmet sandwiches - wraps, baguettes, ciabatta with salads - and an extensive hot and cold drinks menu that includes a choice of coffees, teas and refreshing juices like organic lemonade and pure fruit smoothies. Lunch and dinner menus are more substantial, but the ethos is carried through. Seafood stars in popular dishes like Dundrum Bay mussels Thai style with chilli, garlic, coriander & ginger and seafood chowder with Ardglass crab, salmon & prawns but you'll also find all-time favourites like chicken liver paté with brandy and rosemary (served with crisp ciabatta slices and green salad) and duck confit with caramelised red onion heading up main courses as diverse as Co Down sirloin steak with creamy Ulster champ & brandy peppercorn sauce and a vegetarian dish of aubergine & buffalo mozzarella galette with red pepper pesto & salad. With no drinks licence and a modest £1 corkage, everyone brings their own and part of the charm of the evening is to see what diners on adjoining tables have brought in their carrier bags. Booking is essential. **Seats 30**. No smoking area; air conditioning. Open daily in summer from 9am: L 12-4 daily, D Wed-Sun D 7-9. Set D £19.50, D Wed-Sun. Closed Mon in winter. MasterCard, Visa, Switch. **Directions:** Seafront Newcastle, foot of Mournes.

Newry — The Bank

N Restaurant

2 Trevor Hill Newry Co Down BT3 1DN
Tel: 028 3083 5501

A fine old old banking hall near the bridge makes an impressive setting for this smart contemporary restaurant and bar. Tables in a raised area near the window, where smoking is allowed, are conventionally set up while other dining spaces are provided at high tables with tall stools in the body of the hall, and raised booths along the wall - a good idea as the stools are also just the right height for the tables, allowing larger informal groupings around tables nominally intended for four to six. It fills up quickly at lunch time, when fashionable fare like tortilla rolls, stuffed pitta bread and panini competes with regular sandwiches and old favourites such as pork & spring onion sausages with champ & shallot gravy. Dishes containing chilli or nuts are highlighted on the menu, along with vegetarian dishes some of which, like a crunchy Chinese stir-fry with pilaff rice, are given as an option, eg quorn instead of chicken. Evening menus begin straight after lunch and offer larger portions of slightly more formal dishes. Clearly a hit with the locals, The Bank is just the kind of stylish place that the new City of Newry needs. Not suitable for children after 7pm. Open Mon-Fri 11.30-12.15, Sat 12-2. Food served 12-9, L 12-3, D 3-9. Closed 25 Dec, Good Fri. MasterCard, Visa, Laser, Switch. **Directions:** Town centre. ◇

Newry — Canal Court Hotel

Hotel

Merchants Quay Newry Co Down BT35 8HF
Tel: 028 3025 1234 Fax: 028 3025 1177
Email: manager@canalcourthotel.com Web: www.canalcourthotel.com

This canalside hotel serves Newry well with badly needed facilities, including business/conference services as well as a health & leisure complex and spacious, comfortable accommodation. Conferences(300). Leisure centre (gym, swimming pools, jacuzzi, sauna, steam room). **Rooms 51**. B&B from about £55 pps. Open all year. Amex, Diners, MasterCard, Visa. ◇

Newtownards — Edenvale House

Country House

130 Portaferry Road Newtownards Co. Down BT22 2AH
Tel: 028 9181 4881 Fax: 028 9182 6192
Email: edenvalehouse@hotmail.com Web: www.edenvalehouse.com

Diane Whyte's charming Georgian house is set peacefully in seven acres of garden and paddock, with views over Strangford Lough to the Mourne mountains and a National Trust wildfowl reserve. The house has been sensitively restored and modernised, providing a high standard of accommodation and hospitality. Guests are warmly welcomed and well fed, with excellent traditional breakfasts and afternoon tea with homemade scones. For evening meals, Diane directs guests to one of the local restaurants. Edenvale is close to the National Trust properties Mount Stewart and Castle Ward. Children welcome (under 10s free in parents' room; cots available without charge). Pets permitted. Garden. **Rooms 3** (all no-smoking). B&B £27.50pps, ss £7.50. Closed Christmas. MasterCard, Visa. **Directions:** 2 miles from Newtownards on A20 going towards Portaferry.

Portaferry   The Narrows

Accommodation/Restaurant
8 Shore Road Portaferry Co. Down BT22 1JY
Tel: 028 4272 8148 Fax: 028 4272 8105
Email: info@narrowhouse.co.uk Web: www.narrows.co.uk

On the Portaferry waterfront, an archway in the middle of a primrose yellow facade attracts attention to the inspired 18th century courtyard development that is central to Will and James Browns' unusual guesthouse and conference facilities. The ground floor includes a cosy sitting room with an open fire and a spacious restaurant; the style throughout is light and bright, with lots of natural materials and local art. Uncluttered modern bedrooms are all different and have a serene, almost oriental atmosphere; all are en-suite but only three have baths. For guests with special needs, all the shower rooms are wheelchair-friendly, eight are specially designed and there is a lift. There are two interconnecting rooms and two family rooms; children's tea is available at 5 pm. A fine room over the archway, opening onto a private balcony, provides banqueting/conference facilities for 50. The restaurant is open for lunch and dinner every day and can be most enjoyable at its best, although recent experience has been disappointing. Children welcome. Own parking. Children under 2 free in parents' room; cots available. Pets by arrangement. **Rooms 13** (all no-smoking, 8 for disabled). Lift. B&B £45 pps, ss £15. Meals: L daily 12-2.30 (Sun to 3.30); D daily 6-9 (Sun 5.30-8.30). A la carte. Open all year. Amex, MasterCard, Visa, Switch. **Directions:** A20 to Portaferry, on shore front.

Portaferry   Portaferry Hotel

Hotel
The Strand Portaferry Co Down BT22 1EP
Tel: 028 4272 8231 Fax: 028 4272 8999
Email: info@portaferryhotel.com

This 18th-century waterfront terrace presents a neat, traditional exterior overlooking the Lough to the attractive village of Strangford and the National Trust property, Castleward, home to an opera festival each June. Extensions and refurbishment undertaken by John and Marie Herlihy, who have owned the hotel since 1980, have been sensitively done and the inn is now one of the most popular destinations in Northern Ireland – not least for its food. There's an excellent lunchtime bar menu (including 'Children's Choice') available every day except Sunday. Accommodation is comfortable and most of the individually decorated en-suite bedrooms have views of the water. Small conference/private parties (14/85); Own parking. Children (Under 2s free in parents' room; cots available). No pets. **Rooms 14** (4 no-smoking) B&B about £50 pps, ss £10.
Restaurant: A slightly cottagey style provides the perfect background for good unpretentious food. Local produce features prominently in prime Ulster beef, Mourne lamb and game from neighbouring estates – but it is, of course, the seafood from daily landings at the nearby fishing villages of Ardglass and Portavogie that take pride of place. Well-balanced table d'hôte lunch and dinner menus are offered, plus a short carte, providing plenty of choice although majoring on local seafood. An excellent breakfast is also served in the restaurant. **Seats 80.** Not suitable for children under 12 after 8 pm. L&D daily: 12.30-2.30, 5.30-7, 7-9 (Sat to 10). Set menus & à la carte L available; house wine from about £11.50; sc discretionary. Toilets wheelchair accessible. Open all year. Amex, Diners, MasterCard, Visa. **Directions:** On Portaferry seafront. ◇

Rostrevor   Celtic Fjord

Restaurant
8 Mary Street Rostrevor Co Down BT34 3AY
Tel: 028 4173 8005

In an attractive house on the main street, Cathy (front of house) and Michael (the chef) Keenan have been running a pleasing restaurant here since the summer of 2000. Arriving guests are promptly welcomed and offered an aperitif in the reception, then shown into one of the interesting, warmly decorated dining rooms. Michael's set menus offer plenty of choice - nine or ten dishes on each course at dinner, and are keenly priced The style ranges from the traditional - first courses like soup of the day with freshly-baked bread or chicken liver paté with Cumberland sauce and main courses such as crisp fried haddock with tartare sauce - to more contemporary fare typically including chunky fish cakes with pimento & cucumber relish and tangy mayonnaise and garlic pork tossed with crunchy vegetables, soy, spices and pasta. There is also a separate, individually priced steak menu offering variations on all the popular steak dishes - and a Japanese style sirloin with honey soy and crispy garlic beansprouts. Desserts tend to be classic - French apple flan with crème patissière is typical. This is not cutting edge food but good cooking, pleasantly efficient service and reasonable prices make for a very pleasant dining experience. **Seats 75** (private rooms, 32, 20, 22). L Wed-Sat 12-3, Sun: 12.30-8.30. D Wed-Sun 6-9.30 (Sun to 8.30). 2/3 course Set D £16.95/£21.95. Also a à la carte. Closed Mon, Tue, 25 Dec. MasterCard, Visa, Switch. **Directions:** On Main Street, halfway up the Hill.

Strangford Village — The Cuan

Pub/Guesthouse The Square Strangford Village Co Down BT30 7ND
Tel: 028 4488 1222 Email: info@thecuan.com Web: www.thecuan.com

On the square, just up from the car ferry that goes over to Portaferry, Peter and Caroline McErleann's village hotel presents a neat, inviting face to the world. Over a century old, it has character with open fires, cosy lounges and a homely bar, where good food is available every day - local seafood is the main speciality, notably speciality dishes like seafood crêpe and scampi - also excellent steaks and hearty traditional food like beef & Guinness casserole and venison sausages with champ & onion gravy. There's a good choice for vegetarians too, also a short children's menu. Bedrooms, including two family rooms, are comfortably furnished with good bathrooms (nearly all with bath and shower), television and tea/coffee making facilities. There's also a sitting room for residents, with television and video. Small conferences/banqueting (15/80). Children welcome (under 2s free in parents' room, cots available without charge). **Rooms 9** (2 shower only, all no smoking, 1 for disabled). Limited room service (on request). B&B £39.95, ss £5; SC discretionary. Food served 12-9 daily. Closed 25 Dec. Amex, Diners, MasterCard, Visa, Switch. **Directions:** 7 miles from Downpatrick on the A25; on the square, near the ferry.

Warrenpoint — The Duke Restaurant

🅝 Restaurant 7 Duke Street Warrenpoint Co Down BT34 3JY
Tel: 028 4175 2084 Fax: 028 4175 2084
Web: www.thedukerestaurant.com

Seafood straight from Kilkeel harbour and most other produce sourced with a ten mile radius is the foundation for Ciaran Gallagher's success at his popular restaurant, which occupies the whole of the first floor over a pleasantly traditional pub, The Duke. Arriving up the (rather steep) stairs, guests are met promptly and efficiently, seated at tables laid with the familiar black rubber place mats, good contemporary cutlery, heavy paper napkins and plain white plates. A comfortable mixture of traditional and modern styles, divisions that lend some intimacy, the busy atmosphere and friendly service all add up to a relaxed ambience. Like the surroundings, menus are balanced and well-tailored to the clientele; the midweek set menu is exceptionally good value and goes down a blinder, keeping the restaurant full all week - and there will be four or five daily fish specials at more realistic prices. Crowd pleasers like surf'n'turf and chicken kiev take their regular places alongside some more ambitious dishes for discerning diners, like hake fillet grilled with lemon butter, steamed courgette flower with prawn mousseline & lobster cream sauce - or roast venison with roast vegetables and shallots & cranberry jus. Some dishes might benefit from less embellishment - whole Dover sole, for example, comes with smoked bacon, caper & lemon butter, basil pesto and balsamic syrup, which is several ingredients too many for this wonderfully subtle fish - and desserts are not a strong point either but, on the whole, the cooking is as accomplished as it is generous, the staff cheerful and attentive and the value is terrific: who could ask for more? **Seats 65**. Air conditioning. D Tue-Sat, 6-10, Sun 5.30-9.30. Midweek Special Set D £11.95, also à la carte. House wine from £8.35. No SC. Closed Mon. MasterCard, Visa, Laser, Switch. **Directions:** Just off town square.

COUNTY FERMANAGH

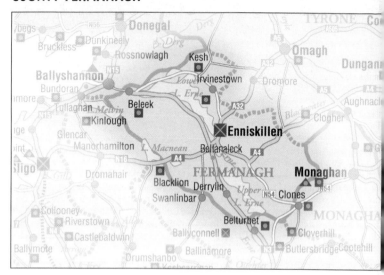

Ireland is a watery place of many lakes, rivers and canals. So it's quite an achievement to be the most watery county of all. Yet this is is but one of Fermanagh's many claims to distinction. It is the only county in Ireland in which you can travel the complete distance between its furthest extremities within the heart of its territory entirely by boat. Elsewhere, rivers often divide one county from another, but Fermanagh is divided - or linked if you prefer - throughout its length by the handsome waters of the River Erne, both river and lake.

Southeast of the county town of Enniskillen, Upper Lough Erne is a maze of small waterways. Northwest of the historic and characterful town, the riverway opens out into the broad spread of Lower Lough Erne, a magnificent inland sea set off against the spectacular heights of the Cliffs of Magho. It's a stunningly beautiful county with much else of interest, including the Marble Arch caves, and the great houses of Castle Coole and Florence Court, the latter with its own forest park nestling under the rising heights of Cuilcagh (667m).

And if you think lakes are for fishing rather than floating over, then in western Fermanagh the village of Garrison gives access to Lough Melvin, an angler's heaven. You just can't escape from water in this county. So much so, in fact, that Fermanagh folk will tell you that during the more summery six months of the year, the lakes are in Fermanagh, but in the damper months of winter, Fermanagh is in the lakes...

Local Attractions and Information

Belleek Porcelain and Explore Erne Exhibition	028 68 659300
Bellanaleck Sheelin Lace Museum	028 66 348052
Enniskillen Ardhowen Lakeside Theatre	028 66 325440
Enniskillen Castle Coole House & Parkland	028 66 322690
Enniskillen Enniskillen Castle	028 66 325000
Enniskillen Florence Court	028 66 348249
Enniskillen Lough Erne Cruises	028 66 322882
Enniskillen Tourism Information	028 66 323110
Enniskillen Waterways Ireland	028 66 323004
Florence Court House and garden	028 66 348249
Florencecourt Marble Arch Caves	028 66 348855
Garrison Lough Melvin Activity Holiday Centre	028 68 658142
Kesh Ardess Craft Centre	028 68 631267
Kesh Castle Archdale Country Park	028 68 621588
Newtownbutler Crom Castle	028 67 738174

Bellanaleck — The Sheelin

Restaurant

Main Street Bellanaleck Co. Fermanagh BT92 2BA
Tel: 028 6634 8232 Fax: 028 6634 8232
Email: a.donnelly@web.de Web: www.thesheelin.com

John and Annett Donnelly's delightful thatched cottage restaurant has been making serious waves in the area since they took over here in 2001: while it always seems as if nothing could change here, their philosophy of food and wine has brought about a quiet revolution in what was already a good little restaurant. It is a simple enough concept on the face of it: over 300 bins in the wine cellars, menus completely changed every six to eight weeks, never more than six choices on any course. Their motto should be music to the ears of discerning diners everywhere: large wine list, small menu, only fresh produce. That produce includes local specialities such as home-smoked kassler (the matured black bacon used is an Enniskillen speciality) and Lough Erne crawfish (a house speciality, grilled in white wine & garlic, and served on salad with lemon crème fraîche). The style is basically fairly classical, but contemporary influences show in irresistible dishes like free range chicken breast on a lemongrass skewer, poached in coconut milk and served with oriental vegetables and saffron rice. Everything is home-made, including accompaniments like spätzle and noodles and a range of usual desserts. Children welcome. **Seats 44** (private room 16). No smoking area. L Tue-Sun, 12.30-3, D Tue-Sun 5-9.30. Set L £12; Set D £15.90-£22.90. House wines (20), from £10. SC discretionary. Closed Mon, all Jan. Diners, MasterCard, Visa, Laser, Switch. **Directions:** Main Enniskillen - Dublin road 3 miles outside of Enniskillen, direction Cavan.

Belleek — Hotel Carlton

Hotel

2 Main Street Belleek Co. Fermanagh BT93 3FX
Tel: 028 6865 8282 Fax: 028 686 59005
Email: reception@hotelcarlton.co.uk Web: www.hotelcarlton.co.uk

Belleek is a smashing little place and one of the friendliest you'll find anywhere. There's Belleek Porcelain to visit of course (which is fascinating and a grand way to spend a wet day), several great music pubs, including Moohans/The Fiddlestone and McMorrows/Franks (both on the main street) and Gilmartins craft shop, which is exceptionally friendly and helpful. Then there's this hospitable waterside hotel, the Carlton which has a welcoming open fire in the bar where meals are served, very helpful staff and comfortable accommodation. It would make a pleasant base for exploring this beautiful, unspoilt area - good value weekend and midweek breaks are offered. Children welcome (cot available without charge). Conference/banqueting (250). Garden, fishing, walking. **Rooms 19** (1 suite, 12 shower only, 4 no smoking). B&B £37.50, ss £15. Closed 24-25 Dec. Amex, MasterCard, Visa, Switch. **Directions:** At the bottom of street, near the bridge.

Belleek — The Thatch

Café

Belleek Co. Fermanagh BT93
Tel: 028 6865 8181

This coffee shop is really special: a listed building dating back to the late eighteenth century, it's the only originally thatched building remaining in County Fermanagh. Home-made food has been served here since the early 1900s and the tradition is being well-maintained today, with home-made soups, a range of freshly made sandwiches and toasted sandwiches all made to order, hot specials like stuffed baked potatoes and (best of all) delicious bakes like chocolate squares, carrot cake and muffins. Drinks include a coffee menu and, more unusually, you can also buy fishing tackle, hire a bike - or even a holiday cottage here. **Directions:** On the main street. ◇

Enniskillen — Blakes of the Hollow

Pub/Restaurant/Café

6 Church Street Enniskillen Co. Fermanagh BT746JE
Tel: 028 6632 2143 Fax: 028 6774 8491
Email: blakep@btconnect.com

One of the great classic pubs of Ireland, Blakes has been in the same family since 1887 and, up to now, has always been one of the few places that could be relied upon to be unchanged. Not a food place, a pub. Maybe a sandwich, but mainly somewhere to have a pint and put the world to rights. It is a great relief to Blakes' many fans all over the world that the building is listed both inside and out because major changes have recently been taking place at this historic establishment. The good news is that the original Victorian bar still remains untouched after 115 years while several new features have been developed on the rest of the site, including Café Merlot (serving informal, bistro-style food) on the lower ground floor, The Atrium - a gothic style bar spread over two floors and Tonic, a brash, buzzy bar with youth appeal. Potentially the most exciting development is Restaurant No 6 @ Blakes of 'The Hollow', due to open shortly after the guide goes to press: the chef, John Williams, is a native of Enniskillen and returning from a highly successful UK restaurant to cook up a storm in his home town. Times and menus to be confirmed. Open all year. Diners, MasterCard, Visa, Switch. **Directions:** Town centre.

Enniskillen — Francos Restaurant

Restaurant · Queen Elizabeth Road Enniskillen Co. Fermanagh BT74
Tel: 028 6632 4183

This large, strikingly decorated restaurant was one of Enniskillen's first contemporary eating places and remains one of the most popular. Informal food, including pizzas, pastas and barbecues, are the order of the day - and it's all done with great style. The range is impressive and really does offer something to everyone, with pasta dishes offered for as little as £6 - and lobster at £29. Seafood from Donegal and Sligo is a speciality (fresh grilled lobster on a bed of colcannon, perhaps), also new age pizzas with Mediterranean style toppings like goats cheese, spinach & pesto. **Seats 140** (private room, 60). Toilets wheelchair accessible. Children welcome. Open Mon-Sat, 12.30-11 (Sun to 10.30 pm). A la carte. Houses wines from £10. Closed 25 Dec. Amex, MasterCard, Visa, Switch.

Enniskillen — Gallery Restaurant

Ⓝ Restaurant/Accommodation · 139 Irvinestown Road Enniskillen
Co. Fermanagh BT74 4RN
Tel: 028 6632 8374 Fax: 028 6632 8263

A large Georgian style countryhouse in a secluded situation with mature trees, the interior - all marble floors and murals of vistas and vines - comes as a surprise, although the accommodation is more in keeping with the countryhouse feel: two of the bedrooms have four-posters and all are comfortably appointed. Since taking over the restaurant in late 2001, chef Gerry Russell has built up a following for accomplished cooking that reflects his experience in Belfast, London and Perth - the latter especially evident in fusion and Thai-influenced dishes (for example, hot and sour broth with pak choi, chestnut mushrooms and a sweet chilli sambal). Good, freshly-made breads are served with dipping oils while your select from short but well-judged menus which are frequently altered to include seasonal produce and typically will include fresh fish, home smoked bacon and dry aged steak as well as a vegetarian option - flavours tend to be complex and interesting side orders are priced separately. A brief dessert menu offers some little gems, like a lemon & lime blur with coconut and white chocolate ice cream, which could well be the highlight of your meal. Occasional wine dinners are offered at a set price, with wines matched to each course. Sunday lunches are price for two or three courses (but side orders charged separately) and there's plenty of room for children to let off steam outside. **Seats 40.** No smoking restaurant. L 12-2.30, D 6-9.30 (Sun 5-8). Set Sun L £11.95/13.95; otherwise à la carte. House wines from £9.95. Closed Mon, Tue. Accommodation: **Rooms 5** (all no smoking). B&B £28 pps, ss £5. MasterCard, Visa, Switch. **Directions:** On the edge of town, signed on main Enniskillen-Irvinestown road.

Enniskillen — Killyhevlin Hotel

Hotel · Dublin Road Enniskillen Co. Fermanagh BT74 6RW
Tel: 028 6632 481 Fax: 028 6632 4726
Email: info@killyhevlin.com Web: www.killyhevlin.com

Just south of Enniskillen, on the A4, this spacious, well-run modern hotel on the banks of the Erne has much to offer, including a warm welcome and comfortable accommodation. It is a popular choice for business guests and would make a relaxing base from which to explore this fascinating and unspoilt area - and it's also a pleasant place to break a journey as there is food available all day and the soothing river views from the Boathouse Grill Bar are lovely. Outdoor activities such as golf and horse-riding are available nearby but, given the location, fishing and river cruising are particular attractions and the hotel gardens reach down to the riverbank and their own pontoon, where visiting cruisers can berth. Conference/banqueting facilities (600/400); business centre, secretarial services, video-conferencing. There are also some holiday chalets in the grounds, with private jetties. Ample parking. Children welcome (under 4s free in parents' room; cots available, £10; playground). Wheelchair accessible. Pets permitted by arrangement. Garden, cycling. **Rooms 43** (1 suite, 1 junior suite, 1 for disabled). B&B £57.50 pps, ss £20; SC incl. Closed 24-25 Dec. Amex, Diners, MasterCard, Visa, Switch. **Directions:** On the A4 just south of Enniskillen.

Enniskillen — Rossahilly House

Guesthouse

Rossahilly Enniskillen Co. Fermanagh BT94 2FP
Tel: 028 6632 2352
Email: enquires@rossahilly.com Web: www.rossahilly.com

Just three miles from Enniskillen, the approach to Monica Poole and Eric Bell's beautifully located 1930s guesthouse may take you past an unsightly disused farmyard but, once you get there, it's definitely worth it. It's on an elevated site with panoramic views overlooking Lower Lough Erne: "A little bit of heaven" is what one guest called it and it's easy to see why. The entrance is through a neat conservatory style entrance with comfortable seating overlooking manicured lawns towards the lough - and there's a lovely traditionally tiled hallway too, setting the tone for a house that has been furnished with character. Accommodation in individually decorated bedrooms has been thoughtfully organised for the maximum comfort and security of guests - not only with phone, TV with video, tea/coffee making and pressing facilities, but also a safe and fax available on request. There is a lot to do in the area - they're specialists in fly-fishing holidays - and there is a tennis court on site. In summer they run a great little restaurant, which is open to non-residents, offering good home cooking (notably excellent baking) for morning and afternoon "bites" and a proper menu for lunch and dinner (at other times they offer dinner for residents and private parties by arrangement. Everything is meticulously sourced and well cooked - presentation is attractive and service, by local waiting staff, both efficient and friendly. Licensed. Children welcome (under 4s free in parents' room). **Rooms 3** (1 suite, 1 junior suite, all no smoking). Room service all day. Restaurant **Seats 20** (private room 10). No smoking restaurant. Open to non-residents high season, 8.30-6 (L 12.30-2, D 7-8.30. Set D £25, L à la carte. House wine £10.) MasterCard, Visa, Switch. **Directions:** 3 miles from Enniskillen on Kesh Road.

Enniskillen — Scoffs Restaurant & Wine Bar

Ⓝ Restaurant

17 Belmore Street Enniskillen Co. Fermanagh BT74 6AA
Tel: 028 663 42622 Fax: 028 663 42622
Email: scottsrest@aol.com

Just a few minutes walk from the town centre, this popular bistro-style restaurant and wine bar has been pleasing a wide range of customers for the last three years - and clearly doing it very successfully as they have just expanded from 60 seats to 140. Early evening opening and a wide-ranging menu - offering everything from inexpensive pastas to more serious (but still moderately priced) 'dinner' dishes - partly explain the wide appeal, but friendly, attentive staff and an atmosphere of relaxed informality are equally attractive. Recent changes (moving the restaurant up to the ground floor) have made for an airier space than previously, with decor retaining the feeling of the former pub - while the wine bar area at the back has more contemporary decor and some zany murals. Large laminated menus include some fascinating choices (like a mixed grill of Cumberland and wild boar sausage with Clonakilty black and white pudding and lambs liver with slow roast tomatoes and baked egg, £11.20) and interesting vegetarian options - which, like those with nuts or flour, are considerably highlighted. Modern classics like slow cooked lamb shank with brunoise of vegetables & creamy mash (£11.80) are well cooked and stylishly presented, and the only down side is that dishes charged extra at £2.80 can add significantly to the costs of a meal. *A daytime sister establishment, Café Cellini, has lovely contemporary decor and riverside views - and they serve a good (Illy) coffee. **Seats 140** (private room, 14). No smoking area. Toilets wheelchair accessible. Children welcome. D daily, 5-11. A la carte. House wine from £9.90. Closed 24-25 Dec. Diners, MasterCard, Visa, Switch. **Directions:** Access from main shopping centre.

Kesh — Lough Erne Hotel

Hotel

Main Street Kesh Co. Fermanagh BT94 1TF
Tel: 028 6863 1275 Fax: 028 6863 1921
Email: info@lougherne hotel.com Web: www.lougherne hotel.com

In a very attractive location on the banks of the Glendurragh River, this friendly village centre hotel has twelve comfortable rooms with en-suite bath/shower rooms, TV and tea/coffee facilities. The hotel is understandably popular for weddings, as the bar and function rooms overlook the river and have access to an attractive paved riverside walkway and garden. Popular for fishing holidays, it would also make a good base for a family break; there is plenty to do in this lovely and unspoilt area, including golf, watersports and horse-riding. Conference/banqueting(200/180). Fishing, cycling, walking. Off-season breaks and self-catering accommodation offered. Garden. Limited wheelchair access. Own parking. Children welcome. Pets permitted in some areas. **Rooms 12** (all en-suite) B&B £35pps, ss £5; sc discretionary. Closed 25 Dec. Amex, Diners, MasterCard, Visa, Switch. **Directions:** From Dublin N3 to Belturbet, A509 to Enniskillen, A32, A35 to Kesh.

Kesh   Lusty Beg Island

Pub/Accommodation   Boa Island Kesh Co. Fermanagh BT93 8AD
Tel: 028 686 32032 Fax: 028 686 32033
Email: reservations@lustybegisland.com Web: www.lustybeg.com

If you arrive by road, a little ferry takes you over to the island (leave your car on the mainland unless you will be staying on the island), or of course, you can call in by boat. It's an unusual place and worth a visit, if only to call into the pleasant waterside pub for a drink, a cup of tea or an informal bite such as smoked salmon and brown bread. However, you could stay much longer as accommodation is available in lodges, chalets and a motel, all spread relatively inconspicuously around the wooded island. Conferences, corporate entertaining and management training are specialities and all sorts of activity breaks are offered. Visiting boats are welcome; phone ahead for details of barbecues and other theme nights; music Saturday nights. Bar food available daily in summer. (Food service variable off-season - phone ahead for details). Conference/banqueting (300/200). **Rooms 18** (all en-suite, 1 disabled) Children welcome (under 5s free in parents' room; cot available, £5; children's games room). Leisure centre: swimming pool, sauna, fitness suite; tennis. Football pitch, canoes, bike hire. B&B £37.50 pps. ss £12.50. Open all year. Amex, Visa, MasterCard. **Directions:** Located off the main Kesh - Belleek Road A47.

Killadeas   Manor House Country Hotel

Hotel/Restaurant   Killadeas Co. Fermanagh BT94 1NY
Tel: 028 6862 2211 Fax: 028 6862 1545
Email: info@manor-house-hotel.com Web: www.manor-house-hotel.com

This impressive lakeside period house makes a fine hotel. The scale of the architecture and the style of furnishings and decor lean very much towards the luxurious in both public areas and accommodation. Spacious bedrooms range from interconnecting family rooms to deluxe doubles and romantic suites with canopied four-poster beds and front rooms have stunning views. Recent changes have included extensive refurbishments and the addition of an impressive new conference and banqueting area with its own separate entrance, which has been discreetly added to the side and rear of the original building and, despite its large size and more contemporary approach, in no way detracts from the appeal of the old house. Leisure centre, indoor swimming pool. Children under 3 free in parents' room. No pets. **Rooms 46** (all en-suite, 6 suites) B&B about £55pps, ss about £30. **The Belleek Restaurant:** is also well positioned to make the most of the lovely view, especially at breakfast and lunchtime. Dominic Almond, who has been head chef "for years" is doing a good job and both food and service match the grand surroundings. Bar meals available 12.30-9 pm daily. **Restaurant seats 65** (private room 30). Non-smoking restaurant. Air Conditioning. L&D daily. [*Information on the nearby Inishclare restaurant, bar & marina complex is available from the hotel, which is in common ownership.] Open all year. Amex, MasterCard, Visa. **Directions:** 6 miles from Enniskillen on the B82. ◊

Killadeas   The Waterfront Restaurant

Restaurant   Rosigh Bay Killadeas Co. Fermanagh BT94
Tel: 028 6862 1938

This beautifully located restaurant has an attractive bar, decorated to a fairly nautical theme with antiques and memorabilia, and a sunny waterside seating area for fine weather. The menu - a fairly extensive à la carte - offers a balanced choice of quite upscale dishes, notably seafood but plenty else besides, including vegetarian dishes. Opening times after Easter:Weds-Sat, 6-9 pm & Sun 12.30-3, followed by teas until 5.30, then the evening a la carte menu. Open daily in July & August. Off season, open Fri, Sat & Sun only, 6-9 pm MasterCard, Visa. ◊

COUNTY LONDONDERRY

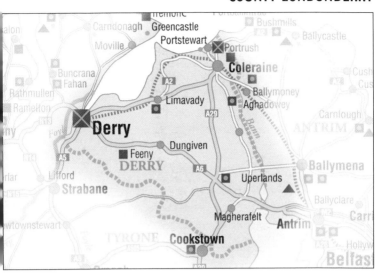

When its boundaries were first defined in modern times, this was actually the County of Coleraine, named for the busy little port on the River Bann a few miles inland from the Atlantic coast. It was an area long favoured by settlers, for Mountsandel - on the salmon-rich Bann a mile south of Coleraine - is where the 9,000 year old traces of one of the sites of some of the oldest-known houses in Ireland have been found.

Today, Coleraine is the main campus of the University of Ulster, with the vitality of student life spreading to the nearby coastal resorts of Portstewart and Portrush in the area known as the "Golden Triangle", appropriately fringed to the north by the two golden miles of Portstewart Strand. Southwestward from Coleraine, the county - which was re-named after the City of Derry became Londonderry in 1613 - offers a fascinating variety of places and scenery, with large areas of fine farmland being punctuated by ranges of hills, while the rising slopes of the Sperrin Mountains dominate the County's southern boundary.

The road from Belfast to Derry sweeps through the Sperrins by way of the stirringly-named Glenshane Pass, and from its heights you begin to get the first glimpses westward of the mountains of Donegal. This is an appropriate hint of the new atmosphere in the City of Derry itself. This lively place could reasonably claim to be the most senior of all Ireland's modern cities, as it can trace its origins back to a monastery of St Colmcille, otherwise Columba, founded in 546AD. Today, the city - with up-dated port facilities on the River Foyle and a cheerfully restored urban heart - is moving into a vibrant future in which it thrives on the energy drawn from its natural position as the focal point of a larger catchment area which takes in much of Donegal to the west in addition to Londonderry to the east.

The area eastward of Lough Foyle is increasingly popular among discerning visitors, the Roe Valley through Dungiven and Limavady being particularly attractive. The re-establishment of the ferry between Magilligan Point and Greencastle in Donegal across the narrow entrance to Lough Foyle has added a new dimension to the region's infrastructure, as does the up-grading of the increasingly busy City of Derry Airport at Eglinton.

Local Attractions and Information

Bellaghy Bellaghy Bawn (Seamus Heaney centre)	028 79 386812
Castlerock Hezlett House	028 70 848567
City of Derry Airport	028 71 810784
Coleraine Guy L Wilson Daffodil Garden	028 70 344141
Coleraine Tourism Information	028 70 344723
Derry City The Fifth Province - Celtic culture	028 71 373177
Derry City Foyle Arts Centre	028 71 266657

Derry City Foyle Cruises (year round)	028 71 362857
Derry City Foyle Valley Railway Centre	028 71 265234
Derry City The Guildhall	028 71 377335
Derry City Harbour Museum	028 71 377331
Derry City Millennium Forum Theatre	028 71 264426
Derry City Orchard Gallery	028 71 269675
Derry City The Playhouse	028 71 268027
Derry City St Columb's Cathedral	028 71 267313
Derry City Tourism Information	028 71 267284
Derry City Tower Museum	028 71 372411
Downhill Mussenden Temple & Gardens	028 70 848728
Draperstown Plantation of Ulster Visitor Centre	028 79 627800
Garvagh Museum & Heritage Centre	028 29 558216
Limavady Roe Valley & Ness Wood Country Parks	028 77 722074
Limavady Tourism Information	028 77 760307
Magherafelt Tourism Information	028 79 631510
Magilligan Lough Foyle Ferry (to Donegal) (ROI t.n.)	077 81901
Moneymore Springhill (NT house)	028 86 748210
Sperrin Mountains Sperrins Tourism	028 79 634570

Aghadowey — The Brown Trout Golf & Country Inn

Hotel/Restaurant 209 Agivey Road Aghadowey Co. Londonderry BT514AD
Tel: 028 7086 8209 Fax: 028 7086 8878
Email: bill@browntroutinn.com Web: www.browntroutinn.com

Golf is the major attraction at this lively country inn, both on-site and in the locality. Newcomers will soon find friends in the convivial bar, where food is served from noon to 10 pm every day. Spacious en-suite rooms with plenty of space for golfing gear are all on the ground floor, arranged around a garden courtyard. New cottage suites overlooking the golf course (just 100 yards from the main building) are the first of this standard to be completed in Northern Ireland. Restaurant: Up a steep staircase (with chair lift for the less able), the restaurant overlooks the garden end of the golf course. Jane O'Hara's good home cooking is based on fresh local ingredients – trout fillet with fresh herbs & lemon butter or sirloin steak with a Bushmills whiskey sauce. High Tea (very popular in this part of the country) is followed by an à la carte dinner menu. Small conference/private parties (40/50); Tennis, horse-riding, golf (9/18), fishing, walking, garden & children's playground available. Children under 4 free in parents' room; cots available). Pets permitted. **Rooms 15** (all en-suite) B&B £42.50pps, ss £15. Stair lift. Restaurant: **Seats 40** (private room, 40). Toilets wheelchair accessible. No smoking restaurant. Open all day (7am-10pm) L 12-3 daily, Set menus from £12.50; also à la carte; house wine about £8.95; sc discretionary. Bar meals: 12-9.30. Open all year. Amex, Diners, MasterCard, Visa, Switch. **Directions:** Intersection of A54/B66 7 miles south of Coleraine.

Aghadowey — Greenhill House

Guesthouse 24 Greenhill Road Aghadowey Co. Londonderry BT51 4EU
Tel: 028 7086 8241 Fax: 028 7086 8365
Email: greenhill.house@btinternet.com Web: www.greenhill.house.btinternet.co.uk

FARMHOUSE OF THE YEAR

Framed by trees with lovely country views, the Hegarty family's Georgian farmhouse is at the centre of a large working farm. In true Northern tradition, Elizabeth Hegarty is a great baker and greets guests in the drawing room with an afternoon tea which includes a vast array of home-made teabreads, cakes and biscuits. There are two large family rooms and, although not luxurious, the thoughtfulness that has gone into furnishing bedrooms makes them exceptionally comfortable – everything is in just the right place to be convenient. Little touches like fresh flowers, a fruit basket, After Eights, tea & coffee making facilities, hair dryer, bathrobe, good quality clothes hangers and even a torch are way above the standard expected of farmhouse accommodation. There's also a safe, fax machine, iron and trouser press available for guests' use on request. Elizabeth provides a home-cooked residents' dinner based on local ingredients by arrangement, served at 6.30pm – please book by noon. (No wine). Guests have been welcomed to Greenhill House since 1980 and, wonderfully comforting and hospitable as it is, Elizabeth constantly seeks ways of improvement, big and small: this lovely house and the way it is run demonstrate rural Irish hospitality at its best: a very worthy recipient of our Farmhouse of the Year Award for 2003. Children welcome, cot available. No pets. Garden. **Rooms 6** (all en-suite, 2 shower only). B&B £27.50 pps, ss £7.50. Closed Nov-Feb. MasterCard, Visa. **Directions:** On B66 Greenhill Road off A29, 7 miles south of Coleraine, 3 miles north of Garvagh.

Coleraine — Charly's Restaurant

Restaurant

34 Newbridge Road Coleraine Co Londonderry BT521TP
Tel: 028 703 52020 Fax: 028 703 55299
Email: chatroom@charlys.com Web: www.charlysrestaurant.com

This big, bright roadside restaurant is inviting, like an American diner, and a great fun place for all age groups, especially the kids. What you get here is good quality fashionable food for all the family - "Charly's Special", a fillet steak with champ, bacon, & garlic mash, is the most expensive dish on the menu at £13.25 - served with speed, efficency and charm. It has heaps of atmosphere and a huge seating capacity but, although tables are turned around quite rapidly, there's no sense that you're being hurried. Most main courses are under about £10; it's great quality for the price and service is `terrific - no wonder it's always busy. **Seats 120.** No smoking area; air conditioning. Children welcome. Open daily high season: 11.30-10; (open low season:L&D Tue-Fri, all day Sat & Sun). A la carte except Set Sun L £10.50 (12-2.30, also main menu, 12-9.30). Closed 25-26 Dec & Mon in low season, also Tue-Fri afternoons, 3-5pm. Amex, MasterCard, Visa, Switch. **Directions:** Belfast-Ballymoney; 1 mile from new hospital. ◇

Feeny — Drumcovitt House

Ⓝ Country House

704 Feeny Road Feeny Co Londonderry BT47 4SU
Tel: 028 7778 1224 Fax: 028 7778 1224
Email: drimcovitt.feeny@btinternet.com Web: www.drumcovitt.com

Drumcovitt is an intriguing house with an impressive Georgian front dating from 1796 - and, behind it a much older farmhouse, built about 1680. It is a listed building and many of the windows and wonderful interior features have been retained but, however interesting its history, today's creature comforts are very much in evidence - central heating extends throughout the house and an adjacent converted barn, and there are big log fires to relax beside while enjoying a fine collection of books, or making a jigsaw. Outdoor pursuits aplenty too: this unspoilt area is perfect for walking, bird-watching, visiting archaeological sites in the Sperrins and much else besides - horseriding, golf and angling are all available nearby and the Giants Causeway, beaches, Bushmills, Derry city and much of Donegal are within easy striking distance. The three guest rooms are the two main front bedrooms (both with a double/ kingsize bed and single) and a twin in the older part; in true country house fashion bathrooms are not en-suite, but two good modern showers (one over bath) are shared by the three rooms; all are spacious and comfortably furnished with tea/coffee-making, television and phone. Florence and Frank Sloan are solicitous but relaxed hosts, who enjoy sharing their unique home and the area around it with guests; Florence also cooks for guests - not just a very fine breakfast menu but a surprisingly extensive dinner menu (from which you can choose before noon for that evening). This is a delightful place, but not one to rush through so allow more than one night if you can. Fax, safe and ironing facilities available for guests' use. Family celebrations/reunions up to about 20 can be catered for in house and three barn cottages, which are available for self-catering. **Rooms 3.** Children welcome (cot available without charge; games room). Pets permitted in some areas by arrangement. B&B £25, no ss. Closed Christmas. Amex, MasterCard, Visa. **Directions:** 0.5 mile east of Feeny Village on B74 off A6.

Limavady — Streeve Hill

🏛 B&B/Country House

25 Dowland Road Limavady Co. Londonderry BT49 9DB
Tel: 028 7776 6563 Fax: 028 7776 8285
Email: pandjwelsh@yahoo.co.uk

Peter and June Welsh have welcomed guests to their lovely 18th century home since they moved here in 1996. It is a very charming house, with a Palladian facade of rose brick and fine views over parkland towards the Sperrin Mountains – but there is also beauty closer to home, in and around the house itself and in the nearby gardens of their former home, Drenagh. The stylish country house accommodation at Streeve Hill is extremely comfortable and the food and hospitality exceptional.

Although the maximum number they can accommodate is six, they are happy for guests to bring friends to dine (provided 24 hours notice is given). They also cater for private dinner parties. Breakfast is another high point and, in the event of fine summer weather, it can be even more enjoyable if served on the terrace outside the drawing room. Horse-riding, walking, fishing, garden available. Children welcome (under 3s free in parents' room; cots available without charge). No Pets. D for residents (and friends) about £30. Please give 24hrs notice. **Rooms 3** (all en-suite & no-smoking,1 shower only). B&B £45pps, ss £10; sc discretionary. Closed Christmas/New Year. Amex, MasterCard, Visa. **Directions:** From Limavady take B021 for Castlerock, follow Estate wall on right. 200 yards past lodge turn right at end of wall.

Limavady — The Lime Tree

Restaurant

60 Catherine Street Limavady Co. Londonderry BT49 9DB
Tel: 028 7776 4300
Email: info@limetreerest.com Web: www.limetreerest.com

Stanley and Maria Matthews' restaurant is on a main street of this handsome, wide-streeted town in a beautiful and prosperous part of the country. There is a great sense of contentment about The Lime Tree; the room is pleasant but quite modest, Stanley is a fine chef and Maria a welcoming and solicitous hostess. Ingredients are carefully sourced, many of them local; menus are generous, with a classical base that Stanley works on to give popular dishes a new twist, in starters like three cheeses tartlette with sun-dried tomatoes & roasted garlic and crab cakes with a chilli jam, for example, while perennial main course favourites include Hunters sirloins steak with a crushed black peppercorn sauce and hake goujons rolled in chopped nuts, with tartare sauce or a lemon mayonnaise dip. Menus are not over-extensive, but change frequently to suit different occasions - there's a keenly-priced set business lunch and a short à la carte lunch menu, for example, then an attractive early dinner menu which is terrific good value, followed by a dressier set dinner for the main evening menu, which also has an accompanying (and more adventurous) à la carte. Sunday lunch brings yet another variation, offering a balanced choice between traditional and more unusual dishes. Stanley's cooking is refreshingly down-to-earth - new dishes are often introduced, but if it's on the menu it's because it works: there are no gimmicks. Good cooking and good value go hand in hand with warm hospitality here and it is always a pleasure to visit The Lime Tree - indeed, some discerning guests enjoy it so much that they travel up from Bangor for lunch at least once a month. Children welcome. A concise, interesting wine list also offers predictably good value. **Seats 30**. No smoking area. L Wed-Sun, 12-2; D Wed-Sun, 6-9 (Sat to 9.30; Sun to 8.30). Set L £6.95/7.95; Set Sun L £13.75. Early D £9.95/£12.95 (6-7 pm only, excl Sat); also à la carte; house wine £9.95; sc discretionary. Toilets wheelchair accessible. Closed Mon,Tue (Sat. lunch booking only), 25-26 Dec, 1 week Feb/Mar, 1 week Jul & 1 week Nov. Amex, MasterCard, Visa, Switch. **Directions:** On the outskirts of town, main Derry-Limavady road.

Londonderry — Beech Hill Country House Hotel

Hotel/Restaurant

32 Ardmore Road Londonderry Co Londonderry BT47 3QP
Tel: 028 7134 9279 Fax: 028 7134 5366
Email: info@beech-hill.com Web: www.beech-hill.com

Beech Hill is just a couple of miles south of Londonderry, in a lovely setting of 42 acres of peaceful woodland, waterfalls and gardens. Built in 1729, the house has retained many of its original details and proprietor Patsy O'Kane makes an hospitable and caring hostess. Comfortable bedrooms vary in size and outlook – many overlook the gardens – but all are thoughtfully and attractively furnished with Mrs O'Kane's ever-growing collection of antiques. Public rooms include a good-sized bar, a fine restaurant (in what was originally the snooker room, now extended into a new conservatory overlooking the gardens) and, unusually, a private chapel, now used for meetings, private parties or small weddings. Facilities include picnic areas in the grounds for fine weather and a fitness suite with sauna, steam room, jacuzzi and weight room. The US Marines had their headquarters here in World War II and an informative small museum of the US Marine Friendship Association is housed within the hotel. Conference/banqueting (100/106); secretarial services. Fitness centre. Tennis, garden, fishing, walking. Children welcome (under 2 free in parents' room; cot £10). **Rooms 27** (4 suites, 2 junior suites, 8 executive rooms, 1 for disabled). Lift. B&B £60pps, ss £32; SC discretionary. Closed 25 Dec.

Ardmore Restaurant: The restaurant has always been a particularly attractive feature of Beech Hill: it is elegantly appointed in traditional style and well-positioned overlooking gardens - and, although the head chef has changed from time to time, a consistently high standard of cooking and service has ensured a loyal local following. A new chef, Philippe Petrani, arrived in the summer of 2002; his style, which is contemporary but soundly based on classical French cooking, is well-suited to both surroundings and clientèle and he makes a point of using as much local (preferably organic) produce as possible. Various combinations of menus are offered, including specials which tend to be very luxurious - a starter of sautéed duck foie gras (fairly priced at £8.95) with vanilla and cardamom sauce, for example - and there's a separate vegetarian listing of five or six interesting dishes which can be served as a starter or main course. The wine list offers good value - and a number of famous New World wines with Northern Irish connections. **Seats 80.** No smoking restaurant. Children welcome. L daily, 12-2.30; D daily 6-9.45. Set L £14.95, set Sun L £17.95. Set 2/3 course D, £19.95/£22.90. Full D menu £27.95. A la carte also available. House wines (6), £12.50-£13.50. SC discretionary. Amex, MasterCard, Visa, Switch. **Directions:** Main Londonderry road A6.

Londonderry	Browns Bar & Brasserie
Restaurant	1-2 Bond Hill Londonderry Co. Londonderry

Tel: 028 7134 5180 Fax: 028 71 345180
Email: browns.tinvteee@aol.com

The city's leading contemporary restaurant has a devoted local following and no wonder - the welcome (and service) may be a little on the cool side, but the cooking's cool too and it's the food that keeps them coming back for more. Recent refurbishment has resulted in a relaxed space with subtle blends of natural colours, textures and finishes - and proprietor-chef Ivan Taylor's approach to food never stands still, and his cooking is consistently terrific. Wide-ranging menus offer a wide range of fresh-flavoured dishes, including delicious starters like an inspired combination of fine beans, Roquefort & walnuts with grilled pancetta & duck 'crackling', and a perfectly judged main dish of mustard glazed tenderloin of pork with roast apples, mushrooms & sauce charcutière - a good example of how to modernise classics without forgetting the basics. Desserts ring some changes with the classics - or espresso, vin santo & home-made biscotti might make a pleasing alternative. All round, there's imagination, a certain amount of style, dedication and consistency - not bad after more than 15 years in business. Tue-Sat: L12-2.15; D 5.30-10.30. Closed Sun, Mon, 1st 2 weeks Aug. Diners, MasterCard, Visa, Laser, Switch. **Directions:** Opposite the old Waterside railway station. ◇

Londonderry	City Hotel
Ⓝ Hotel	Queens Quay Londonderry Co Londonderry BT48 7AS

Tel: 028 7136 5800 Fax: 028 7136 5801
Email: res@derry-gsh.com Web: www.gshotels.com

Centrally located on a quayside site overlooking the River Foyle, Derry's newest hotel is also the latest from what is currently one of Ireland's most vibrant and quality-conscious hotel groups, Great Southern Hotels. Bright and contemporary, it is fashioned in a similar mould to other new hotels in the group such as the highly successful one at Dublin airport and would make an equally attractive base for a leisure visit or for business - all rooms have a workstation with modem/PC connections, voice mail, interactive TV systems and mini-bar and there's a business centre providing secretarial services for guests. Well-located close to the old city, business districts and main shopping areas, it also has free private parking for guests and on-site leisure facilities. Conference/banqueting (450/350). **Rooms 145** (1 suite, 4 junior suites). Lift. 24 hour room service. Children welcome (under 2s free in parents' room, cot available without charge). Leisure centre: swimming pool, Jacuzzi, steam room, sauna, dance suite, gym, hydrotherapy). Room rate: £100 (max 3 guests). Amex, Diners, MasterCard, Visa, Laser. **Directions:** In the heart of Derry City, overlooking the River Foyle.

Londonderry	Exchange Restaurant & Wine Bar
Ⓝ Restaurant	Queens Quay Londonderry Co Londonderry BT48 7AY

Tel: 028 7127 3990 Fax: 028 7127 3991

A great addition to this thriving waterfront area, The Exchange is just outside the walled city and its cool contemporary design makes a great contrast to the age of nearby landmarks. Although seriously modern, this is a friendly and welcoming place that appeals to all age groups and their colourful, fresh-flavoured food suits the mood perfectly. They seem to have a winning formula here as prices are reasonable, ingredients are sourced locally as far as possible and head chef Sean Noonan's cooking fits the bill very well. At first glance the menu seems very international but close examination reveals plenty to please traditionalists too - steaks various ways of course, but also updated roasts like crispy roast duckling with caramelised orange or sweet & sour sauce and straightforward vegetarian dishes such as veggie flan, with garlic, mushroom, spinach and red onion - quite down to earth really, and blackboard specials reflect the same desire to please a wide range of customers. The Exchange has got off to a good start and it should do very well. **Seats 120.** Toilets wheelchair accessible. Children welcome. Air conditioning. L Mon-Sat, 12-2.30; D daily 5.30-10 (Sun to 9.30). A la carte. House wine £9.75. SC discretionary. Closed L Sun, 25 Dec. Amex, MasterCard, Visa, Laser, Switch. **Directions:** Opposite City Hotel.

Londonderry — Fitzroys Restaurant

Restaurant

2-4 Bridge Street 3 Carlisle Road Londonderry Co Londonderey BT55 7EF
Tel: 028 7126 6211 Fax: 028 71 26 4060
Email: fitzroys@lineone.net

This large modern restaurant beside the Foyle Shopping Centre is on two floors and very handy for shoppers, visitors or pre- and post-theatre meals. Menus change through the day and offer a wide range of food in the current international fashion - rack of lamb with hrrb crust, black pudding mash, pea and baby onion jus indicates the evening style while a large daytime menu ranges from hot breakfasts and designer sandwiches to a range of substantial 'chef's specialities'. A useful one to know about. **Seats 80.** Food served all day from 9.30 am (Breakfast to 12.30, lunch to 6, D6-10, à la carte; Sun brasserie menus all day (12-8). Early closing Mon/Tue (7pm). House wine from £7. Closed 26 Dec. MasterCard, Visa, Switch. **Directions:** Beside Foyle Shopping Centre.

Londonderry — Hastings Everglades Hotel

Hotel

Prehen Road Londonderry Co. Londonderry BT47 2NH
Tel: 028 7134 6722 Fax: 028 7134 9200
Email: res@egh.hastingshotels.com Web: www.hastingshotels.com

Situated on the banks of the River Foyle, close to City of Derry airport and just a mile from the city centre, this modern hotel is well located for business and pleasure in a quieter situation than city centre alternatives. Like all the Hastings Hotels, Everglades Hotel undergoes an ongoing system of refurbishment and upgrading, a policy which pays off in comfortable well-maintained bedrooms and public areas which never feel dated. Accommodation is all of a high standard, with good amenities including air conditioning and a spacious desk area, although beds are only standard size which is now unusual in a hotel of this class (and unnecessary as rooms are generally spacious). The hotel is well located for golf, with the City of Derry course just a couple of minutes away and six other courses, including Royal Portrush, within driving distance. Conference/banqueting (400/300); secretarial services; video conferencing (on request). Wheelchair accessible. Own parking. Children under 14 free in parents' room; cots available. No pets. **Rooms 64** (2 suites, 1 junior suite, 4 executive, 24 no-smoking, 1 for disabled). Lift. B&B £67pps, ss £15; no sc. Closed 24-25 Dec. Amex, Diners, MasterCard, Visa, Switch. **Directions:** From Belfast follow M2 (TACW) A6. Hotel is on A5 approx .5 miles from City.

Londonderry — The Merchant's House

Ⓝ B&B

16 Queen Street Londonderry Co Londonderry BT48 7EQ
Tel: 028 7126 9691 Fax: 028 7126 6913
Email: saddlerhouse@btinternet.com Web: www.thesaddlershouse.com

Unusual accommodation is offered at Joan and Dr Peter Pyne's listed Georgian-style townhouse located just outside the city walls. Built in 1867 for Ross Hastings Esq., a city merchant, the house has been adapted for many purposes over the years before being restored in the 1990s by its present owners, as a family home. The interior includes a remarkable first floor drawing room and an elegant period dining room, although bedrooms are less sumptuous than might be expected and - in order to retain the architectural integrity of the building - only one has its own bathroom. This does not bother their fascinated guests, however, for whom the charm and interest of the house outweighs any small practical disadvantages. **Rooms 5** (all no smoking). garden. Children welcome (under 2s free in parents' room, cot available without charge). B&B £22.50, ss £2.50. Open all year. MasterCard, Visa. **Directions:** City centre, off Strand Road.

Londonderry — The Saddler's House

N B&B

36 Great James Street Londonderry Co Londonderry BT 48 &DB
Tel: 028 7126 9691 Fax: 028 7126 6913
Email: saddlerhouse@btinternet.com Web: www.thesaddlershouse.com

Just around the corner from The Merchant's House and in the same ownership, The Saddler's House is a mid-nineteenth century Victorian townhouse in a conservation area. It was built in 1871 for William Dickson Esq, saddler, and remained in the original family until bought by the present owners in 1978; most of the original features survive and there are many fine pieces of furniture in the house. Although less grand or elaborate than its sister property, The Saddler's House seems to have been more suitable for conversion to modern guest accommodation and it has been possible for all rooms to have en-suite shower rooms (also tea/coffee facilities and TV). There is an attractive walled garden behind the house (a very pleasant place to relax after a day out "doing" Derry) and, in the caring hands-on ownership of Dr Peter and Joan Pyne, guests at both properties benefit from having knowledgeable and well-informed hosts - which, as much as the houses themselves, is probably the attraction for their many regular guests connected with the arts and media. **Rooms 7** (all en-suite & no smoking). Children welcome (under 2s free in parents' room, cot available without charge). B&B £27.50 pps, ss 32.50. Open all year. MasterCard, Visa. **Directions:** Central city, off Strand Road.

Londonderry — Tower Hotel Derry

N Hotel

Off The Diamond Londonderry Co Londonderry BT48 6HL
Tel: 028 7137 1000 Fax: 028 7137 1234
Email: reservations@thd.ie Web: wwwtowerhotelderry.com

This attractive new hotel has the distinction of being the only one to have been built inside the city walls and, while this does have its disadvantages (the constraints of the site restricted the amount of parking provided, for example), these are offset by wonderful views over the river and a real sense of being at the heart of the city. Accommodation and facilities have obvious appeal for both leisure and business visitors - the style throughout is bright and sassy, and rooms are pleasingly decorated, with all the necessary modern facilities, including phones/ISDN, hospitality trays, TV, trouser press etc (also a safe in suites). There is a fitness suite with gym and sauna - and a great view. An attractive bistro restaurant off the lobby has the potential to to appeal to non-residents as well as hotel guests. Conference/banqueting 250/180). **Rooms 93** (3 suites, 4 disabled). Lift. Room service (limited hours). Children welcome (cot available without charge). Amex, Diners, MasterCard, Visa, Laser. **Directions:** City centre - old town.

Portstewart — Cromore Halt Licensed Guest Inn

N Guesthouse/Restaurant

158 Station Road Portstewart Co Londonderry BT55 7PU
Tel: 028 7083 6888 Fax: 028 7083 1910
Email: info@cromore.com Web: www.cromore.com

This friendly, family-owned guesthouse and restaurant has been managed by head chef Niall O'Boyle and his wife Kate since it opened in 1994 and it feels like a small hotel. It would make an equally good base for a business or leisure visit as the rooms are furnished to hotel standard in an uncluttered modern style and have all the expected facilities, including satellite television and a comfortable chair as well as direct dial phone with computer line, tea & coffee making, trouser press, keycard & safety deposit box - and there's a quiet first floor residents' lounge well away from the bustle of the busy restaurant downstairs. Although not yet visited by the guide, the restaurant, which is in a large, pleasant room furnished in a relaxed informal style, is open for lunch and dinner every day, and has earned a great reputation in the locality for quality, value and good service. Conference/banqueting (80); secretarial service (video conferencing available). **Rooms 12** (all en-suite & no smoking, 1 disabled). Lift. Children welcome; cot available free of charge. B&B £32.50 MasterCard, Visa, Switch. **Directions:** From Coleraine direction, follow signs for Portstewart take B185 Cromore on left as you enter Portstewart.

Portstewart — Smyths Restaurant

N Restaurant

2-4 Lever Road Portstewart Co Londonderry BT55 7EF
Tel: 028 7083 3564 / 835551 Fax: 028 7083 5551

Alison and Robert Smyth's smart little restaurant is on the ground floor and, up a steep staircase that is a reminder of the home it once was, has a pleasant bar and bistro overlooking The Diamond, used for daytime meals and some evenings (there's live music here two nights a week). The arrival of the talented and energetic team at Smyth's has proved a great asset to the area - chefs Alison Smyth and Anthony Moore direct the kitchen, offering a range of menus tailored to different times of day and days of the week: a shortish 'brasserie menu' suggests lots of delicious dishes for lunch or informal evening meals - stuffed field mushrooms with Cashel Blue cheese & chives, calamari in chilli batter (served with aoïli), chargrilled chicken with aubergine and spicy couscous are all typical, served with lovely side orders including great well-dressed salads, wilted greens and good breads. Evening menus are more extensive, but with the same characteristics: sound flavour combinations are used in colourful, clear-flavoured seasonal food which is attractively presented without gimmicks; vegetarian dishes are imaginative (as in roasted vegetable tarte tatin with a pesto sauce) but creative use of vegetables is an integral part of most dishes (as in pork medallions with braised fennel, caramelised apple ring & baked beetroot, for example). Gorgeous puds too (poached peaches in white wine syrup with panna cotta, perhaps) or Irish farmhouse cheeses to finish. Special evenings are often held (eg an Italian night, or an Irish/French one for the Beaujolais Nouveau) and a wine club is planned for the winter of 2002/3. All this and good service too. **Seats 40** (private room, 20). No smoking area. Music in bar 2 nights a week (traditional/acoustic sets). L Tue-Sun, 12-3, (bar snacks 3-5.30); D Tue-Sun, 5.30-10 (Sun to 8.30). Children's menu 33.95, otherwise à la carte. House wine £8.99. Closed all Mon (except bank hols), 25 Dec, 1 Jan, 1 week Jan. Diners, MasterCard, Visa, Switch. **Directions:** At the Diamond, behind Agherton Church, corner of Church Street & Lever Road.

Upperlands   Ardtara Country House

🏛 Country House

8 Gorteade Road Upperlands Co. Londonderry BT46 5SA
Tel: 028 7964 4490   Fax: 028 7964 5080
Email: valerie@ardtara.fsbusiness.co.uk   Web: www.ardtara.com

Former home to the Clark linen milling family, Ardtara is now an attractive, elegantly decorated Victorian country house with a genuinely hospitable atmosphere. Well-proportioned rooms have antique furnishings and fresh flowers. All the large, luxuriously furnished bedrooms enjoy views of the garden and surrounding countryside and have king size beds and original fireplaces, while bathrooms combine practicality with period details, some including freestanding baths and fireplaces. Breakfast is a high point, so allow time to enjoy it. Tennis, woodland walk, golf practice tee. No pets. Conferences/Banqueting (40/50). **Rooms 8** (3 suites) B&B £75pps, no ss. Restaurant: In a dining room converted from its previous use as a snooker room – still with full Victorian skylight and original hunting frieze – the chef continues the philosophy of using seasonal and local ingredients and offers a balanced choice on the menus, with game well represented in season. **Seats 35** (private room, 10). No smoking restaurant. L&D. Ring to check opening times off-season; closed 25-26 Dec. Amex, MasterCard, Visa, Switch. **Directions:** M2 from from Belfast to A6. After Castledawson take A29 to Maghera. Follow signs to Kilrea until Upperlands.

COUNTY TYRONE

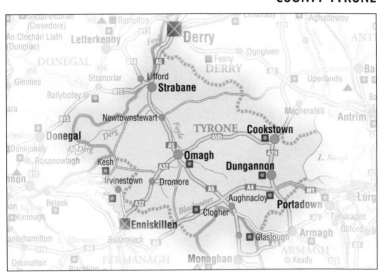

Tyrone is Northern Ireland's largest county, so it is something of a surprise for the traveller to discover that its geography appears to be dominated by a range of mountains of modest height, and nearly half of these peaks seem to be in the neighbouring county of Londonderry.

Yet such is the case with Tyrone and the Sperrins. The village of Sperrin itself towards the head of Glenelly may be in Tyrone, but the highest peak of Sawel (678 m), which looms over it, is actually right on the county boundary. But much of the county is upland territory and moorland, giving the impression that the Sperrins are even more extensive than is really the case.

In such a land, the lower country and the fertile valleys gleam like jewels, and there's often a vivid impression of a living - and indeed prosperity - being wrested from a demanding environment. It's a character-forming sort of place, so it's perhaps understandable that it was the ancestral homeland of a remarkable number of early American Presidents, and this connection is commemorated in the Ulster American Folk Park a few miles north of the county town of Omagh.

Forest parks abound, while attractive towns like Castlederg and Dungannon, as well as villages in the uplands and along the charming Clogher Valley, provide entertainment and hospitality for visitors refreshed by the wide open spaces of the moorlands and the mountains.

Local Attractions and Information

Ardboe Kinturk (Lough Neagh) Cultural Centre	028 86 736512
Benburb Benburb Castle and Valley Park	028 37 548241
Castlederg Visitor Centre (Davy Crockett links)	028 81 670795
Clogher Clogher Valley Rural Centre	028 85 548872
Coagh Kinturk Cultural Centre	028 86 736512
Cookstown Drum Manor Forest Park	028 86 762774
Cookstown Wellbrook Beetling Mill (Corkhill)	028 86 748210
Cranagh (Glenelly) Sperrin Heritage Centre	028 81 648142
Creggan (nr Carrickmore) Visitor Centre	028 80 761112
Dungannon Heritage Centre	028 87 724187
Dungannon Tourism Information	028 87 767259
Dungannon Tyrone Crystal	028 87 725335
Dungannon Ulysses S Grant Ancestral Homestead	028 85 557133
Fivemiletown Clogher Valley Railway Exhibition	028 89 521409
Gortin Ulster History Park	028 81 648188
Newtownstewart Baronscourt Forest Park	028 81 661683
Newtownstewart Gateway Centre & Museum	028 81 662414

Omagh Ulster-American Folk Park	028 82 243292
Omagh Tourism Information	028 82 247831
Strabane Gray's Printing Press (US Independence)	028 71 884094
Strabane Tourism Information	028 71 883735
Strabane President Wilson Ancestral Home	028 71 3844

Dungannon — Grange Lodge

 Country House

7 Grange Road Dungannon Co. Tyrone BT717EJ
Tel: 028 8778 4212 Fax: 028 8778 4313
Email: grangelodge@nireland.com

Norah and Ralph Brown's renowned Georgian retreat offers comfort, true family hospitality and extremely good food. The house is on an elevated site just outside Dungannon, with about 20 acres of grounds; mature woodland and gardens (producing food for the table and flowers for the house) with views over lush countryside. Improvements over the years have been made with great sensitivity and the feeling is of gentle organic growth, culminating in the present warm and welcoming atmosphere. Grange Lodge is furnished unselfconsciously, with antiques and family pieces throughout. Bedrooms (and bathrooms) are exceptionally comfortable and thoughtful in detail. Norah's home cooking is superb and, although they no longer accept bookings from non-residents for dinner, they will cater for groups of 10-30. Grange Lodge is fully licensed and dinner menus change daily (in consultation with guests). Resident dinner (from £24) must be pre-booked, especially if you want to dine on the day of arrival. Breakfasts are also outstanding, so allow time to indulge: a sumptuous buffet beautifully set out on a polished dining table might typically include a large selection of juices, fruit and cereals and porridge is a speciality, served with a tot of Bushmills whiskey, brown sugar and cream... There is, of course, a cooked breakfast menu as well, so go easy on the early temptations, all served with lovely fresh breads and toast and home-made preserves. Just wonderful. (Grange Lodge won our Breakfast Award for the Ulster Region in 2001.) Conferences/banqueting (30) Fishing, walking, garden, snooker. Not suitable for children under12. Pets allowed in some areas. **Rooms 5** (3 shower only, all no smoking) B&B £39 pps, ss £16. Room service (limited hours.) Closed Christmas. MasterCard, Visa. **Directions:** 1 mile from M1 junction 15. A29 Armagh, left at Grange, next right & first white walled entrance on right.

Omagh — Hawthorn House

Guesthouse/Restaurant

72 Old Mountfield Road Omagh Co. Tyrone BT79 7EN
Tel: 028 8225 2005 Fax: 028 8225 2005
Email: information@hawthornhouse.co.uk Web: www.hawthornhouse.co.uk

On the edge of the town, in a lovely part of the country at the foot of the Sperrin Mountains, Hawthorn House is run by owner-chef Michael Gaine - who is from Kenmare, Co Kerry and has many years in the hotel industry under his belt - and his wife, Mary. Public areas, which include a comfortable bar, are furnished to a high standard and bedrooms are large and comfortable, with all the usual amenities; further bedrooms (including one for disabled), a bistro bar and conference facilities were under construction at the time of the Guide's most recent visit and are due for completion for the 2003 season. The restaurant, which is open for both lunch and dinner every day, has earned a reputation for fine contemporary cooking, although there has been a change of style since it was extended in 2002 and, since the Guide's most recent visit, a carvery lunch has been introduced. Conference/banqueting (40/100). Garden, walking. Children welcome (under 6s free in parents' room; cots available without charge). Special breaks offered. No Pets. **Rooms 5** (1 shower only). B&B £30pps, ss £10. Restaurant **seats 100** (private room, 60). L 12-2.30 daily, D 7-9.30 daily. Open all year. MasterCard, Visa, Switch. **Directions:** 5 minutes from Omagh Town Centre.

INDEX